CALCULUS
AND
ANALYTIC GEOMETRY

This book is in the

ADDISON-WESLEY SERIES IN MATHEMATICS

ERIC REISSNER, *Consulting Editor*

CALCULUS
AND
ANALYTIC GEOMETRY

by

GEORGE B. THOMAS, JR.

Department of Mathematics
Massachusetts Institute of Technology

THIRD EDITION

ADDISON-WESLEY PUBLISHING COMPANY, INC.
READING, MASSACHUSETTS, U.S.A.
LONDON, ENGLAND

PREFACE

Calculus and Analytic Geometry is available in one complete volume or as two separate parts: Part 1 covers the subjects of functions of one variable and analytic geometry, and comprises the first twelve chapters of the complete book. Part 2 includes the study of vectors and functions of several variables, which comprises Chapters 13 through 18 of the complete volume. Part 1 is suitable for a full year course, while Part 2 completes the study of the calculus.

It seems to the author that of the two branches of the calculus, the *integral calculus* is the richer, both mathematically and in applicability to the physical sciences and engineering. It is therefore the primary objective of this text to introduce the student to the fundamental concept of the integral as limit of a sum at as early a stage as seems pedagogically practicable. The first five chapters are devoted to the program of presenting the basic concepts of differentiation and integration, with many applications to make the ideas meaningful. An individual teacher may wish to shorten the program by omitting some of these applications, and may safely follow his own taste and experience in this matter. Sufficient material is available so that different applications may be taken up in different years. It is suggested, however, that students at least read all sections which deal with the geometrical applications of the definite integral, in order to appreciate the basic concept of the definite integral as limit of a sum.

A brief review of trigonometry is included in Chapter 4, and the law of cosines and formulas for $\sin{(A \pm B)}$ and $\cos{(A \pm B)}$ are deduced from the distance formula. These are used in getting formulas for derivatives and integrals of the sine and cosine. The derivatives of the other trigonometric functions, the inverse trigonometric functions, the natural logarithm, and the exponential function are studied in Chapter 6. The systematic study of methods of integration in Chapter 7, plus Chapter 10 on hyperbolic functions and Chapter 16 on infinite series, complete the calculus of functions of one real variable.

Chapter 8, on determinants and systems of linear equations, would normally be omitted if the students have studied college algebra. Later chapters use primarily the results for determinants of order three.

Plane analytic geometry and the study of plane motion using vectors are treated in Chapters 9, 11, and 12.

Solid analytic geometry and the calculus of functions of more than one real variable are studied, with frequent use of vectors, in Chapters 13, 14, and 15. Several topics included there, and in Chapter 17 on complex numbers and functions, are often postponed until a course in advanced calculus. However, there seem to be at least two reasons for including these in the first course in calculus, if time permits. First, they are useful to the student in his other studies in physics and in engineering, and should not be too long delayed. Second, the more difficult ideas need repeating. Even though the student of a first course may not master some of these ideas, he will profit from the preview, and will better understand the concepts when he next encounters them.

The treatment of differential equations in Chapter 18 is not exhaustive, but may serve as an introduction to a more systematic study of the important *linear* equations. It was this point of view which led, for example, to the choice of the method of variation of parameters for the solution of the nonhomogeneous linear equation with constant coefficients, even though the more restricted method of undetermined coefficients may be simpler to apply in some cases.

The reader is expected to know high-school algebra, geometry, and trigonometry. Some of the basic formulas from these subjects are collected for reference in an appendix at the end of the book but, in general, the more difficult formulas are reviewed in the text at the time they are needed. The author's experience, both as a student and as a teacher, indicates that one by-product of a good calculus course is likely to be a much firmer grasp of the fundamental skills of high-school mathematics. This is particularly true when the student supplies the missing steps in illustrative examples and elsewhere.

Answers are provided for nearly all problems. Many of the miscellaneous problems were generously furnished by Professors A. W. Tucker of Princeton and T. M. Apostol of the California Institute of Technology, and many of the answers were provided by Richard T. Bumby, Robert R. D. Kemp, and C. Peter Wolk. The author is grateful for this help and for other valuable and friendly assistance.

Some students (and teachers) may like to have a source of review questions to help them go back over the theory and organize their thoughts. Such questions have been included (without answers) at the end of every chapter. It may be desirable to combine two or more chapters for review purposes, and this may easily be done, even if some chapters are taken out of their sequence.

After finishing this text, the reader should be well prepared for a course in differential equations or advanced calculus.

It is a pleasure to acknowledge the fine cooperation of the staff of Addison-Wesley Publishing Company. The author also acknowledges the many helpful suggestions of users of earlier editions of *Calculus and Analytic Geometry*.

Any errors that may appear are, of course, the responsibility of the author. He will very much appreciate having these brought to his attention.

October, 1959

G. B. T., Jr.

CONTENTS

Starred sections may be omitted without loss of continuity.

vii

CHAPTER 1

THE RATE OF CHANGE OF A FUNCTION

1-1 Introduction. Calculus is the mathematics of change and motion. Where there is motion or growth, where forces are at work producing acceleration, calculus is the right mathematical tool. This was true in the beginnings of the subject, and it is true today. Calculus is used to predict the orbits of earth satellites; in the design of inertial navigation systems, cyclotrons, and radar systems; to explore problems of space travel; and to test scientific theories about such things as the dynamics of the atmosphere, ocean currents, and even theories about economic, sociologic, and psychological behavior. Of course the scientist needs a great deal more than mathematical competence, and he needs more mathematics than calculus. But calculus is a tool of great importance and usefulness and is prerequisite for further study in nearly all branches of higher mathematics.

One of the great mathematicians of the twentieth century, John von Neumann (1903–57), has written:* "The calculus was the first achievement of modern mathematics, and it is difficult to overestimate its importance. I think it defines more unequivocally than anything else the inception of modern mathematics, and the system of mathematical analysis, which is its logical development, still constitutes the greatest technical advance in exact thinking."

The calculus is a branch of mathematics which provides methods for solving two large classes of problems. The first of these involves finding the rate at which a variable quantity is changing. For example, when a body, say a stone dropped from a tower, travels in a straight line, its distance from its starting point changes with time and we may ask *how fast* it is moving at any given instant. *Differential calculus* is the branch of calculus which treats such problems.

The second type of problem the calculus deals with is that of finding a function when its rate of change is given. Thus, for example, if we are given the *velocity* of a moving body at every instant of time, we may seek to find the distance it has moved as a function of time. This problem belongs to the domain of *integral calculus*.

Modern science and engineering use both branches of the calculus as a language for expressing physical laws in precise mathematical terms, and

---

* *World of Mathematics*, Vol. 4, "The Mathematician," by John von Neumann. pp. 2053–2063.

as a tool for studying the consequences of those laws. Thus Sir Isaac Newton (1642–1727) was able to explain the motion of the planets relative to the sun as a consequence of the physical assumption known today as the law of gravitational attraction. Some appreciation of the magnitude of his achievement may be gained from realizing that Kepler (1571–1630) spent some twenty years studying observational data and using empirical methods to discover the three laws now known as *Kepler's laws*. They are:

(a) Each planet describes an orbit about the sun which is an ellipse with the sun at one focus.

(b) The line joining the planet and the sun sweeps over equal areas in equal intervals of time.

(c) The squares of the periods of revolution of the planets are proportional to the cubes of their mean distances from the sun.

All three of these laws can be derived, using the calculus as the main mathematical tool, from the "inverse-square" law of gravitational attraction and Newton's laws of motion. A large part of the subject matter of this branch of mathematics was developed by Newton as a tool to help him solve problems which arose in connection with his investigations in physics and astronomy. Credit for the invention of the calculus must also be shared, however, with a German mathematician and philosopher, Gottfried Wilhelm Leibniz (1646–1716), who independently and approximately concurrently also developed a large part of the subject, and whose notation has been almost universally adopted in preference to that used by Newton.

Analytic geometry, which forms a third division of the subject matter of this book, was the creation of several mathematicians.* Two French mathematicians, Pierre de Fermat (1601–1665) and René Descartes (1596–1650) are the chief claimants to the title of inventor of analytic geometry as we now know it. Descartes is credited with the important idea of locating a point in the plane by means of its distances from two perpendicular axes, and his name is commemorated in the terminology "Cartesian coordinates." We discuss coordinates in Article 1–2. The distinguishing characteristic of analytic geometry is that it uses algebraic methods and equations to study geometric problems. Conversely, it permits us to visualize algebraic equations in terms of geometric curves. This frequently adds clarity to abstract concepts. We shall see that most of the theory in calculus can be presented in geometrical terms, so that calculus and analytic geometry may profitably be united and studied as a whole.

----

* See, for example, *World of Mathematics*, Vol. 1, "Commentary on Descartes and Analytical Geometry," pp. 235–237. Also the article "The Invention of Analytic Geometry," by Carl B. Boyer, *Scientific American*. January, 1949.

1–2 Coordinates. The basic idea in analytic geometry is the establishment of a one-to-one correspondence between the points of a plane on the one hand and pairs of numbers (x, y) on the other hand. This correspondence may be established in many ways, but the one most commonly used is as follows.

A horizontal line in the plane, extending indefinitely to the left and to the right, is chosen as the x-axis or axis of *abscissas*. A reference point O on this line and a unit of length are then chosen. The axis is scaled off in terms of this unit of length in such a way that the number zero is attached to O, the number $+a$ is attached to the point which is a units to the right of O, and $-a$ is attached to the symmetrically located point to the left of O. In this way a one-to-one correspondence is established between the points of the x-axis and the set of all *real numbers* (that is, numbers which may be represented by terminating or nonterminating decimals).

Now through O take a second, vertical line in the plane, extending indefinitely up and down. This line becomes the y-axis, or axis of *ordinates*. The unit of length used to represent $+1$ on the y-axis need not be the same as the unit of length used to represent $+1$ on the x-axis. The y-axis is scaled off in terms of the unit of length adopted for it, with the positive number $+b$ attached to the point b units above O and negative number $-b$ attached to the symmetrically located point b units below O.

If a line parallel to the y-axis is drawn through the point marked a on the x-axis, and a line parallel to the x-axis is drawn through the point marked b on the y-axis, their point of intersection P is to be labeled $P(a, b)$. Thus, given the pair of real numbers a and b, we find one and only one point with abscissa a and ordinate b, and this point we denote by $P(a, b)$.

Conversely, if we start with any point P in the plane, we may draw lines through it parallel to the coordinate axes. If these lines intersect the x-axis at a and the y-axis at b, we then regard the pair of numbers (a, b) as corresponding to the point P. We say that the coordinates of P are (a, b).

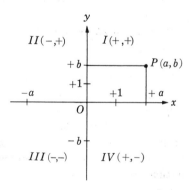

Figure 1–1

The two axes divide the plane into four quadrants, called the first quadrant, second quadrant, and so on, and labeled I, II, III, IV in Fig. 1–1. Points in the first quadrant have both coordinates positive, in the second quadrant the x-coordinate (abscissa) is negative and the y-coordinate (ordinate) is positive. The notations $(-, -)$ and $(+, -)$ in quadrants III and IV of Fig. 1–1 represent the signs of the coordinates of points in these quadrants.

Remark. There are times when it is quite obvious that there is no physical relationship between the unit of measurement of x and the unit of measurement of y. For example, if y is the total cost in dollars, to a certain shoe manufacturer, to produce x pairs of shoes per week, then "1" on the x-scale stands for one pair of shoes, while "1" on the y-scale stands for one dollar. Clearly, there is no reason for using the same scale on the two axes.

On the other hand, in surveying, one foot measured north-and-south should be the same as one foot measured east-and-west. In trigonometry, therefore, it is usually assumed that the units of length on the two axes are the same. This assumption is also made in analytic geometry.

In this book, if coordinates of points are given as pure numbers (i.e., without any physical units attached), it is to be assumed that the scales on the two axes are the same. In particular, this assumption is made wherever angles between lines or lengths of skew line segments are involved.

PROBLEMS

In each of the following problems (1–15), plot the given point P and such of the following points as may apply:

(a) The point Q such that QP is perpendicular to the x-axis and is bisected by it. Give the coordinates of Q.

(b) The point R such that PR is perpendicular to and is bisected by the y-axis. Give the coordinates of R.

(c) The point S such that PS is bisected by the origin. Give the coordinates of S.

(d) The point T such that PT is perpendicular to and is bisected by the 45° line L through the origin bisecting the first and third quadrants. Give the coordinates of T, assuming equal units on the axes.

[*Note:* Q and P are symmetric with respect to the x-axis, R and P with respect to the y-axis, S and P with respect to the origin, and T and P with respect to L.] State rules for finding coordinates of Q, R, S, T in terms of the coordinates of P.

1. $(1, -2)$	2. $(2, -1)$	3. $(-2, 2)$
4. $(-2, 1)$	5. $(2, 2)$	6. $(-2, -2)$
7. $(0, 1)$	8. $(1, 0)$	9. $(-2, 0)$
10. $(0, -3)$	11. $(-1, -3)$	12. $(\sqrt{2}, -\sqrt{2})$
13. $(-\pi, -\pi)$	14. $(-1.5, 2.3)$	15. $(\sqrt{2}, 0)$

In each of the following problems (16 through 20), take the units of length on the two axes to be equal.

16. A straight line is drawn through the point $(0, 0)$ and the point $(1, 1)$. What .acute angle does it make with the positive x-axis? Sketch.

17. A straight line is drawn through the point $A(1, 2)$ and the point $B(2, 4)$. Find $\tan \alpha$, where α is the acute angle that this line makes with the horizontal line through A. Sketch.

18. Show that the line through the pair of points $(1, 1)$ and $(2, 0)$ is parallel to the line through the pair of points $(-1, -1)$ and $(0, -2)$. Sketch.

19. The line through the pair of points $(2, 3)$ and $(1, 1)$ cuts the y-axis at the point $(0, b)$. Find b by using similar triangles. Sketch.

20. Does the line through the pair of points $(-1, -1)$ and $(1, 2)$ pass through the origin? Sketch. Give a reason, other than the evidence of your sketch, for your answer.

1-3 Directed line segments. Given two points A and B on the x-axis, or on a line parallel to the x-axis, the line segment AB *from A to B* extends over a certain number of the units of length used as the x-scale. If the arrow from A to B points to the right, we say that AB is a positive segment. On the other hand, if the arrow from A to B points to the left, we say that AB is a negative segment. Then we assign to the segment AB the number of positive or negative x-units it contains, with appropriate sign. We indicate this signed number by $\overline{AB}$.

To calculate the number (positive or negative) of x-units in the segment AB, let x_2 be the abscissa of B and let x_1 be the abscissa of A. Then, if B is to the right of A, as in Fig. 1-2, the number of x-units in the segment AB is equal to $x_2 - x_1$. We define the segment BA to be the negative of the segment AB. Thus

$$\overline{AB} = x_2 - x_1, \qquad \overline{BA} = x_1 - x_2. \qquad (1)$$

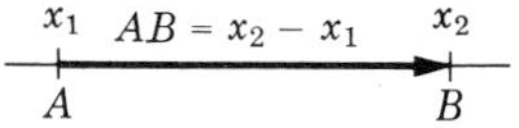

FIGURE 1-2

We may therefore observe that for either a positive or negative segment, *the algebraic number of x-units in a directed segment of the x-axis, or a line parallel to the x-axis, is equal to the abscissa of its terminal point minus the abscissa of its initial point.*

For example, the segment of the x-axis *from -2 to $+3$* contains $+3 - (-2) = +5$ x-units; while the segment *from -1 to -4* contains $-4 - (-1) = -3$ x-units.

We may also think of a directed segment AB along the x-axis as representing the path traversed by a moving particle which starts at A and travels to B. In such motion, the abscissa of the particle changes from x_1 to x_2, and it is customary in calculus to use the notation Δx (read "delta x") to represent this difference $x_2 - x_1$:

$$\Delta x = x_2 - x_1.$$

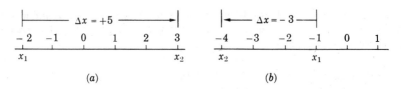

FIGURE 1–3

The symbol Δx thus denotes "change in x" or "difference between two values of x," and does not mean a number multiplied by x.

In Fig. 1–3(a), for example, if we think of a particle that starts at $x_1 = -2$ and travels to $x_2 = +3$, then its abscissa x undergoes a change given by

$$\Delta x = x_2 - x_1 = 3 - (-2) = +5.$$

In Fig. 1–3(b), if the particle travels from $x_1 = -1$ to $x_2 = -4$, then its abscissa changes by the amount

$$\Delta x = x_2 - x_1 = -4 - (-1) = -3.$$

In a precisely analogous fashion, we define the directed segment CD of the y-axis, or parallel to the y-axis, to be positive or negative depending upon whether the arrow from C to D points up (positive direction) or down (negative direction). Then we attach to the segment CD the number of positive or negative y-units that are contained in it. If y_1 is the ordinate of C and y_2 is the ordinate of D, we find that $\overline{CD} = \Delta y$, where

$$\boxed{\Delta y = y_2 - y_1}$$

is equal to the *ordinate of the terminal point D minus the ordinate of the initial point C.*

If, now, we have two points $P_1(x_1, y_1)$ and $P_2(x_2, y_2)$ in the plane, we resolve P_1P_2 into the directed components

$$\overline{P_1R} = \Delta x = x_2 - x_1, \quad (2)$$

$$\overline{RP_2} = \Delta y = y_2 - y_1, \quad (3)$$

that are parallel to the x- and y-axes respectively (Fig. 1–4).

FIGURE 1–4

If the same unit of measurement is used on both axes, then we may also express all distances in the plane in terms of this fundamental unit.

In particular, we readily find by applying the theorem of Pythagoras to the right triangle P_1RP_2 in Fig. 1–4 that the distance d between the two points $P_1(x_1, y_1)$ and $P_2(x_2, y_2)$ is simply

$$d = \sqrt{(\Delta x)^2 + (\Delta y)^2} = \sqrt{(x_2 - x_1)^2 + (y_2 - y_1)^2}. \tag{4}$$

For example, if a particle starts from $P_1(-1, 2)$ and travels in a straight line to the point $P_2(2, -2)$, then its abscissa undergoes a change

$$\Delta x = x_2 - x_1 = 2 - (-1) = 3$$

and its ordinate changes by an amount

$$\Delta y = y_2 - y_1 = -2 - 2 = -4.$$

The distance the particle travels from P_1 to P_2 is

$$d = \sqrt{(\Delta x)^2 + (\Delta y)^2} = \sqrt{9 + 16} = 5.$$

Problems

In each of the following problems, points A and B are given and point C is to be found at the intersection of the horizontal line through A and the vertical line through B. Sketch, and find

(a) the coordinates of C,

(b) the number of x-units ($+$ or $-$) in the line segment $\overline{AC} = \Delta x$,

(c) the number of y-units ($+$ or $-$) in the line segment $\overline{CB} = \Delta y$, and

(d) the length of AB under the assumption that the unit of length on the y-axis is the same as the unit of length on the x-axis.

1. $A(1, 1)$, $B(3, 4)$ 2. $A(3, 4)$, $B(1, 1)$

3. $A(-1, 2)$, $B(2, -1)$ 4. $A(2, -1)$, $B(-1, 2)$

5. $A(-1, -1)$, $B(1, 2)$ 6. $A(1, 2)$, $B(-1, -1)$

7. $A(-3, 2)$, $B(-1, -2)$ 8. $A(-1, -2)$, $B(-3, 2)$

9. $A(-3, -2)$, $B(-1, -1)$ 10. $A(-1, -1)$, $B(-3, -2)$

11. What equation must be satisfied by the coordinates of a point $P(x, y)$ if P is on the circle of radius 5 with center at $C(h, k)$ if:

(a) $(h, k) = (0, 0)$,   (b) $(h, k) = (5, 0)$,

(c) $(h, k) = (3, 4)$,   (d) $(h, k) = (h, k)$?

1–4 Slope of a straight line. Let L be a straight line which is not parallel to the y-axis. Let $P_1(x_1, y_1)$ and $P_2(x_2, y_2)$ be any two distinct points on L (Fig. 1–5a). Then we call

$$\Delta y = y_2 - y_1$$

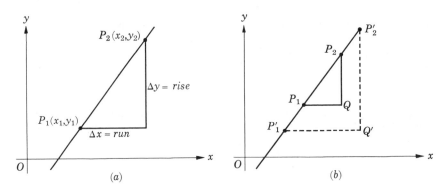

FIGURE 1-5

the "rise" and

$$\Delta x = x_2 - x_1$$

the "run" along L from P_1 to P_2. (Note that either Δx or Δy, or both, may be negative.) We define the *slope of L* as the rate of rise per unit of run,

$$\text{slope} = \frac{\text{rise}}{\text{run}}. \tag{1a}$$

If we denote the slope by m, we have

$$\boxed{m = \frac{\Delta y}{\Delta x} = \frac{y_2 - y_1}{x_2 - x_1}.} \tag{1b}$$

Remark 1. Suppose that instead of using the pair of points P_1 and P_2 to calculate the slope, Eq. (1a), we were to choose a different pair of points $P_1'(x_1', y_1')$, $P_2'(x_2', y_2')$ on L and calculate

$$m' = \frac{y_2' - y_1'}{x_2' - x_1'} = \frac{\Delta y'}{\Delta x'}.$$

Would we get the same answer for the slope? In other words, does

$$m' = m?$$

The answer is "yes." For, in Fig. 1-5(b) the triangles P_1QP_2 and $P_1'Q'P_2'$ are similar, hence

$$m' = \frac{\overline{Q'P_2'}}{\overline{P_1'Q'}} = \frac{\overline{QP_2}}{\overline{P_1Q}} = m.$$

In other words, Eq. (1b) relates the change in x and the change in y between *any* pair of points (x, y) and $(x + \Delta x, y + \Delta y)$ on L.

Remark 2. If we multiply the first two terms of Eq. (1b) by Δx, we obtain

$$\Delta y = m \, \Delta x. \tag{2}$$

This means, in the light of the comment above, that as a particle moves along L, the change in y is proportional to the change in x, and the slope m is the proportionality factor.

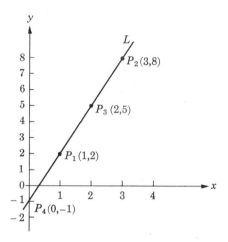

FIGURE 1–6

For example, suppose L is the line determined by the points $P_1(1, 2)$ and $P_2(3, 8)$, Fig. 1–6. Then the slope of L is

$$m = \frac{8 - 2}{3 - 1} = 3.$$

And, if $P(x, y)$, $Q(x + \Delta x, y + \Delta y)$ are any two points on L, then

$$\Delta y = 3 \, \Delta x.$$

That is, for every unit of run, there are three units of rise. Thus, starting from $P_1(1, 2)$, if we increase x by 1 unit we should increase y by 3 units, which would bring us to the point $P_3(2, 5)$. Or, we could decrease x by 1 unit and y by 3 units and obtain the point $P_4(0, -1)$. [*Question:* At what point does L cross the x-axis?]

Remark 3. *Interpolation.* In using a table of logarithms, we may, for example, want to find log 3.1416. Suppose the table gives

log 3.1410 = 0.49707,   log 3.1420 = 0.49721,

and no intermediate values. Then, for any x between 3.1410 and 3.1420, we could approximate the graph of $y = \log x$ by the chord L through the two points $P_1(3.1410, 0.49707)$ and $P_2(3.1420, 0.49721)$. The slope of this chord is

$$m = \frac{\Delta y}{\Delta x} = \frac{14 \times 10^{-5}}{10 \times 10^{-4}} = 1.4 \times 10^{-1}.$$

Then, corresponding to

$$\Delta x = 3.1416 - 3.1410 = 6 \times 10^{-4},$$

we may take

$$\Delta y = 0.14 \, \Delta x = 8.4 \times 10^{-5} \approx 8 \times 10^{-5}.$$

Hence, the ordinate of the point on L with abscissa 3.1416 is

$$0.49707 + 0.00008 = 0.49715.$$

That is, using the chord to approximate the curve, we find

$$\log 3.1416 = 0.49715.$$

Remark 4. If we take equal scales on the x- and y-axes, we may interpret the slope of the line L as the tangent of the angle of inclination that L makes with the positive x-axis. That is,

$$m = \tan \phi.$$

Here ϕ is the angle, $0 \leq \phi < 180°$, that the line makes with the positively directed portion of the x-axis (Fig. 1–7).

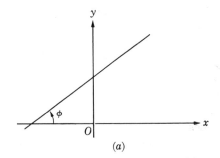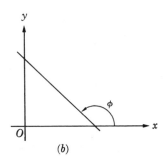

$$(a) \qquad\qquad\qquad (b)$$

FIGURE 1–7

For a line that slopes upward to the right, Fig. 1–7(a), Δy is positive when Δx is. Also, $0 < \phi < 90°$, and $\tan \phi = \Delta y / \Delta x$ is positive.

For a line that slopes downward to the right, Fig. 1–7(b), Δy is negative when Δx is positive. Also, $90° < \phi < 180°$, and $\tan \phi = \Delta y / \Delta x$ is negative.

For a horizontal line, Δy is zero for any Δx. Also $\phi = 0°$ and $\tan \phi = \Delta y/\Delta x$ is zero.

For a vertical line, Δx is zero for any Δy. Then $\Delta y/\Delta x$ is meaningless, since we cannot divide by zero. Also $\phi = 90°$, and $\tan 90°$ does not exist.

Let us examine the slopes of lines whose inclination angles are near $90°$, such as

$$\phi_1 = 89°59', \qquad m_1 = \tan \phi_1 \approx 3437.7$$

and

$$\phi_2 = 90°01', \qquad m_2 = \tan \phi_2 \approx -3437.7.$$

We see that such lines have slopes which are numerically very large. And by taking the angle still closer to $90°$, we can make the slope numerically larger than any preassigned positive number N, no matter how large N may be. It is this fact which is sometimes summarized by the statement that "a vertical line has infinite slope" or, "the slope of the line becomes infinite as its inclination angle approaches $90°$."

The symbol ∞ is used to represent infinity, but we should not use this symbol in computations involving addition, subtraction, multiplication, or division in the way we use ordinary real numbers.

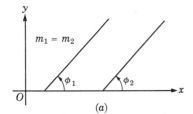 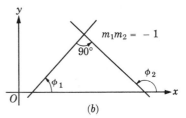

(a)   (b)

FIGURE 1–8

Two *parallel* lines (Fig. 1–8a) have equal angles of inclination and hence have equal slopes

$$\boxed{m_1 = m_2.}$$

Conversely, two lines having equal slopes

$$m_1 = \tan \phi_1, \qquad m_2 = \tan \phi_2$$

also have equal inclinations, since

$$\tan \phi_1 = \tan \phi_2$$

together with

$$0 \leq \phi_1 < 180°, \qquad 0 \leq \phi_2 < 180°$$

implies that ϕ_1 and ϕ_2 are equal.

Next, consider two *perpendicular* lines (Fig. 1–8b). Their inclinations differ by 90°. Suppose, for example, that

$$\phi_2 = 90° + \phi_1.$$

Case 1. If one line is vertical, then the other must be horizontal.
Case 2. If neither line is vertical, then neither ϕ_1 nor ϕ_2 is 90° and

$$m_2 = \tan \phi_2$$
$$= \tan (90° + \phi_1)$$
$$= -\cot \phi_1 = -\frac{1}{\tan \phi_1}$$
$$= -1/m_1.$$

Thus the condition for *perpendicularity* in this case is

$$m_2 = -\frac{1}{m_1}. \tag{3}$$

Problems

In each of the following problems (1 through 15), plot the given points A and B and find the slope of the straight line determined by them and of a perpendicular line.

1. $A(1, 2)$, $B(2, -1)$
2. $A(-1, 2)$, $B(-2, -1)$
3. $A(-2, -1)$, $B(1, -2)$
4. $A(2, -1)$, $B(-2, 1)$
5. $A(1, 0)$, $B(0, 1)$
6. $A(-1, 0)$, $B(1, 0)$
7. $A(2, 3)$, $B(-1, 3)$
8. $A(0, 3)$, $B(2, -3)$
9. $A(0, -2)$, $B(-2, 0)$
10. $A(1, 2)$, $B(1, -3)$
11. $A(\frac{1}{2}, 0)$, $B(0, -\frac{1}{3})$
12. $A(0, 0)$, $B(x, y)$ $(x \neq 0, y \neq 0)$
13. $A(0, 0)$, $B(x, 0)$ $(x \neq 0)$
14. $A(0, 0)$, $B(0, y)$ $(y \neq 0)$
15. $A(a, 0)$, $B(0, b)$ $(a \neq 0, b \neq 0)$

In each of the following problems (16 through 20), plot the given points A, B, C, and D. Determine in each case whether or not $ABCD$ is a parallelogram. Also indicate those parallelograms that are rectangles.

16. $A(0, 1)$, $B(1, 2)$, $C(2, 1)$, $D(1, 0)$
17. $A(3, 1)$, $B(2, 2)$, $C(0, 1)$, $D(1, 0)$
18. $A(-2, 2)$, $B(1, 3)$, $C(2, 0)$, $D(-1, -1)$
19. $A(1, -2)$, $B(2, -1)$, $C(2, 1)$, $D(1, 0)$
20. $A(-1, 0)$, $B(0, -1)$, $C(2, 0)$, $D(0, 2)$

21. Find the coordinates of a point $P(x, y)$ which is so located that the line

OP through the origin and P has slope equal to $+2$, and the line AP through the point $A(-1, 0)$ and P has slope equal to $+1$.

22. A line L goes through the origin and has slope equal to $+3$. If $P(x, y)$ is a point other than the origin and on the line L, show that $y = 3x$. Sketch the line.

In each of the following problems (23 through 27), plot the given points and determine analytically whether or not they all lie on a straight line. Give reasons for your answers.

23. $A(1, 0)$, $B(0, 1)$, $C(2, -1)$

24. $A(-2, 1)$, $B(0, 5)$, $C(-1, 2)$

25. $A(-2, -1)$, $B(-1, 1)$, $C(1, 5)$, $D(2, 7)$

26. $A(-2, 3)$, $B(0, 2)$, $C(2, 0)$

27. $A(-3, -2)$, $B(-2, 0)$, $C(-1, 2)$, $D(1, 6)$

28. Let $P_1(x_1, y_1)$ and $P_2(x_2, y_2)$ be two points. Find the mid-point of the segment P_1P_2.

29. Given $A(0, -1)$, $B(4, 0)$, and $C(3, 4)$, show that ABC is a right triangle and find the center and radius of the circumscribed circle. Sketch.

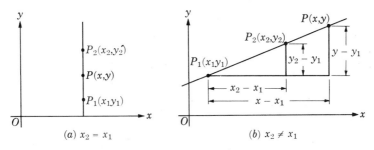

FIGURE 1–9

1–5 Equations of a straight line. In this article we shall discuss algebraic equations that represent straight lines. Suppose we ask ourselves how the two coordinates x and y of a point $P(x, y)$ on the straight line determined by the two points $P_1(x_1, y_1)$ and $P_2(x_2, y_2)$ are related to each other. It is desirable to distinguish between the cases

$$x_2 = x_1 \quad \text{and} \quad x_2 \neq x_1.$$

Case 1. If $x_2 = x_1$, then the line P_1P_2 is vertical and all points on it have the same x-coordinate. Then $P(x, y)$ is on the line if and only if

$$\boxed{x = x_1.} \tag{1}$$

In this case the x- and y-coordinates of P are not related to each other. The ordinate y may have any value whatsoever and the point $P(x, y)$ will be on the line provided its abscissa x has the value x_1.

Case 2. If $x_2 \neq x_1$, we know the slope of the line is

$$m = \frac{y_2 - y_1}{x_2 - x_1}. \tag{2}$$

Then the point $P(x, y)$ is also on the line if (and only if) the slope of P_1P is the same as the slope of P_1P_2. That is, x and y must satisfy the equation

$$\frac{y - y_1}{x - x_1} = m$$

or

$$\boxed{y - y_1 = m(x - x_1),} \tag{3}$$

if P is on the line; and conversely, if x and y do satisfy Eq. (3), then $P(x, y)$ is on the line. If P coincides with P_1, Eq. (3) is still satisfied, even though the slope of P_1P is then undefined.

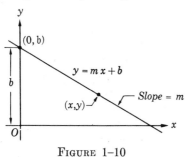

FIGURE 1–10

Equation (3) is called the *point-slope* form of the equation of the line, since it gives the equation in terms of one point $P_1(x_1, y_1)$ on the line and the slope m. The three numbers x_1, y_1, and m are constants in Eq. (3), while x and y are variables. By a *variable* we mean a symbol, such as x, which may take any value in some set of numbers. In Eq. (3), x may take any real value whatever, $-\infty < x < +\infty$, and as x varies continuously from a negative value $-N$ to a positive value $+M$, the corresponding point $P(x, y)$ traces an unbroken portion of the line from left to right.

We may also write Eq. (3) in the equivalent form

$$\boxed{y = mx + b,} \tag{4}$$

where m is the slope of the line and

$$b = y_1 - mx_1$$

is a constant. In fact, $(0, b)$ is the point where the line crosses the y-axis. This point is called the y-intercept of the line. Equation (4) is expressed in terms of the slope m and the y-intercept b, and is therefore called the *slope-intercept* equation of the line.

For example, the equation

$$y = 2x + 3$$

may be compared with (4), with

$$m = 2, \quad b = 3.$$

Thus it represents a straight line having y-intercept $(0, 3)$ and slope 2.

More generally, an equation

$$Ax + By + C = 0, \tag{5}$$

where A, B, and C are constants with at least one of A and B different from zero, represents a *straight line*. For if

$$B = 0, \quad Ax + C = 0, \quad x = -(C/A)$$

and the line is a vertical line as in Eq. (1). On the other hand, if

$$B \neq 0, \quad y = -\frac{A}{B}x - \frac{C}{B},$$

and this represents a straight line of the form of Eq. (4), with

$$m = -\frac{A}{B}, \quad b = -\frac{C}{B}.$$

An equation like (5) that contains only first powers of x and y is said to be "linear in x and in y." Thus we may summarize our discussion by saying that every straight line in the plane is represented by a linear equation and, conversely, every linear equation represents a straight line.

EXAMPLE. Find the slope of the line $2x + 3y = 5$.

Solution. Solving for y, we have

$$y = -\tfrac{2}{3}x + \tfrac{5}{3},$$

which compares with $y = mx + b$, with $m = -\tfrac{2}{3}$ and $b = \tfrac{5}{3}$. Hence the slope is $-\tfrac{2}{3}$.

PROBLEMS

In each of the following problems (1 through 10), plot the given pair of points and find an equation for the line determined by them.

1. $(0, 0)$, $(2, 3)$ 2. $(1, 1)$, $(2, 1)$
3. $(1, 1)$, $(1, 2)$ 4. $(-2, 1)$, $(2, -2)$

5. $(-2, 0)$, $(-2, -2)$ 6. $(1, 3)$, $(3, 1)$
7. $(a, 0)$, $(0, b)$ $(a \neq 0, b \neq 0)$ 8. $(0, 0)$, $(1, 0)$
9. $(0, 0)$, $(0, 1)$ 10. $(2, -1)$; $(-2, 3)$

In each of the following problems (11 through 20), find the slope of the given line.

11. $y = 3x + 5$ 12. $2y = 3x + 5$
13. $x + y = 2$ 14. $2x - y = 4$
15. $x - 2y = 4$ 16. $3x + 4y = 12$
17. $4x - 3y = 12$ 18. $x = 2y - 5$
19. $\dfrac{x}{a} + \dfrac{y}{b} = 1$ $(a, b \text{ constants} \neq 0)$

20. $x_1 x + y_1 y = 1$ $(x_1, y_1 \text{ constants} \neq 0)$

21. Find the line that passes through the point $(1, 2)$ and is parallel to the line $x + 2y = 3$.

22. (a) Find the line L through $A(-2, 2)$ and perpendicular to the line L': $2x + y = 4$

(b) Find the point B where the lines L and L' of part (a) intersect.

(c) Using the result of part (b), find the distance from the point A to the line L' of part (a).

23. Find the line through $(1, 4)$ and having inclination angle $\phi = 60°$.

24. What is the inclination of the line $2x + y = 4$?

25. If A, B, C, C' are constants, show that (a) the lines

$$Ax + By + C = 0,$$
$$Ax + By + C' = 0$$

are parallel, and (b) the lines

$$Ax + By + C = 0,$$
$$Bx - Ay + C' = 0$$

are perpendicular.

26. (a) Let C and F denote, respectively, corresponding centigrade and Fahrenheit temperature readings. Given that the F vs. C graph is a straight line, find its equation from the following data: $C = 0$, $F = 32$ and $C = 100$, $F = 212$ are coordinates of two points on the graph.

(b) Is there a temperature at which $C = F$? If so, what is it?

27. The perpendicular distance ON from the origin to line L is p, and ON makes an angle α with the positive x-axis. Show that L has equation

$$x \cos \alpha + y \sin \alpha = p.$$

1–6 Functions and graphs. We have already mentioned that a *variable* is a symbol, such as x, that may take any value in some specified set of numbers. The set of numbers over which x may vary is called the *domain* of x. In most of our applications, the domains of our variables will be *intervals* of numbers such as the following:

1. The set of all real numbers between two fixed numbers a and b,

$$a < x < b.$$

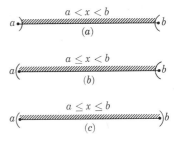

FIGURE 1–11

This means that x is simultaneously greater than a and less than b, hence is strictly between a and b. Such a set of numbers is called an *open interval*. (Fig. 1–11a.)

2. The set $a \le x < b$ of all real numbers x, as above, plus the left end point, $x = a$ (Fig. 1–11b).

3. The set $a \le x \le b$ of all real numbers between a and b and including both end points. This is called a *closed interval* (Fig. 1–11c).

For example, if both x and y are real variables and

$$y = \sqrt{1 - x^2},$$

then x^2 must not be greater than 1, because the square root of a negative number is imaginary. Thus the appropriate domain of x is the closed interval $-1 \le x \le 1$.

Function. In calculus we are most often interested in related variables. For example, the distance an object moves is related to its speed, a person's weight is related to his age, the amount of postage required to mail a letter is related to its weight, and so on. There is an especially important kind of relation between variables which characterizes a *function*. The key idea of a function is that as soon as we know the value of the first variable, the corresponding value of the second variable is also known. Consider the set of all possible ordered pairs of values of x with the corresponding values of y. This set is a function.

DEFINITION. *A function is a set of ordered pairs of numbers* (x, y) *such that to each value of the first variable* (x) *there corresponds a unique value of the second variable* (y).

EXAMPLE 1. Let the domain of x be the set $\{0, 1, 2, 3, 4\}$, and to each value of x let us assign the number $y = x^2$. The function so defined is the set of pairs

$$\{(0, 0), (1, 1), (2, 4), (3, 9), (4, 16)\}.$$

One member of this set is the pair $(2, 4)$. We also say that $(2, 4)$ "belongs to" the function.

EXAMPLE 2. Let the domain of x be the interval $-2 \leq x \leq 2$. Again let us assign to each value of x the number $y = x^2$. The set of all ordered pairs (x, y) such that $-2 \leq x \leq 2$ and $y = x^2$ is written

$$\{(x, y) \mid -2 \leq x \leq 2, \quad y = x^2\}. \quad (1)$$

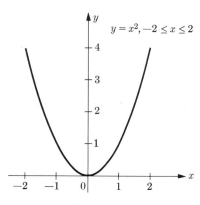

FIGURE 1–12

The outside braces denote "set," (x, y) denotes the typical element of the set, the vertical bar is read "such that," and the statement following the bar is the condition the typical element must satisfy in order to qualify for membership in the set. We must resort to this so-called "set-builder" notation in this instance, since the number of elements belonging to the set is infinite and we cannot possibly enumerate all the elements explicitly, as we did in Example 1. But the key idea is still present: when a value is assigned to the first variable x, there is a unique corresponding value of the second variable y, namely $y = x^2$. For example, if the value assigned to x is $\frac{1}{3}$, the corresponding value of y is $\frac{1}{9}$. The pair $(\frac{1}{3}, \frac{1}{9})$ is one member of the function. The *graph* of the function is the set of points which correspond to the members of the function. See Fig. 1–12.

A function may be denoted by a single letter, say f. Then if a is a particular number in the domain of x, and b is the value of y associated with a, we denote the fact that (a, b) is one of the pairs belonging to f by writing $b = f(a)$, and say that b is the *value* of the function f at a.

EXAMPLE 3. Suppose that with each number x in the closed interval $-1 \leq x \leq 1$ we associate the number $y = \sqrt{1 - x^2}$. The domain is specified, and we have a rule which yields a unique number y when applied to any x in the domain. We imagine the set f of all possible ordered pairs of numbers of the form (x, y) with $-1 \leq x \leq 1$, and $y = \sqrt{1 - x^2}$. The value of this function at 0 is $f(0) = \sqrt{1 - 0^2} = 1$. Its value at $\frac{3}{5}$ is $f(\frac{3}{5}) = \sqrt{1 - (\frac{3}{5})^2} = \frac{4}{5}$, and so on. It is not difficult to see that as x takes on all values from -1 to 0 inclusive, $y = \sqrt{1 - x^2}$ takes on all values from 0 to 1, and these are repeated in reverse order as x takes on the remaining values in its domain, namely from 0 to $+1$. The set of function values $f(x)$ corresponding to all values of x in its domain is called the

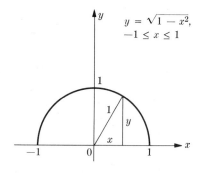

FIGURE 1–13

range of the function. Hence in this example, the range of the function is the closed interval $0 \leq y \leq 1$. The *graph* of any function is the set of all points whose coordinates form a pair (x, y) which belongs to the function. In the present example, the graph is the semicircle shown in Fig. 1–13.

Independent and dependent variables. The variable x which yields the first of the two numbers in the ordered pair (x, y) is often called the *independent* variable, or *argument* of the function f. The second variable y is called the *dependent* variable. The set of all values taken on by the independent variable is called the *domain* of the function. The set of all values taken on by the dependent variable is called the *range* of the function. If the pair (a, b) belongs to the function f, that is, $f(a) = b$, we also say that b is the *image* of a under f. Similarly, the *range* of a function is the *image* of its *domain*. We also say that the function *maps* its domain onto its range.

EXAMPLE 4. With each number $x \neq 0$ associate the number $y = 1/x$ (the reciprocal of x). This describes a function consisting of all pairs of numbers of the form $(x, 1/x)$, $x \neq 0$. Thus $(2, \frac{1}{2})$, $(5, \frac{1}{5})$, $(-\sqrt{2}, -1/\sqrt{2})$ are specific ordered pairs of numbers which belong to this function. The *image* of any number in the domain of the function is its reciprocal. The set of *all* these images, the *range*, is the set of all numbers different from zero, the same as the domain. The graph is shown in Fig. 1–14.

EXAMPLE 5. The domain of a certain function is the set of nonnegative real numbers $x \geq 0$. We shall denote this function by g (to introduce variety), and the value of the function at x will be $g(x) = \sqrt{x}$. Thus $g(0) = 0$, $g(\frac{1}{4}) = \frac{1}{2}$, $g(9) = 3$, $g(10^4) = 10^2$, etc. Since every positive number is the square root of some positive number, the *range* of this function is the set $y \geq 0$, the same set as the domain. The graph is shown in Fig. 1–15.

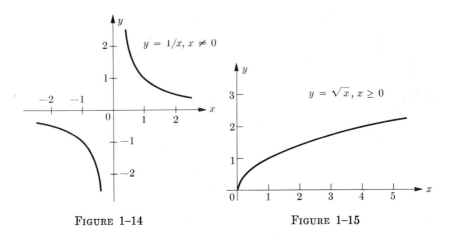

FIGURE 1–14   FIGURE 1–15

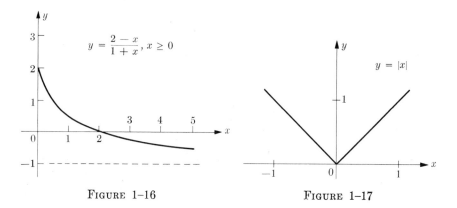

FIGURE 1–16   FIGURE 1–17

EXAMPLE 6. Let the domain of x be the set $x \geq 0$, and let $y = \dfrac{2 - x}{1 + x}$.
Clearly,

$$\left\{ (x, y) \,\middle|\, x \geq 0, \quad y = \frac{2 - x}{1 + x} \right\}$$

is a function, since y is uniquely determined when any nonnegative number is substituted for x. For example, the following pairs belong to the function:

$$(0, 2), \ (1, \tfrac{1}{2}), \ (2, 0), \ (3, -\tfrac{1}{4}), \ (5, -\tfrac{1}{2}), \ (9, -\tfrac{7}{10}), \ (99, -0.97).$$

When x is very large, y is very close to -1. In fact, y takes on all values between 2 and -1, including 2 but not including -1. The *range* is $2 \geq y > -1$. The graph is shown in Fig. 1–16.

EXAMPLE 7. (Fig. 1–17) This function is called the "absolute value of x." Its *domain* is the set of all real numbers x. To the number x it assigns the non-negative number $\sqrt{x^2}$, which is represented by the symbol $|x|$. Therefore the value of the function at x is

$$|x| = \sqrt{x^2} = \begin{cases} x, & \text{if} \quad x \geq 0, \\ -x, & \text{if} \quad x < 0. \end{cases}$$

It maps every positive real number onto itself, and every negative real number onto its negative, which is the corresponding positive number. Thus $|x|$ is never negative; it is like an electric current rectifier that converts either positive or negative current into positive.

Absolute value. The absolute value function discussed in Example 7 may also be given a geometrical interpretation as follows: $|x|$ measures the distance from the origin O to the point P that represents the number x on the scale of real numbers, regardless of whether x is positive or negative. Thus, in Fig. 1–18(a), x_1 is positive, P_1 is to the right of O, and the distance $\overline{OP}_1$ is $|x_1|$; x_2 is negative, P_2 is to the left of O, and the distance $\overline{P_2O}$ is $|x_2|$.

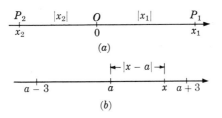

FIGURE 1–18

If we want to say that a number x lies between -1 and $+1$, we can use the alternative expression that x is less than one unit away from zero; that is, $|x| < 1$. In other words, the statements $|x| < 1$ and $-1 < x < +1$ are identical.

The absolute value symbol is so useful in mathematics that it is important to become familiar with further properties of it. If two numbers a and b have the same sign, then $|a + b| = |a| + |b|$, but if they have opposite signs, then $|a + b| < |a| + |b|$. These two cases both fit into the inequality

$$|a + b| \leq |a| + |b|.$$

When we subtract one number from another, for example when we take $a - b$, the sign of the result depends upon which of the two numbers is the larger. But $a - b$ and $b - a$ differ from each other only in sign; hence if only the numerical value of the difference is required, we may take the absolute value of either one of them, that is

$$|a - b| = |b - a|.$$

In fact, this simply measures the distance on the scale of real numbers between the two points which represent a and b respectively.

If we wish to specify that the variable x is to be within 3 units, say, of a given number a (Fig. 1–18b), we may write

$$|x - a| < 3.$$

Since $|x - a|$ measures the distance between a and x, the inequality which says that this distance is less than 3 says, in effect, that x may vary between $a - 3$ and $a + 3$; that is, $|x - a| < 3$ is the same as $a - 3 < x < a + 3$.

A function is determined by the *domain* and by any rule that tells what image in the range is to be associated with each element of the domain. For, once the domain and the rule are given, the set of all ordered pairs (x, y) can, at least in theory, be computed by a machine into which the elements of the domain are fed, one after another. The machine computes the value of y for the input x. Thus if the domain is the set of all real numbers and with the number x the function associates the number

$$y = f(x) = x^2 + 5,$$

we think of a machine so constructed that when a real number x is fed into it, the machine produces $x^2 + 5$ as the result (Fig. 1–19). Whatever argument is substituted for x, the machine squares it and adds 5. For instance,

$$f(2) = 2^2 + 5 = 9,$$

and

$$f(a + 3) = (a + 3)^2 + 5$$

$$= a^2 + 6a + 14.$$

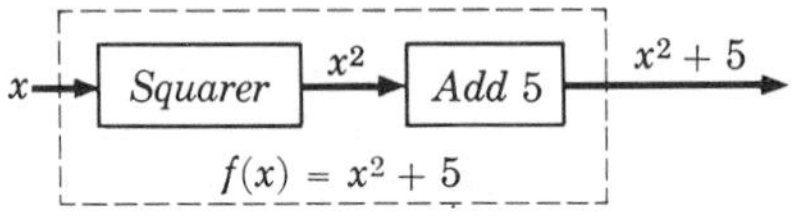

FIGURE 1–19

Remark. Another way that a machine can be used to give the value of a function at a particular x is to store in the machine's "memory" a complete table of the pairs (x, y) that constitute the function. Then tell the machine the value of x and ask it to produce the corresponding y. Or, instead of a complete table, we may store in the machine a partial set of function-values, and compute others from these by interpolation. In practice, the memory of a computer has limited capacity. Hence it is better to compute the function-values as needed, rather than storing them. But whether they are computed or stored in the form of a table, what is important is that there be just one "answer" y corresponding to any given x (from the domain of the function). And when the values are given by a table, we may still say that there is a "rule" for determining the value of the function at a given x—the rule being, "look it up in the table." This is just what we do in evaluating logarithms, for example, though we shall later learn how logarithms are computed from series (Chapter 16).

Since a function is determined by the domain and a rule, we shall often resort to such shorthand expressions as "consider the function $f(x) = x/(x - 2)$, $x \neq 2$" in place of the more precise expression "let f be a function whose domain is the set of all real numbers $x \neq 2$ and which associates with x the number $f(x) = x/(x - 2)$." Or again we may say, simply, "consider the function $y = x^2$," when we actually mean "the function defined on the domain of all real numbers which assigns the value x^2 to the function at x."

Two restrictions should always be kept in mind. First, we must **never divide by zero**. Thus if we see $y = x/(x - 2)$, we must always think "$x \neq 2$," even if this restriction is not stated explicitly. Second, we are dealing exclusively with real-valued functions. This means that the domain must be suitably restricted when we have square roots, or fourth roots, or other even roots. For example, if $y = \sqrt{4 - x^2}$, we should also think "x^2 must not be greater than 4; that is, the domain must not extend beyond the interval $-2 \le x \le +2$, or $|x| \le 2$."

Functions of more than one independent variable. Occasionally we have functions which depend upon several independent variables. For example, if r is the base radius and h is the altitude of a right circular cone (Fig. 1–20), then the volume

$$v = \tfrac{1}{3}\pi r^2 h$$

is uniquely determined when r and h are given definite values. The physical meaning requires that r, h, and v be positive. The set of all ordered triples (r, h, v) with

$$v = \tfrac{1}{3}\pi r^2 h, \qquad r > 0, \quad h > 0$$

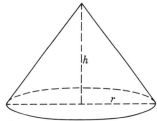

FIGURE 1–20

is an example of a function of two independent variables (r and h). Its *domain* is the set of all pairs (r, h) with $r > 0$, $h > 0$. Its *range* is the set of positive numbers $v > 0$. The variables r and h are *independent* in the sense that the value assigned to either of them need not depend upon the other. But the value of v is fixed by the other two variables, so we call v the *dependent* variable. It is also customary to be briefer, and somewhat less precise, and to say that "the volume of a right circular cone is a function of the radius and altitude," or, still more briefly, "v is a function of r and h." This means two things:

(a) r and h can be assigned values independently, and
(b) when r and h are given, v is uniquely determined.

Similarly, the set of all ordered triples (r, h, s) with

$$s = \pi r\sqrt{r^2 + h^2}, \qquad r > 0, \quad h > 0,$$

is another example of a function of the same two independent variables r and h. Here s is the lateral surface area of the cone. And again we might say, "the lateral surface area of a right circular cone is a function of the radius and altitude," or "s is a function of r and h."

More generally, suppose that some quantity y is uniquely determined by n other quantities $x_1, x_2, x_3, \ldots, x_n$. The set of all ordered ($n + 1$)-tuples $(x_1, x_2, x_3, \ldots, x_n, y)$ that can be obtained by substituting permissible values of the variables $x_1, x_2, \ldots, x_n$ and the corresponding values of y is a function whose domain is the set of all allowable n-tuples $(x_1, x_2, x_3, \ldots, x_n)$ and whose range is the set of all possible values of y corresponding to this domain. If values can be assigned independently to each of the x's, we call them independent variables and say that y is a function of the x's. We also write

$$y = f(x_1, x_2, x_3, \ldots, x_n)$$

to indicate that y is a function of the n x's, just as we write

$$y = f(x)$$

to indicate that y is a function of one independent variable x.

Our primary concern in this book will be with functions of a single independent variable. In such cases there are at least four different ways of representing the functional relationship between the variables x and y, and all four of these methods are probably familiar to the reader. They are:

1. *By tables of values.* For example, the functions $y = \log_{10}x$, $y = \sin(x°)$, $y = \sqrt{x}$, $y = 1/x$, and many others are given in most numerical tables.

2. *By corresponding scales.* For example, the scales of a slide rule may be lined up so that opposite any number x on one scale, we may read $\sqrt{x}$, or x^2, or $\log_{10}x$, and so on, on other scales.

3. *By means of graphs.* Here we usually lay off the x-axis horizontally and the y-axis vertically on graph paper, with their origins coinciding. Then we plot points (x, y) with x in the domain of the function and with $y = f(x)$, and draw a smooth curve through the plotted points, as for example in Fig. 1–16. Observe that it is also customary to make a *table of values* of corresponding numbers x and y before we plot the curve.

4. *By means of equations,* from which we can calculate the value of y that corresponds to any given x.

Of these four methods, the ones most often used in this book will be the third and fourth, namely graphs and equations. However, any rule, whether expressed algebraically or verbally, that produces a value for y when x is given satisfies the requirements of expressing y as a function of x. There need not be a simple equation which gives y in terms of x. Thus, for example, a person's weight is a function of time (the value of his weight can be determined by stepping on scales at a given time), but there is unlikely to be any simple equation relating weight to time. On the other hand, a person's age is a function of time, and this relationship may be expressed by a linear equation.

An example of an interesting function given by a verbal statement is one known as "the greatest integer function." This function is defined on the domain of all real numbers. With any x in the domain, the function associates the algebraically greatest integer which is less than or equal to x. The integer thus associated with x is designated by writing brackets around x, $[x]$. And it has the property of being less than or equal to x, while the next larger integer is greater than x. That is,

$$[x] \leq x < [x] + 1.$$

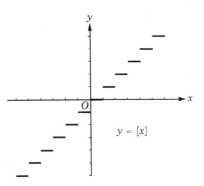

$y = [x]$

FIGURE 1–21

For example, if $x = 3.4$, then $[x] = 3$ is the greatest integer in x. If x is negative, the greatest integer in x, which always lies at or to the left of x on the usual x-axis number scale, may have a larger absolute value than x has. For instance, $[-4.7] = -5$ is the greatest integer in -4.7. The graph of the function $y = [x]$ is shown in Fig. 1–21. Its *range* is just the set of all integers $\ldots, -3, -2, -1, 0, 1, 2, 3, \ldots$ negative, zero, and positive. It is clear from the graph why such a function is called a "step function." There are many examples of step functions in everyday life. The following are typical of situations that may be encountered:

1. The cash value y dollars of a \$100 Series E savings bond x years after the date of issue, $0 \leq x \leq 20$.

2. The postage y cents on a first-class letter weighing x ounces.

3. The toll charge y dollars on a long distance telephone call from Boston to Chicago lasting x minutes.

4. Some physical property y (for example, density, thermal conductivity, or coefficient of thermal expansion) at distance x inches from one end of a compound metal bar composed of two or more different metals joined end-to-end.

Such functions exhibit points of *discontinuity* where the function suddenly jumps from one value to another without taking on any of the intermediate values, as in Fig. 1–21 at $x = 2$ where, as x approaches 2 from the left, y jumps from 1 to 2 without taking any of the intervening values.

PROBLEMS

Solve each of the following equations for x in terms of y. On the basis of the assumption that x and y are real variables, discuss the possible sets of values of x and of y: the *domain* and the *range* of the functions defined by the formulas which here give y in terms of x.

1. $y = x^2$

2. $y = \dfrac{x + 1}{x - 1}$

3. $y = \dfrac{x^2}{x^2 + 1}$ 4. $y = \sqrt{\dfrac{x}{x + 1}}$ 5. $y = x - \dfrac{1}{x}$

6. Separate the equation $x^2 + xy + y^2 = 3$ into two equations, each of which determines y as a function of x.

7. Given the function $f(x) = x^2 + (1/x)$; find $f(2)$, $f(-1)$, $f(1/x)$, $f(x + \Delta x)$.

8. Make a table of values corresponding to $x = 0$, $\frac{1}{2}$, 1, $\frac{3}{2}$, 2, and sketch a graph to represent the function

$$y = \begin{cases} x, & \text{when} & 0 \leq x \leq 1, \\ 2 - x, & \text{when} & 1 < x \leq 2. \end{cases}$$

9. Describe the domain of the variable x without the use of the "absolute value" symbol in each of the following cases: (a) $|x| < 2$, (b) $|x| \geq 2$, (c) $|x - 1| \leq 3$, (d) $|x - 2| < 2$ and simultaneously x must satisfy the additional restriction $|x - 3| \geq 1$.

10. Sketch a graph to represent the function $y = |4 - x^2|$ for $-3 \leq x \leq 3$.

11. When does $|1 - x|$ equal $1 - x$ and when does it equal $x - 1$?

12. Sketch a graph of the function $y = x - [x]$ for $-3 \leq x \leq 3$, where $[x]$ denotes the greatest integer in x.

1–7 Slope of a curve. In Article 1–4 we discussed the slope of a straight line. In this article we shall define what we mean by the *slope of a curve* at a point $P(x, y)$ on the curve. This is the way in which Leibniz himself approached the "differential calculus."

In Fig. 1–22, $P(x_1, y_1)$ is any point on the curve $y = f(x)$, and $Q(x_2, y_2)$ is another point on the same curve. Then the slope of the secant line joining the points P and Q is

$$m_{\text{sec}} = \text{slope of } PQ = \frac{y_2 - y_1}{x_2 - x_1} = \frac{\Delta y}{\Delta x}. \tag{1}$$

Suppose now we hold P fixed and move Q along the curve toward P. As we do so, the slope of the secant line PQ will probably vary. But it may happen (and does for most curves encountered in practice) that as Q moves closer and closer to P, the slope of the secant line varies by smaller and smaller amounts and, in fact, approaches a constant limiting value. When this happens, as it does in the following example, we call this limiting value *the slope of the tangent to the curve at P* or, more briefly, *the slope of the curve at P*.

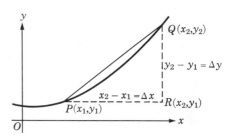

FIGURE 1–22

EXAMPLE. Consider the curve

$$y = x^3 - 3x + 3. \qquad (2)$$

If $P(x_1, y_1)$ is a point on this curve, then its coordinates must satisfy the equation

$$y_1 = x_1^3 - 3x_1 + 3. \qquad (3a)$$

If $Q(x_2, y_2)$ is a second point on the curve, and if

$$\Delta x = x_2 - x_1, \qquad \Delta y = y_2 - y_1,$$

then

$$x_2 = x_1 + \Delta x, \qquad y_2 = y_1 + \Delta y$$

must also satisfy Eq. (2). That is,

$$y_1 + \Delta y = (x_1 + \Delta x)^3 - 3(x_1 + \Delta x) + 3$$
$$= x_1^3 + 3x_1^2 \Delta x + 3x_1 (\Delta x)^2 + (\Delta x)^3 - 3x_1 - 3\Delta x + 3. \quad (3b)$$

When we subtract the members of Eq. (3a) from Eq. (3b) we obtain

$$\Delta y = 3x_1^2 \Delta x + 3x_1 (\Delta x)^2 + (\Delta x)^3 - 3\Delta x. \qquad (4)$$

From this we readily find the slope of the secant line PQ to be

$$m_{\text{sec}} = \frac{\Delta y}{\Delta x} = 3x_1^2 + 3x_1 \Delta x + (\Delta x)^2 - 3. \qquad (5)$$

Now comes the most important step! When Q approaches P along the curve, Δx and Δy both approach zero. Thus the slope of PQ will be the ratio of two small numbers. This information is not helpful, since the ratio of two small numbers may be practically anything. But we have further information here, since we also know from Eq. (5) that

$$m_{\text{sec}} = (3x_1^2 - 3) + (3x_1 + \Delta x) \Delta x.$$

The right side of this equation is the sum of two terms, one of which,

$$3x_1^2 - 3,$$

remains constant as Δx approaches zero, while the other,

$$(3x_1 + \Delta x) \Delta x,$$

becomes smaller and, in fact, itself approaches zero when Δx does. We summarize this by saying that

the limit of m_{sec} as Δx approaches zero is $3x_1^2 - 3,$

and by definition, this limit is the slope of the tangent to the curve, or the slope of the curve, at the point (x_1, y_1). Since (x_1, y_1) might have been *any* point on the curve of Eq. (2), we may delete the subscript 1 and say that

$$m = 3x^2 - 3 \qquad (6)$$

gives the slope of the curve at any point $P(x, y)$ on it.

We can make use of the slope as well as the equation of the curve itself to learn more about the shape of the curve than we would be likely to discover if we did not have this additional information. For example, we see that the tangent to the curve is horizontal, that is, $m = 0$, when $x = \pm 1$. We also see that the slope is negative for x between -1 and $+1$, and that elsewhere it is positive. If we substitute values of x between -2 and $+2$, say, into Eq. (2) to find y and into Eq. (6) to find m, we obtain the following table of values:

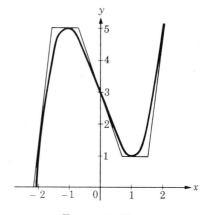

FIGURE 1–23

x	y	m
-2	1	9
-1	5	0
0	3	-3
1	1	0
2	5	9

When these points are plotted and the tangent line at each point is drawn, we get a very good picture of the shape of the curve. Of course the curve itself is smooth and does not follow the tangent lines, but these lines do afford material aid in sketching the curve (Fig. 1–23).

PROBLEMS

Use the method illustrated in this article to find the slope of each of the following curves at a point (x, y) on the curve. Use the equation of the curve and the equation you get for its slope to make a table of values. Include in your table all points where the curve has a horizontal tangent. Sketch the curve, making use of all the information in your table of values.

1. $y = x^2 - 2x - 3$ 2. $y = 2x^2 - x - 1$

3. $y = 4 - x^2$ 4. $y = x^2 - 4x$

5. $y = x^2 - 4x + 4$ 6. $y = x^2 + 4x + 4$

7. $y = 6 + x - x^2$ 8. $y = 6 + 5x - x^2$

9. $y = x^2 + 3x + 2$ 10. $y = 2 - x - x^2$

11. $y = 2x^3 + 3x^2 - 12x + 7$ 12. $y = x^3 - 3x$

13. $y = x^3 - 12x$ 14. $y = x^2(4x + 3) + 1$

15. $y = x^3 - 3x^2 + 4$

1–8 Derivative of a function. We now formulate the method for finding the slope of a curve representing the more general functional equation $y = f(x)$. Let $P(x_1, y_1)$ be a fixed point on the curve. The subscript 1 is used to emphasize that x_1 and y_1 are to be held constant throughout the following discussion. If $Q(x_1 + \Delta x, y_1 + \Delta y)$ is another point on the curve, then

$$y_1 + \Delta y = f(x_1 + \Delta x),$$

and from this we subtract

$$y_1 = f(x_1)$$

to obtain (Fig. 1–24)

$$\Delta y = f(x_1 + \Delta x) - f(x_1).$$

Then the slope of the secant line PQ is

$$m_{\text{sec}} = \frac{\Delta y}{\Delta x} = \frac{f(x_1 + \Delta x) - f(x_1)}{\Delta x}.$$

(1)

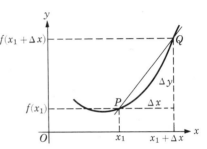

FIGURE 1–24

The division in Eq. (1) can only be *indicated* when we are talking about a general function $f(x)$, but for any specific equation such as $f(x) = x^3 - 3x + 3$ in Eq. (2) of Article 1–7, this division of Δy by Δx is actually to be carried out [as we did in going from Eq. (4) to Eq. (5)] *before* we do the next operation.

Having performed the division indicated in Eq. (1), we now investigate what happens if we hold x_1 fixed and take Δx to be smaller and smaller, approaching zero. If m_{sec} approaches a constant value, we call this value its *limit* and define this to be the slope m_{tan} of the tangent to the curve at P. The mathematical symbols which summarize this discussion are

$$m_{\text{tan}} = \lim_{Q \to P} m_{\text{sec}} = \lim_{\Delta x \to 0} \frac{\Delta y}{\Delta x} = \lim_{\Delta x \to 0} \frac{f(x_1 + \Delta x) - f(x_1)}{\Delta x}.$$

(2)

The symbol "lim" with "$\Delta x \to 0$" written beneath it is read "the limit, as Δx approaches zero, of ..."

The result of carrying out the operations represented by the last term in Eq. (2) produces a number which we have called m_{tan}, or the slope of the tangent to the curve $y = f(x)$ at the point $P(x_1, y_1)$. It is also customary to indicate that this number is related to the original function f by writing it as $f'(x_1)$ (read "f-prime at x_1"). Thus $f'(x_1)$ is *defined* by

$$f'(x_1) = \lim_{\Delta x \to 0} \frac{f(x_1 + \Delta x) - f(x_1)}{\Delta x}. \tag{3}$$

As mentioned above, the subscript 1 is used to emphasize the fact that x_1 is held constant while the various operations indicated on the right side of Eq. (3) are performed. The indicated limit may exist for some values of x_1 and fail to exist for other values. (We shall discuss this situation in more detail below.) At each point x_1 where the limit does exist, the function f is said to have a *derivative* (or to be *differentiable*) and the number $f'(x_1)$ is said to be the derivative of f at x_1.

The process of *finding the derivative of a function* is the fundamental operation of differential calculus. In fact we may now define *differential calculus* to be that branch of mathematics which is concerned with studying the following two general problems.

Problem I. Given a function f, determine those values of x (in the domain of f) at which the function possesses a derivative.

Problem II. Given a function f and an x at which the derivative exists, find $f'(x)$.

For example, in studying Eq. (2) of Article 1–7,

$$f(x) = x^3 - 3x + 3, \tag{4}$$

we found that for any x_1 whatever, the result of applying the operations on the right side of Eq. (3) gave us $3x_1^2 - 3$. That is, the function f in Eq. (4) possesses a derivative whose value at *any* x_1 is

$$f'(x_1) = 3x_1^2 - 3. \tag{5}$$

Thus the answer to Problem I above is: "The function f, Eq. (4), possesses a derivative at any x in the domain $-\infty < x < +\infty$," and the answer to Problem II is given by Eq. (5).

Now for most of the functions considered in this book, it will turn out that the answer to Problem I is that the derivative exists at all but a few values of x; that is, the places where the derivative fails to exist will be exceptional. Then the x_1 in Eq. (3) may be *any* of the nonexceptional values of x. Therefore, we might as well write x instead of x_1 in Eq. (3) if we remember that

x is to be held constant, while

Δx varies and approaches zero

in the calculation of the derivative

$$f'(x) = \lim_{\Delta x \to 0} \frac{f(x + \Delta x) - f(x)}{\Delta x}. \tag{6}$$

With this understanding, we shall henceforth omit the subscript 1 in talking about the derivative and shall use Eq. (6) to define the derivative of f, with respect to x, at any x in its domain for which the limit exists.

The derived function. Let x_1 be a number in the domain of the function f. If the limit indicated in Eq. (3) exists, then it provides a rule for associating a number $f'(x_1)$ with the number x_1. The set of all pairs of numbers $(x_1, f'(x_1))$ that can be formed by this process is called the *derived function* f'. The *domain* of f' is a subset of the domain of f. It contains all numbers x_1 in the domain of f such that the limit in (3) exists, but does not contain those exceptional values where the derivative fails to exist. The derived function f' is also called the *derivative* of f.

EXAMPLE 1. Consider the absolute value function

$$f(x) = |x|, \qquad -\infty < x < +\infty.$$

From the graph in Fig. 1–17 it is clear that the slope is $+1$ when x is positive and -1 when x is negative. But at $x_1 = 0$, the derivative fails to exist [the graph has no tangent at $(0, 0)$]. Hence the *domain* of the derived function does not include 0. It consists of all real numbers $x \neq 0$. The values of the derived function are given by the rule

$$f'(x) = \begin{cases} -1 & \text{if} \quad x < 0, \\ +1 & \text{if} \quad x > 0. \end{cases}$$

(See Problem 21, p. 34.)

Notations. In addition to $f'(x)$, various notations are used to denote the derivative of $y = f(x)$ with respect to x. The ones most commonly used are

$$y', \qquad \frac{dy}{dx}, \qquad \text{and} \qquad D_x y.$$

The last two of these may be interpreted as

$$\frac{dy}{dx} = \frac{d}{dx}(y),$$

where $\dfrac{d}{dx} \ldots$ stands for the operation "derivative with respect to x of" the expression following, and

$$D_x y = D_x(y)$$

with D_x ... meaning the same thing as $\dfrac{d}{dx}$ ... , namely, "derivative with respect to x of" the expression which follows it.

EXAMPLE 2. Find $f'(x)$ for the function

$$f(x) = x^2 + \frac{1}{x}, \qquad x \neq 0.$$

Solution. We carry out the operations indicated on the right side of Eq. (6) in the following order:

1. $f(x + \Delta x) = (x + \Delta x)^2 + \dfrac{1}{x + \Delta x}$

   $\qquad = x^2 + 2x\,\Delta x + (\Delta x)^2 + \dfrac{1}{x + \Delta x}$.

2. $f(x) = x^2 + \dfrac{1}{x}$.

Subtract 2 from 1:

3. $f(x + \Delta x) - f(x) = 2x\,\Delta x + (\Delta x)^2 + \dfrac{1}{x + \Delta x} - \dfrac{1}{x}$

   $\qquad = 2x\,\Delta x + (\Delta x)^2 + \dfrac{x - (x + \Delta x)}{x(x + \Delta x)}$

   $\qquad = \Delta x \left(2x + \Delta x - \dfrac{1}{x(x + \Delta x)} \right)$.

Divide by Δx:

4. $\dfrac{f(x + \Delta x) - f(x)}{\Delta x} = 2x + \Delta x - \dfrac{1}{x(x + \Delta x)}$.

5. $f'(x) = \lim\limits_{\Delta x \to 0} \dfrac{f(x + \Delta x) - f(x)}{\Delta x}$

   $\qquad = \lim\limits_{\Delta x \to 0} \left(2x + \Delta x - \dfrac{1}{x(x + \Delta x)} \right)$ \hfill (a)

   $\qquad = 2x + 0 - \dfrac{1}{x(x + 0)}$ \hfill (b)

   $\qquad = 2x - \dfrac{1}{x^2}$.

In a later article we shall discuss the validity of the various limit operations involved in going from (a) to (b) above. If we anticipate these results, we may say that *after* the division by Δx has been carried out and the expression has been reduced to a form [as in (a) above] which "makes sense" (that is, does not involve division by zero) when Δx is taken equal to zero, then the limit as Δx *approaches* zero does exist and may be found by simply replacing Δx by zero in this reduced form.

EXAMPLE 3. Find dy/dx if $y = \sqrt{x}$ and $x > 0$.

Solution. Let $y = \sqrt{x}$, $y + \Delta y = \sqrt{x + \Delta x}$, so that

$$\frac{\Delta y}{\Delta x} = \frac{\sqrt{x + \Delta x} - \sqrt{x}}{\Delta x}$$

$$= \frac{(\sqrt{x + \Delta x} - \sqrt{x})(\sqrt{x + \Delta x} + \sqrt{x})}{\Delta x(\sqrt{x + \Delta x} + \sqrt{x})} \qquad (a)$$

$$= \frac{(x + \Delta x) - x}{\Delta x(\sqrt{x + \Delta x} + \sqrt{x})} = \frac{1}{\sqrt{x + \Delta x} + \sqrt{x}}.$$

In step (a) we multiplied by a fraction equal to 1 and having a form such that it enabled us to get rid of the square roots in the numerator. Then in the next step we were able to carry out the division by Δx. Now we let Δx approach zero in the final form and have

$$\frac{dy}{dx} = \lim_{\Delta x \to 0} \frac{\Delta y}{\Delta x} = \lim_{\Delta x \to 0} \frac{1}{\sqrt{x + \Delta x} + \sqrt{x}} = \frac{1}{2\sqrt{x}}.$$

PROBLEMS

For each of the following functions f, find the derivative $f'(x)$, by means of the definition in Eq. (6).

1. $f(x) = x^2$

2. $f(x) = x^3$

3. $f(x) = 2x + 3$

4. $f(x) = x^2 - x + 1$

5. $f(x) = \dfrac{1}{x}$

6. $f(x) = \dfrac{1}{x^2}$

7. $f(x) = \dfrac{1}{2x + 1}$

8. $f(x) = \dfrac{x}{x + 1}$

9. $f(x) = 2x^2 - x + 5$

10. $f(x) = x^3 - 12x + 11$

11. $f(x) = x^4$

12. $f(x) = ax^2 + bx + c$ (a, b, c constants)

13. $f(x) = x - \dfrac{1}{x}$

14. $f(x) = ax + \dfrac{b}{x}$ (a, b constants)

15. $f(x) = \sqrt{2x}$

16. $f(x) = \sqrt{x + 1}$

17. $f(x) = \sqrt{2x + 3}$

18. $f(x) = \dfrac{1}{\sqrt{x}}$

19. $f(x) = \dfrac{1}{\sqrt{2x + 3}}$

20. $f(x) = \sqrt{x^2 + 1}$

21. In Example 1, $f(x) = |x|$, what is the *range* of the derived function f'? What is its graph? Compare the graphs of $y = f'(x)$ and $y = |x|/x, x \neq 0$.

1–9 Velocity and rates. When a body moves in a straight line, it is customary to represent the line of motion by a coordinate axis, select a reference point O on the line as origin, adopt a positive direction and a unit of distance on the line, and then describe the motion by means of an equation which gives the coordinate of the body as a function of the time t that has elapsed since the start of the motion.

Thus for a freely falling body, the equation of motion is

$$s = \tfrac{1}{2}gt^2, \tag{1}$$

where g is the acceleration due to gravity and is approximately 32 (ft/sec²), and s is the distance in feet that the body has fallen in t seconds from the start.

More generally, suppose the law of motion is given by a function f,

$$s = f(t), \tag{2}$$

and that we are required to find the *velocity* of the body at some instant of time t. First of all, how shall we *define* the instantaneous velocity of a moving body?

If we assume that *distance* and *time* are the fundamental physical quantities which we can measure, we may be led to reason as follows. At time t, the body is in the position

$$s = f(t), \tag{3}$$

and at time $t + \Delta t$ the body is in the position

$$s + \Delta s = f(t + \Delta t). \tag{4}$$

Hence during the interval of time from t to $t + \Delta t$, it has undergone a displacement

$$\Delta s = f(t + \Delta t) - f(t). \tag{5}$$

The quantities in Eqs. (3), (4), and (5) are all physical quantities which can be measured (by clocks and tapelines, say).

We now define the *average velocity* to be Δs divided by Δt:

$$v_{\text{av}} = \frac{\Delta s}{\Delta t} = \frac{f(t + \Delta t) - f(t)}{\Delta t}. \tag{6}$$

We are all familiar with applications of Eq. (6) in everyday life. For example, a sprinter runs 100 yards in 10 seconds. His average velocity is therefore

$$v_{av} = \frac{\Delta s}{\Delta t} = \frac{100 \ (yd)}{10 \ (sec)} = 10 \ (yd/sec).$$

In order to obtain the *instantaneous* velocity at time t, we take the average velocity over shorter and shorter intervals of time Δt. We are thereby led to the definition of instantaneous velocity, or what we call the velocity at time t, as the *limit* of v_{av} as Δt approaches zero; that is,

$$v = \lim_{\Delta t \to 0} \frac{\Delta s}{\Delta t} = \lim_{\Delta t \to 0} \frac{f(t + \Delta t) - f(t)}{\Delta t}. \tag{7}$$

We recognize that Eq. (7) is the same as the definition of the derivative

$$v = \frac{ds}{dt} = f'(t). \tag{8}$$

EXAMPLE. For the motion governed by Eq. (1),

$$s = \tfrac{1}{2}gt^2,$$

we find, by the methods of the previous article, that the velocity at time t is

$$v = \frac{ds}{dt} = gt.$$

When we refer to Fig. 1–25, we see that

$$v_{av} = \frac{\Delta s}{\Delta t}$$

is the slope of the secant line PQ in the sense of measuring its rate of rise in units of s per unit of t. Here there is no reason to suppose that the unit of length used on the t-axis to represent one second is the same as the unit of length used on the s-axis to represent one foot. And certainly the geometrical inclination ϕ of the secant line PQ depends upon the scales used to represent the units of time and distance on the two axes. We can still say, however, that the average velocity equals the ratio of the opposite side to the adjacent side in the triangle PRQ, each with its proper units (and proper sign). Then the instantaneous velocity can also be interpreted geometrically as the rate of rise of the tangent line in units of s per unit of t.

This geometrical interpretation is sometimes used to estimate the velocity when the motion is given by means of a graph instead of by an equation $s = f(t)$.

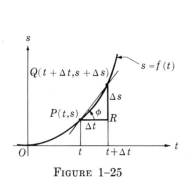

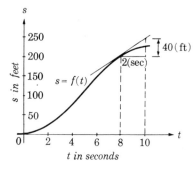

FIGURE 1–25   FIGURE 1–26

For example, in the graph of Fig. 1–26, s represents the coordinate of some point of a bicycle which a boy is riding along a straight road. At $t = 8$, the tangent line appears to be rising at the rate of 40 s-units in an interval of 2 t-units; that is, the velocity at time $t = 8$ is apparently

$$\frac{40 \ (\text{ft})}{2 \ (\text{sec})} = 20 \ (\text{ft/sec}).$$

We say the velocity is "apparently" 20 ft/sec because we cannot be sure that we have accurately constructed the tangent to the curve. Indeed, an accurate construction would require that we know the derivative $f'(t)$, exactly, at $t = 8$ and this is the very thing we are trying to estimate. On the other hand, we can make a fair approximation to the tangent line by inspection and this is what we have done in the graph.

There are many other applications of the notion of average rate and instantaneous rate. For example, the quantity of water Q (gal) in a reservoir at time t (min) is a function of t. Water may flow into or out of the reservoir. As it does so, suppose that Q changes by an amount ΔQ from time t to time $t + \Delta t$. Then the average rate of change of Q with respect to t is

$$\frac{\Delta Q}{\Delta t} \ (\text{gal/min})$$

and the instantaneous rate of change of Q with respect to t is

$$\frac{dQ}{dt} = \lim_{\Delta t \to 0} \frac{\Delta Q}{\Delta t} \ (\text{gal/min}).$$

Derivatives are important in economic theory, where they are usually indicated by the adjective "*marginal.*" Suppose, for example, that a manufacturer produces x tons of steel per week at a total cost of $y = f(x)$ dollars. This total cost includes such items as a proportionate part of the cost of building and maintaining the company's steel mills, salaries of executives, taxes, office maintenance, cost of raw materials, labor, etc. Suppose that in order to produce $x + \Delta x$ tons of steel weekly, it would cost $y + \Delta y$ dollars. The increase in cost per unit increase in output would be $\Delta y/\Delta x$. The limit of this ratio, as Δx tends to zero, is called the *marginal cost*. In other words, if total cost is y for weekly output x, then the *marginal* cost is just the derivative of y with respect to x. It gives the rate of increase of cost per unit increase of output from the level x.

The manufacturer is also interested in revenue and in profits. In order to sell his output of x tons per week he finds that he may charge a price $P = F(x)$ per ton. [Usually, at a higher price he would sell less; at a lower price he could sell more.] Then his *revenue* is the product $xP = xF(x)$. The *marginal* revenue is the *derivative* of xP with respect to x. It gives the rate of increase of revenue per unit increase in output. The manufacturer's profit, T, is the difference between revenue and cost:

$$T = xP - y.$$

In Chapter 3 we shall see how the manufacturer should adjust his production to achieve maximum profit. The adjustment involves his *marginal* profit, $\dfrac{dT}{dx}$, which is the rate of increase of profit per unit increase of production. (For a further discussion of applications to economics, see the book *Mathematical Analysis for Economists* by R. G. D. Allen, published by the Macmillan Co., New York, 1939. In particular, marginal cost and marginal revenue are discussed on pp. 152 ff.)

Any derivative may be interpreted as the instantaneous rate of change of one variable per unit change in the other. Thus, if the function defined by $y = f(x)$ has a derivative

$$f'(x) = \lim_{\Delta x \to 0} \frac{\Delta y}{\Delta x} = \lim_{\Delta x \to 0} \frac{f(x + \Delta x) - f(x)}{\Delta x},$$

we may interpret $\Delta y/\Delta x$ as *average* rate of change and

$$f'(x) = \lim_{\Delta x \to 0} \frac{\Delta y}{\Delta x}$$

as *instantaneous* rate of change of y with respect to x. Such a rate tells us the amount of change that would be produced in y by a change of one unit in x, provided the rate of change remained constant.

The *average* rate of change of y per unit change in x, $\Delta y/\Delta x$, when multiplied by the number of units change in x, Δx, gives the actual change in y:

$$\Delta y = \frac{\Delta y}{\Delta x}\, \Delta x.$$

The *instantaneous* rate of change of y per unit change in x, $f'(x)$, multiplied by the number of units change in x, Δx, gives the change that would be produced in y if the point (x, y) were to move along the *tangent line* instead of moving along the curve; that is (Fig. 1–27),

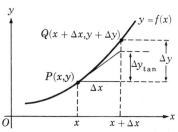

$$\Delta y_{\text{tan}} = f'(x) \cdot \Delta x.$$

One reason calculus is important is that it enables us to find quantitatively how a change in one of two related variables affects the second variable.

FIGURE 1–27

PROBLEMS

1. If a, b, c are constants and

$$f(t) = at^2 + bt + c,$$

show that

$$f'(t) = \lim_{\Delta t \to 0} \frac{f(t + \Delta t) - f(t)}{\Delta t} = 2at + b.$$

In the following problems (2 through 10), the law of motion gives s as a function of t. Apply the *result* found in Problem 1 above to write the velocity, $v = \dfrac{ds}{dt}$, by inspection.

2. $s = 2t^2 + 5t - 3$

3. $s = \frac{1}{2}gt^2 + v_0t + s_0$
   (g, v_0, s_0 constants)

4. $s = 4t + 3$

5. $s = t^2 - 3t + 2$

6. $s = 4 - 2t - t^2$

7. $s = (2t + 3)^2$

8. $s = (2 - t)^2$

9. $s = 3 - 2t^2$

10. $s = 64t - 16t^2$

11. The following data give the coordinate s of a moving body for various values of t. Plot s vs. t on coordinate paper and sketch a smooth curve through the given points. Assuming that this smooth curve represents the motion of the body, estimate the velocity (a) at $t = 1.0$, (b) at $t = 2.5$, (c) at $t = 2.0$.

s (in ft)	10	38	58	70	74	70	58	38	10
t (in sec)	0	0.5	1.0	1.5	2.0	2.5	3.0	3.5	4.0

12. A swimming pool is to be drained for cleaning. If Q represents the number of gallons of water in the pool t minutes after the pool has started to drain, and $Q = 200 (30 - t)^2$, how fast is the water running out at the end of 10

minutes? What is the *average* rate at which the water flows out during the first 10 minutes?

13. (a) If the radius of a circle changes from r to $r + \Delta r$, what is the average rate of change of the area of the circle with respect to the radius? (b) Find the instantaneous rate of change of the area with respect to the radius.

14. The volume V (ft^3) of a sphere of radius r (ft) is $V = \frac{4}{3}\pi r^3$. Find the rate of change of V with respect to r.

15. The radius r and altitude h of a certain cone are equal at all times. Find the rate of change of the volume $V = \frac{1}{3}\pi r^2 h$ with respect to h.

1–10 Properties of limits. The calculation of the derivative of a function,

$$y = f(x), \tag{1}$$

involves the calculation of a limit

$$f'(x) = \lim_{\Delta x \to 0} \frac{f(x + \Delta x) - f(x)}{\Delta x}, \tag{2}$$

as illustrated in the preceding articles. In the next chapter we shall develop some rules which make it very easy to find the derivatives of many functions without having to go through the computations involved in a direct application of Eq. (2). These rules must ultimately rest upon this defining equation, however, and must themselves be derived from this fundamental definition of the derivative.

In this article we shall investigate more carefully what it means to say that something "has a limit." The limits we are most concerned with are of the kind indicated in Eq. (2). Let us return once more to the specific example

$$f(x) = x^3 - 3x + 3, \tag{3}$$

which we investigated in Article 1–7, Eqs. (2) through (6). By algebra we find that

$$\frac{f(x + \Delta x) - f(x)}{\Delta x} = 3x^2 - 3 + 3x\,\Delta x + (\Delta x)^2. \tag{4}$$

So far the notion of limit has not entered. But now we say "hold x fixed and make Δx approach zero." That is, Δx is to vary in Eq. (4), while x is held constant. What is the *domain* of the variable Δx in this equation? The answer is that Δx in the first place must be such that the function in (3) is defined at $x + \Delta x$; that is, $f(x + \Delta x)$ must make sense. But in the present case, this in itself places no restriction on Δx, since Eq. (3) is defined for all real $x + \Delta x$, $-\infty < x + \Delta x < +\infty$. There is also a second restriction on Δx, namely, Δx must be *different from zero*. Why? Because the left side of Eq. (4) would become $0/0$, which is meaningless, if we were to put $\Delta x = 0$ in it. Thus we have reached a crucial point.

We are interested in what happens in Eq. (4) as Δx is taken nearer and nearer to zero, yet we cannot in all honesty take $\Delta x = 0$ because then we have a meaningless expression on the left.

Two things should now be emphasized. The first of these is that the *division* in Eq. (2) is to be performed *before* we let Δx approach zero. Thus, in Eq. (4), no matter how small Δx is, provided it is not zero, the division as indicated gives the expression on the right side of the equation. The second point to be emphasized is that the expression on the right side of (4), which depends upon both x and Δx and which we shall therefore indicate as a function F of x and Δx,

$$F(x, \Delta x) = 3x^2 - 3 + 3x\,\Delta x + (\Delta x)^2, \tag{5}$$

can be made to be as *nearly equal* to

$$L(x) = 3x^2 - 3 \tag{6}$$

as we wish (provided we don't wish for *exact* equality) by taking Δx *sufficiently close* to zero.

In common terms, let us say that we are manufacturers of a product [in this case our factory produces $F(x, \Delta x)$ as in Eq. (5)] which, if we could achieve absolute *perfection*, would be the $L(x)$ in Eq. (6). A buyer comes to us to place an order. He is very particular, but he does not expect perfection. He requires only that we guarantee to produce a product which differs from absolute perfection by an amount less than some "tolerance limit" which he will specify. In other words, he will buy our $F(x, \Delta x)$ if we guarantee that it lies between

$$L(x) - \epsilon \quad \text{and} \quad L(x) + \epsilon,$$

where ϵ (epsilon) is a positive number representing the "tolerance limit" he will prescribe. Now the way we control the quality of the product we make, i.e., $F(x, \Delta x)$, is by making Δx small. By taking pains, we can make Δx as close to zero (either positive or negative) as we wish. The amount of "imperfection" in our product, namely

$$F(x, \Delta x) - L(x) = 3x\,\Delta x + (\Delta x)^2, \tag{7}$$

is to be made to lie between $-\epsilon$ and $+\epsilon$:

$$-\epsilon < 3x\,\Delta x + (\Delta x)^2 < +\epsilon, \tag{8}$$

by making Δx *close* to zero. Now it is clear that we can satisfy the most exacting customer. He places his order and specifies his ϵ. Then for any fixed x, the inequalities in (8) can be satisfied simply by making Δx come *close* to zero. That is, there is a positive number δ (delta), which may be very small, such that if we control the precision of Δx to a fineness $-\delta < \Delta x < +\delta$, ($\Delta x \neq 0$), we can guarantee the accuracy demanded by (8).

These preliminary remarks should now enable us to understand the following definition of a limit.

DEFINITION. *Let $F(x, \Delta x)$ be defined for some fixed value of x and for all values of Δx (different from zero) in some interval $-h < \Delta x < +h$, that is, for $-h < \Delta x < 0$ and for $0 < \Delta x < +h$. Let there be a number $L(x)$ (which may depend upon x), such that to any positive number ϵ, there corresponds a positive number δ, $0 < \delta < h$, having the property that $F(x, \Delta x)$ differs from $L(x)$ by less than ϵ when $|\Delta x|$ is different from zero and is less than δ. That is, if*

$$0 < |\Delta x| < \delta, \tag{9a}$$

then

$$|F(x, \Delta x) - L(x)| < \epsilon. \tag{9b}$$

We then say that $L(x)$ is the *limit* of $F(x, \Delta x)$ as Δx approaches zero, and abbreviate this by writing

$$L(x) = \lim_{\Delta x \to 0} F(x, \Delta x). \tag{10}$$

The notation in the definition above is complicated by the fact that the function $F(x, \Delta x)$ whose limit we have been discussing depends upon both x and Δx, although only Δx varies during the limit process. If we ignore the x completely and use another letter, say t instead of Δx, to stand for the variable, we obtain a simpler definition of limit as follows.

DEFINITION. *A function F which is defined on the domain*

$$t_1 < t < c \quad and \quad c < t < t_2$$

is said to approach the limit L as t approaches c, and we write

$$\lim_{t \to c} F(t) = L$$

FIGURE 1–28

if, given any positive number ϵ, there is a positive number δ such that the functional values $F(t)$ are within ϵ of L whenever t is within δ of c, $t \neq c$:

$$\boxed{|F(t) - L| < \epsilon \quad when \quad 0 < |t - c| < \delta.}$$

Note that saying "$F(t)$ approaches L" is the same as saying "$F(t) - L$ approaches zero."

The function F may or may not be defined at $t = c$. We shall illustrate the meaning of the definition by several examples.

EXAMPLE 1. $F(t) = t^2$, $c = 3$, $\lim_{t \to 3} t^2 = 9$. Here the function F is defined for all real t, $|t| < \infty$.

If challenged with a "tolerance limit" ϵ which is required only to be *positive*, and may be very small, we ask ourselves how close t must be to $c = 3$ in order to make the functional values t^2 lie between $9 - \epsilon$ and $9 + \epsilon$. In other words, we are *to find a positive number δ* such that

$$|t^2 - 9| < \epsilon \qquad \text{when} \qquad 0 < |t - 3| < \delta.$$

We see that

$$t^2 - 9 = (t - 3)(t + 3)$$

is the product of a factor $t - 3$, *which we can force to be small* by taking t close to 3, and a factor $t + 3$, which will be approximately equal to $3 + 3 = 6$ when t is close to 3. Certainly this larger factor can be made less than 7, say, if we make the requirement

$$|t - 3| < 1.$$

We do this. Then t lies between 2 and 4, and hence

$$|t + 3| < 7.$$

Therefore we have the inequality

$$|t^2 - 9| = |(t + 3)(t - 3)| < 7|t - 3|.$$

Now we further restrict t so that

$$7|t - 3| < \epsilon,$$

that is,

$$|t - 3| < \frac{\epsilon}{7}.$$

If we now take δ equal to the smaller of $(\epsilon/7, 1)$, we can be sure that

$$|t^2 - 9| < \epsilon$$

is satisfied provided

$$0 < |t - 3| < \delta.$$

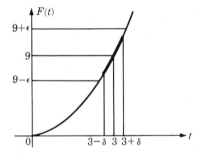

FIGURE 1–29

Figure 1–29 shows the geometrical significance of ϵ and δ. We see that $F(t) = t^2$ lies between $9 - \epsilon$ and $9 + \epsilon$ when t lies between $3 - \delta$ and $3 + \delta$.

EXAMPLE 2. Let us find the limit of

$$F(t) = \frac{t^2 - 9}{t - 3}$$

as t approaches 3. Now the function we are dealing with is defined everywhere *except at* $t = 3$. If we try to substitute $t = 3$ to calculate $F(3)$, we get

$$\frac{t^2 - 9}{t - 3} = \frac{9 - 9}{3 - 3} = \frac{0}{0},$$

which is meaningless. But the definition of

$$\lim_{t \to 3} F(t) = L$$

does not require that the function $F(t)$ be defined at $t = 3$. All that matters is what happens when t is *nearly* equal to 3. Now, using elementary algebra and factoring $t^2 - 9$, we find that

$$F(t) = \frac{(t - 3)(t + 3)}{(t - 3)} = t + 3 \qquad \text{when} \qquad t \neq 3.$$

That is, for *all* values of t *different from* 3,

$$F(t) = t + 3.$$

Then when t is nearly equal to 3, $F(t)$ is *nearly* equal to 6. Hence we assert that

$$\lim_{t \to 3} \frac{t^2 - 9}{t - 3} = \lim_{t \to 3} (t + 3) = 6.$$

Let us now show that the conditions of our definition of a limit are satisfied by taking $L = 6$. To this end, let ϵ be any positive number (*presumably small*). Then

$$F(t) - L = \frac{t^2 - 9}{t - 3} - 6 = (t + 3) - 6 = t - 3,$$

and in order to make

$$|F(t) - L| < \epsilon$$

we need only require

$$0 < |t - 3| < \epsilon.$$

Here we may take $\delta = \epsilon$ or any smaller positive number.

EXAMPLE 3. Find the limit of the function F (Fig. 1–30) defined by

$$F(t) = [t] = (\text{"greatest integer in } t\text{"})$$

as t approaches 3. Our first guess might be that the required limit is $L = 3$, since certainly the functional values of $F(t) = [t]$ are close to 3 when t is equal to or slightly *greater* than 3. But when t is slightly *less* than 3, say $t = 2.9999$, then $[t] = 2$. That is, if δ is any positive number less than unity, $0 < \delta < 1$, then

$$[t] = 2 \qquad \text{if} \qquad 3 - \delta < t < 3,$$

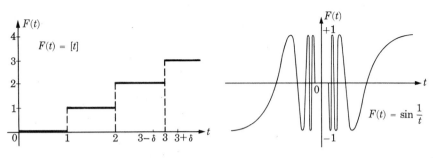

FIGURE 1–30   FIGURE 1–31

while $[t] = 3$ if $3 < t < 3 + \delta.$

Hence if we are challenged with a small positive ϵ, for example $\epsilon = 0.01$, we cannot find $\delta > 0$, which makes

$$|[t] - 3| < \epsilon \qquad \text{for} \qquad 0 < |t - 3| < \delta.$$

In fact, there is no number L that will work as the limit in this case, since when t is near 3 *some* of the functional values of $[t]$ are 2 while others are 3, and hence they are not all close to any one number L. That is,

$$\lim_{t \to 3} [t] \text{ does not exist.}$$

The so-called "right- and left-hand limits" do, however, exist. As the names imply, the right-hand limit $L+$ is a number such that the functional values of $F(t)$ are close to $L+$ when t is slightly greater than 3 (that is, to the right of 3), and the left-hand limit $L-$ is a number such that $F(t)$ is close to $L-$ when t is slightly less than 3. In our example,

$$L+ = \lim_{t \to 3+} [t] = 3, \qquad L- = \lim_{t \to 3-} [t] = 2.$$

The notation $t \to 3+$ may be read "t approaches 3 from above" (or "from the right," or "through values larger than 3") with an analogous meaning for $t \to 3-$.

EXAMPLE 4. The function F, $F(t) = \sin (1/t)$, $t \neq 0$, possesses no limit as $t \to 0$. This is a consequence of the fact that in every neighborhood of $t = 0$ the function F takes all values between -1 and $+1$. Hence there is no single number L such that the functional values $F(t)$ are *all* close to L when t is close to zero. These remarks apply even when we restrict t to positive values or to negative values. In other words, this function does not even have a right-hand limit or a left-hand limit as t approaches zero. (See Fig. 1–31.)

Many more examples could be given, but we must now turn our attention instead to some fundamental properties of limits. We shall state these properties in the form of a theorem for future reference.

THEOREM 1. *If $L_1 = \lim\limits_{t \to c} F_1(t)$ and $L_2 = \lim\limits_{t \to c} F_2(t)$ both exist and are finite, then*

(i) $\lim [F_1(t) + F_2(t)] = \lim F_1(t) + \lim F_2(t) = L_1 + L_2,$

(ii) $\lim [kF_1(t)] = k \lim F_1(t) = kL_1$ (*k any number*),

(iii) $\lim [F_1(t) \cdot F_2(t)] = \lim F_1(t) \cdot \lim F_2(t) = L_1L_2,$

(iv) $\lim \dfrac{F_1(t)}{F_2(t)} = \dfrac{\lim F_1(t)}{\lim F_2(t)} = \dfrac{L_1}{L_2},$ *if* $L_2 \neq 0,$

it being understood that all of the limits are to be taken as $t \to c$.

We shall not give a formal proof of this theorem, but shall only indicate the method used in part (iii). The same technique applies in the other cases as well. We therefore assume that

$$\lim F_1(t) = L_1,$$
$$\lim F_2(t) = L_2.$$

This means that by taking t close to c we can make the "errors"

$$F_1(t) - L_1 = \epsilon_1,$$
$$F_2(t) - L_2 = \epsilon_2,$$

arbitrarily small. Then we have

$$F_1(t) = L_1 + \epsilon_1,$$
$$F_2(t) = L_2 + \epsilon_2,$$
$$F_1(t)F_2(t) = L_1L_2 + \epsilon_1L_2 + \epsilon_2L_1 + \epsilon_1\epsilon_2.$$

Suppose now that we are challenged with an $\epsilon > 0$. As $t \to c$ the terms involving ϵ_1 and ϵ_2 on the right side of the last equation can each be made smaller than $\epsilon/3$, say, by restricting t to lie sufficiently near c; that is, we may find a $\delta > 0$ such that

$$|\epsilon_1L_2| < \frac{\epsilon}{3}, \qquad |\epsilon_2L_1| < \frac{\epsilon}{3}, \qquad |\epsilon_1\epsilon_2| < \frac{\epsilon}{3}$$

when

$$0 < |t - c| < \delta.$$

Thus the conditions for the existence of a limit are satisfied with

$$L = L_1L_2 \qquad \text{and} \qquad F(t) = F_1(t)F_2(t).$$

It should be noted that the limits must be *finite* in this theorem, and that (iv) applies only if the denominator does not tend to zero.

We should add a word about the meaning to be attached to such statements as: "When t approaches zero, $1/t$ approaches infinity" or, in symbols,

$$\lim_{t\to 0} \frac{1}{t} = \infty.$$

The usual meaning of the more general expression

$$\lim_{t\to c} F(t) = \infty$$

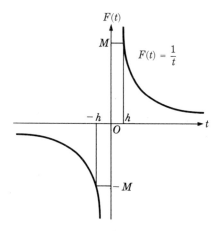

FIGURE 1–32

is: "For any M, however large it may be, there is an $h > 0$ such that $|F(t)| > M$ for all t satisfying $0 < |t - c| < h$." Note that this allows $F(t)$ to be either negative or positive provided only that the *numerical* or *absolute* value of $F(t)$ can be made indefinitely large by taking t sufficiently close to c. If we may replace $|F(t)| > M$ by $F(t) > M$ in the above statement, we say $\lim F(t) = +\infty$, and if we may replace $|F(t)| > M$ by $F(t) < -M$, we say $\lim F(t) = -\infty$. Thus

$$\lim_{t\to 0} \frac{1}{t} = \infty, \qquad \lim_{t\to 0} \frac{1}{t^2} = +\infty.$$

If we distinguish between left-hand limits and right-hand limits, we may write

$$\lim_{t\to 0-} \left(\frac{1}{t}\right) = -\infty, \qquad \lim_{t\to 0+} \left(\frac{1}{t}\right) = +\infty,$$

where by $t \to 0-$ and $t \to 0+$, we mean that t tends to zero through negative or positive values respectively. Thus when speaking of infinity as the limit of a function f, we do not mean that the difference between $f(t)$ and infinity becomes small, but rather that $f(t)$ is numerically large when t is near c.

The condition $L_2 \neq 0$ in part (iv) of the theorem means, of course, that such limits as were required in the determination of instantaneous velocity and the slope of a curve, all of which would have *both* L_1 and L_2 equal to zero, cannot be evaluated by the direct use of (iv), which would give $(L_1/L_2) = (0/0)$. Such limits, for example, as

$$\lim_{t\to 3} \frac{t^2 - t - 6}{t - 3},$$

with $F_1(t) = t^2 - t - 6$ and $F_2(t) = t - 3$, for which $L_1 = 9 - 3 - 6 = 0$ and $L_2 = 3 - 3 = 0$, are to be evaluated as we have done in the past by *dividing first*, then taking the limit, thus:

$$\lim_{t \to 3} \frac{t^2 - t - 6}{t - 3} = \lim_{t \to 3} (t + 2) = 5.$$

We conclude this article with a theorem which is used repeatedly in our later work.

THEOREM 2. *Suppose $f(t) \leq g(t) \leq h(t)$ for all values of t near c. Furthermore, suppose that the function values $f(t)$ and $h(t)$ approach a common limit L as t approaches c. Then $g(t)$ also approaches L as limit when t approaches c.*

Proof. By hypothesis, to any positive number ϵ there corresponds a positive number δ such that both $f(t)$ and $h(t)$ lie between $L - \epsilon$ and $L + \epsilon$ when t is within δ units of c; that is,

$$L - \epsilon < f(t) < L + \epsilon, \qquad L - \epsilon < h(t) < L + \epsilon$$

when

$$0 < |t - c| < \delta.$$

But this also implies

$$L - \epsilon < f(t) \leq g(t) \leq h(t) < L + \epsilon$$

or

$$L - \epsilon < g(t) < L + \epsilon.$$

In other words,

$$|g(t) - L| < \epsilon \qquad \text{when} \qquad 0 < |t - c| < \delta.$$

This establishes the conclusion,

$$\lim_{t \to c} g(t) = L. \qquad \text{Q.E.D.}$$

PROBLEMS

Evaluate the limits indicated in Problems 1–7.

1. $\lim_{t \to 2} \dfrac{t + 3}{t + 2}$

2. $\lim_{x \to 1} \dfrac{x^2 - 1}{x - 1}$

3. $\lim_{y \to 2} \dfrac{y^2 + 5y + 6}{y + 2}$

4. $\lim_{y \to 2} \dfrac{y^2 - 5y + 6}{y - 2}$

5. $\lim\limits_{x \to -3} \dfrac{x^2 + 4x + 3}{x + 3}$ 6. $\lim\limits_{t \to \infty} \dfrac{t + 1}{t^2 + 1} \left[\text{Let } t = \dfrac{1}{h}, \ h \to 0 \right]$

7. $\lim\limits_{t \to \infty} \dfrac{t^2 - 2t + 3}{2t^2 + 5t - 3}$

8. Find some neighborhood of $t = 3$, that is, a domain $0 < |t - 3| < \delta$, such that when t is restricted to this domain the difference between $t^2 + t$ and 12 will be numerically smaller than (a) $\frac{1}{10}$, (b) $\frac{1}{100}$, (c) ϵ, where ϵ may be any positive number.

9. As $x \to 0+$, the functions $1/x$, $1/x^2$, $1/\sqrt{x}$ all become infinite. Which one increases most rapidly and which one least rapidly?

REVIEW QUESTIONS AND EXERCISES FOR CHAPTER 1

1. Define what is meant by the *slope* of a straight line. How would you find the slope of a straight line from its graph? From its equation?

2. In Fig. 1–33, the lines L_1, L_2, and L_3 have slopes m_1, m_2, m_3, respectively. Which slope is algebraically least? Greatest? Write the three slopes in order of increasing size with the symbols for "less than" or "greater than" correctly inserted between them.

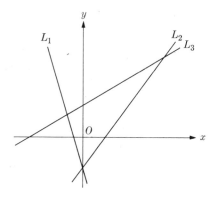

FIG. 1–33. Lines L_1, L_2, L_3 have slopes m_1, m_2, m_3, respectively.

3. Describe the family of lines $y - y_1 = m(x - x_1)$:

(a) If (x_1, y_1) is fixed and different lines are drawn for different values of m.

(b) If m and x_1 are fixed and different lines are drawn for different values of y_1.

4. Define *function*. What is the *domain* of a function? What is its *range*?

5. The domain of a certain function is the set $0 \le x \le 2$. The range of the function is the single number $y = 1$.

(a) Sketch and describe the graph of the function.

(b) Write an expression for the function.

(c) If we interchange the axes in part (a), does the new graph so obtained represent a function? Explain.

6. Give an example, different from those mentioned in the text, of a step-function.

7. Give an example, different from those in the text, of a function whose domain could be the set of all real numbers, $-\infty < x < +\infty$.

8. **DEFINITION.** *A rational number is one that can be expressed in the form* p/q, *where* p *and* q *are integers with no common divisor greater than one, and* $q > 0$. *A real number that is not rational is called* irrational.

With these definitions in mind, plot a few points on the graph of the function that maps the rational number p/q (reduced to lowest terms as above) into $1/q$, and maps each irrational number into zero. This function has been described as the "ruler function" because of the resemblance of its graph to the markings on an ordinary ruler showing inches, half-inches, quarters, eighths, and sixteenths by lines of different lengths. The edge of the ruler corresponds to the x-axis. Do you see why this terminology is rather appropriate?

9. Is it appropriate to define a *tangent line* to a curve C at a point P on C as a line that has just the one point P in common with C? Illustrate your discussion with graphs.

10. Define, carefully, the concept of slope of a tangent to a curve at a point on the curve.

11. Define the concept of *average velocity*, of *instantaneous velocity*.

12. What more general concept includes both the concept of slope of the tangent to a curve and the concept of instantaneous velocity?

13. Define the derivative of a function at a point in its domain. Illustrate your definition by applying it to the function f defined by $f(x) = x^2$, at the point $x = 2$.

14. A function f, whose domain is the set of all real numbers, has the property that $f(x + h) = f(x) \cdot f(h)$ for all x and h; and $f(0) \neq 0$.

(a) Show that $f(0) = 1$. [*Hint:* Let $h = x = 0$.]

(b) If f has a derivative at 0, show that f has a derivative at every real number x, and that

$$f'(x) = f(x) \cdot f'(0).$$

15. Give an example of a function, defined for all real x, that fails to have a derivative (a) at some point, (b) at several points, (c) at infinitely many points.

16. Suppose F is a function whose values are all less than or equal to some constant M; $F(t) \leq M$. Prove: If $\lim_{t \to c} F(t) = L$, then $L \leq M$.

[*Suggestion:* An indirect proof may be used to show that $L > M$ is false. For, if $L > M$, we may take $\frac{1}{2}(L - M)$ as a positive number ϵ, apply the definition of limit, and arrive at a contradiction.]

MISCELLANEOUS PROBLEMS FOR CHAPTER 1

1. (a) Plot the points $A(8, 1)$, $B(2, 10)$, $C(-4, 6)$, $D(2, -3)$, $E(4\frac{2}{3}, 6)$.

(b) Find the slopes of the lines AB, BC, CD, DA, CE, BD.

(c) Do four of the five points A, B, C, D, E form a parallelogram? (Why?)

(d) Do three of the five points lie on a common straight line? (Why?)

(e) Does the origin $(0, 0)$ lie on a straight line through two of the five points? (Why?)

(f) Find equations of the lines AB, CD, AD, CE, BD.

(g) Find the coordinates of the points in which the lines AB, CD, AD, CE, BD intersect the x- and y-axes.

2. Given the straight line $2y - 3x = 4$ and the point $(1, -3)$.

(a) Find the equation of the straight line through the given point and perpendicular to the given line.

(b) Find the shortest distance from the given point to the given line.

3. Plot the three points $A(6, 4)$, $B(4, -3)$, and $C(-2, 3)$.

(a) Is triangle ABC a right triangle? Why?

(b) Is it isosceles? Why?

(c) Does the origin lie inside, outside, or on the boundary of the triangle? Why?

(d) If C is replaced by a point $C'(-2, y)$ such that angle $C'BA$ is a right angle, find y, the ordinate of C'.

4. Find the equations of the straight lines passing through the origin which are tangent to the circle of center $(2, 1)$ and radius 2.

5. Let $P_1(x_1, y_1)$ and $P_2(x_2, y_2)$ be any two points. Find the coordinates of the midpoint of the line segment P_1P_2.

6. The x- and y-intercepts of a line L are respectively a and b. Show that an equation of L is $(x/a) + (y/b) = 1$.

7. Given the line L: $ax + by + c = 0$. Find (a) its slope, (b) its y-intercept, (c) its x-intercept, (d) the line through the origin perpendicular to L.

8. Show that the distance from a point $P(x_1, y_1)$ to a line $ax + by + c = 0$ is equal to

$$\frac{|ax_1 + by_1 + c|}{\sqrt{a^2 + b^2}}.$$

(There are neat solutions of this problem in Vol. 59, 1952, of the *American Mathematical Monthly*, pp. 242 and 248.)

9. How many circles can you find that are tangent to the three lines

$$L_1: x + y = 1; \quad L_2: y = x + 1; \quad L_3: x - 3y = 1?$$

Give the center and radius of at least one such circle. You may use the result of Problem 8 that the distance from a point $P(x_1, y_1)$ to a line $ax + by + c = 0$ is

$$\frac{|ax_1 + by_1 + c|}{\sqrt{a^2 + b^2}}$$

10. Find, in terms of b, b', and m, the perpendicular distance between the parallel lines $y = mx + b$ and $y = mx + b'$.

11. Given the two lines

$$L_1: a_1x + b_1y + c_1 = 0; \qquad L_2: a_2x + b_2y + c_2 = 0.$$

If k is a constant, what is the locus whose equation is

$$(a_1x + b_1y + c_1) + k(a_2x + b_2y + c_2) = 0?$$

12. Determine the coordinates of the point on the straight line $y = 3x + 1$ that is equidistant from $(0, 0)$ and $(-3, 4)$.

13. Find the equation of a straight line which is perpendicular to $5x - y = 1$ and is such that the area of the triangle formed by the x-axis, the y-axis, and the straight line is equal to 5.

14. Given the equation $y = (x^2 + 2)/(x^2 - 1)$. Express x in terms of y and determine the range of values of y for which x is real.

15. Express the area A and the circumference C of a circle as functions of the radius r. Express A as a function of C.

16. In each of the following functions, what is the largest domain of x and the corresponding range of y?

(a) $y = \dfrac{1}{1+x}$; \qquad (b) $y = \dfrac{1}{1+x^2}$; \qquad (c) $y = \dfrac{1}{1+\sqrt{x}}$.

17. Without the use of the absolute value symbol, describe the domain of x for which $|x + 1| < 4$.

18. If $y = 2x + |2 - x|$, determine x as a function of y.

19. For what range of values of y does the equation $y = x + |2 - x|$ determine x as a single-valued function of y? Solve for x in terms of y on this range of values.

20. If $y = x + (1/x)$, express x as a function of y and determine the range of y for which x is real.

21. (a) If $f(x) = x^2 + 2x - 3$, find $f(-2); f(-1); f(x_1); f(x_1 + \Delta x)$.

(b) If $f(x) = x - (1/x)$, show that $f(1/x) = -f(x) = f(-x)$.

22. Sketch the graph of each of the following equations:

(a) $y = |x - 2| + 2$; \qquad\qquad (b) $y = x^2 - 1$.

(c) Find the point on the curve in part (b) where the tangent to the curve makes an angle of $45°$ with the positive x-axis.

23. Sketch a graph of the function $y = |x + 2| + x$ for the domain $-5 \le x \le 2$. What is the range?

24. Show that the expression $M(a, b) = (a + b)/2 + |a - b|/2$ is equal to a when $a \ge b$ and is equal to b when $b \ge a$. In other words, $M(a, b)$ gives the larger of the two numbers a and b. Find a similar expression, $m(a, b)$, which gives the smaller of the two numbers.

25. For each of the following expressions $f(x)$, sketch first the graph of $y = f(x)$, then the graph of $y = |f(x)|$ and finally the graph of $y = f(x)/2 + |f(x)|/2$.

(a) $f(x) = (x - 2)(x + 1)$;   (b) $f(x) = x^2$;

(c) $f(x) = -x^2$;   (d) $f(x) = 4 - x^2$.

26. *Lagrange interpolation formula.* Let (x_1, y_1), (x_2, y_2), ..., (x_n, y_n) be n points in the plane, no two of them having the same abscissas. Find a polynomial, $f(x)$, of degree $(n - 1)$ which takes the value y_1 at x_1, y_2 at x_2, ..., y_n at x_n; that is, $f(x_i) = y_i$ ($i = 1, 2, \ldots, n$). [*Hint:* $f(x) = y_1\phi_1(x) + y_2\phi_2(x) + \cdots + y_n\phi_n(x)$, where $\phi_k(x)$ is a polynomial which is zero at x_i ($i \neq k$) and $\phi_k(x_k) = 1$.]

27. Let $f(x) = ax + b$ and $g(x) = cx + d$. What condition must be satisfied by the constants a, b, c, and d in order that $f(g(x))$ and $g(f(x))$ shall be identical?

28. Let $f(x) = (ax + b)/(cx + d)$. If $d = -a$, show that $f(f(x)) = x$, identically.

29. If $f(x) = x/(x - 1)$, find (a) $f(1/x)$, (b) $f(-x)$, (c) $f(f(x))$, (d) $f(1/f(x))$.

30. Using the definition of the derivative, find $f'(x)$ if $f(x)$ is

(a) $(x - 1)/(x + 1)$,   (b) $x^{3/2}$,   (c) $x^{1/3}$.

31. Use the definition of the derivative to find

(a) $f'(x)$ if $f(x) = x^2 - 3x - 4$,

(b) $\dfrac{dy}{dx}$ if $y = \dfrac{1}{3x} + 2x$,

(c) $f'(t)$ if $f(t) = \sqrt{t - 4}$.

32. (a) By means of the Δ-method, find the slope of the curve $y = 2x^3 + 2$ at the point $(1, 4)$. (b) At which point of the curve in (a) is the tangent to the curve parallel to the x-axis? Sketch the curve.

33. If $f(x) = 2x/(x - 1)$, find (a) $f(0), f(-1), f(1/x)$; (b) $\Delta f(x)/\Delta x$; (c) $f'(x)$, using the result of part (b).

34. Given $y = 180x - 16x^2$. Using the method of Article 1–7, find the slope of the curve at the point (x_1, y_1). Sketch the curve. At what point does the curve have a horizontal tangent?

35. Find the velocity $v = ds/dt$ if the distance a particle moves in time t is given by $s = 180t - 16t^2$. When does the velocity vanish?

36. If a ball is thrown vertically upward with a velocity of 32 ft/sec, its height after t sec is given by the equation $s = 32t - 16t^2$. At what instant will the ball be at its highest point, and how high will it rise?

37. If the pressure P and volume V of a certain gas are related by the formula $P = 1/V$, find (a) the average rate of change of P with respect to V, (b) the rate of change of P with respect to V at the instant when $V = 2$.

38. The volume V (in^3) of water remaining in a leaking pail after t sec is $V = 2000 - 40t + 0.2t^2$. How fast is the volume decreasing when $t = 30$?

39. Given $y = (x - 1)/(2x^2 - 7x + 5) = f(x)$. Find (a) the limit of $f(x)$ as $x \to \infty$, (b) the limit of $f(x)$ as $x \to 1$, (c) $f(-1/x), f(0), 1/f(x)$.

40. Compute the coordinates of the point of intersection of the straight lines $3x + 5y = 1$, $(2 + c)x + 5c^2y = 1$, and determine the limiting position of this point as c tends to 1.

41. Find (a) $\lim_{n\to\infty} (\sqrt{n^2+1} - n)$, (b) $\lim_{n\to\infty} (\sqrt{n^2+n} - n)$.

42. Given $\epsilon > 0$, find $\delta > 0$ such that $\sqrt{t^2-1} < \epsilon$ when $0 < |t-1| < \delta$.

43. Given $\epsilon > 0$, find M such that

$$\left| \frac{t^2+t}{t^2-1} - 1 \right| < \epsilon$$

when $t > M$.

44. Show that $\lim_{t\to 0} t \sin (1/t)$ exists and is zero, even though $\sin (1/t)$ has no limit as t approaches zero.

45. Prove that if $f(t)$ is bounded (that is, $|f(t)| < M$ for some constant M) and $g(t)$ approaches zero as t approaches a, then $\lim_{t\to a} f(t)\, g(t) = 0$.

46. Prove that if $f(t)$ has a finite limit as t approaches a, then there exist numbers m, M, and $h > 0$ such that $m < f(t) < M$ if $0 < |t-a| < h$.

47. *Properties of inequalities.* If a and b are any two real numbers, we say a is less than b and write $a < b$ if (and only if) $b - a$ is positive. If $a < b$ we also say that b is greater than a $(b > a)$. Prove the following properties of inequalities:

(a) If $a < b$, then $a \pm c < b \pm c$ for any real number c.

(b) If $a < b$ and $c < d$, then $a + c < b + d$. Is it also true that $a - c < b - d$? If so, prove it; if not, give an example to support your contention.

(c) If a and b are both positive (or both negative) and $a < b$, then $1/b < 1/a$.

(d) If $a < 0 < b$, then $1/a < 0 < 1/b$.

(e) If $a < b$ and $c > 0$, then $ac < bc$.

(f) If $a < b$ and $c < 0$, then $bc < ac$.

48. *Properties of absolute values.*

(a) Prove that $|a| < |b|$ if, and only if, $a^2 < b^2$.

(b) Prove that $|a + b| \le |a| + |b|$.

(c) Prove that $|a - b| \ge ||a| - |b||$.

(d) Prove, by mathematical induction, that

$$|a_1 + a_2 + \cdots + a_n| \le |a_1| + |a_2| + \cdots + |a_n|.$$

(e) Using the result from part (d), prove that

$$|a_1 + a_2 + \cdots + a_n| \ge |a_1| - |a_2| - \cdots - |a_n|.$$

CHAPTER 2

DERIVATIVES OF ALGEBRAIC FUNCTIONS

2–1 Polynomial functions and their derivatives. A single term of the form cx^n, where c is a constant and n is zero or a positive integer, is called a *monomial* in x. A function which is the sum of a finite number of monomial terms is called a *polynomial* in x. For example,

$$f(x) = x^3 - 5x + 7, \qquad g(x) = (x^2 + 3)^3, \qquad h(x) = 4x, \qquad \phi(x) = 5$$

are special cases of polynomials in x and

$$s = \tfrac{1}{2}gt^2, \qquad v = v_0 + gt$$

are polynomials in t.

We shall now derive some formulas which will enable us to find the derivatives of polynomial functions very easily. In every case we derive the formula by means of the basic definition:

Let $y = f(x)$ define a function f. If the limit

$$\frac{dy}{dx} = \lim_{\Delta x \to 0} \frac{\Delta y}{\Delta x}, \tag{1a}$$

meaning

$$f'(x) = \lim_{\Delta x \to 0} \frac{f(x + \Delta x) - f(x)}{\Delta x}, \tag{1b}$$

exists and is finite, we call this limit the derivative of y with respect to x and say that f is differentiable at x.

1. *The derivative of a constant is zero.* The geometric meaning of this result is that the graph of the equation $y = c$ is everywhere parallel to the x-axis (Fig. 2–1). To prove it analytically, let

$$y = c,$$

where c is a constant. Then when $x = x_1$ and again when $x = x_1 + \Delta x$, y has the same value c, hence

$$y = c$$

and

$$y + \Delta y = c,$$

so that

$$\Delta y = 0.$$

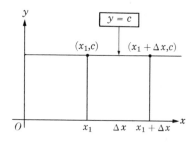

FIGURE 2–1

54

Then, dividing by Δx, we have

$$\frac{\Delta y}{\Delta x} = 0$$

and

$$\frac{dy}{dx} = \lim_{\Delta x \to 0} \frac{\Delta y}{\Delta x} = 0.$$

2. *The derivative, with respect to x, of x^n is nx^{n-1} when n is any positive integer.* To prove this result, we let

$$y = x^n,$$

where n may be any positive integer. Then, by the binomial theorem,

$$y + \Delta y =$$

$$(x + \Delta x)^n = \begin{cases} x + \Delta x & \text{if } n = 1, \\ x^2 + 2x\,\Delta x + (\Delta x)^2 & \text{if } n = 2, \\ x^3 + 3x^2\,\Delta x + 3x\,(\Delta x)^2 + (\Delta x)^3 & \text{if } n = 3, \\ x^n + nx^{n-1}\,\Delta x + (\text{terms in } x \text{ and } \Delta x) \cdot (\Delta x)^2 & \text{if } n > 3. \end{cases}$$

From this we subtract $y = x^n$ and obtain

$$\Delta y = \begin{cases} \Delta x & \text{if } n = 1, \\ 2x\,\Delta x + (\Delta x)^2 & \text{if } n = 2, \\ 3x^2\,\Delta x + (3x + \Delta x) \cdot (\Delta x)^2 & \text{if } n = 3, \\ nx^{n-1}\,\Delta x + (\text{terms in } x \text{ and } \Delta x) \cdot (\Delta x)^2 & \text{if } n > 3. \end{cases}$$

Dividing by Δx, we find next that

$$\frac{\Delta y}{\Delta x} = \begin{cases} 1 & \text{if } n = 1, \\ 2x + \Delta x & \text{if } n = 2, \\ 3x^2 + (3x + \Delta x) \cdot \Delta x & \text{if } n = 3, \\ nx^{n-1} + (\text{terms in } x \text{ and } \Delta x) \cdot \Delta x & \text{if } n > 3. \end{cases}$$

Finally, we let Δx approach zero and find

$$\frac{dy}{dx} = \lim_{\Delta x \to 0} \frac{\Delta y}{\Delta x} = \begin{cases} 1 & \text{if } n = 1, \\ 2x & \text{if } n = 2, \\ 3x^2 & \text{if } n = 3, \\ nx^{n-1} & \text{if } n > 3. \end{cases}$$

In particular, the case $n = 1$ tells us that

$$\frac{dx}{dx} = 1.$$

Since the results for $n = 1, 2, 3$ are simply special cases of the general result, we have

$$\boxed{\frac{dy}{dx} = nx^{n-1} \quad \text{if} \quad y = x^n} \tag{2}$$

and

$$n = \text{any positive integer.}$$

In words, this says: *"To find the derivative of x to the power n, simply multiply that power times x to a power one less."*

3. *If $u = f(x)$ is a differentiable function of x and c is a constant, then*

$$\boxed{\frac{d(cu)}{dx} = c\,\frac{du}{dx}.} \tag{3}$$

Proof. Let

$$y = cu, \tag{4a}$$

where

$$u = f(x).$$

Then if x is replaced by $x + \Delta x$, we have

$$y + \Delta y = c(u + \Delta u), \tag{4b}$$

where

$$u + \Delta u = f(x + \Delta x).$$

Subtracting (4a) from (4b), we obtain

$$\Delta y = c\,\Delta u$$

and dividing this by Δx, we have

$$\frac{\Delta y}{\Delta x} = c\,\frac{\Delta u}{\Delta x}. \tag{4c}$$

Since u has a derivative

$$\frac{du}{dx} = \lim_{\Delta x \to 0} \frac{\Delta u}{\Delta x},$$

the limit of the right side of Eq. (4c), when Δx approaches zero, is simply

$$\lim_{\Delta x \to 0} c\,\frac{\Delta u}{\Delta x} = c\,\frac{du}{dx}.$$

Since both sides of Eq. (4c) are equal, its left side must have the same limit. But this limit is also equal to dy/dx from the definition of the derivative. All of this is summarized in the following equation, which follows by taking limits in Eq. (4c):

$$\frac{dy}{dx} = \lim_{\Delta x \to 0} \frac{\Delta y}{\Delta x} = \lim_{\Delta x \to 0} c\,\frac{\Delta u}{\Delta x} = c\,\frac{du}{dx}.$$

Since $y = cu$, this is the same as

$$\boxed{\frac{d(cu)}{dx} = c\,\frac{du}{dx},}$$

which we wished to show.

In particular, if c is a constant and n is a positive integer, Eqs. (3) and (2) together tell us that

$$\boxed{\frac{d(cx^n)}{dx} = cnx^{n-1}.} \tag{5}$$

For example, if

$$y = 7x^5$$

then

$$\frac{dy}{dx} = 35x^4.$$

4. *The derivative of the sum of a finite number of differentiable functions is equal to the sum of their derivatives.* To prove this, we first consider the sum of two terms,

$$y = u + v,$$

where we suppose that u and v are differentiable functions of x whose derivatives are

$$\frac{du}{dx} = \lim_{\Delta x \to 0} \frac{\Delta u}{\Delta x}$$

and

$$\frac{dv}{dx} = \lim_{\Delta x \to 0} \frac{\Delta v}{\Delta x}.$$

When x is replaced by $x + \Delta x$, the new values of the variables will satisfy the equation

$$y + \Delta y = (u + \Delta u) + (v + \Delta v).$$

We subtract

$$y = u + v$$

from this and obtain

$$\Delta y = \Delta u + \Delta v,$$

and hence

$$\frac{\Delta y}{\Delta x} = \frac{\Delta u}{\Delta x} + \frac{\Delta v}{\Delta x}.$$

When Δx approaches zero, we get

$$\frac{dy}{dx} = \lim_{\Delta x \to 0} \frac{\Delta y}{\Delta x} = \lim_{\Delta x \to 0} \left(\frac{\Delta u}{\Delta x} + \frac{\Delta v}{\Delta x} \right),$$

$$\boxed{\frac{d(u+v)}{dx} = \frac{du}{dx} + \frac{dv}{dx}.}$$

This equation expresses the result that the derivative of the sum of two terms is the sum of their derivatives.

We may proceed by induction to establish the result for the sum of any finite number of terms. For example, if

$$y = u_1 + u_2 + u_3,$$

where u_1, u_2, and u_3 are differentiable functions of x, then we may take

$$u = u_1 + u_2, \qquad v = u_3,$$

and apply the result already established for the sum of two terms, namely,

$$\frac{dy}{dx} = \frac{d(u_1 + u_2)}{dx} + \frac{du_3}{dx}.$$

Since the first term is again a sum of two terms, we have

$$\frac{d(u_1 + u_2)}{dx} = \frac{du_1}{dx} + \frac{du_2}{dx},$$

so that

$$\frac{d(u_1 + u_2 + u_3)}{dx} = \frac{du_1}{dx} + \frac{du_2}{dx} + \frac{du_3}{dx}.$$

Finally, if it has been established for some integer n that

$$\frac{d(u_1 + u_2 + \cdots + u_n)}{dx} = \frac{du_1}{dx} + \frac{du_2}{dx} + \cdots + \frac{du_n}{dx},$$

and we let

$$y = u + v,$$

with

$$u = u_1 + u_2 + \cdots + u_n,$$

$$v = u_{n+1},$$

we find in the same way as above that

$$\frac{d(u_1 + u_2 + \cdots + u_{n+1})}{dx} = \frac{du_1}{dx} + \frac{du_2}{dx} + \cdots + \frac{du_{n+1}}{dx}.$$

This enables us to conclude that if the theorem is true for a sum of n terms it is also true for a sum of $(n + 1)$ terms, and since it is already established for the sum of two terms, we conclude that it is true for the sum of any finite number of terms.

EXAMPLE 1. Find dy/dx if $y = x^3 + 7x^2 - 5x + 4$.

By the result just established, we may find the derivatives of the separate terms of a sum and add the results. Thus

$$\frac{dy}{dx} = \frac{d(x^3)}{dx} + \frac{d(7x^2)}{dx} + \frac{d(-5x)}{dx} + \frac{d(4)}{dx}$$
$$= 3x^2 + 14x - 5x^0 + 0$$
$$= 3x^2 + 14x - 5.$$

EXAMPLE 2. What is the slope of the curve

$$y = x^3 - 6x + 2$$

where it crosses the y-axis?

The slope at the point (x, y) is equal to

$$\frac{dy}{dx} = 3x^2 - 6.$$

The curve crosses the y-axis when $x = 0$. Hence its slope at that point is

$$m = (3x^2 - 6)_{x=0} = -6.$$

The derivative with respect to x of $y' = dy/dx$ is called the *second derivative* of y with respect to x and is denoted by y''. That is,

$$y' = \frac{dy}{dx}$$

is the first derivative of y with respect to x, and its derivative

$$y'' = \frac{dy'}{dx} = \frac{d}{dx}\left(\frac{dy}{dx}\right)$$

is the second derivative of y with respect to x. The operation of taking the derivative of a function twice in succession, denoted by

$$\frac{d}{dx}\left(\frac{d}{dx}\cdots\right),$$

is also indicated by the notation

$$\frac{d^2}{dx^2}(\cdots).$$

In this notation, we write the second derivative of y with respect to x as

$$\frac{d^2y}{dx^2}.$$

More generally, the result of differentiating a function $y = f(x)$ n times in succession is denoted by $y^{(n)}$, $f^{(n)}(x)$, or by $d^n y/dx^n$.

EXAMPLE 3. For example, if $y = x^3 - 3x^2 + 2$, then

$$y' = \frac{dy}{dx} = 3x^2 - 6x, \qquad y''' = \frac{d^3y}{dx^3} = 6,$$

$$y'' = \frac{d^2y}{dx^2} = 6x - 6, \qquad y^{(iv)} = \frac{d^4y}{dx^4} = 0.$$

In mechanics, if $s = f(t)$ gives the position of a moving body at time t, then

the first derivative ds/dt gives the *velocity*, and

the second derivative d^2s/dt^2 gives the *acceleration*

of the body at time t.

EXAMPLE 4. A body moves in a straight line according to the law of motion

$$s = t^3 - 4t^2 - 3t.$$

Find its acceleration at each instant when the velocity is zero.
Here we find the velocity v and acceleration a are

$$v = \frac{ds}{dt} = 3t^2 - 8t - 3, \qquad a = \frac{dv}{dt} = 6t - 8.$$

The velocity is zero when

$$3t^2 - 8t - 3 = (3t + 1)(t - 3) = 0,$$

that is, when

$$t = -\tfrac{1}{3} \qquad \text{or} \qquad t = 3.$$

The corresponding values of the acceleration are

$$t = -\tfrac{1}{3}, \quad a = -10; \qquad t = 3, \quad a = 10.$$

PROBLEMS

In Problems 1–5, s represents the position of a moving body at time t. Find the velocity $v = ds/dt$ and the acceleration $a = dv/dt = d^2s/dt^2$.

1. $s = t^2 - 4t + 3$ 2. $s = 2t^3 - 5t^2 + 4t - 3$

3. $s = gt^2/2 + v_0t + s_0$; (g, v_0, s_0 constants)

4. $s = 3 + 4t - t^2$ 5. $s = (2t + 3)^2$

Find $y' = dy/dx$ and $y'' = dy'/dx$ in Problems 6–15.

6. $y = x^4 - 7x^3 + 2x^2 + 5$ 7. $y = 5x^3 - 3x^5$

8. $y = 4x^2 - 8x + 1$ 9. $y = \dfrac{x^4}{4} - \dfrac{x^3}{3} + \dfrac{x^2}{2} - x + 3$

10. $y = 2x^4 - 4x^2 - 8$ 11. $12y = 6x^4 - 18x^2 - 12x$

12. $y = 3x^7 - 7x^3 + 21x^2$ 13. $y = x^2(x^3 - 1)$

14. $y = (x - 2)(x + 3)$ 15. $y = (3x - 1)(2x + 5)$

16. A particle projected vertically upward with a speed of 160 ft/sec reaches an elevation $s = 160t - 16t^2$ at the end of t seconds. (a) How high does it rise? (b) How fast is it traveling when it reaches an elevation of 256 feet going up and again when it reaches this elevation coming down?

17. Find the line tangent to the curve $y = 2x^2 + 4x - 3$ at the point (1, 3).

18. Find the lines tangent to the curve $y = x^3 + x$, where the slope is equal to 4. What is the smallest value the slope of this curve can ever have and where on the curve does the slope equal this smallest value?

19. Find the points on the curve $y = 2x^3 - 3x^2 - 12x + 20$, where the tangent is parallel to the x-axis.

20. Find the values of the constants a, b, and c if the curve $y = ax^2 + bx + c$ is to pass through the point (1, 2) and is to be tangent to the line $y = x$ at the origin.

21. Find the constants a, b, and c so that the two curves $y = x^2 + ax + b$ and $y = cx - x^2$ shall be tangent to each other at the point (1, 0).

22. Find the constant c if the curve $y = x^2 + c$ is to be tangent to the line $y = x$.

2–2 Rational functions and their derivatives.

In the preceding article we learned how to find the derivative of a polynomial very quickly by using certain simple formulas. First we found the derivative of a monomial in x,

$$\frac{d}{dx}(cx^n) = cnx^{n-1},$$

and then we proved that the derivative of the sum of a finite number of such terms is the sum of their derivatives.

In this article we shall derive formulas for finding the derivative with respect to x of

$$\text{products: } y = uv,$$

$$\text{quotients: } y = u/v,$$

$$\text{powers: } \quad y = u^n,$$

when u and v are any differentiable functions of x. For the present, this will mean that u and v may be polynomials in x, for example; but after we learn to differentiate other functions like $\sin x$ and $\log x$, the same basic formulas will apply to combinations of these as well.

The product of two polynomials in x is again a polynomial in x; hence if u and v are polynomials the product uv is also a polynomial. Similarly, if n is a positive integer and u is a polynomial, then u^n is again a polynomial. For example, if

$$u = x^2 + 1, \quad v = x^3 + 3, \qquad \text{then} \qquad uv = x^5 + x^3 + 3x^2 + 3,$$

and if

$$u = x^2 + 1, \quad n = 2, \qquad \text{then} \qquad u^n = x^4 + 2x^2 + 1.$$

But the ratio u/v of two polynomials is, in general, not a polynomial in x. Such a function is called a *rational* function of x, where the word *ratio* is the key to the real meaning of the word rational.

1. *The derivative of the product*

$$y = uv$$

of two differentiable functions of x is given by

$$\boxed{\frac{d(uv)}{dx} = u\frac{dv}{dx} + v\frac{du}{dx}.} \tag{1}$$

To prove this result, we let

$$y = uv,$$

where u and v are differentiable functions of x. Let x be given an increment Δx, and let the corresponding increments in y, u, v be denoted by Δy, Δu, Δv. (These "increments" may be either positive or negative.) Then the new values of the variables satisfy the equation

$$y + \Delta y = (u + \Delta u)(v + \Delta v)$$
$$= uv + u\,\Delta v + v\,\Delta u + \Delta u\,\Delta v.$$

When we subtract from this the equation

$$y = uv,$$

we obtain

$$\Delta y = u\,\Delta v + v\,\Delta u + \Delta u\,\Delta v.$$

Next we must divide by Δx,

$$\frac{\Delta y}{\Delta x} = u\,\frac{\Delta v}{\Delta x} + v\,\frac{\Delta u}{\Delta x} + \Delta u\,\frac{\Delta v}{\Delta x}.$$

Finally, when Δx approaches zero, so will Δu and Δv, since

$$\lim \Delta u = \lim\left(\frac{\Delta u}{\Delta x}\,\Delta x\right) = \lim \frac{\Delta u}{\Delta x}\,\lim \Delta x = \frac{du}{dx}\cdot 0.$$

Thus,

$$\lim \frac{\Delta y}{\Delta x} = \lim\left(u\,\frac{\Delta v}{\Delta x} + v\,\frac{\Delta u}{\Delta x} + \Delta u\,\frac{\Delta v}{\Delta x}\right)$$

$$= \lim u\,\frac{\Delta v}{\Delta x} + \lim v\,\frac{\Delta u}{\Delta x} + \lim \Delta u\,\frac{\Delta v}{\Delta x}$$

$$= \lim u \lim \frac{\Delta v}{\Delta x} + \lim v \lim \frac{\Delta u}{\Delta x} + \lim \Delta u \lim \frac{\Delta v}{\Delta x}$$

$$= u\,\frac{dv}{dx} + v\,\frac{du}{dx} + 0\cdot\frac{dv}{dx}.$$

That is,

$$\frac{dy}{dx} = u\,\frac{dv}{dx} + v\,\frac{du}{dx},$$

which establishes (1).

Note that the derivative of a product is *not* the product of the derivatives. Instead, we add together two terms $u(dv/dx)$ and $v(du/dx)$. In the first of these we leave u untouched and differentiate v, and in the second we differentiate u and leave v alone. In fact, it is possible to extend the formula, by the method of mathematical induction, to show that the derivative of a product

$$y = u_1 u_2 \ldots u_n$$

of a finite number of differentiable functions is given by

$$\frac{d}{dx}(u_1 u_2 \cdots u_n) = \frac{du_1}{dx}\cdot u_2 \cdots u_n + u_1\,\frac{du_2}{dx}\cdots u_n + \cdots + u_1 u_2 \cdots \frac{du_n}{dx}, \quad (2)$$

where the right side of the equation consists of the sum of the n terms obtained by multiplying the derivative of each one of the factors by the other $(n-1)$ factors undifferentiated.

2. *At a point where $v \neq 0$, the derivative of the quotient*

$$y = \frac{u}{v}$$

of two differentiable functions u and v is given by

$$\frac{d}{dx}\left(\frac{u}{v}\right) = \frac{v\,\dfrac{du}{dx} - u\,\dfrac{dv}{dx}}{v^2}.$$ (3)

To prove this, consider a point $x = c$ where $v \neq 0$ and where u and v are differentiable. Let x be given an increment Δx and let Δy, Δu, Δv be the corresponding increments in y, u, v. Then, as $\Delta x \to 0$,

$$\lim (v + \Delta v) = \lim v + \lim \Delta v$$

while

$$\lim \Delta v = \lim \frac{\Delta v}{\Delta x} \cdot \Delta x = \frac{dv}{dx} \cdot 0 = 0.$$

Therefore the value of $v + \Delta v$ is close to the value of v when $x + \Delta x$ is close to c, that is, when Δx is near zero. In particular, since $v \neq 0$ at $x = c$, it follows that $v + \Delta v \neq 0$ when Δx is *near* zero, say when $0 < |\Delta x| < h$. Let Δx be so restricted. Then $v + \Delta v \neq 0$ and

$$y + \Delta y = \frac{u + \Delta u}{v + \Delta v}.$$

From this we subtract

$$y = \frac{u}{v}$$

and obtain

$$\Delta y = \frac{u + \Delta u}{v + \Delta v} - \frac{u}{v}$$

$$= \frac{(vu + v\,\Delta u) - (uv + u\,\Delta v)}{v(v + \Delta v)}$$

$$= \frac{v\,\Delta u - u\,\Delta v}{v(v + \Delta v)}.$$

We divide this by Δx by dividing the numerator of the fraction on the right by Δx and have

$$\frac{\Delta y}{\Delta x} = \frac{v\,\dfrac{\Delta u}{\Delta x} - u\,\dfrac{\Delta v}{\Delta x}}{v(v + \Delta v)}.$$

When Δx approaches zero, we obtain

$$\lim \frac{\Delta u}{\Delta x} = \frac{du}{dx},$$

$$\lim \frac{\Delta v}{\Delta x} = \frac{dv}{dx},$$

$$\lim v(v + \Delta v) = \lim v \lim (v + \Delta v) = v^2 \neq 0,$$

and

$$\lim \frac{\Delta y}{\Delta x} = \frac{\lim \left(v \dfrac{\Delta u}{\Delta x} - u \dfrac{\Delta v}{\Delta x} \right)}{\lim v(v + \Delta v)},$$

or

$$\frac{dy}{dx} = \frac{v \dfrac{du}{dx} - u \dfrac{dv}{dx}}{v^2},$$

which establishes Eq. (3).

3. *If $u = g(x)$ is a differentiable function of x and n is a positive integer or zero, then*

$$\frac{d}{dx}(u^n) = nu^{n-1}\frac{du}{dx}. \tag{4}$$

We let

$$y = u^n,$$

where u and n satisfy the hypotheses, give x an increment Δx, and call the increments of y and u, Δy and Δu. Then

$$y + \Delta y = (u + \Delta u)^n$$
$$= u^n + nu^{n-1}\,\Delta u + \frac{n(n-1)}{2}\,u^{n-2}\,(\Delta u)^2 + \cdots + (\Delta u)^n.$$

From this we subtract the original equation and obtain

$$\Delta y = nu^{n-1}\,\Delta u + (\text{terms in } u \text{ and } \Delta u)(\Delta u)^2.$$

Next, we divide by Δx:

$$\frac{\Delta y}{\Delta x} = nu^{n-1}\frac{\Delta u}{\Delta x} + (\text{terms in } u \text{ and } \Delta u)\,\frac{(\Delta u)^2}{\Delta x}.$$

Now when Δx approaches zero,

$$\lim \frac{\Delta u}{\Delta x} = \frac{du}{dx}$$

by the definition of the derivative, while

$$\lim \frac{(\Delta u)^2}{\Delta x} = \lim \left(\frac{\Delta u}{\Delta x}\,\Delta u \right)$$
$$= \lim \frac{\Delta u}{\Delta x} \lim \Delta u = \frac{du}{dx} \cdot 0 = 0.$$

Hence, $$\lim \frac{\Delta y}{\Delta x} = \lim \left[nu^{n-1} \frac{\Delta u}{\Delta x} + (\cdots) \frac{(\Delta u)^2}{\Delta x} \right]$$

$$= \lim nu^{n-1} \frac{\Delta u}{\Delta x} + \lim (\cdots) \frac{(\Delta u)^2}{\Delta x}$$

$$= nu^{n-1} \frac{du}{dx} + 0,$$

that is,

$$\frac{dy}{dx} = nu^{n-1} \frac{du}{dx},$$

which establishes Eq. (4).

4. *At a point where* $u = g(x)$ *is differentiable and different from zero, the derivative of*

$$y = u^n$$

is given by

$$\frac{d(u^n)}{dx} = nu^{n-1} \frac{du}{dx} \tag{5}$$

if n is a negative integer.

Note that this formula (5) is the extension of (4) to the case where n is a *negative integer*. To prove it, we combine the results in Eqs. (3) and (4) as follows. Let

$$y = u^{-m} = \frac{1}{u^m},$$

where $n = -m$ is a negative integer, so that m is a positive integer. Then, using (3) for the derivative of a quotient, we have

$$\frac{dy}{dx} = \frac{d\left(\frac{1}{u^m}\right)}{dx} = \frac{u^m \frac{d(1)}{dx} - 1 \frac{d(u^m)}{dx}}{(u^m)^2} \tag{6}$$

at any point where u is differentiable and different from zero. Now the various derivatives on the right side of (6) can be evaluated by formulas already proved, namely,

$$\frac{d(1)}{dx} = 0,$$

since 1 is a constant, and

$$\frac{d(u^m)}{dx} = mu^{m-1} \frac{du}{dx},$$

since m is a *positive integer*. Therefore,

$$\frac{dy}{dx} = \frac{u^m \cdot 0 - 1 \cdot mu^{m-1} \frac{du}{dx}}{u^{2m}} = -mu^{-m-1} \frac{du}{dx}.$$

If $-m$ is replaced by its equivalent value n, the formula reduces to Eq. (5).

EXAMPLE 1. $y = x^2 + 1/x^2$, $x \neq 0$. We may write

$$y = x^2 + x^{-2}.$$

Then

$$\frac{dy}{dx} = 2x^{2-1}\frac{dx}{dx} + (-2)x^{-2-1}\frac{dx}{dx}$$

$$= 2x - 2x^{-3}.$$

EXAMPLE 2. $y = \dfrac{x^2 + 1}{x^2 - 1}$, $x^2 \neq 1$. We apply the formula, Eq. (3), for the derivative of a fraction and have

$$\frac{dy}{dx} = \frac{(x^2 - 1) \cdot 2x - (x^2 + 1) \cdot 2x}{(x^2 - 1)^2}$$

$$= \frac{-4x}{(x^2 - 1)^2}.$$

EXAMPLE 3. $y = (x^2 + 1)^3(x^3 - 1)^2$. We could, of course, expand everything here and write y as a polynomial in x, but this is not necessary. Instead, we use Eq. (1) for the derivative of a product:

$$\frac{dy}{dx} = (x^2 + 1)^3 \frac{d}{dx}(x^3 - 1)^2 + (x^3 - 1)^2 \frac{d}{dx}(x^2 + 1)^3.$$

The derivatives which are now to be evaluated are of the type in Eq. (4),

$$\frac{d}{dx}(x^3 - 1)^2 = 2(x^3 - 1)\frac{d}{dx}(x^3 - 1)$$

$$= 2(x^3 - 1) \cdot 3x^2 = 6x^2(x^3 - 1),$$

and

$$\frac{d}{dx}(x^2 + 1)^3 = 3(x^2 + 1)^2 \frac{d}{dx}(x^2 + 1)$$

$$= 3(x^2 + 1)^2 \cdot 2x = 6x(x^2 + 1)^2.$$

We substitute these into the earlier equation and have

$$\frac{dy}{dx} = (x^2 + 1)^3 6x^2(x^3 - 1) + (x^3 - 1)^2 6x(x^2 + 1)^2$$

$$= 6x(x^2 + 1)^2(x^3 - 1)[x(x^2 + 1) + (x^3 - 1)]$$

$$= 6x(x^2 + 1)^2(x^3 - 1)(2x^3 + x - 1).$$

PROBLEMS

Find dy/dx in each of the following problems (1 through 8).

1. $y = x^3/3 - x^2/2 + x - 1$ 2. $y = (x - 1)^3(x + 2)^4$

3. $y = (x^2 + 1)^5$ 4. $y = (x^3 - 3x)^4$

5. $y = (x + 1)^2(x^2 + 1)^{-3}$ 6. $y = \dfrac{2x + 1}{x^2 - 1}$

7. $y = \dfrac{2x + 5}{3x - 2}$ 8. $y = \left(\dfrac{x + 1}{x - 1}\right)^2$

Find ds/dt in each of the following problems (9 through 15).

9. $s = \dfrac{t}{t^2 + 1}$ 10. $s = (2t + 3)^3$

11. $s = (t^2 - t)^{-2}$ 12. $s = t^2(t + 1)^{-1}$

13. $s = \dfrac{2t}{3t^2 + 1}$ 14. $s = (t + t^{-1})^2$

15. $s = (t^2 + 3t)^3$

16. With the book closed, state and prove the formula for the derivative of the product of two differentiable functions u and v.

17. With the book closed, state and prove the formula for the derivative of the quotient u/v of two differentiable functions u and v.

18. With the book closed, state and prove the formula for the derivative with respect to x of u^n, where n is a positive integer and u is a differentiable function of x.

2–3 Implicit relations and their derivatives. The functions we have dealt with so far have been of the form $y = f(x)$, which express y explicitly in terms of x. Quite often, however, we encounter equations like

$$x^2 + y^2 = 1, \qquad\qquad xy = 1,$$
$$y^2 = x, \qquad x^2 + xy + y^2 = 3,$$

which involve x and y in such a manner that they do not give y explicitly in terms of x. Nevertheless each of the equations listed defines a relation between y and x. When a definite number from some domain is substituted for x, the resulting equation determines one or more values of y to be associated with the given value of x. We therefore say that the equation determines y as one or more *implicit functions* of x. The domain of x is usually restricted so that y is real.

It happens that each of the equations given above can actually be solved to give y explicitly in terms of x, but such is not the case for an equation like

$$x^5 + 4xy^3 - 3y^5 = 2. \tag{1}$$

Nevertheless, it is possible to calculate dy/dx from such an equation by the method known as *implicit differentiation*. In this method we simply treat y as an unknown but differentiable function of x and apply the rules for finding derivatives of u^n, uv, u/v, etc., which we have already developed. [For a discussion of the validity of the assumption that the equation does define y as one or more differentiable functions of x, we must refer the reader to more advanced textbooks such as Fine, *Calculus*, p. 248; Macmillan (1937).]

EXAMPLE 1. Find dy/dx if y is related to x by Eq. (1).

Solution. We simply differentiate both sides of the given equation with respect to x, thus

$$\frac{d}{dx}(x^5) + \frac{d}{dx}(4xy^3) - \frac{d}{dx}(3y^5) = \frac{d}{dx}(2),$$

or

$$5x^4 + 4\left(x\frac{d(y^3)}{dx} + y^3\frac{dx}{dx}\right) - 15y^4\frac{dy}{dx} = 0,$$

$$5x^4 + 4\left(3xy^2\frac{dy}{dx} + y^3\right) - 15y^4\frac{dy}{dx} = 0,$$

$$(12xy^2 - 15y^4)\frac{dy}{dx} = -(5x^4 + 4y^3),$$

and finally, at all points where

$$12xy^2 - 15y^4 \neq 0,$$

we have

$$\frac{dy}{dx} = \frac{5x^4 + 4y^3}{15y^4 - 12xy^2}.$$

Note that the rule

$$\frac{d}{dx}u^n = nu^{n-1}\frac{du}{dx}$$

becomes

$$\frac{dy^5}{dx} = 5y^4\frac{dy}{dx}$$

when applied to y^5.

The result of applying this method to any of the equations listed above will be to give an expression for dy/dx in terms of both x and y. This is no real handicap since, if we want the slope of the tangent to a curve at a point (x_1, y_1), for instance, we need merely substitute x_1 for x and y_1 for y in the final expression for dy/dx.

EXAMPLE 2. Find the slope of the tangent to the curve $x^2 + xy + y^2 = 7$ at the point $(1, 2)$.

Solution. We differentiate both sides of the equation with respect to x, noting that xy is a product, uv, and that y^2 is of the form u^n, while 7 is a constant.

Thus

$$2x \frac{dx}{dx} + \left(x \frac{dy}{dx} + y \frac{dx}{dx} \right) + 2y \frac{dy}{dx} = 0,$$

$$(x + 2y) \frac{dy}{dx} = -(2x + y),$$

and wherever $x + 2y \neq 0$, we have

$$\frac{dy}{dx} = - \frac{2x + y}{x + 2y}.$$

In particular, at $(1, 2)$ we have

$$\left(\frac{dy}{dx} \right)_{(1,2)} = - \frac{4}{5}.$$

The method of implicit differentiation enables us to show also that *if u is a differentiable function of x and*

$$y = u^{p/q},$$

where p and q are integers with $q > 0$, then

$$\frac{dy}{dx} = \frac{p}{q} u^{(p/q)-1} \frac{du}{dx}$$

provided $u \neq 0$ if $p/q < 1$.

Note that this is the familiar rule for the derivative of u^n, but this time applied to the case where $n = p/q$ is any rational number. Of course, the domain of x is restricted to values for which $u^{p/q}$ is well defined. For example, if $u = 1 - x^2$ and $p/q = \frac{1}{2}$, then $|x| \leq 1$ in order to produce real values of

$$y = (1 - x^2)^{1/2}.$$

The restriction $u \neq 0$ if $p/q < 1$ is necessary in order to avoid division by zero, which is never permitted.

To establish the result, let

$$y = u^{p/q},$$

which means that

$$y^q = u^p.$$

Then, differentiating both sides of the equation implicitly and using the familiar formulas for the derivatives of y^q and u^p (since p and q are integers, these formulas are valid), we obtain

$$qy^{q-1} \frac{dy}{dx} = pu^{p-1} \frac{du}{dx}.$$

Hence if $y \neq 0$, we have

$$\frac{dy}{dx} = \frac{pu^{p-1}}{qy^{q-1}} \frac{du}{dx}.$$

But

$$y^{q-1} = (u^{p/q})^{q-1} = u^{p-(p/q)},$$

so that

$$\frac{dy}{dx} = \frac{p}{q} \frac{u^{p-1}}{u^{p-(p/q)}} \frac{du}{dx}$$

$$= \frac{p}{q} u^{(p/q)-1} \frac{du}{dx}.$$

The restriction $y \neq 0$ is the same as the restriction $u \neq 0$ but was made without reference to whether p/q was or was not less than one. The restriction is certainly not needed if $p/q = 1$, since then we simply have $y = u$ and

$$\frac{dy}{dx} = \frac{du}{dx}.$$

The case

$$y = x^{3/2}$$

is typical of the case

$$y = u^{p/q}, \qquad p/q > 1,$$

and we shall show that for this case the slope of the curve is 0 at $x = 0$. We may work directly with the definition of the tangent to the curve at $(0, 0)$ as the limiting position of a secant line through $(0, 0)$ and a second point $P_1(x_1, y_1)$ on the curve as P_1 approaches the origin. Then the slope of OP_1 is

$$m = \frac{\text{rise}}{\text{run}} = \frac{y_1 - 0}{x_1 - 0} = \frac{x_1^{3/2}}{x_1} = x_1^{1/2}.$$

Now as P_1 approaches O, we have

$$m_0 = \lim_{x_1 \to 0} m = \lim_{x_1 \to 0} x_1^{1/2} = 0;$$

that is, the slope of the tangent to the curve at O is zero. If we use the formula just derived, we obtain

$$y = x^{3/2},$$

$$\frac{dy}{dx} = \frac{3}{2} x^{1/2},$$

and at $x = 0$ this also equals zero.

In the strictest sense, this curve doesn't actually have a derivative at $x = 0$, since the curve does

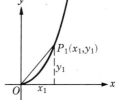

FIGURE 2–2

not exist to the left of the origin. This means that only the right-hand limit,

$$\lim_{\Delta x \to 0+} \frac{f(x + \Delta x) - f(x)}{\Delta x},$$

can be calculated at $x = 0$. Nevertheless, it is customary to say that the curve (see Fig. 2–2) has a horizontal tangent at the origin, since the only secant lines which can be drawn from $O(0, 0)$ to points P on the curve tend to a unique limiting position as P approaches O along the curve.

PROBLEMS

In Problems 1–23, find dy/dx.

1. $x^2 + y^2 = 1$

2. $y^2 = \dfrac{x - 1}{x + 1}$

3. $x^2 + xy = 2$

4. $x^2y + xy^2 = 6$

5. $y^2 = x^3$

6. $x^{2/3} + y^{2/3} = 1$

7. $x^{1/2} + y^{1/2} = 1$

8. $x^3 - xy + y^3 = 1$

9. $x^2 = \dfrac{x - y}{x + y}$

10. $y = \dfrac{x}{\sqrt{x^2 + 1}}$

11. $y = x\sqrt{x^2 + 1}$

12. $y^2 = x^2 + \dfrac{1}{x^2}$

13. $2xy + y^2 = x + y$

14. $y = \sqrt{x} + \sqrt[3]{x} + \sqrt[4]{x}$

15. $y^2 = \dfrac{x^2 - 1}{x^2 + 1}$

16. $(x + y)^3 + (x - y)^3 = x^4 + y^4$

17. $(3x + 7)^5 = 2y^3$

18. $y = (x + 5)^4(x^2 - 2)^3$

19. $\dfrac{1}{y} + \dfrac{1}{x} = 1$

20. $y = (x^2 + 5x)^3$

21. $y^2 = x^2 - x$

22. $x^2y^2 = x^2 + y^2$

23. $y = \dfrac{\sqrt[3]{x^2 + 3}}{x}$

24. (a) By differentiating the equation $x^2 - y^2 = 1$ implicitly, show that $dy/dx = x/y$.

(b) By differentiating both sides of the equation $dy/dx = x/y$ implicitly, show that

$$\frac{d^2y}{dx^2} = \frac{y - x\left(\dfrac{dy}{dx}\right)}{y^2} = \frac{y - \dfrac{x^2}{y}}{y^2} = \frac{y^2 - x^2}{y^3}$$

or, since $y^2 - x^2 = -1$ from the original equation,

$$\frac{d^2y}{dx^2} = \frac{-1}{y^3}.$$

Use the method outlined in Problem 24 to find dy/dx and d^2y/dx^2 in each of the following problems (25 through 28).

25. $x^2 + y^2 = 1$ 　　　　　　　　26. $x^3 + y^3 = 1$

27. $x^{2/3} + y^{2/3} = 1$ 　　　　　28. $xy + y^2 = 1$

29. A particle of mass m moves along the x-axis. The velocity $v = dx/dt$ and position x satisfy the equation

$$m(v^2 - v_0^2) = k(x_0^2 - x^2),$$

where k, v_0, and x_0 are constants. Show, by implicitly differentiating this equation with respect to t, that whenever $v \neq 0$,

$$m \frac{dv}{dt} = -kx.$$

Find the lines that are respectively *tangent* and *normal* to the following curves at the points indicated as P_0. (A line is said to be *normal* to a curve at a point P_0 if it is perpendicular to the tangent at P_0.)

30. $x^2 + xy - y^2 = 1$, 　　　$P_0(2, 3)$

31. $x^2 + y^2 = 25$, 　　　　　$P_0(3, -4)$

32. $x^2 y^2 = 9$, 　　　　　　　$P_0(-1, 3)$

33. $\dfrac{x - y}{x - 2y} = 2$, 　　　　$P_0(3, 1)$

34. $(y - x)^2 = 2x + 4$, 　　　$P_0(6, 2)$

2-4 The increment of a function. In this article, we shall learn how to estimate the change Δy produced in a function $y = f(x)$ when x changes by a small amount Δx. To be precise, let us focus our attention on a portion of the graph of $y = f(x)$ in the neighborhood of a point $P(x, y)$ where the function is differentiable. Then, if $Q(x + \Delta x, y + \Delta y)$ is a second point on the curve, with $\Delta x \neq 0$, we know that

$$\text{the slope of the secant line } PQ = \frac{\Delta y}{\Delta x}$$

approaches the limiting value

$$\frac{dy}{dx} = f'(x)$$

as Δx approaches zero. Therefore, the difference

$$\frac{\Delta y}{\Delta x} - \frac{dy}{dx}$$

is numerically small when $|\Delta x|$ is small. Let us denote this difference by ϵ:

$$\frac{\Delta y}{\Delta x} - \frac{dy}{dx} = \epsilon. \tag{1}$$

Then, saying that

$$\lim_{\Delta x \to 0} \frac{\Delta y}{\Delta x} = \frac{dy}{dx} = f'(x) \tag{2}$$

is equivalent to saying that

$$\lim_{\Delta x \to 0} \epsilon = 0. \tag{3}$$

In other words, we may deduce from Eqs. (1), (2), and (3) that

$$\frac{\Delta y}{\Delta x} = \frac{dy}{dx} + \epsilon, \tag{4a}$$

where

$$\epsilon \to 0 \quad \text{as} \quad \Delta x \to 0. \tag{4b}$$

If we multiply both sides of (4a) by Δx, we also have

$$\boxed{\Delta y = \frac{dy}{dx} \Delta x + \epsilon \, \Delta x.} \tag{4c}$$

Although Eq. (4c) was derived under the assumption that $\Delta x \neq 0$, it is still a true equation even when $\Delta x = 0$. In fact, if we define ϵ by Eq. (1) when $\Delta x \neq 0$, and take $\epsilon = 0$ when $\Delta x = 0$, then Eqs. (4b, c) hold whether $\Delta x = 0$ or not.

If we compare Fig. 2–3 with Fig. 1–27, Article 1–9, we see that the first term on the right side of Eq. (4c) is equal to the change Δy_{tan} that would be produced in y by a change Δx in x if the point (x, y) were to move along the tangent line. This is called the *principal part* of Δy since, for small values of Δx, it usually is large in comparison with the second term, $\epsilon \, \Delta x$.

The significance of Eqs. (4b, c) is that

$$\boxed{\Delta y = \Delta y_{\text{tan}} + \epsilon \, \Delta x = \text{change in } y \textit{ along the curve}}$$

and

$$\boxed{\Delta y_{\text{tan}} = \frac{dy}{dx} \Delta x = \text{change in } y \textit{ along the tangent line}}$$

differ by an amount

$$\epsilon \, \Delta x,$$

which tends to zero more rapidly than Δx does when Δx approaches zero.

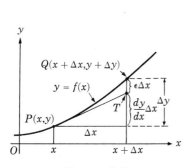

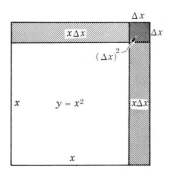

FIGURE 2–3   FIGURE 2–4

For example, if

$$y = x^2 = f(x),$$

then

$$\frac{dy}{dx} = 2x = f'(x)$$

and the principal part of Δy is

$$\frac{dy}{dx} \Delta x = 2x \, \Delta x.$$

On the other hand, the exact value of Δy is

$$\Delta y = 2x \, \Delta x + (\Delta x)^2.$$

We compare this with Eq. (4c) and see that, for this particular example, the part which is denoted by $\epsilon \Delta x$ in (4c) is

$$\epsilon \, \Delta x = (\Delta x)^2.$$

When Δx is small, $(\Delta x)^2$ is the square of a small number and this is much smaller than Δx itself.

This example,

$$y = x^2, \qquad \text{(principal part of } \Delta y) = 2x \, \Delta x,$$

also lends itself to an interesting geometrical interpretation, as illustrated by Fig. 2–4. The original square, having sides x by x, has area $y = x^2$. When the sides are increased to $x + \Delta x$ by $x + \Delta x$, the area is increased by $\Delta y = 2x \, \Delta x + (\Delta x)^2$. When Δx is small in comparison with x, most of the change in y is given by the two rectangular pieces x by Δx and only a very small part is given by the small square Δx by Δx. Thus, if the original square has sides

$$x = 2 \text{ (in.)}$$

and the larger square has sides

$$x + \Delta x = 2.01 \text{ (in.),}$$

so that

$$\Delta x = +0.01 \text{ (in.)},$$

the area of the original square is

$$y = x^2 = 4 \text{ (in}^2)$$

and the area of the larger square is

$$y + \Delta y = (x + \Delta x)^2 = x^2 + 2x\,\Delta x + (\Delta x)^2$$
$$= 4 + 0.04 + 0.0001 \text{ (in}^2).$$

The increment,

$$\Delta y = 0.04 + 0.0001 \text{ (in}^2)$$

has its principal part equal to

$$2x\,\Delta x = 0.04 \text{ (in}^2)$$

and its remainder

$$(\Delta x)^2 = 0.0001 \text{ (in}^2).$$

If we were to use only the principal part of Δy as an approximation to Δy itself, we would thereby introduce an error of magnitude 0.0001 (in^2), which is just under one-fourth of one percent of Δy.

Since the principal part of Δy usually gives a good approximation to Δy itself (at least when Δx is small compared with dy/dx), it is customary to use the approximation

$$\Delta y \approx \frac{dy}{dx}\,\Delta x = \Delta y_{\text{tan}} \tag{5}$$

in numerical calculations. (The symbol $\approx$ means "is approximately equal to.")

EXAMPLE 1. Use the approximation in Eq. (5) to approximate the change in $y = x^3$ when x changes from 3 to 2.98.

Solution. We take $x = 3$ and $x + \Delta x = 2.98$, so that $\Delta x = 2.98 - 3 = -0.02$. Since

$$\frac{dy}{dx} = 3x^2,$$

we find, using Eq. (5), that

$$\Delta y \approx 3x^2\,\Delta x = 27\,(-0.02) = -0.54.$$

EXAMPLE 2. Using the approximation in Eq. (5), determine a reasonable approximation to $(2.98)^3$.

Solution. As in Example 1, we consider

$$y = x^3.$$

Since 2.98 is near to 3 and $3^3 = 27$ is easily calculated, we think of starting from the point

$$x = 3, \qquad y = 27$$

and trying to reach the point

$$x + \Delta x = 2.98, \qquad y + \Delta y = (2.98)^3 = ?$$

Now instead of calculating $(2.98)^3$ exactly, we shall make use of the *approximation*

$$\Delta y \approx \frac{dy}{dx} \, \Delta x = 3x^2 \, \Delta x = -0.54.$$

Hence, adding this to $y = x^3 = 27$, we have

$$(2.98)^3 = y + \Delta y \approx y + \frac{dy}{dx} \, \Delta x = 27 - 0.54$$

or

$$(2.98)^3 \approx 26.46.$$

Problems

For each of the following functions, find (a) Δy, (b) the principal part of Δy, namely, $\Delta y_{\text{tan}} = (dy/dx)\Delta x$, (c) the difference, $\Delta y - \Delta y_{\text{tan}}$.

1. $y = x^2 + 2x$ 2. $y = 2x^2 + 4x - 3$
3. $y = x^3 - x$ 4. $y = x^4$
5. $y = x^{-1}$

For each of the following functions $y = f(x)$, *estimate* $y + \Delta y = f(x + \Delta x)$ by calculating y plus the principal part of Δy for the given data.

6. $y = \sqrt{x}, \quad x = 4, \quad \Delta x = 0.5$ 7. $y = \sqrt[3]{x}, \quad x = 8, \quad \Delta x = -0.5$
8. $y = x^{-1}, \quad x = 2, \quad \Delta x = 0.1$
9. $y = \sqrt{x^2 + 9}, \quad x = -4, \quad \Delta x = -0.2$
10. $y = \dfrac{x}{x + 1}, \quad x = 1, \quad \Delta x = 0.3$

11. The volume $y = x^3$ of a cube of edge x increases by an amount Δy when x increases by an amount Δx. Show that Δy may be represented geometrically as the sum of the volumes of:

(a) three slabs of dimensions x by x by Δx,
(b) three bars of dimensions x by Δx by Δx,
(c) one cube of dimensions Δx by Δx by Δx.

Illustrate by a sketch.

2–5 The chain rule for derivatives. When a particle moves in a curved plane path rather than in a straight line, it is customary to specify its position at any time t by means of equations which give both x and y as

functions of t. For example, the
equations of the trajectory of a projectile have approximately the form

$$x = c_1 t, \qquad y = c_2 t - \tfrac{1}{2}g t^2,$$

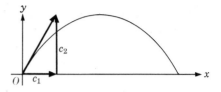

FIGURE 2-5

where c_1 and c_2 are the initial velocity components at time $t = 0$.
The exact equations, which must also take air resistance and other factors
into account, are much more complicated. We are not in a position to
go into details here.

More generally, equations of the form

$$x = f(t), \qquad y = g(t) \tag{1}$$

can be used to specify the position of (x, y) in terms of t. Such equations
are called *parametric equations* and t is called the parameter. If we eliminate t from the equations, then we obtain an equation of the form

$$y = F(x). \tag{2}$$

One might reasonably ásk how $dy/dx = F'(x)$ from Eq. (2) is related to
$dy/dt = g'(t)$ and $dx/dt = f'(t)$ from Eq. (1). The answer to this question is contained in the following *chain rule for derivatives.*

*If $y = F(x)$ is a differentiable function of x and $x = f(t)$ is a differentiable
function of t, then $y = F[f(t)] = g(t)$ is a differentiable function of t and*

$$g'(t) = F'(x)f'(t), \tag{3a}$$

or, in other words,

$$\boxed{\frac{dy}{dt} = \frac{dy}{dx}\frac{dx}{dt}.} \tag{3b}$$

This is called the chain rule of differentiation, since finding the derivative
with respect to t of

$$y = F[f(t)]$$

involves the following chain of steps. *First,* differentiate the outside function

$$y = F(x)$$

with respect to x. *Second,* differentiate the inside function

$$x = f(t)$$

with respect to t.

The product of these derivatives gives dy/dt.

To establish the result, we let t be given an increment $\Delta t \neq 0$ and denote the corresponding x and y increments by Δx and Δy. Then, since $y = F(x)$ is a differentiable function of x, we know, from Eqs. (4a, b, c) of Article 2–4, that we may write

$$\Delta y = \frac{dy}{dx}\Delta x + \epsilon\,\Delta x, \tag{4a}$$

where

$$\epsilon \to 0 \quad \text{as} \quad \Delta x \to 0. \tag{4b}$$

We divide (4a) by Δt

$$\frac{\Delta y}{\Delta t} = \frac{dy}{dx}\frac{\Delta x}{\Delta t} + \epsilon\frac{\Delta x}{\Delta t} \tag{4c}$$

and take limits as $\Delta t \to 0$. Since $x = f(t)$ is a differentiable function of t, we have

$$\lim_{\Delta t \to 0} \Delta x = \lim_{\Delta t \to 0}\left(\frac{\Delta x}{\Delta t}\Delta t\right) = \frac{dx}{dt}\cdot 0 = 0.$$

Therefore Δx approaches zero when Δt does, and

$$\lim_{\Delta t \to 0} \epsilon = \lim_{\Delta x \to 0} \epsilon = 0.$$

Hence the last term in Eq. (4c) has the limit zero and we have

$$\frac{dy}{dt} = \lim_{\Delta t \to 0}\frac{\Delta y}{\Delta t} = \lim_{\Delta t \to 0}\frac{dy}{dx}\frac{\Delta x}{\Delta t} + \lim_{\Delta t \to 0}\left(\epsilon\frac{\Delta x}{\Delta t}\right) = \frac{dy}{dx}\frac{dx}{dt} + 0,$$

as we wished to show.

EXAMPLE 1.

$$y = x^3 - 3x^2 + 5x - 4 = F(x), \qquad x = t^2 + t = f(t).$$

Solution. From these equations, we find

$$\frac{dy}{dx} = 3x^2 - 6x + 5 = 3(t^2 + t)^2 - 6(t^2 + t) + 5,$$

$$\frac{dx}{dt} = 2t + 1,$$

so that Eq. (3b) becomes

$$\frac{dy}{dt} = \frac{dy}{dx}\frac{dx}{dt}$$

$$= [3(t^2 + t)^2 - 6(t^2 + t) + 5](2t + 1).$$

If, on the other hand, we first substitute the value of x in terms of t into the equation for y, we have

$$y = (t^2 + t)^3 - 3(t^2 + t)^2 + 5(t^2 + t) - 4.$$

When we differentiate this with respect to t, we get

$$\frac{dy}{dt} = 3(t^2 + t)^2(2t + 1) - 6(t^2 + t)(2t + 1) + 5(2t + 1)$$

$$= [3(t^2 + t)^2 - 6(t^2 + t) + 5](2t + 1),$$

which agrees with the previous answer.

Remark 1. So far we have not defined dy and dx as separate entities, but have used the complete symbol dy/dx as the name for $\lim (\Delta y/\Delta x)$ as $\Delta x \rightarrow 0$. Now that we have established Eq. (3), we are in a position where we can (and we shall in the next article) define dy and dx as separate quantities whose ratio is the derivative of y with respect to x. Then Eq. (3b) is the form of the chain rule which is most easily remembered, since it suggests that dx may be cancelled from the two fractions on the right.

Remark 2. If $dx/dt \neq 0$, we may divide both sides of Eq. (3b) by dx/dt and write it in the equivalent form

$$\boxed{\frac{dy}{dx} = \frac{dy/dt}{dx/dt}.} \tag{5}$$

This form of the equation is particularly useful in dealing with the parametric equations

$$x = f(t), \qquad y = g(t),$$

since it enables us to find the derivative of y with respect to x directly from these equations.

EXAMPLE 2. The parametric equations

$$x = 2t + 3, \qquad y = t^2 - 1$$

represent a curve whose equation in the form of $y = f(x)$ may be found by substituting

$$t = \frac{x - 3}{2}$$

from the first equation into the second; that is,

$$y = \tfrac{1}{4}(x - 3)^2 - 1.$$

If we work with the original equations and calculate

$$\frac{dx}{dt} = 2, \qquad \frac{dy}{dt} = 2t,$$

then Eq. (5a) gives

$$\frac{dy}{dx} = \frac{dy/dt}{dx/dt} = \frac{2t}{2} = t = \frac{x-3}{2}.$$

On the other hand, from the equation for y in terms of x, we find

$$\frac{dy}{dx} = \frac{1}{2}(x-3)\frac{d}{dx}(x-3) = \frac{x-3}{2}.$$

Remark 3. The chain rule is also frequently expressed using other letters to represent the variables. The most common of these is the case where y is a function of u and u is a function of x,

$$y = F(u), \qquad u = f(x).$$

Then the rule says

$$\boxed{\frac{dy}{dx} = \frac{dy}{du}\frac{du}{dx}.} \qquad (6)$$

We have already had an illustration of this formula in the case of the derivative with respect to x of

$$y = u^n.$$

Then

$$\frac{dy}{du} = nu^{n-1}$$

and

$$\frac{dy}{dx} = \frac{dy}{du}\frac{du}{dx} = nu^{n-1}\frac{du}{dx}.$$

Problems

In Problems 1–4, each pair of equations represents a curve in parametric form. In each case, find the equation of the curve in the form $y = F(x)$ by eliminating t, then calculate dy/dt, dy/dx, and dx/dt and verify that they satisfy the chain rule, Eq. (3b).

1. $x = 3t + 1, \quad y = t^2$ 2. $x = t^2, \quad y = t^3$

3. $x = \dfrac{t}{1-t}, \quad y = t^2$ 4. $x = \dfrac{t}{1+t}, \quad y = \dfrac{t^2}{1+t}$

5. If a point traces the circle $x^2 + y^2 = 25$ and if $dx/dt = 4$ when the point reaches $(3, 4)$, find dy/dt there.

In each of the following problems (6 through 10), find dy/dx, (a) by using the chain rule and also (b) by first expressing y directly in terms of x, and then differentiating.

6. $y = u^2 + 3u - 7$; $u = 2x + 1$ 7. $y = \dfrac{u^2}{u^2 + 1}$; $u = \sqrt{2x + 1}$

8. $y = z^{2/3}$; $z = x^2 + 1$ 9. $y = w^2 - w^{-1}$; $w = 3x$

10. $y = 2v^3 + \dfrac{2}{v^3}$; $v = (3x + 2)^{2/3}$

2–6 The differentials dx and dy. We are now prepared to define dx and dy in such a way that their ratio, when $dx \neq 0$, will be the same as the derivative of y with respect to x. This is very easy to do in the case where x is the *independent variable* and y is a function of x. When x is the independent variable and

$$y = F(x),$$

we shall adopt the following *definitions:*

(a) dx, *called the "differential of x," may be any real number whatever; that is, dx is another independent variable and its domain is* $-\infty < dx < +\infty$, *and*

(b) dy, *called the "differential of y," is a function of x and dx given by*

$$\boxed{dy = F'(x)\, dx,} \tag{1}$$

where $F'(x)$ is the derivative at x of the function F.

It is clear from (1) that the differentials dx and dy have the properties

(1) if $dx = 0$, then $dy = 0$, and
(2) if $dx \neq 0$, then

$$\frac{dy}{dx} = \frac{\text{the differential of } y \text{ in terms of } x \text{ and } dx}{\text{the differential of } x}$$

$$= \frac{F'(x)\, dx}{dx} = F'(x) \tag{2}$$

is the derivative of y with respect to x.

There is certainly nothing mysterious about this last result, since we deliberately defined dy by Eq. (1) so that Eq. (2) would be true. In other words, we planned it that way!

For example, if

$$y = x^3 = F(x)$$

then

$$F'(x) = 3x^2$$

and

$$dy = F'(x)\, dx = 3x^2\, dx.$$

We also have been accustomed to writing

$$\frac{dy}{dx} = 3x^2,$$

and if we treat this as a fraction and multiply both sides by dx, we obtain again

$$dy = 3x^2 \, dx.$$

Again, if

$$y = x = F(x)$$

then

$$F'(x) = 1$$

and

$$dy = F'(x) \, dx = dx.$$

That is, the *function* $F(x) = x$ has its differential, as given by Eq. (1), equal to the differential of the *independent variable* x. This is not a profound result; it simply shows that in the case where both (a) and (b) apply, the differential is the same whether given by (a) or by (b); that is, the two rules are *consistent*.

The geometric interpretation of dy becomes clear when we refer to Fig. 2–6, where in each part we indicate a curve $y = F(x)$ and a line segment PT tangent to the curve at P. The differential $dx = PR$ in each figure is considered positive if R is to the right of P [as in (a) and (c)], and negative when R is to the left of P. The sign of dy is positive if T is above R [as in (a) and (d)] and negative if T is below R. In any

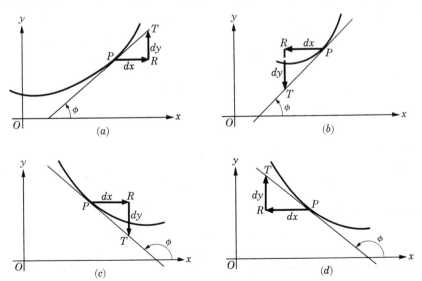

FIGURE 2–6

case, we find that

$$\frac{dy}{dx} = \frac{RT}{PR} = \tan \phi = F'(x)$$

gives the slope of the tangent to the curve at P, and

$$dy = F'(x)\,dx = (\tan \phi)(PR) = RT$$

is the *amount* of change in y along this tangent line that would be produced by a change dx in x. We thus have

(a) dy/dx is the *rate* of change of y per unit change in x, and

(b) dy is the *amount* of change of y for dx units of change in x along the *tangent* to the curve at P.

Therefore, if we take $dx = \Delta x$, then dy is the same as $\Delta y_{\tan}$ (Fig. 1–27), which is the principal part of Δy. In problems dealing with increments we therefore do take $dx = \Delta x$ and use dy as an approximation to Δy.

EXAMPLE. Find a reasonable approximation to the value of

$$(1.001)^7 - 2(1.001)^{4/3} + 3.$$

Solution. At

$$x_0 = 1$$

the function

$$F(x) = x^7 - 2x^{4/3} + 3$$

has the easily calculated value

$$y_0 = F(1) = 2.$$

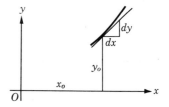

FIGURE 2–7

The tangent to this curve $y = F(x)$ at $(1, 2)$ will remain near the curve for values of x close to x_0. As x changes from $x_0 = 1$ to $x_0 + dx = 1.001$, the change in y *along this tangent line* will be

$$dy = F'(x_0)\,dx.$$

Since

$$F'(x) = 7x^6 - \tfrac{8}{3}x^{1/3}$$

has the value

$$F'(x_0) = \tfrac{13}{3}$$

at $x_0 = 1$, when we take $dx = 0.001$, we have

$$dy = \tfrac{13}{3}(0.001) = 0.0043.$$

When this change in y is added to y_0, we have

$$y_0 + dy = 2.0043$$

as a good approximation to the value of y at the point on the curve for which $x = x_0 + dx$.

Suppose next that x is not the independent variable, but that x and y are both to be regarded as functions of t. Let

$$y = F(x), \qquad x = f(t),$$
$$y = F[f(t)] = g(t), \tag{3}$$

with t now the independent variable. Then to be consistent with our previous definitions, we shall have the definitions:

(a) dt is arbitrary, that is, another independent variable with the range $-\infty < dt < +\infty$, but

(b) $dx = f'(t)\, dt$, and $\tag{4a}$

(c) $dy = g'(t)\, dt$. $\tag{4b}$

Our notation is the same as that used in establishing Eq. (3a), Article 2–5, so we may substitute

$$g'(t) = F'(x)f'(t)$$

into (4b) and find

$$dy = F'(x)f'(t)\, dt,$$

and reference to (4a) shows that this implies

$$dy = F'(x)\, dx. \tag{4c}$$

What is the significance of (4c) and how does it differ from (1)? To answer the latter question first: In (4c), $dy = g'(t)\, dt$ is expressed in terms of t and dt; likewise $dx = f'(t)\, dt$ is expressed in terms of t and dt, whereas in (1), dx is an independent variable and dy is expressed directly in terms of x and dx. Thus the significance of (4c) is that from it we may write

$$F'(x) = \frac{dy \text{ (in terms of } t \text{ and } dt)}{dx \text{ (in terms of } t \text{ and } dt)}, \qquad \text{if } dx \neq 0,$$

that is,

$$\text{the derivative of } y \text{ with respect to } x = \frac{\text{the differential of } y}{\text{the differential of } x}, \qquad \text{if } dx \neq 0,$$

whether the differentials are in terms of x and dx or in terms of t and dt. [When dx equals zero, Eq. (4c) tells us only that dy also equals zero, and of course tells us nothing about $F'(x)$.]

It is this property of the differentials that makes it possible to treat the derivative as the ratio of dy and dx, whether x is the independent variable or not, and enables us to take full advantage of the Leibniz notation.

As an illustration of these ideas, if we let

$$y = t^2 \quad \text{and} \quad x = t^3,$$

we have

$$\frac{dy}{dt} = 2t, \quad \frac{dx}{dt} = 3t^2,$$

$$dy = 2t\,dt, \quad dx = 3t^2\,dt,$$

$$\frac{dy}{dx} = \frac{2t\,dt}{3t^2\,dt} = \frac{2}{3t}.$$

If we eliminate t before taking derivatives,

$$y = x^{2/3},$$

$$\frac{dy}{dx} = \frac{2}{3}x^{-1/3} = \frac{2}{3x^{1/3}} = \frac{2}{3t},$$

in agreement with the answer above.

Second derivative. The second derivative of y with respect to x has been interpreted as the result obtained from y by doing twice in succession the operation "differentiate with respect to x"; i.e.,

$$\frac{d^2y}{dx^2} = \frac{d}{dx}\left[\frac{d}{dx}(y)\right].$$

It is also possible to define a second differential, d^2y, in such a way that the second derivative of y with respect to x is equal to d^2y divided by $(dx)^2$. However, things get rather complicated in the case of parametric equations

$$x = f(t), \quad y = F(x) = F[f(t)] = g(t).$$

In such cases, it is simplest to calculate second and higher order derivatives by using such rules as

$$\frac{dy}{dx} = y' = \frac{dy/dt}{dx/dt},$$

$$\frac{d^2y}{dx^2} = y'' = \frac{dy'}{dx} = \frac{dy'/dt}{dx/dt}.$$

It is important to note that to get the second derivative of y with respect to x, when the first derivative $dy/dx = y'$ is expressed in terms of t, we may differentiate y' with respect to t, provided we divide the result by dx/dt.

EXAMPLE. Find d^2y/dx^2 if $x = t - t^2$ and $y = t - t^3$.

Solution.
$$y' = \frac{dy}{dx} = \frac{dy/dt}{dx/dt} = \frac{1 - 3t^2}{1 - 2t},$$

$$\frac{d^2y}{dx^2} = y'' = \frac{dy'}{dx} = \frac{dy'/dt}{dx/dt} = \frac{\frac{d}{dt}\left[\frac{1 - 3t^2}{1 - 2t}\right]}{(1 - 2t)}$$

$$= \frac{(1 - 2t) \cdot (-6t) - (1 - 3t^2) \cdot (-2)}{(1 - 2t)^3} = \frac{2 - 6t + 6t^2}{(1 - 2t)^3}.$$

2–7 Formulas for differentiation repeated in the notation of differentials. Earlier in this chapter we derived formulas for the derivatives listed below on the left. By multiplying each one by dx we now obtain the corresponding formulas for differentials.

Derivatives	*Differentials*
I. $\dfrac{dc}{dx} = 0$	I'. $dc = 0$
II. $\dfrac{d(cu)}{dx} = c\dfrac{du}{dx}$	II'. $d(cu) = c\,du$
III. $\dfrac{d(u + v)}{dx} = \dfrac{du}{dx} + \dfrac{dv}{dx}$	III'. $d(u + v) = du + dv$
IV. $\dfrac{d(uv)}{dx} = u\dfrac{dv}{dx} + v\dfrac{du}{dx}$	IV'. $d(uv) = u\,dv + v\,du$
V. $\dfrac{d\left(\frac{u}{v}\right)}{dx} = \dfrac{v\dfrac{du}{dx} - u\dfrac{dv}{dx}}{v^2}$	V'. $d\left(\dfrac{u}{v}\right) = \dfrac{v\,du - u\,dv}{v^2}$
VI. $\dfrac{du^n}{dx} = nu^{n-1}\dfrac{du}{dx}$	VI'. $d(u^n) = nu^{n-1}\,du$
VIa. $\dfrac{dcx^n}{dx} = cnx^{n-1}$	VI'a. $d(cx^n) = cnx^{n-1}\,dx$

We collect these formulas primarily for future reference. Any problem involving differentials, say that of finding dy when y is a given function of x, may be handled either

(a) by finding the derivative dy/dx and then multiplying by dx, or
(b) by direct use of formulas I'–VI'a.

For instance, if we let
$$y = x^3 + 5x^2 - 7x + 4,$$
then
$$\frac{dy}{dx} = 3x^2 + 10x - 7,$$
and
$$dy = (3x^2 + 10x - 7)\, dx,$$

or we may calculate directly:

$$dy = d(x^3 + 5x^2 - 7x + 4)$$
$$= d(x^3) + d(5x^2) + d(-7x) + d(4) \qquad \text{(III')}$$
$$= 3x^2\, dx + 10x\, dx - 7\, dx + 0 \qquad \text{(VI'a)}$$
$$= (3x^2 + 10x - 7)\, dx.$$

It should be noted that a *differential* on the left side of an equation, say dy, also calls for a *differential*, usually dx, on the right side of the equation. Thus we never have $dy = 3x^2$, but instead $dy = 3x^2\, dx$.

The term "differentiate" means either to find the derivative or to find the differential and either operation is referred to as "differentiation."

Problems

In each of the following problems (1 through 8), find dy.

1. $y = x^3 - 3x^2 + 5x - 7$ 2. $y^2 = (3x^2 + 1)^{3/2}$

3. $xy^2 + x^2y = 4$ 4. $y = \dfrac{2x}{1 + x^2}$

5. $y = x\sqrt{1 - x^2}$ 6. $y = \dfrac{x + 1}{x^2 - 2x + 4}$

7. $y = \dfrac{(1 - x)^3}{2 - 3x}$ 8. $y = \dfrac{1 + x - x^2}{1 - x}$

Use differentials to obtain reasonable approximations to the following:

9. $\sqrt{145}$ 10. $(2.1)^3$

11. $\sqrt[4]{17}$ 12. $\sqrt[3]{0.126}$

13. $(8.01)^{4/3} + (8.01)^2 - \dfrac{1}{\sqrt[3]{8.01}}$

Given the following functions $x = f(t)$, $y = g(t)$.
(a) Express dx and dy in terms of t and dt.
(b) Use the results of (a) to find, at the point for which $t = 2$, the slope of the locus of the point (x, y).

(c) Use the results of (b) to find an equation of the line tangent to the curve at the point for which $t = 2$.

14. $x = t + \dfrac{1}{t}, \quad y = t - \dfrac{1}{t}$ $\qquad$ 15. $x = \sqrt{2t^2 + 1}, \quad y = (2t + 1)^2$

16. $x = t\sqrt{2t + 5}, \quad y = (4t)^{1/3}$ $\qquad$ 17. $x = \dfrac{t - 1}{t + 1}, \quad y = \dfrac{t + 1}{t - 1}$

18. $x = \dfrac{1}{t^2}, \quad y = \sqrt{t^2 + 12}$

19. Find d^2y/dx^2 from the parametric equations in Problem 14.
20. Find d^2y/dx^2 from the parametric equations in Problem 17.
21. Given the parametric equations $x = f(t), y = g(t)$. Show that

$$\frac{d^2y}{dx^2} = \frac{\dfrac{dx}{dt}\dfrac{d^2y}{dt^2} - \dfrac{d^2x}{dt^2}\dfrac{dy}{dt}}{(dx/dt)^3}.$$

22. [Franklin: *Treatise on Advanced Calculus* (Wiley, 1940), p. 110.] Let

$$y = F(x), \quad x = f(t); \quad F[f(t)] = g(t).$$

Using a subscript to denote the independent variable, define second differentials as follows:

$$(d^2y)_x = F''(x) \cdot (dx)^2, \ (d^2y)_t = g''(t) \cdot (dt)^2, \ (d^2x)_t = f''(t) \cdot (dt)^2.$$

Then show that
$$(d^2y)_t = (d^2y)_x + F'(x)(d^2x)_t.$$

[*Hint:* By the chain rule, $g'(t) = F'(x)f'(t)$. From this deduce that $g''(t) = F'(x)f''(t) + F''(x)[f'(t)]^2$.]

2–8 Continuity. Before we take up applications of differentiation (Chapter 3), it is desirable to discuss the *continuity* of a function. We shall see that continuity is even more basic than differentiability.

DEFINITION. *A function f which is defined in some neighborhood of c is said to be* continuous *at c provided*

(a) *the function has a definite finite value $f(c)$ at c, and*
(b) *as x approaches c, $f(x)$ approaches $f(c)$ as limit:*

$$\lim_{x \to c} f(x) = f(c).$$

If a function is continuous at all points of an interval $a \le x \le b$ (or $a < x < b$, etc.), then it is said to be continuous on, or in, that interval.

As an example of a continuous function, let us investigate

$$f(x) = x^2$$

at some fixed value $x = c$. Certainly requirement (a) of the definition is satisfied, since the function has the value

$$f(c) = c^2$$

at $x = c$. Furthermore, the difference

$$f(x) - f(c) = x^2 - c^2 = (x - c)(x + c)$$

approaches zero as a limit when $x - c$ approaches zero, since as $x \to c$ we have

$$\lim [f(x) - f(c)] = \lim (x - c) \lim (x + c)$$
$$= 0 \cdot 2c = 0.$$

Therefore this function, $f(x) = x^2$, is continuous at *any* $x = c$; that is, it is continuous for all x, $-\infty < x < +\infty$.

The graph of a function which is continuous on an interval $a \le x \le b$ consists of an unbroken curve over that interval. This fact is of practical importance in using curves to represent functions. It makes it possible, for example, to sketch a curve by constructing a table of values (x, y), plotting relatively few points from this table, and then sketching a continuous (i.e., unbroken) curve through these points. For example, suppose we carry through the steps discussed for the simple case $y = x^2$.

We first make a short table of values:

x	0	±0.5	±1	±2
y	0	0.25	1	4

then plot these points and draw a continuous curve through them, as shown in Fig. 2–8. Then we might go one step further and use the curve itself to find the value of x^2 corresponding to an x different from those used in making the table of values. For example, in Fig. 2–8, $x = 1.6$ is indicated on the x-scale and the corresponding reading on the y-scale gives $x^2 \approx 2.6$. Of course, the graph probably won't give *exact* values except at those points which have been plotted exactly. But it will give values which are near the exact values, if the calculated points aren't spread too far apart.

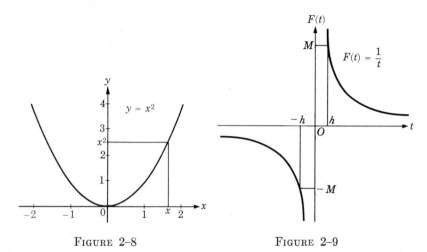

FIGURE 2–8   FIGURE 2–9

In order to appreciate the concept of continuity more fully, it is desirable to have some examples of the opposite behavior which some functions exhibit at certain points, that is, discontinuity. For example, the function $F(t) = 1/t$ is discontinuous at $t = 0$ because it violates both requirements (a) and (b) (see Fig. 2–9). This function has an infinite discontinuity at $t = 0$.

The function

$$F(t) = \text{greatest integer in } t = [t],$$

on the other hand, is discontinuous at $t = n$ for every integer $n = 0, \pm 1, \pm 2, \ldots$, but its discontinuities are all finite. This function changes abruptly by unity when t decreases by ever so small an amount from 3 to $3 - \delta$, for example, no matter how small the positive number δ may be. (See Fig. 2–10.)

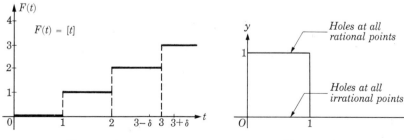

FIGURE 2–10   FIGURE 2–11

An extreme example of a discontinuous function is afforded by the function defined by the rule

$$f(x) = \begin{cases} 0, \text{ when } x \text{ is rational,} \\ 1, \text{ when } x \text{ is irrational.} \end{cases}$$

This function has a perfectly definite value for every x in the interval $0 \leq x \leq 1$. But no matter what c is chosen in this interval, there are points x which are arbitrarily close to c but having functional values $f(x)$ which differ from $f(c)$ by unity. That is, $|f(x) - f(c)|$ is not arbitrarily small for all $x \neq c$ in some small neighborhood of c. This function is discontinuous at all points in the interval $(0, 1)$. Its graph cannot be drawn, but it can be described by saying that it consists of all the rational points on the x-axis from 0 to 1, with the irrational points all pushed up one unit above the x-axis. (See Fig. 2–11.) Thus it consists of two parallel line segments, each of which is full of holes!

With these examples before us, the question arises as to how, in practice, we can tell whether or not a given function is continuous. When we sketch its graph, should we be sure to sketch a connected, unbroken curve, as for the graph of $y = x^2$, or must we be careful *not* to connect all of the points as, for example, in the case $y = 1/x$, where points in the third quadrant must not be connected with points in the first quadrant?

Since we have studied differentiation, the following theorem, which says that every function which has a derivative at a point is also continuous at that point, enables us to conclude that:

(a) every polynomial

$$f(x) = ax^n + bx^{n-1} + \cdots + px + q$$

is continuous for all x, $-\infty < x < +\infty$, and

(b) every rational function

$$f(x) = \frac{F(x)}{G(x)},$$

$F(x)$ and $G(x)$ being polynomials, is continuous for all x where the denominator, $G(x)$, is not zero.

Thus, for example, the graphs of

$$y = x^3, \qquad y = 2x^2 - x + 3, \qquad y = \frac{x^2 - 1}{x^2 + 1}$$

are continuous, connected curves over the domain $-\infty < x < +\infty$.

On the other hand, the graph of

$$y = \frac{x^2 + 1}{x^3 - 4x} \tag{1}$$

goes shooting off toward $\pm \infty$ as x approaches one of the three values

$$x = -2, \qquad x = 0, \qquad x = +2,$$

where the denominator vanishes. But, over the intervals $-\infty < x < -2$, $-2 < x < 0, 0 < x < 2$, and $2 < x < +\infty$, the graph consists of separate continuous curves, since the denominator does not vanish in any of these intervals. The reader will find it instructive to work out the graph of Eq. (1) for himself on the basis of the discussion above.

Let us now state and prove the theorem we mentioned above.

THEOREM 1. *If the function f has a finite derivative*

$$f'(c) = \lim_{\Delta x \to 0} \frac{f(c + \Delta x) - f(c)}{\Delta x} \tag{2}$$

at x = c, then f is continuous at x = c.

Proof. For the limit in (2) to exist, it is necessary that $f(c)$ and $f(c + \Delta x)$ both exist, at least for all Δx near zero. We change the notation slightly by writing x in place of $c + \Delta x$. Then

$$x = c + \Delta x$$

is near c when

$$\Delta x = x - c$$

is near zero. Equation (2) now may be written in the form

$$f'(c) = \lim_{x \to c} \frac{f(x) - f(c)}{x - c}.$$

Suppose then that $f'(c)$ exists and is finite. We want to prove that $f(x) - f(c)$ tends to zero as $x \to c$. This follows at once from

$$\lim_{x \to c} [f(x) - f(c)] = \lim_{x \to c} \left[(x - c) \frac{f(x) - f(c)}{x - c} \right]$$

$$= \lim_{x \to c} (x - c) \cdot \lim_{x \to c} \frac{f(x) - f(c)}{x - c}$$

$$= 0 \cdot f'(c) = 0. \qquad \text{Q.E.D.}$$

We have just shown that differentiability implies continuity. The converse, however, is not true, as is easily seen by considering the example

$$f(x) = |x|,$$

which is continuous at $x = 0$ but does not possess a derivative at that point.

The fact that $f(x) = |x|$ has no derivative at $x = 0$ follows from the fact that

$$\frac{f(0 + \Delta x) - f(0)}{\Delta x} = \frac{|\Delta x|}{\Delta x}$$

$$= \begin{cases} +1, & \text{when} & \Delta x > 0, \\ -1, & \text{when} & \Delta x < 0, \end{cases}$$

and

$$\lim_{\Delta x \to 0} \frac{|\Delta x|}{\Delta x} \text{ does not exist.}$$

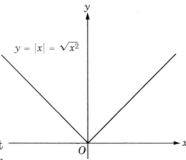

$$y = |x| = \sqrt{x^2}$$

FIGURE 2–12

Until the middle of the 19th century it was generally believed that a continuous function would at least have a derivative at most places, even though there might be isolated points (as at $x = 0$, in our example) where the derivative did not exist. However, the German mathematicians Riemann (1826–1866) and Weierstrass (1815–1897) gave examples of functions which are continuous but which fail to have derivatives anywhere. For a readable account of this, see *World of Mathematics*, Vol. 3, p. 1963.

We conclude this chapter with some theorems which we shall state without proofs. Some of these theorems follow rather simply from the corresponding theorems on limits. Others require, for rigorous proofs, a more penetrating investigation of the properties of the real number system than we are able to make at this time.

THEOREM 2. *Suppose f and g are two functions that are continuous at $x = c$. Then the functions F_1, F_2, F_3 defined by*

$$F_1(x) = f(x) + g(x),$$

$$F_2(x) = kf(x), \qquad k \text{ any number,}$$

$$F_3(x) = f(x) \cdot g(x)$$

are also continuous at $x = c$. Furthermore, if $g(c)$ is not zero, then F_4,

$$F_4(x) = \frac{f(x)}{g(x)}$$

is also continuous at $x = c$.

THEOREM 3.   *A function f that is continuous for all x in the closed interval $a \leq x \leq b$ has the following properties:*

(i) *It has a minimum value m and a maximum value M; that is, there are numbers α and β in the interval such that $m = f(\alpha)$ and $M = f(\beta)$, and such that for all x in the interval, the condition*

$$m \leq f(x) \leq M$$

is satisfied.

(ii) *If N is any number between $f(a)$ and $f(b)$, then there is at least one number c between a and b such that $f(c) = N$.* *

(iii) *Given any positive number ϵ there is a positive number δ (which may depend upon ϵ but does not depend upon x_1 or x_2) such that if x_1 and x_2 belong to the interval $a \leq x \leq b$ and $|x_1 - x_2| < \delta$, then $|f(x_1) - f(x_2)| < \epsilon$.*

Remark. A function that satisfies the condition (iii) above is said to be *uniformly continuous* for $a \leq x \leq b$ and the theorem says that a function that is continuous on a *closed* interval is automatically *uniformly continuous* there.   The function $f(x) = 1/x$ is, on the other hand, continuous in the *open* interval $0 < x < 1$, but is not uniformly continuous there.

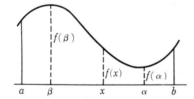 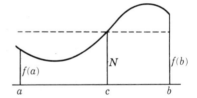

FIGURE 2–13

The following physical interpretation of continuity may be of some value in throwing more light on the distinction between the notion of "continuous at every point of an interval" on the one hand and "uniformly continuous in an interval" on the other. We recall that a function is continuous at $x = c$ if $f(c)$ exists and $f(x) \to f(c)$ as $x \to c$. This means that if we are challenged with a positive "tolerance limit" ϵ and required to make

$$|f(x) - f(c)| < \epsilon \tag{3}$$

for *all* x sufficiently close to c, we must produce a positive number δ such that condition (3) is met whenever

$$|x - c| < \delta. \tag{4}$$

Let us translate this into physical terms.

---

* This is known as the *intermediate value theorem.*

Suppose we have a pair of dividers (Fig. 2–14) with a meter attached and having the property that when the points of the dividers are set at c and x respectively, the meter registers the numerical value of the difference in the functional values at c and x; that is,

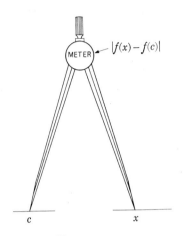

FIGURE 2–14

the meter reads $|f(x) - f(c)|$ when the points touch x and c.

Suppose now we hold one prong of the dividers at c and move the other prong around near c, either to the left of c or to its right. Suppose that to *each* positive number ϵ we are able to assign a band of width 2δ around c,

$$c - \delta < x < c + \delta,$$

such that whenever the second prong is inside this band the meter reading is less than ϵ. Then the function is, by our definition, continuous at c.

Now the "bandwidth" 2δ will in general depend upon ϵ. That is, the smaller the tolerance limit ϵ that is required, the more narrowly must we restrict the range of x around c. Furthermore, the "bandwidth" 2δ will also, in general, depend upon c. That is, for a given function $f(x)$,

$$\delta = \delta(c, \epsilon)$$

is a function of both c and ϵ. Now if the function $f(x)$ is continuous for all values of x in some domain, then with each x_0 in the domain and with each $\epsilon > 0$ we can associate a positive number $\delta = \delta(x_0, \epsilon)$ such that if x is in the domain and if $|x - x_0| < \delta(x_0, \epsilon)$, then

$$|f(x) - f(x_0)| < \epsilon.$$

Finally, as we vary x_0, it may happen that all of these numbers $\delta(x_0, \epsilon)$ are at least as large as some positive number $k = k(\epsilon)$. Then, given $\epsilon > 0$, we could use a band of constant width $2k$ around *any* x_0 of the domain, and have

$$|f(x) - f(x_0)| < \epsilon$$

whenever x is in the domain and $|x - x_0| < k$. For, the band $x_0 - k < x < x_0 + k$ surely lies inside the band $x_0 - \delta(x_0, \epsilon) < x < x_0 + \delta(x_0, \epsilon)$, since $\delta(x_0, \epsilon) \geq k$. In other words, if the two prongs of the dividers are spread apart any distance smaller than this k and the dividers are then placed so that they touch *any two points* x_1, x_2, in the domain of x, in the circumstances described above it will turn out that the meter reading is less than ϵ. This exemplifies what is meant by *uniform* continuity.

To summarize these remarks we may say that

(a) *ordinary continuity* at a point c means that the bandwidth depends not only upon the tolerance ϵ but also upon c, whereas

(b) *uniform continuity* means that with any positive ϵ we may associate *one* bandwidth that works for *all* points in the domain.

PROBLEMS

1. (a) Prove that the function $f(x) = x^3$ is continuous at $x = c$ for any real c. (b) If $c = 5$, and ϵ is a preassigned positive number, find

$$\delta \text{ such that } |x^3 - 5^3| < \epsilon \quad \text{when} \quad |x - 5| < \delta.$$

2. For what values of x is each of the following functions discontinuous?

(a) $f(x) = \dfrac{x}{x+1}$,

(b) $f(x) = \dfrac{x+1}{x^2 - 4x + 3}$.

3. Is the function f defined by the rule

$$f(x) = \begin{cases} \dfrac{x^2 - 1}{x - 1}, & \text{when} \quad x \neq 1, \\ 2, & \text{when} \quad x = 1, \end{cases}$$

continuous or discontinuous at $x = 1$? Prove your result.

4. The function $f(x) = |x|$ is continuous at $x = 0$. Given a positive number ϵ, how large may δ be in order that $|f(x) - 0| < \epsilon$ when $|x - 0| < \delta$?

5. What is the maximum of $f(x) = |x|$ for $-1 \leq x \leq 1$? What is the minimum? Sketch.

6. Does the function $f(x) = x^2$ have a maximum for $0 < x < 1$? Does it have a minimum? Give reasons for your answers.

7. A continuous function $y = f(x)$ is known to be negative at $x = 0$ and positive at $x = 1$. Why is it true that the equation $f(x) = 0$ has at least one root between $x = 0$ and $x = 1$? Illustrate with a sketch.

8. Is the function $f(x) = \sqrt[3]{x}$ continuous at $x = 0$? Is it differentiable there? Give reasons for your answers.

9. *Prove the following theorem.* Let f be continuous and positive at $x = c$. Prove that there is some interval around $x = c$, say $c - \delta < x < c + \delta$, throughout which $f(x)$ remains positive. [*Hint:* In the definition of continuity, Eqs. (3) and (4), take $\epsilon = \frac{1}{2}f(c)$.] Illustrate with a sketch.

10. For $x \neq 2$, the function $f(x)$ is equal to $(x^2 + 3x - 10)/(x - 2)$. What value should be assigned to $f(2)$ to make $f(x)$ continuous at $x = 2$?

REVIEW QUESTIONS AND EXERCISES FOR CHAPTER 2

1. Using the definition of the derivative, deduce the formula for the derivative of a product uv of two differentiable functions.

2. In the formula for the derivative of uv, let $v = u$, and thereby deduce a formula for the derivative of u^2. Repeat the process, with $v = u^2$, and get a formula for the derivative of u^3. Extend the result, by the method of mathematical induction, to deduce the formula for the derivative of u^n for every positive integer n.

3. Explain how the three formulas

$$\text{(a) } \frac{d(x^n)}{dx} = nx^{n-1}, \quad \text{(b) } \frac{d(cu)}{dx} = c\frac{du}{dx}, \quad \text{(c) } \frac{d(u+v)}{dx} = \frac{du}{dx} + \frac{dv}{dx}$$

are sufficient to differentiate any polynomial.

4. What formula do we need, in addition to the three listed in Problem 3 above, in order to differentiate rational functions?

5. Does the derivative of a polynomial function exist at every point of its domain? What is the largest domain the function can have? Does the derivative of a rational function exist at every point in its domain? What real numbers, if any, must be excluded from the domain of a rational function?

6. *Definition of algebraic function.* Let $y = f(x)$ define a function of x such that every pair of numbers (x, y) belonging to f satisfy an irreducible equation of the form

$$P_0(x)y^n + P_1(x)y^{n-1} + \cdots + P_{n-1}(x)y + P_n(x) = 0 \qquad (\alpha)$$

for some positive integer n, with coefficients $P_0(x), \ldots, P_n(x)$ polynomials in x, and $P_0(x)$ not identically zero. Then f is said to be an *algebraic function*. What technique of this chapter can be used to find the derivative of an algebraic function if the polynomial coefficients $P_0(x), \ldots, P_n(x)$ in its defining equation (α) are given?

7. Show that the function f defined by $f(x) = x^{2/3}$ is an algebraic function by finding an appropriate equation of the type (α) in the definition in Problem 6 above. On what domain of values of x is this function defined? Where is it continuous? Where is it differentiable?

8. Show that every rational function is algebraic. Do you think the converse is also true? Explain.

9. It can be shown (though not very easily) that sums, quotients, products, powers, and roots of algebraic functions are algebraic functions. Thus

$$f(x) = x\sqrt{3x^2 + 1} + 5x^{4/3}/(3x + 2), \qquad x \neq -\tfrac{2}{3},$$

defines an algebraic function. Find its derivative. What formulas of this chapter are used in finding derivatives of functions like this one?

10. Show that $y = |x|$ satisfies the equation $y^2 - x^2 = 0$. Is the absolute value function algebraic? What is its derivative? Where does the derivative exist? Where is the absolute value function continuous?

11. Define differentials. If $y = f(x)$ defines a differentiable function, how are dy and dx related? Give geometrical interpretations of dx and dy.

12. State the chain rule for derivatives. Prove it, with the book closed.

13. Show how the chain rule is used to prove that the derivative of y with respect to x is the ratio of dy to dx when x and y are both differentiable functions of t, and $dx \neq 0$.

14. Give an example of a function that is defined and bounded on $0 \leq t \leq 1$, continuous in the open interval $0 < t < 1$, and discontinuous at $t = 0$.

15. State and prove a theorem about the relationship between continuity and differentiability of a function, at a point in its domain.

16. Read the article "The Lever of Mahomet," by R. Courant and H. Robbins, and the accompanying "Commentary on Continuity," by J. R. Newman, in *World of Mathematics*, Vol. 4, pp. 2410–2413.

MISCELLANEOUS PROBLEMS FOR CHAPTER 2

Find dy/dx in each of the following problems (1 through 33).

1. $y = \dfrac{x}{\sqrt{x^2 - 4}}$

2. $x^2 + xy + y^2 - 5x = 2$

3. $xy + y^2 = 1$

4. $x^3 + 4xy - 3y^3 = 2$

5. $x^2y + xy^2 = 6$

6. $y = (x + 1)^2(x^2 + 2x)^{-2}$

7. $y = \dfrac{x}{\sqrt{1 - x^2}}$

8. $x^2 + 3xy^2 + y^3 = 2$

9. $y = \dfrac{x}{x + 1}$

10. $y = \sqrt{2x + 1}$

11. $y = x^2\sqrt{x^2 - a^2}$

12. $y = \dfrac{2x + 1}{2x - 1}$

13. $y = \dfrac{x^2}{1 - x^2}$

14. $y = (x^2 + x + 1)^3$

15. $y = \dfrac{1}{\sqrt{x^2 + x - 1}}$

16. $y = \dfrac{x^3 - 1}{x - 1}$

17. $y = \dfrac{(2x^2 + 5x)^{3/2}}{3}$

18. $y = \dfrac{3}{(2x^2 + 5x)^{3/2}}$

19. $xy^2 + \sqrt{xy} = 2$

20. $x^2 + y^2 = xy$

21. $x^{2/3} + y^{2/3} = a^{2/3}$

22. $x^{1/2} + y^{1/2} = a^{1/2}$

23. $xy = 1$

24. $\sqrt{xy} = 1$

25. $(x + 2y)^2 + 2xy^2 = 6$

26. $y = \sqrt{\dfrac{1 - x}{1 + x^2}}$

27. $y^2 = \dfrac{x}{x + 1}$

28. $x^2y + xy^2 = 6(x^2 + y^2)$

29. $xy + 2x + 3y = 1$

30. $y = u^2 - 1,\ x = u^2 + 1$

31. $y = \sqrt{2t + t^2},\ t = 2x + 3$

32. $x = \dfrac{t}{1 + t^2},\ y = 1 + t^2$

33. $t = \dfrac{x}{1 + x^2},\ y = x^2 + t^2$

34. Find the slope of $y = x/(x^2 + 1)$ at the origin. Write the equation of the tangent line at the origin.

35. Write the equation of the tangent to the curve $x^2 - 2xy + y^2 + 2x + y - 6 = 0$ at $(2, 2)$.

36. Determine the constant c such that the straight line joining the points $(0, 3)$ and $(5, -2)$ is tangent to the curve $y = c/(x + 1)$.

37. What is the slope of the curve $y = 2x^2 - 6x + 3$ at the point on the curve where $x = 2$? What is the equation of the tangent line to the curve at this point?

38. Find the points on the curve $y = 2x^3 - 3x^2 - 12x + 20$ where the tangent is parallel to the x-axis.

39. Find the derivatives of the following functions:

(a) $y = (x^2 + 2x)^5$;

(b) $f(t) = \sqrt{3t^2 - 2t}$;

(c) $f(r) = \sqrt{r^2 + 5} + \sqrt{r^2 - 5}$;

(d) $f(x) = \dfrac{x^2 - 1}{x^2 + 1}$.

40. Find the equation of the tangent to the curve $y = 2/\sqrt{x - 1}$ at the point on the curve where $x = 10$.

41. Write the equation of the straight line passing through the point $(1, 2)$ and normal to the curve $x^2 = 4y$.

42. Use the definition of the derivative to find dy/dx for $y = \sqrt{2x + 3}$ and then check the result by finding the same derivative by the power formula.

43. Find the value of

$$\lim_{\Delta x \to 0} \frac{[2 - 3(x + \Delta x)]^2 - [2 - 3x]^2}{\Delta x}$$

and specify the function $f(x)$ of which this is the derivative.

44. Find the slope of the curve $x^2y + xy^2 = 6$ at the point $(1, 2)$.

45. A cylindrical can of height 6 (in.) and radius r (in.) has volume $V = 6\pi r^2$ (in³). What is the difference between ΔV and its principal part as r varies? What is the geometric significance of the principal part?

46. If a hemispherical bowl of radius 10 in. is filled with water to a depth of x in., the volume of water is given by $v = \pi[10 - (x/3)]x^2$. Find the rate of increase of the volume per inch increase of the depth.

47. A bus will hold 60 people. If the number x of persons per trip who use the bus is related to the fare charged (p nickels), by the law $p = [3 - (x/40)]^2$, write the function expressing the total revenue per trip received by the bus company. What is the number x_1 of people per trip that will make the marginal revenue equal to zero? What is the corresponding fare?

48. Prove Eq. (2), Article 2–2, by mathematical induction.

49. Given $y = x - x^2$, find the rate of change of y^2 with respect to x^2 (expressed in terms of x).

50. If $x = 3t + 1$ and $y = t^2 + t$, find dy/dt, dx/dt, and dy/dx. Eliminate t to obtain y as a function of x, and then determine dy/dx directly. Do the results check?

51. A particle projected vertically upward with a speed of a ft/sec reaches an elevation $s = at - 16t^2$ ft at the end of t sec. What must the initial velocity be in order for the particle to travel 49 ft upward before it starts coming back down?

52. Find the rate of change of $\sqrt{x^2 + 16}$ with respect to $x/(x - 1)$ at $x = 3$.

53. The circle $(x - h)^2 + (y - k)^2 = r^2$, center at (h, k), radius $= r$ (see Article 9–5), is tangent to the curve $y = x^2 + 1$ at the point $(1, 2)$. (a) Find the locus of the point (h, k). (b) If, also, the circle and the curve have the same second derivative at $(1, 2)$, find h, k, and r. Sketch the curve and the circle.

54. If $y = x^2 + 1$ and $u = \sqrt{x^2 + 1}$, find dy/du.

55. If $x = y^2 + y$ and $u = (x^2 + x)^{3/2}$, find dy/du.

56. If $f'(x) = \sqrt{3x^2 - 1}$ and $y = f(x^2)$, find dy/dx.

57. If $f'(x) = \sin(x^2)$ and $y = f\left(\dfrac{2x - 1}{x + 1}\right)$, find $\dfrac{dy}{dx}$.

58. Find $y' = dy/dx$ and $y'' = dy'/dx$ if $y = x^2 - 3x + 5$.

59. If s represents the distance a body moves in time t, determine the acceleration $a = d^2s/dt^2$ if $s = 250 + 40t - 16t^2$.

60. If $y = x\sqrt{2x - 3}$, find d^2y/dx^2.

61. Find the value of d^2y/dx^2 in the equation $y^3 + y = x$ at the point $(2, 1)$.

62. If $x = t - t^2$, $y = t - t^3$, find the values of dy/dx and d^2y/dx^2 at $t = 1$.

63. Prove Leibniz's rule:

(a) $\dfrac{d^2(uv)}{dx^2} = \dfrac{d^2u}{dx^2} \cdot v + 2 \dfrac{du}{dx}\dfrac{dv}{dx} + u \dfrac{d^2v}{dx^2}$,

(b) $\dfrac{d^3(uv)}{dx^3} = \dfrac{d^3u}{dx^3} \cdot v + 3 \dfrac{d^2u}{dx^2}\dfrac{dv}{dx} + 3 \dfrac{du}{dx}\dfrac{d^2v}{dx^2} + u \dfrac{d^3v}{dx^3}$,

(c) $\dfrac{d^n(uv)}{dx^n} = \dfrac{d^nu}{dx^n} \cdot v + n \dfrac{d^{n-1}u}{dx^{n-1}}\dfrac{dv}{dx} + \cdots$

$\qquad + \dfrac{n(n - 1) \cdots (n - k + 1)}{k!} \dfrac{d^{n-k}u}{dx^{n-k}}\dfrac{d^kv}{dx^k} + \cdots + u \dfrac{d^nv}{dx^n}$.

The terms on the right side of this equation may be obtained from the terms in the binomial expansion $(a + b)^n$ by replacing $a^{n-k}b^k$ by $(d^{n-k}u/dx^{n-k}) \cdot (d^kv/dx^k)$ for $k = 0, 1, 2, \ldots, n$, and interpreting d^0u/dx^0 as being u itself.

64. Find d^3y/dx^3 in each of the following cases:

(a) $y = \sqrt{2x - 1}$;   (b) $y = \dfrac{1}{3x + 2}$;   (c) $y = ax^3 + bx^2 + cx + d$.

65. If $f(x) = (x - a)^n g(x)$, where $g(x)$ is a polynomial and $g(a) \neq 0$, show that $f(a) = 0 = f'(a) = \cdots = f^{(n-1)}(a)$; but $f^{(n)}(a) = n!g(a) \neq 0$.

66. If $y = 2x^2 - 3x + 5$, find Δy for $x = 3$ and $\Delta x = 0.1$. Approximate Δy by finding its principal part.

67. Find an approximate value of $\sqrt{26}$ by considering the function $y = \sqrt{x}$ when $x = 25$ and $\Delta x = 1$. Also find an approximate value of $\sqrt[3]{26}$. (Specify the function used for the purpose and the values of x and Δx.)

68. By means of differentials, find an approximate value of $\sqrt[10]{0.999}$.

69. To compute the height h of a lamppost, the length a of the shadow of a six-foot pole is measured. The pole is 20 ft from the lamppost. If $a = 15$ ft, with a possible error of less than one inch, find the height of the lamppost and estimate the error in height.

70. Find the differential dy in each of the following cases:

(a) $y = x^2/(1 + x)$; (b) $x^2 - y^2 = 1$; (c) $xy + y^2 = 1$.

71. Given a function f satisfying the following two conditions for all x and y:

(a) $f(x + y) = f(x) \cdot f(y)$;   (b) $f(x) = 1 + xg(x)$, where $\lim\limits_{x \to 0} g(x) = 1$.

Prove that (a) the derivative $f'(x)$ exists, (b) $f'(x) = f(x)$.

72. Let $f(x) = x^2 + 1$. Given $\epsilon > 0$, find $\delta > 0$ such that $|f(x_1) - f(x_2)| < \epsilon$ whenever $|x_1 - x_2| < \delta$ and x_1, x_2 both lie in the closed interval $-2 \leq x \leq 2$. State precisely what this means concerning the continuity of this function.

73. Given a function $f(x)$, defined for all real x, and a positive constant c such that $|f(x + h) - f(x)| \leq ch^2$ for all real h. Prove that (a) $f(x)$ is uniformly continuous, (b) $f'(x) = 0$ for all x.

74. A function $f(x)$ is said to satisfy a Lipschitz condition of order m on the closed interval $a \leq x \leq b$ if there is a constant C such that

$$|f(x_2) - f(x_1)| \leq C|x_2 - x_1|^m$$

for all values of x_1, x_2 on $[a, b]$. Prove that a function which satisfies a Lipschitz condition of order $m > 0$ on $[a, b]$ is uniformly continuous there.

75. Suppose $[a, b]$ is the interval $[-1, 1]$ and $f(x) = \sqrt{1 - x^2}$. Find appropriate values of C and of m to satisfy the conditions in Problem 74. [Hint: Show that if $y_2 > y_1 > 0$ and $y_2 - y_1 = h$, then $|\sqrt{y_2} - \sqrt{y_1}| \leq \sqrt{h}$.]

CHAPTER 3

APPLICATIONS

3–1 Sign of the first derivative. Application to curve sketching. We have previously illustrated the use of the slope of a curve to gain information beyond that given by the table of (x, y) values. We wish now to consider how just the sign of the derivative at a point gives information about the curve. Figure 3–1 shows a curve $y = f(x)$ on which we have indicated certain points $A, B, C, D,$ and E. At A we say that y is an increasing function of x, by which we mean that the function values increase as x increases. At such a point the slope of the tangent to the curve, dy/dx, is positive. The same applies at E, while

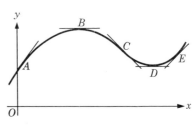

FIGURE 3–1

at C we say the function f is a decreasing function of x and this will be indicated by a negative value of dy/dx at C. At B and D the slope is zero.

We apply these ideas to the problem of sketching the curve:

$$y = \tfrac{1}{3}x^3 - 2x^2 + 3x + 2.$$

The slope at (x, y) is

$$\frac{dy}{dx} = x^2 - 4x + 3 = (x - 1)(x - 3).$$

To determine where dy/dx is positive and where it is negative, we first determine where it is zero:

$$\frac{dy}{dx} = 0 \qquad \text{when} \qquad x = 1 \quad \text{or} \quad x = 3,$$

since these points will mark the transition from positive to negative or from negative to positive slopes. The sign of dy/dx depends upon the signs of both factors $(x - 1)$ and $(x - 3)$, and since the sign of $(x - 1)$ is negative when x is to the left of 1 and positive to the right, we have the pattern of signs indicated in Fig. 3–2(a). Similarly, the sign of $(x - 3)$ is as shown in Fig. 3–2(b), and the sign of $dy/dx = (x - 1)(x - 3)$ as shown in Fig. 3–2(c). We can get a rough idea of the shape of the curve just from this pattern of signs of its slope, if we sketch a curve which is

104

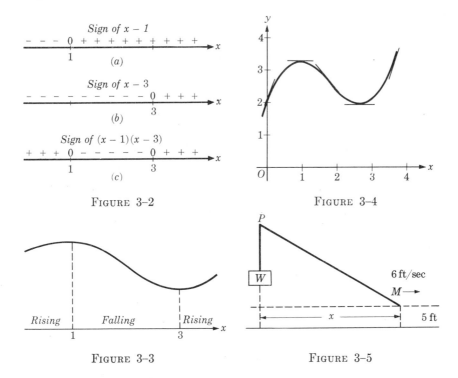

FIGURE 3–2

FIGURE 3–4

FIGURE 3–3

FIGURE 3–5

rising, falling, and rising again for $x < 1$, $1 < x < 3$, and $x > 3$, respectively (Fig. 3–3).

To get a more accurate curve, we would construct a table for some range of values extending, say, from $x = 0$ to $x = 4$, which includes the transition points between rising and falling portions of the curve (Fig. 3–4).

The terms "rising" and "falling," or "increasing" and "decreasing" are always taken to apply to the behavior of the curve as the point that is tracing it moves from left to right or, in other words, relative to its behavior as x increases.

The same concepts apply to functions that vary with time. For example, Fig. 3–5 represents a rope running through a pulley at P, bearing a weight W at one end. The other end is held in a man's hand M at a distance of 5 feet above the ground as he walks in a straight line at the rate of 6 ft/sec. If, as in the figure, x represents the distance in feet of the man's hand away from the vertical line PW, then x is an increasing function of t and we are given the rate at which it changes with t, namely, 6 ft/sec. This would be stated in mathematical terms by saying $dx/dt = +6$ (ft/sec). On the other hand, if the man were to walk toward the line PW at the rate of 6 ft/sec, we would have $dx/dt = -6$ (ft/sec), because x would then be a decreasing function of t.

PROBLEMS

In each of the following exercises, determine dy/dx and find the sets of values of x where the graph of y versus x is rising (to the right) and where it is falling. Sketch each curve, showing in particular the points of transition between falling and rising portions of the curve.

1. $y = x^2 - x + 1$

2. $y = \dfrac{x^3}{3} - \dfrac{x^2}{2} - 2x + \dfrac{1}{3}$

3. $y = 2x^3 - 3x^2 + 3$

4. $y = x^3 - 27x + 36$

5. $y = x^4 - 8x^2 + 16$

3–2 Related rates. In the example at the end of Article 3–1, suppose that the pulley is 25 ft above the ground, the rope is 45 ft long, and at a given instant the distance x is 15 ft and the man is walking away from the pulley. How fast is the weight being raised at this particular instant?

In Fig. 3–6, M represents the man's hand, P the pulley, W the weight, and OM is a horizontal line at the level of the man's hand which is 5 ft above the ground, so that P is 20 ft above O. The figure is drawn to illustrate the situation at any time t and *not just at* the instant in question. The reason for this is that certain of the distances, namely, x, y, z, and h in the illustration, are quantities which vary and it is important to treat them as such and not as constants.

Having drawn a figure to illustrate the relationship between the various variable quantities involved in the problem, let us now state what is given and what the problem asks for in terms of these variables.

Given: (a) Relationships between the variables which are to hold for all instants of time:

$$y + z = 45,$$

$$h + y = 20,$$

$$20^2 + x^2 = z^2.$$

(b) At a given instant, which we may take to be $t = 0$:

$$x = 15, \qquad \frac{dx}{dt} = 6.$$

To find: $dh/dt = $ (?) at the given instant $t = 0$.

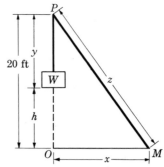

FIGURE 3–6

Such a problem involving rates of related variables is called "a problem in related rates." It is typical of such problems that

(a) certain variables are related in a definite way for all values of t under consideration,

(b) the values of some or all of these variables and the rates of change of some of them are given at some particular instant, and

(c) it is required to find the rate of change of one or more of them at this instant.

The variables may then all be considered to be functions of time, and if the equations which relate them for all values of t are differentiated with respect to t, the new equations so obtained will tell how their rates of change are related. From this information it should be possible to answer the question posed by the problem.

In our problem, we shall modify the procedure outlined above by first obtaining a single equation relating the variable x (whose rate is given) and the variable h (whose rate is wanted) before we take derivatives. Using the equations given, we find successively:

$$z = 45 - y, \qquad y = 20 - h,$$
$$z = 45 - (20 - h) = (25 + h),$$
$$20^2 + x^2 = z^2 = (25 + h)^2,$$

that is,

$$20^2 + x^2 = (25 + h)^2.$$

This last equation relates the variables x and h for all values of t under consideration (namely, in an interval of values of t near $t = 0$). Both sides of this equation are functions of t, and the equality says they represent the same function of t. Thus when we differentiate both sides of the equation with respect to t, we will have another equation:

$$\frac{d}{dt}(20^2 + x^2) = \frac{d}{dt}(25 + h)^2,$$

$$0 + 2x\frac{dx}{dt} = 2(25 + h)\frac{dh}{dt}.$$

This may be solved for the rate we want, namely,

$$\frac{dh}{dt} = \frac{x}{25 + h}\frac{dx}{dt}.$$

Now at the given instant, we have

$$x = 15, \qquad \frac{dx}{dt} = 6,$$

and we find h at this instant from the equation

$$20^2 + 15^2 = (25 + h)^2, \qquad 25 + h = 25.$$

When we substitute these values, we obtain

$$\frac{dh}{dt} = \frac{18}{5} = 3\tfrac{3}{5} \ (\text{ft/sec})$$

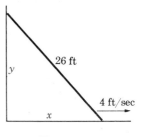

26 ft

4 ft/sec

FIGURE 3–7

as the rate at which the weight is being raised at the instant in question.

As a second example, consider a ladder 26 ft long which leans against a vertical wall. At a particular instant, the foot of the ladder is 10 ft out from the base of the wall and is being drawn away from the wall at the rate of 4 ft/sec. How fast is the top of the ladder moving down the wall at this instant? Figure 3–7 represents the position of the ladder, with the distance from the base of the wall to the foot of the ladder labeled x to indicate the fact that it is a variable, and the distance from the ground to the top of the ladder labeled y because it varies also. The statement of the problem may then be translated into mathematical terms as follows:

Given: $x^2 + y^2 = 26^2$.

To find: $\dfrac{dy}{dt} = (?)$

when

$$x = 10 \ (\text{ft}) \qquad \text{and} \qquad \frac{dx}{dt} = 4 \ (\text{ft/sec}).$$

We differentiate the given equation implicitly with respect to t and get

$$2x\frac{dx}{dt} + 2y\frac{dy}{dt} = 0.$$

Hence

$$\frac{dy}{dt} = \frac{-x}{y}\frac{dx}{dt}.$$

When $x = 10$, $y = 24$, $dx/dt = 4$, this leads to $dy/dt = -\tfrac{5}{3}$. That is, y is *decreasing* (the top of the ladder is moving *down*) at the rate of $\tfrac{5}{3}$ ft/sec.

As a final example, consider the conical reservoir, Fig. 3–8, into which water runs at the constant rate of 2 ft^3 per minute. How fast is the water level rising when it is 6 ft deep?

First, we must translate the problem into mathematical terms. To do this, we let

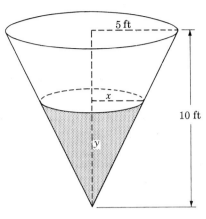

FIGURE 3–8

v = volume (ft³) of water in the tank at time t (min),

x = radius (ft) of the section of the cone at the water line,

y = depth (ft) of water in the tank at time t.

Then, the statement that water runs into the tank at the rate of 2 ft³/min becomes

$$\frac{dv}{dt} = 2.$$

The question we are to answer is

$$\frac{dy}{dt} = (?) \quad \text{when} \quad y = 6.$$

The relationship between the volume of water v and depth y is expressed by the equation

$$v = \tfrac{1}{3}\pi x^2 y.$$

But this involves the additional variable x as well as v and y. However, we may eliminate x since, by similar triangles, we have

$$\frac{x}{y} = \frac{5}{10} \quad \text{or} \quad x = \tfrac{1}{2}y.$$

Therefore

$$v = \tfrac{1}{12}\pi y^3,$$

and when we differentiate this with respect to t, we have

$$\frac{dv}{dt} = \frac{1}{4}\pi y^2 \frac{dy}{dt}.$$

Hence
$$\frac{dy}{dt} = \frac{4 \, dv/dt}{\pi y^2},$$
and when
$$\frac{dv}{dt} = 2 \quad \text{and} \quad y = 6,$$
this gives
$$\frac{dy}{dt} = \frac{2}{9\pi} \approx 0.071 \text{ (ft/min)}.$$

Problems

1. Let A be the area of a circle of radius r. How is dA/dt related to dr/dt?

2. Let V be the volume of a sphere of radius r. How is dV/dt related to dr/dt?

3. Sand falls onto a conical pile at the rate of 10 ft^3/min. The radius of the base of the pile is always equal to one-half of its altitude. How fast is the altitude of the pile increasing when it is 5 ft deep?

4. Suppose that a raindrop is a perfect sphere. Assume that, through condensation, the raindrop accumulates moisture at a rate proportional to its surface area. Show that the radius increases at a constant rate.

5. Point A moves along the x-axis at the constant rate of a ft/sec while point B moves along the y-axis at the constant rate of b ft/sec. Find how fast the distance between them is changing when A is at the point $(x, 0)$ and B is at the point $(0, y)$.

6. A spherical balloon is inflated with gas at the rate of 100 ft^3/min. Assuming that the gas pressure remains constant, how fast is the radius of the balloon increasing at the instant when the radius is 3 ft?

7. A boat is pulled in to a dock by means of a rope with one end attached to the bow of the boat, the other end passing through a ring attached to the dock at a point 4 ft higher than the bow of the boat. If the rope is pulled in at the rate of 2 ft/sec, how fast is the boat approaching the dock when 10 ft of rope are out?

8. A balloon is 200 ft off the ground and rising vertically at the constant rate of 15 ft/sec. An automobile passes beneath it traveling along a straight road at the constant rate of 45 mi/hr = 66 ft/sec. How fast is the distance between them changing one second later?

9. Water is withdrawn from a conical reservoir 8 ft in diameter and 10 ft deep (vertex down) at the constant rate of 5 ft^3/min. How fast is the water level falling when the depth of water in the reservoir is 6 ft?

10. A particle moves around the circle $x^2 + y^2 = 1$ with an x-velocity component $dx/dt = y$. Find dy/dt. Does the particle travel in the clockwise or counterclockwise direction around the circle?

11. A man 6 ft tall walks at the rate of 5 ft/sec toward a street light that is 16 ft above the ground. At what rate is the tip of his shadow moving? At what rate is the length of his shadow changing when he is 10 ft from the base of the light?

12. When air expands adiabatically, the pressure p and volume v satisfy the relationship $pv^{1.4} =$ constant. At a certain instant the pressure is 50 lb/in^2

and the volume is 32 in³ and is decreasing at the rate of 4 in³/sec. How rapidly is the pressure changing at this instant?

13. A light is at the top of a pole 50 ft high. A ball is dropped from the same height from a point 30 ft away from the light. How fast is the shadow of the ball moving along the ground ½ sec later? (Assume the ball falls a distance $s = 16t^2$ ft in t seconds.)

14. A boy flies a kite at a height of 300 ft, the wind carrying the kite horizontally away from the boy at a rate of 25 ft/sec. How fast must the boy pay out the string when the kite is 500 ft away from him?

15. A spherical iron ball 8 in. in diameter is coated with a layer of ice of uniform thickness. If the ice melts at the rate of 10 in³ per minute, how fast is the thickness of the ice decreasing when it is 2 in. thick? How fast is the outer surface area of ice decreasing?

16. Two ships A and B are sailing away from the point O along routes such that the angle $AOB = 120°$. How fast is the distance between them changing if, at a certain instant, $OA = 8$ mi, $OB = 6$ mi, ship A is sailing at the rate of 20 mi/hr, and ship B at the rate of 30 mi/hr? [*Hint:* Use the law of cosines.]

3–3 Significance of the sign of the second derivative. We have already seen how we may use the information given by dy/dx about the slope of the tangent to a curve to help in sketching it. We recall that in an interval where dy/dx is positive, the curve is rising to the right, while if dy/dx is negative the curve is falling to the right. Also it is evident that the regions of rise and fall are usually separated by high or low points where dy/dx is zero and the tangent is horizontal. However, it is possible for dy/dx to be zero at points which are neither high nor low points of the curve.

For example, if
$$y = (x - 2)^3 + 1,$$
then
$$\frac{dy}{dx} = 3(x - 2)^2,$$
and although
$$\frac{dy}{dx} = 0 \quad \text{at} \quad x = 2,$$

for all values of x other than 2, the slope is positive and y is an increasing function of x (Fig. 3–9, p. 112).

The regions of rise and fall may also be separated by points where the derivative fails to exist.

For example, if $y = x^{2/3}$, then
$$\frac{dy}{dx} = \frac{2}{3}x^{-1/3} = \frac{2}{3\sqrt[3]{x}}$$

is positive when x is positive, and negative when x is negative. At the transition

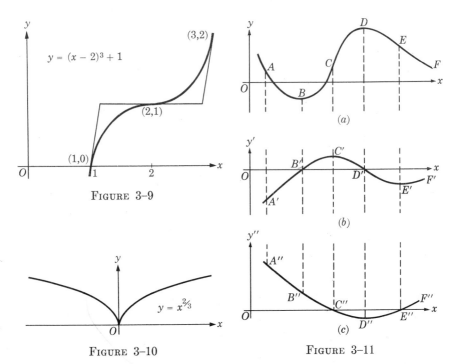

$y = (x - 2)^3 + 1$

(3,2)

(2,1)

(1,0)

FIGURE 3–9

$y = x^{2/3}$

FIGURE 3–10

(a)

(b)

(c)

FIGURE 3–11

point $x = 0$, dy/dx does not exist, but $dx/dy = \frac{3}{2}x^{1/3}$ is zero, which means that the tangent to the curve at $(0, 0)$ is vertical instead of horizontal (Fig. 3–10).

Next we shall see that the sign of the second derivative tells whether the graph of $y = f(x)$ is concave upward (y'' positive) or downward (y'' negative).

Consider, for example, the curve in Fig. 3–11(a). The first and second derivatives are represented by the curves in Fig. 3–11 (b) and (c). The arc ABC of the y-curve is concave upward; CDE is concave downward; EF is again concave upward. To focus attention, let us consider a section near A on arc ABC. Here y' is negative and the y-curve slopes downward to the right. But as we travel through A, moving from left to right, we find the slope becomes less negative. That is, y' is an *increasing* function of x. Therefore the y'-curve slopes upward at A'. Hence its slope (that is, y'') is positive there. The same kind of argument applies at all points along the arc ABC; namely, y' is an increasing function of x, so its derivative (that is, y'') is positive. This is indicated by drawing the arc $A''B''C''$ of the y''-curve above the x-axis.

Similarly, where the y-curve is concave downward (along CDE), the y'-curve is falling, so its slope (that is, y'') is negative.

The direction of concavity is, therefore,

upward if the second derivative is *positive*,

downward if the second derivative is *negative*.

In the first case we could also say the curve is cupped so as to "hold water"; in the second case it would "spill water."

Points of inflection. A point where the curve changes the direction of its concavity from downward to upward or vice versa is called a *point of inflection*. Inflection points occur at C and E in Fig. 3–11(a), and are characterized by a change in the sign of d^2y/dx^2. Such a change of sign may occur where

(a) $d^2y/dx^2 = 0$, or

(b) d^2y/dx^2 fails to exist (for example, it may become infinite at such a point).

In Fig. 3–11, case (a) is shown. Case (b) is shown in Fig. 3–12, where the curve is

$$y = x^{1/3},$$

from which we find

$$y' = \tfrac{1}{3}x^{-(2/3)},$$

$$y'' = -\tfrac{2}{9}x^{-(5/3)},$$

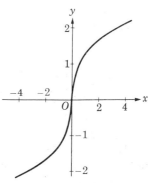

so that both y' and y'' become infinite when x approaches zero. On the other hand,

$$y' = \frac{1}{3x^{2/3}} = \frac{1}{3y^2}$$

Figure 3–12

is always positive for both positive and negative values of x, so the curve is always rising and has a vertical tangent at $(0, 0)$. Also,

$$y'' = -\frac{2}{9}\left(\frac{1}{\sqrt[3]{x}}\right)^5 = \frac{-2}{9y^5}$$

is positive (the curve "holds water") when x is negative, and is negative (the curve "spills water") when x is positive, so that $(0, 0)$ is a point of inflection.

The example just given would have been much simpler to discuss if we had written the equation in the form $x = y^3$, and then

$$\frac{dx}{dy} = 3y^2, \qquad \frac{d^2x}{dy^2} = 6y,$$

so that we have

$$\frac{dx}{dy} = 0 \quad \text{and} \quad \frac{d^2x}{dy^2} = 0$$

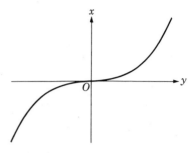

FIGURE 3–13

at $(0, 0)$. It is clear that dx/dy is positive for all y different from zero and d^2x/dy^2 has the same sign as y and therefore changes its sign at $y = 0$. If we interchange the x- and y-axes so as to take the x-axis to be vertical and the y-axis to be horizontal, the curve will be as shown in Fig. 3–13.

3–4 Curve plotting. The discussion in Article 3–3 may be summarized and stated in the following outline of procedure to apply in sketching the graph of an equation $y = f(x)$.

A. Calculate dy/dx and d^2y/dx^2.

B. Find the values of x for which dy/dx is positive and for which it is negative. Calculate y and d^2y/dx^2 at the points of transition between positive and negative values of dy/dx. These may give maximum or minimum points on the curve. (See Figs. 3–4, 3–10, and 3–11a.)

C. Find the values of x for which d^2y/dx^2 is positive and for which it is negative. Calculate y and dy/dx at the points of transition between positive and negative values of d^2y/dx^2. These may give points of inflection of the curve. (See Figs. 3–11 and 3–12.)

D. Plot a few additional points. In particular, points which lie between the transition points already determined or points which lie to the left and to the right of all of them will ordinarily be useful. The nature of the curve for large values of $|x|$ should also be indicated.

E. Sketch a smooth curve through the points found above, unless there are discontinuities in the curve or its slope. Have the curve pass through its points rising or falling as indicated by the sign of dy/dx, and concave upward or downward as indicated by the sign of d^2y/dx^2.

We shall now apply this technique to a few examples.

EXAMPLE 1. (Fig. 3–14b)

$$y = \frac{1}{6}(x^3 - 6x^2 + 9x + 6).$$

Solution. $\quad \dfrac{dy}{dx} = \dfrac{1}{6}(3x^2 - 12x + 9) = \dfrac{1}{2}(x^2 - 4x + 3),$

$$\frac{d^2y}{dx^2} = \frac{1}{2}(2x - 4) = x - 2.$$

In the factored form,

$$\frac{dy}{dx} = \frac{1}{2}(x - 1)(x - 3),$$

and the two factors change their signs at $x = 1$ and $x = 3$. (See Fig. 3–14a.)

It is readily seen that $d^2y/dx^2 = x - 2$ is negative to the left of $x = 2$ and is positive to the right of $x = 2$, so that an inflection point occurs at $x = 2$. A fairly good sketch of the curve can now be made by using the information in the following table.

x	y	y'	y''	Remarks
-1	$-\frac{5}{3}$	$+$	$-$	Rising; concave down
0	1	$+\frac{3}{2}$	$-$	Rising; concave down
1	$\frac{5}{3}$	0	$-$	"Spills water"; max.
2	$\frac{4}{3}$	$-\frac{1}{2}$	0	Falling; point of inflection
3	1	0	$+$	"Holds water"; min.
4	$\frac{5}{3}$	$+\frac{3}{2}$	$+$	Rising; concave up

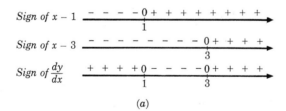

(a)

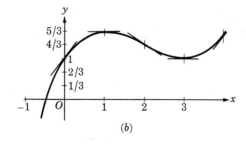

(b)

Figure 3–14

EXAMPLE 2. (Fig. 3–15b)

$$y = x + \frac{1}{x} = x + x^{-1}.$$

Solution. $$\frac{dy}{dx} = 1 - x^{-2} = 1 - \frac{1}{x^2} = \frac{x^2 - 1}{x^2},$$

$$\frac{d^2y}{dx^2} = 2x^{-3} = \frac{2}{x^3}.$$

The sign of dy/dx will be the same as the sign of $x^2 - 1 = (x - 1)(x + 1)$.
(See Fig. 3–15a.) But when x is near zero, $|y|$ will be large and y, dy/dx, d^2y/dx^2
all become infinite as x approaches zero. This curve is discontinuous at $x = 0$.

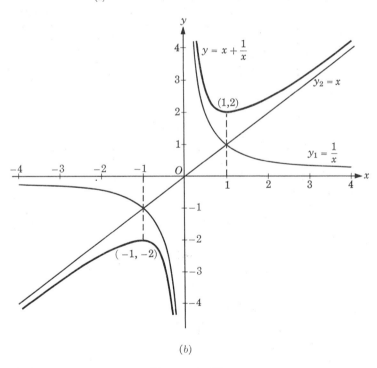

FIGURE 3–15

Also, for large values of x, the $1/x$ term becomes small and $y \approx x$. In fact,

$$\text{when } |x| \text{ is small,} \qquad y \approx \frac{1}{x},$$

$$\text{when } |x| \text{ is large,} \qquad y \approx x,$$

so that it is helpful to sketch (as can quickly be done) the curves

$$y_1 = \frac{1}{x}, \qquad y_2 = x,$$

as well as

$$y = x + \frac{1}{x} = y_1 + y_2.$$

Actually, replacing x by $-x$ merely changes the sign of y, so that it would suffice to sketch the portion of the curve in the first quadrant and then reflect the result with respect to the origin to get the portion in the third quadrant (Fig. 3–15b).

x	y_1	y_2	y	y'	y''	Remarks
-4	$-\frac{1}{4}$	-4	$-\frac{17}{4}$	$+$	$-$	Rising; concave down
-2	$-\frac{1}{2}$	-2	$-\frac{5}{2}$	$+$	$-$	Rising; concave down
-1	-1	-1	-2	0	-2	"Spills water"; max.
$-\frac{1}{2}$	-2	$-\frac{1}{2}$	$-\frac{5}{2}$	$-$	$-$	Falling; concave down
$-\frac{1}{4}$	-4	$-\frac{1}{4}$	$-\frac{17}{4}$	$-$	$-$	Falling; concave down
$+\frac{1}{4}$	4	$\frac{1}{4}$	$\frac{17}{4}$	$-$	$+$	Falling; concave up
$\frac{1}{2}$	2	$\frac{1}{2}$	$\frac{5}{2}$	$-$	$+$	Falling; concave up
1	1	1	2	0	$+2$	"Holds water"; min.
2	$\frac{1}{2}$	2	$\frac{5}{2}$	$+$	$+$	Rising; concave up
4	$\frac{1}{4}$	4	$\frac{17}{4}$	$+$	$+$	Rising; concave up

Problems

In each of the following problems (1 through 5), find intervals of values of x for which the curve is (a) rising, (b) falling, (c) concave upward, (d) concave downward. Sketch the curves, showing the high turning points M, low turning points m, and points of inflection I.

1. $y = x^2 - 4x + 3$ 2. $y = \dfrac{x}{x+1}$ 3. $y = 4 + 3x - x^3$

4. $y = \dfrac{x^3}{3} - \dfrac{x^2}{2} - 6x$ 5. $y = x + \dfrac{4}{x}$

6. Sketch a smooth curve $y = f(x)$ illustrating

$f(1) = 0,$ $f'(x) < 0$ for $x < 1,$ $f'(x) > 0$ for $x > 1.$

7. Sketch a smooth curve $y = f(x)$ illustrating

$f(1) = 0,$ $f''(x) < 0$ for $x < 1,$ $f''(x) > 0$ for $x > 1.$

Sketch each of the following curves (8 through 12), indicating high and low turning points and points of inflection

8. $y = 6 - 2x - x^2$ 9. $y = 2x^2 - 4x + 3$
10. $y = 12 - 12x + x^3$ 11. $y = x^4 - 32x + 48$
12. $y = x^3 - 3x^2 + 2$

For the following curves (13 through 16), find vertical tangents and sketch the curves.

13. $x = y^3 + 3y^2 + 3y + 2$ 14. $x = y^3 + 3y^2 - 9y - 11$

15. $x = y^4 - 2y^2 + 2$ 16. $x = y^2 + \dfrac{2}{y}$

17. Sketch a continuous curve $y = f(x)$ having the following characteristics:

$f(-2) = 8,$ $f'(2) = f'(-2) = 0,$
$f(0) = 4,$ $f'(x) < 0$ for $|x| < 2,$
$f(2) = 0,$ $f''(x) < 0$ for $x < 0,$
$f'(x) > 0$ for $|x| > 2,$ $f''(x) > 0$ for $x > 0.$

18. Sketch a continuous curve $y = f(x)$ having

$f'(x) > 0$ for $x < 2,$ $f'(x) < 0$ for $x > 2,$

(a) if $f'(x)$ is continuous at $x = 2,$
(b) if $f'(x) \to 1$ as $x \to 2-$ and $f'(x) \to -1$ as $x \to 2+,$
(c) if $f'(x) = 1$ for all $x < 2$ and $f'(x) = -1$ for all $x > 2.$

19. Sketch a continuous curve $y = f(x)$ for $x > 0$ if

$f(1) = 0$ and $f'(x) = 1/x$ for all $x > 0.$

Is such a curve necessarily concave upward or concave downward?

20. Show that the sum of any positive real number and its reciprocal is at least 2.

21. Sketch the curve

$$y = 2x^3 + 2x^2 - 2x - 1$$

after locating its maximum, minimum, and inflection points. Then answer the following questions from your graph:

(a) How many times and approximately where does the curve cross the x-axis?

(b) How many times and approximately where would the curve cross the x-axis if $+3$ were added to all the y-values?

(c) How many times and approximately where would the curve cross the x-axis if -3 were added to all the y-values?

3–5 Maxima and minima. Theory. A function f is said to have a relative, or local, *maximum* at $x = a$ if

$$f(a) \geq f(a + h)$$

for all positive and negative values of h sufficiently near zero. For a local *minimum* at $x = b$,

$$f(b) \leq f(b + h)$$

for values of h close to zero. The word *relative* or *local* is used to distinguish such a point from an *absolute* maximum or minimum that would occur if we could say, for example,

$$f(a) \geq f(x)$$

for all x and not just for all x close to a. In Fig. 3–15(b), for example, the point $(1, 2)$ is a *relative* minimum of the function

$$f(x) = x + \frac{1}{x}$$

because

$$x + \frac{1}{x} \geq 2$$

for all values of x close to 1. But certainly when x is negative, the inequality is no longer satisfied. Indeed, the function $f(x) = x + 1/x$ has no absolute minimum and no absolute maximum.

In Fig. 3–16 we indicate the graph of a function $y = f(x)$ defined only for the domain $0 \leq x \leq L$. This function has a relative minimum at C, which is also an absolute minimum. It also has relative maxima at A and at B, and an absolute maximum at B.

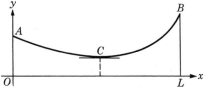

FIGURE 3–16

We have encountered relative maxima and minima in sketching curves and have observed that they occur at transition points between rising and falling portions of a curve. At such transition points we have also observed that dy/dx is usually zero, but may in exceptional cases become infinite (Fig. 3–10). We shall now prove the following theorem.

THEOREM. *Let the function f be defined for $a \leq x \leq b$ and have a relative maximum or minimum at $x = c$, where $a < c < b$. If the derivative $f'(x)$ exists as a finite number at $x = c$, then*

$$f'(c) = 0. \tag{1}$$

Proof. We shall give the proof for the case of a relative minimum at $x = c$; namely,

$$f(c) \leq f(c + h)$$

for all h close to zero (that is, when $c + h$ is close to c). By hypothesis,

$$f'(c) = \lim_{h \to 0} \frac{f(c + h) - f(c)}{h} \tag{2}$$

exists as a definite number which we want to prove is zero. In the ratio whose limit is $f'(c)$, when h is small, we have

$$\frac{f(c + h) - f(c)}{h} \geq 0 \quad \text{if} \quad h > 0$$

and

$$\frac{f(c + h) - f(c)}{h} \leq 0 \quad \text{if} \quad h < 0,$$

because in both cases the numerator is either positive or is zero. Hence if we let $h \to 0$ through positive values, we have

$$f'(c) \geq 0$$

from the first case; but if we let $h \to 0$ through negative values, we also have

$$f'(c) \leq 0$$

from the second case. Since the derivative is assumed to exist, we must have the same limit in both cases, so

$$0 \leq f'(c) \leq 0,$$

and the only way this can happen is to have

$$f'(c) = 0. \qquad \text{Q.E.D.}$$

The proof in case of a relative maximum at $x = c$ is similar.

Remark. The reader is cautioned not to read into the theorem more than it says. It does not say what happens if a maximum or minimum occurs

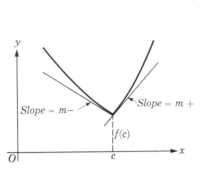

FIGURE 3–17   FIGURE 3–18

(a) at a point c where the derivative fails to exist, or

(b) at an end point of the interval of definition of the function. Neither does it say that the function necessarily does have a maximum or minimum at every place where the derivative is zero.

In Fig. 3–17, for example,

$$\lim_{h \to 0} \frac{f(c + h) - f(c)}{h} = m- \quad \text{or} \quad m+,$$

depending upon whether h approaches zero through negative or positive values respectively. Unless these two numbers $m-$ and $m+$ are equal, the derivative $f'(c)$ does not exist.

For example, if the function is given by

$$y = f(x) = \begin{cases} 3 - x, & \text{for} \quad x \le 2, \\ \tfrac{1}{2}x^2 - 1, & \text{for} \quad x > 2, \end{cases}$$

its graph is the continuous curve shown in Fig. 3–18. The slope is

$$\frac{dy}{dx} = \frac{d(3 - x)}{dx} = -1 \quad \text{for} \quad x < 2,$$

$$\frac{dy}{dx} = \frac{d(\tfrac{1}{2}x^2 - 1)}{dx} = x \quad \text{for} \quad x > 2,$$

and at the point $x = 2$, the left-hand tangent has slope $m- = -1$ and the right-hand tangent has slope $m+ = 2$. Clearly, the curve is falling before $x = 2$ and rising after $x = 2$, and has a minimum at $x = 2$, $y = 1$.

It is also easy to see from the proof of the theorem that when a maximum or minimum occurs at the end of a curve which exists only over a limited interval, the derivative need not vanish at such a point. For example, if the point $x = c$ is at the left end of such a curve, then in the limit in Eq. (2) it is not possible to take h to be negative, because $f(c + h)$ with h negative does not exist in this case. Strictly speaking, $f'(c)$ does not exist in these circumstances, although there may be a right-hand tangent at one end of the curve and a left-hand tangent at the other end (Fig. 3–16).

The point $(0, 0)$ on the curve $y = x^3$ is an example of a point where a curve has zero slope without having either a maximum or a minimum there.

It is customary to refer to a point on a curve $y = f(x)$ at which $f'(x) = 0$ as a "stationary point" on the curve. Values of x which satisfy the equation $f'(x) = 0$ are also called "critical values." In other words, a "critical value" of x corresponds to a "stationary point" on the curve $y = f(x)$.

3–6 Maxima and minima. Problems. The differential calculus is a powerful tool for solving problems that call for minimizing or maximizing a function. We shall illustrate how this is done in several instances, and then summarize the technique in a list of specific rules.

EXAMPLE 1. Find two positive numbers whose sum is 20 and such that their product is as large as possible.

Solution. If one of the numbers is x, the other is $(20 - x)$ and their product is

$$y = x(20 - x) = 20x - x^2. \tag{1}$$

Since both numbers are to be positive,

$$x > 0 \quad \text{and} \quad 20 - x > 0,$$

or

$$0 < x < 20.$$

From (1), we find

$$\frac{dy}{dx} = 20 - 2x = 2(10 - x),$$

which is

positive when $x < 10$,

negative when $x > 10$,

zero when $x = 10$.

Furthermore,

$$\frac{d^2y}{dx^2} = -2$$

is always negative and the curve representing (1) is concave downward at every point on it. The graph is the curve shown in Fig. 3–19, which has an absolute maximum at $x = 10$. The two numbers are thus $x = 10$, $20 - x = 10$.

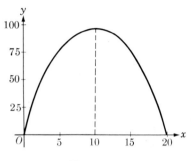

FIGURE 3–19   FIGURE 3–20

EXAMPLE 2. A square sheet of tin a inches on a side is to be used to make an open-top box by cutting a small square of tin from each corner and bending up the sides. How large a square should be cut from each corner in order that the box shall have as large a volume as possible?

Solution. We first draw a figure to illustrate the problem (Fig. 3–20). In the figure, the side of the square cut from each corner is taken to be x inches and the volume of the box in cubic inches is then given by

$$y = x(a - 2x)^2, \qquad 0 \le x \le a/2. \qquad (2)$$

The restrictions placed on x in (2) are clearly those imposed by the fact that one can neither cut a negative amount of material from a corner, nor can one cut away an amount which is more than the total amount present. It is also evident that $y = 0$ when $x = 0$ or when $x = a/2$, so that the maximum volume y must occur at some value of x between 0 and $a/2$. The function in (2) possesses a derivative at every such point, hence

when y is a maximum, dy/dx must be zero.

From (2), we find

$$y = a^2 x - 4ax^2 + 4x^3,$$

$$\frac{dy}{dx} = a^2 - 8ax + 12x^2$$

$$= (a - 2x)(a - 6x),$$

so that

$$\frac{dy}{dx} = 0 \qquad \text{when} \qquad x = \frac{a}{2} \text{ or } \frac{a}{6}.$$

We gain additional information about the shape of the curve representing (2) from

$$\frac{d^2 y}{dx^2} = 24x - 8a = 24\left(x - \frac{a}{3}\right),$$

which shows that the curve is

$$\text{concave downward for } x < \frac{a}{3},$$

$$\text{concave upward} \quad \text{for } x > \frac{a}{3}.$$

In particular,

$$\text{at} \quad x = \frac{a}{6}: \quad \frac{dy}{dx} = 0, \quad \frac{d^2y}{dx^2} = -4a,$$

$$\text{at} \quad x = \frac{a}{2}: \quad \frac{dy}{dx} = 0, \quad \frac{d^2y}{dx^2} = +4a. \tag{3}$$

From (3) we see that if we were to draw the graph of the curve (2) it would "spill water" at $x = (a/6)$ and this is the only point between $x = 0$ and $x = (a/2)$ where a relative maximum of the volume y may occur (Fig. 3–21). Each corner square should thus have dimensions $a/6$ by $a/6$ to produce a box of maximum volume.

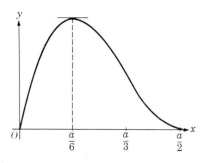

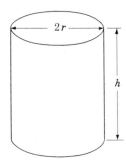

FIGURE 3–21   FIGURE 3–22

EXAMPLE 3. An oil can is to be made in the form of a right circular cylinder to contain one quart of oil. What dimensions of the can will require the least amount of material?

Solution. Again we start with a figure to illustrate the problem (Fig. 3–22). Clearly, the requirement that the can hold a quart of oil is the same as

$$V = \pi r^2 h = a^3, \tag{4a}$$

if the radius r and altitude h are in inches and a^3 is the number of cubic inches in a quart ($a^3 = 57.75$). How shall we interpret the phrase "least amount of material"? A reasonable interpretation arises from neglecting the thickness of the material and the waste due to the manufacturing process. Then we ask for dimensions r and h that make the total surface area

$$A = 2\pi r^2 + 2\pi r h \tag{4b}$$

as small as possible while still satisfying (4a).

We are not quite ready to apply the methods used in Examples 1 and 2, because Eq. (4b) expresses A as a function of *two* variables, r and h, and our methods call for A to be expressed as a function of just *one* variable. However, Eq. (4a) may be used to express one of the variables r or h in terms of the other; in fact, we find

$$h = \frac{a^3}{\pi r^2} \tag{4c}$$

or

$$r = \sqrt{\frac{a^3}{\pi h}}. \tag{4d}$$

The division in (4c) and (4d) is legitimate because neither r nor h can be zero, and only the positive square root is used in (4d) because the radius r can never be negative. If we substitute from (4c) into (4b), we have

$$A = 2\pi r^2 + \frac{2a^3}{r}, \qquad 0 < r < \infty, \tag{4e}$$

and now we may apply our previous methods. A minimum of A can occur only at a point where

$$\frac{dA}{dr} = 4\pi r - 2a^3 r^{-2} \tag{4f}$$

is zero, that is, where

$$4\pi r = \frac{2a^3}{r^2}, \qquad r = \frac{a}{\sqrt[3]{2\pi}}. \tag{4g}$$

At such a value of r, we shall have

$$\frac{d^2 A}{dr^2} = 4\pi + 4a^3 r^{-3} = 12\pi > 0,$$

so the curve representing A as a function of r has $dA/dr = 0$ and d^2A/dr^2 positive ("holds water") at $r = a/\sqrt[3]{2\pi}$, which must therefore produce a relative minimum. Since the second derivative is *always positive* for $0 < r < \infty$, the curve is concave upward everywhere, and there can be no other relative minimum, so we have also found the absolute minimum. From (4g) and (4c), we find

$$r = a/\sqrt[3]{2\pi} = \sqrt[3]{V/2\pi},$$

$$h = 2a/\sqrt[3]{2\pi} = 2\sqrt[3]{V/2\pi}$$

as the dimensions of the can of volume V having minimum surface area. Figure 3–23 shows a curve representing A as a function of r as given by (4e).

There is an alternative method of solving problems of this type. Namely,

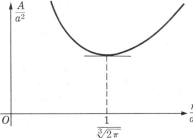

FIGURE 3–23

instead of solving (4a) for h in terms of r, say, we differentiate both (4a) and (4b) with respect to r, remembering that h is a function of r. Thus, we have

$$V = \pi r^2 h,$$

$$A = 2\pi r^2 + 2\pi rh,$$

and since

$$V \text{ is a constant,} \quad dV/dr = 0,$$

and since we want to find when A will be a minimum, we put

$$\frac{dA}{dr} = 0$$

also. Hence

$$\frac{dV}{dr} = \pi \left(r^2 \frac{dh}{dr} + 2rh \right) = 0, \qquad \frac{dh}{dr} = -\frac{2h}{r}, \tag{4h}$$

$$\frac{dA}{dr} = 2\pi \left(2r + r\frac{dh}{dr} + h \right) = 2\pi(2r - h). \tag{4i}$$

Therefore dA/dr is zero when

$$h = 2r. \tag{4j}$$

When this is substituted into (4a), we have

$$V = \pi r^2 h = 2\pi r^3,$$

so that

$$r = \sqrt[3]{V/2\pi}, \qquad h = 2r = 2\sqrt[3]{V/2\pi}$$

give the critical dimensions for a cylindrical can of volume V.

We may use d^2A/dr^2 to test these critical values. We have

$$\frac{dA}{dr} = 2\pi(2r - h),$$

so that, if we take account of (4h), we find

$$\frac{d^2A}{dr^2} = 2\pi \left(2 - \frac{dh}{dr} \right) = 2\pi \left(2 + \frac{2h}{r} \right).$$

This is positive for all positive values of r and h, and hence A has a minimum at $r = r_{\text{crit}}$ where $dA/dr = 0$ and d^2A/dr^2 is positive.

EXAMPLE 4. A wire of length L is to be cut into two pieces, one of which is bent to form a circle and the other to form a square. How should the wire be cut if the sum of the areas enclosed by the two pieces is to be a maximum?

Solution. In the notation of Fig. 3–24, the sum of the combined areas is

$$A = \pi r^2 + x^2, \tag{5a}$$

where r and x must satisfy the equation

$$L = 2\pi r + 4x. \qquad \text{(5b)}$$

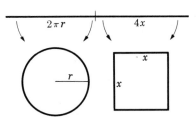

We could solve (5b) for x in terms of r, but instead we shall differentiate both (5a) and (5b), treating A and x as functions of r for $0 \le 2\pi r \le L$. Then

$$\frac{dA}{dr} = 2\pi r + 2x\frac{dx}{dr}, \qquad \text{(5c)}$$

FIGURE 3–24

and

$$\frac{dL}{dr} = 2\pi + 4\frac{dx}{dr} = 0, \qquad \frac{dx}{dr} = -\frac{\pi}{2}, \qquad \text{(5d)}$$

where dL/dr is zero because L is a constant. If we substitute dx/dr from (5d) into (5c), we get

$$\frac{dA}{dr} = \pi(2r - x) \qquad \text{(5e)}$$

and, for future reference, we note that

$$\frac{d^2 A}{dr^2} = \pi\left(2 - \frac{dx}{dr}\right) = \pi\left(2 + \frac{\pi}{2}\right) \qquad \text{(5f)}$$

is a positive constant, so that the curve which represents A as a function of r is always concave upward (Fig. 3–25).

Now

$$\frac{dA}{dr} = 0 \qquad \text{when} \qquad x = 2r,$$

and when we substitute this into (5b),

$$L = 2\pi r + 4(2r) = (2\pi + 8)r,$$

we have

$$\frac{dA}{dr} = 0 \quad \text{when} \quad r = \frac{L}{2\pi + 8}, \qquad x = \frac{L}{\pi + 4}.$$

But the fact that the second derivative is positive means that this value of r gives a *minimum* for A. The problem asks for the *maximum* of A.

Since r is limited to

$$0 \le r \le \frac{L}{2\pi},$$

we examine the values of A at the ends of this interval. When

$$r = 0: \qquad x = \frac{L}{4}, \qquad A = \frac{1}{16}L^2,$$

and when

$$r = \frac{L}{2\pi}: \qquad x = 0, \qquad A = \frac{1}{4\pi} L^2.$$

At the minimum,

$$r = \frac{1}{2} \frac{L}{\pi + 4}, \qquad x = \frac{L}{\pi + 4}, \qquad A = \frac{1}{4\pi + 16} L^2.$$

Using these values to make a rough sketch of A as a function of r (Fig. 3–25), it is readily seen that the maximum value of A occurs when $r = L/2\pi$, which means that the wire should not be cut at all, but all of it should be bent into the circle for maximum total area. Or, if we adopt the point of view that the wire *must* be cut, then there is no answer to the problem. For no matter how little of it is used for the square, we could always get a larger total area by using still less of it for the square.

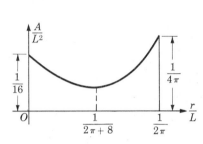

FIGURE 3–25

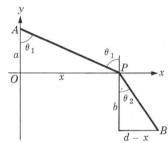

FIGURE 3–26

EXAMPLE 5. Fermat's principle in optics states that light travels from a point A to a point B along that path for which the time of travel is a minimum. Let us find the path that a ray of light will follow in going from a point A in a medium where the velocity of light is c_1 to a point B in a second medium where the velocity of light is c_2, when both points lie in the xy-plane and the x-axis separates the two media.

Solution. In either medium where the velocity of light remains constant, the light ray will follow a straight path, since then "shortest time" and "shortest distance" amount to the same thing. Hence the path will consist of a straight line segment from A to P in the first medium and another line segment PB in the second medium. The time required for the light to travel from A to P is

$$t_1 = \frac{\sqrt{a^2 + x^2}}{c_1},$$

and from P to B the time required is

$$t_2 = \frac{\sqrt{b^2 + (d - x)^2}}{c_2}.$$

We therefore seek to minimize

$$t = t_1 + t_2 = \frac{\sqrt{a^2 + x^2}}{c_1} + \frac{\sqrt{b^2 + (d - x)^2}}{c_2}. \tag{6a}$$

We find

$$\frac{dt}{dx} = \frac{x}{c_1\sqrt{a^2 + x^2}} - \frac{(d - x)}{c_2\sqrt{b^2 + (d - x)^2}} \tag{6b}$$

or

$$\frac{dt}{dx} = \frac{\sin \theta_1}{c_1} - \frac{\sin \theta_2}{c_2}, \tag{6c}$$

if we make use of the angles θ_1 and θ_2 in the figure.

If we restrict x to the interval $0 \le x \le d$, t has a negative derivative at $x = 0$ and a positive derivative at $x = d$, while at the value of x, say x_c, for which

$$\frac{\sin \theta_1}{c_1} = \frac{\sin \theta_2}{c_2}, \tag{6d}$$

dt/dx is zero. Figure 3–27 indicates the directions of the tangents to the curve giving t as a function of x, at these three points, and suggests that t will indeed be a minimum at $x = x_c$. If we want further information on this point, by referring to Fig. 3–26 we see that a decrease in x will cause P to move to the left, making θ_1 smaller, and hence also $\sin \theta_1$ smaller, but will have the opposite effect on θ_2 and $\sin \theta_2$. Figure 3–28 shows that since $(\sin \theta_1)/c_1$ is an increasing function of x which is zero at $x = 0$, while $(\sin \theta_2)/c_2$ is a decreasing function of x which is zero at $x = d$, the two curves can cross at only one point, $x = x_c$, between 0 and d. To the right of x_c, the curve for $(\sin \theta_1)/c_1$ is above the curve for $(\sin \theta_2)/c_2$, but these roles are reversed to the left of x_c, so that

$$\frac{dt}{dx} = \frac{\sin \theta_1}{c_1} - \frac{\sin \theta_2}{c_2} \begin{cases} \text{is negative for } x < x_c, \\ \text{is zero for } x = x_c, \\ \text{is positive for } x > x_c, \end{cases}$$

and the minimum of t does indeed occur at $x = x_c$.

Instead of determining this value of x explicitly, it is customary to characterize the path followed by the ray of light by leaving the equation for $dt/dx = 0$ in the form (6d), which is known as the law of refraction or Snell's law. [See Sears, *Optics*, p. 27. Addison-Wesley (1949).]

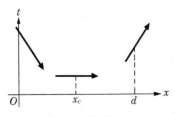

FIGURE 3–27

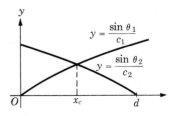

FIGURE 3–28

The reader will very likely have noticed in the above problems that the techniques summarized in the following rules have been used.

First. When possible, draw a figure to illustrate the problem and label those parts that are important in the problem. Constants and variables should be clearly distinguished.

Second. Write an equation for the quantity that is to be a maximum or a minimum. If this quantity is denoted by y, it is desirable to express it in terms of a single independent variable x. This may require some algebraic manipulation to make use of auxiliary conditions of the problem.

Third. If $y = f(x)$ is the quantity to be a maximum or a minimum, find those values of x for which

$$\frac{dy}{dx} = f'(x) = 0.$$

Fourth. Test each value of x for which $f'(x) = 0$ to determine whether it provides a maximum or minimum or neither. The usual tests are:

(a) If $\frac{d^2y}{dx^2}$ is positive when $\frac{dy}{dx} = 0$, y is a minimum.

If $\frac{d^2y}{dx^2}$ is negative when $\frac{dy}{dx} = 0$, y is a maximum.

If $\frac{d^2y}{dx^2} = 0$ when $\frac{dy}{dx} = 0$, the test fails.

(b) If

$$\frac{dy}{dx} \text{ is } \begin{cases} \text{positive for } x < x_c, \\ \text{zero for } x = x_c, \\ \text{negative for } x > x_c, \end{cases}$$

then a maximum occurs at x_c. But if dy/dx changes from negative to zero to positive as x advances through x_c, there is a minimum. If dy/dx does not change its sign, neither a maximum nor a minimum occurs.

Fifth. If the derivative fails to exist at some point, examine this point as possible maximum or minimum. (See Fig. 3–18.)

Sixth. If the function $y = f(x)$ is defined for only a limited range of values $a \leq x \leq b$, examine $x = a$ and $x = b$ for possible extreme values of y. (See Fig. 3–25.)

Remark. The following useful argument applies in many problems. It is often obvious from the formulas, or from physical conditions, that we have a continuous and everywhere-differentiable function that does not attain its maximum at an end point. Hence it has at least one maximum at an interior point, at which its derivative must be zero. So if we find just one zero for the derivative, we have the maximum without any appeal to second-derivative or other tests.

EXAMPLE 6. Suppose a manufacturer can sell x items per week at a price $P = 200 - 0.01x$ cents, and that it costs $y = 50x + 20{,}000$ cents to produce the x items. What is the production level for maximum profits?

Solution. The total revenue per week on x items is

$$xP = 200x - 0.01x^2.$$

The manufacturer's profit T is revenue minus cost:

$$T = xP - y = (200x - 0.01x^2) - (50x + 20{,}000)$$
$$= 150x - 0.01x^2 - 20{,}000.$$

To maximize T, we find

$$dT/dx = 150 - 0.02x,$$

which is zero when

$$x = 7500.$$

We know that this production level gives maximum profit, since the second derivative $d^2T/dx^2 = -0.02$ is negative, or by the argument in the "Remark" above. To sell the 7500 items, the manufacturer should charge \$1.25 per item.

PROBLEMS

1. Show that the rectangle that has maximum area for a given perimeter is a square.

2. Find the dimensions of the rectangle of greatest area that can be inscribed in a semicircle of radius r.

3. Find the area of the largest rectangle with lower base on the x-axis and upper vertices on the curve $y = 12 - x^2$.

4. An open rectangular box is to be made from a piece of cardboard 8 in. wide and 15 in. long by cutting a square from each corner and bending up the sides. Find the dimensions of the box of largest volume.

5. One side of an open field is bounded by a straight river. How would you put a fence around the other three sides of a rectangular plot in order to enclose as great an area as possible with a given length of fence?

6. An open storage bin with square base and vertical sides is to be constructed from a given amount of material. Determine its dimensions if its volume is a maximum. Neglect the thickness of the material and waste in construction.

7. A box with square base and open top is to hold 32 in³. Find the dimensions that require the least amount of material. Neglect the thickness of the material and waste in construction.

8. A variable line through the point $(1, 2)$ intersects the x-axis at $A(a, 0)$ and the y-axis at $B(0, b)$. Find the area of the triangle AOB of least area if both a and b are positive.

9. A poster is to contain 50 in^2 of printed matter with margins of 4 in. each at top and bottom and 2 in. at each side. Find the over-all dimensions if the total area of the poster is a minimum.

10. A right triangle of given hypotenuse is rotated about one of its legs to generate a right circular cone. Find the cone of greatest volume.

11. It costs a manufacturer c dollars each to manufacture and distribute a certain item. If he sells it at x dollars each, he estimates that the number he can sell is given by $n = a/(x - c) + b(100 - x)$, where a and b are certain positive constants. What selling price will bring him a maximum profit?

12. A cantilever beam of length L has one end built into a wall, while the other end is simply supported. If the beam weighs w lb per unit length, its deflection y at distance x from the built-in end satisfies the equation

$$48EIy = w(2x^4 - 5Lx^3 + 3L^2x^2),$$

where E and I are constants depending upon the material of the beam and the shape of its cross section. How far from the built-in end does the maximum deflection occur?

13. Determine the constant a in order that the function

$$f(x) = x^2 + \frac{a}{x}$$

may have (a) a relative minimum at $x = 2$, (b) a relative minimum at $x = -3$, (c) a point of inflection at $x = 1$. (d) Show that the function cannot have a relative maximum for any value of a.

14. Determine the constants a and b in order that the function

$$f(x) = x^3 + ax^2 + bx + c$$

may have (a) a relative maximum at $x = -1$ and a relative minimum at $x = 3$, (b) a relative minimum at $x = 4$ and a point of inflection at $x = 1$.

15. A wire of length L is cut into two pieces, one being bent to form a square and the other to form an equilateral triangle. How should the wire be cut (a) if the sum of the two areas is a minimum, (b) if the sum of the areas is a maximum?

16. Find the points on the curve $5x^2 - 6xy + 5y^2 = 4$ that are nearest the origin.

17. The distance between the points (x_1, y_1) and (x_2, y_2) is

$$\sqrt{(x_2 - x_1)^2 + (y_2 - y_1)^2}.$$

Find the point on the curve $y = \sqrt{x}$ nearest the point $(c, 0)$, (a) if $c \geq \frac{1}{2}$, (b) if $c < \frac{1}{2}$.

18. Find the volume of the largest right circular cone that can be inscribed in a sphere of radius r.

19. Find the volume of the largest right circular cylinder that can be inscribed in a sphere of radius r.

20. Show that the volume of the largest right circular cylinder that can be inscribed in a given right circular cone is $\frac{4}{9}$ the volume of the cone.

21. The strength of a rectangular beam is proportional to the product of its width and the square of its depth. Find the dimensions of the strongest beam that can be cut from a circular cylindrical log of radius r.

22. The stiffness of a rectangular beam is proportional to the product of its breadth and the cube of its depth. Find the stiffest beam that can be cut from a log of given diameter.

23. The intensity of illumination at any point is proportional to the product of the strength of the light source and the inverse of the square of the distance from the source. If two sources of relative strengths a and b are a distance c apart, at what point on the line joining them will the intensity be a minimum? Assume the intensity at any point is the sum of intensities from the two sources.

24. A window is in the form of a rectangle surmounted by a semicircle. If the rectangle is of clear glass while the semicircle is of colored glass which transmits only half as much light per square foot as clear glass does, and the total perimeter is fixed, find the proportions of the window that will admit the most light.

25. Right circular cylindrical tin cans are to be manufactured to contain a given volume. There is no waste involved in cutting the tin that goes into the vertical sides of the can, but each end piece is to be cut from a square and the corners of the square wasted. Find the ratio of height to diameter for the most economical cans.

26. A silo is to be made in the form of a cylinder surmounted by a hemisphere. The cost of construction per square foot of surface area is twice as great for the hemisphere as for the cylinder. Determine the dimensions to be used if the volume is fixed and the cost of construction is to be a minimum. Neglect the thickness of the silo and waste in construction.

27. If the sum of the areas of a cube and a sphere is constant, what is the ratio of the diameter of the sphere to an edge of the cube when (a) the sum of their volumes is a minimum, (b) the sum of their volumes is a maximum?

28. Two towns, located on the same side of a straight river, agree to construct a pumping station and filtering plant at the river's edge, to be used jointly to supply the towns with water. If the distances of the two towns from the river are a and b and the distance between them is c, show that the sum of the lengths of the pipe lines joining them to the pumping station is at least as great as $\sqrt{c^2 + 4ab}$.

29. Light emanating from a source A is reflected to a point B by a plane mirror. If the time required for the light to travel from A to the mirror and then to B is a minimum, show that the angle of incidence is equal to the angle of reflection.

30. Show that a manufacturer's profit is maximized (or minimized) at a level of production where his marginal revenue equals marginal cost.

31. Suppose the government imposes a tax of ten cents, for each item sold, on the product of Example 6, but other features are unchanged. How much of the tax should the manufacturer absorb and how much should he pass on to the customer? Why? Compare his profits before and after the tax.

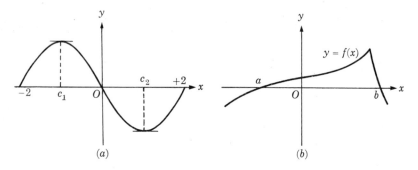

FIGURE 3–29

3–7 Rolle's Theorem. There is strong geometrical evidence to support the belief that between two points where a smooth curve $y = f(x)$ crosses the x-axis there must be at least one point where it has a horizontal tangent (Fig. 3–29a). But such is not the case if the curve has a corner, as in Fig. 3–29(b), where the derivative fails to exist. More precisely, we have the following theorem.

ROLLE'S THEOREM.* *Let the function f be defined and continuous on the closed interval $a \leq x \leq b$ and differentiable in the open interval $a < x < b$. Furthermore, let*

$$f(a) = f(b) = 0.$$

Then there is at least one number c between a and b where $f'(x)$ is zero; i.e.,

$$f'(c) = 0 \quad \textit{for some } c \quad a < c < b.$$

Proof. Either $f(x)$ is identically equal to zero for all x, $a \leq x \leq b$, or else $f(x)$ is different from zero for some values of x in this interval. In the former case, $f'(x)$ is also identically zero and the theorem is true for this case.

But if $f(x)$ is not zero everywhere between a and b, then either it is positive some place, or negative some place, or both. In any case, the function will then have a maximum positive value or a minimum negative value, or both. That is, it has an extreme value at a point c where $f(c)$ is negative (in the case of a minimum) or $f(c)$ is positive (in the case of a maximum). In either case, c is neither a nor b, since

$$f(a) = f(b) = 0, \quad f(c) \neq 0.$$

---

* Published in 1691 in *Methode pour Résoudre les Egalitez* by the French mathematician Michel Rolle. See *Source Book in Mathematics* by D. E. Smith, p. 253.

Therefore c is between a and b and the theorem of Article 3–5 applies, showing that the derivative must be zero at $x = c$:

$$f'(c) = 0 \quad \text{for some } c \quad a < c < b. \quad\quad \text{Q.E.D.}$$

Remark 1. There may be more than one place between a and b where the derivative is zero. In Fig. 3–29(a), for example, dy/dx is zero at c_1 and at c_2 and they both lie between $a = -2$ and $b = +2$.

EXAMPLE. The polynomial

$$y = x^3 - 4x = f(x)$$

is continuous and differentiable for all x, $-\infty < x < +\infty$. If we take

$$a = -2, \quad b = +2,$$

the hypotheses of Rolle's Theorem are satisfied, since

$$f(-2) = f(+2) = 0.$$

Thus

$$f'(x) = 3x^2 - 4$$

must be zero at least once between -2 and $+2$. In fact, we find

$$3x^2 - 4 = 0$$

at

$$x = c_1 = -2\sqrt{3}/3 \quad \text{and} \quad x = c_2 = +2\sqrt{3}/3.$$

Remark 2. The reader may combine Rolle's Theorem with part (ii) of Theorem 3 of Article 2–8 to obtain the following criterion for isolating the real roots of an equation $f(x) = 0$. Suppose a and b are two real numbers such that

(a) $f(x)$ and its first derivative $f'(x)$ are continuous for $a \leq x \leq b$,
(b) $f(a)$ and $f(b)$ have opposite signs,
(c) $f'(x)$ is different from zero for all values of x between a and b.

Then there is one and only one real root of the equation $f(x) = 0$ between a and b.

To see the significance of this, suppose the equation is

$$f(x) = x^3 + 3x + 1 = 0.$$

Then

$$f'(x) = 3x^2 + 3$$

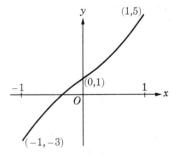

FIGURE 3–30

is always positive, so that the equation $f'(x) = 0$ can have no real roots. Hence the original equation $f(x) = 0$ cannot have as many as two real roots. It does, in fact, have exactly one real root, since the graph of

$$y = x^3 + 3x + 1$$

crosses the x-axis between $x = -1$ and $x = 0$ but can never cross the x-axis at any other point. (If it did, the derivative would have to be zero at some point between.)

PROBLEMS

Without trying to solve the equations exactly, show that the equation $f(x) = 0$ has one and only one real root between the given pair of numbers for each of the following functions $f(x)$.

1. $x^4 + 3x + 1$ $(-2, -1)$
2. $x^4 + 2x^3 - 2$ $(0, 1)$
3. $2x^3 - 3x^2 - 12x - 6$ $(-1, 0)$

4. Let $f(x)$, together with its first two derivatives $f'(x)$ and $f''(x)$, be continuous for $a \le x \le b$. Suppose the curve $y = f(x)$ intersects the x-axis in at least three different places between a and b inclusive. Using Rolle's Theorem, show that the equation $f''(x) = 0$ has at least one real root between a and b. Generalize this result.

3–8 The Mean Value Theorem. In this article we shall prove the Mean Value Theorem, which is a generalization of Rolle's Theorem. Again we shall be concerned with a function $y = f(x)$ which is continuous for $a \le x \le b$ and which has a nonvertical tangent at each point between $A[a, f(a)]$ and $B[b, f(b)]$, although the tangent may be vertical at one or both of the end points A and B (Fig. 3–31). For example, the function might be

$$f(x) = \sqrt{a^2 - x^2}, \qquad -a \le x \le a,$$

which represents a semicircle that fulfills the requirements above.

Discussion. Geometrically, the Mean Value Theorem states that if the function $y = f(x)$ is continuous for $a \le x \le b$ and has a derivative at each value of x for $a < x < b$, then there is at least one point c between a and b where the tangent to the curve will be parallel to the chord through the two points $A[a, f(a)]$ and $B[b, f(b)]$. This is intuitively plausible, for if we consider

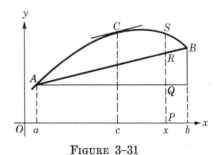

FIGURE 3–31

displacing the chord AB in Fig. 3–31 upward, keeping it parallel to AB, there will be a transition between positions where it cuts the curve in two nearby points and where it will fail to touch the curve, and the transition will take place at a point C where the line will be tangent to this curve. This transition will occur where the vertical distance between the chord AB and the curve is a maximum.

The analytic proof of the Mean Value Theorem has its key idea in this last statement. The vertical distance between the chord and the curve is measured by RS in Fig. 3–31 and

$$RS = PS - PR.$$

Now PS is simply the ordinate y on the curve $y = f(x)$, so that

$$PS = f(x).$$

On the other hand, PR is the ordinate on the chord AB and may be found by using the equation

$$y - f(a) = m(x - a),$$

which is the equation of the straight line AB through the point $A[a, f(a)]$ with slope

$$m = \frac{f(b) - f(a)}{b - a}.$$

That is, the ordinate y of the point R on the line AB is

$$y = PR = f(a) + \frac{f(b) - f(a)}{b - a}(x - a).$$

Hence

$$RS = f(x) - f(a) - \frac{f(b) - f(a)}{b - a}(x - a) \tag{1}$$

measures the vertical displacement from the chord AB to the curve $y = f(x)$ for any x between a and b.

Proof of the Mean Value Theorem. Denote the expression on the right side of Eq. (1) by $F(x)$, that is,

$$F(x) = f(x) - f(a) - \frac{f(b) - f(a)}{b - a}(x - a). \tag{2}$$

Then

$$F(a) = f(a) - f(a) - \frac{f(b) - f(a)}{b - a}(a - a) = 0$$

and

$$F(b) = f(b) - f(a) - \frac{f(b) - f(a)}{b - a}(b - a) = 0,$$

so that this function $F(x)$ is zero at both $x = a$ and $x = b$. But since $f(x)$ and $x - a$ in Eq. (2) are continuous for $a \leq x \leq b$ and differentiable for $a < x < b$, and the other expressions on the right side of the equation are constants, the function $F(x)$ satisfies all the hypotheses of Rolle's Theorem. Therefore its derivative must be zero at some place between a and b; that is,

$$F'(c) = 0 \quad \text{for some } c, \quad a < c < b. \tag{3a}$$

If we take the derivative of both sides of (2), we get

$$F'(x) = f'(x) - \frac{f(b) - f(a)}{b - a} \cdot \frac{d(x - a)}{dx}$$

and the result (3a) is equivalent to stating

$$f'(c) = \frac{f(b) - f(a)}{b - a} \tag{3b}$$

or

$$f(b) - f(a) = f'(c)(b - a) \quad \text{for some } c, \quad a < c < b. \tag{4}$$

These results are summarized in the following theorem.

THE MEAN VALUE THEOREM. *Let $y = f(x)$ be continuous for $a \leq x \leq b$, and possess a derivative at each x for $a < x < b$. Then there is at least one number c between a and b such that*

$$\boxed{f(b) - f(a) = f'(c)(b - a).}$$

We note that (3b) states that the slope $f'(c)$ of the curve at $C[c, f(c)]$ is the same as the slope $[f(b) - f(a)]/(b - a)$ of the chord joining the point $A[a, f(a)]$ and $B[b, f(b)]$; this is a form that is easily recalled.

Equation (4) contains a symbol c which is not very well defined except by this equation itself. For a specific function f and specific values of a and b, however, the equation can be used to find one or more values of c.

EXAMPLE 1. (Fig. 3–32) Let $f(x) = x^3$, $a = -2$, and $b = +2$. Then

$$f'(x) = 3x^2, \quad f'(c) = 3c^2,$$

$$f(b) = 2^3 = 8, \quad f(a) = (-2)^3 = -8,$$

$$\frac{f(b) - f(a)}{b - a} = \frac{8 - (-8)}{2 - (-2)} = \frac{16}{4} = 4,$$

so that

$$f'(c) = \frac{f(b) - f(a)}{b - a}$$

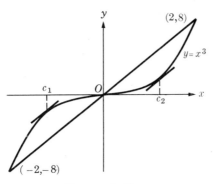

FIGURE 3–32

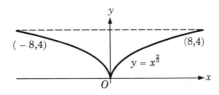

FIGURE 3–33

becomes

$$3c^2 = 4, \qquad c = \pm\tfrac{2}{3}\sqrt{3}.$$

There are thus two values of c, namely,

$$c_1 = -\tfrac{2}{3}\sqrt{3}, \qquad c_2 = +\tfrac{2}{3}\sqrt{3},$$

between $a = -2$ and $b = +2$, where the tangent to the curve $y = x^3$ is parallel to the chord through the points $(-2, -8)$ and $(+2, +8)$.

EXAMPLE 2. (Fig. 3–33) Let $f(x) = x^{2/3}$, $a = -8$, $b = +8$. Then

$$f'(x) = \frac{2}{3}x^{-1/3} = \frac{2}{3\sqrt[3]{x}}$$

exists everywhere between a and b *except* at $x = 0$. We find that

$$\frac{f(b) - f(a)}{b - a} = \frac{(8)^{2/3} - (-8)^{2/3}}{8 - (-8)} = \frac{4 - 4}{16} = 0,$$

and

$$f'(c) = \frac{2}{3\sqrt[3]{c}}$$

is not zero for any finite value of c. The result (3b) need not hold, and does not hold, in this case due to the failure of the derivative to exist at a point, namely $x = 0$, between $a = -8$ and $b = +8$.

Remark. The Mean Value Theorem has the following interesting interpretation when applied to an equation of motion $s = f(t)$. $\Delta s = f(b) - f(a)$ is the change in s corresponding to $\Delta t = b - a$ and the right side of Eq. (3b) is

$$\frac{\Delta s}{\Delta t} = \frac{f(b) - f(a)}{b - a} = \text{average velocity from } t = a \text{ to } t = b. \qquad (5)$$

The equation then tells us that there is an instant $t = c$ between a and b at which the instantaneous velocity $f'(c)$ is equal to the average velocity. The theorem may therefore be paraphrased as follows: If a motorist makes a trip in which his *average* velocity is 30 mi/hr, then at least once during the trip his speedometer must also have registered precisely 30 mi/hr.*

COROLLARY 1. *If a function F has a derivative which is equal to zero for all values of x in an interval $a < x < b$,*

$$F'(x) \equiv 0, \qquad a < x < b, \qquad (6a)$$

then the function is constant throughout the interval:

$$F(x) \equiv \text{constant}, \qquad a < x < b. \qquad (6b)$$

Proof. Suppose (6a) is satisfied. Let x_1 and x_2 be any two points in the interval with $a < x_1 < x_2 < b$. Then, since the function is differentiable for $x_1 \le x \le x_2$, it is also continuous in the same closed interval. Hence the Mean Value Theorem applies. That is, there is at least one number c, $x_1 < c < x_2$, such that

$$F(x_1) - F(x_2) = F'(c)(x_1 - x_2).$$

But $F'(c)$ is zero by hypothesis. Therefore

$$F(x_1) = F(x_2).$$

That is, the value of the function at any point x_1 is the same as its value at any other point x_2, for all x_1, x_2 in the interval (a, b). This is what is meant by Eq. (6b). Q.E.D.

COROLLARY 2. *If F_1 and F_2 are two functions each of which has its derivative equal to $f(x)$ for $a < x < b$, that is,*

$$\frac{dF_1(x)}{dx} = \frac{dF_2(x)}{dx} = f(x), \qquad a < x < b,$$

---

* The author wishes to thank Professor Raphael Salem for this interesting paraphrase.

then
$$F_1(x) - F_2(x) \equiv \text{constant}, \qquad a < x < b.$$

Proof. Apply Corollary 1, above, to the function $F(x) = F_1(x) - F_2(x)$.

PROBLEMS

In each of the following problems (1 through 5), a, b, and c refer to the equation $f(b) - f(a) = (b - a) f'(c)$, which expresses the Mean Value Theorem. Given $f(x)$, a, and b, find c.

1. $f(x) = x^2 + 2x - 1$; $a = 0$, $b = 1$.

2. $f(x) = x^3$; $a = 0$, $b = 3$.

3. $f(x) = x^{2/3}$; $a = 0$, $b = 1$.

4. $f(x) = x + \dfrac{1}{x}$; $a = \frac{1}{2}$, $b = 2$.

5. $f(x) = \sqrt{x - 1}$; $a = 1$, $b = 3$.

6. Suppose you know that $f'(x)$ always has a value between -1 and $+1$. Show that
$$|f(x) - f(a)| \leq |x - a|.$$

7. The Mean Value Theorem gives the equation
$$f(b) = f(a) + (b - a)f'(c),$$

c between a and b. When all terms on the right side of this equation are known, the equation determines $f(b)$ for us. Usually, however, $f'(c)$ is not known unless $f(b)$ is known. But when b is near a, then c will also be near a, and the approximation
$$f'(c) \approx f'(a)$$
leads to the approximation
$$f(b) \approx f(a) + (b - a)f'(a).$$

Using this approximation, calculate

(a) $\sqrt{10}$ by taking $f(x) = \sqrt{x}$, $a = 9$, $b = 10$;

(b) $(2.003)^2$ by taking $f(x) = x^2$, $a = 2$, $b = 2.003$;

(c) $1/99$ by taking $f(x) = 1/x$, $a = 100$, $b = 99$.

8. Let $P_1(x_1, y_1)$ and $P_2(x_2, y_2)$ be any two points on the parabola $y = ax^2 + bx + c$, and let $P_3(x_3, y_3)$ be the point on the arc P_1P_2 where the tangent is parallel to the chord P_1P_2. Show that $x_3 = (x_1 + x_2)/2$.

3–9 Extension of the Mean Value Theorem. In Article 3–8 we established the existence of a number c, between a and b, such that

$$f(b) - f(a) = f'(c)(b - a), \qquad (1)$$

under suitable hypotheses on the function f. If the number c is replaced by a on the right side of Eq. (1), the equality must be changed to an approximation, which turns out to be the approximation we obtain by using the line tangent to the curve at $(a, f(a))$ to approximate the curve $y = f(x)$ at $x = b$. When b is close to a, we expect the approximation to be quite good. The following theorem tells us that if the function has a second derivative, as well as a first, then the difference between the tangent approximation and the function itself is proportional to $(b - a)^2$.

EXTENDED MEAN VALUE THEOREM (*Special Case*). *Let $f(x)$ and its first derivative $f'(x)$ be continuous on the closed interval $a \leq x \leq b$, and suppose its second derivative $f''(x)$ exists in the open interval $a < x < b$. Then there is a number c_2 between a and b such that*

$$f(b) = f(a) + f'(a)(b - a) + \tfrac{1}{2}f''(c_2)(b - a)^2. \tag{2}$$

Proof. Let K be the number defined by the equation

$$f(b) = f(a) + f'(a)(b - a) + K(b - a)^2. \tag{3}$$

Consider the function $F(x)$ that we get by replacing b by x in Eq. (3) and subtracting the right side from the left:

$$F(x) = f(x) - f(a) - f'(a)(x - a) - K(x - a)^2. \tag{4}$$

Then, by substitution in (4), we find

$$F(a) = 0.$$

Also, from (3), we have

$$F(b) = 0.$$

Moreover, F and its first derivative are continuous on $a \leq x \leq b$, and

$$F'(x) = f'(x) - f'(a) - 2K(x - a). \tag{5}$$

Therefore, F satisfies the hypotheses of Rolle's Theorem, so there is a number c_1 between a and b such that

$$F'(c_1) = 0.$$

And, by substitution in (5), we also have

$$F'(a) = 0.$$

The derived function F' satisfies Rolle's Theorem on the interval $a \leq x \leq c_1$. Hence there is a number c_2 between a and c_1 such that

$$F''(c_2) = 0.$$

We differentiate (5) and get

$$F''(x) = f''(x) - 2K. \tag{6}$$

If we put $x = c_2$ in (6), set the result equal to zero, and solve for K, we have

$$K = \tfrac{1}{2}f''(c_2).$$

When this is substituted into Eq. (3), we have Eq. (2).   Q.E.D.

By a similar method, it is easy to prove the more general Extended Mean Value Theorem.

EXTENDED MEAN VALUE THEOREM (*General Case*).   *Let $f(x)$ and its first $n - 1$ derivatives $f'(x), f''(x), \ldots, f^{(n-1)}(x)$ be continuous on the closed interval $a \leq x \leq b$, and suppose the nth derivative $f^{(n)}(x)$ exists at least in the open interval $a < x < b$. Then there is a number c_n between a and b such that*

$$
\begin{aligned}
f(b) = f(a) &+ f'(a)(b - a) + \frac{1}{2}f''(a)(b - a)^2 \\[6pt]
&+ \frac{1}{6}f'''(a)(b - a)^3 + \cdots \\[6pt]
&+ \frac{1}{(n-1)!}f^{(n-1)}(a)(b - a)^{n-1} \\[6pt]
&+ \frac{1}{n!}f^{(n)}(c_n)(b - a)^n.
\end{aligned} \tag{7}
$$

Remark. The law of formation of the terms on the right side of Eq. (7) may be discovered by continuing a term at a time from $n = 1$ to $n = 2$ (as we have done), then to $n = 3$, and so on. Equation (7) is the basis of a powerful general method for evaluating a large class of functions that have derivatives of all orders. The proof of the general case of the Mean Value Theorem is left as an exercise. (See Problem 74 at the end of this chapter.)

PROBLEMS

1. Prove the special case $n = 3$ of the Extended Mean Value Theorem, Eq. (7).

2. Prove the case $n = 4$ of the Extended Mean Value Theorem, Eq. (7).

3. Verify the validity of the Extended Mean Value Theorem for each of the following polynomials, for the given values of a and n:

(a) $f(x) = 3x^2 + 2x + 4;$ $a = 1,$ $n = 2.$

(b) $f(x) = x^3 + 5x - 7;$ $a = 1,$ $n = 3.$

4. Using the Extended Mean Value Theorem, prove that a polynomial $f(x)$ of degree n may be written, precisely, in the form:

$$f(x) = f(a) + f'(a)(x - a) + \frac{f''(a)}{2}(x - a)^2 + \cdots$$
$$+ \frac{f^{(n)}(a)}{n!}(x - a)^n.$$

5. Use the Extended Mean Value Theorem for $n = 2$, Eq. (2), to prove the following: Let $f(x)$ be continuous and have continuous first and second derivatives. Suppose that $f'(a) = 0$. Then $f(x)$ has:

   (a) a relative maximum at a if its second derivative is less than or equal to zero throughout some neighborhood of a,
   (b) a relative minimum at a if its second derivative is greater than or equal to zero throughout some neighborhood of a.

[A "neighborhood" of a is an open interval centered at a, thus an interval of the form $a - h < x < a + h$ for some positive h.]

   * 3–10 Applications of the Mean Value Theorem to curve tracing. The discussion of the signs of dy/dx and d^2y/dx^2 in Articles 3–1 and 3–3 can be made more rigorous by applying the Mean Value Theorems to prove the following results.

   THEOREM 1. *Let $y = f(x)$ be continuous in the closed interval $a \leq x \leq b$ and differentiable in the open interval $a < x < b$. Then,*

   if dy/dx is positive for $a < x < b$, the curve $y = f(x)$ steadily rises,

   if dy/dx is negative for $a < x < b$, the curve $y = f(x)$ steadily falls

   as x increases from a to b.

   Proof. (The reader should make his own sketch to illustrate the following statements.) Let x_1 and x_2 be any two points in the closed interval (a, b) with x_1 to the left of x_2; that is,

$$a \leq x_1 < x_2 \leq b.$$

Then by the Mean Value Theorem, there is a number c between x_1 and x_2 such that
$$f(x_2) - f(x_1) = f'(c) \cdot (x_2 - x_1).$$

---

* This section may be omitted without loss of continuity. The results are not used in later chapters.

Since $x_2 - x_1$ is positive, the sign of the right side of this equation is the same as the sign of the derivative $f'(c)$. Therefore

$$y_2 = f(x_2) \text{ is greater than } y_1 = f(x_1) \text{ if } f'(c) \text{ is positive,}$$

and

$$y_2 = f(x_2) \text{ is less than } y_1 = f(x_1) \text{ if } f'(c) \text{ is negative.}$$

In other words, when dy/dx is positive, the point $P_2(x_2, y_2)$ is to the right of and above the point $P_1(x_1, y_1)$ and when dy/dx is negative, the point $P_2(x_2, y_2)$ is to the right of and below the point $P_1(x_1, y_1)$, as the theorem asserts. Q.E.D.

Second derivative test for maxima and minima. In Article 3–6 we found that we can sometimes tell a relative maximum from a minimum of a function by the sign of the second derivative at a point where the first derivative is zero. When the second derivative is also zero at the same point, the test fails. But we may use the second derivative, even when it is zero at the point a where $f'(a) = 0$, provided there is some *interval* $a - h < x < a + h$, containing a, where the second derivative does not change its sign. Theorem 2 explains this procedure.

THEOREM 2. *Let f be continuous and twice differentiable in some open interval containing a, and suppose that the first derivative is zero at a:*

$$f'(a) = 0. \tag{1}$$

Then $f(x)$ has a relative maximum at $x = a$ if its second derivative $f''(x)$ is negative or zero in some interval $a - h < x < a + h$, and has a relative minimum if $f''(x)$ is positive or zero there.

Proof. Let h be a number such that $f''(x)$ exists for $a - h < x < a + h$. Let b be any number between $a - h$ and $a + h$. By the Extended Mean Value Theorem for $n = 2$, we know that there is a number c between a and b such that

$$f(b) - f(a) = f'(a)(b - a) + \tfrac{1}{2}f''(c)(b - a)^2.$$

This reduces to

$$f(b) - f(a) = \tfrac{1}{2}f''(c)(b - a)^2, \tag{2}$$

in view of the hypothesis (1). The right side of Eq. (2) has the same sign as $f''(c)$. If the second derivative is negative or zero throughout $a - h < x < a + h$, then $f(b) - f(a) \le 0$ and $f(b) \le f(a)$; hence f has a relative maximum at a. If the second derivative is positive or zero throughout $a - h < x < a + h$, then $f(b) \ge f(a)$ and f has a relative minimum at a. Q.E.D.

EXAMPLE 1. The function

$$f(x) = x^4 - 4x^3 + 6x^2 - 4x + 4$$

is differentiable any number of times for all values of x. Its first two derivatives are

$$f'(x) = 4x^3 - 12x^2 + 12x - 4 = 4(x - 1)^3,$$
$$f''(x) = 12x^2 - 24x + 12 = 12(x - 1)^2.$$

The first derivative is zero at $x = 1$. So is the second derivative. But the second derivative is positive everywhere else, so the function has a minimum at $x = 1$.

Curves concave upward or downward. By using the Extended Mean Value Theorem for $n = 2$, we can now give an analytic proof of the results in Article 3–3 on the direction of concavity of a curve.

THEOREM 3. *Let $y = f(x)$ be continuous together with its first derivative $y' = f'(x)$ in the closed interval $a \le x \le b$. Let the second derivative $y'' = f''(x)$ exist at least over the open interval $a < x < b$. Then the curve $y = f(x)$ is*

concave upward if $f''(x)$ is positive,

and

concave downward if $f''(x)$ is negative,

for $a < x < b$.

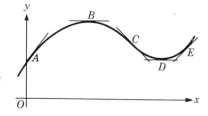

FIGURE 3–34

Remark. To prove Theorem 3 we need a more precise formulation of what the phrases "concave upward" and "concave downward" mean. A portion of a curve is *concave upward* if the chord PQ lies above the arc PQ for all pairs of points P and Q on it, as in the region CDE in Fig. 3–34. Similarly, it is *concave downward* when each chord lies below its arc, as in the region ABC in the figure.

Proof of Theorem 3. In Fig. 3–35(a), $P_1(x_1, y_1)$ and $P_2(x_2, y_2)$ represent two points on the curve $y = f(x)$ with $a \le x_1 < x_2 \le b$. The point P_L is on the chord P_1P_2. Its abscissa x lies between x_1 and x_2. By similar triangles, we have

$$\frac{y_L - y_1}{h_1} = \frac{y_2 - y_L}{h_2}$$

or

$$y_L = \frac{h_1 y_2 + h_2 y_1}{h_1 + h_2}.$$

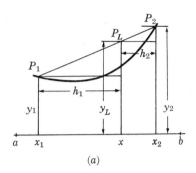

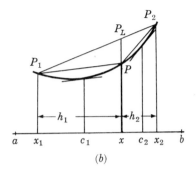

FIGURE 3–35

Suppose now that $P(x, y)$ is the point of abscissa x on the curve $y = f(x)$. Then we know that

$$P \text{ lies above the chord if } y > y_L,$$
$$P \text{ lies on the chord if } \quad y = y_L,$$
$$P \text{ lies below the chord if } y < y_L.$$

To be specific, let us consider the case where the second derivative $f''(x)$ is positive for $a < x < b$. By the Extended Mean Value Theorem with $n = 2$ we have

$$f(x_1) - f(x) = f'(x)(x_1 - x) + \tfrac{1}{2}f''(c)(x_1 - x)^2, \qquad (3a)$$

$$f(x_2) - f(x) = f'(x)(x_2 - x) + \tfrac{1}{2}f''(e)(x_2 - x)^2 \qquad (3b)$$

for some numbers c, between x_1 and x, and e, between x and x_2. We multiply (3a) by $x_2 - x = h_2$ and (3b) by $x - x_1 = h_1$ and add, thereby eliminating the terms in $f'(x)$. We obtain

$$h_2[f(x_1) - f(x)] + h_1[f(x_2) - f(x)] = \tfrac{1}{2}[h_2 f''(c)h_1^2 + h_1 f''(e)h_2^2]. \quad (4)$$

If f'' is positive throughout the interval (a, b), all terms on the right side of (4) are positive and we have

$$h_2 f(x_1) + h_1 f(x_2) - (h_1 + h_2)f(x) > 0$$

or

$$\frac{h_2 f(x_1) + h_1 f(x_2)}{h_1 + h_2} > f(x) \qquad (5)$$

or

$$\frac{h_1 y_2 + h_2 y_1}{h_1 + h_2} > y.$$

The expression on the left side of this inequality is the ordinate y_L of the point P_L on the chord P_1P_2. Since y is less than y_L, the point $P(x, y)$ is below the chord. Since this is true for any position of the points P_1 and P_2, provided only that $a \leq x_1 < x_2 \leq b$, and for any intermediate point P of abscissa x between x_1 and x_2, it follows that the curve is concave upward in this case, that is, when the second derivative is positive for $a < x < b$.

In case the second derivative is negative over $a < x < b$, the inequalities above are reversed, and we find that

$$y_L < y \qquad \text{when} \qquad f''(x) \text{ is negative.}$$

That is, the curve-point $P(x, y)$ is above the chord-point $P_L(x, y_L)$. This means that the curve is concave downward when the second derivative is negative. Q.E.D.

REVIEW QUESTIONS AND EXERCISES FOR CHAPTER 3

1. Discuss the significance of the signs of the first and second derivatives. Sketch a small portion of a curve, illustrating how it looks near a point where:

(a) both y' and y'' are positive;
(b) $y' > 0, y'' < 0$;
(c) $y' < 0, y'' > 0$;
(d) $y' < 0, y'' < 0$.

2. Define: *point of inflection.* How do you find points of inflection from an equation of a curve?

3. How do you locate local maximum and minimum points of a curve? Discuss exceptional points, such as end points and points where the derivative fails to exist, in addition to the nonexceptional type. Illustrate with graphs.

4. Let n be a positive integer. For which values of n does the curve $y = x^n$ have (a) a local minimum at the origin, (b) a point of inflection at the origin?

5. Outline a general method of attack for solving "related rates" problems.

6. Outline a general method of attack for solving "max-min" problems.

7. What are the hypotheses of Rolle's theorem? What is the conclusion?

8. Is the converse of Rolle's theorem true?

9. With the book closed, state and prove the Mean Value Theorem. What is its geometrical interpretation?

10. We know that if $F(x) = x^2$, then $F'(x) = 2x$. If someone knows a function G such that $G'(x) = 2x$ but $G(x) \neq x^2$, what can be said about the difference $G(2) - G(1)$? Explain.

11. Use the Extended Mean Value Theorem, with $n = 2$, to estimate $\sqrt[3]{9}$. [*Hint:* Let $f(x) = x^{1/3}$ and take $a = 8, b = 9$, in Eq. (7), Article 3-9.] Compare the answer with what you get using $n = 1$.

12. Read the article "Mathematics in Warfare" by F. W. Lanchester, *World of Mathematics*, Vol. 4, pp. 2138–2157, as a discussion of a practical problem in "related rates."

MISCELLANEOUS PROBLEMS FOR CHAPTER 3

In each of the following exercises (1 through 14) find y' and y''. Determine in each case the sets of values of x for which

(a) y is increasing (as x increases),
(b) y is decreasing (as x increases),
(c) the graph is concave upward,
(d) the graph is concave downward.

Also sketch the graph in each case, indicating *high* and *low* turning points and points of inflection.

1. $y = 9x - x^2$
2. $y = x^3 - 5x^2 + 3x$
3. $y = 4x^3 - x^4$
4. $y = 4x + x^{-1}$
5. $y = x^2 + 4x^{-1}$
6. $y = x + 4x^{-2}$
7. $y = 5 - x^{2/3}$
8. $y = \dfrac{x - 1}{x + 1}$
9. $y = x - \dfrac{4}{x}$
10. $y = x^4 - 2x^2$
11. $y = \dfrac{x^2}{ax + b}$; $a > 0, b > 0$
12. $y = 2x^3 - 9x^2 + 12x$
13. $y = (x - 1)(x + 1)^2$
14. $y = x^2 - \frac{1}{6}x^3$

15. The slope of a curve at any point (x, y) is given by the equation

$$\frac{dy}{dx} = 6(x - 1)(x - 2)^2(x - 3)^3(x - 4)^4.$$

(a) For what value (or values) of x is y a maximum? Why?
(b) For what value (or values) of x is y a minimum? Why?

16. A particle moves along the x-axis with velocity $v = dx/dt = f(x)$. Show that its acceleration is $f(x)f'(x)$.

17. A meteorite entering the earth's atmosphere has velocity inversely proportional to $\sqrt{s}$ when at distance s from the center of the earth. Show that its acceleration is inversely proportional to s^2.

18. If the velocity of a falling body is $k\sqrt{s}$ at the instant when the body has fallen a distance s, find its acceleration.

19. The volume of a cube is increasing at a rate of 300 in^3/min at the instant when the edge is 20 in. Find the rate at which the edge is changing.

20. Sand falling at the rate of 3 ft^3/min forms a conical pile whose radius always equals twice the height. Find the rate at which the height is changing at the instant when the height is 10 ft.

21. The volume of a sphere is decreasing at the rate of 12π ft^3/min. Find the rates at which the radius and the surface area are changing at the instant when the radius is 20 ft. Also find approximately how much the radius and surface area may be expected to change in the following 6 sec.

22. At a certain instant airplane A is flying a level course at 500 mi/hr. At the same time, airplane B is directly above airplane A and flying at the rate of 700 mi/hr on a course that intercepts A's course at a point C that is 4 mi from B and 2 mi from A. (a) At the instant in question, how fast is the distance between the airplanes decreasing? (b) What is the minimum distance between the airplanes, if they continue on the present courses at constant speed?

23. A point moves along the curve $y^2 = x^3$ in such a way that its distance from the origin increases at the constant rate of 2 units per second. Find dx/dt at $(2, 2\sqrt{2})$.

24. Refer to the triangle in Fig. 3-7. How fast is its area changing when $x = 17\sqrt{2}$?

25. Suppose the cone in Fig. 3-8 has a small opening at the vertex through which the water escapes at the rate of $0.08\sqrt{y}$ ft³/min when its depth is y. Water is also running into the cone at a constant rate of c ft³/min. When the depth is $6\frac{1}{4}$ ft it is observed to be increasing at the rate 0.02 ft/min. Under these conditions, will the tank fill? Give a reason for your answer.

26. A particle projected vertically upward from the surface of the earth with initial velocity v_0 has velocity $\sqrt{v_0^2 - 2gR[1 - (R/s)]}$ when it reaches a distance s from the *center* of the earth. Here R is the radius of the earth. Show that the acceleration is inversely proportional to s.

27. Given a triangle ABC. Let D and E be points on the sides AB and AC, respectively, such that DE is parallel to BC. Let the distance between BC and DE equal x. Show that the derivative, with respect to x, of the area $BCED$ is equal to the length of DE.

28. Points A and B move along the x- and y-axes, respectively, in such a way that the perpendicular distance r (inches) from the origin to AB remains constant. How fast is OA changing, and is it increasing or decreasing, when $OB = 2r$ and B is moving toward O at the rate of 0.3r in/sec?

29. Ships A and B start from O at the same time. Ship A travels due east at a rate of 15 mi/hr. Ship B travels in a straight course making an angle of 60° with the path of ship A at a rate of 20 mi/hr. How fast are they separating at the end of 2 hr?

30. Water is being poured into an inverted conical tank (vertex down) at the rate of 2 ft³/min. How fast is the water level rising when the depth of the water is 5 ft? The radius of the base of the cone is 3 ft and the altitude is 10 ft.

31. Divide 20 into two parts (not necessarily integers) such that the product of one part with the square of the other shall be a maximum.

32. Find the largest value of $f(x) = 4x^3 - 8x^2 + 5x$ for $0 \le x \le 2$. Give reasons for your answer.

33. Find two *positive* numbers whose sum is 36 and such that their product is as large as possible. Can the problem be solved if the product is to be as small as possible?

34. Determine the coefficients a, b, c, d so that the curve whose equation is $y = ax^3 + bx^2 + cx + d$ has a maximum at $(-1, 10)$ and an inflection point at $(1, -6)$.

35. Find that number which most exceeds its square.

36. The perimeter p and area A of a circular sector ("piece of pie") of radius

r and arc length s are given by $p = 2r + s$; $A = \frac{1}{2}rs$. If the perimeter is known to be 100 ft, what value of r will produce a maximum area?

37. If a ball is thrown vertically upward with a velocity of 32 ft/sec, its height after t sec is given by the equation $s = 32t - 16t^2$. At what instant will the ball be at its highest point, and how high will it rise?

38. A right circular cone has altitude 12 ft and radius of base 6 ft. A cone is inscribed with its vertex at the center of the base of the given cone and its base parallel to the base of the given cone. Find the dimensions of the cone of maximum volume that can be so inscribed.

39. An oil can is to be made in the form of a right circular cylinder to contain 16π in³. What dimensions of the can will require the least amount of material?

40. An isosceles triangle is drawn with its vertex at the origin, its base parallel to and above the x-axis and the vertices of its base on the curve $12y = 36 - x^2$. Determine the area of the largest such triangle.

41. A tire manufacturer is able to make x (hundred) grade A tires and y (hundred) grade B tires per day, where $y = (40 - 10x)/(5 - x)$, $0 \leq x \leq 4$. If the profit on each grade A tire is twice the profit on a grade B tire, how many grade A tires per day should he make?

42. Find the points on the curve $x^2 - y^2 = 1$ which are nearest the point $P(a, 0)$ in case (a) $a = 4$, (b) $a = 2$, (c) $a = \sqrt{2}$.

43. A motorist is stranded in a desert 5 mi from a point A, which is the point on a long straight road nearest to him. He wishes to get to a point B on the road. If he can travel at 15 mi/hr on the desert and 39 mi/hr on the road, find the point at which he must meet the road to get to B in the shortest possible time if (a) B is 5 mi from A, (b) B is 10 mi from A, (c) B is 1 mi from A.

44. Points A and B are ends of a diameter of a circle and C is a point on the circumference. Which of the following statements about triangle ABC is (or are) true?

(a) The area is a maximum when the triangle is isosceles.
(b) The area is a minimum when the triangle is isosceles.
(c) The perimeter is a maximum when the triangle is isosceles.
(d) The perimeter is a minimum when the triangle is isosceles.

45. The base and the perimeter of a triangle are fixed. Determine the remaining two sides if the area is to be a maximum.

46. The base b and the area k of a triangle are fixed. Determine the base angles if the angle at the vertex opposite b is to be a maximum.

47. A line is drawn through a fixed point (a, b) to meet the axes Ox, Oy in P and Q. Show that the minimum values of PQ, $OP + OQ$, and $OP \cdot OQ$ are respectively $(a^{2/3} + b^{2/3})^{3/2}$, $(\sqrt{a} + \sqrt{b})^2$, and $4ab$.

48. Find the smallest value of the constant m if $mx - 1 + (1/x)$ is to be greater than or equal to zero for all positive values of x.

49. Let s be the distance from the fixed point $P_1(x_1, y_1)$ to a point $P(x, y)$ on the line L: $ax + by + c = 0$. Using calculus methods, (a) show that s^2 is a minimum when P_1P is perpendicular to L, and (b) show that the minimum distance is $|ax_1 + by_1 + c|/\sqrt{a^2 + b^2}$.

50. A playing field is to be built in the shape of a rectangle plus a semicircular area at each end. A 440-yd race track is to form the perimeter of the field. Find the dimensions of the field if the rectangular part is to have as large an area as possible.

51. If $ax + (b/x) \geq c$ for all positive values of x, where a, b, and c are positive constants, show that $ab \geq c^2/4$.

52. Prove that if $ax^2 + (b/x) \geq c$ for all positive values of x, where a, b, and c are positive constants, then $27ab^2 \geq 4c^3$.

53. Given $f(x) = ax^2 + 2bx + c$ with $a > 0$. By considering the minimum, prove that $f(x) \geq 0$ for all real x if, and only if, $b^2 - ac \leq 0$.

54. In Problem 53, take

$$f(x) = (a_1x + b_1)^2 + (a_2x + b_2)^2 + \cdots + (a_nx + b_n)^2,$$

and deduce Schwarz's inequality:

$$(a_1b_1 + a_2b_2 + \cdots + a_nb_n)^2 \leq (a_1^2 + a_2^2 + \cdots + a_n^2)(b_1^2 + b_2^2 + \cdots + b_n^2).$$

55. In Problem 54, prove that equality can hold only in case there is a real number x such that $b_i = -a_ix$ for every $i = 1, 2, \ldots, n$.

56. If x is positive and m is greater than one, prove that $x^m - 1 - m(x - 1)$ is not negative.

57. What are the dimensions of the rectangular plot of greatest area which can be laid out within a triangle of base 36 ft and altitude 12 ft? Assume that one side of the rectangle lies on the base of the triangle.

58. Find the width across the top of an isosceles trapezoid of base 12 in. and slant sides 6 in. if its area is a maximum.

59. A fence h ft high runs parallel to and w ft from a vertical wall. Find the length of the shortest ladder which will reach from the ground across the top of the fence to the wall.

60. Assuming that the cost per hour of running the Queen Mary is $a + bv^n$, where a, b, and n are positive constants, $n > 1$, and v is the velocity through the water, find the speed for making the run from Liverpool to New York at minimum cost.

61. A flower bed is to be in the shape of a circular sector of radius r and central angle θ (i.e., like a piece of pie). Find r and θ if the area is fixed and the perimeter is a minimum.

62. A reservoir is to be built in the form of a right circular cone and the lateral area waterproofed. If the capacity of the reservoir is to be 72π ft³ and one gallon of waterproofing material will cover 80 ft², how many gallons are required?

63. Given two concentric circles, C_1 of radius r_1 and C_2 of radius r_2, $r_2 > r_1 > 0$. Let A be the area between them. (a) How fast is A increasing (or decreasing) when $r_1 = 4$ in. and is increasing at the rate of 0.02 in/sec while $r_2 = 6$ in. and is increasing at the rate of 0.01 in/sec?

(b) Suppose that at time $t = 0$, r_1 is 3 in. and r_2 is 5 in., and that for $t > 0$, r_1 increases at the constant rate of a in/sec and r_2 increases at the constant rate of b in/sec. If $(\frac{3}{5})a < b < a$, find when the area A will be a maximum.

64. Given two concentric spheres, S_1 of radius r_1 and S_2 of radius r_2, $r_2 > r_1 > 0$. Let V be the volume between them. Suppose that at time $t = 0$, $r_1 = r$ in. and $r_2 = R$ in., and that for $t > 0$, r_1 increases at the constant rate of a in/sec and r_2 increases at the constant rate of b in/sec. If $a > b > ar^2/R^2$, find when V will be a maximum.

65. The motion of a particle in a straight line is given by $s = \lambda t - (1 + \lambda^4)t^2$. Show that the particle moves forward initially when λ is positive but ultimately retreats. Show also that for different values of λ the maximum possible distance that the particle can move forward is $\frac{1}{8}$.

66. Let $h(x) = f(x)g(x)$ be the product of two functions that have first and second derivatives and are positive; that is, $f(x) > 0$, $g(x) > 0$.

(a) Is it true, if f and g both have a relative maximum at $x = a$, that h has a relative maximum at $x = a$?

(b) Is it true, if f and g both have a point of inflection at $x = a$, that h has a point of inflection at $x = a$?

For both (a) and (b) either give a proof or construct a numerical example showing that the statement is false.

67. The numbers $c_1, c_2, \ldots, c_n$ are recorded in an experiment. It is desired to determine a number x with the property that $(c_1 - x)^2 + (c_2 - x)^2 + (c_3 - x)^2 + \cdots + (c_n - x)^2$ shall be a minimum. Find x.

68. The 4 points $(-2, -\frac{1}{2})$, $(0, 1)$, $(1, 2)$, and $(3, 3)$ are observed to lie more or less close to a straight line of equation $y = mx + 1$. Find m if the sum

$$(y_1 - mx_1 - 1)^2 + (y_2 - mx_2 - 1)^2 + (y_3 - mx_3 - 1)^2 + (y_4 - mx_4 - 1)^2$$

is to be a minimum, where $(x_1, y_1), \ldots, (x_4, y_4)$ are the coordinates of the given points.

69. The *geometric mean* of the n positive numbers $a_1, a_2, \ldots, a_n$ is the nth root of $a_1 a_2 \ldots a_n$ and the arithmetic mean is $(a_1 + a_2 + \cdots + a_n)/n$. Show that if $a_1, a_2, \ldots, a_{n-1}$ are fixed and $a_n = x$ is permitted to vary over the set of positive real numbers, the ratio of the arithmetic mean to the geometric mean is a minimum when x is the arithmetic mean of $a_1, a_2, \ldots, a_{n-1}$.

70. The curve $(y + 1)^3 = x^2$ passes through the points $(1, 0)$ and $(-1, 0)$. Does Rolle's Theorem justify the conclusion that dy/dx vanishes for some value of x in the interval $-1 \leq x \leq 1$? Give reasons for your answer.

71. If $a < 0 < b$ and $f(x) = x^{-1/3}$, show that there is no c that satisfies Eq. (4), Article 3–8. Illustrate with a sketch of the graph.

72. If $a < 0 < b$ and $f(x) = x^{1/3}$, show that there is a value of c that satisfies Eq. (4), Article 3–8, even though the function fails to have a derivative at $x = 0$. Illustrate with a sketch of the graph.

73. Show that the equation $f(x) = 2x^3 - 3x^2 + 6x + 6 = 0$ has exactly one real root and find its value accurate to two significant figures. [*Hint*: $f(-1) = -5$, $f(0) = +6$, and $f'(x) > 0$ for all real x.]

74. Extended Mean Value Theorem. Suppose $f(x)$ and its derivatives $f'(x)$, $f''(x), \ldots, f^{(n-1)}(x)$ of order one through $n - 1$ are continuous on $a \leq x \leq b$,

and $f^{(n)}(x)$ exists for $a < x < b$. If

$$F(x) = f(x) - f(a) - (x - a)f'(a) - (x - a)^2 f''(a)/2! - \cdots$$

$$- \frac{(x - a)^{n-1} f^{(n-1)}(a)}{(n - 1)!} - K(x - a)^n,$$

where K is chosen so that $F(b) = 0$, show that:

(a) $F(a) = F(b) = 0$,

(b) $F'(a) = F''(a) = \cdots = F^{(n-1)}(a) = 0$,

(c) there exist numbers $c_1, c_2, c_3, \ldots, c_n$ such that

$$a < c_n < c_{n-1} < \cdots < c_2 < c_1 < b$$

and such that

$$F'(c_1) = 0 = F''(c_2) = F'''(c_3) = \cdots = F^{(n-1)}(c_{n-1}) = F^{(n)}(c_n).$$

(d) Hence, deduce that $K = [f^{(n)}(c_n)]/n!$ for c_n as above in (3); or, in other words, since $F(b) = 0$,

$$f(b) = f(a) + f'(a)(b - a) + \frac{f''(a)}{2!}(b - a)^2 + \cdots$$

$$+ \frac{f^{(n-1)}(a)}{(n - 1)!}(b - a)^{n-1} + \frac{f^{(n)}(c_n)}{n!}(b - a)^n$$

for some c_n, $a < c_n < b$.

75. Suppose that it costs a manufacturer $y = a + bx$ dollars to produce x units per week. Assume that the price, P dollars per item, at which he can sell x items per week is $P = c - ex$. (a) What level of production maximizes his profits? (b) What is the corresponding price? (c) What is his profit (per week) at this level of production? (d) If a tax of t dollars per item sold is imposed on this product, and the manufacturer still wishes to maximize his profit, at what price should he sell each item? Comment on the difference between this price and the price before tax.

CHAPTER 4

INTEGRATION

4–1 Introduction. In the preceding chapters we have pursued one of the two main branches of the calculus, namely, *differential calculus.* We shall now turn our attention to the other main branch of the subject, *integral calculus.* Today, "to integrate" has two meanings when used in connection with calculus. The deeper and more fundamental meaning is nearly the same as the nontechnical definition: "to indicate the whole of; to give the sum or total of" (Webster). The mathematical meaning of the word in this sense will be amply illustrated in finding areas bounded by curves, volumes of various solids, lengths of curves, centers of gravity, and other applications.

The second mathematical meaning of the verb "to integrate" is "to find a function whose derivative is given." This is the aspect of integration that we shall discuss in the next two articles.

The two kinds of integration are called respectively *definite* and *indefinite,* and the connection between the two is given by a theorem which is called the *fundamental theorem* of integral calculus.

4–2 The indefinite integral. Suppose that we are given the derivative dy/dx as a function

$$\frac{dy}{dx} = f(x), \qquad a < x < b, \tag{1}$$

and are asked to find $y = F(x)$.

For example, we might be asked to find y as a function of x if

$$\frac{dy}{dx} = 2x.$$

From our experience with derivatives, we can find one answer, namely,

$$y = x^2.$$

On the other hand, we realize that this is not the only answer, since

$$y = x^2 + 1, \qquad y = x^2 - \sqrt{2}, \qquad y = x^2 + 5\pi$$

are also valid answers. Indeed,

$$y = x^2 + C$$

is an answer if C is any constant.

DEFINITION 1. *An equation such as* (1), *which specifies the derivative as a function of x* (*or as a function of x and y*), *is called a* differential equation.

For example,

$$\frac{dy}{dx} = 2xy^2$$

is a differential equation. Second, third, and higher order derivatives may also occur in differential equations, such as

$$\frac{d^2y}{dx^2} + 6xy\frac{dy}{dx} + 3x^2y^3 = 0,$$

and so on. For the time being we shall restrict attention to the special type of differential equation considered in Eq. (1). Differential equations of more general types will be considered in Chapter 18.

DEFINITION 2. *A function* $y = F(x)$ *is called a* solution *of the differential equation* (1) *if, over the domain* $a < x < b$, $F(x)$ *is differentiable and*

$$\frac{dF(x)}{dx} = f(x). \tag{2}$$

We also say, in these circumstances, that $F(x)$ *is an integral of* $f(x)$ *with respect to x.*

Remark. It is clear from this definition that if $F(x)$ is an integral of $f(x)$ with respect to x, then $F(x) + C$ is also such an integral when C is any constant whatever. For if Eq. (2) is satisfied, then we also have

$$\frac{d}{dx}[F(x) + C] = \frac{dF(x)}{dx} + \frac{dC}{dx}$$
$$= f(x) + 0 = f(x).$$

What is not clear, however, is whether there are other integrals of $f(x)$ not contained in this collection given by the formula $F(x) + C$.

Specifically, we know that $y = x^2 + C$ is a solution, for any constant C, of the differential equation $dy/dx = 2x$. But are there any other solutions?

This question is answered by the second corollary of the Mean Value Theorem, Article 3–8. For if both $F_1(x)$ and $F_2(x)$ are integrals of $f(x)$, then

$$\frac{dF_1(x)}{dx} = \frac{dF_2(x)}{dx} = f(x)$$

or

$$\frac{d[F_1(x) - F_2(x)]}{dx} = 0,$$

and hence

$$F_1(x) - F_2(x) = C,$$

where C is a constant. Hence, if we take $F_2(x) = F(x)$, we have $F_1(x) = F(x) + C$.

Therefore, if

$$y = F(x)$$

is any solution whatever of Eq. (1), then *all* solutions are contained in the formula

$$y = F(x) + C,$$

where C is an arbitrary constant. This is indicated by writing

$$\int f(x) \, dx = F(x) + C, \tag{3}$$

where the symbol $\int$ is called an "integral sign" and Eq. (3) is read "The integral of $f(x) \, dx$ is $F(x)$ plus C." This is a standard notation. We may interpret it in either of two ways:

1. We may think of the symbol

$$\int \ldots dx \tag{4}$$

as meaning "integral, with respect to x, of ..." The symbol (4) is then interpreted as the inverse of the symbol

$$\frac{d}{dx} \ldots ,$$

which means "derivative, with respect to x, of ..." In this interpretation the integral sign and the dx go together; the integral sign specifies the operation of integration, and the dx tells us that the "variable of integration" is x.

2. Or, we may think of Eq. (2) as written in *differential* form:

$$dF(x) = f(x) \, dx, \tag{5}$$

before the operation indicated by the integral sign is performed. Then, when we introduce the integral sign in Eq. (5) (that is, when we "integrate" both sides of the equation), we get

$$\int dF(x) = \int f(x) \, dx.$$

If we compare this with Eq. (3), we have

$$\int dF(x) = F(x) + C. \tag{6}$$

In other words, when we integrate the *differential* of a function we get that function plus an arbitrary constant. In this interpretation, we therefore think of the symbol $\int$ for integration (without absorbing the dx as part of the symbol) as meaning the operation which is the inverse of the operation denoted by the symbol d for differentiation. This is the interpretation which we shall adopt in this book.

Thus, if we want to solve the differential equation

$$\frac{dy}{dx} = 3x^2,$$

we use the definition of the differential

$$dy = \frac{dy}{dx}\,dx$$

to change it to the differential form

$$dy = 3x^2\,dx.$$

Now we know, from past experience, that

$$d(x^3) = 3x^2\,dx.$$

Hence we have

$$y = \int 3x^2\,dx = \int d(x^3) = x^3 + C.$$

If both x and y occur in the differential equation, but in such a way that we can separate the variables so as to combine all y terms with dy and all x terms with dx, we then integrate as in the following example.

EXAMPLE. Solve the differential equation

$$\frac{dy}{dx} = x^2\sqrt{y}, \qquad y > 0. \tag{7}$$

Solution. We change to differentials

$$dy = x^2\sqrt{y}\,dx$$

and then divide by $\sqrt{y}$ to obtain

$$y^{-(1/2)}\,dy = x^2\,dx,$$

in which the variables have been separated. The left side of this equation is

$$d(2y^{1/2}) = y^{-(1/2)}\,dy,$$

while the right side is

$$d(x^3/3) = x^2\,dx.$$

Therefore

$$d(2y^{1/2}) = d(x^3/3).$$

When we integrate this equation, we may write

$$2y^{1/2} + C_1 = \frac{x^3}{3} + C_2$$

or

$$2y^{1/2} = \frac{x^3}{3} + C,$$

where we have combined the two constants C_1 and C_2 into a single constant

$$C = C_2 - C_1.$$

In fact, when we integrate the two sides of a differential equation, it always suffices to add the arbitrary constant C to just one side of the equation since, in any case, if we add constants to both sides of the equation they may always be combined into a single constant.

Integration, as defined above, requires the ability to guess the answer. But the following formulas help to reduce the amount of guesswork in many cases. In these formulas, u and v denote differentiable functions of some independent variable (say of x) and a, n, and C are constants.

$$\int du = u + C, \tag{a}$$

$$\int a\,du = a\int du, \tag{b}$$

$$\int (du + dv) = \int du + \int dv, \tag{c}$$

$$\int u^n\,du = \frac{u^{n+1}}{n+1} + C, \qquad (n \neq -1). \tag{d}$$

In words, these formulas say that:

(a) The integral of the differential of a function u is u plus an arbitrary constant C.

(b) A constant may be moved across the integral sign. [*Caution:* Variables must *not* be moved across the integral sign.]

(c) The integral of the sum of two differentials is the sum of their integrals. This may be extended to the sum of any *finite* number of differentials:

$$\int (du_1 + du_2 + \cdots + du_n) = \int du_1 + \int du_2 + \cdots + \int du_n.$$

(d) If n is not equal to minus one, the integral of $u^n\, du$ is obtained by adding one to the exponent and dividing by the new exponent. For example:

$$\int x^{1/2}\, dx = \frac{x^{3/2}}{3/2} + C = \tfrac{2}{3}x^{3/2} + C.$$

Caution: One *must* have precisely du as well as u^n in order to use this formula. For example,

$$\int \sqrt{2x + 1}\, dx$$

does not fit the formula if we let

$$u = 2x + 1, \qquad n = \tfrac{1}{2},$$

because then

$$du = \frac{du}{dx}\cdot dx = 2\, dx$$

is *not* present precisely. But only the constant factor 2 is missing, and this factor can be introduced after the integral sign provided we compensate for it by a factor of $\tfrac{1}{2}$ in front of the integral sign [by(b)]. Thus we write

$$\int \sqrt{2x + 1}\, dx = \frac{1}{2}\int \sqrt{2x + 1}\cdot 2\, dx$$

$$= \frac{1}{2}\int u^{1/2}\, du \qquad [u = 2x + 1, \quad du = 2\, dx]$$

$$= \frac{1}{2}\frac{u^{3/2}}{3/2} + C$$

$$= \frac{1}{3}(2x + 1)^{3/2} + C.$$

Problems

Solve the following differential equations.

1. $\dfrac{dy}{dx} = x^2 + 1$

2. $\dfrac{dy}{dx} = \dfrac{1}{x^2} + x, \quad x > 0$

3. $\dfrac{dy}{dx} = \dfrac{x}{y}, \quad y > 0$

4. $\dfrac{dy}{dx} = \sqrt{xy}, \quad x > 0, \ y > 0$

5. $\dfrac{dy}{dx} = \sqrt[3]{y/x}, \quad x > 0, \ y > 0$

6. $\dfrac{dy}{dx} = 2xy^2, \quad y > 0$

7. $\dfrac{dy}{dx} = 3x^2 - 2x + 5$

8. $\dfrac{ds}{dt} = 3t^2 + 4t - 6$

9. $\dfrac{dr}{dz} = (2z + 1)^3$

10. $\dfrac{du}{dv} = 2u^2(4v^3 + 4v^{-3}), \quad v > 0, \quad u > 0$

11. $\dfrac{dx}{dt} = 8\sqrt{x}, \quad x > 0$ 12. $\dfrac{dy}{dt} = (2t + t^{-1})^2, \quad t > 0$

13. $\dfrac{dy}{dz} = \sqrt{(z^2 - z^{-2})^2 + 4}, \quad z > 0$

Evaluate the following integrals:

14. $\displaystyle\int (2x + 3)\, dx$ 15. $\displaystyle\int (x^2 - \sqrt{x})\, dx$

16. $\displaystyle\int (3x - 1)^{234}\, dx$ 17. $\displaystyle\int (2 - 7t)^{2/3}\, dt$

18. $\displaystyle\int \sqrt{2 + 5y}\, dy$ 19. $\displaystyle\int \dfrac{dx}{(3x + 2)^2}$

20. $\displaystyle\int \dfrac{3r\, dr}{\sqrt{1 - r^2}}$ 21. $\displaystyle\int \sqrt{2x^2 + 1}\; x\, dx$

22. $\displaystyle\int t^2(1 + 2t^3)^{-(2/3)}\, dt$ 23. $\displaystyle\int \dfrac{y\, dy}{\sqrt{2y^2 + 1}}$

24. $\displaystyle\int \left(\sqrt{x} + \dfrac{1}{\sqrt{x}}\right) dx$ 25. $\displaystyle\int \dfrac{(z + 1)\, dz}{\sqrt[3]{z^2 + 2z + 2}}$

4-3 Applications of indefinite integration. Differential equations, such as Eq. (1) or (7) of Article 4–2, arise in chemistry, physics, mathematics, and all branches of engineering. Some of these applications will be illustrated in the examples that follow. Before proceeding with these, however, let us consider the meaning of the arbitrary constant C, which always enters when we integrate a differential equation. If we draw one of the integral curves $y = F(x)$ (corresponding to taking $C = 0$), then any other integral curve $y = F(x) + C$ is obtained by simply shifting this curve through a vertical displacement C. Thus we obtain, as in Fig. 4–1, a family of "parallel" curves. They are parallel in the sense that the slope of the tangent to any one of them, at the point of abscissa x, is $f(x)$, the same for all curves $y = F(x) + C$. Now clearly this family of parallel curves

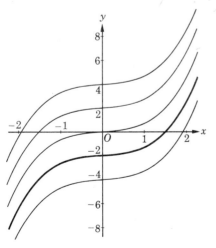

FIGURE 4–1

has the property that, given any point (x_0, y_0) with x_0 in the allowed domain of the independent variable x, there is one and only one curve of the family that passes through this particular point. For in order that the curve shall pass through the point, the equation must be satisfied by these particular coordinates. This uniquely specifies the value of C, namely,

$$C = y_0 - F(x_0).$$

With C thus determined, we get a definite function expressing y in terms of x.

The condition imposed that $y = y_0$ when $x = x_0$ is often referred to as an "initial condition." This terminology is particularly appropriate in connection with mechanical problems, where time is the independent variable and initial velocities or initial positions of moving bodies are specified.

EXAMPLE 1. The velocity, at time t, of a moving body is given by

$$v = at,$$

where a is a constant. If the body's coordinate is s_0 at time $t = 0$, find the distance s as a function of t.

Solution. The velocity v is the same as the derivative ds/dt. Hence we want to solve the problem that consists of

$$\text{the differential equation:} \frac{ds}{dt} = at \tag{1}$$

and

$$\text{the initial condition:} s = s_0 \qquad \text{when} \qquad t = 0. \tag{2}$$

From Eq. (1), we have

$$ds = at \, dt,$$

$$s = \int at \, dt = a\frac{t^2}{2} + C.$$

The constant of integration may now be determined from the initial condition, which requires that

$$s_0 = C.$$

Hence, the solution of the problem is

$$s = a\frac{t^2}{2} + s_0.$$

EXAMPLE 2. (Fig. 4–1) Find the curve whose slope at the point (x, y) is $3x^2$ if the curve is also required to pass through the point $(1, -1)$.

Solution. In mathematical language, we have the following problem:

$$\text{differential equation:} \frac{dy}{dx} = 3x^2$$

$$\text{initial condition:} \ y = -1 \quad \text{when} \quad x = 1.$$

First, we integrate the differential equation:

$$dy = 3x^2 \, dx,$$

$$y = \int 3x^2 \, dx = x^3 + C.$$

Then we impose the initial condition to evaluate the constant C:

$$-1 = 1^3 + C; \quad C = -2.$$

We substitute the value of C into the solution of the differential equation, and obtain the particular integral curve that passes through the given point, namely,

$$y = x^3 - 2.$$

PROBLEMS

In each of the following problems (1 through 6), find the position s as a function of t from the given velocity $v = ds/dt$. Evaluate the constant of integration so as to have $s = s_0$ when $t = 0$.

1. $v = 3t^2$ 2. $v = 2t + 1$
3. $v = (t + 1)^2$ 4. $v = (t^2 + 1)^2$
5. $v = (t + 1)^{-2}$ 6. $v = \sqrt{2gs}$ (g = constant)

In each of the following problems (7 through 11), find the velocity v and position s as functions of t from the given acceleration $a = dv/dt$. Evaluate the constants of integration so as to have $v = v_0$ and $s = s_0$ when $t = 0$.

7. $a = g$ (constant)   8. $a = t$
9. $a = \sqrt[3]{2t + 1}$ 10. $a = (2t + 1)^{-3}$
11. $a = (t^2 + 1)^2$

12. The gravitational attraction exerted by the earth on a particle of mass m at distance s from the center is given by $F = -mgR^2 s^{-2}$, where R is the radius of the earth and F is negative because the force acts in opposition to increasing s. If a particle is projected vertically upward from the surface of the earth with initial velocity $v_0 = \sqrt{2gR}$, apply Newton's second law $F = ma$ with $a = v(dv/ds)$ to show that $v = v_0\sqrt{R/s}$ and that $s^{3/2} = R^{3/2}[1 + (3v_0t/2R)]$.

Remark. The initial velocity $v_0 = \sqrt{2gR}$ (approximately 7 miles per second) is known as the "velocity of escape," since the displacement s tends to infinity with increasing t provided the initial velocity is this large. Actually, a somewhat larger initial velocity is required for escape from the earth's gravitational attraction, due to the retardation effect of air resistance, which we have here neglected for the sake of simplicity.

Solve the following differential equations subject to the prescribed initial conditions.

13. $\dfrac{dy}{dx} = x\sqrt{y};$ $x = 0, \quad y = 1.$

14. $\dfrac{dy}{dx} = 2xy^2;$ $x = 1, \quad y = 1.$

15. $\dfrac{dy}{dx} = x\sqrt{1 + x^2};$ $x = 0, \quad y = -3.$

16. $\dfrac{dy}{dx} = \dfrac{4\sqrt{(1 + y^2)^3}}{y};$ $x = 0, \quad y = 1.$

4–4 Brief review of trigonometry. Many natural phenomena are periodic; that is, they repeat after definite periods of time. Such phenomena are most readily studied through the use of the trigonometric functions, particularly sines and cosines. Our object in this article is to apply the operations of the calculus to these functions, but before we do so, we shall review some of their properties.

When the angle θ is placed in standard position at the center of a circle of radius r, the trigonometric functions of θ are defined by the equations

$$\sin \theta = \frac{y}{r} = \frac{1}{\csc \theta}, \qquad \cos \theta = \frac{x}{r} = \frac{1}{\sec \theta}, \qquad \tan \theta = \frac{y}{x} = \frac{1}{\cot \theta}. \qquad (1)$$

Since, by the theorem of Pythagoras, we have

$$x^2 + y^2 = r^2,$$

it follows that

$$\cos^2 \theta + \sin^2 \theta = 1. \qquad (2)$$

It is also useful to express the coordinates of P in terms of r and θ as follows:

$$x = r \cos \theta, \qquad y = r \sin \theta. \qquad (3)$$

When $\theta = 0$ in Fig. 4–2, we have $y = 0$ and $x = r$; hence, from the definitions (1), we obtain

$$\sin 0 = 0, \qquad \cos 0 = 1.$$

Similarly, when $\theta = 90°$ we have $x = 0, y = r$; hence

$$\sin 90° = 1, \qquad \cos 90° = 0.$$

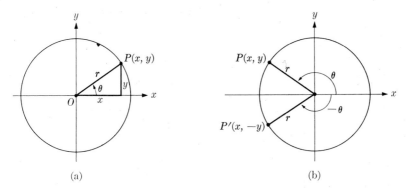

Fig. 4-2. (a) Angle θ in standard position. (b) Angles of opposite signs.

Figure 4-2(b) shows two angles of opposite sign and equal in magnitude. By symmetry, the points $P(x, y)$ and $P'(x, -y)$, where the two rays θ and $-\theta$ intersect the circle, have equal abscissas and ordinates that differ only in sign. Hence we have

$$\sin{(-\theta)} = \frac{-y}{r} = -\sin{\theta},$$

$$\cos{(-\theta)} = \frac{x}{r} = \cos{\theta}.$$

In particular,

$$\sin{(-90°)} = -\sin{90°} = -1,$$

$$\cos{(-90°)} = \cos{90°} = 0.$$

Both $\sin\theta$ and $\cos\theta$ are continuous functions of the angle θ, since a small change in θ produces a corresponding small change in both x and y. However, $\tan\theta$ is discontinuous at angles θ for which $x = 0$, that is, for θ equal to an odd integral multiple of $\pm 90°$. Likewise, $\sec\theta$ is discontinuous when $x = 0$, while $\cot\theta$ and $\csc\theta$ are discontinuous when $y = 0$ in Eqs. (1).

It will be helpful, for reasons which will soon be made apparent, to review the formulas

$$\sin{(A + B)} = \sin A \cos B + \cos A \sin B, \qquad (4a)$$

and

$$\cos{(A + B)} = \cos A \cos B - \sin A \sin B, \qquad (4b)$$

together with two formulas obtained from these by replacing B by $-B$ and recalling that

$$\sin{(-B)} = -\sin B, \quad \cos{(-B)} = \cos B, \qquad (4c)$$

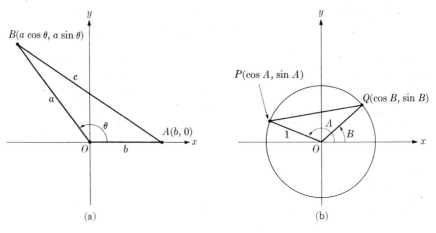

Fig. 4–3. (a) Law of cosines. (b) Diagram for $\cos(A - B)$.

namely,

$$\sin(A - B) = \sin A \cos B - \cos A \sin B, \tag{4d}$$

$$\cos(A - B) = \cos A \cos B + \sin A \sin B. \tag{4e}$$

Equation (4e) may easily be established for all angles A and B by two applications of the formula for the distance between two points:

$$d = \sqrt{(x_2 - x_1)^2 + (y_2 - y_1)^2}.$$

The first application gives the law of cosines. The second then yields the identity (4e). The other formulas (4a, b, d) can be derived from (4e) as shown below.

Law of cosines. In Fig. 4–3(a), triangle OAB has been placed with one vertex O at the origin, a second vertex A on the x-axis at $A(b, 0)$. The third vertex B has coordinates

$$x = a \cos \theta, \qquad y = a \sin \theta,$$

as given by Eq. (3) with $r = a$. The angle included between sides OA and OB is θ. By the formula for the distance between two points, the square of the distance c from A to B is

$$\begin{aligned} c^2 &= (a \cos \theta - b)^2 + (a \sin \theta)^2 \\ &= a^2 (\cos^2 \theta + \sin^2 \theta) + b^2 - 2ab \cos \theta, \end{aligned}$$

or

$$c^2 = a^2 + b^2 - 2ab \cos \theta. \tag{5}$$

In words: "the square of any side of a triangle is equal to the sum of the squares of the other two sides minus twice the product of those two sides and the cosine of their included angle." When the angle θ is a right angle, its cosine is zero, and Eq. (5) reduces to the theorem of Pythagoras. Equation (5) holds for a general angle θ, since it is based solely on the distance formula and on Eqs. (3) for the coordinates of a point.

Addition formulas. Equation (4e) follows from the law of cosines applied to the triangle OPQ in Fig. 4–3(b). We take $OP = OQ = r = 1$. Then the coordinates of P are

$$x_P = \cos A, \qquad y_P = \sin A$$

and of Q,

$$x_Q = \cos B, \qquad y_Q = \sin B.$$

Hence the square of the distance between P and Q is

$$
\begin{aligned}
(PQ)^2 &= (x_Q - x_P)^2 + (y_Q - y_P)^2 \\
&= (x_Q^2 + y_Q^2) + (x_P^2 + y_P^2) - 2(x_Q x_P + y_Q y_P) \\
&= 2 - 2\,(\cos A \cos B + \sin A \sin B).
\end{aligned}
$$

But angle $QOP = A - B$, and the law of cosines gives

$$
\begin{aligned}
(PQ)^2 &= (OP)^2 + (OQ)^2 - 2(OP)(OQ) \cos (A - B) \\
&= 2 - 2 \cos (A - B).
\end{aligned}
$$

When we equate these two expressions for $(PQ)^2$, we obtain

$$\boxed{\cos (A - B) = \cos A \cos B + \sin A \sin B.} \qquad (4e)$$

We now deduce Eqs. (4a, b, c, d) from Eq. (4e) and the results

$$
\begin{aligned}
\sin 0° = 0, \qquad \sin 90° = 1, \qquad \sin (-90°) = -1, \\
\cos 0° = 1, \qquad \cos 90° = 0, \qquad \cos (-90°) = 0,
\end{aligned}
\qquad (6)
$$

which follow at once from the definitions in Eqs. (1).

1. Since (4e) is an identity, it is true when we replace A by $0°$ and use (6). The result is

$$\cos (-B) = \cos B. \qquad (7a)$$

2. Next replace A by $90°$ in (4e), and use (6). The result is

$$\cos (90° - B) = \sin B. \qquad (7b)$$

This expresses the familiar result that the sine of an angle is the cosine of the complementary angle. The companion result

$$\cos B = \sin (90° - B) \qquad (7c)$$

follows from Eq. (7b) by replacing B by $90° - B$ and $90° - B$ by $90° - (90° - B) = B$.

3. We next put $B = -90°$ in (4e), and use (6) to get

$$\cos (A + 90°) = -\sin A. \tag{7d}$$

In (7b) we may replace B by $-A$ to obtain

$$\cos (90° + A) = \sin (-A).$$

When we compare this with (7d) above, we find

$$\sin (-A) = -\sin A. \tag{7e}$$

4. Notice that Eqs. (7a, e) agree with Eqs. (4c) and have been derived from the fundamental identity for $\cos (A - B)$. In it, we now replace B by $-B$ and make use of (4c) to get

$$\cos (A + B) = \cos A \cos B - \sin A \sin B. \tag{4b}$$

5. To derive formulas for $\sin (A \pm B)$, we use the identity (7b) with B replaced by $A + B$ or by $A - B$. Thus we have

$$\begin{aligned} \sin (A + B) &= \cos (90° - (A + B)) \\ &= \cos (90° - A - B) \\ &= \cos (90° - A) \cos B + \sin (90° - A) \sin B \\ &= \sin A \cos B + \cos A \sin B. \end{aligned} \tag{4a}$$

And Eq. (4d) follows from this if we replace B by $-B$.

These are the key results of analytic trigonometry, and all have been derived simply from the distance formula and the definitions of sine and cosine. The most important formulas to remember are:

$$\sin (A + B) = \sin A \cos B + \cos A \sin B, \tag{4a}$$

$$\cos (A + B) = \cos A \cos B - \sin A \sin B, \tag{4b}$$

$$\sin (-B) = -\sin B, \quad \cos (-B) = \cos B. \tag{4c}$$

If we let

$$\alpha = A + B \quad \text{and} \quad \beta = A - B,$$

so that

$$A = \tfrac{1}{2}(\alpha + \beta), \quad B = \tfrac{1}{2}(\alpha - \beta),$$

and subtract Eq. (4d) from Eq. (4a), we obtain the further useful identity

$$\sin \alpha - \sin \beta = 2 \cos \frac{\alpha + \beta}{2} \sin \frac{\alpha - \beta}{2}. \tag{8}$$

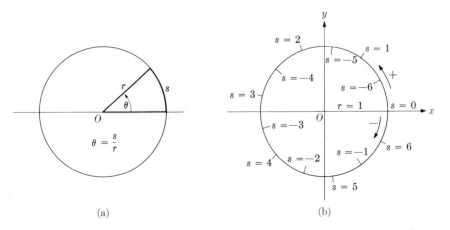

Fig. 4-4. (a) Unit circle with angle θ. (b) Curved "s-axis" wrapped around unit circle.

Radian measure. In all work with the trigonometric functions in the calculus, it is desirable to measure the angle in *radians*. The number of radians in the angle θ in Fig. 4-4(a) is defined as the number of "radius units" contained in the arc s subtended by the central angle θ; that is

$$\theta \text{ (in radians)} = \frac{s}{r}. \tag{9a}$$

This also implies that

$$s = r\theta \qquad (\theta \text{ in radians}). \tag{9b}$$

Another useful interpretation of radian measure is easy to get if we take $r = 1$ in (9b). Then the central angle θ, in radians, is just equal to the arc s subtended by θ. We may imagine the circumference of the circle marked off with a scale from which we may read θ. We think of a number scale, like the y-axis shifted one unit to the right, as having been wrapped around the circle. The unit on this number scale is the same as the unit radius. We put the zero of the scale at the place where the initial ray crosses the circle, and wrap the positive end of the scale around the circle in the counterclockwise direction, negative in the opposite direction (see Fig. 4-4b). Then θ can be read from this curved s-"axis." A unit of arc length, $s = 1$ radius, subtends a central angle of $57°18'$ (approximately); so

$$1 \text{ radian} \approx 57°18'. \tag{10}$$

We find this, and other relations between degree measure and radian measure, by using the fact that the full circumference has arc length $s = 2\pi r$ and central angle $360°$. Therefore

$$\boxed{360° = 2\pi \text{ radians,}} \tag{11a}$$

$$180° = \pi = 3.14159\ldots \text{ radians,} \tag{11b}$$

$$\left(\frac{360}{2\pi}\right)^° = 1 \text{ radian} = 57°17'44.8'', \tag{11c}$$

$$1° = \frac{2\pi}{360} = \frac{\pi}{180} \approx 0.01745 \text{ radian.} \tag{11d}$$

It should be emphasized, however, that the radian measure of an angle is dimensionless, since r and s in Eqs. (9a, b) both represent lengths measured in identical units, for instance feet, inches, centimeters, or light years. Thus $\theta = 2.7$ is to be interpreted as a pure number. The sine and cosine of 2.7 are the ordinate and abscissa, respectively, of the point $P(x, y)$ on a circle of radius r at the end of an arc of length 2.7 radii. For practical purposes we would convert 2.7 radians to 2.7 $(360/2\pi)$ degrees and say

$$\sin 2.7 = \sin\left[2.7\left(\frac{360}{2\pi}\right)^°\right] \approx \sin[154°41'55''] \approx 0.42738.$$

We include here a short table of the angles most frequently used, their radian measures, and their sines and cosines.

Degrees	0°	30°	45°	60°	90°	180°	270°	360°
Radians	0	$\pi/6$	$\pi/4$	$\pi/3$	$\pi/2$	π	$3\pi/2$	2π
Sines	0	1/2	$\sqrt{2}/2$	$\sqrt{3}/2$	1	0	−1	0
Cosines	1	$\sqrt{3}/2$	$\sqrt{2}/2$	1/2	0	−1	0	1

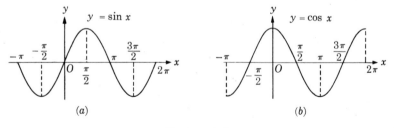

FIGURE 4–5

Figures 4–5(a), (b) show graphs of the curves $y = \sin x$ and $y = \cos x$. The portion of either curve between 0 and 2π is repeated endlessly to the left and to the right. It should also be noted that the cosine curve is the same as the sine curve shifted to the left an amount $\pi/2$.

PROBLEMS

In Problems 1 through 6, sketch the graph of the given equation.

1. $y = 2 \sin x$

2. $y = 3 \sin 2x$

3. $y = A \sin (Bx + C)$, A, B, C constants $\neq 0$

4. $y = 2 \cos 3x$

5. $y = 3 \cos (2x + \pi/4)$

6. $y = 2 \tan x/3$

7. Show that the area of a sector of a circle having central angle θ and radius r is $\frac{1}{2}r^2\theta$, if θ is measured in radians.

8. Let $A(r, 0)$ be the point where the positive x-axis cuts a circle of radius r, center at the origin O. Let $P(r \cos \theta, r \sin \theta)$ be a point on the circle in the first quadrant, with angle $AOP = \theta$ radians. Let AT be tangent to the circle at A and suppose it intersects the line OP at T. By considering the areas of triangle AOP, sector AOP, and triangle AOT, prove the following inequality:

$$\sin \theta < \theta < \tan \theta, \quad \text{if} \quad 0 < \theta < \pi/2.$$

9. In Eq. (4e) take $B = A$. Does the result agree with something else you know?

10. In Eq. (4d) take $B = A$. Does the result agree with something you already know?

11. Derive a formula for $\tan (A - B)$ from Eqs. (4d, e).

12. Derive a formula for $\tan (A + B)$ from Eqs. (4a, b).

13. Express all of the trigonometric functions of a general angle θ in terms of $\sin \theta$ and $\cos \theta$.

14. A function $f(\theta)$ is said to be

$$\text{an even function of } \theta \text{ if } f(-\theta) = f(\theta),$$
$$\text{an odd function of } \theta \text{ if } f(-\theta) = -f(\theta).$$

Which of the six trigonometric functions are even, and which are odd?

15. Deduce formulas for $\cos 2A$ and $\sin 2A$ from Eqs. (4a, b).

16. Let P and Q be points on a circle with radius $r = 1$, center at the origin O, and such that OP makes an angle $-B$ with the positive x-axis, OQ an angle A. Use the law of cosines to derive a formula for $\cos (A + B)$ directly from this configuration.

4–5 Differentiation and integration of sines and cosines. We shall now apply the operations of the calculus to the sine and cosine functions. We need the result given by the following theorem.

THEOREM. *Let θ be measured in radians. Then*

$$\lim_{\theta \to 0} \frac{\sin \theta}{\theta} = 1. \tag{1}$$

Proof. First we shall suppose that θ is a small positive angle at the center of a circle of radius $r = 1$ (Fig. 4–6). In the figure, OP and OQ are sides of the angle, PT is tangent to the circle at P and intersects the side OQ at T. We observe that

$$\text{area } \triangle OPQ < \text{area sector } OPQ < \text{area } \triangle OPT. \tag{2}$$

These areas may be expressed in terms of θ as follows:

$$\text{area } \triangle OPQ = \tfrac{1}{2}\overline{OP} \cdot \overline{OQ} \cdot \sin \theta = \tfrac{1}{2} \sin \theta, \tag{3a}$$

$$\text{area sector } OPQ = \tfrac{1}{2}r^2\theta = \tfrac{1}{2}\theta, \tag{3b}$$

$$\text{area } \triangle OPT = \tfrac{1}{2}\overline{OP} \cdot \overline{PT} = \tfrac{1}{2} \tan \theta. \tag{3c}$$

We substitute from Eqs. (3a, b, c) into (2) and obtain

$$\tfrac{1}{2} \sin \theta < \tfrac{1}{2}\theta < \tfrac{1}{2} \tan \theta, \qquad \text{when} \qquad 0 < \theta < \pi/2. \tag{4}$$

Since $\sin \theta$ is positive in (4), the inequality signs will go the same way if we divide all three terms by $\tfrac{1}{2} \sin \theta$. Therefore,

$$1 < \frac{\theta}{\sin \theta} < \frac{1}{\cos \theta}, \qquad \text{when} \qquad 0 < \theta < \pi/2. \tag{5a}$$

We next take reciprocals in (5a), which requires that we reverse the inequality signs:

$$1 > \frac{\sin \theta}{\theta} > \cos \theta, \qquad \text{when} \qquad 0 < \theta < \pi/2. \tag{5b}$$

This quickly brings us to our goal. Since $\cos \theta$ approaches 1 as θ approaches zero, the difference between 1 and $\cos \theta$ tends to zero, while (5b) shows that the difference between 1 and $(\sin \theta)/\theta$ is even smaller:

$$\left| 1 - \frac{\sin \theta}{\theta} \right| < |1 - \cos \theta|.$$

Therefore,

$$\lim_{\theta \to 0} \frac{\sin \theta}{\theta} = 1. \qquad \text{Q.E.D.}$$

Although the geometrical argument leading to Eq. (1) is based on the assumption that θ is positive, the same limit is obtained if θ approaches zero through negative values. For if $\theta = -\alpha$ and α is positive, then when α approaches zero, we have

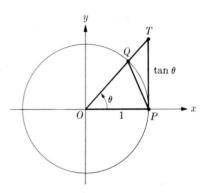

$$\frac{\sin \theta}{\theta} = \frac{\sin (-\alpha)}{-\alpha} = \frac{-\sin \alpha}{-\alpha} = \frac{\sin \alpha}{\alpha} \to 1.$$

If θ were not measured in radians but in degrees, the limit that we would obtain in place of Eq. (1) would be

FIG. 4-6. Area $\triangle OPQ <$ area sector $OPQ <$ area $\triangle OPT$.

$$\lim_{\theta \to 0} \frac{\sin \theta°}{\theta°} = \frac{\pi}{180}.$$

It is the contrast between the simplicity of the result in Eq. (1) and the factor $\pi/180$ in this equation that makes it desirable to use radian measure in all calculus operations with the trigonometric functions.

The following table shows $\sin \theta$ and $(\sin \theta)/\theta$ for a few selected values of θ near zero. To get the effect of $(\sin \theta)/\theta$ approaching 1, we read the last column upward from the bottom.

Degrees	θ (radians)	$\sin \theta$	$\dfrac{\sin \theta}{\theta}$
0°	0	0	undefined
1°	0.017453	0.017452	0.99994
2°	0.034907	0.034900	0.9998
5°	0.08727	0.08716	0.9987
10°	0.17453	0.17365	0.995

Derivative of sin u. We now consider a function defined by

$$y = \sin u$$

and calculate the derivative from the definition

$$\frac{dy}{du} = \lim_{\Delta u \to 0} \frac{\Delta y}{\Delta u}.$$

Let u be given an increment Δu and y a corresponding increment Δy. Then

$$y + \Delta y = \sin (u + \Delta u),$$

and hence

$$\Delta y = \sin (u + \Delta u) - \sin u \qquad \text{(a)}$$

$$= 2 \cos \left(u + \frac{\Delta u}{2}\right) \sin \frac{\Delta u}{2}, \qquad \text{(b)}$$

where we have made use of Eq. (8) of Article 4–4, with $\alpha = u + \Delta u$ and $\beta = u$, in going from (a) to (b). If we divide (b) by Δu, we have

$$\frac{\Delta y}{\Delta u} = 2 \cos \left(u + \frac{\Delta u}{2}\right) \frac{\sin (\Delta u/2)}{\Delta u} = \cos (u + \theta) \frac{\sin \theta}{\theta},$$

where $\theta = \Delta u/2$. We now let θ approach zero and make use of Eq. (1), and obtain

$$\lim_{\Delta u \to 0} \frac{\Delta y}{\Delta u} = \lim_{\theta \to 0} \left[\cos (u + \theta) \frac{\sin \theta}{\theta} \right] = \cos u.$$

But since $y = \sin u$, this means that

$$\frac{dy}{du} = \frac{d (\sin u)}{du} = \cos u.$$

If u is a differentiable function of x, we may apply the chain rule

$$\frac{dy}{dx} = \frac{dy}{du} \frac{du}{dx}$$

to this, with the result that we obtain

$$\boxed{\frac{d (\sin u)}{dx} = \cos u \cdot \frac{du}{dx}.} \qquad \text{VII}$$

Thus to find the derivative of the sine of a function, we take the cosine of the same function and multiply it by the derivative of the function.

For example, if

$$y = \sin 2x,$$

then

$$\frac{dy}{dx} = \cos 2x \cdot \frac{d(2x)}{dx} = 2 \cos 2x.$$

Derivative of cos u. To obtain a formula for the derivative of $\cos u$, we make use of the identities

$$\cos u = \sin \left(\frac{\pi}{2} - u\right), \qquad \sin u = \cos \left(\frac{\pi}{2} - u\right).$$

Thus

$$\frac{d\,(\cos u)}{dx} = \frac{d\sin\left(\frac{\pi}{2} - u\right)}{dx}$$

$$= \cos\left(\frac{\pi}{2} - u\right) \cdot \frac{d\left(\frac{\pi}{2} - u\right)}{dx}$$

$$= \sin u \cdot -\frac{du}{dx},$$

or

$$\boxed{\frac{d\,(\cos u)}{dx} = -\sin u \cdot \frac{du}{dx}.} \qquad \text{VIII}$$

This equation tells us that the derivative of the cosine of a function is minus the sine of the same function, times the derivative of the function.

For example, let

$$y = \cos(x^2),$$

then

$$\frac{dy}{dx} = -\sin(x^2)\frac{d(x^2)}{dx} = -2x \sin(x^2).$$

The formulas VII and VIII may be combined with the formulas given previously, as in the following examples.

EXAMPLE 1. Let

$$y = \sin^2(3x) = u^2 \qquad \text{with} \qquad u = \sin 3x.$$

Solution.

$$\frac{dy}{dx} = 2u\frac{du}{dx} = 2\sin 3x\,\frac{d\,(\sin 3x)}{dx}$$

$$= 2\sin 3x \cdot \cos 3x\,\frac{d(3x)}{dx}$$

$$= 6\sin 3x \cos 3x.$$

EXAMPLE 2. Let

$$y = \sec^2 5x = (\cos 5x)^{-2}.$$

Solution. First we must apply the formula for the derivative of a function to a power,

$$\frac{d(u^n)}{dx} = nu^{n-1}\frac{du}{dx}.$$

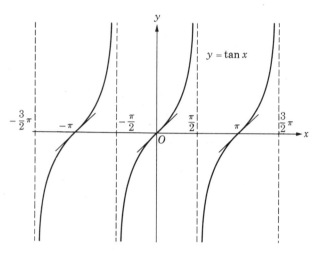

FIGURE 4–7

We then have
$$\frac{dy}{dx} = -2 \, (\cos 5x)^{-3} \, \frac{d \, (\cos 5x)}{dx}$$

$$= (-2 \sec^3 5x) \left(-\sin 5x \, \frac{d(5x)}{dx}\right)$$

$$= +10 \sec^3 5x \sin 5x.$$

EXAMPLE 3. Show that the function

$$f(x) \;=\; \tan x$$

is an increasing function of x at any point where $\cos x \neq 0$.

Solution. To show this (Fig. 4–7), we let

$$y = f(x) = \tan x \qquad \text{or} \qquad y = \frac{\sin x}{\cos x}.$$

Then
$$\frac{dy}{dx} = \frac{\cos x \, \dfrac{d \, (\sin x)}{dx} - \sin x \, \dfrac{d \, (\cos x)}{dx}}{\cos^2 x}$$

$$= \frac{\cos x \cdot \cos x \, \dfrac{dx}{dx} - \sin x \left(-\sin x \, \dfrac{dx}{dx}\right)}{\cos^2 x}$$

$$= \frac{\cos^2 x + \sin^2 x}{\cos^2 x} = \frac{1}{\cos^2 x} = f'(x).$$

exists and is positive at any point where $\cos x \neq 0$. Since $f'(x)$ is positive, $f(x)$ is an increasing function of x. In fact, since $\cos^2 x \leq 1$, we observe that $dy/dx \geq 1$ at every point on the curve $y = \tan x$. (When $\cos x = 0$, $\tan x$ does not exist.)

EXAMPLE 4. Find the velocity and acceleration of a particle moving in a circle of radius r with constant angular velocity ω, $\omega > 0$.

Solution. In Fig. 4–8, if the position of the particle at time t is $P(x, y)$, then

$$x = r \cos \theta, \qquad y = r \sin \theta, \qquad \text{(6a)}$$

and it is given that the angular velocity

$$\frac{d\theta}{dt} = \omega \qquad \text{(6b}$$

is constant. The velocity is a vector with components

$$v_x = \frac{dx}{dt} = \frac{dx}{d\theta}\frac{d\theta}{dt},$$

$$v_y = \frac{dy}{dt} = \frac{dy}{d\theta}\frac{d\theta}{dt} \qquad \text{(6c)}$$

parallel to the x- and y-axes respectively. Also, the acceleration is a vector with components

$$a_x = \frac{dv_x}{dt}, \qquad a_y = \frac{dv_y}{dt} \qquad \text{(6d)}$$

parallel to the coordinate axes. From (6a) and (6b), we find

$$v_x = \frac{dx}{dt} = -r \sin \theta \, \frac{d\theta}{dt}$$

$$= -\omega r \sin \theta = -\omega y,$$

$$v_y = \frac{dy}{dt} = r \cos \theta \, \frac{d\theta}{dt} \qquad \text{(6e)}$$

$$= \omega r \cos \theta = \omega x,$$

and from these we find in turn

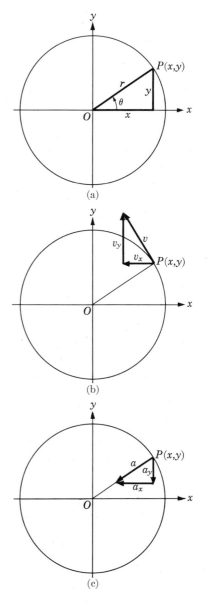

(a)

(b)

(c)

FIGURE 4–8

$$a_x = \frac{dv_x}{dt} = -\omega \frac{dy}{dt} = -\omega^2 x, \qquad a_y = \frac{dv_y}{dt} = \omega \frac{dx}{dt} = -\omega^2 y. \tag{6f}$$

The velocity vector has both magnitude and direction. Its magnitude is

$$\sqrt{v_x^2 + v_y^2} = \sqrt{\omega^2 y^2 + \omega^2 x^2} = \omega\sqrt{y^2 + x^2} = \omega r,$$

which is the angular velocity ω times the radius of the circle. Its direction is specified, except for sense, by its slope, which is given by

$$\frac{v_y}{v_x} = \frac{dy/dt}{dx/dt} = \frac{dy}{dx},$$

which is the same as the slope of the tangent to the curve at P. The sense is seen graphically (Fig. 4–8b) to be in the counterclockwise direction, since from (6e) the x-component has a sign opposite to the sign of y if, as we assume, ω is positive.

Similarly, the acceleration vector has magnitude

$$\sqrt{a_x^2 + a_y^2} = \omega^2\sqrt{x^2 + y^2} = \omega^2 r,$$

and its direction will be opposite to that of the vector from O to P, since the latter has components x and y, while (6f) shows that the acceleration has its corresponding components just $(-\omega^2)$ times these; that is,

$$\text{the acceleration vector } \mathbf{a} = -\omega^2 \overrightarrow{OP}.$$

This shows that the acceleration is toward the center of the circle at each instant and has a constant magnitude $\omega^2 r$.

To summarize: If a particle moves in a circle of radius r with constant angular velocity ω, then its velocity vector is tangent to the circle and has magnitude ωr, while its acceleration vector points toward the center of the circle and has magnitude $\omega^2 r$. Hence (by Newton's second law) the force needed to keep a particle of mass m moving at constant speed ωr in a circle of radius r is $m\omega^2 r$, directed toward the center of the circle.

Integration of sines and cosines. Corresponding to the derivative formulas VII and VIII, we also have the differential formulas

$$d(\sin u) = \cos u \, du, \qquad\qquad\qquad \text{VII}'$$

$$d(\cos u) = -\sin u \, du, \qquad\qquad\qquad \text{VIII}'$$

and the integration formulas

$$\int \cos u \, du = \sin u + C,$$

$$\int \sin u \, du = -\cos u + C. \tag{7}$$

EXAMPLE 5. $\displaystyle\int \cos 2t \, dt = \tfrac{1}{2} \int \cos 2t \cdot 2dt$

$$= \tfrac{1}{2} \int \cos u \, du \quad (u = 2t)$$

$$= \tfrac{1}{2} \sin 2t + C.$$

EXAMPLE 6. Evaluate the integral

$$\int \frac{\cos 2x}{\sin^3 2x} \, dx.$$

Solution. Since

$$d\,(\sin 2x) = 2 \cos 2x \, dx,$$

we recognize the numerator as being

$$\tfrac{1}{2} d\,(\sin 2x).$$

Hence we have

$$\int \frac{\cos 2x \, dx}{\sin^3 2x} = \int (\sin 2x)^{-3} \cdot \tfrac{1}{2} d\,(\sin 2x)$$

$$= \frac{1}{2} \int u^{-3} \, du \quad (u = \sin 2x)$$

$$= \frac{1}{2} \frac{u^{-2}}{-2} + C$$

$$= \frac{-1}{4 \sin^2 2x} + C.$$

PROBLEMS

Evaluate the following limits (1 through 20) by making use of Eq. (1) together with appropriate trigonometric identities and theorems on limits:

1. $\displaystyle\lim_{\theta \to 0} \frac{\tan \theta}{\theta}$

2. $\displaystyle\lim_{\theta \to \pi} \frac{\sin \theta}{\pi - \theta}$ [*Hint:* let $x = \pi - \theta$.]

3. $\displaystyle\lim_{\theta \to 0} \frac{\sin 2\theta}{\theta}$

4. $\displaystyle\lim_{x \to 0} \frac{\sin x}{3x}$

5. $\displaystyle\lim_{x \to 0} \frac{\sin 5x}{\sin 3x}$

6. $\displaystyle\lim_{x \to 0} \tan 2x \csc 4x$

7. $\displaystyle\lim_{\theta \to 0} \frac{\sin^2 \theta}{\theta}$

8. $\displaystyle\lim_{\theta \to 0} \frac{1 - \cos \theta}{\theta}$ $\left[\textit{Hint:} \text{ If } |\theta| < \pi, \, 1 - \cos \theta = \dfrac{\sin^2 \theta}{1 + \cos \theta}. \right]$

9. $\lim\limits_{\theta \to 0} \dfrac{1 - \cos \theta}{\theta^2}$

10. $\lim\limits_{y \to 0} \dfrac{\tan 2y}{3y}$

11. $\lim\limits_{u \to 0} \dfrac{3u}{\sin 5u}$

12. $\lim\limits_{x \to \infty} x \sin \dfrac{1}{x}$ $\left[\textit{Hint: } \text{Let } \dfrac{1}{x} = u. \right]$

13. $\lim\limits_{y \to \infty} 2y \tan \dfrac{\pi}{y}$

14. $\lim\limits_{x \to \pi/2} \dfrac{2x - \pi}{\cos x}$

15. $\lim\limits_{\theta \to 0} \theta \cot 2\theta$

16. $\lim\limits_{x \to 0} \dfrac{x^2 + 2x}{\sin 2x}$

17. $\lim\limits_{x \to 0} \dfrac{\sin 2x}{2x^2 + x}$

18. $\lim\limits_{h \to 0} \dfrac{\sin (a + h) - \sin a}{h}$

19. $\lim\limits_{h \to 0} \dfrac{\cos (a + h) - \cos a}{h}$

20. $\lim\limits_{h \to 2} \dfrac{\cos (\pi/h)}{h - 2}$

In each of the following problems (21 through 36), find dy/dx.

21. $y = \sin (3x + 4)$

22. $y = x \sin x$

23. $y = \dfrac{\sin x}{x}$

24. $y = \cos 5x$

25. $y = x^2 \sin 3x$

26. $y = \sqrt{2 + \cos 2x}$

27. $y = \sin^2 x + \cos^2 x$

28. $y = \dfrac{2}{\cos 3x}$

29. $y = 3 \sin 2x - 4 \cos 2x$

30. $y = 3 \cos^2 2x - 3 \sin^2 2x$

31. $y = 2 \sin x \cos x$

32. $y = \dfrac{1}{\sin x}$

33. $y = \cos^2 3x$

34. $y = \cot x$

35. $x \sin 2y = y \cos 2x$

36. $y^2 = \sin^4 2x + \cos^4 2x$

37. Using the Mean Value Theorem, prove that

$$|\sin b - \sin a| \le |b - a|.$$

38. Show that the curve

$$y = x + \sin x$$

has no relative maxima or minima even though it does have points where dy/dx is zero. Sketch the curve.

39. A particle moves on the curve

$$x = a \cos \omega t, \qquad y = b \sin \omega t,$$

where a, b, and ω are constants. Show that the acceleration components are

$$a_x = -\omega^2 x \qquad \text{and} \qquad a_y = -\omega^2 y.$$

Evaluate the following integrals, Problems 40 through 60.

40. $\displaystyle\int \sin 3x \, dx$ 41. $\displaystyle\int \cos (2x + 4) \, dx$

42. $\displaystyle\int x \sin (2x^2) \, dx$ 43. $\displaystyle\int (\cos \sqrt{x}) \, \frac{dx}{\sqrt{x}}$

44. $\displaystyle\int \sin 2t \, dt$ 45. $\displaystyle\int \cos (3\theta - 1) \, d\theta$

46. $\displaystyle\int 4 \cos 3y \, dy$ 47. $\displaystyle\int 2 \sin z \cos z \, dz$

48. $\displaystyle\int \sin^2 x \cos x \, dx$ 49. $\displaystyle\int \cos^2 2y \sin 2y \, dy$

50. $\displaystyle\int (1 - \sin^2 3t) \cos 3t \, dt$ 51. $\displaystyle\int \frac{\sin x \, dx}{\cos^2 x}$

52. $\displaystyle\int \frac{\cos x \, dx}{\sin^2 x}$ 53. $\displaystyle\int \sqrt{2 + \sin 3t} \cos 3t \, dt$

54. $\displaystyle\int \frac{\sin 2t \, dt}{\sqrt{2 - \cos 2t}}$ 55. $\displaystyle\int \sin^3 \frac{y}{2} \cos \frac{y}{2} \, dy$

56. $\displaystyle\int \frac{\sin \dfrac{z - 1}{3} \, dz}{\cos^2 \dfrac{z - 1}{3}}$ 57. $\displaystyle\int \cos^2 \frac{2x}{3} \sin \frac{2x}{3} \, dx$

58. $\displaystyle\int (1 + \sin 2t)^{3/2} \cos 2t \, dt$ 59. $\displaystyle\int (3 \sin 2x + 4 \cos 3x) \, dx$

60. $\displaystyle\int \sin t \cos t \, (\sin t + \cos t) \, dt$

4–6 Area under a curve. In geometry we learned how to find areas of certain polygons: rectangles, triangles, parallelograms, trapezoids. Indeed, the area of any polygon can be found by cutting it into triangles.

The area of a circle is easily computed from the familiar formula $A = \pi r^2$. But the idea behind this simple formula isn't so simple. In fact, it is the subtle concept of a *limit*, the area of the circle being *defined* as the limit of areas of inscribed (or circumscribed) regular polygons as the number of sides increases without bound. A similar idea is involved in the definition we now introduce for other plane areas.

Let $y = f(x)$ define a continuous function of x on the closed interval $a \leq x \leq b$. For simplicity, we shall also suppose that $f(x)$ is positive for $a \leq x \leq b$. We consider the problem of calculating the area bounded

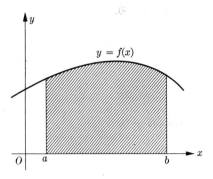

FIG. 4–9. Area under a curve.

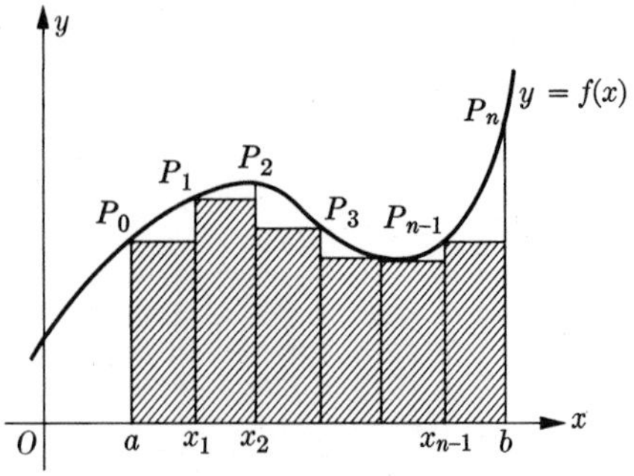

FIG. 4–10. Area under a curve $y = f(x)$ divided into strips. Each strip is approximated by a rectangle.

above by the graph of the function, on the sides by vertical lines through $x = a$ and $x = b$, and below by the x-axis (Fig. 4–9).

We divide the area into n thin strips of uniform width $\Delta x = (b - a)/n$ by lines perpendicular to the x-axis through the end points $x = a$ and $x = b$ and many intermediate points, which we number as $x_1, x_2, \ldots, x_{n-1}$ (Fig. 4–10). We use an inscribed rectangle to approximate the area in each strip. For instance, in the figure, we approximate the area of the strip $aP_0P_1x_1$ by the shaded rectangle of altitude aP_0 and base $a \ldots x_1$. The area of this rectangle is

$$f(a) \cdot (x_1 - a) = f(a) \cdot \Delta x,$$

since the length of the altitude aP_0 is the value of f at $x = a$, and the length of the base is $x_1 - a = \Delta x$. Similarly, the inscribed rectangle in the second strip has area

$$f(x_1) \cdot \Delta x.$$

Continuing in this fashion, we inscribe a rectangle in each strip.

In the special case where the function increases with x as in Fig. 4–11, we always use the ordinate at the left edge of the strip as the altitude of the corresponding rectangle. Then we have

$$\text{area of first rectangle} \quad= f(a) \cdot \Delta x,$$
$$\text{area of second rectangle} = f(x_1) \cdot \Delta x,$$
$$\text{area of third rectangle} \quad= f(x_2) \cdot \Delta x,$$
$$\vdots$$
$$\text{area of } n\text{th and last rectangle} = f(x_{n-1}) \cdot \Delta x.$$

EXAMPLE. Suppose $f(x) = 1 + x^2$; $a = 0$, $b = 1$, and $n = 4$. There are $n - 1 = 3$ intermediate points $x_1 = \frac{1}{4}$, $x_2 = \frac{1}{2}$, and $x_3 = \frac{3}{4}$, which divide the

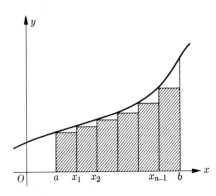

FIG. 4–11. Rectangles under graph of an increasing function.

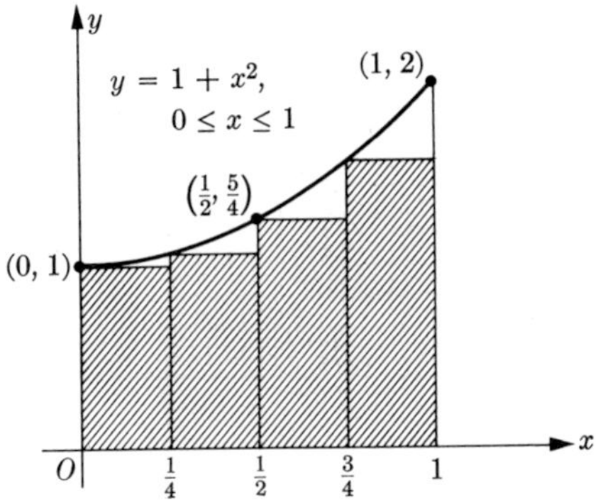

FIG. 4–12. Rectangles under graph of $y = 1 + x^2$, $0 \leq x \leq 1$.

interval $0 \leq x \leq 1$ into $n = 4$ subintervals, each of length $\Delta x = \frac{1}{4}$. The inscribed rectangles (Fig. 4–12) have areas

$$f(0) \cdot \Delta x = 1 \cdot \tfrac{1}{4} = \tfrac{16}{64}$$
$$f(\tfrac{1}{4}) \cdot \Delta x = \tfrac{17}{16} \cdot \tfrac{1}{4} = \tfrac{17}{64}$$
$$f(\tfrac{1}{2}) \cdot \Delta x = \tfrac{5}{4} \cdot \tfrac{1}{4} = \tfrac{20}{64}$$
$$f(\tfrac{3}{4}) \cdot \Delta x = \tfrac{25}{16} \cdot \tfrac{1}{4} = \tfrac{25}{64}$$
$$\text{Sum} = \tfrac{78}{64} = 1.21875.$$

Since the area under the curve is larger than the sum of the areas of these inscribed rectangles, we may expect it to be somewhat larger than 1.22. In fact, by using methods we shall soon develop, we shall find that the area is exactly $\frac{4}{3}$. Thus our estimate of 1.22 is about 8% too small. There are easy ways of improving the accuracy, for example by using trapezoids in place of rectangles to approximate each strip, but we defer that to a later time.

If the curve slopes downward as in Fig. 4–13, the inscribed rectangles have areas as follows:

$$\begin{array}{ll} \text{first rectangle} & f(x_1) \cdot \Delta x, \\ \text{second rectangle} & f(x_2) \cdot \Delta x, \\ \text{third rectangle} & f(x_3) \cdot \Delta x, \\ \quad\vdots & \\ n\text{th and last} & f(b) \quad \cdot \Delta x. \end{array}$$

More generally, the curve may rise and fall between $x = a$ and $x = b$, as in Fig. 4–14. But there is a number c_1 between a and x_1 inclusive such that the first inscribed rectangle has area $f(c_1) \cdot \Delta x$; and a number c_2 in the second closed subinterval such that the area of the second inscribed

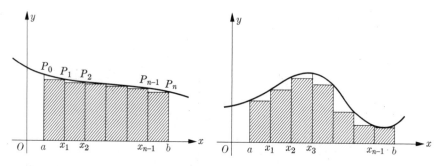

FIG. 4-13. Rectangles under graph of a decreasing function.

FIG. 4-14. Rectangles under a curve which rises and falls between a and b.

rectangle is $f(c_2) \cdot \Delta x$; and so on. The number c_1 is the place between a and x_1 inclusive where f is minimized for the first subinterval. Similarly, the minimum value of f for x in the second subinterval is attained at c_2, and so on.

The sum of the areas of these inscribed rectangles is

$$S_n = f(c_1) \cdot \Delta x + f(c_2) \cdot \Delta x + \cdots + f(c_n) \cdot \Delta x. \tag{1}$$

We may also write this in more abbreviated form by using the sigma notation,

$$S_n = \sum_{k=1}^{n} f(c_k) \cdot \Delta x. \tag{2}$$

The Greek letter Σ (capital sigma) is used this way in mathematics to denote a sum. Note that each term of the sum in (1) is of the form $f(c_k) \cdot \Delta x$, with only the subscript on c changing from one term to another. We have indicated the subscript by k, but we could equally well have used i or j or any other symbol except a letter which is already in use for something else. In the first term in the sum on the right side of Eq. (1) the subscript is $k = 1$; in the second, $k = 2$; and so on to the last, or nth in which $k = n$. We indicate this by writing $k = 1$ below the Σ in (2), to say that the sum is to *start* with the term we get by replacing k in the expression that follows by 1. The n above the sigma tells us where to *stop*. For instance, if $n = 4$, we have

$$\sum_{k=1}^{4} f(c_k) \cdot \Delta x = f(c_1) \cdot \Delta x + f(c_2) \cdot \Delta x + f(c_3) \cdot \Delta x + f(c_4) \cdot \Delta x.$$

The only thing that changes from one summand to the next is the numeral in the place indicated by k. First we replace k by 1, then by 2, then 3, then 4. And we add.

Here are a few other examples of $\Sum$ notation:

(a) $\displaystyle\sum_{k=1}^{5} k^2 = 1^2 + 2^2 + 3^2 + 4^2 + 5^2$,

(b) $\displaystyle\sum_{k=1}^{3} \frac{k}{k+1} = \frac{1}{1+1} + \frac{2}{2+1} + \frac{3}{3+1}$,

(c) $\displaystyle\sum_{j=0}^{2} \frac{j+1}{j+2} = \frac{0+1}{0+2} + \frac{1+1}{1+2} + \frac{2+1}{2+2}$,

(d) $\displaystyle\sum_{i=1}^{4} x_i = x_1 + x_2 + x_3 + x_4$,

(e) $\displaystyle\sum_{k=1}^{4} x^k = x + x^2 + x^3 + x^4$.

We turn our attention once more to the area under a curve. We *define* it to be **the limit of the sums of the areas of inscribed rectangles as their number increases without bound.** In symbols,

$$
\begin{aligned}
A &= \lim_{n\to\infty} [f(c_1)\,\Delta x + f(c_2)\,\Delta x + \cdots + f(c_n)\,\Delta x] \\
&= \lim_{n\to\infty} \sum_{k=1}^{n} f(c_k)\,\Delta x.
\end{aligned}
\tag{3}
$$

Remark 1. The limit indicated in Eq. (3) exists, provided f is continuous. That is, by taking larger and larger values of n and computing the sum of the areas of inscribed rectangles for each n, we get answers which differ from one another (and from what we would intuitively call the area under the curve) by amounts which become arbitrarily small as n increases.

Remark 2. We could have used circumscribed instead of inscribed rectangles. We would then replace the c_k in Eq. (3) by other numbers, say e_k. These would be the places in the subintervals where the function takes on its *maximum* instead of minimum values. The corresponding sums would tend to overestimate the exact area, but in the limit we would get the same answer whether we used inscribed or circumscribed rectangles. The fact that the two kinds of sums of areas of rectangles give the same limit is a consequence of the *uniform continuity* of the function f over the domain $a \le x \le b$. It is a theorem which is usually proved in more advanced courses in mathematical analysis. (It is also implied by the inequalities and equations (10) through (14) of Article 4–9.)

Remark 3. Just as we use the simple formula $A = \pi r^2$ to find the area of a circle, rather than resorting to a calculation of the limit of areas of inscribed polygons, so with the area under a curve. We shall not actually compute many areas directly from the definition in Eq. (3). Rather we shall develop from it a method for getting answers very quickly and simply. But first we need the definition of area, as given above, as a starting place.

Problems

In each of the following problems (1 through 5), sketch the graph of the given equation over the interval $a \leq x \leq b$. Divide the interval into $n = 4$ subintervals each of length $\Delta x = (b - a)/4$. (a) Sketch the inscribed rectangles and compute the sum of their areas. (b) Do the same using the circumscribed in place of the inscribed rectangle in each subinterval.

1. $y = 2x + 1$, $a = 0$, $b = 1$.   2. $y = x^2$, $a = -1$, $b = 1$.

3. $y = \sin x$, $a = 0$, $b = \pi$.   4. $y = 1/x$, $a = 1$, $b = 2$.

5. $y = \sqrt{x}$, $a = 0$, $b = 4$.

4–7 Computation of areas as limits. In Article 4–6 we defined the area under the graph of $y = f(x)$ over the interval $a \leq x \leq b$ as the *limit* of sums of areas of inscribed rectangles. We computed a few sums, but no limits. To compute the limits we need some algebraic formulas. We now develop these. Then we compute some areas as limits to show how it can be done. In Article 4–8 we show how much easier it is using calculus. We need the following formulas:

$$\sum_{k=1}^{n} k = 1 + 2 + 3 + \cdots + n = \frac{n(n + 1)}{2}$$

$$\sum_{k=1}^{n} k^2 = 1^2 + 2^2 + 3^2 + \cdots + n^2 = \frac{n(n + 1)(2n + 1)}{6},$$

which we shall prove by the method of mathematical induction. This consists in showing that each formula is true when $n = 1$, and that if the formula is true for any integer n, then it is also true for the next integer, $n + 1$. We shall also show how such formulas might be discovered.

First, consider the sum of first powers:

$$F(n) = 1 + 2 + 3 + \cdots + n.$$

Here is a short table that shows how $F(n)$ increases with n. The last column exhibits $F(n)/n$, the ratio of $F(n)$ to n.

n	$F(n)$	$F(n)/n$
1	1	$1 = \frac{2}{2}$
2	$1 + 2 = 3$	$\frac{3}{2} = \frac{3}{2}$
3	$1 + 2 + 3 = 6$	$\frac{6}{3} = \frac{4}{2}$
4	$1 + 2 + 3 + 4 = 10$	$\frac{10}{4} = \frac{5}{2}$
5	$1 + 2 + 3 + 4 + 5 = 15$	$\frac{15}{5} = \frac{6}{2}$
6	$1 + 2 + 3 + 4 + 5 + 6 = 21$	$\frac{21}{6} = \frac{7}{2}$

The last column seems to indicate that the ratio $F(n)/n$ is equal to $(n + 1)/2$. At least such is the case for all the entries in the table ($n = 1, 2, 3, 4, 5, 6$). In other words, the formula

$$\frac{F(n)}{n} = \frac{n + 1}{2}$$

or

$$1 + 2 + 3 + \cdots + n = \frac{n(n + 1)}{2} \qquad (1)$$

is true for $n = 1, 2, 3, 4, 5, 6$. Suppose now that n is any integer for which (1) is known to be true (at the moment, n could be any integer from 1 through 6). Then if $(n + 1)$ were added to both sides of the equation, the new equation

$$1 + 2 + 3 + \cdots + n + (n + 1) = \frac{n(n + 1)}{2} + (n + 1) \qquad (2)$$

would also be true for that same n. But the right side of (2) is

$$\frac{n(n + 1)}{2} + (n + 1) = \frac{(n + 1)}{2}(n + 2) = \frac{(n + 1)(n + 2)}{2},$$

so that (2) becomes

$$1 + 2 + 3 + \cdots + n + (n + 1) = \frac{(n + 1)((n + 1) + 1)}{2},$$

which is just like Eq. (1) except that n is replaced by $n + 1$. Thus if Eq. (1) is true for an integer n, it is also true for the next integer $n + 1$. Hence we now know that it is true for $n + 1 = 7$, since it was true for $n = 6$. Then we can say it is true for $n + 1 = 8$, since it is true for $n = 7$. By the principle of mathematical induction, then, it is true for every positive integer n.

Now let's consider the squares. Let

$$Q(n) = 1^2 + 2^2 + 3^2 + \cdots + n^2$$

be the sum of the squares of the first n positive integers. Obviously this grows faster than the sum of first powers, but let us look at the ratio to compare them.

n	$F(n)$	$Q(n)$	$Q(n)/F(n)$
1	1	$1^2 = 1$	$\frac{1}{1} = \frac{3}{3}$
2	3	$1^2 + 2^2 = 5$	$\frac{5}{3} = \frac{5}{3}$
3	6	$1^2 + 2^2 + 3^2 = 14$	$\frac{14}{6} = \frac{7}{3}$
4	10	$1^2 + 2^2 + 3^2 + 4^2 = 30$	$\frac{30}{10} = \frac{9}{3}$
5	15	$1^2 + 2^2 + 3^2 + 4^2 + 5^2 = 55$	$\frac{55}{15} = \frac{11}{3}$
6	21	$1^2 + 2^2 + 3^2 + 4^2 + 5^2 + 6^2 = 91$	$\frac{91}{21} = \frac{13}{3}$

We note how regular the last column is: $\frac{3}{3}, \frac{5}{3}, \frac{7}{3}$, and so on. In fact it is just $(2n + 1)/3$ for $n = 1, 2, 3, 4, 5, 6$; that is,

$$Q(n) = F(n) \cdot \frac{2n + 1}{3}.$$

But from Eq. (1), $F(n) = n(n + 1)/2$, and hence

$$Q(n) = 1^2 + 2^2 + 3^2 + \cdots + n^2 = \frac{n(n + 1)(2n + 1)}{6} \qquad (3)$$

is true for the integers n from 1 through 6. To establish it for all other positive integers, we proceed as before. Start with any n for which (3) is true and add $(n + 1)^2$. Then

$$1^2 + 2^2 + 3^2 + \cdots + n^2 + (n + 1)^2 = \frac{n(n + 1)(2n + 1)}{6} + (n + 1)^2$$

$$= \frac{(n + 1)}{6} [n(2n + 1) + 6(n + 1)]$$

$$= \frac{(n + 1)}{6} (2n^2 + 7n + 6)$$

$$= \frac{(n + 1)(n + 2)(2n + 3)}{6}. \qquad (4)$$

We note that the last expression in (4) is the same as the last expression in (3) with n replaced by $n + 1$. In other words, if the formula in (3) is true for any integer n, we have just shown that it is true for $n + 1$. Since we know it is true for $n = 6$, it is also true for $n + 1 = 7$. And now that we know it is true for $n = 7$, it follows that it is true for $n + 1 = 8$, and so on. It is true for every positive integer n by the principle of mathematical induction.

We now apply these formulas to find areas under two graphs.

EXAMPLE 1. Consider the line $y = mx$ (Fig. 4–15). Let b and a be any positive numbers, $b > a$. Let n be a positive integer and divide the interval $a \ldots b$ into n subintervals each of length $\Delta x = (b - a)/n$, by inserting the points

$$x_1 = a + \Delta x,$$
$$x_2 = a + 2\,\Delta x,$$
$$x_3 = a + 3\,\Delta x,$$
$$\vdots$$
$$x_{n-1} = a + (n - 1)\,\Delta x.$$

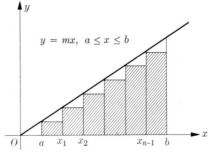

$y = mx, \ a \le x \le b$

FIG. 4–15. Area under $y = mx$, $a \le x \le b$.

The inscribed rectangles have areas

$$f(a)\,\Delta x = ma \cdot \Delta x,$$
$$f(x_1)\,\Delta x = m(a + \Delta x) \cdot \Delta x,$$
$$f(x_2)\,\Delta x = m(a + 2\,\Delta x) \cdot \Delta x,$$
$$\vdots$$
$$f(x_{n-1})\,\Delta x = m[a + (n - 1)\,\Delta x] \cdot \Delta x,$$

whose sum is

$$
\begin{aligned}
S_n &= m[a + (a + \Delta x) + (a + 2\,\Delta x) + \cdots + (a + (n - 1)\,\Delta x)] \cdot \Delta x \\
&= m[na + (1 + 2 + \cdots + (n - 1))\,\Delta x]\,\Delta x \\
&= m\left[na + \frac{(n - 1)n}{2}\,\Delta x \right]\Delta x \\
&= m\left[a + \frac{n - 1}{2}\,\Delta x \right] n\,\Delta x \quad \left(\Delta x = \frac{b - a}{n} \right) \\
&= m\left[a + \frac{b - a}{2} \cdot \frac{n - 1}{n} \right] \cdot (b - a).
\end{aligned}
$$

The area under the graph is defined to be the limit of S_n as $n \to \infty$. In the final form, the only place n appears is in the fraction

$$\frac{n - 1}{n} = 1 - \frac{1}{n},$$

and $1/n \to 0$ as $n \to \infty$, so

$$\lim \frac{n - 1}{n} = 1.$$

Therefore,

$$
\begin{aligned}
\lim S_n &= m\left(a + \frac{b - a}{2} \right) \cdot (b - a) \\
&= \frac{ma + mb}{2} \cdot (b - a).
\end{aligned}
$$

This is easily interpreted as the area of a trapezoid, with "bases" (in this case vertical) ma and mb and with altitude $(b - a)$.

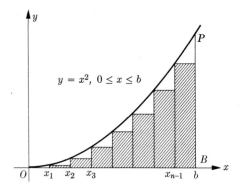

FIG. 4–16. Area under $y = x^2$, $0 \leq x \leq b$.

EXAMPLE 2. Consider the graph of $y = x^2$, $0 \leq x \leq b$, Fig. 4–16. Let n be a positive integer; divide the interval $0 \leq x \leq b$ into n subintervals each of length $\Delta x = b/n$, by inserting the points

$$x_1 = \Delta x, \quad x_2 = 2\,\Delta x, \quad x_3 = 3\,\Delta x, \quad \ldots, \quad x_{n-1} = (n-1)\,\Delta x.$$

The inscribed rectangles have areas

$$f(0)\,\Delta x = 0,$$
$$f(x_1)\,\Delta x = (\Delta x)^2\,\Delta x,$$
$$f(x_2)\,\Delta x = (2\,\Delta x)^2\,\Delta x,$$
$$f(x_3)\,\Delta x = (3\,\Delta x)^2\,\Delta x,$$
$$\vdots$$
$$f(x_{n-1})\,\Delta x = ((n-1)\,\Delta x)^2\,\Delta x.$$

The sum of these areas is

$$S_n = (1^2 + 2^2 + 3^2 + \cdots + (n-1)^2)(\Delta x)^3$$

$$= \frac{(n-1)n(2n-1)}{6} \cdot \left(\frac{b}{n}\right)^3$$

$$= \frac{b^3}{6} \cdot \frac{n-1}{n} \cdot \frac{n}{n} \cdot \frac{2n-1}{n}$$

$$= \frac{b^3}{6} \cdot \left(1 - \frac{1}{n}\right) \cdot \left(2 - \frac{1}{n}\right).$$

To find the area under the graph, we let n increase without bound and get

$$A = \lim S_n = \frac{b^3}{3}.$$

Therefore the area under the curve is $\frac{1}{3}$ the base b times the "altitude" b^2. The triangle OBP, Fig. 4–16, has area $\frac{1}{2}b \cdot b^2 = b^3/2$, and the area under the curve turns out to be somewhat smaller, as we should expect.

PROBLEMS

1. Verify the formula

$$\sum_{k=1}^{n} k^3 = 1^3 + 2^3 + \cdots + n^3 = \left(\frac{n(n+1)}{2}\right)^2$$

for $n = 1, 2, 3$. Then add $(n+1)^3$ and thereby prove by mathematical induction (as in the text) that the formula is true for all positive integers n.

2. Using the result of Problem 1 and the method of Example 2 in the text, show that the area under the graph of $y = x^3$ over the interval $0 \leq x \leq b$ is $b^4/4$.

3. Find the area under the graph of $y = mx$ over the interval $a \leq x \leq b$ by using *circumscribed* rectangles in place of the inscribed rectangles of Example 1 in the text.

4. Find the area under the curve $y = x^2$ over the interval $0 \leq x \leq b$ by using circumscribed rectangles in place of the inscribed rectangles of Example 2 in the text.

5. Do Problem 2 above by using circumscribed rectangles instead of inscribed rectangles.

6. Establish the formulas given below, for every positive integer n, by showing (a) that the formula is correct for $n = 1$, and (b) if true for n, the formula is also true for $n + 1$.

$$\sum_{k=1}^{n} (2k - 1) = 1 + 3 + 5 + \cdots + (2n - 1) = n^2,$$

$$\sum_{k=1}^{n} \frac{1}{k(k+1)} = \frac{1}{1 \cdot 2} + \frac{1}{2 \cdot 3} + \cdots + \frac{1}{n \cdot (n+1)} = \frac{n}{n+1}.$$

4–8 Areas by calculus. In Article 4–6 we defined the area under a curve and showed how we could estimate it by computing sums of areas of rectangles. Nothing more than arithmetic is involved in these calculations, but we pay the price of getting only an estimate of the true area. On the other hand, in Article 4–7 we used algebraic techniques and actually computed *limits*, thus getting exact areas at the cost of fairly extensive algebraic preliminaries. In this article we shall follow the path blazed by Leibnitz and Newton to show how exact areas can be easily computed by using calculus.

To begin we need some preliminary results. We consider a function f which is positive-valued and continuous over the domain $a \le x \le b$. Let A_a^c, A_c^b, A_a^b denote the areas under the graph and above the x-axis from a to c, from c to b, and from a to b, respectively (Fig. 4–17). If c is between a and b, we have

$$\boxed{A_a^c + A_c^b = A_a^b.} \tag{1}$$

And this is also true when $c = a$ if we define the area from a to a to be zero,

$$\boxed{A_a^a = 0.} \tag{2}$$

Equation (1) is also true if c is beyond b, provided we adopt some conventions about signed areas. Let us say that area above the x-axis is positive if we go from left to right, and negative if we go from right to left. Thus in Fig. 4–17 A_a^c, A_c^b, and A_a^b are all positive, while

$$\boxed{A_c^a = -A_a^c, \qquad A_b^c = -A_c^b, \qquad A_b^a = -A_a^b} \tag{3}$$

are negative. So formula (1) is also true in the form

$$A_a^b + A_b^c = A_a^c, \tag{4}$$

because adding A_b^c to A_a^b just subtracts A_c^b from the latter, leaving A_a^c (Fig. 4–17).

The following theorem will also be used.

THE INTERMEDIATE VALUE THEOREM. *Let f be a positive-valued continuous function over the domain $a \le x \le b$. Let A_a^b denote the area under the graph of f over the domain. Then there is at least one number c between a and b such that*

$$\boxed{A_a^b = f(c) \cdot (b - a).} \tag{5}$$

Proof. Suppose m and M are respectively the minimum and maximum values of f over the domain $a \dots b$. Then

$$m(b - a) \le A_a^b \le M(b - a),$$

and therefore

$$m \le \frac{A_a^b}{b - a} \le M.$$

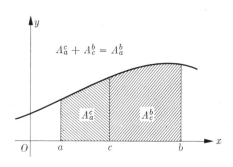

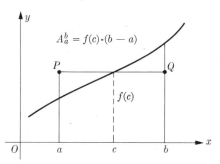

FIG. 4-17. $A_a^c + A_c^b = A_a^b$.

FIG. 4-18. Area under curve is equal to area of rectangle $aPQb$:
$$A_a^b = f(c) \cdot (b - a).$$

Since $A_a^b/(b - a)$ lies between the minimum and maximum values of $f(x)$ for $a \leq x \leq b$, there is at least one place c between a and b where $f(c)$ is equal to this number:

$$f(c) = \frac{A_a^b}{b - a}, \qquad \text{[Article 2-8, Theorem 3].}$$

Equation (5) follows.

Remark. The geometric interpretation of the Intermediate Value Theorem is this. A line drawn parallel to the x-axis at the right place between m and M units above the x-axis will serve as upper boundary of a rectangle having the same area as that under the curve, and it will surely cut the curve at least once between $x = a$ and $x = b$. The abscissa of that cut is a suitable value of c in Eq. (5). (See Fig. 4-18).

To compute the area A_a^b, we now consider any abscissa x between a and b, the area A_a^x, and the area $A_a^{x+\Delta x}$, where $\Delta x \neq 0$ (Fig. 4-19). We shall derive a differential equation for the area function A_a^x. The solution of this differential equation, with the initial condition

$$A_a^a = 0,$$

will enable us to compute the area from a to any x and, in particular, from a to b.

From Eq. (1) we have

$$A_a^x + A_x^{x+\Delta x} = A_a^{x+\Delta x},$$

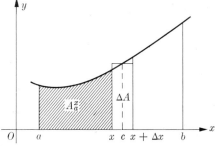

FIG. 4-19. Increment of area function.

so that

$$\Delta(A_a^x) = A_a^{x+\Delta x} - A_a^x = A_x^{x+\Delta x}. \tag{6a}$$

Then, by Eq. (5),

$$A_x^{x+\Delta x} = f(c) \cdot \Delta x, \tag{6b}$$

where c is a number between x and $x + \Delta x$, which must therefore approach x as Δx approaches zero. Combining (6a) and (6b) and dividing by Δx, we get

$$\frac{\Delta A_a^x}{\Delta x} = f(c), \tag{7}$$

and therefore

$$\begin{aligned}
\frac{dA_a^x}{dx} &= \lim_{\Delta x \to 0} \frac{\Delta A_a^x}{\Delta x} \\
&= \lim_{c \to x} f(c) \\
&= f(x),
\end{aligned}$$

where the last line follows from the fact that f is continuous.

Therefore the area function A_a^x satisfies the differential equation

$$\boxed{\frac{dA_a^x}{dx} = f(x)} \tag{8a}$$

and the initial condition

$$\boxed{A_a^a = 0.} \tag{8b}$$

Thus if $F(x)$ is any integral of $f(x)\, dx$, we have

$$A_a^x = \int f(x)\, dx = F(x) + C \tag{9a}$$

and

$$A_a^a = 0 = F(a) + C.$$

Hence

$$C = -F(a)$$

and

$$A_a^x = F(x) - F(a).$$

Finally, by taking $x = b$ we get

$$A_a^b = F(b) - F(a). \tag{9b}$$

Equations (9a) and (9b) summarize the method for finding the area under a curve by integration. If the equation of the curve is $y = f(x)$, we integrate this function f to find

$$F(x) + C = \int f(x) \, dx. \qquad (10a)$$

If the interval is $a \leq x \leq b$, we then compute

$$A_a^b = F(x)]_a^b = F(b) - F(a). \qquad (10b)$$

The standard notation $F(x)]_a^b$ in Eq. (10b) simply means: first replace x by the upper value b to calculate $F(b)$ and from this subtract the value $F(a)$ obtained by setting $x = a$. For example,

$$2x + 3\Big]_1^5 = 13 - 5 = 8.$$

It is worth noting that the constant of integration may be omitted in evaluating Eq. (10b). For if we use $F(x) + C$ in place of $F(x)$ in (10b), we find

$$F(x) + C\Big]_a^b = [F(b) + C] - [F(a) + C]$$

$$= F(b) - F(a)$$

$$= F(x)\Big]_a^b.$$

EXAMPLE 1. The area under the graph of $y = mx$, $a \leq x \leq b$, Fig. 4–15, is

$$\int mx \, dx\Big]_a^b = \frac{mx^2}{2}\Big]_a^b = \frac{mb^2}{2} - \frac{ma^2}{2}$$

$$= \frac{mb + ma}{2} \cdot (b - a).$$

EXAMPLE 2. The area under the graph of $y = x^2$, $0 \leq x \leq b$, Fig. 4–16, is

$$\int x^2 \, dx\Big]_0^b = \frac{x^3}{3}\Big]_0^b = \frac{b^3}{3}.$$

Compare both the results and the methods with Examples 1 and 2 of Article 4–7.

EXAMPLE 3. As another illustration of the method of finding areas, let us calculate the area bounded by the parabola $y = 6 - x - x^2$ and the x-axis.

Solution. We find where the curve crosses the x-axis by setting

$$y = 0 = 6 - x - x^2 = (3 + x)(2 - x),$$

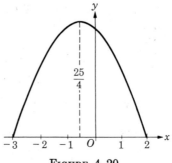

FIGURE 4–20

which gives

$$x = -3 \quad \text{or} \quad x = 2.$$

The curve is sketched in Fig. 4–20.

According to Eqs. (10a, b), the area is

$$A^2_{-3} = \int (6 - x - x^2)\, dx \Big]_{-3}^2 = 6x - \frac{x^2}{2} - \frac{x^3}{3}\Big]_{-3}^2$$

$$= (12 - 2 - \tfrac{8}{3}) - (-18 - \tfrac{9}{2} + \tfrac{27}{3}) = 20\tfrac{5}{6}.$$

The curve in Fig. 4–20 is an arch of a parabola, and it is interesting to note that the area is exactly equal to two-thirds the base times the altitude:

$$\tfrac{2}{3}(5)(\tfrac{25}{4}) = \tfrac{125}{6} = 20\tfrac{5}{6}.$$

EXAMPLE 4. Show that the area under one arch of the curve $y = \sin x$ is 2.

Solution. One arch of the sine curve extends from $x = 0$ to $x = \pi$ (Fig. 4–5a). Therefore the area is

$$A^\pi_0 = \int \sin x\, dx\Big]_0^\pi = -\cos x\Big]_0^\pi$$

$$= -\cos \pi + \cos 0.$$

Since $\cos \pi = -1$ while $\cos 0 = +1$, this gives

$$A^\pi_0 = 2.$$

PROBLEMS

In Problems 1 through 10, find the area bounded by the x-axis, the given curve $y = f(x)$, and the given vertical lines:

1. $y = x^2 + 1$; $x = 0$, $x = 3$.

2. $y = 2x + 3$; $x = 0$, $x = 1$.

3. $y = \sqrt{2x + 1}$; $x = 0$, $x = 4$.

4. $y = \dfrac{1}{\sqrt{2x + 1}}$; $x = 0$, $x = 4$.

5. $y = \dfrac{1}{(2x + 1)^2}$; $x = 1$, $x = 2$.   6. $y = (2x + 1)^2$; $x = -1$, $x = 3$.

7. $y = x^3 + 2x + 1$; $x = 0$, $x = 2$.   8. $y = x\sqrt{2x^2 + 1}$; $x = 0$, $x = 2$.

9. $y = \dfrac{x}{\sqrt{2x^2 + 1}}$; $x = 0$, $x = 2$.   10. $y = \dfrac{x}{(2x^2 + 1)^2}$; $x = 0$, $x = 2$.

11. Find the area bounded by the coordinate axes and the line $x + y = 1$.

12. Find the area between the curve $y = 4 - x^2$ and the x-axis.

13. Find the area between the curve $y = 1/\sqrt{x}$, the x-axis, and the lines $x = 1$, $x = 4$.

14. Find the area between the curve $y = \sqrt{1 - x}$ and the coordinate axes.

15. Find the area between the curve $x = 1 - y^2$ and the y-axis.

16. Find the area contained between the x-axis and one arch of the curve $y = \cos 3x$.

*17. Take $B = A$ in Eq. (4b), Article 4–4, and show that

$$\cos 2A = \cos^2 A - \sin^2 A.$$

Combine this with the identity

$$1 = \cos^2 A + \sin^2 A$$

to show that

$$\cos^2 A = \tfrac{1}{2}(1 + \cos 2A), \qquad \sin^2 A = \tfrac{1}{2}(1 - \cos 2A).$$

Make use of the last of these identities to find the area contained between the x-axis and one arch of the curve $y = \sin^2 3x$.

18. The graph of $y = \sqrt{a^2 - x^2}$ over $-a \le x \le a$ is a semicircle of radius a. (a) Using this fact, explain why it is true that

$$\int \sqrt{a^2 - x^2}\, dx \Big]_{-a}^{a} = \frac{1}{2}\,\pi a^2.$$

(b) Evaluate $\int \sqrt{a^2 - x^2}\, dx]_0^a$.

19. The integral in Problem 18 above can be evaluated by using the substitution

$$x = a \cos \theta, \qquad \pi \ge \theta \ge 0$$

to replace $\sqrt{a^2 - x^2}\, dx$ by $-a^2 \cos^2 \theta\, d\theta$. Combine this with Problem 17 above to show that

$$\int \sqrt{a^2 - x^2}\, dx \Big]_{-a}^{a} = \int -a^2 \cos^2 \theta\, d\theta \Big]_{\pi}^{0} = -\frac{a^2}{2} \int (1 + \cos 2\theta)\, d\theta \Big]_{\pi}^{0},$$

and thus verify the result given in Problem 18(a), by evaluating this final integral.

---

* The method used in this problem should be used in several later problems involving integration of squares of sines and cosines.

4–9 The definite integral and the Fundamental Theorem of integral calculus. In Articles 4–6, 4–7, and 4–8, we made a systematic study of the area problem. We have arrived at the following result.

If the function f is positive and continuous over the domain $a \leq x \leq b$, then the area under its graph is

$$A_a^b = \lim \sum f(c_k)\, \Delta x = \int f(x)\, dx]_a^b = F(x)]_a^b = F(b) - F(a). \quad (1)$$

The first part of this equation is just the definition of the area as the limit of the sum of areas of inscribed rectangles. The last part of the equation gives a short way of evaluating this limit, that is, by calculus. Therein lies one of the most powerful ideas of "modern" mathematics ("modern" in the sense of post-Renaissance); for the key idea is this: the limit can be evaluated by integration. This, essentially, is what is known as the *Fundamental Theorem* of integral calculus. It ties together the summation process (which Archimedes used over two thousand years ago for finding areas, volumes, and centers of gravity) and the differentiation process, from which one may find the tangent to a curve. It is a remarkable fact that the inverse of the "tangent problem" (that is, the inverse of differentiation) provides a ready tool for solving the summation problem. And its applications, as we shall see, extend far beyond the finding of areas. They include volumes of solids, lengths of curves, areas of surfaces of revolution, centers of gravity, work done by a variable force, and gravitational and electrical potential.

While Eq. (1) above is expressed in terms of area, and up until now has been restricted to positive-valued functions, the Fundamental Theorem is less restrictive.

FUNDAMENTAL THEOREM OF INTEGRAL CALCULUS. *Let f be a function which is continuous over the domain $a \leq x \leq b$. Let*

$$a, x_1, x_2, \ldots, x_{n-1}, b \quad (2)$$

be a set of numbers $a < x_1 < x_2 < \ldots < x_{n-1} < b$ which partition the interval $a \ldots b$ into n equal subintervals each of length

$$\Delta x = (b - a)/n. \quad (3)$$

Let $c_1, c_2, \ldots, c_n$ be a set of n numbers, one in each subinterval,

$$a \leq c_1 \leq x_1, \quad x_1 \leq c_2 \leq x_2, \quad \ldots, \quad x_{n-1} \leq c_n \leq b. \quad (4)$$

Let

$$S_n = f(c_1)\, \Delta x + f(c_2)\, \Delta x + \cdots + f(c_n)\, \Delta x$$

$$= \sum_{k=1}^{n} f(c_k)\, \Delta x. \quad (5)$$

Finally, let $F(x)$ be any integral of $f(x)\,dx$,

$$F(x) = \int f(x)\,dx. \tag{6}$$

Then, as $n \to \infty$,

$$\lim S_n = \lim \sum f(c_k)\,\Delta x = F(b) - F(a). \tag{7}$$

Proof. We shall first prove (7) for the special set of numbers $c_1, c_2, \ldots,$ c_n that we get by applying the Mean Value Theorem of Article 3–8 to the function F in each subinterval. We can do this because F is differentiable and continuous. Thus, remembering that $F'(x) = f(x)$, we have

$$F(x_1) - F(a) = F'(c_1) \cdot (x_1 - a) = f(c_1)\,\Delta x,$$
$$F(x_2) - F(x_1) = F'(c_2) \cdot (x_2 - x_1) = f(c_2)\,\Delta x,$$
$$F(x_3) - F(x_2) = F'(c_3) \cdot (x_3 - x_2) = f(c_3)\,\Delta x, \tag{8}$$
$$\vdots$$
$$F(x_{n-1}) - F(x_{n-2}) = F'(c_{n-1}) \cdot (x_{n-1} - x_{n-2}) = f(c_{n-1})\,\Delta x,$$
$$F(b) - F(x_{n-1}) = F'(c_n) \cdot (b - x_{n-1}) = f(c_n)\,\Delta x.$$

We add Eqs. (8), and note that $F(x_1)$, $F(x_2)$, $\ldots$, $F(x_{n-1})$ all appear twice on the left side, once positive and once negative. Hence these terms cancel out, leaving only $F(b) - F(a)$ in the sum. Thus we get

$$F(b) - F(a) = f(c_1)\,\Delta x + f(c_2)\,\Delta x + \cdots + f(c_n)\,\Delta x. \tag{9}$$

Since the left side of this equation does not in any way involve n, it remains fixed as we let $n \to \infty$, thus establishing Eq. (7), for this particular way of choosing the numbers $c_1, c_2, \ldots, c_n$.

But the theorem states that the same answer is obtained no matter how the c's are chosen in the subintervals, so long as there is one and only one c in each. To establish this final result, we recall that the function f is continuous on the closed interval $a \le x \le b$, and therefore is *uniformly* continuous there [Article 2–8, Theorem 3, (iii)]. Hence, if ϵ is any positive number, there exists a positive number δ, depending only upon ϵ, such that

$$|f(c_k) - f(c'_k)| < \epsilon \tag{10}$$

whenever

$$|c_k - c'_k| < \delta. \tag{11}$$

And we can make $\Delta x = (b - a)/n < \delta$ by making

$$n > (b - a)/\delta. \tag{12}$$

For all sufficiently large n, (12) is satisfied. Now let c_1, c_1' be two numbers in the first subinterval, c_2, c_2' in the second, and so on. Form the sums

$$S_n = \sum_{k=1}^{n} f(c_k)\, \Delta x,$$

$$S_n' = \sum_{k=1}^{n} f(c_k')\, \Delta x.$$

Their difference is less than or equal to

$$|f(c_1) - f(c_1')|\, \Delta x + |f(c_2) - f(c_2')|\, \Delta x + \cdots + |f(c_n) - f(c_n')|\, \Delta x. \quad (13)$$

Every term in (13) is less than $\epsilon \cdot \Delta x$, by (10), and there are n terms. Therefore

$$|S_n - S_n'| < n \cdot (\epsilon \cdot \Delta x) = \epsilon \cdot (n\, \Delta x) = \epsilon \cdot (b - a), \quad (14)$$

provided condition (12) is satisfied. This inequality, (14), says that the sums S_n and S_n' that we get from two different choices of the c's in the subintervals can be made to differ by as little as we please [no more than $\epsilon \cdot (b - a)$] by making n sufficiently large. But for the particular choice of the c's in Eqs. (8), we have

$$S_n = F(b) - F(a).$$

Therefore S_n' differs arbitrarily little from $F(b) - F(a)$ when n is sufficiently large. This means that

$$\lim S_n' = F(b) - F(a). \quad (15)$$

Equation (15) completes the proof.

Remark 1. The integral sign, $\int$, is a modified capital S (for sum), intended to remind us of the close connection between integration and summation.

Remark 2. The limit in Eq. (7),

$$\lim \sum f(c_k)\, \Delta x,$$

is called the *definite integral* of f from a to b. It is denoted by the symbol $\int_a^b f(x)\, dx$. The Fundamental Theorem tells us how to evaluate this definite integral provided we know any indefinite integral of the integrand $f(x)\, dx$. We just subtract the value of the indefinite integral F at a (the *lower limit* of integration) from its value at b (the *upper limit*).

Remark 3. If the function has only nonnegative (that is, positive or

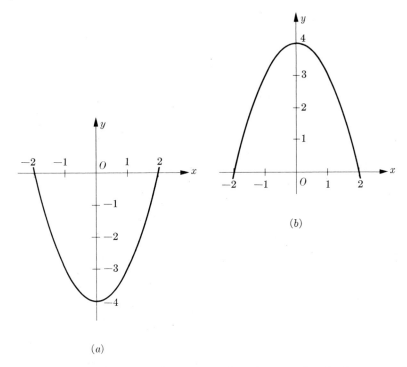

FIG. 4–21. (a) Graph of $y = x^2 - 4$, $-2 \le x \le 2$. (b) Graph of $y = 4 - x^2$, $-2 \le x \le 2$.

zero) values over $a \le x \le b$, then the definite integral

$$\int_a^b f(x)\, dx = F(x)\Big]_a^b = F(b) - F(a) \qquad (16)$$

represents the area under its graph, above the x-axis, between the ordinates at $x = a$ and $x = b$. If, on the other hand, the function f were everywhere negative between a and b, the summands $f(c_k)\,\Delta x$ would all be negative (assuming $b > a$ and $\Delta x = (b - a)/n$ is positive) and the integral, (16), would be negative.

EXAMPLE 1. For $|x| < 2$, $f(x) = x^2 - 4$ is negative (Fig. 4–21a).

$$\int_{-2}^{2} f(x)\, dx = \frac{x^3}{3} - 4x \Big]_{-2}^{2} = (\tfrac{8}{3} - 8) - (-\tfrac{8}{3} + 8) = -\tfrac{32}{3}.$$

The area between the curve and the x-axis, from $x = -2$ to $x = +2$, contains $\tfrac{32}{3}$ units of area. The sign is negative because the area is below the x-axis. Clearly, the graph (Fig. 4–21b) of

$$y = g(x) = -f(x) = 4 - x^2, \qquad -2 \le x \le 2$$

is just the mirror image, with respect to the x-axis as mirror, of the curve in Fig. 4-21(a). The area between the graph of $y = g(x)$ and the x-axis is

$$\int_{-2}^{2} g(x)\, dx = 4x - \frac{x^3}{3}\Big]_{-2}^{2} = \tfrac{32}{3}.$$

The absolute value is the same as for the integral of $f(x)\, dx$ between the same limits. For $g(x)\, dx$ the sign is positive, since the area between the g-curve and the x-axis is above the axis.

Remark 4. If the graph of $y = f(x)$, $a \leq x \leq b$, is partly below and partly above the x-axis, as in Fig. 4-22, then

$$\lim \sum f(c_k)\, \Delta x = \int_{a}^{b} f(x)\, dx = F(x)\Big]_{a}^{b} = F(b) - F(a)$$

is the algebraic sum of *signed* areas, positive areas above the x-axis, negative areas below. For example, if the absolute values of the areas between the curve and the x-axis in Fig. 4-22 are A_1, A_2, A_3, A_4, then the definite integral of f from a to b is equal to

$$\int_{a}^{b} f(x)\, dx = -A_1 + A_2 - A_3 + A_4.$$

Thus if we wanted the sum of the absolute values of these signed areas, that is

$$A = |-A_1| + A_2 + |-A_3| + A_4,$$

we should need to find the abscissas s_1, s_2, s_3 of the points P_1, P_2, P_3 where the curve crosses the x-axis. We would then compute, separately,

$$-A_1 = \int_{a}^{s_1} f(x)\, dx, \qquad A_2 = \int_{s_1}^{s_2} f(x)\, dx,$$

$$-A_3 = \int_{s_2}^{s_3} f(x)\, dx, \qquad A_4 = \int_{s_3}^{b} f(x)\, dx,$$

and add their absolute values.

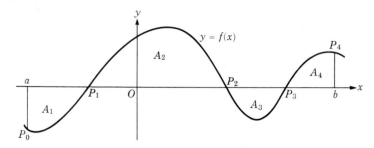

FIGURE 4-22

EXAMPLE 2. Find the total area bounded by the curve $y = x^3 - 4x$ and the x-axis.

Solution. The graph, Fig. 4–23, lies above the x-axis from -2 to 0, below from 0 to $+2$. (The polynomial $x^3 - 4x$ factors as

$$x^3 - 4x = x(x - 2)(x + 2).$$

It is easy to determine the sign of the product from the signs of the three factors.)

$$A_1 = \int_{-2}^{0} (x^3 - 4x)\, dx = \left.\frac{x^4}{4} - 2x^2\right]_{-2}^{0} = 0 - (4 - 8) = +4,$$

$$-A_2 = \int_{0}^{2} (x^3 - 4x)\, dx = \left.\frac{x^4}{4} - 2x^2\right]_{0}^{2} = (4 - 8) - 0 = -4,$$

$$A_1 + |-A_2| = 4 + |-4| = 8.$$

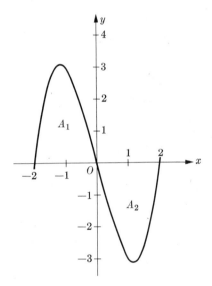

FIG. 4–23. Graph of $y = x^3 - 4x$, $-2 \le x \le 2$.

Remark 5. The definite integral, as a limit of sums, provides a new way of defining functions. The integral of any continuous function $f(t)$ from $t = a$ to $t = x$ defines a number

$$F(x) = \int_{a}^{x} f(t)\, dt, \tag{17a}$$

which can be computed as a limit (at least in theory). The function F defined by this formula has the property that its derivative at any x is the value of the integrand f at x:

$$F'(x) = f(x). \tag{17b}$$

To show this, we use the definition of the derivative

$$F'(x) = \lim_{\Delta x \to 0} \frac{F(x + \Delta x) - F(x)}{\Delta x}$$

$$= \lim_{\Delta x \to 0} \frac{1}{\Delta x} \int_x^{x+\Delta x} f(t)\, dt.$$

By the Intermediate Value Theorem, Article 4–8, Eq. (5), we have

$$\int_x^{x+\Delta x} f(t)\, dt = f(c)\, \Delta x$$

for some c between x and $x + \Delta x$. When we divide both sides of this equation by Δx, and then let Δx approach zero, c approaches x and $f(c)$ approaches $f(x)$. (Why?) Hence

$$F'(x) = \lim_{\Delta x \to 0} \left[\frac{1}{\Delta x} f(c) \cdot \Delta x \right] = \lim_{c \to x} f(c) = f(x).$$

EXAMPLE 3. Suppose $F(x) = \int_0^x \sqrt{1 - t^2}\, dt$, $0 < x < 1$. Then $F'(x) = \sqrt{1 - x^2}$.

Remark 6. The Fundamental Theorem is sometimes used as a tool for approximating sums. This is the reverse of what we did in Article 4–7. There we found formulas for sums of first powers, and of squares, of the positive integers 1 through n. Then we used these formulas to compute limits of sums of areas of inscribed rectangles for the graphs of $y = mx$, $a \le x \le b$, and of $y = x^2$, $0 \le x \le b$. In the following example, we work back from the definite integral (or, what amounts to the same thing, the area under the graph) to an approximation for the sum of the square roots of the integers 1 through n. The process is not completely reversible. We can go from exact formulas for sums to definite integrals by way of limits, but we cannot go back from the definite integral to an exact formula for the sum, because we don't know which terms went to zero in the limit process, and hence we cannot recover them.

EXAMPLE 4. Consider the function defined by $f(x) = \sqrt{x}$, $0 \le x \le 1$. Let n be a positive integer, and $\Delta x = 1/n$. In Eq. (7) take $c_1 = x_1 = \Delta x$, $c_2 = x_2 = 2\,\Delta x, \ldots, c_n = b = 1 = n\,\Delta x$. Then

$$S_n = \sqrt{c_1}\,\Delta x + \sqrt{c_2}\,\Delta x + \cdots + \sqrt{c_n}\,\Delta x$$

$$= \frac{\sqrt{1} + \sqrt{2} + \cdots + \sqrt{n}}{n^{3/2}}$$

$$\rightarrow \int \sqrt{x}\,dx \Big]_0^1 = \frac{x^{3/2}}{3/2}\Big]_0^1 = \frac{2}{3}, \qquad \text{as } n \rightarrow \infty.$$

When n is large, S_n will be close to its limit $\frac{2}{3}$. This means that the numerator

$\sqrt{1} + \sqrt{2} + \cdots + \sqrt{n}$ is approximately equal to $\frac{2}{3}n^{3/2}$.

For $n = 10$, the sum of the square roots is 22.5^-, while $\frac{2}{3}n^{3/2}$ is 21.1^-, so that the approximation is in error by about 6%.

PROBLEMS

1. For each of the following cases, integrate the given function f to find a new function F, defined by $F(x) = \int f(x)\,dx$. Apply the Mean Value Theorem to this new function F to find an expression for c_k in terms of x_k and x_{k-1} such that

$$F(x_k) - F(x_{k-1}) = F'(c_k)(x_k - x_{k-1}).$$

(a) $f(x) = x$,   (b) $f(x) = x^2$,   (c) $f(x) = x^3$,   (d) $f(x) = 1/\sqrt{x}$.

2. Consider the function defined by $f(x) = x$ and take $a = 0$, $b > 0$. Show that by taking

$$c_k = \tfrac{1}{2}(x_k + x_{k-1})$$

in Eq. (5), the resulting sum has the constant value

$$S_n = \tfrac{1}{2}b^2,$$

independent of the value of n. (Let $a = x_0$ and $b = x_n$.)

3. Take $f(x) = x^2$, $a = 0$, $b > 0$ and form S_n, Eq. (5), using

$$c_k = \sqrt{\frac{x_k^2 + x_k x_{k-1} + x_{k-1}^2}{3}}.$$

Show that no matter what value n has, the resulting sum S_n has the constant value

$$S_n = \tfrac{1}{3}b^3.$$

(Let $a = x_0$ and $b = x_n$.) What is the limit of S_n as $n \rightarrow \infty$? Note that one should substitute $x_k - x_{k-1}$ for Δx and recognize that

$$\left(\frac{x_k^2 + x_k x_{k-1} + x_{k-1}^2}{3} \right) \Delta x = \frac{x_k^3 - x_{k-1}^3}{3}.$$

4. Take $f(x) = x^3$, $a = 0$, $b > 0$, and calculate S_n, Eq. (5), taking

$$c_k = \sqrt[3]{\frac{x_k^3 + x_k^2 x_{k-1} + x_k x_{k-1}^2 + x_{k-1}^3}{4}}.$$

Express the result in a form which is independent of the number of subdivisions n. (Let $a = x_0$ and $b = x_n$.)

5. Take $f(x) = 1/\sqrt{x}$, $a = 1$, $b > 1$. Use the intermediate values

$$c_k = \left(\frac{\sqrt{x_{k-1}} + \sqrt{x_k}}{2}\right)^2$$

and calculate S_n, Eq. (5). Express the result in a form which is independent of the number of subdivisions. (Let $a = x_0$, and $b = x_n$.)

Evaluate each of the following definite integrals (6 through 16).

6. $\int_1^2 (2x + 5)\, dx$ 7. $\int_0^1 (x^2 - 2x + 3)\, dx$

8. $\int_{-1}^1 (x + 1)^2\, dx$ 9. $\int_0^2 \sqrt{4x + 1}\, dx$

10. $\int_0^\pi \sin x\, dx$ 11. $\int_0^\pi \cos x\, dx$

12. $\int_{\pi/4}^{\pi/2} \frac{\cos x\, dx}{\sin^2 x}$ (Let $u = \sin x$.)   13. $\int_0^{\pi/6} \frac{\sin 2x}{\cos^2 2x}\, dx$

*14. $\int_0^\pi \sin^2 x\, dx$ *15. $\int_0^{2\pi/\omega} \cos^2(\omega t)\, dt$ (ω constant)   16. $\int_0^1 \frac{dx}{(2x + 1)^3}$

17. (a) Express the area between the curves $y = x^2$, $y = 18 - x^2$ as a *limit of a sum* of areas of rectangles. (b) Evaluate the area of part (a) by Eq. (7).

18. Approximate the area under the curve $y = 1/x$ between $x = 1$ and $x = 2$ by five rectangles, each of base $\Delta x = 0.2$. Use the ordinate of the curve at the *midpoint* of each subinterval as the altitude of the approximating rectangle. The following short table of reciprocals may be used for convenience:

x	1.1	1.3	1.5	1.7	1.9
$1/x$	0.909	0.769	0.667	0.588	0.526

(Compare your answer with 0.693, which is the value of $\int_1^2 dx/x$ to 3 decimals.)

In each of the following problems (19 through 25), use Eqs. (17a, b) to find $F'(x)$ for the given functions F:

19. $F(x) = \int_0^x \sqrt{1 + t^2}\, dt$ 20. $F(x) = \int_1^x \frac{dt}{t}$

21. $F(x) = \int_x^1 \sqrt{1 - t^2}\, dt$ 22. $F(x) = \int_0^x \frac{dt}{1 + t^2}$

----

* See Problem 17, Article 4–8.

23. $F(x) = \int_1^{2x} \cos(t^2)\, dt$ [*Hint:* Use the chain rule with $u = 2x$.]

24. $F(x) = \int_1^{x^2} \dfrac{dt}{1 + \sqrt{1 - t}}$ 25. $F(x) = \int_{\sin x}^0 \dfrac{dt}{2 + t}$

4–10 The trapezoidal rule for approximating an integral. Any definite integral may be thought of as an area, or an algebraic sum of signed areas, as discussed in Article 4–9. We know how to evaluate a definite integral when an indefinite integral of the integrand is known. But there are simple integrands, for example $(\sin x)/x$, for which no simple indefinite integral is known. In such instances, as long as the integrand is continuous, the definite integral still exists and we may wish to evaluate it numerically. We can often obtain good accuracy by using numerical methods for approximating a definite integral. These methods are also important for computations done by machines. One of the simplest of these numerical methods is the *trapezoidal rule,* which we shall now derive. (See Fig. 4–24.)

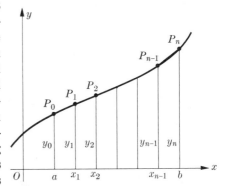

FIG. 4–24. Sum of areas of trapezoids approximates area under the curve.

Suppose that the definite integral $\int_a^b f(x)\, dx$ is to be evaluated. We divide the interval $a \le x \le b$ into n subintervals, each of length $\Delta x = (b - a)/n$, in the usual way by inserting the points

$$x_1 = a + \Delta x, \quad x_2 = a + 2\,\Delta x, \quad \ldots, \quad x_{n-1} = a + (n - 1)\,\Delta x$$

between

$$x_0 = a \quad \text{and} \quad x_n = b.$$

The integral from a to b is just the sum of the integrals from a to x_1, from x_1 to x_2, etc., and finally, the integral from x_{n-1} to b;

$$\int_a^b f(x)\, dx = \int_a^{x_1} f(x)\, dx + \int_{x_1}^{x_2} f(x)\, dx + \cdots + \int_{x_{n-1}}^b f(x)\, dx$$

$$= \sum_{k=1}^n \int_{x_{k-1}}^{x_k} f(x)\, dx.$$

The integral over the first subinterval is now *approximated* by the area of the trapezoid $aP_0P_1x_1$, which equals $\frac{1}{2}(y_0 + y_1)\,\Delta x$; over the second subinterval by the area of the trapezoid $x_1P_1P_2x_2$, which is $\frac{1}{2}(y_1 + y_2)\Delta x$; and so on. The *trapezoidal rule* is: To estimate the definite integral $\int_a^b f(x)\,dx$, use the *trapezoidal approximation* T given by

$$
\begin{aligned}
T &= \tfrac{1}{2}(y_0 + y_1)\,\Delta x + \tfrac{1}{2}(y_1 + y_2)\,\Delta x + \cdots \\
&\quad + \tfrac{1}{2}(y_{n-2} + y_{n-1})\,\Delta x + \tfrac{1}{2}(y_{n-1} + y_n)\,\Delta x \\
&= (\tfrac{1}{2}y_0 + y_1 + y_2 + \cdots + y_{n-1} + \tfrac{1}{2}y_n)\,\Delta x,
\end{aligned}
\tag{1a}
$$

where

$$
y_0 = f(x_0), \quad y_1 = f(x_1), \quad \ldots, \quad y_{n-1} = f(x_{n-1}), \quad y_n = f(x_n). \tag{1b}
$$

EXAMPLE 1. Use the trapezoidal rule with $n = 4$ to estimate $\int_1^2 x^2\,dx$ and compare this approximation with the exact value of the integral.

Solution. The exact value of this integral is

$$
\int_1^2 x^2\,dx = \frac{x^3}{3}\Big]_1^2 = \frac{7}{3}.
$$

For the trapezoidal approximation we have

$$
x_0 = a = 1, \quad x_n = b = 2, \quad n = 4,
$$

$$
\Delta x = (b - a)/n = (2 - 1)/4 = \tfrac{1}{4},
$$

so that

$$
\begin{array}{llll}
x_0 = a & = 1, & y_0 = f(x_0) = & 1^2 = \tfrac{16}{16} \\
x_1 = a + \Delta x = \tfrac{5}{4}, & & y_1 = f(x_1) = (\tfrac{5}{4})^2 = \tfrac{25}{16} \\
x_2 = a + 2\,\Delta x = \tfrac{6}{4}, & & y_2 = f(x_2) = (\tfrac{6}{4})^2 = \tfrac{36}{16} \\
x_3 = a + 3\,\Delta x = \tfrac{7}{4}, & & y_3 = f(x_3) = (\tfrac{7}{4})^2 = \tfrac{49}{16} \\
x_4 = b & = 2, & y_4 = f(x_4) = (\tfrac{8}{4})^2 = \tfrac{64}{16}
\end{array}
$$

and

$$
\begin{aligned}
T &= (\tfrac{1}{2}y_0 + y_1 + y_2 + y_3 + \tfrac{1}{2}y_4)\,\Delta x \\
&= (\tfrac{75}{8})\,\Delta x = \tfrac{75}{32} = 2.34375.
\end{aligned}
$$

Thus the approximation is too large by about 1 part in 233, or less than one-half of one percent.

The graph in Fig. 4–25 shows clearly that each approximating trapezoid contains slightly more area than the corresponding strip of area under the

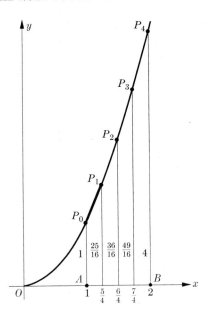

FIG. 4–25.   Trapezoidal approximation to area under graph of $y = x^2$, $1 \leq x \leq 2$.

curve. But the polygonal line $P_0P_1P_2P_3P_4$ lies very close to the curve, so we would expect the area under the curve to be quite close to the area of the polygon $AP_0P_1P_2P_3P_4BA$, which is the trapezoidal approximation.

Accuracy of the trapezoidal approximation. It is easy to prove that as n increases and Δx approaches zero the trapezoidal approximation approaches the exact value of the definite integral as limit. For we have

$$T = (y_1 + y_2 + \cdots + y_n)\, \Delta x + \tfrac{1}{2}(y_0 - y_n)\, \Delta x$$

$$= \sum_{k=1}^{n} f(x_k)\, \Delta x + \tfrac{1}{2}[f(a) - f(b)]\, \Delta x. \tag{2}$$

When n increases without bound and Δx approaches zero, the sum indicated by the sigma approaches $\int_a^b f(x)\, dx$ as limit, and the last term in (2) approaches zero. Therefore,

$$\lim T = \int_a^b f(x)\, dx.$$

This means, of course, that by taking n sufficiently large the difference between T and the integral can be made as small as desired.

By methods studied in more advanced calculus (an extension of the

Mean Value Theorem), it is possible to prove* that, if f is continuous on $a \leq x \leq b$, and twice differentiable on $a < x < b$, then there is a number e between a and b such that

$$\int_a^b f(x) \, dx = T - \frac{b-a}{12} f''(e) \cdot (\Delta x)^2. \tag{3}$$

Thus as Δx approaches zero the "error," that is, the difference between the integral and the trapezoidal approximation, approaches zero as the *square* of Δx. By estimating the size of the second derivative of f between a and b, we can get a good estimate of how accurate T is as an approximation to the integral.

EXAMPLE 2. In Example 1 above, $f(x) = x^2$, $f''(x) = 2$, and the predicted error in (3) is

$$-\frac{b-a}{12} f''(e) \cdot (\Delta x)^2 = -\frac{2-1}{12} \cdot 2 \cdot \frac{1}{16} = -\frac{1}{96}.$$

This is precisely what we find when we subtract $T = \frac{75}{32}$ from $\int_1^2 x^2 \, dx = \frac{7}{3}$, since $\frac{7}{3} - \frac{75}{32} = -\frac{1}{96}$. Here we are able to give the error *exactly*, since the second derivative of $f(x) = x^2$ is a constant and we have no uncertainty caused by not knowing e in the term $f''(e)$. Of course we are not always this lucky, and in most cases the best we can do is to *estimate* the difference between the integral and T.

EXAMPLE 3. Suppose the trapezoidal rule, with $n = 5$, is used to approximate $\int_1^2 (1/x) \, dx$. Estimate the error.

Solution. Here

$$f(x) = x^{-1}, \qquad f'(x) = -x^{-2}, \qquad f''(x) = 2x^{-3} = 2/x^3.$$

Since $f''(x)$ steadily decreases from

$$f''(1) = 2 \qquad \text{to} \qquad f''(2) = \tfrac{1}{4},$$

we can estimate the error only as lying between

$$-\tfrac{1}{12} \cdot 2 \cdot \tfrac{1}{25} = -\tfrac{1}{150} \approx -0.0067$$

and

$$-\tfrac{1}{12} \cdot \tfrac{1}{4} \cdot \tfrac{1}{25} = -\tfrac{1}{1200} \approx -0.0008.$$

Therefore the integral lies between $T - \frac{1}{150}$ and $T - \frac{1}{1200}$, so that it is slightly

---

* See, for example, J. M. H. Olmsted, *Intermediate Analysis* (Appleton-Century-Crofts, 1956), p. 145.

less than T, but differs from it by less than 0.01. In other words, we can get about two-decimal place accuracy for the integral by using the trapezoidal rule with $n = 5, \Delta x = \frac{1}{2}$. By taking $n = 10, \Delta x = \frac{1}{10}$, the error is cut by approximately a factor of 4 (the e of $f''(e)$ in the error may change when n does, and hence we cannot say that the error is cut precisely by a factor of 4).

Problems

1. Interpret the meaning of the sign of the correction term in Eq. (3) in case the graph of $y = f(x)$ is: (a) concave upward over $a < x < b$, (b) concave downward. Illustrate both cases with sketches

Test the accuracy of the trapezoidal approximation to the definite integral $\int_a^b f(x)\,dx$ in each of the following problems (2 through 5).

2. $f(x) = x$;　　$a = 0$,　　$b = 2$,　　$n = 4$.
3. $f(x) = x^3$;　　$a = 0$,　　$b = 2$,　　$n = 4$.
4. $f(x) = \sqrt{x}$;　　$a = 0$,　　$b = 2$,　　$n = 4$.
5. $f(x) = 1/x^2$;　　$a = 1$,　　$b = 2$,　　$n = 2$.

4–11 Some comments on notation. In each application of the definite integral it is reasonably easy to set up sums which approximate the answer to some physical problem. In general, it will even be possible (though not necessary) to find *particular* choices of the points c_k such that the *particular* sums

$$S_n = \sum_{k=1}^{n} f(c_k)\,\Delta x$$

give the *exact* value. Then

$$\lim_{n \to \infty} S_n = \int_a^b f(x)\,dx = F(x)\Big]_a^b = F(b) - F(a)$$

also gives the *exact* value. But since all sums S_n give the *same* answer in the limit (provided the function $f(x)$ is continuous for $a \le x \le b$, and this condition will usually be satisfied by the functions we shall encounter), we could get the same limit from

$$S_n = \sum_{k=1}^{n} f(x_k)\,\Delta x. \tag{1a}$$

Finally, we modify this notation slightly by dropping the subscript k entirely and writing simply

$$S_a^b = \sum_a^b f(x)\,\Delta x, \tag{1b}$$

where we write a and b to indicate that we have a sum of expressions, each of the form $f(x)\,\Delta x$, extending over a set of subintervals from $x = a$ to $x = b$. Of course it is not the *sum* (1b) that we are interested in, but rather the *limit* of the sum as given by the definite integral, and the notation (1b) is most suggestive of the final form, namely,

$$\lim_{\Delta x \to 0} S_a^b = \lim_{\Delta x \to 0} \sum_a^b f(x)\,\Delta x = \int_a^b f(x)\,dx = F(x)\bigg]_a^b. \qquad (2)$$

As remarked in Article 4–9, it was the close relationship between sums and integrals which led to the adoption of the symbol $\int$ (a modified S) to denote integration.

It should also be noted that *since it is the integral* which gives the *exact* answer in (2), and since the expression $f(x)\,dx$ after the integral sign is the same as the differential of $F(x)$,

$$\frac{dF(x)}{dx} = f(x), \qquad (3a)$$

$$dF(x) = f(x)\,dx, \qquad (3b)$$

we would arrive at the *correct final result* for the area under the curve $y = f(x)$ between $x = a$ and $x = b$, say, if we were to write

$$dA = f(x)\,dx, \qquad A = \int_a^b f(x)\,dx. \qquad (4)$$

It is easy to attach a geometric interpretation to (4), but it is also easy to be misled by this interpretation into feeling that the integral in (4) gives only an approximation to the area, rather than giving its exact value. Enough has already been said on this latter point, however, so that the careful reader need not be a victim of this delusion. If we accept the interpretation simply as a short-cut for setting up the *integral whose value gives the exact result*, we may thereby gain from its simplicity. Namely, if we again think of the area from the left boundary a to a right boundary x, this area is a function of x, with derivative $dA/dx = y = f(x)$, as we found in Article 4–8. When we multiply both sides of this equation by dx, we get the result $dA = f(x)\,dx$, as in (4). But if we think of dx as a small increment in x, we may also interpret this as the

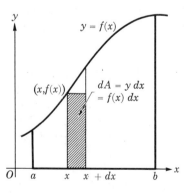

FIGURE 4–26

area of a small rectangle with base extending along the x-axis from x to $x + dx$, and with altitude $f(x) = y$ equal to the ordinate of the curve (see Fig. 4–26). Then this rectangle gives an *approximation* to that portion of the area under the curve lying between x and $x + dx$, and we think of the integral

$$A = \int_a^b f(x) \, dx$$

as adding together all of these small rectangles from $x = a$ to $x = b$ and then taking the *limit* of the sum so as to give the *exact value*.

It should be borne in mind that what has just been discussed should in no way obscure the fact that a *precise* formulation of the problem would involve a process of

(a) subdividing the interval $a \leq x \leq b$,

(b) forming a sum $\sum_a^b f(x) \, \Delta x$,

(c) taking the limit, $\lim\limits_{\Delta x \to 0} \sum_a^b f(x) \, \Delta x$, and

(d) applying the fundamental theorem to evaluate this limit,

$$\lim_{\Delta x \to 0} \sum_a^b f(x) \, \Delta x = \int_a^b f(x) \, dx = F(x) \Big]_a^b.$$

Insofar as the short-cut described above leads to the same final answer, without leading to confusion or feelings of misgiving, it may be helpful and time-saving. But whenever there is doubt that the final answer may only be an approximation instead of a mathematically exact answer, a reconsideration, along the lines which led up to the fundamental theorem, should be made. It is probably desirable, at least in the beginning, to go through the precise formulation first, and then it is but a matter of seconds to repeat the setup of the problem by the short-cut method.

4–12 Summary. Much that we have done in this chapter is related to area. This is useful and gives us a way of interpreting sums like those in Eq. (5), Article 4–9, and Eq. (1a) in Article 4–11. But it is also good to express the main results in ways that don't depend upon area. In this article we shall summarize six results of major importance. Although we have appealed to the notion of area in presenting them in earlier sections, they can all be proved by purely analytical methods, with no reference to area. (See, for example, Apostol, *Modern Mathematical Analysis*, or Buck, *Advanced Calculus*, or Rudin, *Principles of Analysis*.)

Once again we start with a function f defined on an interval $a \leq x \leq b$. We partition the interval into n subintervals by inserting points x_1, $x_2, \ldots, x_{n-1}$ between $a = x_0$ and $b = x_n$. We do not require that the points be uniformly spaced. The kth subinterval has length $\Delta x_k = x_k - x_{k-1}$, which may vary with k. In the kth subinterval a number c_k is chosen arbitrarily, for each k from 1 through n. Then we form the sum

$$\sum_{k=1}^{n} f(c_k) \cdot (x_k - x_{k-1}). \tag{1}$$

This sum depends upon the function f, the points $x_0, x_1, x_2, \ldots, x_n$ and upon the c's. However, for a given function f and interval $[a, b]$ it may happen that all sums like (1) are nearly equal to some constant, provided the subintervals are all sufficiently short. If this is true, then that constant is called the *Riemann integral* of f from a to b, and is variously denoted by $R_a^b(f)$, or $\int_a^b f$, or $\int_a^b f(x)\, dx$, or $\int_a^b f(t)\, dt$, or $\int_a^b f(u)\, du$, and so on.

DEFINITION OF RIEMANN INTEGRAL. *Let f be a function whose domain includes the interval $[a, b]$, $a < b$. Let f have the property that there exists a number $R_a^b(f)$ so related to f that to each positive number ϵ there corresponds a positive number δ such that every sum (1) differs from $R_a^b(f)$ by less than ϵ whenever all subintervals have lengths Δx_k less than δ. Then:*

   (a) *f is said to be* Riemann-integrable *(or, more briefly, integrable) over $[a, b]$, and*

   (b) *$R_a^b(f)$ is called the* Riemann integral *(or, more briefly, the integral) of f from a to b.*

THEOREM 1. *If f is Riemann-integrable over an interval $[a, b]$, then it is also integrable over any subinterval contained in $[a, b]$.*

THEOREM 2. *Every function that is continuous on a closed bounded interval $[a, b]$ is Riemann-integrable there.*

Remark. Although we are mainly interested in continuous functions, they are not the only ones that are integrable. All bounded functions that are *piecewise*-continuous are also integrable. "Piecewise-continuous" means that the interval can be divided into a finite number of nonoverlapping open subintervals over each of which the function is continuous. "Bounded" means that, for some finite constant M, $|f(x)| \leq M$ for all values of x in the interval. Figure 4–27 shows the graph of a bounded piecewise-continuous function over $[a, b]$. For this example, the integral $R_a^b(f)$ would be computed as the sum

$$R_a^b(f) = R_a^u(f) + R_u^v(f) + R_v^w(f) + R_w^z(f) + R_z^b(f).$$

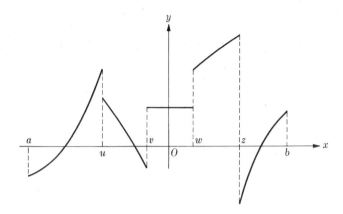

Fig. 4–27. Piecewise-continuous graph.

If $b < a$ and $R_b^a(f)$ exists, then we define $R_a^b(f)$ to be its negative:

$$R_a^b(f) = -R_b^a(f). \tag{2}$$

If $a = b$, we define $R_a^a(f)$ to be zero.

THEOREM 3. *Let a, b, c be three numbers belonging to an interval over which the Riemann integral of f exists. Then*

$$R_a^c(f) = R_a^b(f) + R_b^c(f). \tag{3}$$

THEOREM 4. *Let f be Riemann-integrable over $[a, b]$. Let x be any number between a and b at which f is continuous. Then $R_a^x(f)$ is differentiable at x and its derivative there is $f(x)$:*

$$\frac{d}{dx} R_a^x(f) = f(x). \tag{4}$$

THEOREM 5. THE MEAN VALUE THEOREM FOR INTEGRALS. *Let f be continuous on $[a, b]$. Then there exists at least one number c between a and b such that*

$$R_a^b(f) = f(c) \cdot (b - a). \tag{5}$$

THEOREM 6. FUNDAMENTAL THEOREM OF INTEGRAL CALCULUS. *Let f be Riemann-integrable over $[a, b]$. Let F be any continuous indefinite integral of f, that is,*

$$F'(x) = f(x) \qquad for \qquad a < x < b.$$

Then

$$R_a^b(f) = F(b) - F(a). \tag{6}$$

Problems

1. Rewrite Equations (2) through (6), Article 4–12, using the notation $\int_a^b f(t)\, dt$ in place of $R_a^b(f)$ for the Riemann integral of f from a to b.

2. Sketch graphs of each of the following piecewise-continuous functions on $(0, 2)$ and compute $\int_0^2 f(x)\, dx$:

(a) $f(x) = \begin{cases} x, \text{ for } 0 \leq x < 1 \\ \sin(\pi x), \text{ for } 1 \leq x \leq 2. \end{cases}$

(b) $f(x) = \begin{cases} \sqrt{1 - x}, & \text{for } 0 \leq x \leq 1 \\ (7x - 6)^{-1/3}, & \text{for } 1 < x \leq 2. \end{cases}$

3. Find $F'(x)$ for $x = \frac{1}{2}$ and for $x = \frac{3}{2}$ if $F(x) = \int_0^x f(t)\, dt$ and (a) f is defined as in Problem 2(a) above, (b) f is defined as in Problem 2(b) above, (c) $f(t) = \dfrac{\sin(\pi t)}{1 + t}$.

REVIEW QUESTIONS AND EXERCISES FOR CHAPTER 4

1. The process of "indefinite integration" is sometimes called "antidifferentiation." Explain why the two terms should be synonymous.

2. Can there be more than one indefinite integral of a given function? If more than one exist, how are they related? What theorem of Chapter 3 is the key to this relationship?

3. If the acceleration of a moving body is given as a function of time (t), what further information do you need in order to find the law of motion, $s = f(t)$? How is s found?

4. Develop the law of cosines from the formula for the distance between two points.

5. Develop the formula for $\cos(A - B)$ from the law of cosines.

6. Write expressions for $\sin(A + B)$ and $\sin(A - B)$. Set $\alpha = A + B$, $\beta = A - B$ and develop a formula for $\sin \alpha - \sin \beta$.

7. Under what assumptions is it true that $\lim \dfrac{\sin \theta}{\theta} = 1$? Prove the result.

8. Write expressions for $\cos(A + B)$ and $\cos(A - B)$. Set $\alpha = A + B$, $\beta = A - B$, and develop a formula for $\cos \alpha - \cos \beta$. Use the result to develop a formula for the derivative of $\cos x$, from the definition

$$\frac{d(\cos x)}{dx} = \lim_{\Delta x \to 0} \frac{\cos(x + \Delta x) - \cos x}{\Delta x}.$$

9. Let A_n be the area bounded by a regular n-sided polygon inscribed in a circle of radius r. Show that $A_n = (n/2)r^2 \sin(2\pi/n)$. Find $\lim A_n$ as $n \to \infty$. Does the result agree with what you know about the area of a circle?

10. Write a formula for the area bounded above by the semicircle $y = \sqrt{r^2 - t^2}$, below by the t-axis, on the left by the y-axis, and on the right by

the line $t = x$. Without making any calculations, what do you know must be the derivative, with respect to x, of this expression? Explain.

11. What property of continuous functions is used in the proof of the Intermediate Value Theorem?

12. Is every Riemann-integrable function also differentiable? Give a reason for your answer.

13. Is the function f defined on the domain $0 \leq x \leq 1$ by

$$f(x) = \begin{cases} 0 \text{ when } x \text{ is rational} \\ 1 \text{ when } x \text{ is irrational} \end{cases}$$

Riemann-integrable over $(0, 1)$? Give a reason for your answer.

14. If you could not find an indefinite integral of $f(x)\ dx$, how could you still calculate $\int_a^b f(x)\ dx$ to any specified number of decimal places of accuracy, assuming f is continuous over $a \leq x \leq b$? Illustrate for $f(x) = 1/x$, $a = 1$, $b = 2$, and one-decimal-place accuracy.

MISCELLANEOUS PROBLEMS FOR CHAPTER 4*

Solve the differential equations in Problems 1–5.

1. $\dfrac{dy}{dx} = xy^2$

2. $\dfrac{dy}{dx} = \sqrt{1 + x + y + xy}$

3. $\dfrac{dy}{dx} = \dfrac{x^2 - 1}{y^2 + 1}$

4. $\dfrac{dx}{dy} = \dfrac{y - \sqrt{y}}{x + \sqrt{x}}$

5. $\dfrac{dx}{dy} = \left(\dfrac{2 + x}{3 - y}\right)^2$

6. Solve each of the following differential equations subject to the prescribed initial conditions:

(a) $\dfrac{dy}{dx} = x\sqrt{x^2 - 4}$; $x = 2$, $y = 3$.   (b) $\dfrac{dy}{dx} = xy^3$; $x = 0$, $y = 1$.

7. Can there be a curve satisfying the following conditions? d^2y/dx^2 is everywhere equal to zero and, when $x = 0$, $y = 0$ and $dy/dx = 1$. Give a reason for your answer.

8. Find an equation of the curve whose slope at the point (x, y) is $3x^2 + 2$, if the curve is required to pass through the point $(1, -1)$.

9. A particle moves along the x-axis. Its acceleration is $a = -t^2$. At $t = 0$, the particle is at the origin. In the course of its motion, it reaches the point $x = b$, where $b > 0$, but no point beyond b. Determine its velocity at $t = 0$.

10. A particle moves with acceleration $a = \sqrt{t} - (1/\sqrt{t})$. Assuming that the velocity $v = 2$ and the distance $s = 5$ when $t = 0$, find (a) the velocity v in terms of t, (b) the distance s in terms of t.

11. A particle is accelerated with acceleration $3 + 2t$, where t is the time. At $t = 0$, the velocity is 4. Find the velocity as a function of time and the distance between the position of the particle at time zero and at time 4.

12. The acceleration of a particle moving along the x-axis is given by $d^2x/dt^2 = -4x$. If the particle starts from rest at $x = 5$, find the velocity when it first reaches $x = 3$.

13. Let $f(x)$, $g(x)$ be two continuously differentiable functions satisfying the relationships $f'(x) = g(x)$; $f''(x) = -f(x)$.   Let $h(x) = f^2(x) + g^2(x)$. If $h(0) = 5$, find $h(10)$.

14. The family of straight lines $y = ax + b$ (a, b arbitrary constants) can be characterized by the relation $y'' = 0$. Find a similar relation satisfied by the family of all circles $(x - h)^2 + (y - h)^2 = r^2$, where h and r are arbitrary constants. [*Hint:* Eliminate h and r from the set of three equations including the given one and two obtained by successive differentiation.]

15. Assume that the brakes of an automobile produce a constant deceleration of k ft/sec^2. (a) Determine what k must be to bring an automobile traveling 60 mi/hr (88 ft/sec) to rest in a distance of 100 ft from the point where the brakes

---

* These problems can be taken up during, or after, the study of Chapter 7.

are applied. (b) With the same k, how far would a car traveling 30 mi/hr travel before being brought to a stop?

16. Solve the differential equation $dy/dx = x\sqrt{1 + x^2}$ subject to the condition that $y = -2$ when $x = 0$.

17. The acceleration due to gravity is -32 ft/sec^2. A stone is thrown upward from the ground with a speed of 96 ft/sec. Find the height to which the stone rises in t sec. What is the maximum height reached by the stone?

18. (*Amer. Math. Monthly*, 1955, M. S. Klamkin.) Show that the following procedure will produce a continuous polygonal "curve" whose slope at the point (x_k, y_k) will be $f(x_k)$. First, sketch the auxiliary curve $C{:}y = xf(x)$. Then through the point $P_0(x_0, y_0)$, draw the ordinate $x = x_0$ intersecting C in $Q_0(x_0, x_0 f(x_0))$. Through P_0 draw a line segment $P_0 P_1$ parallel to OQ_0. Then the slope of $P_0 P_1$ is $f(x_0)$. Now take $P_1(x_1, y_1)$ on this segment to lie close to P_0. For example, take $x_1 = x_0 + h$, where h is small. Then find $Q_1(x_1, x_1 f(x_1))$ on C and through P_1 draw a line segment $P_1 P_2$ parallel to OQ_1. Continue the process by taking $P_2(x_2, y_2)$ close to P_1, with $x_2 = x_1 + h$; then find $Q_2(x_2, x_2 f(x_2))$ on C and through P_2 draw a line segment $P_2 P_3$ parallel to OQ_2; and so on.

19. (a) Apply the procedure of Problem 18 to the case $f(x) = 1/x$ with $x_0 = 1$, $y_0 = 1$, and $h = \frac{1}{4}$. Continue the process until you reach the point $P_4(x_4, y_4)$. What is your value of y_4? (b) Repeat the construction of part (a), but with $h = \frac{1}{8}$, and continue until you reach $x_8 = 2$. What is your value of y_8?

20. A body is moving with velocity 16 ft/sec when it is suddenly subjected to a deceleration. If the deceleration is proportional to the square root of the velocity, and the body comes to rest in 4 sec, (a) how fast is the body moving 2 sec after it begins decelerating, and (b) how far does the body travel before coming to rest?

Evaluate the integrals in Problems 21 through 33:

21. $\displaystyle \int \frac{x^3 + 1}{x^2} \, dx$

22. $\displaystyle \int y\sqrt{1 + y^2} \, dy$

23. $\displaystyle \int t^{1/3}(1 + t^{4/3})^{-7} \, dt$

24. $\displaystyle \int \frac{(1 + \sqrt{u})^{1/2} \, du}{\sqrt{u}}$

25. $\displaystyle \int \frac{dr}{\sqrt[3]{(7 - 5r)^2}}$

26. $\displaystyle \int \cos 4x \, dx$

27. $\displaystyle \int \sin^2 3x \cos 3x \, dx$

28. $\displaystyle \int \frac{\cos x \, dx}{\sqrt{\sin x}}$

29. $\displaystyle \int \cos (2x - 1) \, dx$

30. $\displaystyle \int \frac{y \, dy}{\sqrt{25 - 4y^2}}$

31. $\displaystyle \int \frac{dt}{t\sqrt{2t}}$

32. $\displaystyle \int (x^2 - \sqrt{x}) \, dx$

33. $\displaystyle \int \frac{dx}{(2 - 3x)^2}$

Find dy/dx in Problems 34 through 38:

34. $y = \cos (1 - 2x)$ 35. $y = \dfrac{\cos x}{\sin x}$

36. $y = \sec^2 (5x)$ 37. $y = \sin^4 5x$

38. $y^3 = \sin^3 x + \cos^3 x$

39. Given $y = 3 \sin 2x$ and $x = u^2 + \pi$, find the value of dy/du when $u = 0$.

40. If $0 < x < \pi/2$, prove that $x > \sin x > 2x/\pi$.

41. If one side and the opposite angle of a triangle are fixed, prove that the area is a maximum when the triangle is isosceles.

42. A light hangs above the center of a table of radius r ft. The illumination at any point on the table is directly proportional to the cosine of the angle of incidence (i.e., the angle a ray of light makes with the normal) and is inversely proportional to the square of the distance from the light. How far should the light be above the table in order to give the strongest illumination at the edge of the table?

43. If A, B, C are constants, $AB \neq 0$, prove that the graph of the curve $y = A \sin (Bx + C)$ is always concave toward the x-axis and that its points of inflection coincide with its points of intersection with the x-axis.

44. Two particles move on the same straight line so that their distances from a fixed point O, at any time t, are $x_1 = a \sin bt$ and $x_2 = a \sin [bt + (\pi/3)]$, where a and b are constants, $ab \neq 0$. Find the greatest distance between them.

45. If the identity $\sin (x + a) = \sin x \cos a + \cos x \sin a$ is differentiated with respect to x, is the resulting equation also an identity? Does this principle apply to the equation $x^2 - 2x - 8 = 0$? Explain.

46. A revolving beacon light in a lighthouse $\frac{1}{2}$ mile offshore makes two revolutions per minute. If the shoreline is a straight line, how fast is the ray of light moving along the shore when it passes a point one mile from the lighthouse?

47. The coordinates of a moving particle are $x = a \cos^3 \theta$, $y = a \sin^3 \theta$. If a is a positive constant and θ increases at the constant rate of ω rad/sec, find the magnitude of the velocity vector.

48. The area bounded by the x-axis, the curve $y = f(x)$, and the lines $x = a$, $x = b$ is equal to $\sqrt{b^2 - a^2}$ for all $b > a$. Find $f(x)$.

49. Evaluate the following limits:

(a) $\displaystyle \lim_{x \to 0} \dfrac{2 \sin 5x}{3x}$;   (b) $\displaystyle \lim_{x \to 0} \sin 5x \cot 3x$;   (c) $\displaystyle \lim_{x \to 0} x \csc^2 \sqrt{2x}$.

50. Find dy/dx and d^2y/dx^2 if $x = \cos 3t$ and $y = \sin^2 3t$.

51. Let $f(x)$ be a continuous function. Express

$$\lim_{n \to \infty} \frac{1}{n} \left[f\left(\frac{1}{n}\right) + f\left(\frac{2}{n}\right) + \cdots + f\left(\frac{n}{n}\right) \right]$$

as a definite integral.

52. Use the result of Problem 51 to evaluate:

(a) $\displaystyle \lim_{n \to \infty} \frac{1}{n^{16}} [1^{15} + 2^{15} + 3^{15} + \cdots + n^{15}]$,

(b) $\lim\limits_{n\to\infty} \dfrac{\sqrt{1}+\sqrt{2}+\sqrt{3}+\cdots+\sqrt{n}}{n^{3/2}}$,

(c) $\lim\limits_{n\to\infty} \dfrac{1}{n}\left[\sin\dfrac{\pi}{n}+\sin\dfrac{2\pi}{n}+\sin\dfrac{3\pi}{n}+\cdots+\sin\dfrac{n\pi}{n}\right]$.

Find:

(d) $\lim\limits_{h\to 0} \dfrac{1}{h}\displaystyle\int_x^{x+h} \dfrac{du}{u+\sqrt{u^2+1}}$,   (e) $\lim\limits_{x\to x_1}\left[\dfrac{x}{x-x_1}\displaystyle\int_{x_1}^x f(t)\,dt\right]$.

53. Variables x and y are related by the equation

$$x = \int_0^y \frac{1}{\sqrt{1+4t^2}}\,dt.$$

Show that d^2y/dx^2 is proportional to y and find the constant of proportionality.

54. (a) Show that the perimeter P_n of an n-sided regular polygon inscribed in a circle of radius r is $P_n = 2nr \sin(\pi/n)$. (b) Find the limit of P_n as $n \to \infty$. Is the answer consistent with what you know about the circumference of a circle?

CHAPTER 5

APPLICATIONS OF THE DEFINITE INTEGRAL

5–1 Introduction. In Chapter 4 we discovered a close connection between sums of the form

$$S_a^b = \sum_a^b f(x)\,\Delta x \tag{1}$$

and integration, the inverse of differentiation. When f is continuous on $a \le x \le b$, we found that the *limit* of S_a^b as Δx approaches zero is just $F(b) - F(a)$, where F is any integral of f:

$$F(x) = \int f(x)\,dx. \tag{2}$$

We applied this to the problem of computing the area between the x-axis and the graph of $y = f(x)$, $a \le x \le b$. In this chapter we shall extend the applications to the following topics: area between two curves, distance, volumes, lengths of curves, areas of surfaces of revolution, average value of a function, center of mass, centroid, work, and hydrostatic force. Further applications will be taken up in Chapter 15 in connection with double and triple integrals.

5–2 Area between two curves. Suppose that

$$y_1 = f_1(x), \qquad y_2 = f_2(x)$$

define two functions of x that are continuous for $a \le x \le b$, and furthermore, suppose that

$$f_1(x) \ge f_2(x) \qquad \text{for} \qquad a \le x \le b.$$

Then the y_1 curve is above the y_2 curve from a to b (Fig. 5–1) and we consider the problem of finding the area bounded above by the y_1 curve, below by the y_2 curve, and on the sides by the vertical lines $x = a$, $x = b$. If the x-interval from a to b is divided into n equal subintervals, each of width $\Delta x = (b - a)/n$, and a rectangle of width Δx and altitude extending from the y_2 curve to the y_1 curve is used to approximate that portion of the area between the curves that lies between x and $x + \Delta x$, we find the area of such a rectangle is

$$(y_1 - y_2)\,\Delta x = [f_1(x) - f_2(x)]\,\Delta x.$$

222

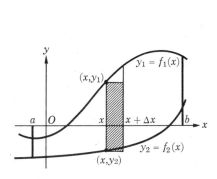

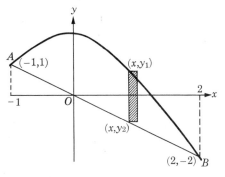

FIGURE 5–1   FIGURE 5–2

The total area in question is *approximated* by adding together the areas of all such rectangles

$$A \approx \sum_{a}^{b} [f_1(x) - f_2(x)]\, \Delta x.$$

Finally, if we let $\Delta x \to 0$, we obtain the exact area:

$$A = \lim_{\Delta x \to 0} \sum_{a}^{b} [f_1(x) - f_2(x)]\, \Delta x = \int_{a}^{b} [f_1(x) - f_2(x)]\, dx. \qquad (1)$$

EXAMPLE.   Find the area (Fig. 5–2) bounded by the parabola

$$y = 2 - x^2$$

and the straight line

$$y = -x.$$

Solution.   We first find where the curves intersect by finding points that satisfy both equations simultaneously.   That is, we solve

$$2 - x^2 = -x$$

or

$$x^2 - x - 2 = 0, \qquad (x - 2)(x + 1) = 0, \qquad x = -1,\ 2.$$

The points of intersection are thus $A(-1, 1)$ and $B(2, -2)$.   For all values of x between -1 and $+2$, the curve

$$y_1 = 2 - x^2$$

is above the line

$$y_2 = -x$$

by an amount

$$y_1 - y_2 = (2 - x^2) - (-x) = 2 - x^2 + x.$$

This is the altitude of a typical rectangle used to approximate that portion of the area lying between x and $x + \Delta x$. The total area is approximated by

$$A^2_{-1} \approx \sum_{-1}^{2} (y_1 - y_2) \, \Delta x = \sum_{-1}^{2} (2 - x^2 + x) \, \Delta x$$

and is given exactly by

$$A^2_{-1} = \lim_{\Delta x \to 0} \sum_{-1}^{2} (2 - x^2 + x) \, \Delta x = \int_{-1}^{2} (2 - x^2 + x) \, dx = 4\tfrac{1}{2}.$$

Problems

1. Make a sketch to represent a region that is bounded on the right by a continuous curve $x = f(y)$, on the left by a continuous curve $x = g(y)$, below by the line $y = a$, and above by the line $y = b$. Divide the region into n horizontal strips each of altitude $\Delta y = (b - a)/n$ and express the area of the region (a) as a limit of a sum of areas of rectangles, and (b) as an appropriate definite integral.

2. Find the area bounded by the x-axis and the curve $y = 2x - x^2$.

3. Find the area bounded by the y-axis and the curve $x = y^2 - y^3$.

4. Find the area bounded by the curve $y^2 = x$ and the line $x = 4$.

5. Find the area bounded by the curve $y = 2x - x^2$ and the line $y = -3$.

6. Find the area bounded by the curve $y = x^2$ and the line $y = x$.

7. Find the area bounded by the curve $x = 3y - y^2$ and the line $x + y = 3$.

8. Find the area bounded by the curves $y = x^4 - 2x^2$ and $y = 2x^2$.

9. Find the area of the "triangular" shaped region in the first quadrant bounded by the y-axis and the curves $y = \sin x$, $y = \cos x$.

10. The area bounded by the curve $y = x^2$ and the line $y = 4$ is divided into two equal portions by the line $y = c$. Find c.

11. Find the area bounded by the curve $\sqrt{x} + \sqrt{y} = 1$ and the coordinate axes.

5–3 Distance. As a second application of the basic principles involved in the use of the Fundamental Theorem of the calculus, we shall calculate the distance traveled by a body moving with velocity

$$v = f(t). \tag{1}$$

To simplify the discussion we shall assume that $f(t)$ is positive, as well as being continuous, for $a \leq t \leq b$. This means that the body moves only in one direction and does no backing up.

Now there are two ways in which we can calculate the distance traveled by the body between $t = a$ and $t = b$.

First method. If we can integrate the differential equation

$$ds = f(t) \, dt, \tag{2}$$

which we get by substituting ds/dt for v in Eq. (1), then we can determine the position s of the body as a function of t, say

$$s = F(t) + C. \tag{3}$$

The distance traveled by the body between $t = a$ and $t = b$ is then given by

$$s \Big]_{t=a}^{t=b} = F(t) + C \Big]_{a}^{b} = F(b) - F(a).$$

We recognize this, of course, as saying that the distance is given by the definite integral

$$s \Big]_{t=a}^{t=b} = \int_{a}^{b} f(t)\, dt = F(t) \Big]_{a}^{b} = F(b) - F(a). \tag{4}$$

Second method. In this method, we imagine the total time interval $a \leq t \leq b$ as divided into n subintervals, each of duration $\Delta t = (b - a)/n$. The velocity at the beginning of the first subinterval is

$$v_1 = f(t_1) = f(a).$$

If Δt is small, the velocity remains nearly constant throughout the time from a to $a + \Delta t$. Hence during the first subinterval of time, the body travels a distance Δs_1 which is approximately equal to $v_1\, \Delta t$:

$$\Delta s_1 \approx v_1\, \Delta t = f(t_1)\, \Delta t. \tag{5}$$

If, instead of using the velocity v_1 at time t_1, we were to use the *average* velocity

$$\overline{v_1} = \frac{\Delta s_1}{\Delta t}, \tag{6a}$$

we could write

$$\Delta s_1 = \overline{v_1}\, \Delta t \tag{6b}$$

exactly. Now by the Mean Value Theorem, we know that there is some instant, say T_1, between t_1 and $t_1 + \Delta t$ where the instantaneous velocity is equal to the average velocity $\overline{v_1}$. In other words,

$$f(T_1) = \overline{v_1} \text{ for some } T_1, \qquad t_1 < T_1 < t_1 + \Delta t, \tag{6c}$$

and therefore

$$\Delta s_1 = f(T_1)\, \Delta t$$

exactly. By reasoning in the same manner for the second, third, $\ldots$, nth subintervals, we conclude that there are instants of time $T_2, T_3, \ldots, T_n$

in these respective intervals such that

$$\Delta s_2 = f(T_2) \, \Delta t,$$

$$\Delta s_3 = f(T_3) \, \Delta t,$$

$$\vdots$$

$$\Delta s_n = f(T_n) \, \Delta t,$$

where $\Delta s_2, \Delta s_3, \ldots, \Delta s_n$ represent the distances traveled during these respective time subintervals. Therefore the total distance traveled between $t = a$ and $t = b$ is

$$s\Big]_{t=a}^{t=b} = \Delta s_1 + \Delta s_2 + \Delta s_3 + \cdots + \Delta s_n$$

$$= f(T_1) \, \Delta t + f(T_2) \, \Delta t + \cdots + f(T_n) \, \Delta t$$

$$= \sum_{k=1}^{n} f(T_k) \, \Delta t. \tag{7}$$

Let us now take finer and finer subdivisions Δt and let n increase without limit. For each n we select the appropriate instants of time $T_1, T_2, \ldots, T_n$ according to the method described above. Then the particular sums used in Eq. (7) tend to the definite integral

$$\lim_{n \to \infty} \sum_{k=1}^{n} f(T_k) \, \Delta t = \int_a^b f(t) \, dt \tag{8}$$

as limit, by virtue of the Fundamental Theorem. On the other hand, these sums all give the distance traveled by the body. Therefore the distance traveled is equal to the integral in Eq. (8) [or Eq. (4)].

Remark 1. If, instead of using the velocities at the instants of time $T_1, T_2, \ldots, T_n$ described above, we had used the velocities

$$v_1 = f(t_1), \qquad v_2 = f(t_2), \qquad \ldots, \qquad v_n = f(t_n)$$

at the beginnings of the various subintervals, then we would have had n *approximations* like (5) with subscripts $1, 2, \ldots, n$. Then we would have obtained an *approximation*

$$\Delta s_1 + \Delta s_2 + \cdots + \Delta s_n \approx f(t_1) \, \Delta t + f(t_2) \, \Delta t + \cdots + f(t_n) \, \Delta t,$$

or

$$s\Big]_{t=a}^{t=b} \approx \sum_{k=1}^{n} f(t_k) \, \Delta t. \tag{9}$$

Now since $f(t)$ is continuous, the sums (7) and (9) have the same *limit* as $n \rightarrow \infty$. In other words, the approximation (9) gets better as n increases, and the *limit* again gives the exact value, namely, the integral in Eq. (8).

Remark 2. Of course, the two methods give the same result, Eqs. (4) and (8). The second method is useful primarily (a) because it shows how the simple formula

$$\text{distance} = \text{velocity} \times \text{time,}$$

which applies only to the case of *constant* velocity, can be extended to the case of variable velocity, provided we apply it to short subintervals Δt; and (b) because it can be used [in the form of the approximation (9)] to estimate the distance in cases where the velocity is given empirically by a table of values or a graph instead of by a formula $f(t)$ with known indefinite integral $F(t)$.

Remark 3. If the velocity changes sign during the interval (a, b), then the integral in Eq. (4) gives only the *net* change in s. This permits cancellation of distances traveled forwards and backwards. For example, it would give an answer of 2 miles if the body traveled forward 7 miles and backed up 5 miles. If we want to determine the actual total distance traveled, we should calculate the integral of the *absolute value* of the velocity,

$$\int_a^b |f(t)|\, dt. \qquad (10)$$

This would be done by integrating separately over the intervals where v is positive and where v is negative and adding the absolute values of the results.

Remark 4. The preceding discussion shows that the distance traveled is given by precisely the same expression as that for the area bounded

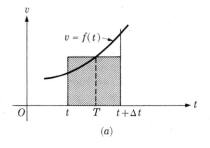

(a)

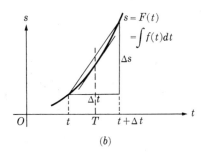

(b)

FIGURE 5–3

by the curve

$$v = f(t)$$

and the t-axis from a to b. All of the discussion above can be interpreted geometrically. For example, T is chosen between t and $t + \Delta t$ in such a way that the area of the rectangle of base Δt and altitude $f(T)$ (Fig. 5–3a) is precisely equal to the area under the velocity curve between t and $t + \Delta t$. This is also the place where the slope of the curve $s = F(t)$ (Fig. 5–3b) is equal to the slope of the chord.

Problems

In each of the following problems (1 through 8), the function $v = f(t)$ represents the velocity v (ft/sec) of a moving body as a function of the time t (sec). Sketch the graph of v versus t and find that portion of the given time interval $a \le t \le b$ in which the velocity is (a) positive, and (b) negative. Then find the total distance traveled by the body between $t = a$ and $t = b$.

1. $v = 2t + 1; \ 0 \le t \le 2$ 2. $v = t^2 - t - 2; \ 0 \le t \le 3$

3. $v = t - \dfrac{8}{t^2}; \ 1 \le t \le 3$ 4. $v = |t - 1|; \ 0 \le t \le 2$

5. $v = 6 \sin 3t; \ 0 \le t \le \dfrac{\pi}{2}$ 6. $v = 4 \cos 2t; \ 0 \le t \le \pi$

7. $v = \sin t + \cos t; \ 0 \le t \le \pi$

8. $v = \sin t \sqrt{2 + 2 \cos t}; \ 0 \le t \le \pi$

In each of the following problems (9 through 13), the function $a = f(t)$ represents the acceleration (ft/sec^2) of a moving body and v_0 is its velocity at time $t = 0$. Find the *distance* traveled by the body between time $t = 0$ and $t = 2$.

9. $a = \sin t; v_0 = 2$ 10. $a = 1 - \cos t; v_0 = 0$

11. $a = g$ (const.); $v_0 = 0$ 12. $a = \sqrt{4t + 1}; \ v_0 = -4\frac{1}{3}$

13. $a = \dfrac{1}{\sqrt{4t + 1}}; \ v_0 = 1$

14. Suppose water flows into a tank at the rate of $f(t)$ (gal/min), where f is a given, positive, continuous function of t. Let the amount of water in the tank at time $t = 0$ be Q_0 (gal). Apply the Fundamental Theorem to show that the amount of water in the tank at any later time $t = b$ is

$$Q = Q_0 + \int_0^b f(t) \, dt.$$

15. Use the trapezoidal rule, Article 4–10, to find (approximately) the distance traveled between $t = 0$ and $t = 2$ by a body whose velocity is given by the following table of values.

v (ft/sec)	2.2	2.5	3.0	3.8	5.0
t (sec)	0	0.5	1.0	1.5	2.0

Also find (approximately) the average velocity during the time $t = 0$ to $t = 2$.

5-4 Volumes. The volumes of many solids can be found by an application of the "method of slicing." Suppose, for example, that the solid is bounded by two parallel planes perpendicular to the x-axis at $x = a$ and $x = b$. Imagine the solid cut into thin slices of thickness Δx by planes perpendicular to the x-axis. Then the total volume V of the solid is the sum of the volumes of these slices.

Let ΔV be the volume of the representative slice between x and $x + \Delta x$. Then if A' and A'' are respectively the smallest and largest cross-sectional areas of the solid between x and $x + \Delta x$, it will be seen at once that

$$A' \, \Delta x \le \Delta V \le A'' \, \Delta x$$

or

$$\Delta V = A(\bar{x}) \, \Delta x,$$

where $A(\bar{x})$ denotes an appropriate intermediate cross-sectional area of the solid at some $\bar{x}$ between x and $x + \Delta x$. Then

$$V = \sum_{a}^{b} A(\bar{x}) \, \Delta x$$

will give the total volume of the solid exactly. If, instead of choosing the exactly appropriate intermediate point $\bar{x}$ in the typical subinterval, we use the area $A(x)$ of the cross section at x, we have only an approximation,

$$V \approx \sum_{a}^{b} A(x) \, \Delta x.$$

But now let $\Delta x \to 0$. Then, if the cross-sectional area is a continuous function of x, all these sums will approach the same limit. Since one se-

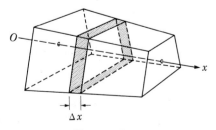

FIGURE 5-4

quence of sums always gives the value V, it will have this value as its limit. Hence the other sums will also give the value V in the limit,

that is,
$$V = \lim_{\Delta x \to 0} \sum_a^b A(x)\,\Delta x = \int_a^b A(x)\,dx. \tag{1}$$

Volume of a solid of revolution. The solid generated by rotating a plane area about an axis in its plane is called a solid of revolution. To find the volume of a solid such as shown in Fig. 5–5, we need only observe that the cross-sectional area $A(x)$ in Eq. (1) is the area of a circle of radius $r = y = f(x)$, so that
$$A(x) = \pi r^2 = \pi[f(x)]^2. \tag{2}$$

EXAMPLE 1. Suppose the curve in Fig. 5–5 represents the graph of
$$y = \sqrt{x}$$
from (0, 0) to (4, 2). Then the volume of the representative slice is
$$\Delta V \approx \pi y^2\,\Delta x = \pi(\sqrt{x})^2\,\Delta x,$$
and the total volume is approximately
$$V \approx \sum_0^4 \pi x\,\Delta x.$$

Exactly, we have
$$V = \lim_{\Delta x \to 0} \sum_0^4 \pi x\,\Delta x = \int_0^4 \pi x\,dx = \pi\frac{x^2}{2}\Big]_0^4 = 8\pi.$$

Method of cylindrical shells. Suppose the area $PQRS$ in Fig. 5–6 is revolved around the y-axis. We can compute the volume generated in the

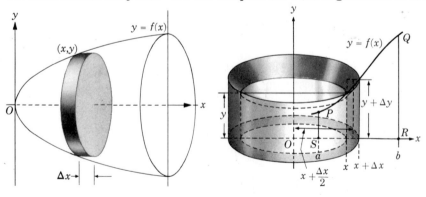

FIGURE 5–5   FIGURE 5–6

following way. Consider a strip of area between the ordinate at x and the ordinate at $x + \Delta x$. When this strip is revolved around the y-axis, it generates a hollow, thin-walled shell of inner radius x, outer radius $x + \Delta x$, and volume ΔV. The base of this shell is a ring bounded by two concentric circles. The inner radius is

$$r_1 = x$$

and the outer radius is

$$r_2 = x + \Delta x.$$

The area of the ring is

$$\Delta A = \pi(r_2^2 - r_1^2) = 2\pi \left(\frac{r_2 + r_1}{2} \right) (r_2 - r_1) = 2\pi r \, \Delta x.$$

Here

$$r = \frac{r_2 + r_1}{2} = x + \frac{\Delta x}{2}$$

is the radius of the circle midway between the inner and outer boundaries of the ring, and $2\pi r$ is its circumference.

Now if we had a cylindrical shell of constant altitude y standing on this base, its volume would be

$$\text{altitude} \times \text{base} = y \, \Delta A.$$

In the present case, the altitude of the shell varies between y and $y + \Delta y$. Its volume therefore lies between $y \, \Delta A$ and $(y + \Delta y) \, \Delta A$. That is,

$$y \, \Delta A \leq \Delta V \leq (y + \Delta y) \, \Delta A$$

or

$$y \cdot 2\pi r \, \Delta x \leq \Delta V \leq (y + \Delta y) \cdot 2\pi r \, \Delta x.$$

The total volume V is contained between the "lower" sum

$$s = \sum_a^b y \cdot 2\pi \left(x + \frac{\Delta x}{2} \right) \Delta x$$

and the "upper" sum

$$S = \sum_a^b (y + \Delta y) \cdot 2\pi \left(x + \frac{\Delta x}{2} \right) \Delta x.$$

As Δx approaches zero, both of these sums approach the following integral as limit (see Article 5–5). Hence this limit must also be equal to the volume V, namely,

$$V = \lim_{\Delta x \to 0} s = \lim_{\Delta x \to 0} S = \int_a^b y \cdot 2\pi x \, dx = \int_a^b 2\pi x f(x) \, dx.$$

Remark. An easy way to visualize this result is to imagine that the volume element ΔV has been cut along a generator of the cylinder and that the shell has been rolled out flat like a thin sheet of tin. The sheet then has dimensions very nearly equal to $2\pi x$ by $y = f(x)$ by Δx. Hence

$$\Delta V \approx 2\pi x \cdot f(x) \cdot \Delta x,$$

and the total volume is given approximately by

$$V \approx \sum_a^b 2\pi x \cdot f(x) \cdot \Delta x.$$

As Δx approaches zero, we obtain a limit that is equal to the exact volume:

$$V = \lim_{\Delta x \to 0} \sum_a^b 2\pi x \cdot f(x) \cdot \Delta x$$

$$= \int_a^b 2\pi x f(x)\, dx.$$

EXAMPLE 2. In Example 1 above, where the area under the curve $y = \sqrt{x}$ is revolved around the x-axis, we may take a horizontal strip of area between the lines at distances y and $y + \Delta y$ above the x-axis. The volume generated by revolving this strip around the x-axis is a hollow cylindrical shell of inner circumference $2\pi y$, inner length $4 - x$, and wall thickness Δy. Hence, the total volume V is approximately

$$V \approx \sum_{y=0}^{2} 2\pi y(4 - x)\, \Delta y$$

and is exactly equal to the limit of this sum as Δy approaches zero:

$$V = \lim_{\Delta y \to 0} \sum_{y=0}^{2} 2\pi y(4 - x)\, \Delta y$$

$$= \int_0^2 2\pi y(4 - y^2)\, dy$$

$$= 2\pi \left[2y^2 - \frac{y^4}{4} \right]_0^2 = 8\pi.$$

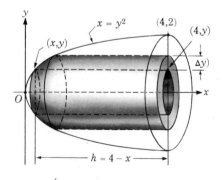

FIGURE 5–7

Various methods for finding volumes are illustrated in the following examples.

EXAMPLE 3. The circle

$$x^2 + y^2 = a^2$$

is rotated about the x-axis to generate a sphere. Find its volume.

Solution. We imagine the sphere cut into thin slices by planes perpendicular to the x-axis (Fig. 5–8). The volume of a typical slice between two planes at x and $x + \Delta x$ is approximately

$$\pi y^2 \, \Delta x = \pi(a^2 - x^2) \, \Delta x,$$

and the sum of all slices is approximately

$$V_{-a}^{a} \approx \sum_{-a}^{a} \pi(a^2 - x^2) \, \Delta x.$$

The exact volume is given by

$$V_{-a}^{a} = \lim_{\Delta x \to 0} \sum_{-a}^{a} \pi(a^2 - x^2) \, \Delta x$$

$$= \int_{-a}^{a} \pi(a^2 - x^2) \, dx$$

$$= \pi \left[a^2 x - \frac{x^3}{3} \right]_{-a}^{a} = \tfrac{4}{3}\pi a^3.$$

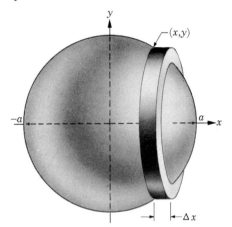

FIGURE 5–8

EXAMPLE 4. A hole of diameter a is bored through the center of the sphere in Example 3 above. Find the remaining volume.

The volume in question could be generated by rotating about the y-axis the area inside the circle $x^2 + y^2 = a^2$ lying to the right of the line $x = a/2$ (Fig. 5–9a). The line and the circle intersect at the points $(a/2, \pm a\sqrt{3}/2)$. There are at least three methods for finding the required volume.

Method 1. The volume is

$$V = V_1 - V_2,$$

where V_1(Fig. 5–9b) is the volume of the segment of the sphere contained between the two planes perpendicular to the y-axis at $y = \pm a\sqrt{3}/2$, and V_2 is the volume of a right circular cylinder of radius $a/2$ and altitude $2(a\sqrt{3}/2) = a\sqrt{3}$, so that

$$V_2 = \frac{\sqrt{3}}{4} \pi a^3.$$

To find V_1, imagine the solid as being cut into thin slices by planes perpendicular

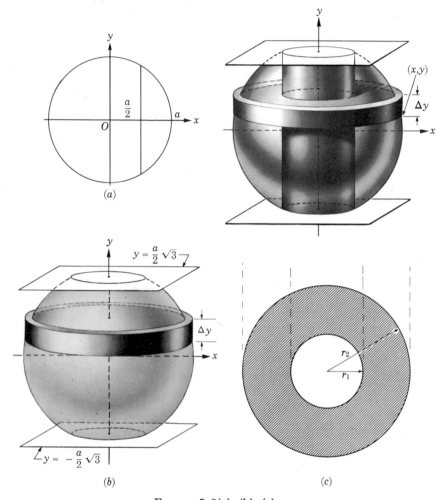

FIGURE 5–9(a), (b), (c).

to the y-axis. The slice between y and $y + \Delta y$ is approximated by a cylinder of altitude Δy and cross-sectional area $\pi x^2 = \pi(a^2 - y^2)$, so that we have the approximation

$$V_1 \approx \sum_{-a\sqrt{3}/2}^{a\sqrt{3}/2} \pi(a^2 - y^2)\, \Delta y$$

and the exact value

$$V_1 = \int_{-a\sqrt{3}/2}^{a\sqrt{3}/2} \pi(a^2 - y^2)\, dy = \frac{3\sqrt{3}}{4}\pi a^3.$$

Thus

$$V = V_1 - V_2 = \frac{3\sqrt{3}}{4}\pi a^3 - \frac{\sqrt{3}}{4}\pi a^3 = \frac{\sqrt{3}}{2}\pi a^3.$$

Method 2. Instead of subtracting volumes, we may work directly with the volume required. Again we imagine the solid to be cut into thin slices by planes perpendicular to the y-axis. Each slice (Fig. 5–9c) is now like a washer of thickness Δy, inner radius

$$r_1 = \frac{a}{2},$$

and outer radius

$$r_2 = x = \sqrt{a^2 - y^2}.$$

The area of a face of such a washer is

$$\pi r_2^2 - \pi r_1^2 = \pi(\tfrac{3}{4}a^2 - y^2)$$

and the volume of the solid is approximately

$$V \approx \sum_{-a\sqrt{3}/2}^{a\sqrt{3}/2} \pi(\tfrac{3}{4}a^2 - y^2)\,\Delta y,$$

while its exact value is

$$V = \lim_{\Delta y \to 0} \sum_{-a\sqrt{3}/2}^{a\sqrt{3}/2} \pi(\tfrac{3}{4}a^2 - y^2)\,\Delta y$$

$$= \int_{-a\sqrt{3}/2}^{a\sqrt{3}/2} \pi(\tfrac{3}{4}a^2 - y^2)\,dy$$

$$= \frac{\sqrt{3}}{2}\pi a^3.$$

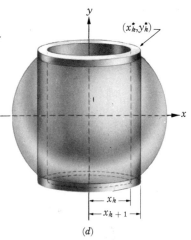

FIGURE 5–9(d).

Method 3. This time we imagine the solid to be cut into a number of hollow cylindrical shells (Fig. 5–9d) by cylinders having the y-axis as their common axis and having radii

$$x_1 = \frac{a}{2}, \quad x_2, \quad x_3, \quad \ldots, \quad x_n, \quad x_{n+1} = a.$$

The first shell has inner radius x_1 and outer radius x_2, the second shell has inner radius x_2 and outer radius x_3, and so on, the kth shell having inner radius x_k and outer radius x_{k+1}. The volume of the kth shell is approximately

$$2\pi x_k^* \cdot \Delta x_k \cdot 2y_k^* = 4\pi x_k^* \sqrt{a^2 - (x_k^*)^2}\,\Delta x_k,$$

where (x_k^*, y_k^*), Fig. 5–9(f), is the point of abscissa

$$x_k^* = \tfrac{1}{2}(x_k + x_{k+1})$$

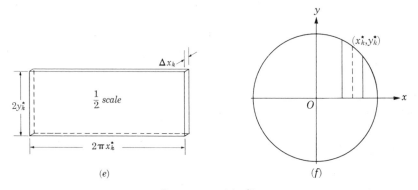

FIGURE 5–9(e), (f).

on the circle in the first quadrant. (Imagine the kth cylindrical shell to have been cut along a generator and flattened into a sheet of length $2\pi x_k^*$, altitude $2y_k^*$, and thickness Δx_k, Fig. 5-9e.) Then the entire volume will be approximated by

$$V \approx \sum_{k=1}^{n} 4\pi x_k^* \sqrt{a^2 - (x_k^*)^2}\, \Delta x_k$$

$$\approx \sum_{a/2}^{a} 4\pi x \sqrt{a^2 - x^2}\, \Delta x.$$

The exact value will be the *limit* of this sum, namely,

$$V = \lim_{\Delta x \to 0} \sum_{a/2}^{a} 4\pi x \sqrt{a^2 - x^2}\, \Delta x$$

$$= \int_{a/2}^{a} 4\pi x \sqrt{a^2 - x^2}\, dx.$$

To evaluate this integral, we let

$$u = a^2 - x^2,$$

then

$$V = 4\pi \int_{a/2}^{a} \sqrt{a^2 - x^2}\, (x\, dx)$$

$$= 4\pi \int u^{1/2}(-\tfrac{1}{2}\, du) = -\frac{4\pi}{3}\left[(a^2 - x^2)^{3/2} \right]_{a/2}^{a} = \frac{\sqrt{3}}{2}\, \pi a^3.$$

EXAMPLE 5. A wedge is cut from a right circular cylinder of radius r by two planes, one perpendicular to the axis of the cylinder while the second makes an angle α with the first and intersects it at the center of the cylinder. Find the volume of the wedge.

Solution. The volume ΔV of the slice between y and $y + \Delta y$ in Fig. 5–10 is approximately

$$\Delta V \approx A(y) \, \Delta y,$$

where

$$A(y) = \tfrac{1}{2}xh$$

is the area of the triangle that forms one face of the slice and is to be expressed as a function of y. By trigonometry,

$$h = x \tan \alpha,$$

and by the theorem of Pythagoras,

$$x^2 + y^2 = r^2$$

or

$$x^2 = r^2 - y^2.$$

Hence

$$A(y) = \tfrac{1}{2}x^2 \tan \alpha = \tfrac{1}{2} \tan \alpha \, (r^2 - y^2).$$

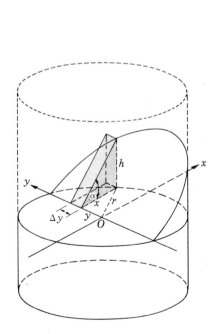

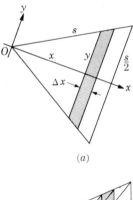

(a)

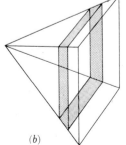

(b)

FIGURE 5–10   FIGURE 5–11

The total volume is given by

$$V = \lim_{\Delta y \to 0} \sum_{-r}^{r} A(y)\,\Delta y$$

$$= \int_{-r}^{r} \frac{1}{2} \tan \alpha (r^2 - y^2)\,dy.$$

Remembering that the factor $\frac{1}{2}\tan\alpha$ is a constant, we find

$$V = \tfrac{2}{3}\,r^3 \tan \alpha.$$

EXAMPLE 6. The base of a certain solid is an equilateral triangle of side s, with one vertex at the origin and an altitude along the x-axis. Each plane section perpendicular to the x-axis is a square, one side of which lies in the base of the solid. Find the volume of the solid.

Solution. Figure 5–11(a) represents the base of the solid with a strip of width Δx, which corresponds to a slice of the solid of volume

$$\Delta V \approx A(x)\,\Delta x,$$

where

$$A(x) = (2y)^2 = 4y^2$$

is the area of a face of the slice. The slice extends upward from the plane of the paper in Fig. 5–11(a). It is possible to find the required volume from the statement of the problem by reference to this figure and without visualizing the actual solid. A perspective view of the solid is, however, given in Fig. 5–11(b). It is required to find y in terms of x so that the area $A(x)$ will be given as a function of x. Since the base triangle is equilateral, its altitude h is given by

$$h^2 = s^2 - (s/2)^2 = \tfrac{3}{4}s^2$$

or

$$h = \frac{s}{2}\sqrt{3}.$$

Then, by similar triangles, we find

$$\frac{2y}{x} = \frac{s}{h} = \frac{2}{\sqrt{3}}$$

or

$$y = \frac{x}{\sqrt{3}}.$$

Then

$$V = \int_{0}^{h} A(x)\,dx$$

$$= \int_{0}^{s\sqrt{3}/2} \frac{4}{3}x^2\,dx = \frac{s^3}{2\sqrt{3}} = \frac{1}{3}hs^2.$$

Problems

In Problems 1 through 8, find the volumes generated when the areas bounded by the given curves and lines are rotated about the x-axis. [*Note:* $x = 0$ is the y-axis and $y = 0$ is the x-axis.]

1. $x + y = 2$; $x = 0$, $y = 0$

2. $y = \sin x$; $y = 0$ $(0 \le x \le \pi)$
[See Problem 17, Article 4–8.]

3. $y = x - x^2$; $y = 0$

4. $y = 3x - x^2$; $y = x$

5. $x = 2y - y^2$; $x = 0$
(Use cylindrical shells.)

6. $y = x$, $y = 1$; $x = 0$

7. $y = x^2$; $y = 4$

8. $y = 3 + x^2$; $y = 4$

9. By integration find the volume generated by the triangle with vertices at $(0, 0)$, $(h, 0)$, (h, r) when it is rotated (a) about the x-axis, (b) about the y-axis.

10. (a) The area bounded by the curve $y = x^2$ and the line $y = x$ is revolved around the y-axis. Find the volume generated. (b) Find the volume generated if the area is revolved around the x-axis.

11. The area bounded by the curve $y = x^2$ and the line $y = 4$ generates various solids of revolution when rotated as follows:

(a) about the y-axis,

(b) about the line $y = 4$,

(c) about the x-axis,

(d) about the line $y = -1$,

(e) about the line $x = 2$.

Find the volume generated in each case.

12. (a) A hemispherical bowl of radius a contains water to a depth h. Find the volume of water in the bowl. (b) (Review problem on related rates.) Water runs into a hemispherical bowl of radius 5 ft at the rate of 0.2 ft^3/sec. How fast is the water level in the bowl rising when the water is 4 ft deep?

13. A football has a volume that is approximately the same as the volume generated by rotating the area inside the ellipse $b^2x^2 + a^2y^2 = a^2b^2$ (where a and b are constants) about the x-axis. Find the volume so generated.

14. The cross sections of a certain solid by planes perpendicular to the x-axis are circles with diameters extending from the curve $y = x^2$ to the curve $y = 8 - x^2$. The solid lies between the points of intersection of these two curves. Find its volume.

15. The base of a certain solid is the circle $x^2 + y^2 = a^2$. Each plane section of the solid cut out by a plane perpendicular to the x-axis is a square with one edge of the square in the base of the solid. Find the volume of the solid.

16. Two great circles, lying in planes that are perpendicular to each other, are marked on a sphere of radius a. A portion of the sphere is then shaved off in such a manner that any plane section of the remaining solid, perpendicular to the common diameter of the two great circles, is a square with vertices on these circles. Find the volume of the solid that remains.

17. The base of a certain solid is the circle $x^2 + y^2 = a^2$. Each plane section of the solid cut out by a plane perpendicular to the y-axis is an isosceles right triangle with one leg in the base of the solid. Find the volume.

18. The base of a certain solid is the region between the x-axis and the curve $y = \sin x$ between $x = 0$ and $x = \pi/2$. Each plane section of the solid perpendicular to the x-axis is an equilateral triangle with one side in the base of the solid. Find the volume.

19. A rectangular swimming pool is 30 ft wide and 50 ft long. The depth of water h(ft) at distance x (ft) from one end of the pool is measured at 5-ft intervals and found to be as follows:

x (ft)	0	5	10	15	20	25	30	35	40	45	50
h (ft)	6.0	8.2	9.1	9.9	10.5	11.0	11.5	11.9	12.3	12.7	13.0

Use the trapezoidal rule to find (approximately) the volume of water in the pool.

20. The circle $x^2 + y^2 = a^2$ is rotated about the line $x = b$ $(b > a)$ to generate a torus. Find the volume generated. [*Hint:* $\int_{-a}^{a} \sqrt{a^2 - x^2}\, dx = \pi a^2/2$, since it is the area of a semicircle of radius a.]

5–5 Approximations. By now it is apparent that each application of the Fundamental Theorem that we have so far made has involved the following steps:

1. Select an independent variable, say x, such that the quantity U to be computed can be represented as a sum of pieces ΔU, where ΔU is that part of U that is associated with the subinterval $(x, x + \Delta x)$ of the domain $a \leq x \leq b$ of the variable x.

2. Subdivide the domain (a, b) into n subintervals. For the sake of simplicity we usually take the lengths all to be the same, namely, equal to $\Delta x = (b - a)/n$.

3. Approximate that portion ΔU of U that is associated with the subinterval $(x, x + \Delta x)$ by an expression of the form

$$\Delta U \approx f(X)\, \Delta x. \tag{1}$$

In this expression, X is to be some point in the subinterval $(x, x + \Delta x)$ and the function f is to be continuous over the entire domain $a \leq x \leq b$.

4. Then the total quantity U is given *approximately* by

$$U \approx \sum_a^b f(X)\, \Delta x. \tag{2}$$

5. Take the limit, as Δx approaches zero, of the sum in Eq. (2). This limit is the definite integral

$$\lim_{\Delta x \to 0} \sum_a^b f(X)\, \Delta x = \int_a^b f(x)\, dx. \tag{3}$$

Is this limit also an approximation to U or does it give U exactly?

In the case of area, distance, and volume we have seen that the *limit* in (3) does give U exactly. In order for us to be able to apply these methods to new situations as they arise, we need an answer to the following question.

Question: How accurate must the approximations in (1) and (2) be in order to say that all of the error is squeezed out in going to the limit, (3), with the result that the exact value of U is given by the limit

$$U = \lim_{\Delta x \to 0} \sum_a^b f(X)\, \Delta x = \int_a^b f(x)\, dx? \tag{4}$$

Answer: Denote by $\alpha\, \Delta x$ the correction that must be added to the right side of Eq. (1) to give ΔU exactly. That is, suppose that

$$\Delta U = f(X)\, \Delta x + \alpha\, \Delta x, \tag{5}$$

exactly.

First case. Suppose these correction terms are no larger than a constant K times $(\Delta x)^2$,

$$|\alpha\, \Delta x| \leq K\, (\Delta x)^2,$$

where K is a constant the same for all subintervals and all methods of subdivision. Then we have

$$\Delta U = f(X)\, \Delta x + \alpha\, \Delta x,$$

$$U = \sum_a^b f(X)\, \Delta x + \sum_a^b \alpha\, \Delta x$$

and

$$\left| U - \sum_a^b f(X)\, \Delta x \right| = \left| \sum_a^b \alpha\, \Delta x \right| \leq \sum_a^b K\, (\Delta x)^2. \tag{6}$$

This last sum consists of n terms each of which is equal to $K(\Delta x)^2$, where $\Delta x = (b - a)/n$. Therefore

$$\sum_a^b K\, (\Delta x)^2 = nK(b - a)^2/n^2 = K(b - a)^2/n = K(b - a)\, \Delta x,$$

and (6) becomes

$$\left| U - \sum_a^b f(X)\, \Delta x \right| \leq K(b - a)\, \Delta x. \tag{7}$$

In other words, if the error in the approximation (1) to each individual ΔU is no more than a constant times the *square* of Δx, then the error in the approximation (2) to the *total* U is no more than a constant times the *first power* of Δx. Now let Δx approach zero in (7). The sum on the left becomes the definite integral (3), and the term on the right becomes zero. In other words, U is exactly equal to the definite integral in this case.

Second case. Suppose the correction terms are numerically no larger than a constant K' times Δx times δy:

$$|\alpha \, \Delta x| \leq K' \, \Delta x \, \delta y,$$

where K' is the same for all subintervals and all methods of subdivision, and where δy is the oscillation in the interval $(x, \, x + \Delta x)$ of a function $y = \phi(x)$ that is continuous over the closed interval $(a, \, b)$. Then one finds in this case that the total error in the approximation (2) is no larger than

$$K'(b - a) \text{ times (max. } \delta y).$$

But the maximum δy also approaches zero when Δx does, so again we find that U is given exactly by the definite integral.

We have given criteria such as

$$|\alpha \, \Delta x| \leq K \, (\Delta x)^2 \qquad \text{or} \qquad |\alpha \, \Delta x| \leq K' \, \Delta x \, \delta y,$$

where K and K' are constants. Usually, in an application, we have a function of x in place of K or K' in these inequalities. But a function of x that is continuous over the closed interval $a \leq x \leq b$ has a maximum absolute value M on that interval, and we could take K (or K') equal to M in such a case. Also, the correction terms $\alpha \, \Delta x$ could involve finite combinations of the two cases discussed above, provided the inequality

$$|\alpha \, \Delta x| \leq K \, (\Delta x)^2 + K' \, \Delta x \, \delta y$$

is satisfied for some choice of the constants K and K'.

Roughly speaking, we may say that in the approximation

$$\Delta U \approx f(X) \, \Delta x$$

we must include all first power Δx terms but we may omit higher power terms like $(\Delta x)^2$, $(\Delta x)^3$, and so on, or we may omit such mixed terms as $(\Delta x)(\Delta y)$, $(\Delta x)^2(\Delta y)$, $(\Delta x) \, (\Delta y)^2$, and so on. If each separate piece ΔU is estimated to this degree of accuracy, then the total quantity U which is given approximately by the sum (2) will be given exactly by the limit of the sum, namely, by the integral (4).

In discussing the cylindrical shell method of finding a volume of revolution, Article 5–4, we found that we could estimate the volume ΔV in a hollow shell as follows:

$$2\pi\left(x + \frac{\Delta x}{2}\right) \cdot y \cdot \Delta x \leq \Delta V \leq 2\pi\left(x + \frac{\Delta x}{2}\right)(y + \Delta y)\,\Delta x. \qquad (8)$$

Multiplied out, this becomes

$$2\pi xy\,\Delta x + \pi y\,(\Delta x)^2 \leq \Delta V \leq 2\pi xy\,\Delta x + \pi y\,(\Delta x)^2 + 2\pi x\,\Delta x\Delta y + \pi\Delta y(\Delta x)^2.$$

If we ignore all except the first power terms in Δx, we have the approximation

$$\Delta V \approx 2\pi xy\,\Delta x,$$

with an error that involves combinations like $\pi y\,(\Delta x)^2$, $2\pi x\,\Delta y\,\Delta x$, $\pi\Delta y(\Delta x)^2$. All such terms may be safely ignored when we go to the *limit* of the sum:

$$V = \lim_{\Delta x \to 0} \sum_a^b 2\pi xy\,\Delta x = \int_a^b 2\pi xy\,dx = \int_a^b 2\pi xf(x)\,dx.$$

Infinitesimals. A variable, such as Δx above, that approaches zero as a limit is called an infinitesimal. Terms that approach zero as the first power of Δx are said to be of the *same order* as Δx, but terms which approach zero as $(\Delta x)^2$ or as $\Delta y\,\Delta x$ are called infinitesimals·of *higher order* than Δx. In setting up a definite integral, we must retain those infinitesimals that are of the same order as Δx, but we may omit those infinitesimals·that are of higher order than Δx. Thus we may omit the term $\alpha\,\Delta x$, Eq. (5), if α is an infinitesimal of the same order as Δx (or higher order) or of the same order as δy (or higher order), and the *limit* in (4) will give the exact value of U.

PROBLEMS

1. In Fig. 5–6, Article 5–4, let V_a^x denote the volume generated by rotating about the y-axis the area under the curve $y = f(x)$ between the ordinate at a and the ordinate at x, $(x > a)$. By making use of the inequality (8) in this section, show that

$$\frac{dV_a^x}{dx} = \lim_{\Delta x \to 0} \frac{\Delta V_a^x}{\Delta x} = 2\pi xf(x).$$

From this, deduce that

$$V_a^b = \int_a^b 2\pi xf(x)\,dx.$$

2. Let U_a^x denote the amount of the quantity U associated with the interval

(a, x) and let ΔU in Eq. (5) represent $U_a^{x+\Delta x} - U_a^x = U_x^{x+\Delta x}$. If the function $f(x)$ in Eq. (5) is continuous over the closed interval $a \le x \le b$ and $|\alpha \Delta x| \le K(\Delta x)^2$, where K is a constant, show that

$$\frac{dU_a^x}{dx} = \lim_{\Delta x \to 0} \frac{\Delta U}{\Delta x} = f(x).$$

From this, deduce that $U_a^b = \int_a^b f(x)\,dx$.

3. In Problem 2, replace the condition $|\alpha \Delta x| \le K(\Delta x)^2$ by the condition

$$|\alpha \Delta x| \le |K' \Delta x\; \delta y|,$$

where K' is a constant and δy is the oscillation over the interval $(x, x + \Delta x)$ of a function $y = g(x)$ that is continuous over the closed interval $a \le x \le b$, and derive the same conclusion as in Problem 2.

5–6 Length of a plane curve. Divide the arc AB, Fig. 5–12, into n pieces and join the successive points of division by straight lines. A representative line, such as PQ, will have length

$$PQ = \sqrt{(\Delta x_k)^2 + (\Delta y_k)^2}.$$

The length of the curve AB is approximately

$$L_A^B \approx \sum_{k=1}^{n} \sqrt{(\Delta x_k)^2 + (\Delta y_k)^2}.$$

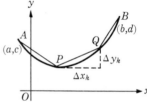

FIGURE 5–12

When the number of division points is increased indefinitely while the lengths of the individual segments tend to zero, we obtain

$$L_A^B = \lim_{n \to \infty} \sum_{k=1}^{n} \sqrt{(\Delta x_k)^2 + (\Delta y_k)^2}, \tag{1}$$

provided the limit exists.* The sum on the right side of (1) is not in the standard form to which we can apply the Fundamental Theorem of the integral calculus, but it can be put into such a form as follows.

Suppose that the function $y = f(x)$ is continuous and possesses a continuous derivative at each point of the curve from $A[a, f(a)]$ to $B[b, f(b)]$. Then, by the Mean Value Theorem, there is some point $P^*(x_k^*, y_k^*)$ be-

---

* For most smooth curves encountered in practice, the limit does exist. Such curves are called rectifiable. An example of a continuous curve that is not rectifiable is given by the curve

$$y = \begin{cases} x \sin 1/x & \text{when} & x \ne 0, \\ 0 & \text{when} & x = 0, \end{cases} \quad \frac{-\pi}{2} \le x \le \frac{\pi}{2}.$$

tween P and Q on the curve where the tangent to the curve is parallel to the chord PQ. That is,

$$f'(x_k^*) = \frac{\Delta y_k}{\Delta x_k}$$

or

$$\Delta y_k = f'(x_k^*)\, \Delta x_k.$$

Hence (1) may also be written in the form

$$L_A^B = \lim_{n \to \infty} \sum_{k=1}^{n} \sqrt{(\Delta x_k)^2 + (f'(x_k^*)\, \Delta x_k)^2}$$

$$= \lim_{\Delta x \to 0} \left(\sum_a^b \sqrt{1 + (f'(x^*))^2}\, \Delta x \right)$$

or

$$L_A^B = \int_a^b \sqrt{1 + \left(\frac{dy}{dx}\right)^2}\, dx, \qquad (2a)$$

where we have written dy/dx for $f'(x)$.

We may remark that it is sometimes convenient, if x may be expressed as a single-valued function of y, to interchange the roles of x and y (indeed, the *length* of a curve does not depend upon the particular axes used) and the length is also given by

$$L_A^B = \int_c^d \sqrt{1 + \left(\frac{dx}{dy}\right)^2}\, dy. \qquad (2b)$$

In many applications, the curve is traced by a moving particle whose coordinates x and y are given as functions of some third variable, such as the time t. Let the equations of motion be

$$x = g(t), \qquad y = h(t), \qquad (3)$$

and let t_k, t_{k+1} be the values of t at P and Q respectively. Suppose the arc AB is described just once by $P(x, y)$ as t goes from t_a at A to t_b at B. If the functions $g(t)$ and $h(t)$ are continuously differentiable for t between t_a and t_b inclusive, the Mean Value Theorem may be applied to Eq. (3) to give

$$\Delta x_k = x_{k+1} - x_k = g(t_{k+1}) - g(t_k) = g'(t_k')\, \Delta t_k,$$

$$\Delta y_k = y_{k+1} - y_k = h(t_{k+1}) - h(t_k) = h'(t_k'')\, \Delta t_k,$$

where t'_k and t''_k are two suitably chosen values of t between t_k and t_{k+1}. Then (1) becomes

$$
L_A^B = \lim_{n \to \infty} \sum_{k=1}^{n} \sqrt{(g'(t'_k))^2 + (h'(t''_k))^2}\, \Delta t_k
$$

$$
= \int_{t_a}^{t_b} \sqrt{\left(\frac{dx}{dt}\right)^2 + \left(\frac{dy}{dt}\right)^2}\, dt.
$$

(4)

Clearly, there is nothing inherently dependent upon the fact that t stands for time in Eqs. (3) and (4). Any other variable could serve as well, and if θ is used instead of t in (3) in representing the curve, then we need only replace t by θ in (4) as well.

EXAMPLE 1. The coordinates (x, y) of a point on a circle of radius r can be expressed in terms of the central angle θ, Fig. 5–13, as follows:

$$
x = r \cos \theta, \qquad y = r \sin \theta.
$$

The point $P(x, y)$ moves once around the circle as θ varies from 0 to 2π, so that the circumference of the circle is given by

$$
C = \int_0^{2\pi} \sqrt{\left(\frac{dx}{d\theta}\right)^2 + \left(\frac{dy}{d\theta}\right)^2}\, d\theta.
$$

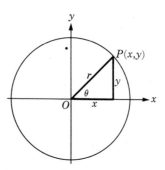

FIGURE 5–13

We find

$$
\frac{dx}{d\theta} = -r \sin \theta, \qquad \frac{dy}{d\theta} = r \cos \theta,
$$

so that

$$
\left(\frac{dx}{d\theta}\right)^2 + \left(\frac{dy}{d\theta}\right)^2 = r^2(\sin^2 \theta + \cos^2 \theta) = r^2,
$$

and hence

$$
C = \int_0^{2\pi} r\, d\theta = r[\theta]_0^{2\pi} = 2\pi r.
$$

It should be remarked that Eq. (4) is frequently written in terms of differentials in place of derivatives. This is done formally by writing $(dt)^2$ under the radical in place of the dt outside the radical, and then writing

$$
(dx)^2 = \left(\frac{dx}{dt}\, dt\right)^2 = \left(\frac{dx}{dt}\right)^2 (dt)^2
$$

and

$$(dy)^2 = \left(\frac{dy}{dt}\, dt\right)^2 = \left(\frac{dy}{dt}\right)^2 (dt)^2.$$

It is also customary to eliminate the parentheses in $(dx)^2$ and write dx^2 instead, so that Eq. (4) is written

$$L = \int \sqrt{dx^2 + dy^2}. \tag{5}$$

Of course, dx and dy must both be expressed in terms of one and the same variable, and appropriate limits must be supplied in (5) before the integration can be performed

A useful mnemonic device is also associated with (5). Namely, it is customary to write

$$ds = \sqrt{dx^2 + dy^2} \tag{6}$$

and treat ds as the differential of arc length, which can be integrated (between appropriate limits) to give the total length of a curve. Figure 5–14(a) gives the exact interpretation of ds corresponding to Eq. (6). Figure 5–14(b) is not strictly accurate, but is to be thought of as a simplified version of Fig. 5–14(a). The inaccuracies in this simplified version will be compensated if the arc of the curve is treated as the hypotenuse ds of a right triangle of sides dx and dy.

EXAMPLE 2. Find the length of the curve $y = x^{2/3}$ between $x = -1$ and $x = 8$.

Solution. From the equation of the curve, we find

$$\frac{dy}{dx} = \frac{2}{3} x^{-1/3}.$$

Since this becomes infinite at the origin (see Fig. 5–15), we use Eq. (2b) instead of (2a) to find the length of the curve. Then we need to find dx/dy. Since the

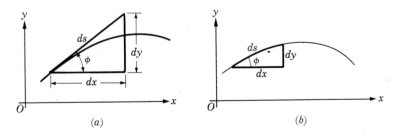

(a)   (b)

FIGURE 5–14

equation of the curve,

$$y = x^{2/3},$$

can also be written as

$$x = \pm y^{3/2},$$

we find

$$\frac{dx}{dy} = \pm \frac{3}{2} y^{1/2},$$

or

$$dx = \pm \frac{3}{2} y^{1/2} dy.$$

Then

$$ds^2 = dx^2 + dy^2 = (\tfrac{9}{4}y + 1) dy^2,$$

so that

$$ds = \sqrt{\tfrac{9}{4}y + 1} \, dy.$$

The portion of the curve between $A(-1, 1)$ and the origin has length

$$L_1 = \int_0^1 \sqrt{\tfrac{9}{4}y + 1} \, dy,$$

while the rest of the curve from the origin to $B(8, 4)$ has length

$$L_2 = \int_0^4 \sqrt{\tfrac{9}{4}y + 1} \, dy,$$

and the total length is

$$L = L_1 + L_2.$$

It is necessary to calculate the two lengths L_1 and L_2 as separate integrals, since $x = \pm y^{3/2}$ needs to be separated into two distinct functions of y. For the portion AO of the curve, we have $x = -y^{3/2}$, $0 \le y \le 1$; while on the arc OB, we have $x = +y^{3/2}$, $0 \le y \le 4$.

To evaluate the given integrals, we let

$$u = \tfrac{9}{4}y + 1,$$

then

$$du = \tfrac{9}{4}dy, \qquad dy = \tfrac{4}{9}du,$$

and

$$\int (\tfrac{9}{4}y + 1)^{1/2} dy = \tfrac{4}{9} \int u^{1/2} du = \tfrac{8}{27} u^{3/2}.$$

Therefore,

$$L = \tfrac{8}{27}\Big\{ (\tfrac{9}{4}y + 1)^{3/2} \Big]_0^1 + (\tfrac{9}{4}y + 1)^{3/2} \Big]_0^4 \Big\}$$

$$= \tfrac{1}{27}(13\sqrt{13} + 80\sqrt{10} - 16) = 10.5.$$

As a check against gross errors, we calculate the sum of the lengths of the two inscribed chords:

$$AO + OB = \sqrt{2} + \sqrt{80} = 10.4.$$

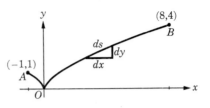

FIGURE 5–15

The check appears to be satisfactory.

The curve in Fig. 5–15 has a cusp at (0,0) where the slope becomes infinite. If we were to reconstruct the derivation of Eq. (2) for this particular curve, we would see that the crucial step that required an application of the Mean Value Theorem could not have been taken for the case of a chord PQ from a point P to the left of the cusp to a point Q to its right. For this reason, if for no other, when one or more cusps occur between the ends of a portion of a curve whose length is to be calculated, it is best to calculate the lengths of portions of the curve between cusps and add the results. We recall that the Mean Value Theorem is still valid even when the derivative becomes infinite at an extremity of the interval where it is to be applied, so that the derivation of Eq. (2) would be valid for the separate portions of a curve lying *between* cusps (or other discontinuities of dy/dx, such as occur at corners). Thus in the example just worked, we find the lengths L_1 from $A(-1, 1)$ to O (up to the cusp) and L_2 from O to $B(8, 4)$, then add the results to obtain $L = L_1 + L_2$. This was done by the sum of the two integrals. Had there been no point of discontinuity of dy/dx, it would not have been necessary to take two separate integrals, and Eq. (2a) could have been used.

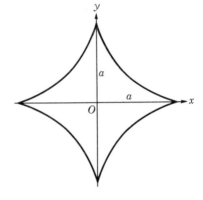

FIGURE 5–16

EXAMPLE 3. The coordinates of the point $P(x, y)$ on the four-cusped hypocycloid are given by

$$x = a \cos^3 \theta, \qquad y = a \sin^3 \theta.$$

Find the total length of the curve (Fig. 5–16).

Solution. When θ varies from 0 to $\pi/2$, P traces out the portion of the curve in the first quadrant. Also, from the fact that

$$x^{2/3} + y^{2/3} = a^{2/3} \ (\cos^2 \theta + \sin^2 \theta) = a^{2/3}$$

it will be seen that for every point (x, y) on the curve in the first quadrant, the corresponding points $(-x, y)$, $(-x, -y)$, and $(x, -y)$ in the other three quadrants are also on the curve, which is therefore symmetrical about both axes.

The portion of the curve in the first quadrant lies *between* two cusps and is one-quarter of the total length of the curve. Therefore

$$L = 4 \int_{\theta=0}^{\theta=\pi/2} \sqrt{dx^2 + dy^2}.$$

From the equation of the curve, we find

$$\frac{dx}{d\theta} = -3a \cos^2 \theta \sin \theta, \qquad dx = 3a \cos \theta \sin \theta \ (-\cos \theta) \ d\theta,$$

$$\frac{dy}{d\theta} = 3a \sin^2 \theta \cos \theta, \qquad dy = 3a \cos \theta \sin \theta \ (\sin \theta) \ d\theta,$$

and hence

$$ds^2 = dx^2 + dy^2 = (3a \cos \theta \sin \theta)^2 \ (\cos^2 \theta + \sin^2 \theta) \ (d\theta)^2$$

or

$$ds^2 = (3a \cos \theta \sin \theta \ d\theta)^2.$$

Hence, for θ between 0 and $\pi/2$,

$$ds = 3a \cos \theta \sin \theta \ d\theta$$

and

$$L = 4 \int_0^{\pi/2} 3a \cos \theta \sin \theta \ d\theta.$$

To evaluate this integral, we let

$$u = \sin \theta, \qquad du = \cos \theta \ d\theta,$$

and

$$\int \cos \theta \sin \theta \ d\theta = \int u \ du = \tfrac{1}{2} u^2 = \tfrac{1}{2} \sin^2 \theta,$$

so that

$$L = (12a) \left(\tfrac{1}{2} \sin^2 \theta \right) \Big]_0^{\pi/2} = 6a.$$

PROBLEMS

1. Find the length of the curve $y = \tfrac{1}{3}(x^2 + 2)^{3/2}$ from $x = 0$ to $x = 3$.
2. Find the length of the curve $y = x^{3/2}$ from $(0, 0)$ to $(4, 8)$.
3. Find the length of the curve $9x^2 = 4y^3$ from $(0, 0)$ to $(2\sqrt{3}, 3)$.
4. Find the length of the curve $y = x^3/3 + 1/(4x)$ from $x = 1$ to $x = 3$.
5. Find the length of the curve $x = y^4/4 + 1/(8y^2)$ from $y = 1$ to $y = 2$.
6. Find the length of the curve $(y + 1)^2 = 4x^3$ from $x = 0$ to $x = 1$.
7. Find the distance traveled between $t = 0$ and $t = \pi/2$ by a particle $P(x, y)$

whose position at time t is given by

$$x = a \cos t + at \sin t, \qquad y = a \sin t - at \cos t,$$

where a is a positive constant.

8. Find the distance traveled by the particle $P(x, y)$ between $t = 0$ and $t = 4$ if the position at time t is given by

$$x = \frac{t^2}{2}, \qquad y = \tfrac{1}{3}(2t + 1)^{3/2}.$$

9. The position of a particle $P(x, y)$ at time t is given by

$$x = \tfrac{1}{3}(2t + 3)^{3/2}, \qquad y = \frac{t^2}{2} + t.$$

Find the distance it travels between $t = 0$ and $t = 3$.

5–7 Area of a surface of revolution. Suppose that the curve in Fig. 5–17 is rotated about the x-axis. It will generate a surface in space. The inscribed polygonal line segments will generate inscribed frustums of cones. The sum of the lateral areas of these frustums will be an approximation to the area of the surface. To obtain an analytic expression for

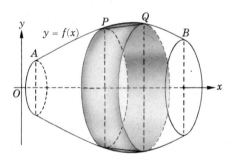

FIGURE 5–17

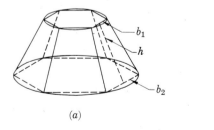

(a)

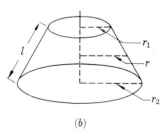

(b)

FIGURE 5–18

this approximation, we require the formula

$$A = \pi(r_1 + r_2)l \tag{1}$$

for the lateral area A of a frustum of slant height l, where r_1 and r_2 are the radii of its bases.

To establish Eq. (1), we may imagine the frustum of a cone to be the limit of inscribed frustums of pyramids (see Fig. 5–18a). If each base of an inscribed frustum of a pyramid is a regular polygon of n sides, and b_1 is the length of one side in the upper face, while b_2 is the length of a side in the lower face, then the lateral area will consist of n trapezoids each having an area

$$\tfrac{1}{2}(b_1 + b_2)h.$$

Hence the n trapezoids have area

$$\tfrac{1}{2}(nb_1 + nb_2)h.$$

As n increases indefinitely, we have

$$\lim_{n\to\infty} nb_1 = 2\pi r_1, \qquad \lim_{n\to\infty} nb_2 = 2\pi r_2,$$

and

$$\lim_{n\to\infty} h = l,$$

so that

$$A = \lim_{n\to\infty} \tfrac{1}{2}(nb_1 + nb_2)h = \tfrac{1}{2}(2\pi r_1 + 2\pi r_2)l = \pi(r_1 + r_2)l,$$

which establishes Eq. (1). Note that if $r_1 = r_2$, Eq. (1) reduces to the correct formula for the lateral area of a cylinder, and if $r_1 = 0$, it gives the correct result for the lateral area of a cone. It can also be put into the form

$$A = 2\pi rl$$

where

$$r = \tfrac{1}{2}(r_1 + r_2)$$

is the radius of the mid-section of the frustum. In this form, (1) says that the lateral area of a frustum of a cone = (circumference of mid-section) $\times$ (slant height).

We now consider the portion of the surface ΔS generated by the arc PQ, and its inscribed frustum of a cone generated by the chord PQ. Call the coordinates of P: (x, y), and of Q: $(x + \Delta x, y + \Delta y)$, and take

$$r_1 = y, \qquad r_2 = y + \Delta y, \qquad l = \sqrt{(\Delta x)^2 + (\Delta y)^2}$$

in Eq. (1). Then we have the approximation

$$S \approx \sum_{x=a}^{b} \pi(2y + \Delta y) \sqrt{(\Delta x)^2 + (\Delta y)^2}$$

or

$$S \approx \sum_{a}^{b} 2\pi \left(y + \frac{1}{2}\Delta y\right) \sqrt{1 + \left(\frac{\Delta y}{\Delta x}\right)^2} \, \Delta x.$$

If y and dy/dx are continuous functions of x and we omit products like $(\Delta y)(\Delta x)$ and higher powers of Δx in this approximation, we have

$$S \approx \sum_{a}^{b} 2\pi y \sqrt{1 + \left(\frac{dy}{dx}\right)^2} \, \Delta x.$$

Then taking the limit as Δx tends to zero, we get

$$S = \lim_{\Delta x \to 0} \sum_{a}^{b} 2\pi y \sqrt{1 + \left(\frac{dy}{dx}\right)^2} \, \Delta x$$

or

$$S = \int_{a}^{b} 2\pi y \sqrt{1 + \left(\frac{dy}{dx}\right)^2} \, dx. \qquad (2)$$

Our end result, Eq. (2), is easily remembered if we write

$$\sqrt{1 + \left(\frac{dy}{dx}\right)^2} \, dx = ds$$

and take

$$S = \int 2\pi y \, ds. \qquad (3)$$

If we let

$$dS \doteq 2\pi y \, ds,$$

so that

$$S = \int dS,$$

we may interpret dS as the product of a

$$\text{circumference} = 2\pi y$$

and a

$$\text{slant height} = ds.$$

Thus dS gives the lateral area of a frustum of a cone of slant height ds if the point (x, y) is the mid-point of the element of arc length ds (Fig. 5–19).

A question which often occurs to the alert student is the following. Why not approximate the surface area S by inscribed *cylinders* and arrive at a result

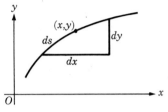

$$S = \int 2\pi y \, dx,$$

FIGURE 5–19

having dx instead of ds, to replace Eq. (3)? This is a reasonable question. Since we know from our discussion on volume that inscribed cylinders work perfectly well for *volumes* of revolution, why not use them for *surfaces* of revolution also? The answer hinges on the fact that the approximation.

$$\Delta V \approx \pi y^2 \, \Delta x$$

for the volume of a slice involves, at worst, terms which are products like (Δx) (Δy) and higher powers of Δx and these contribute zero to the *limit* of the sum of volumes of the inscribed cylinders. (See Article 5–5.) But the approximations

$$\text{(a)} \quad \Delta S \approx 2\pi y \, \Delta x$$

and

$$\text{(b)} \quad \Delta S \approx 2\pi y \sqrt{(\Delta x)^2 + (\Delta y)^2}$$

for the surface area of a slice cannot *both* be this accurate. For their ratio is

$$\frac{2\pi y \sqrt{(\Delta x)^2 + (\Delta y)^2}}{2\pi y \, \Delta x} = \sqrt{1 + \left(\frac{\Delta y}{\Delta x}\right)^2},$$

which has the limiting value

$$\lim_{\Delta x \to 0} \sqrt{1 + \left(\frac{\Delta y}{\Delta x}\right)^2} = \sqrt{1 + \left(\frac{dy}{dx}\right)^2},$$

and this will be different from one (unless $dy/dx = 0$, which would not be generally true), whereas two approximations that differ only by terms involving products like $(\Delta y)(\Delta x)$ and higher powers of Δx have a ratio whose limiting value is unity. Since the approximations (a) and (b) above will usually lead to different answers when we pass to the corresponding definite integrals, they cannot both be correct, and we must abandon one or both of them. But the approximation (b) is clearly the one which corresponds to a natural way of defining the surface area of a surface of revolution and it leads to (3).

If the axis of revolution is the y-axis, the corresponding formula that replaces (3) is

$$S = \int 2\pi x \, ds,$$

while, more generally, we may write

$$S = \int 2\pi\rho \, ds$$

(4)

if ρ is the distance from the axis of revolution to the element of arc length ds. Both ρ and ds need to be expressed in terms of some one variable and proper limits must be supplied to (4) in any particular problem.

EXAMPLE 1. The circle

$$x^2 + y^2 = r^2$$

is revolved about the x-axis (Fig. 5–20). Find the area of the sphere generated.

Solution. We write

$$dS = 2\pi y \, ds,$$

$$ds = \sqrt{dx^2 + dy^2},$$

and use

$$x = r \cos\theta, \qquad y = r \sin\theta$$

to represent the circle. Then

$$dx = -r \sin\theta \, d\theta, \qquad dy = r \cos\theta \, d\theta,$$

so that

$$ds = r \, d\theta$$

and

$$dS = 2\pi y \, ds = 2\pi(r \sin\theta) \, r \, d\theta$$

$$= 2\pi r^2 \sin\theta \, d\theta.$$

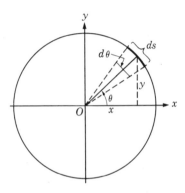

FIGURE 5–20

The top half of the circle generates the entire sphere, and the representative point (x, y) traces out this upper semicircle as θ varies from 0 to π. Hence

$$S = \int_0^\pi 2\pi r^2 \sin\theta \, d\theta$$

$$= 2\pi r^2 \left[-\cos\theta \right]_0^\pi = 4\pi r^2.$$

EXAMPLE 2. The circle in Example 1 is revolved about the line $y = -r$, which is tangent to the circle at the point $(0, -r)$ (Fig. 5–21). Find the area of the surface generated.

Solution. Here it takes the whole circle to generate the surface, and in terms of the previous example, this means that we must let θ vary from 0 to 2π. The radius of rotation now becomes

$$\rho = y + r,$$

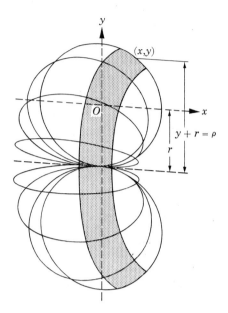

FIGURE 5–21

and we have

$$dS = 2\pi\rho \, ds = 2\pi(y + r)r \, d\theta = 2\pi(r \sin \theta + r)r \, d\theta.$$

Hence

$$S = \int_0^{2\pi} 2\pi \, (\sin \theta + 1)r^2 \, d\theta = 2\pi r^2 \left[-\cos \theta + \theta \right]_0^{2\pi} = 4\pi^2 r^2.$$

PROBLEMS

1. Find the area of the surface generated by rotating the hypocycloid $x = a \cos^3 \theta$, $y = a \sin^3 \theta$ about the x-axis.

2. Find the area of the surface generated by rotating the portion of the curve $y = \frac{1}{3}(x^2 + 2)^{3/2}$ between $x = 0$ and $x = 3$ about the y-axis.

3. Find the area of the surface generated by rotating about the x-axis the arc of the curve $y = x^3$ between $x = 0$ and $x = 1$.

4. Find the area of the surface generated by rotating about the y-axis the arc of the curve $y = x^2$ between $(0, 0)$ and $(2, 4)$.

5. The arc of the curve $y = x^3/3 + 1/(4x)$ from $x = 1$ to $x = 3$ is rotated about the line $y = -1$. Find the surface area generated.

6. The arc of the curve $x = y^4/4 + 1/(8y^2)$ from $y = 1$ to $y = 2$ is rotated about the x-axis. Find the surface area generated.

7. The curve described by the particle $P(x, y)$,

$$x = t + 1, \qquad y = \frac{t^2}{2} + t,$$

from $t = 0$ to $t = 4$, is rotated about the y-axis. Find the surface area that is generated.

8. The loop of the curve $9x^2 = y(3 - y)^2$ is rotated about the x-axis. Find the surface area generated.

5–8 Average value of a function. The process of finding the average value of a finite number of data is familiar to all students. For example, if $y_1, y_2, \ldots, y_n$ are the grades of a class of n students on a certain calculus quiz, then the class average on that quiz is

$$y_{av} = \frac{y_1 + y_2 + \cdots + y_n}{n}. \tag{1}$$

When the number of data is infinite, it is not feasible to use Eq. (1) (since it is likely to take on the meaningless form ∞/∞). This situation arises, in particular, when the data y are given by a continuous function

$$y = f(x), \qquad a \le x \le b.$$

In this case, the average value of y, with respect to x, is defined to be

$$(y_{av})_x = \frac{1}{b - a} \int_a^b f(x) \, dx. \tag{2}$$

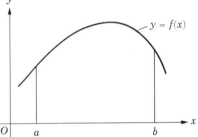

FIGURE 5–22

The curve in Fig. 5–22, for example, might represent temperature as a function of time over a twenty-four hour period. Equation (2) would then give the "average temperature" for the day.

Remark 1. It may be possible to express y as a function of x, or, alternatively, as a function of u. Then $(y_{av})_x$ and $(y_{av})_u$ need not be equal. For example, for a freely falling body starting from rest,

$$s = \tfrac{1}{2}gt^2, \qquad v = gt, \qquad v = \sqrt{2gs}.$$

Suppose we calculate the average velocity, first with respect to t and second with respect to s, from $t_1 = 0$, $s_1 = 0$ to $t_2 > 0$, $s_2 = \tfrac{1}{2}gt_2^2$. Then, by definition,

$$(v_{av})_t = \frac{1}{t_2 - 0} \int_0^{t_2} gt \, dt = \tfrac{1}{2}gt_2 = \tfrac{1}{2}v_2,$$

$$(v_{av})_s = \frac{1}{s_2 - 0} \int_0^{s_2} \sqrt{2gs} \, ds = \tfrac{2}{3}\sqrt{2gs_2} = \tfrac{2}{3}v_2.$$

Remark 2. If both sides of Eq. (2) are multiplied by $b - a$, we have

$$(y_{\text{av}})_x \cdot (b - a) = \int_a^b f(x)\, dx. \tag{3}$$

The right side of Eq. (3) represents the area bounded above by the curve $y = f(x)$, below by the x-axis, and on the sides by the ordinates $x = a$, $x = b$. The left side of the equation can be interpreted as the area of a rectangle of altitude $(y_{\text{av}})_x$ and of base $b - a$. Hence, Eq. (3) provides a geometric interpretation of $(y_{\text{av}})_x$ as that ordinate of the curve $y = f(x)$ that should be used as altitude if one wishes to construct a rectangle whose base is the interval $a \le x \le b$ and whose area is equal to the area under the curve (Fig. 5–23). In the narrower sense of area, this statement is only valid when the curve lies above the x-axis. In case the curve lies partly or entirely

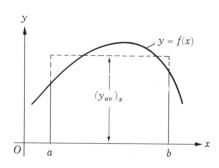

FIGURE 5–23

below the x-axis, we would count areas below the x-axis as negative. In such a case there might well be a certain amount of canceling of positive and negative areas.

Remark 3. Equation (2) is a *definition*, and hence is not subject to proof. Nevertheless, some discussion may help to explain why this particular formula is used to define the average. One might arrive at it as follows. From the total "population" of x-values, $a \le x \le b$, we select a representative "sample," $x_1, x_2, \ldots, x_n$, uniformly distributed between a and b. Then, using Eq. (1), we calculate the average of the functional values

$$y_1 = f(x_1), \qquad y_2 = f(x_2), \qquad \ldots, \qquad y_n = f(x_n)$$

associated with these representative x's. This gives us

$$\frac{y_1 + y_2 + \cdots + y_n}{n} = \frac{f(x_1) + f(x_2) + \cdots + f(x_n)}{n}. \tag{4}$$

Since we require that the x's be uniformly distributed between a and b, let us take the spacing to be Δx, with

$$x_2 - x_1 = x_3 - x_2 = \cdots = x_n - x_{n-1} = \Delta x$$

and

$$\Delta x = \frac{b - a}{n}.$$

Then, in (4), let us replace the n in the denominator by $(b - a)/\Delta x$, thus obtaining

$$\frac{f(x_1) + f(x_2) + \cdots + f(x_n)}{(b - a)/\Delta x} = \frac{f(x_1)\, \Delta x + f(x_2)\, \Delta x + \cdots + f(x_n)\, \Delta x}{b - a}.$$

If, now, n is very large (Δx small), the expression

$$f(x_1)\, \Delta x + f(x_2)\, \Delta x + \cdots + f(x_n)\, \Delta x = \sum_{k=1}^{n} f(x_k)\, \Delta x$$

is very nearly equal to $\int_a^b f(x)\, dx$. In fact, if we take limits, letting $n \to \infty$, we obtain precisely

$$\lim_{n \to \infty} \frac{f(x_1)\, \Delta x + f(x_2)\, \Delta x + \cdots + f(x_n)\, \Delta x}{b - a} = \frac{1}{b - a} \int_a^b f(x)\, dx.$$

This is the expression used to define the average value of y in Eq. (2).

Problems

In each of the following problems (1 through 5), find the average value with respect to x, over the given domain, of the given function $f(x)$. In each case, draw a graph of the curve $y = f(x)$, and sketch a rectangle whose altitude is the average ordinate.

1. (a) $\sin x$, $0 \le x \le \pi/2$ 2. (a) $\sin^2 x$, $0 \le x \le \pi/2$
   (b) $\sin x$, $0 \le x \le 2\pi$ (b) $\sin^2 x$, $\pi \le x \le 2\pi$

3. $\sqrt{2x + 1}$, $4 \le x \le 12$ 4. $\frac{1}{2} + \frac{1}{2} \cos 2x$, $0 \le x \le \pi$
5. $\alpha x + \beta$; $a \le x \le b$ $[\alpha, \beta, a, b,$ constants]

6. Given a circle C of radius a, and a diameter AB of C. Chords are drawn perpendicular to AB, intercepting equal segments along AB. Find the limit of the average of the lengths of these chords, as the number of chords tends to infinity. [*Hint:* $\int_{-a}^{a} \sqrt{a^2 - x^2}\, dx$ is $\frac{1}{2}\pi a^2$, since it is the area of a semicircle of radius a.]

7. Solve Problem 6 under the modified assumption that the chords intercept equal arcs along the circumference of C.

8. Solve Problem 6 using the *squares* of the lengths, in place of the lengths of the chords.

9. Solve Problem 7 using the *squares* of the lengths, in place of the lengths of the chords.

5–9 Moments and center of mass. If several masses $m_1, m_2, \ldots, m_n$ are placed along the x-axis at distances $x_1, x_2, \ldots, x_n$ respectively from the origin (Fig. 5–24), then their moment about the origin is defined to be

$$x_1 m_1 + x_2 m_2 + \cdots + x_n m_n = \sum_{k=1}^{n} x_k m_k. \tag{1}$$

If all the mass

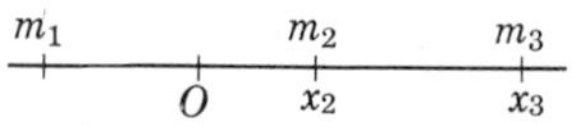

$$m_1 + m_2 + \cdots + m_n = \sum_{k=1}^{n} m_k \quad (2)$$

$m_1 \qquad m_2 \qquad m_3$

$O \quad x_2 \qquad x_3$

FIGURE 5–24

is concentrated at one point of abscissa $\bar{x}$, the total moment is

$$\bar{x}\left(\sum_{k=1}^{n} m_k\right).$$

The position of $\bar{x}$ for which this is the same as the total moment in (1) is called the *center of mass*. The condition

$$\bar{x}\sum_{k=1}^{n} m_k = \sum_{k=1}^{n} x_k m_k$$

thus determines

$$\bar{x} = \frac{\displaystyle\sum_{k=1}^{n} x_k m_k}{\displaystyle\sum_{k=1}^{n} m_k}. \quad (3)$$

EXAMPLE 1. The principle of a moment underlies the simple seesaw. For instance (Fig. 5–25), suppose one child weighs 80 lb and sits 5 ft from the point O, while the other child weighs 100 lb and is 4 ft from O. Then the child at the left end of the seesaw produces a moment of $80 \times 5 = 400$ (lb-ft), which tends to rotate the plank counterclockwise about O. The child at the right end of the plank produces a moment of $100 \times 4 = 400$ (lb-ft), which tends to rotate the plank clockwise around O. If we introduce coordinates $x_1 = -5$ and $x_2 = +4$, we find

$$x_1 m_1 + x_2 m_2 = (-5)(80) + (4)(100)$$

$$= -400 + 400 = 0$$

as the resultant moment about O. The same moment, zero, would be obtained if both children were at O, which is the center of their mass.

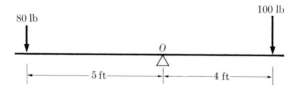

80 lb

100 lb

O

5 ft —— 4 ft

FIGURE 5–25

If, instead of being placed on the x-axis, the masses are located in the xy-plane at points $(x_1, y_1,)$ (x_2, y_2), . . . , (x_n, y_n), in that order, then we define their moments with respect to the y-axis and with respect to the x-axis as

$$M_y = x_1 m_1 + x_2 m_2 + \cdots + x_n m_n = \sum_{k=1}^{n} x_k m_k,$$

$$M_x = y_1 m_1 + y_2 m_2 + \cdots + y_n m_n = \sum_{k=1}^{n} y_k m_k.$$

The center of mass is the point $(\bar{x}, \bar{y})$,

$$\bar{x} = \frac{\sum x_k m_k}{\sum m_k}, \qquad \bar{y} = \frac{\sum y_k m_k}{\sum m_k}, \tag{4}$$

where the total mass could be concentrated and still give the same total moments M_y and M_x.

In space, three coordinates are needed to specify the position of a point. If the masses are located at the points (x_1, y_1, z_1), (x_2, y_2, z_2), . . . , (x_n, y_n, z_n), we define their moments with respect to the various coordinate planes as

$$M_{yz} = x_1 m_1 + x_2 m_2 + \cdots + x_n m_n = \sum_{k=1}^{n} x_k m_k,$$

$$M_{zx} = y_1 m_1 + y_2 m_2 + \cdots + y_n m_n = \sum_{k=1}^{n} y_k m_k,$$

$$M_{xy} = z_1 m_1 + z_2 m_2 + \cdots + z_n m_n = \sum_{k=1}^{n} z_k m_k.$$

$(M_{yz} = $ moment with respect to the yz-plane, etc.)

The center of mass $(\bar{x}, \bar{y}, \bar{z})$ is the point where the total mass could be concentrated without altering these moments. Its coordinates therefore are given by

$$\bar{x} = \frac{\sum x_k m_k}{\sum m_k}, \qquad \bar{y} = \frac{\sum y_k m_k}{\sum m_k}, \qquad \bar{z} = \frac{\sum z_k m_k}{\sum m_k}. \tag{5}$$

Now most physical objects with which we deal are composed of enormously large numbers of molecules. It would be extremely difficult, and in most cases unnecessary, for us to concern ourselves with the molecular structure of a physical object, such as a pendulum, whose motion as a whole is to be studied. Instead, we make certain simplifying assumptions which we recognize as being only approximately correct. One such assumption is that the matter in a given solid is continuously distributed throughout the solid. Furthermore, if P is a point in the solid and ΔV is an element of volume which contains P, and if Δm is the mass of ΔV, then we assume that the ratio $\Delta m / \Delta V$ tends to a definite limit

$$\delta = \lim_{\Delta V \to 0} \frac{\Delta m}{\Delta V}, \tag{6}$$

as the largest dimension of ΔV approaches zero. The limit δ is called the *density* of the solid at the point P. It is customary to write Eq. (6) in the alternative forms

$$\delta = dm/dV, \qquad dm = \delta \, dV. \tag{7}$$

If now a solid is divided into small pieces ΔV of mass Δm and if $P(\tilde{x}, \tilde{y}, \tilde{z})$ is a point in ΔV and δ is the density at P, then

$$\Delta m \approx \delta \, \Delta V.$$

The moments of Δm with respect to the coordinate planes are not defined by what we have done thus far. But now we may think of replacing the Δm that fills the volume ΔV by an equal mass all concentrated at the point P. The moments of this concentrated mass with respect to the coordinate planes are

$$\tilde{x} \, \Delta m, \qquad \tilde{y} \, \Delta m, \qquad \tilde{z} \, \Delta m.$$

Now we add the moments of all the concentrated masses in all the volume elements ΔV and take the limit as the ΔV's approach zero. This leads us to the following *definitions* of the moments M_{yz}, etc., for the mass as a whole:

$$M_{yz} = \lim_{\Delta m \to 0} \sum \tilde{x} \, \Delta m = \int \tilde{x} \, dm,$$

$$M_{zx} = \lim_{\Delta m \to 0} \sum \tilde{y} \, \Delta m = \int \tilde{y} \, dm,$$

$$M_{xy} = \lim_{\Delta m \to 0} \sum \tilde{z} \, \Delta m = \int \tilde{z} \, dm.$$

From these, we then deduce the equations

$$\boxed{\bar{x} = \frac{\int \tilde{x} \, dm}{\int dm}, \qquad \bar{y} = \frac{\int \tilde{y} \, dm}{\int dm}, \qquad \bar{z} = \frac{\int \tilde{z} \, dm}{\int dm}} \tag{8}$$

for the center of mass of the solid as a whole.

In theory, the element dm is approximately the mass in a volume element dV which has three small dimensions as in Fig. 5–26. In a later chapter we shall see how to evaluate the integrals (8) which arise when this is done. In practice, however, we can usually take

$$dm = \delta \, dV$$

with a volume element dV which has only one small dimension. Then we must interpret $\tilde{x}, \tilde{y}, \tilde{z}$ in the integrands in (8) as the coordinates of the **center of mass** of the **element** dm.

In many problems of practical importance the density δ is constant and the solid possesses a plane of symmetry. Then it is easy to see that the center of mass lies in this plane of symmetry. For we may, with no loss of generality, choose our coordinate reference frame in such a way that the yz-plane is the plane of symmetry. Then for every element of mass Δm with a positive $\tilde{x}$ there is a symmetrically located element of mass with a corresponding negative $\tilde{x}$. These two elements have moments which are equal in magni-

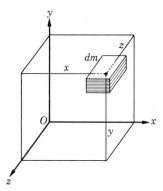

FIGURE 5–26

tude and of opposite signs. The whole mass is made up of such symmetric pairs of elements and the sum of their moments about the yz-plane is zero. Therefore $\tilde{x} = 0$; that is, the center of mass lies in the plane of symmetry. If there are two planes of symmetry, their intersection is an axis of symmetry and the center of mass must lie on this axis, since it lies in both planes of symmetry.

The most frequently encountered distributions of mass are

(a) along a thin wire or filament: $dm = \delta_1 \, ds$,
(b) in a thin plate or shell: $dm = \delta_2 \, dA$ or $\delta_2 \, dS$,
(c) in a solid: $dm = \delta_3 \, dV$,

where

$$ds = \text{element of arc length,}$$
$$\delta_1 = \text{mass per unit length of the wire,}$$
$$dA \text{ or } dS = \text{element of area,}$$
$$\delta_2 = \text{mass per unit area of the plate or shell,}$$
$$dV = \text{element of volume,}$$
$$\delta_3 = \text{mass per unit volume of the solid.}$$

EXAMPLE 1. Find the center of mass of a thin homogeneous triangular plate of base b and altitude h.

Solution. Divide the triangle into strips of width dy parallel to the x-axis. A representative strip is shown in Fig. 5–27. The mass of the strip is approximately

$$dm = \delta_2 \, dA,$$

where

$$dA = l \, dy$$

and l is the width of the triangle at distance y above its base. By similar triangles,

$$\frac{l}{b} = \frac{h - y}{h}$$

or

$$l = \frac{b}{h} (h - y),$$

so that

$$dm = \delta_2 \frac{b}{h} (h - y) \, dy.$$

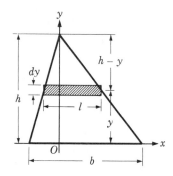

FIGURE 5–27

For the y-coordinate of the center of mass of the element dm, we have $\tilde{y} = y$. For the entire plate,

$$\bar{y} = \frac{\displaystyle\int y \, dm}{\displaystyle\int dm} = \frac{\displaystyle\int_0^h \delta_2 \frac{b}{h} y(h - y) \, dy}{\displaystyle\int_0^h \delta_2 \frac{b}{h} (h - y) \, dy} = \frac{1}{3} h.$$

Thus the center of mass lies above the base of the triangle at a distance one-third of the way toward the opposite vertex. By considering each side in turn as being a base of the triangle, this result shows that the center of gravity lies at the intersection of the medians.

EXAMPLE 2. A thin homogeneous wire is bent to form a semicircle of radius r (Fig. 5–28). Find its center of mass.

Solution. Here we take

$$dm = \delta_1 \, ds,$$

where ds is an element of arc length of the wire and

$$\delta_1 = \frac{M}{L} = \frac{M}{\pi r}$$

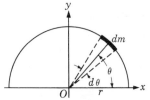

FIGURE 5–28

is the mass per unit length of the wire. In terms of the central angle θ measured in radians (as usual), we have

$$ds = r\, d\theta$$

and

$$\tilde{x} = r\cos\theta, \qquad \tilde{y} = r\sin\theta.$$

Hence

$$\bar{x} = \frac{\displaystyle\int_0^\pi r\cos\theta\,\delta_1\,r\,d\theta}{\displaystyle\int_0^\pi \delta_1\,r\,d\theta} = \frac{\delta_1 r^2 \Big[\sin\theta\Big]_0^\pi}{\delta_1 r \Big[\theta\Big]_0^\pi} = 0,$$

$$\bar{y} = \frac{\displaystyle\int_0^\pi r\sin\theta\,\delta_1\,r\,d\theta}{\displaystyle\int_0^\pi \delta_1\,r\,d\theta} = \frac{\delta_1 r^2 \Big[-\cos\theta\Big]_0^\pi}{\delta_1 r \Big[\theta\Big]_0^\pi} = \frac{2}{\pi}\,r.$$

The center of mass is therefore on the y-axis at a distance $2/\pi$ (roughly $\tfrac{2}{3}$) of the way up from the origin toward the intercept $(0, r)$.

EXAMPLE 3. Find the center of mass of a solid hemisphere of radius r if its density at any point P is proportional to the distance of P from the base of the hemisphere.

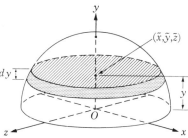

FIGURE 5–29

Solution. Imagine the solid cut into slices of thickness dy by planes perpendicular to the y-axis (Fig. 5–29), and take

$$dm = \delta_3\, dV,$$

where

$$dV = A(y)\, dy$$

is the volume of the representative slice at distance y above the base of the hemisphere, which is in the xz-plane, and where

$$\delta_3 = ky \qquad (k = \text{constant})$$

is the density of the solid in this slice. The area of a face of the slice dV is

$A(y) = \pi x^2$, where $x^2 + y^2 = r^2$, that is,

$$dV = A(y)\,dy = \pi(r^2 - y^2)\,dy,$$

so that

$$dm = k\pi(r^2 - y^2)y\,dy.$$

The center of mass of the slice may be taken at its geometrical center, that is

$$(\bar{x},\,\bar{y},\,\bar{z}) = (0,\,y,\,0),$$

so that

$$\bar{x} = \bar{z} = 0$$

and

$$\bar{y} = \frac{\displaystyle\int y\,dm}{\displaystyle\int dm}$$

$$= \frac{\displaystyle\int_0^r k\pi(r^2 - y^2)y^2\,dy}{\displaystyle\int_0^r k\pi(r^2 - y^2)y\,dy} = \frac{k\pi\left[\dfrac{r^2 y^3}{3} - \dfrac{y^5}{5}\right]_0^r}{k\pi\left[\dfrac{r^2 y^2}{2} - \dfrac{y^4}{4}\right]_0^r}$$

$$= \frac{8}{15}r.$$

Problems

In each of the following problems (1 through 5), find the center of mass of a thin homogeneous plate covering the given portion of the xy-plane.

1. The first quadrant of the circle $x^2 + y^2 = a^2$.
2. The area bounded by the parabola $y = h^2 - x^2$ and the x-axis.
3. The "triangular" shaped area in the first quadrant between the circle $x^2 + y^2 = a^2$ and the lines $x = a$, $y = a$.
4. The area between the x-axis and the curve $y = \sin x$ between $x = 0$ and $x = \pi$. [*Hint:* Take $dA = y\,dx$ and $\bar{y} = \frac{1}{2}y$.]
5. The area between the y-axis and the curve $x = 2y - y^2$.
6. Find the distance, from the base, of the center of mass of a thin triangular plate of base b and altitude h if its density varies as the square root of the distance from the base.
7. In Problem 6, suppose that the density varies as the square of the distance.
8. Find the center of mass of a homogeneous solid right circular cone.
9. Find the center of mass of a solid right circular cone if the density varies as the distance from the base.
10. In Problem 9 suppose that the density varies as the square of the distance.
11. In Example 2 (see Fig. 5–28) suppose that the density is $\delta_1 = k \sin \theta$, k being constant. Find the center of mass.

5–10 Centroid and center of gravity.   In the case of a mass having uniform density, Eqs. (8), Article 5–9, reduce to

$$
\bar{x} = \frac{\int \bar{x}\delta_3\, dV}{\int \delta_3\, dV} = \frac{\delta_3 \int \bar{x}\, dV}{\delta_3 \int dV} = \frac{\int \bar{x}\, dV}{\int dV},
$$

$$
\bar{y} = \frac{\int \bar{y}\, dV}{\int dV}, \qquad \bar{z} = \frac{\int \bar{z}\, dV}{\int dV}.
$$

(1)

for a solid, with similar equations having dA or ds in place of dV in the case of a plate or a wire. Since these expressions involve only the geometric objects, namely, volumes, areas, and curves, we speak of the point $(\bar{x}, \bar{y}, \bar{z})$ in such cases as the *centroid* of the object. The term *center of gravity* is also used, since the line of action of the forces due to gravity acting on the elements of the object pass through this point. (See Sears, *Mechanics, Heat, and Sound*, Chapters 3 and 7, for a discussion of physical concepts involved.)

EXAMPLE 1. Find the center of gravity of a solid hemisphere of radius r.

Solution. As in Example 3, Article 5–9, imagine the solid (Fig. 5–29) cut into slices of thickness dy by planes perpendicular to the y-axis. The centroid of a slice is its geometrical center, on the y-axis, at $(0, y, 0)$. Its moment with respect to the xz-plane is

$$
dM_{xz} = y\, dV
$$
$$
= y\pi(r^2 - y^2)\, dy.
$$

Hence

$$
M_{xz} = \pi \int_0^r (r^2 y - y^3)\, dy = \frac{\pi r^4}{4}.
$$

Since the volume of the hemisphere is

$$
V = \frac{2}{3}\pi r^3,
$$

we have

$$
\bar{y} = \frac{M_{xz}}{V} = \frac{3}{8} r.
$$

EXAMPLE 2. Find the center of gravity of a thin hemispherical shell of inner radius r and thickness t.

Solution. We shall solve this problem, (a) exactly, by using the results of the preceding example, then (b) we shall see how the position of the center of gravity changes as we hold r fixed and let $t \to 0$. Finally, (c) we shall solve the problem approximately without using the results of Example 1, by considering the center of mass of an imaginary distribution of mass over the surface of the hemisphere of radius r, assuming that the thickness t is negligible in comparison with r. (As, for example, the gold leaf covering the dome of the State House in Boston.)

(a) Let M_1, M_2, and M; V_1, V_2, and V denote respectively the moments with respect to the xz-plane and the volumes of the solid hemisphere of radius r, the solid hemisphere of radius $(r + t)$, and the hemispherical shell of thickness t and inner radius r. Since the moment of the sum of two masses is the sum of their moments and

$$V_1 + V = V_2,$$

we also have

$$M_1 + M = M_2,$$

that is

$$M = M_2 - M_1.$$

But by Example 1,

$$M_2 = \frac{\pi}{4}(r + t)^4, \qquad M_1 = \frac{\pi}{4}r^4,$$

so that

$$M = \frac{\pi}{4}[(r + t)^4 - r^4]$$

$$= \frac{\pi}{4}[4r^3t + 6r^2t^2 + 4rt^3 + t^4],$$

while

$$V = V_2 - V_1 = \tfrac{2}{3}\pi[(r + t)^3 - r^3]$$

$$= \tfrac{2}{3}\pi(3r^2t + 3rt^2 + t^3);$$

hence

$$\bar{y} = \frac{M}{V} = \frac{1}{2}\frac{[r^3 + \frac{3}{2}r^2t + rt^2 + \frac{1}{4}t^3]}{[r^2 + rt + \frac{1}{3}t^2]}.$$

(b) In the case of a shell where the thickness t is negligible in comparison with r, this reduces to $\bar{y} = \frac{1}{2}r$, by writing

$$\bar{y} = \frac{1}{2}\frac{r^3\left[1 + \frac{3}{2}\left(\frac{t}{r}\right) + \left(\frac{t}{r}\right)^2 + \frac{1}{4}\left(\frac{t}{r}\right)^3\right]}{r^2\left[1 + \left(\frac{t}{r}\right) + \frac{1}{3}\left(\frac{t}{r}\right)^2\right]},$$

and then letting $(t/r) \to 0$.

(c) To solve the problem directly, without reference to Example 1, consider the mass of the shell as being uniformly distributed over its surface so that the mass of any portion cut from the shell will be proportional to its (inner) surface area. The proportionality factor,

$$\sigma = \delta t,$$

where δ is the volume density and t the thickness of the shell, is frequently referred to as a surface density factor. (Thus in working with sheet metal stock, say aluminum of uniform thickness and density, we might speak of it as weighing so many pounds *per square foot*. This would be our σ, and A square feet of this particular stock would weigh σA pounds.) Then the slice of shell between planes perpendicular to the y-axis at distances y and $y + \Delta y$ respectively above the xz-plane has mass

$$\Delta m = \sigma \, \Delta S,$$

where ΔS is the surface area of the slice (see Fig. 5–30). The moment of this slice with respect to the xz-plane then lies between

$$y \, \Delta m \qquad \text{and} \qquad (y + \Delta y) \, \Delta m,$$

and hence differs from $y \, \Delta m$ by at most $\Delta y \, \Delta m$. The sum of the moments of the slices has a limit, as Δy approaches zero, equal to $\int y \, dm$. We are thus led to

$$\bar{y} = \frac{\int y \, dm}{\int dm} = \frac{\int \sigma y \, dS}{\int \sigma \, dS} = \frac{\sigma \int y \, dS}{\sigma \int dS},$$

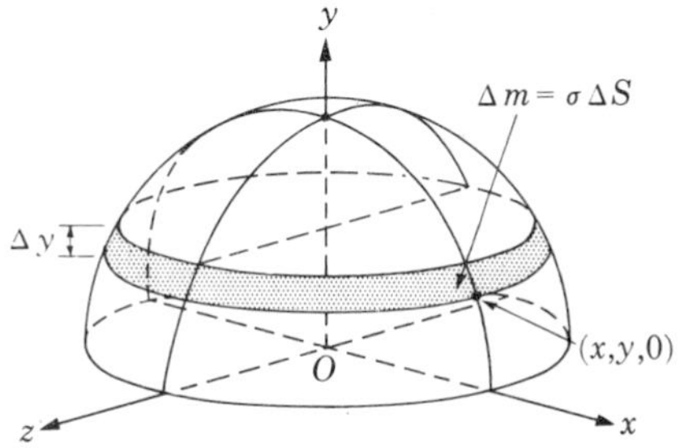

since σ is constant by our hypotheses. Here

$$dS = 2\pi x \, ds = 2\pi (r \cos \theta) r \, d\theta$$

if we use

$$x = r \cos \theta, \qquad y = r \sin \theta$$

FIGURE 5–30

to represent the circle $x^2 + y^2 = r^2$. Hence

$$\bar{y} = \frac{\int_0^{\pi/2} r \sin \theta \cdot 2\pi (r \cos \theta) \cdot r \, d\theta}{\int_0^{\pi/2} 2\pi (r \cos \theta) r \, d\theta}$$

$$= \frac{2\pi r^3 \int_0^{\pi/2} \sin \theta \cos \theta \, d\theta}{2\pi r^2 \int_0^{\pi/2} \cos \theta \, d\theta} = r \frac{\left[\frac{1}{2} \sin^2 \theta \right]_0^{\pi/2}}{\left[\sin \theta \right]_0^{\pi/2}} = \frac{1}{2} r.$$

Observe that the element of arc ds which, when rotated about the y-axis, generates dS, need only move along the arc of the circle in the first quadrant, namely, $0 \leq \theta \leq \pi/2$, in order to give us the entire hemisphere.

By the symmetry of the shell, the center of gravity lies on the y-axis, that is,

$$(\bar{x}, \, \bar{y}, \, \bar{z},) = (0, \, \tfrac{1}{2} r, \, 0).$$

Problems

In Problems 1 through 5 find the center of gravity of the areas bounded by the given curves and lines.

1. The x-axis and the curve $y = c^2 - x^2$.
2. The y-axis and the curve $x = y - y^3$, $\quad 0 \leq y \leq 1$.
3. The curve $y = x^2$ and the line $y = 4$.
4. The curve $y = x - x^2$ and the line $x + y = 0$.
5. The curve $x = y^2 - y$ and the line $y = x$.
6. Find the center of gravity of a solid right circular cone of altitude h and base-radius r.
7. Find the center of gravity of the solid generated by rotating, about the y-axis, the area bounded by the curve $y = x^2$ and the line $y = 4$.
8. The area bounded by the curve $x = y^2 - y$ and the line $y = x$ is rotated about the x-axis. Find the center of gravity of the solid thus generated.
9. Find the center of gravity of a very thin right circular conical shell of base-radius r and altitude h.
10. Find the center of gravity of the surface area generated by rotating about the line $x = -r$, the arc of the circle $x^2 + y^2 = r^2$ that lies in the first quadrant. (Use $x = r \cos \theta$, $y = r \sin \theta$ to represent the circle.)
11. Find the moment, about the x-axis, of the arc of the parabola $y = \sqrt{x}$ lying between $(0, 0)$ and $(4, 2)$.
12. Find the center of gravity of the arc length of one quadrant of a circle.

5–11 The Theorems of Pappus. When a plane area, such as A in Fig. 5–31, is rotated about an axis in its plane that does not intersect the area, there is a useful formula that relates the volume swept out by the area to the path described by its centroid.

THEOREM 1.   *If a plane area is revolved about a line that lies in its plane but does not intersect the area, then the volume generated is equal to the product of the area and the distance traveled by its center of gravity.*

To prove this result, which is one of the Theorems of Pappus, let the x-axis coincide with the axis of revolution and divide the area into strips of width Δy by lines parallel to the x-axis. The entire volume is the sum of the volumes generated by these strips of area. Let $l = f(y)$ be the width of the area at distance y above the x-axis, $c \leq y \leq d$. By the same argument we used in Article 5–5 to justify the

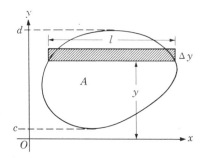

FIGURE 5–31

cylindrical shell method of computing volumes, we have

$$V = \lim_{\Delta y \to 0} \sum 2\pi yl \, \Delta y = \int_c^d 2\pi yl \, dy. \qquad (1)$$

But the ordinate $\bar{y}_A$ of the center of gravity of the area A is given by

$$\bar{y}_A = \frac{\int y \, dA}{\int dA} = \frac{\int_c^d yl \, dy}{A},$$

so that

$$\int_c^d yl \, dy = A\bar{y}_A,$$

and hence Eq. (1) becomes

$$V = 2\pi \bar{y}_A A. \qquad (2)$$

Since $2\pi \bar{y}_A$ is the distance traveled by the center of gravity of the area, the theorem is established.

EXAMPLE 1. (Fig. 5–32) Find the volume of the torus (doughnut) generated by rotating a circle of radius r about an axis in its plane at a distance b from its center, $b > r$.

Solution. The center of the circle is its center of gravity, and this travels a distance $2\pi b$. The area of the circle is πr^2, so by Eq. (2) the volume of the torus is

$$V = (2\pi b)(\pi r^2) = 2\pi^2 br^2.$$

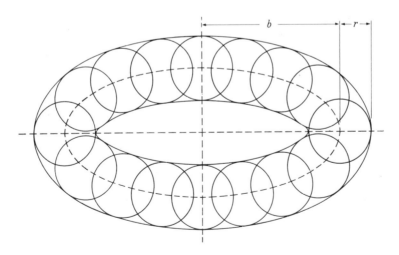

FIGURE 5–32

THEOREM 2. *If an arc of a plane curve is revolved about a line that lies in its plane but does not intersect the arc, then the surface area generated by the arc is equal to the product of the length of the arc and the distance traveled by its center of gravity.*

In this, another Theorem of Pappus, the center of gravity is that of the curve (or of a fine homogeneous wire whose centerline coincides with the curve), and is generally different from the center of gravity of the enclosed plane area (if the curve is a closed curve). To prove the theorem, refer the curve to x- and y-axes in its plane and let the x-axis coincide with the axis of revolution (see Fig. 5–33). Then the surface area generated is

$$S = \int_{x=a}^{x=b} 2\pi y \, ds, \tag{3}$$

as we found in Article 5–7. But the center of gravity of the curve has ordinate

$$\bar{y}_c = \frac{\int y \, ds}{\int ds} = \frac{\int y \, ds}{L},$$

where

$$L = \int ds$$

is the length of the arc. Hence

$$S = 2\pi \int_{x=a}^{x=b} y \, ds = 2\pi \bar{y}_c L. \qquad \text{Q.E.D.} \tag{4}$$

EXAMPLE 2. The surface area of the torus in the previous example is given by

$$S = (2\pi b)(2\pi r) = 4\pi^2 br.$$

The two Theorems of Pappus are useful in determining volumes or surface areas of solids of revolution when the centers of gravity are

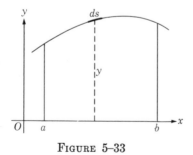

FIGURE 5–33   FIGURE 5–34

known. They are equally useful in determining the centers of gravity when the volume and surface area are known.

EXAMPLE 3. Use the first Theorem of Pappus and the fact that the volume of a sphere of radius r is

$$V = \tfrac{4}{3}\pi r^3$$

to find the center of gravity of the area of a semicircle.

Solution. Note that we generate a sphere by rotating a semicircle about its diameter (Fig. 5–34). Then the axis of revolution does not intersect the area, and since

$$A = \tfrac{1}{2}\pi r^2,$$

while

$$V = 2\pi \bar{y} A,$$

we find

$$\bar{y} = \frac{V}{2\pi A} = \frac{\tfrac{4}{3}\pi r^3}{2\pi \cdot \tfrac{1}{2}\pi r^2} = \frac{4}{3\pi} r.$$

PROBLEMS

1. Use the Theorems of Pappus to find the lateral surface area and the volume of a right circular cone.

2. Use the second Theorem of Pappus and the fact that the surface area of a sphere of radius r is $4\pi r^2$ to find the center of gravity of the semicircular arc

$$y = \sqrt{r^2 - x^2}, \qquad -r \le x \le r.$$

3. The semicircular arc $y = \sqrt{r^2 - x^2}$, $-r \le x \le r$, is rotated about the line $y = r$. Use the second Theorem of Pappus together with the answer to the preceding problem to find the surface area generated.

4. The center of gravity of the area bounded by the x-axis and the semicircle $y = \sqrt{r^2 - x^2}$ is at $[0, (\tfrac{4}{3}\pi)r]$ (see Example 3, above). Find the volume generated when this area is rotated about the line $y = -r$.

5. The area in the preceding example is rotated about the line $y = x - r$. Find the volume generated.

6. Use the answer to Problem 2 above to find the surface area generated by rotating the semicircular arc $y = \sqrt{r^2 - x^2}$, $-r \le x \le r$, about the line $y = x - r$.

7. Find the moment about the x-axis of the area in the semicircle of Fig. 5–34, Example 2, above. (If you use results already known, you won't need to integrate.)

8. Find the moment about the line $y = -r$ of the area in the semicircle of Fig. 5–34.

9. Find the moment about the line $y = x - r$ of the area in the semicircle of Fig. 5–34.

5–12 Hydrostatic pressure. If a flat-bottomed container is filled with water to a depth h, the resulting force due to the pressure of the liquid it contains is

$$F = whA, \tag{1}$$

where w is the weight-density, which is nearly 62.5 lb/ft^3, and A is the area of the bottom of the container. Obviously, the units in Eq. (1) must be compatible, say h in feet, A in square feet, w in pounds per cubic foot, giving F in pounds. It is a remarkable fact that this force does not depend upon the shape of the sides of the vessel, the force on the bottom being the same in both (a) and (b) in Fig. 5–35, for example, if both

FIGURE 5–35

containers have the same area at their bases and both have the same "head" h. (See Sears, *Mechanics, Heat, and Sound*, Chapter 16.) The *pressure*, or *force per unit area*, at the bottom of the container is therefore

$$p = wh. \tag{2}$$

Next consider any body of water, such as the water in a reservoir or behind a dam. According to Pascal's principle, the pressure $p = wh$ at depth h in such a body of water is the same *in all directions*. For a flat plate submerged *horizontally*, the downward *force* acting on its upper face due to this liquid pressure is the same as that given by Eq. (1). If the plate is submerged *vertically*, however, then the pressure against it will be different at different depths and Eq. (1) no longer is usable in that form because we would have different h factors for points at different depths. We circumvent this difficulty in a manner which should by now be fairly familiar to the reader, namely, by dividing the plate into many narrow strips, the representative strip having its upper edge at depth h and its lower edge at depth $h + \Delta h$ below the surface of the water. If the area of this strip is called ΔA, and the force on one side of it ΔF, then Eq. (1) suggests that

$$wh \, \Delta A \le \Delta F \le w(h + \Delta h) \, \Delta A,$$

since the pressure will vary from wh to $w(h + \Delta h)$ in this strip. When we add the forces for all strips, then take the limit of such sums as $\Delta h \to 0$, we may disregard the infinitesimals of higher order, such as $\Delta h \, \Delta A$, and we are led to

$$F = \lim_{\Delta h \to 0} \sum_a^b wh \, \Delta A$$

or

$$F = \int_{h=a}^{h=b} wh \, dA = \int_a^b whl \, dh, \tag{3}$$

where $dA = l \, dh$ (see Fig. 5–36).

As a corollary of Eq. (3), if we denote the depth of the center of gravity of the area A by $\bar{h}$, then

$$\bar{h} = \frac{\int h \, dA}{\int dA}$$

or

$$\int h \, dA = \bar{h}A.$$

Since w is a constant which may be moved across the integral sign in (3), we have

$$F = w\bar{h}A. \tag{4}$$

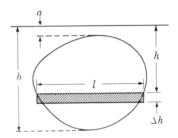

FIGURE 5–36

This states that the total force of the liquid pressing against one face of the plate (an equal and opposite force presses against the other face unless the plate forms part of a wall of the container) is the same as it would be according to (1) if all of the area A were at the depth $\bar{h}$ below the surface.

Equation (4) is the working tool used most frequently by the engineer in finding such hydrostatic forces as we have discussed. He can refer to a handbook to obtain the center of gravity of simple plane areas and from this he quickly finds $\bar{h}$. Of course, the location of the center of gravity which he finds in his handbook was calculated by someone who performed an integration equivalent to evaluating the integral in Eq. (3). It is recommended that the reader solve problems of this type by thinking through the steps which lead up to Eq. (3) by integration, and that he then check his results, when he can conveniently do so, by Eq. (4).

EXAMPLE 1. A trapezoid is submerged vertically in water with its upper edge 4 ft below the surface and its lower edge 10 ft below the surface. If the upper and lower edges are respectively 6 ft and 8 ft long, find the total force on one face of the trapezoid.

Solution. In Fig. 5–37, we have, by similar triangles,

$$\frac{l - 6}{2} = \frac{h - 4}{6},$$

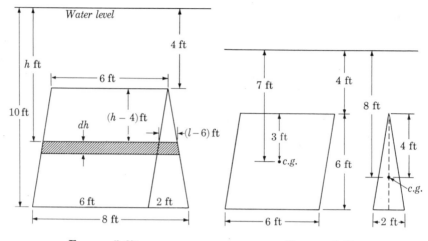

FIGURE 5–37   FIGURE 5–38

so that

$$l = \frac{h + 14}{3}.$$

Then the force is

$$F = \int_4^{10} wh \left(\frac{h + 14}{3} \right) dh = 300w.$$

Since

$$w = 62.5 \ (\text{lb/ft}^3) = \tfrac{1}{32}(\text{ton/ft}^3),$$

we have

$$F = 9\tfrac{3}{8} \text{ tons.}$$

Now we check by using Eq. (4). The trapezoid can be resolved into a parallelogram plus a triangle (Fig. 5–38). For the parallelogram,

$$\bar{h}_1 = 7, \qquad A_1 = 36; \qquad F_1 = 252w.$$

For the triangle,

$$\bar{h}_2 = 8, \qquad A_2 = 6; \qquad F_2 = 48w.$$

For the trapezoid,

$$F = F_1 + F_2 = 300w.$$

EXAMPLE 2. Find the moment produced about the lower edge of the trapezoid by the forces in the preceding example.

Solution. The force on the representative strip may be denoted by

$$dF = wh \, dA = wh \left(\frac{h + 14}{3} \right) dh.$$

For the moment of this force about the lower edge of the trapezoid, we must multiply this force by the moment arm,

$$r = 10 - h,$$

to give the moment

$$dM = r\, dF = wh(10 - h)\,\frac{h + 14}{3}\, dh.$$

The total moment due to forces on all the strips is

$$M = \frac{w}{3}\int_{4}^{10} (140h - 4h^2 - h^3)\, dh = 732w$$

or

$$M = 22\tfrac{7}{8} \text{ (foot-tons)}.$$

PROBLEMS

1. The vertical ends of a water trough are isosceles triangles of base 4 ft and altitude 3 ft. Find the force on one end if the trough is full of water weighing 62.5 lb/ft^3.

2. Find the force in the previous problem if the water level in the trough is lowered one foot.

3. A triangular plate ABC is submerged in water with its plane vertical. The side AB, 4 ft long, is 1 ft below the surface, while C is 5 ft below AB. Find the total force on one face of the plate.

4. Find the force on one face of the triangle ABC of Problem 3 if AB is one foot below the surface as before, but the triangle is rotated 180° about AB so as to bring the vertex C 4 ft above the surface.

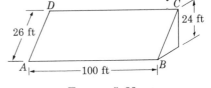

FIGURE 5–39

5. A semicircular plate is submerged in water with its plane vertical and its diameter in the surface. Find the force on one face of the plate if its diameter is 2 ft.

6. The face of a dam is a rectangle, $ABCD$, of dimensions $AB = CD = 100$ ft, $AD = BC = 26$ ft. Instead of being vertical, the plane $ABCD$ is inclined as indicated in Fig. 5–39, so that the top of the dam is 24 ft higher than the bottom. Find the force due to water pressure on the dam when the surface of the water is level with the top of the dam.

7. Find the moment, about AB, of the force in Problem 6.

5–13 Work. When a constant force F (pounds) acts throughout a distance s (feet), the *work* done (in foot-pounds) is the product of force and distance,

$$W = Fs. \qquad (1)$$

When the force is not constant, as for instance in stretching or compressing a spring, then Eq. (1) cannot be used directly to give the work done. The law in (1) can be used, however, to find approximately the work done over a *short* interval Δs if the force is a continuous function of s. The integral process then enables us to extend the law in (1) to find the total work done.

To illustrate, suppose we consider the work done in compressing a spring from its natural unstressed length L to a length $\frac{3}{4}L$ (Fig. 5–40) if the force required to hold it under compression is

$$F = cx, \qquad (2)$$

where x is the amount it has been compressed and c is a proportionality factor (called the "spring constant"). Thus to compress the spring by an amount $L/4$, the force must be increased from

$$F_0 = c \times 0 = 0$$

to

$$F_1 = c\frac{L}{4},$$

and as it does so the point of application of the force will move from $x = 0$ to $x = L/4$ in Fig. 5–40. How, then, shall we find the *work* done during the process? We imagine the x-interval from 0 to $L/4$ to be divided into a large number of subintervals, each of length Δx. As the spring is compressed an amount Δx, so that its left end moves across the representative subinterval from x to $x + \Delta x$, the *force* will vary from cx to $c(x + \Delta x)$, and since it acts through a *distance* Δx, the work done for this small compression will lie between

$$cx\ \Delta x \qquad \text{and} \qquad c(x + \Delta x)\ \Delta x,$$

so that the total work will be given approximately by

$$W \approx \sum_{x=0}^{L/4} cx\ \Delta x,$$

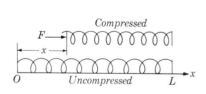

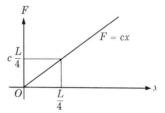

FIGURE 5–40   FIGURE 5–41

or

$$W = \sum_{x=0}^{L/4} c\tilde{x}\,\Delta x$$

for appropriate choices of the $\tilde{x}$ between x and $x + \Delta x$. In the limit as Δx tends to zero, we have

$$W = \lim_{\Delta x \to 0} \sum_{x=0}^{L/4} cx\,\Delta x = \int_0^{L/4} cx\,dx = \frac{cL^2}{32}$$

or

$$W = \tfrac{1}{2}(cL/4)(L/4).$$

In this last form, the factor $\tfrac{1}{2}c(L/4)$ is one-half the final value reached by F when the spring has been compressed to $\tfrac{3}{4}$ of its original length, and the factor $L/4$ is the total distance through which the variable force has acted. This suggests

$$W = \overline{F}s \tag{3}$$

as a suitable modification of Eq. (1) when the force is variable, where $\overline{F}$ represents the *average* value of the variable force throughout the total displacement. However, the determination of $\overline{F}$ itself involves an integration in the general case, so that it is usually as easy to apply the principles illustrated in the example just considered as it is to apply Eq. (3). In fact, Eq. (3) may be interpreted as *defining* $\overline{F}$.

In a manner entirely analogous to that in the above example, it is easily seen that

$$\boxed{W = \int_a^b F\,ds} \tag{4}$$

gives the work done by a variable force (which, however, always acts along a given direction) as the point of application undergoes a displacement from $s = a$ to $s = b$. This leads to the following interesting theorem of mechanics.

THEOREM. *Let F denote the resultant of all forces acting on a particle of mass m. Let the direction of F remain constant. Then whether the magnitude of F is constant or variable, the work done on the particle by the force F is equal to the change in the kinetic energy of the particle.*

The ingredients required for a proof of this theorem are:

(a) Eq. (4), which gives the work,
(b) the definition of kinetic energy, K.E. $= \tfrac{1}{2}mv^2$, and
(c) Newton's second law: $F = m(dv/dt)$.

The fact that

$$v = \frac{ds}{dt}$$

and

$$\frac{dv}{dt} = \frac{dv}{ds}\frac{ds}{dt} = \frac{dv}{ds}v$$

and Newton's second law enable us to write Eq. (4) in the form

$$W = \int_{s=a}^{s=b} mv\frac{dv}{ds}\,ds = \int_{v=v_a}^{v=v_b} mv\,dv,$$

which leads to

$$W = \frac{1}{2}mv^2\Big]_{v_a}^{v_b} = \frac{1}{2}mv_b^2 - \frac{1}{2}mv_a^2.$$

That is, the work done by the force F is the kinetic energy at b minus the kinetic energy at a or, more simply, the change in kinetic energy:

$$W = \Delta(\text{K.E.}).$$

As a second example of work in a situation where the simple Eq. (1) cannot be applied to the *total* but can be applied to a *small piece*, we consider the problem of pumping all the water from a full hemispherical bowl of radius r (feet) to a distance h (feet) above the top of the bowl (see Fig. 5–42).

We introduce coordinate axes as shown in Fig. 5–42 and imagine the bowl to be divided into a large number of thin slices by planes perpendicular to the x-axis between $x = 0$ and $x = r$. The representative

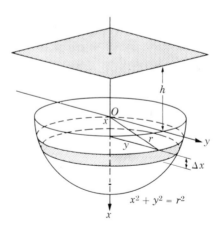

FIGURE 5–42

slice between the planes at x and $x + \Delta x$ has volume ΔV which, if we neglect only infinitesimals of higher order than Δx, is given approximately by

$$\Delta V \approx \pi y^2 \, \Delta x = \pi(r^2 - x^2) \, \Delta x.$$

To the same order of approximation, the force F required to lift *this slice* is equal to its weight:

$$w \, \Delta V \approx \pi w(r^2 - x^2) \, \Delta x,$$

where w is the weight of a cubic foot of water. Finally, the *distance* through which this force must act lies between

$$h + x \qquad \text{and} \qquad h + x + \Delta x,$$

so that the work ΔW done in *lifting this one slice* is approximately

$$\Delta W \approx \pi w(r^2 - x^2)(h + x) \, \Delta x,$$

where we again have suppressed all higher powers of Δx. This is justified in the *limit* of the sum, and the total work is

$$\begin{aligned}
W &= \lim_{\Delta x \to 0} \sum_0^r \pi w(r^2 - x^2)(h + x) \, \Delta x \\
&= \int_0^r \pi w(h + x)(r^2 - x^2) \, dx \\
&= hw \int_0^r \pi(r^2 - x^2) \, dx + w \int_0^r \pi x(r^2 - x^2) \, dx \\
&= hwV + \bar{x}wV.
\end{aligned}$$

Here (wV) is the weight of the whole bowlful of water of volume V, and the second integral may be interpreted physically as giving the work required in pumping *all* the water from the depth of the center of gravity of the bowl to the level $x = 0$, while the first integral gives the work done in pumping the whole bowlful of water from the level $x = 0$ up a distance of h feet. The actual evaluation of the integrals leads to

$$W = \tfrac{2}{3}\pi r^3 w(h + \tfrac{3}{8}r).$$

Can you prove for yourself that no matter what the shape of the container in Fig. 5–42, the total work is the sum of two terms, one of which is

$$W_1 = hw \int dV$$

and represents the total work done in lifting a bowlful of water a distance

h, while the other is

$$W_2 = w \int x \, dV$$

and represents the work done in lifting a bowlful of water a distance equal to the depth of the center of gravity of the bowl?

PROBLEMS

1. If the spring in Fig. 5–40 has natural length $L = 18$ in., and a force of 10 lb is sufficient to compress it to a length of 16 in., what is the value of the "spring constant" c for the particular spring in question? How much work is done in compressing it from a length of 16 in. to a length of 12 in.?

2. Answer the questions of Problem 1 if the law of force is $F = c \sin (\pi x/2L)$ in place of Eq. (2).

3. Two electrons repel each other with a force inversely proportional to the square of the distance between them. Suppose one electron is held fixed at the point $(1, 0)$ on the x-axis. Find the work required to move a second electron along the x-axis from the point $(-1, 0)$ to the origin.

4. If two electrons are held stationary at the points $(-1, 0)$ and $(1, 0)$ on the x-axis, find the work done in moving a third electron from $(5, 0)$ to $(3, 0)$ along the x-axis.

5. If a straight hole could be bored through the center of the earth, a particle of mass m falling in this hole would be attracted toward the center of the earth with a force $mg \, r/R$ when it is at distance r from the center. (R is the radius of earth; g is the acceleration due to gravity at the surface of the earth.) How much work is done on the particle as it falls from the surface to the center of the earth?

6. A bag of sand originally weighing 144 lb is lifted at a constant rate of 3 ft/min. The sand leaks out uniformly at such a rate that half of the sand is lost when the bag has been lifted 18 ft. Find the work done in lifting the bag this distance.

7. Gas in a cylinder of constant cross-sectional area A expands or is compressed by the motion of a piston. If p is the pressure of the gas in pounds per square inch and v is its volume in cubic inches, show that the work done by the gas as it goes from an initial state (p_1, v_1) to a second state (p_2, v_2) is

$$W = \int_{(p_1, v_1)}^{(p_2, v_2)} p \, dv \text{ (inch-pounds).}$$

[*Hint:* Take the x-axis perpendicular to the face of the piston. Then $dv = A \, dx$ and $F = pA$.]

8. Use the result of Problem 7 to find the work done on the gas in compressing it from $v_1 = 243$ in^3 to $v_2 = 32$ in^3 if the initial pressure $p_1 = 50$ lb/in^2 and the pressure and volume satisfy the law for adiabatic change of state, $pv^{1.4} = $ constant.

9. Find the work done in pumping all the water out of a conical reservoir of radius 10 ft at the top, altitude 8 ft, to a height of 6 ft above the top of the reservoir.

10. Find the work done in Problem 9 if at the beginning the reservoir is filled to a depth of 5 ft and the water is pumped just to the top of the reservoir.

REVIEW QUESTIONS AND EXERCISES FOR CHAPTER 5

1. List nine applications of the definite integral presented in this chapter.

2. How do you define the area bounded above by a curve $y = f_1(x)$, below by a curve $y = f_2(x)$, and on the sides by $x = a$ and $x = b$, $a < b$?

3. How do you define the volume generated by rotating a plane area about an axis in its plane and not intersecting the area?

4. How do you define the length of a plane curve? Can you extend this to a curve in three-dimensional space?

5. How do you define the surface area of a sphere? Of other surfaces of revolution?

6. How do you define the average value of a function over an interval?

7. How do you define center of mass?

8. How do you define work done by a variable force?

9. How do you define the hydrostatic force on the face of a dam?

MISCELLANEOUS PROBLEMS FOR CHAPTER 5

1. Sketch the graphs of the equations $y = 2 - x^2$ and $x + y = 0$ in one diagram, and find the area bounded by them.

2. Find the maximum and minimum points of the curve $y = x^3 - 3x^2$ and find the total area bounded by this curve and the x-axis. Sketch.

In the following problems (3–15), find the area bounded by the given curves and lines. Use the trapezoidal rule, Article 4–10, to approximate any integral you cannot evaluate by the Fundamental Theorem. A sketch is usually helpful.

3. $y = x, \quad y = \dfrac{1}{x^2}, \quad x = 2$ 4. $y = x, \quad y = \dfrac{1}{\sqrt{x}}, \quad x = 2$

5. $y = x + 1, \quad y = 3 - x^2$ 6. $y = 2x^2, \quad y = x^2 + 2x + 3$

7. $x = 2y^2, \quad x = 0, \quad y = 3$ 8. $4x = y^2 - 4, \quad 4x = y + 16$

9. $x^{1/2} + y^{1/2} = a^{1/2}, \quad x = 0, \quad y = 0$

10. $y = \sqrt{9 + x^2}, \quad y = 0, \quad x = 0, \quad x = 4$

11. $y^2 = 9x, \quad y = \dfrac{3x^2}{8}$

12. $y = \dfrac{1}{1 + x^2}, \quad y = 0, \quad x = 0, \quad x = 1$

13. $y = x\sqrt{2x^2 + 1}, \quad x = 0, \quad x = 2$

14. $y^2 = 4x$ and $y = 4x - 2$ 15. $y = 2 - x^2$ and $y = x^2 - 6$

16. The function $v = 3t^2 - 15t + 18$ represents the velocity v (ft/sec) of a moving body as a function of the time t (sec). (a) Find that portion of the time interval $0 \le t \le 3$ in which the velocity is positive. (b) Find that portion where v is negative. (c) Find the total distance traveled by the body from $t = 0$ to $t = 3$.

17. The area from 0 to x under a certain graph is given to be

$$A = (1 + 3x)^{1/2} - 1, \quad x \ge 0.$$

(a) Find the *average* rate of change of A with respect to x as x increases from 1 to 8. (b) Find the *instantaneous* rate of change of A with respect to x at $x = 5$. (c) Find the ordinate (height) y of the graph as a function of x. (d) Find the average value of the ordinate (height) y, with respect to x, as x increases from 1 to 8.

18. A solid is generated by rotating, about the x-axis, the area bounded by the curve $y = f(x)$, the x-axis, and the lines $x = a$, $x = b$. Its volume, for all $b > a$, is $b^2 - ab$. Find $f(x)$.

19. Find the volume generated by rotating the area bounded by the given curves and lines about the line indicated:

(a) $y = x^2, \quad y = 0, \quad x = 3$; about the x-axis.
(b) $y = x^2, \quad y = 0, \quad x = 3$; about the line $x = -3$.

(c) $y = x^2$, $y = 0$, $x = 3$; about the y-axis, first integrating with respect to x and then integrating with respect to y.

(d) $x = 4y - y^2$, $x = 0$; about the y-axis.

(e) $x = 4y - y^2$, $x = 0$; about the x-axis.

20. A solid is generated by rotating $f(x)$, $(0 \leq x \leq a)$, about the x-axis. Its volume for all a is $a^2 + a$; find $f(x)$.

21. The area bounded by the curve $y^2 = 4x$ and the straight line $y = x$ is rotated about the x-axis. Find the volume generated.

22. Sketch the area bounded by the curve $y^2 = 4ax$, the line $x = a$, and the x-axis. Find the respective volumes generated by rotating this area in the following ways: (a) about the x-axis, (b) about the line $x = a$, (c) about the y-axis.

23. The area bounded by the curve $y = x/\sqrt{x^3 + 8}$, the x-axis, and the line $x = 2$ is rotated about the y-axis, generating a certain volume. Set up the integral that should be used to evaluate the volume and then evaluate the integral.

24. Find the volume of the solid generated by rotating the area bounded by $y^2 = x - 1$, $x = 3$, and $y = 1$ about the y-axis.

25. The area bounded by the curve $y^2 = 4ax$ and the line $x = a$ is rotated about the line $x = 2a$. Find the volume generated.

26. A twisted solid is generated as follows: We are given a fixed line L in space, and a square of side s in a plane perpendicular to L. One vertex of the square is on L. As this vertex moves a distance h along L, the square turns through a full revolution, with L as the axis. Find the volume generated by this motion. What would the volume be if the square had turned through two full revolutions in moving the same distance along L?

27. Two circles have a common diameter and lie in perpendicular planes. A square moves in such a way that its plane is perpendicular to this diameter and its diagonals are chords of the circles. Find the volume generated.

28. Find the volume generated by rotating about the x-axis the area bounded by the x-axis and one arch of the curve $y = \sin 2x$.

29. A round hole of radius $\sqrt{3}$ ft is bored through the center of a solid sphere of radius 2 ft. Find the volume cut out.

30. The cross section of a certain solid in any plane perpendicular to the x-axis is a circle having diameter AB with A on the curve $y^2 = 4x$ and B on the curve $x^2 = 4y$. Find the volume of the solid lying between the points of intersection of the curves.

31. The base of a solid is the area bounded by $y^2 = 4ax$ and $x = a$. Each cross section perpendicular to the x-axis is an equilateral triangle. Find the volume of the solid.

32. Find the length of the curve $y = (\tfrac{2}{3})x^{3/2} - (\tfrac{1}{2})x^{1/2}$ from $x = 0$ to $x = 4$.

33. Find the surface area generated when the curve of Problem 32 is rotated about the y-axis.

34. Find the length of the curve $x = (\tfrac{3}{5})y^{5/3} - (\tfrac{3}{4})y^{1/3}$ from $y = 0$ to $y = 1$.

35. Find the surface area generated when the curve of Problem 34 is rotated about the line $y = -1$.

36. Find the average value of y with respect to x for that part of the curve $y = \sqrt{ax}$ between $x = a$ and $x = 3a$.

37. Find the average value of y^2 with respect to x for the curve $ay = b\sqrt{a^2 - x^2}$ between $x = 0$ and $x = a$. Also find the average value of y with respect to x^2 for $0 \leq x \leq a$.

38. Consider the curve $y = f(x)$, $x \geq 0$ such that $f(0) = a$. Let $s(x)$ denote the arc length along the curve from $(0, a)$ to $(x, f(x))$. Find $f(x)$ if (a) $s(x) = Ax$. (What are the permissible values of A?) (b) Is it possible for $s(x) = x^n$, $n > 1$? Give a reason for your answer.

39. A point moves in a straight line during the time from $t = 0$ to $t = 3$ according to the law $s = 120t - 16t^2$. (a) Find the average value of the velocity, with respect to time, for these three seconds. [Compare with the "average velocity," Article 1-9, Eq. (6).] (b) Find the average value of the velocity with respect to the distance s during the three seconds.

40. Sketch a smooth curve through the points $A(1, 3)$, $B(3, 5)$, $C(5, 6)$, $D(7, 6)$, $E(9, 7)$, $F(11, 10)$. The area bounded by this curve, the x-axis, and the lines $x = 1$, $x = 11$ is rotated about the x-axis to generate a solid. Use the trapezoidal rule to approximate the volume generated. Also determine approximately the average value of the circular cross-sectional area (with respect to x).

41. Determine the center of mass of a thin homogeneous plate covering the area enclosed by the curves $y^2 = 8x$ and $y = x^2$.

42. Find the center of mass of a homogeneous plate covering the area in the first quadrant bounded by the curve $4y = x^2$, the y-axis, and the line $y = 4$.

43. Find the center of gravity of the area bounded by the curve $y = 4x - x^2$ and the line $2x - y = 0$.

44. Find the center of mass of a thin homogeneous plate covering the portion of the xy-plane, in the first quadrant, bounded by the curve $y = x^2$, the x-axis, and the line $x = 1$.

45. Consider a thin metal plate of area A and constant density and thickness. Show that if its first moment about the y-axis is M, its moment about the line $x = b$ is $M - bA$. Indicate why this result actually shows that the center of gravity is a physical property of the body, independent of the coordinate system used for finding its location.

46. Find the center of mass of a thin plate covering the region bounded by the curve $y^2 = 4ax$ and the line $x = a$, $a =$ positive constant, if the density at (x, y) is directly proportional to (a) x, (b) $|y|$.

47. Find the centroid of the area, in the first quadrant, bounded by two concentric circles and the coordinate axes, if the circles have radii a and b, $b > a > 0$, and their centers are at the origin. Also find the limits of the coordinates of the centroid as a approaches b, and discuss the meaning of the result.

48. (a) Find the centroid of the arc of the curve $x = a \cos^3 \phi$, $y = a \sin^3 \phi$ that is in the first quadrant. (b) Find the centroid of the surface generated by rotating the arc of part (a) about the y-axis.

49. A triangular corner is cut from a square 1 ft on a side. The area of the cutoff triangle is 36 in^2. If the centroid of the remaining area is 7 in. from one side of the original square, how far is it from the remaining sides?

50. A triangular plate ABC is submerged in water with its plane vertical. The side AB, 4 ft long, is 6 ft below the surface of the water, while the vertex C is 2 ft below the surface. Find the force of liquid pressure on one face of the plate.

51. A dam is in the form of a trapezoid, with its two horizontal sides 200 and 100 ft, respectively, the longer side being at the top; the height is 20 ft. What is the force of pressure on the dam when the water is level with the top of the dam?

52. The center of pressure on a submerged plane area is defined to be the point at which the total force could be applied without changing its total moment about any axis in the plane. Find the depth to the center of pressure (a) on a vertical rectangle of height h and width b if its upper edge is in the surface of the water, (b) on a vertical triangle of height h and base b if the vertex opposite b is a ft, and the base b is $a + h$ ft, below the surface of the water.

53. A container is filled with two nonmixing liquids with respective densities d_1 and d_2, $d_1 < d_2$. Find the force on one face of a square $ABCD$, $6\sqrt{2}$ feet on a side, immersed in the liquids with the diagonal AC normal to the free surface, if the highest point A of the square is 2 ft below the free surface and BD lies on the surface separating the two liquids.

54. A particle of mass M starts from rest at time $t = 0$ and is moved with constant acceleration a from $x = 0$ to $x = h$ against a variable force $F(t) = t^2$. Find the work done.

55. When a particle of mass M is at $(x, 0)$ it is attracted toward the origin with a force whose magnitude is k/x^2. If the particle starts from rest at $x = b$ and is acted upon by no other forces, find the work done on it by the time it reaches $x = a, 0 < a < b$.

56. Below the surface of the earth the force of its gravitational attraction is directly proportional to the distance from its center. Find the work done in lifting an object, whose weight at the surface is w lb, from a distance r ft below the earth's surface to the surface.

57. A storage tank is a right circular cylinder 20 ft long and 8 ft in diameter with its axis horizontal. If the tank is half full of oil weighing w lb/ft^3, find the work done in emptying it through a pipe that runs from the bottom of the tank to an outlet that is 6 ft above the top of the tank.

CHAPTER 6

TRANSCENDENTAL FUNCTIONS

6–1 The trigonometric functions. We have learned how to differentiate and integrate polynomials, and certain other algebraic functions including some rational functions and fractional powers. By definition, y is an *algebraic* function of x if it is a function that satisfies an irreducible algebraic equation of the form

$$P_0(x)y^n + P_1(x)y^{n-1} + \cdots + P_{n-1}(x)y + P_n(x) = 0,$$

with n a positive integer and with coefficients $P_0(x)$, $P_1(x)$, ... that are polynomials in x. For instance, $y = \sqrt{x}$, $x > 0$, defines an algebraic function whose elements (x, y) satisfy the irreducible equation

$$y^2 - x = 0.$$

Sums, products, quotients, powers, and roots of algebraic functions are in turn algebraic functions.

A function that is not algebraic is called *transcendental*. The class of transcendental functions includes the trigonometric, logarithmic, exponential, and inverse trigonometric functions, and many more which are less familiar.

We have learned how to differentiate and integrate two transcendental functions—the sine and cosine. In this chapter we shall add to this list the derivatives of the remaining trigonometric functions, their inverse functions, and the logarithmic and exponential functions.

At this stage it is well to recall the following formulas for derivatives and differentials:

Derivatives	*Differentials*
I. $\dfrac{dc}{dx} = 0.$	I′. $dc = 0.$
II. $\dfrac{d(cu)}{dx} = c\dfrac{du}{dx}.$	II′. $d(cu) = c\,du.$
III. $\dfrac{d(u + v)}{dx} = \dfrac{du}{dx} + \dfrac{dv}{dx}.$	III′. $d(u + v) = du + dv.$
IV. $\dfrac{d(uv)}{dx} = u\dfrac{dv}{dx} + v\dfrac{du}{dx}.$	IV′. $d(uv) = u\,dv + v\,du.$

V. $\dfrac{d\left(\frac{u}{v}\right)}{dx} = \dfrac{v\dfrac{du}{dx} - u\dfrac{dv}{dx}}{v^2}.$ 　　　 V'. $d\left(\dfrac{u}{v}\right) = \dfrac{v\,du - u\,dv}{v^2}.$

VI. $\dfrac{d(u^n)}{dx} = n\,u^{n-1}\dfrac{du}{dx}.$ 　　　 VI'. $d(u^n) = n\,u^{n-1}\,du.$

VII. $\dfrac{d\,(\sin u)}{dx} = \cos u\dfrac{du}{dx}.$ 　　　 VII'. $d\,(\sin u) = \cos u\,du.$

VIII. $\dfrac{d\,(\cos u)}{dx} = -\sin u\dfrac{du}{dx}.$ 　　　 VIII'. $d\,(\cos u) = -\sin u\,du.$

The first six of these by themselves enable us to differentiate the *algebraic* functions, which include polynomials, ratios of polynomials, and roots or powers of either of these types. VII, VII', VIII, and VIII' are discussed in Article 4–5.

When we combine formulas V, VII, and VIII and apply them to the trigonometric identities

$$\tan u = \frac{\sin u}{\cos u}, \qquad \cot u = \frac{\cos u}{\sin u},$$

$$\sec u = \frac{1}{\cos u}, \qquad \csc u = \frac{1}{\sin u}, \tag{1}$$

it is a simple matter to complete the list of formulas for differentiating the trigonometric functions and, doing so, we obtain:

IX. $\dfrac{d\,(\tan u)}{dx} = \sec^2 u\dfrac{du}{dx}.$ 　　　 IX'. $d\,(\tan u) = \sec^2 u\,du.$

X. $\dfrac{d\,(\cot u)}{dx} = -\csc^2 u\dfrac{du}{dx}.$ 　　　 X'. $d\,(\cot u) = -\csc^2 u\,du.$

XI. $\dfrac{d\,(\sec u)}{dx} = \sec u \tan u\dfrac{du}{dx}.$ 　　　 XI'. $d\,(\sec u) = \sec u \tan u\,du.$

XII. $\dfrac{d\,(\csc u)}{dx} = -\csc u \cot u\dfrac{du}{dx}.$ 　　　 XII'. $d\,(\csc u) = -\csc u \cot u\,du.$

The proofs of the formulas given above should be carried through by the reader.

These are the forms which are customarily used, though there are alternate forms such as

$$\frac{d\,(\sec u)}{dx} = \frac{\sin u}{\cos^2 u}\frac{du}{dx}\cdot$$

which are obtained from the expressions given by using some trigonometric identities. One reason for preferring the forms above is that they are quite easy to remember if we note that *the derivative of every cofunction (i.e., cos, cot, csc) can be obtained from the derivative of the corresponding function (i.e., sin, tan, sec)* by

(a) *introducing a minus sign,* and
(b) *replacing each function by its cofunction.*

Apply this, for example, to the formula

$$\frac{d\,(\sec u)}{dx} = \sec u \tan u\frac{du}{dx}\cdot$$

Replace sec u and tan u by their *cofunctions* on *both sides* of the equation and put in a *minus* sign; the result is

$$\frac{d\,(\csc u)}{dx} = -\csc u \cot u\frac{du}{dx}\cdot$$

Thus it is really only necessary to "memorize" the two new formulas

$$\frac{d\,(\tan u)}{dx} = \sec^2 u\frac{du}{dx},$$

$$\frac{d\,(\sec u)}{dx} = \sec u \tan u\frac{du}{dx},$$

and the above rule produces the other two.

The formulas IX′–XII′ for differentials immediately produce the four new integration formulas:

$$\int \sec^2 u\,du = \tan u + C, \qquad \int \sec u \tan u\,du = \sec u + C,$$

$$\int \csc^2 u\,du = -\cot u + C, \qquad \int \csc u \cot u\,du = -\csc u + C. \tag{2}$$

EXAMPLE 1. Find dy/dx if $y = \tan^2 3x$.
First we apply the power formula VI,

$$\frac{dy}{dx} = 2\tan 3x\,\frac{d\,(\tan 3x)}{dx}$$

and then IX,

$$\frac{d\,(\tan 3x)}{dx} = \sec^2 3x\,\frac{d(3x)}{dx},$$

and then II,

$$\frac{d(3x)}{dx} = 3\frac{dx}{dx} = 3.$$

When these are combined, we get

$$\frac{dy}{dx} = 6 \tan 3x \sec^2 3x.$$

EXAMPLE 2. Integrate $\int \tan^2 3x\, dx$.

At first sight, this seems to be impossible with the formulas we have for integration. But the trigonometric identity

$$\sin^2 3x + \cos^2 3x = 1$$

becomes

$$\tan^2 3x + 1 = \sec^2 3x$$

when we divide both sides by $\cos^2 3x$. Hence,

$$\tan^2 3x = \sec^2 3x - 1$$

and

$$\int \tan^2 3x\, dx = \int (\sec^2 3x - 1)\, dx = \int \sec^2 3x\, dx - \int 1\, dx$$

$$= \tfrac{1}{3} \int \sec^2 3x\, d(3x) - \int 1\, dx = \tfrac{1}{3} \tan 3x - x + C.$$

PROBLEMS

Sketch the graphs of the following equations, Problems 1–10.

1. $y = \sin x$
2. $y = \cos x$
3. $y = \tan x$
4. $y = \cot x$
5. $y = \sec x$
6. $y = \csc x$
7. $y = 3 \sin 2x$
8. $y = 4 \cos (x/3)$
9. $y = \sin^2 x$
10. $y = \tfrac{1}{2} + \tfrac{1}{2} \cos 2x$
11. (a) Derive formula IX
    (b) Derive formula XI
12. (a) Derive formula X
    (b) Derive formula XII

Find dy/dx in each of the following problems (13 through 33):

13. $y = \tan (3x^2)$
14. $y = \tan^2 (\cos x)$
15. $y = \cot (3x + 5)$
16. $y = \sqrt{\cot x}$
17. $y = \sec^2 x - \tan^2 x$
18. $y = \tfrac{1}{3} \sec^3 x$
19. $y = 3x + \tan 3x$
20. $y = 3 \tan 2x$
21. $y = x - \tan x$
22. $y = \sec^4 x - \tan^4 x$
23. $y = (\csc x + \cot x)^2$
24. $y = 2 \sin^2 3x$

25. $y = \frac{1}{2}x - \frac{1}{4}\sin 2x$

26. $y = \frac{1}{2}x + \frac{1}{4}\sin 2x$

27. $y = \sin^3 \frac{x}{3} - 3\sin \frac{x}{3}$

28. $y = 3\cos^2 \frac{x}{2}$

29. $y = 2\sin \frac{1}{2}x - x\cos \frac{1}{2}x$

30. $x^2 = \sin y + \sin 2y$

31. $y = \sin^3 x - \sin 3x$

32. $y = \frac{1}{3}\sin^3 5x - \sin 5x$

33. $x + \tan(xy) = 0$

34. Find the maximum height of the curve $y = 6\cos x - 8\sin x$ above the x-axis.

35. Find the maximum and minimum values of the function $y = 2\sin x + \cos 2x$ for $0 \le x \le \pi/2$.

36. Show that the function $f(x) = x + \sin x$ has no relative maxima or minima.

37. Show that the curve $y = x\sin x$ is tangent to the line $y = x$ whenever $\sin x = 1$, and is tangent to the line $y = -x$ whenever $\sin x = -1$.

38. A revolving light 3 miles from a straight shoreline makes 8 revolutions per minute. Find the velocity of the beam of light along the shore at the instant when it makes an angle of 45° with the shoreline.

39. A rope with a ring in one end is looped over two pegs in a horizontal line. The free end, after being passed through the ring, has a weight suspended from it, so that the rope hangs taut. If the rope slips freely through the ring, the weight will descend as far as possible. Find the angle formed at the bottom of the loop. (Assume that the length of the rope is at least four times as great as the distance between the pegs.)

Evaluate the following integrals:

40. $\int \sin 3t \, dt$

41. $\int \sec^2 2\theta \, d\theta$

42. $\int \tan^3 x \sec^2 x \, dx$

43. $\int \sec^3 x \tan x \, dx$

44. $\int \sec \frac{x}{2} \tan \frac{x}{2} \, dx$

45. $\int \cos^2 y \, dy$

46. $\int \frac{d\theta}{\cos^2 \theta}$

47. $\int \frac{d\theta}{\sin^2 (\theta/3)}$

48. Find the area bounded by the curve $y = \tan x \sec^2 x$, the x-axis, and the line $x = \pi/3$.

49. The area bounded above by the curve $y = \tan x$, below by the x-axis, and on the right by the line $x = \pi/4$ is revolved about the x-axis. Find the volume generated.

6–2 The inverse trigonometric functions. The equation

$$x = \sin y \tag{1}$$

determines infinitely many real values of y for each x in the range $-1 \le x \le 1$.

For example, if $x = \frac{1}{2}$ then we ask for all angles y such that $\sin y = \frac{1}{2}$. The two angles 30° and 150° in the first and second quadrants occur to us immediately. But any whole multiple of 360° may be either added to or subtracted from these and the sine of the resulting angle will still be $\frac{1}{2}$. Expressing these facts in mathematical language and using radian measure for the angles, we have $\sin y = \frac{1}{2}$ if

$$y = \begin{cases} \dfrac{\pi}{6} + 2n\pi \\[2ex] \dfrac{5\pi}{6} + 2n\pi \end{cases} \qquad n = 0, \pm 1, \pm 2, \ldots$$

Similarly, we find that $\sin y = -\frac{1}{2}$ if

$$y = \begin{cases} -\dfrac{\pi}{6} + 2n\pi \\[2ex] -\dfrac{5\pi}{6} + 2n\pi \end{cases} \qquad n = 0, \pm 1, \pm 2, \ldots$$

Now it is desirable, for some of our later applications, to adopt a rule for picking a *principal value* of y. We shall require that the rule (a) produce one and only one value of y for each x, $-1 \le x \le 1$, such that $\sin y = x$; and (b) give two "nearly equal" values of y for two "nearly equal" values of x.

To state requirement (b) more specifically, we require that if x_1 and x_2 are two values of x both between -1 and $+1$, and y_1 and y_2 are the corresponding values of y such that $\sin y = x$, then $y_2 - y_1$ should tend to zero if $x_2 - x_1$ does. The portion of the curve AOB shown heavily marked in Fig. 6-2 fulfills these requirements. For any x between -1 and $+1$ there is one and only one corresponding point (x, y) on this portion of the curve, and the y-value satisfies $\sin y = x$. Furthermore, this is a continuous curve, so that if (x_1, y_1) and (x_2, y_2) are two points on it and $(x_2 - x_1) \to 0$, then also $(y_2 - y_1) \to 0$.

To be sure that the point (x, y) stays on the portion AOB of Fig. 6-2, we need only restrict y:

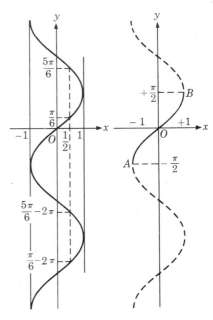

FIGURE 6-1   FIGURE 6-2

$$\sin y = x, \qquad -\frac{\pi}{2} \leq y \leq \frac{\pi}{2}. \tag{2}$$

The restrictions placed on y give a continuous function

$$y = \sin^{-1} x, \qquad -\frac{\pi}{2} \leq y \leq \frac{\pi}{2}, \tag{3}$$

called the "inverse sine of x" which is defined on the domain $-1 \leq x \leq 1$ and has values on the range $-\pi/2 \leq y \leq +\pi/2$. Note that the minus one in Eq. (3), although written as an exponent, does *not* mean

$$(\sin x)^{-1} = \frac{1}{\sin x} = \csc x.$$

Actually, Eq. (3) merely gives a name to a new function that is defined implicitly by Eq. (2). The symbol $f^{-1}(x)$ is often used to denote the function y defined implicitly by $f(y) = x$, that is,

$$y = f^{-1}(x).$$

The notation arcsin x is also used to represent the function that we have denoted by $\sin^{-1} x$, but the latter notation is now more commonly used. Thus,

$$\sin^{-1}\left(\frac{1}{2}\right) = \frac{\pi}{6}, \qquad \sin^{-1}\left(-\frac{1}{2}\right) = -\frac{\pi}{6}.$$

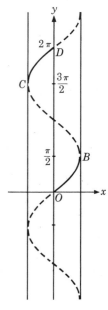

In terms of angles referred to standard position in the various quadrants, Eq. (2) and the restriction $-\pi/2 \leq y \leq \pi/2$ mean that the answer to the question: "What is the angle y whose sine is x?" is always an angle in the *first* or *fourth* quadrant, but if it is in the *fourth* quadrant, it is to be expressed as the *negative* of an angle between 0 and $\pi/2$ and not as a positive angle $\geq 3\pi/2$, since the latter would violate the restriction in (2).

At the risk of appearing to labor a point which is already clear, we also note that the inverse sine is an *odd* function of x. This means that

$$\sin^{-1}(-x) = -\sin^{-1}(x).$$

Keeping this fact firmly in mind will prevent us from using values of y corresponding to points on the discontinuous curve composed of the portions OB and CD on the curve in Fig. 6–3. The objection to using these is that for a small positive value of x, say $x_1 = +0.01$,

FIGURE 6–3

the point is near O and $y_1 \approx 0.01$; while for a small negative value of x, say $x_2 = -0.01$, the point is near D and $y_2 \approx 2\pi - 0.01$. The difference $y_2 - y_1$ is nearly $2\pi = 6.28+$, whereas the difference $x_1 - x_2$ is, in this case, only 0.02. This difficulty is not encountered if we restrict the value of y as in (3), which confines us to the *continuous* curve AOB of Fig. 6–2.

To each of the other trigonometric functions there also corresponds an *inverse* trigonometric function. In each case, we restrict the angle in such a way that the function is *single-valued*.

The same reasoning that led us to adopt the particular range

$$-\frac{\pi}{2} \le y \le \frac{\pi}{2}$$

for the principal value of $y = \sin^{-1} x$ prompts us to adopt a similar range for the principal value of y satisfying the equation $x = \tan y$ (see Fig. 6–4). Thus we write

$$y = \tan^{-1} x, \qquad -\frac{\pi}{2} < y < \frac{\pi}{2} \qquad (4)$$

to mean the same as

$$\tan y = x, \qquad -\frac{\pi}{2} < y < \frac{\pi}{2}. \qquad (5)$$

The inverse tangent function, (4), is defined on the *domain* $-\infty < x < +\infty$, that is, for all real x. Its *range* is $-\pi/2 < y < +\pi/2$. The values $y = \pm\pi/2$ are to be excluded, since the tangent becomes infinite as the angle approaches $\pm\pi/2$.

When we come to the inverse cosine function, we simply *define* it by the equation

$$\cos^{-1} x = \frac{\pi}{2} - \sin^{-1} x. \qquad (6)$$

Since

$$-\frac{\pi}{2} \le \sin^{-1} x \le \frac{\pi}{2},$$

the range of principal values for (6) is

$$0 \le \cos^{-1} x \le \pi. \qquad (7)$$

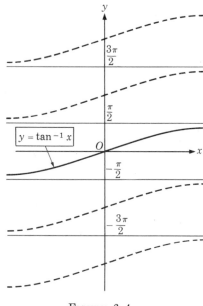

FIGURE 6–4   FIGURE 6–5

The *domain* of the inverse cosine function is $-1 \le x \le 1$. Its *range* is $0 \le y \le \pi$. The principal value is thus represented by the heavily marked portion of the curve

$$x = \cos y$$

shown in Fig. 6–5.

The reason for defining $\cos^{-1} x$ by Eq. (6) is as follows. In the right triangle in Fig. 6–6, the acute angles α and β are complementary, that is

$$\alpha + \beta = \frac{\pi}{2}.$$

But we also have

$$\sin \alpha = x = \cos \beta,$$

so that

$$\alpha = \sin^{-1} x, \qquad \beta = \cos^{-1} x,$$

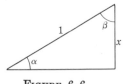

FIGURE 6–6

and the relation $\alpha + \beta = \pi/2$ is the same as $\beta = \pi/2 - \alpha$; that is,

$$\cos^{-1} x = \frac{\pi}{2} - \sin^{-1} x.$$

Thus Eq. (6) expresses the fact that the angle whose cosine is x is the complement of the angle whose sine is x.

For exactly analogous reasons, we also define the inverse cotangent to be

$$\cot^{-1} x = \frac{\pi}{2} - \tan^{-1} x, \tag{8}$$

and we thus restrict the principal value to

$$0 < \cot^{-1} x < \pi. \tag{9}$$

The inverse secant and inverse cosecant functions will be single-valued functions of x on the domain $|x| \geq 1$ if we adopt the definitions

$$\sec^{-1} x = \cos^{-1}\left(\frac{1}{x}\right), \tag{10a}$$

$$\csc^{-1} x = \sin^{-1}\left(\frac{1}{x}\right), \tag{10b}$$

with their principal values confined to the ranges

$$0 \leq \sec^{-1} x \leq \pi, \tag{11a}$$

$$-\frac{\pi}{2} \leq \csc^{-1} x \leq \frac{\pi}{2}. \tag{11b}$$

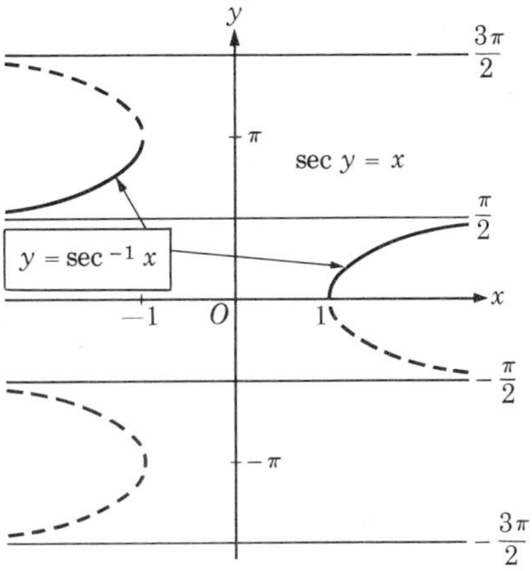

FIGURE 6–7

The reason for adopting the definitions above is based on the following considerations. If $\sec y = x$, then $\cos y = 1/x$, and we simply ask that the principal values of y be the same in these two cases, that is

$$y = \sec^{-1} x = \cos^{-1}\left(\frac{1}{x}\right).$$

It should be noted, however, that some writers choose the principal value of the inverse secant of x to lie between 0 and $\pi/2$ when x is positive, and between $-\pi$ and $-\pi/2$ (hence, as a negative angle in the third quadrant) when x is negative. This latter method has the advantage of simplifying the formula for the derivative of $\sec^{-1} x$, but has the disadvantage of failing to satisfy the relationship expressed in Eq. (10a) when x is negative. Either method leads to a function which is discontinuous, as is inherent in the nature of the secant function itself, since to pass from a point where the secant is negative to a point where the secant is positive requires crossing one of the discontinuities of the curve.

PROBLEMS

1. Given that $\alpha = \sin^{-1} \frac{1}{2}$, find $\cos \alpha$, $\tan \alpha$, $\sec \alpha$, $\csc \alpha$.
2. Given that $\alpha = \cos^{-1}\left(-\frac{1}{2}\right)$, find $\sin \alpha$, $\tan \alpha$, $\sec \alpha$, $\csc \alpha$.

3. Evaluate $\sin^{-1}(1) - \sin^{-1}(-1)$.   4. Evaluate $\tan^{-1}(1) - \tan^{-1}(-1)$.

5. Evaluate $\sec^{-1}(2) - \sec^{-1}(-2)$.

6. A picture a feet high is placed on a wall with its base b feet above the level of an observer's eye. If the observer stands x feet from the wall, show that the angle of vision α subtended by the picture is given by

$$\alpha = \cot^{-1}\frac{x}{a+b} - \cot^{-1}\frac{x}{b}.$$

7. Prove:

(a) $\tan^{-1}(-x) = -\tan^{-1}x$,   (b) $\cos^{-1}(-x) = \pi - \cos^{-1}x$,

(c) $\sec^{-1}(-x) = \pi - \sec^{-1}(x)$.

8. Simplify each of the following expressions:

(a) $\sin(\sin^{-1}0.735)$,   (b) $\cos(\sin^{-1}0.8)$,   (c) $\sin(2\sin^{-1}0.8)$,

(d) $\tan^{-1}(\tan \pi/3)$,   (e) $\cos^{-1}(-\sin \pi/6)$,   (f) $\sec^{-1}(\sec(-30°))$.

6–3 Derivatives of the inverse trigonometric functions. The following formulas may now be derived.

XIII. $\dfrac{d(\sin^{-1}u)}{dx} = \dfrac{du/dx}{\sqrt{1-u^2}}$.   XIII'. $d(\sin^{-1}u) = \dfrac{du}{\sqrt{1-u^2}}$.

XIV. $\dfrac{d(\cos^{-1}u)}{dx} = -\dfrac{du/dx}{\sqrt{1-u^2}}$.   XIV'. $d(\cos^{-1}u) = -\dfrac{du}{\sqrt{1-u^2}}$.

XV. $\dfrac{d(\tan^{-1}u)}{dx} = \dfrac{du/dx}{1+u^2}$.   XV'. $d(\tan^{-1}u) = \dfrac{du}{1+u^2}$.

XVI. $\dfrac{d(\cot^{-1}u)}{dx} = -\dfrac{du/dx}{1+u^2}$.   XVI'. $d(\cot^{-1}u) = -\dfrac{du}{1+u^2}$.

XVII. $\dfrac{d(\sec^{-1}u)}{dx} = \dfrac{du/dx}{|u|\sqrt{u^2-1}}$.   XVII'. $d(\sec^{-1}u) = \dfrac{du}{|u|\sqrt{u^2-1}}$.

XVIII. $\dfrac{d(\csc^{-1}u)}{dx} = \dfrac{-du/dx}{|u|\sqrt{u^2-1}}$.   XVIII'. $d(\csc^{-1}u) = \dfrac{-du}{|u|\sqrt{u^2-1}}$.

To illustrate how these are derived, we shall prove formulas XIII and XVII. Let

$$y = \sin^{-1}u, \qquad -\frac{\pi}{2} \le y \le \frac{\pi}{2}.$$

Then
$$\sin y = u,$$

$$\cos y \frac{dy}{dx} = \frac{du}{dx}, \qquad \frac{dy}{dx} = \frac{1}{\cos y} \frac{du}{dx}.$$

To express the right side in terms of u, we use the fact that

$$\cos y = \pm\sqrt{1 - \sin^2 y} = \pm\sqrt{1 - u^2}.$$

When $-\pi/2 \leq y \leq \pi/2$, $\cos y$ is not negative; hence

$$\cos y = +\sqrt{1 - u^2}$$

and

$$\frac{dy}{dx} = \frac{1}{\sqrt{1 - u^2}} \frac{du}{dx},$$

which establishes XIII.

Next, let
$$y = \sec^{-1} u, \qquad 0 \leq y \leq \pi.$$

Then

$$\sec y = u, \qquad \sec y \tan y \frac{dy}{dx} = \frac{du}{dx},$$

$$\frac{dy}{dx} = \frac{1}{\sec y \tan y} \frac{du}{dx}.$$

Substituting

$$\sec y = u, \qquad \tan y = \pm\sqrt{\sec^2 y - 1} = \pm\sqrt{u^2 - 1},$$

we have

$$\frac{dy}{dx} = \frac{1}{u(\pm\sqrt{u^2 - 1})} \frac{du}{dx}.$$

The ambiguous sign is determined by the sign of $\tan y$, and hence is

$$+ \text{ if } 0 < y < \frac{\pi}{2}; \qquad \text{that is, if } u \text{ is } +,$$

$$- \text{ if } \frac{\pi}{2} < y < \pi; \qquad \text{that is, if } u \text{ is } -.$$

That is,

$$\frac{dy}{dx} = \frac{1}{u\sqrt{u^2 - 1}} \frac{du}{dx} \qquad \text{if } u > 0$$

$$= \frac{1}{-u\sqrt{u^2 - 1}} \frac{du}{dx} \qquad \text{if } u < 0,$$

and both of these are summarized in the single formula

$$\frac{dy}{dx} = \frac{1}{|u|\sqrt{u^2 - 1}} \frac{du}{dx}.$$

The formulas XIII to XVIII are used directly as given, but even more important are the integration formulas obtained immediately from the differential formulas XIII′ to XVIII′, namely,

$$\int \frac{du}{\sqrt{1 - u^2}} = \sin^{-1} u + C, \qquad \int \frac{du}{1 + u^2} = \tan^{-1} u + C,$$

$$\int \frac{du}{u\sqrt{u^2 - 1}} = \int \frac{d(-u)}{(-u)\sqrt{u^2 - 1}} = \sec^{-1} |u| + C. \tag{1}$$

Note that $\sec^{-1} u$ and $\sec^{-1} |u|$ are meaningless unless $|u| \geq 1$ (see Fig. 6–7).

EXAMPLE.

$$\int_0^1 \frac{dx}{1 + x^2} = \tan^{-1} x \Big]_0^1 = \tan^{-1} 1 - \tan^{-1} 0 = \frac{\pi}{4}.$$

PROBLEMS

1. Derive formula XIV.   2. Derive formula XV.

3. Derive formula XVI.   4. Derive formula XVIII.

Find dy/dx in each of the following:

5. $y = \sin^{-1} \dfrac{x}{2}$ 6. $y = \dfrac{1}{3} \tan^{-1} \dfrac{x}{3}$

7. $y = \sec^{-1} 5x$ 8. $y = \cos^{-1} 2x$

9. $y = \cot^{-1} \dfrac{2}{x} + \tan^{-1} \dfrac{x}{2}$ 10. $y = \sin^{-1} \dfrac{x - 1}{x + 1}$

11. $y = \tan^{-1} \dfrac{x - 1}{x + 1}$ 12. $y = x \sin^{-1} x + \sqrt{1 - x^2}$

13. $y = x (\sin^{-1} x)^2 - 2x + 2\sqrt{1 - x^2} \sin^{-1} x$

14. $y = x \cos^{-1} 2x - \frac{1}{2}\sqrt{1 - 4x^2}$

15. How far from the wall should the observer stand in order to maximize the angle of vision α in Problem 6, Article 6–2?

Evaluate the following integrals:

16. $\displaystyle\int_0^{1/2} \frac{dx}{\sqrt{1 - x^2}}$ 17. $\displaystyle\int_{-1}^1 \frac{dx}{1 + x^2}$ 18. $\displaystyle\int_{\sqrt{2}}^2 \frac{dx}{x\sqrt{x^2 - 1}}$

19. $\displaystyle\int_{-2}^{-\sqrt{2}} \frac{dx}{x\sqrt{x^2-1}}$ 20. $\displaystyle\int \frac{dx}{\sqrt{1-4x^2}}$ 21. $\displaystyle\int_{1/\sqrt{3}}^{1} \frac{dx}{x\sqrt{4x^2-1}}$

6–4 The natural logarithm. We have so far studied functions which are fairly familiar. Polynomials, rational functions, and other algebraic functions result from the familiar operations of arithmetic and algebra. The trigonometric functions can be identified with coordinates of points on a unit circle and with their ratios and reciprocals. The inverse trigonometric functions are probably less familiar, but nevertheless they can be understood without any knowledge of the calculus. But we are now going to study a function, the natural logarithm, which depends upon the calculus for its very definition.

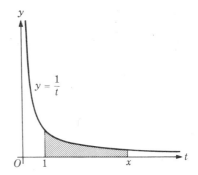

The natural logarithm* of x, which is indicated by the notation $\ln x$, is defined, for positive x, as the integral

$$\ln x = \int_{1}^{x} \frac{1}{t}\, dt. \qquad (1)$$

Fig. 6–8 Shaded area is $\ln x$.

For any x greater than 1, this integral represents the area bounded above by the curve $y = 1/t$, below by the t-axis, on the left by the line $t = 1$, and on the right by the line $t = x$. (See Fig. 6–8.)

If $x = 1$, the left and right boundaries of the area are identical and the area is zero,

$$\ln 1 = \int_{1}^{1} \frac{1}{t}\, dt = 0. \qquad (2)$$

If x is less than 1, then the left boundary is the line $t = x$ and the right boundary is $t = 1$. In this case,

$$\ln x = \int_{1}^{x} \frac{1}{t}\, dt = -\int_{x}^{1} \frac{1}{t}\, dt \qquad (3)$$

is the negative of the area under the curve between x and 1.

---

* The first discovery of logarithms is credited to a Scottish nobleman, John Napier (1550–1617). For a biographical sketch of Napier, see the *World of Mathematics*, Vol. 1, "The Great Mathematicians," by H. W. Turnbull, pp. 121–125.

In all cases, if x is any positive number, the value of the definite integral in Eq. (1) can be calculated to as many decimal places as may be desired by using inscribed rectangles, circumscribed rectangles, or trapezoids to approximate the appropriate area. (See Chapter 4. Another method for computing natural logarithms, by means of series, will also be discussed in Chapter 16. Also see Problem 8 below.) In any event, Eq. (1) defines a computable function of x over the domain $0 < x < +\infty$. We study its range in Article 6–7.

PROBLEMS

Use trapezoids of altitude $\Delta t = 0.1$ to approximate the appropriate areas to obtain approximations to the following natural logarithms, Problems 1–4.

1. ln 1.2　　　　2. ln 1.4　　　　3. ln 2　　　　4. ln 0.5

5. (a) Suppose h is small and positive. Does the approximation $\ln (1 + h) \approx h$ correspond to using an inscribed rectangle or a circumscribed rectangle to approximate the area from 1 to $1 + h$ under the curve $y = 1/t$? (b) Answer the same question in case h is negative.

6. Approximate $\ln (1 + h)$ by using the line L that is tangent to the curve $y = 1/t$ at $A(1, 1)$, as upper boundary of a trapezoid of altitude $|h|$. Sketch. Show that this leads to the approximation

$$\ln (1 + h) \approx h - \frac{h^2}{2}.$$

Use this result to approximate: (a) ln 1.04, (b) ln 0.96.

7. Let $aACBb$ be the polygon whose vertices are $a(1, 0)$, $A(1, 1)$, C $(\frac{4}{3}, \frac{2}{3})$, $B(2, \frac{1}{2})$, and $b(2, 0)$. Show that AC and CB are tangent to the hyperbola $y = 1/t$ at A and at B respectively. Use the area of the polygon to find an approximation to ln 2. Sketch.

8. (a) Show, by long division or otherwise, that

$$\frac{1}{1 + u} = 1 - u + u^2 - \frac{u^3}{1 + u}.$$

(The division could be continued. We stop here only for sake of illustration.)

(b) In Eq. (1), make the substitution

$$t = 1 + u, \qquad dt = du$$

and make the corresponding change in the limits of integration, thus obtaining

$$\ln x = \int_0^{x-1} \frac{du}{1 + u}.$$

(c) Combine the results of (a) and (b) to obtain

$$\ln x = \int_0^{x-1} \left(1 - u + u^2 - \frac{u^3}{1+u}\right) du,$$

or

$$\ln x = (x-1) - \tfrac{1}{2}(x-1)^2 + \tfrac{1}{3}(x-1)^3 - R,$$

where

$$R = \int_0^{x-1} \frac{u^3}{1+u}\, du.$$

(d) Show that, if $x > 1$ and $0 \le u \le x - 1$, then

$$\frac{u^3}{1+u} \le u^3.$$

Hence, deduce that

$$R \le \int_0^{x-1} u^3\, du = \frac{(x-1)^4}{4}.$$

(e) Combining the results of (c) and (d), show that the approximation

$$\ln x \approx (x-1) - \tfrac{1}{2}(x-1)^2 + \tfrac{1}{3}(x-1)^3$$

tends to overestimate the value of $\ln x$, but with an error not greater than $(x-1)^4/4$.

(f) Use the result of (e) to estimate $\ln 1.2$.

6–5 The derivative of ln x. Since the function $F(x) = \ln x$ is defined by the integral

$$F(x) = \int_1^x \frac{1}{t}\, dt \qquad (x > 0) \tag{1}$$

(see Fig. 6–9, p. 304), it follows at once, from Theorem 4 of Article 4–12 that

$$F'(x) = \frac{1}{x}.$$

That is,

$$\frac{d\,(\ln x)}{dx} = \frac{1}{x}. \tag{2}$$

We can obtain a slightly more general formula by considering $\ln u$, where u is a positive, differentiable, function of x. By the chain rule for derivatives,

$$\boxed{\frac{d \ln u}{dx} = \frac{d \ln u}{du}\frac{du}{dx} = \frac{1}{u}\frac{du}{dx}} \qquad\qquad \text{XIX}$$

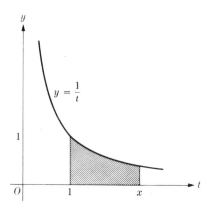

FIG. 6–9. $\ln x = \displaystyle\int_1^x \frac{1}{t}\,dt, \quad \frac{d(\ln x)}{dx} = \frac{1}{x}.$

or, in terms of differentials,

$$\boxed{d \ln u = \frac{du}{u}.}$$
                                            XIX′

EXAMPLE 1. Find dy/dx if $y = \ln(3x^2 + 4)$.

Solution. $\dfrac{dy}{dx} = \dfrac{1}{3x^2 + 4} \dfrac{d(3x^2 + 4)}{dx} = \dfrac{6x}{3x^2 + 4}.$

Equation (XIX′) leads at once to the integration formula

$$\int \frac{du}{u} = \ln u + C, \tag{3a}$$

provided u is positive. On the other hand, if u is negative then $-u$ is positive and

$$\int \frac{du}{u} = \int \frac{d(-u)}{-u} = \ln(-u) + C. \tag{3b}$$

The two results (3a, b) can be combined into a single result, namely,

$$\int \frac{du}{u} = \begin{cases} \ln u + C & \text{if} \quad u > 0, \\ \ln(-u) + C & \text{if} \quad u < 0, \end{cases}$$

or

$$\boxed{\int \frac{du}{u} = \ln |u| + C.} \tag{4}$$

We recall that the formula

$$\int u^n \, du = \frac{u^{n+1}}{n+1} + C, \qquad n \neq -1$$

failed to cover one case, namely, $n = -1$. Now Eq. (4) covers this case for us, since it tells us that

$$\int u^{-1} \, du = \int \frac{du}{u} = \ln |u| + C.$$

It is important, of course, to remember that

$$\int \frac{dx}{x^2} = \int x^{-2} \, dx = \frac{x^{-1}}{-1} + C$$

is, not a logarithm.

EXAMPLE 2. Integrate

$$\int \frac{\cos \theta \, d\theta}{1 + \sin \theta}.$$

Solution. In Eq. (4), let

$$u = 1 + \sin \theta.$$

Then

$$du = \frac{du}{d\theta} \, d\theta = \cos \theta \, d\theta$$

so that

$$\int \frac{\cos \theta \, d\theta}{1 + \sin \theta} = \int \frac{du}{u} = \ln |u| + C$$

$$= \ln |1 + \sin \theta| + C.$$

PROBLEMS

Find dy/dx in each of the following problems (1 through 18).

1. $y = \ln (x^2 + 2x)$ 2. $y = (\ln x)^3$

3. $y = \ln (\cos x)$ 4. $y = \ln (\tan x + \sec x)$

5. $y = \ln (x\sqrt{x^2 + 1})$ 6. $y = \ln (3x\sqrt{x + 2})$

7. $y = x \ln x - x$ 8. $y = x^3 \ln (2x)$

9. $y = \frac{1}{2} \ln \frac{1 + x}{1 - x}$ 10. $y = \frac{1}{3} \ln \frac{x^3}{1 + x^3}$

11. $y = \ln \frac{x}{2 + 3x}$ 12. $y = \ln (x^2 + 4) - x \tan^{-1} \frac{x}{2}$

13. $y = \ln x - \dfrac{1}{2}\ln(1 + x^2) - \dfrac{\tan^{-1} x}{x}$

14. $y = x(\ln x)^3$ 15. $y = x[\sin(\ln x) + \cos(\ln x)]$

16. $y = x\sec^{-1} x - \ln(x + \sqrt{x^2 - 1}),\quad (x > 1)$

17. $y = x\ln(a^2 + x^2) - 2x + 2a\tan^{-1}\dfrac{x}{a}$

18. $y = \ln(\ln x)$

Evaluate the following integrals:

19. $\displaystyle\int \frac{dx}{2x + 3}$

20. $\displaystyle\int \frac{dx}{2 - 3x}$

21. $\displaystyle\int \frac{x\,dx}{4x^2 + 1}$

22. $\displaystyle\int \frac{\sin x\,dx}{2 - \cos x}$

23. $\displaystyle\int \frac{\cos x\,dx}{\sin x}$

24. $\displaystyle\int \frac{2x - 5}{x}\,dx$

25. $\displaystyle\int \frac{x\,dx}{x + 1}$

26. $\displaystyle\int \frac{x^2\,dx}{4 - x^3}$

27. $\displaystyle\int \frac{x\,dx}{1 - x^2}$

28. $\displaystyle\int \frac{dx}{\sqrt{x}\,(1 + \sqrt{x})}$

29. $\displaystyle\int (\ln x)^2\,\frac{dx}{x}$

30. $\displaystyle\int \frac{dx}{(2x + 3)^2}$

6–6 Properties of natural logarithms. In this article we shall establish the following properties of the natural logarithm:

$$\ln ax = \ln a + \ln x, \tag{1}$$

$$\ln \frac{x}{a} = \ln x - \ln a, \tag{2}$$

$$\ln x^n = n\ln x, \tag{3}$$

provided x and a are positive and n is a rational number.

The proofs of these results are all based on the fact that

$$y = \ln x$$

satisfies the differential equation

$$\frac{dy}{dx} = \frac{1}{x} \quad \text{for all} \quad x > 0,$$

plus the fact that if two functions have the same derivative for all $x > 0$, then the two functions can differ only by a constant. That is, if

$$\frac{dy_1}{dx} = \frac{dy_2}{dx} \quad \text{for all} \quad x > 0,$$

then

$$y_1 = y_2 + \text{constant} \quad \text{for all} \quad x > 0.$$

Now to prove Eq. (1), let

$$y_1 = \ln ax, \qquad y_2 = \ln x.$$

Then

$$\frac{dy_1}{dx} = \frac{1}{ax} \frac{d(ax)}{dx} = \frac{a}{ax} = \frac{1}{x} = \frac{dy_2}{dx}. \tag{4}$$

Therefore we have

$$\ln ax = \ln x + C. \tag{5}$$

To evaluate C it suffices to substitute $x = 1$:

$$\ln a = \ln 1 + C = 0 + C,$$

which gives

$$C = \ln a.$$

Hence, by (5),

$$\ln ax = \ln x + \ln a. \qquad \text{Q.E.D.}$$

To prove Eq. (2), we first put $x = 1/a$ in Eq. (1) and recall that $\ln 1 = 0$:

$$0 = \ln 1 = \ln a + \ln (1/a)$$

so that

$$\ln \frac{1}{a} = -\ln a. \tag{6}$$

Now apply Eq. (1) with a replaced by $1/a$ and $\ln a$ replaced by $\ln (1/a) = -\ln a$. The result is Eq. (2).

To prove Eq. (3), let

$$y_1 = \ln x^n.$$

Then

$$\frac{dy_1}{dx} = \frac{1}{x^n} \cdot nx^{n-1} = \frac{n}{x} = \frac{d}{dx}(n \ln x).$$

Hence $y_1 = \ln x^n$ and $y_2 = n \ln x$ have equal derivatives, so they differ at most by a constant:

$$\ln x^n = n \ln x + C. \tag{7}$$

But by taking $x = 1$, and remembering that $\ln 1 = 0$, we find $C = 0$, which gives Eq. (3). In particular, if $n = 1/m$, where m is a positive integer, we have

$$\ln \sqrt[m]{x} = \ln x^{1/m} = \frac{1}{m} \ln x. \tag{8}$$

Problems

Express the following logarithms in terms of the two given logarithms $a = \ln 2$, $b = \ln 3$. [For example: $\ln 1.5 = \ln \frac{3}{2} = \ln 3 - \ln 2 = b - a$.]

1. $\ln 16$ 2. $\ln \sqrt[3]{9}$ 3. $\ln 2\sqrt{2}$

4. $\ln 0.25$ 5. $\ln \frac{4}{9}$ 6. $\ln 12$

7. $\ln \frac{9}{8}$ 8. $\ln 36$ 9. $\ln 4.5$

10. $\ln \sqrt{13.5}$

6–7 Graph of $y = \ln x$. The slope of the curve

$$y = \ln x \tag{1}$$

is given by

$$\frac{dy}{dx} = \frac{1}{x}, \tag{2}$$

which is positive for all $x > 0$. Hence the graph of $y = \ln x$ steadily rises from left to right. Since the derivative is continuous, the function $\ln x$ is itself continuous, and the curve has a continuously turning tangent.

The second derivative,

$$\frac{d^2y}{dx^2} = -\frac{1}{x^2}, \tag{3}$$

is always negative, so the curve (1) is everywhere concave downward.

The curve passes through the point $(1, 0)$, since $\ln 1 = 0$. At this point its slope is $+1$, so the tangent line at this point makes an angle of $45°$ with the x-axis (if we use equal units on the x- and y-axes).

If we refer to the definition of $\ln 2$ as an integral,

$$\ln 2 = \int_1^2 \frac{1}{t}\, dt,$$

we see that it may be interpreted as the area in Fig. 6–8 with $x = 2$. By considering the areas of rectangles of base 1 and altitudes 1 or $\frac{1}{2}$, respectively circumscribed over or inscribed under the given area, we see that

$$0.5 < \ln 2 < 1.0.$$

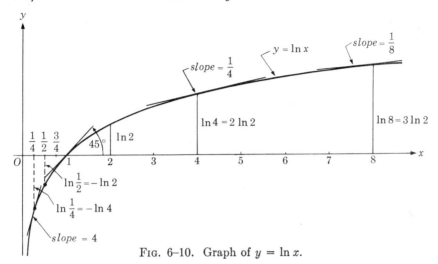

FIG. 6–10. Graph of $y = \ln x$.

In fact, by more extensive calculations, the value of $\ln 2$ to 5 decimal places has been found to be

$$\ln 2 \approx 0.69315.$$

By Eq. (3) of Article 6–6 we have

$$\ln 4 = \ln 2^2 = 2 \ln 2 \approx 1.38630,$$
$$\ln 8 = \ln 2^3 = 3 \ln 2 \approx 2.07945,$$
$$\ln \tfrac{1}{2} = \ln 2^{-1} = -\ln 2 \approx -0.69315,$$
$$\ln \tfrac{1}{4} = \ln 2^{-2} = -2 \ln 2 \approx -1.38630,$$

and so on.

We now plot the points that correspond to $x = \tfrac{1}{4}, \tfrac{1}{2}, 1, 2, 4, 8$ on the curve $y = \ln x$ and connect them with a smooth curve. The curve we draw should have slope $1/x$ at the point of abscissa x and should everywhere be concave downward. The curve is shown in Fig. 6–10.

Since $\ln 2$ is greater than 0.5 and $\ln 2^n = n \ln 2$, it is clear that

$$\ln 2^n > 0.5n,$$

and hence $\ln x$ increases without limit as x does. That is,

$$\ln x \to +\infty \quad \text{as} \quad x \to +\infty. \tag{4}$$

On the other hand, as x approaches zero through positive values, $1/x$ tends to plus infinity. Hence, taking Eq. (6) of Article 6–6 into account, we have

$$\ln x = -\ln \frac{1}{x} \to -\infty \quad \text{as} \quad x \to 0+. \tag{5}$$

Summary. The natural logarithm, $y = \ln x$, is a function with the following properties:

1. Its *domain* is the set of positive real numbers, $x > 0$.

2. Its *range* is the set of all real numbers, $-\infty < y < +\infty$.

3. It is a *continuous, increasing* function of x everywhere on its domain. If $x_1 > x_2 > 0$, then $\ln x_1 > \ln x_2$. It provides a one-to-one mapping from its domain to its range.

4. *Multiplication* of numbers in the domain corresponds to *addition* of numbers in the range. That is, if

$$x_1 > 0, \qquad y_1 = \ln x_1,$$

$$x_2 > 0, \qquad y_2 = \ln x_2,$$

then

$$x_1 x_2 > 0 \qquad \text{and} \qquad y_1 + y_2 = \ln (x_1 x_2).$$

5. The *derivative* of $y = \ln x$ is $dy/dx = 1/x$.

PROBLEMS

1. Take $\ln 3 = 1.09861$ as known. Plot the points corresponding to $x = \frac{1}{9}$, $\frac{1}{3}$, 1, 3, and 9 on the curve $y = \ln x$. Also construct, through each of these points, a line segment tangent to the curve. Then sketch the curve itself. From the curve, read off $\ln 2$.

2. Let x_0 be the abscissa of the point $(x_0, 1)$ in which the line $y = 1$ intersects the curve $y = \ln x$. Show that the curve $y = x \ln x$ has a minimum at $[1/x_0, -(1/x_0)]$ and sketch the curve for $x > 0$. Does this curve possess a point of inflection? If so, find it (or them), and if not, state why not. (See Problem 5.)

3. Sketch the curve $x = \ln y$ for $y > 0$. What is its slope at the point (x, y)? Is it always concave upward, or downward, or does it have inflection points? Give reasons for your answers.

4. The curve $y = \ln x$ in Fig. 6–10 has the property that y becomes infinite when x does. But the ratio $(\ln x)/x$ approaches zero as x becomes infinite. Prove this latter statement by showing, first, that for $x > 1$

$$\ln x = \int_1^x \frac{1}{t}\, dt \le \int_1^x \frac{1}{\sqrt{t}}\, dt = 2(\sqrt{x} - 1).$$

[*Hint:* Compare the areas under the curves $y_1 = 1/t$ and $y_2 = 1/\sqrt{t}$ for $1 \le t \le x$.]

5. From the result of Problem 4 that

$$\lim_{x \to +\infty} \frac{\ln x}{x} = 0,$$

deduce that $\lim_{x \to 0+} x \ln x = 0$. [*Hint:* Let $x = 1/u$, $u \to +\infty$.]

6. Show that the curve $y = \ln x - (x - 1) + \frac{1}{2}(x - 1)^2$ has a point of inflection and a horizontal tangent at $(1, 0)$. Sketch the curve for $0 < x < 2$. (Compare Problem 8, Article 6–4.)

7. Suppose you had a table of natural logarithms giving $\ln x$ for each $x > 0$. How could you use this to find $\log_{10} N$, where $\log_{10} N = b$ means $N = 10^b$?

6–8 The exponential function. In Article 6–7 we discussed and sketched the graph of the curve $y = \ln x$ (Fig. 6–10). We now make the observation that the curve $y = \ln x$ must cross the horizontal line $y = 1$ for some value of x between 2 and 4, since $\ln x$ is continuous and $\ln 2$ is less than 1 while $\ln 4$ is greater than 1. The value of x for which $\ln x = 1$ is denoted by the letter e. It is one of the most important numbers in mathematics. It satisfies the basic equation

$$\ln e = 1. \tag{1}$$

From our discussion above, it follows that e lies between 2 and 4. In Chapter 16 we shall see how its value may be computed to any desired number of decimal places by using series. Its value to 15 decimal places is

$$e = 2.7 \ \ 1828 \ \ 1828 \ \ 45 \ \ 90 \ \ 45 \ldots \tag{2}$$

By Eq. (3), Article 6–6, and Eq. (1) above, we have

$$\ln e^n = n \ln e = n \tag{3}$$

for any rational number n. Thus, for example, we have

$$\ln e^2 = 2, \quad \ln e^3 = 3, \quad \ln e^{-1} = -1, \quad \ln \sqrt{e} = \tfrac{1}{2},$$

and so on. Since only one number can have its natural logarithm equal to n, for any given n, we may restate Eq. (3) by saying that the number whose natural logarithm is n is e^n; i.e., the anti-natural-logarithm of n is e^n.

We now propose to study the antilogarithm, i.e., the *inverse* of the *logarithm*, as a function. To obtain this inverse function, we let

$$y = \text{inverse natural logarithm of } x$$

or

$$x = \ln y. \tag{4}$$

The equation $x = \ln y$ defines a unique x for each positive real number y. Values of y greater than 1 correspond to x greater than zero; $y = 1$ to $x = 0$; $y < 1$ to $x < 0$. To each positive real number y there corresponds just one real number x such that $x = \ln y$. And conversely, to each real number x there corresponds just one positive real number y such that $x = \ln y$. The correspondence is one-to-one between the sets $y > 0$ and $-\infty < x < +\infty$, and hence it may be used to *define* y as a *function* of x, on the domain of all real numbers $-\infty < x < +\infty$. The *range* of this function is the set of all positive real numbers $y > 0$.

We have just seen, Eq. (3), that $x = \ln y = n$ if and only if $y = e^n$, provided n is a rational number. That is, Eq. (4) is equivalent to the equation

$$y = e^x \tag{5}$$

for all rational values of x. We are therefore led to define e^x for all real values of x, irrational as well as rational, to be that number y whose natural logarithm is x:

$$\boxed{y = e^x \qquad \text{if and only if} \qquad x = \ln y.} \tag{6}$$

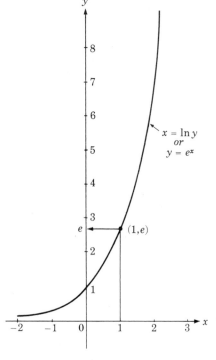

The resulting function is a continuous, single-valued function of x, defined for all real x, $-\infty < x < +\infty$. It is called the *exponential function*, with e as base and exponent x. **The exponential function is the inverse of the natural logarithm.** Its graph, Fig. 6–11, may be obtained by reflecting the curve in Fig. 6–10 across the 45° line $y = x$. Notice, in particular, that $e^0 = 1$ since $\ln 1 = 0$.

To find the derivative of

$$y = e^x, \tag{7}$$

we differentiate both sides of the equivalent equation

$$x = \ln y$$

implicitly with respect to x. Then

$$1 = \frac{1}{y} \cdot \frac{dy}{dx} \quad \text{or} \quad \frac{dy}{dx} = y. \tag{8}$$

$x = \ln y$
or
$y = e^x$

$(1,e)$

FIGURE 6–11

Taking account of Eq. (7), we therefore have

$$\frac{de^x}{dx} = e^x.$$

Here is a function which is not changed by differentiation! It is indestructible. It can be differentiated again and again without changing.

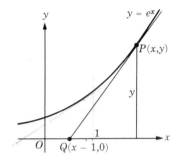

FIGURE 6–12

In Fig. 6–12 the line QP through the points $Q(x - 1, 0)$ and $P(x, e^x)$ is tangent to the curve $y = e^x$ at P, for the slope of QP is $y/1$ and the slope of the curve, at P, is also equal to y, by Eq. (8).

We obtain a slightly more general formula for the derivative of e^u, where u is a differentiable function of x, by applying the chain rule

$$\frac{de^u}{dx} = \frac{de^u}{du}\frac{du}{dx} = e^u \frac{du}{dx}.$$

XX

In terms of differentials, we have from XX,

$$de^u = e^u \, du.$$

XX′

This in turn leads to the integration formula

$$\int e^u \, du = e^u + C.$$

(9)

EXAMPLE 1. Find dy/dx if $y = e^{\tan^{-1} x}$.

Solution.

$$\frac{dy}{dx} = e^{\tan^{-1} x} \frac{d \tan^{-1} x}{dx}$$

$$= e^{\tan^{-1} x} \cdot \frac{1}{1 + x^2} \cdot \frac{dx}{dx}$$

$$= \frac{e^{\tan^{-1} x}}{1 + x^2}.$$

EXAMPLE 2. Find the area under the curve $y = e^{-x}$ from $x = 0$ to $x = b(> 0)$ and show that this area *remains finite* as $b \to +\infty$.

Solution. The area from $x = 0$ to $x = b$ is given by

$$A_0^b = \int_0^b y \, dx = \int_0^b e^{-x} \, dx.$$

To evaluate this integral, we compare it with our standard forms and see that it is almost, but not exactly, like

$$\int e^u \, du = e^u + C.$$

To bring it into precisely this form, we let

$$u = -x, \qquad du = -dx$$

or

$$dx = -du,$$

so that

$$\int e^{-x} \, dx = \int e^u \, (-du) = -\int e^u \, du = -e^u + C = -e^{-x} + C.$$

Therefore

$$A_0^b = -e^{-x} \Big]_0^b = -e^{-b} + e^0 = 1 - e^{-b}.$$

From this we see that the number of square units of area in the shaded region of Fig. 6-13 is somewhat less than unity, for b large and positive, and moreover

$$\lim_{b \to +\infty} A_0^b = \lim_{b \to +\infty} (1 - e^{-b}) = 1,$$

since [see Eq. (11) below]

$$\lim_{b \to +\infty} e^{-b} = \lim_{b \to +\infty} \frac{1}{e^b} = 0.$$

Some properties of the function

$$y = e^x$$

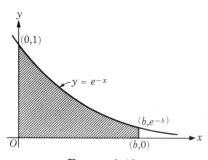

FIGURE 6-13

are worthy of additional comment.

In the first place, the exponential function satisfies the law

$$\boxed{e^{x_1} \cdot e^{x_2} = e^{x_1 + x_2}.} \tag{10}$$

For, if

$$y_1 = e^{x_1} \qquad \text{and} \qquad y_2 = e^{x_2}$$

then, by definition,

$$x_1 = \ln y_1 \quad \text{and} \quad x_2 = \ln y_2,$$

so that

$$x_1 + x_2 = \ln y_1 + \ln y_2 = \ln y_1 y_2$$

by Eq. (1), Article 6–6. Therefore, by definition,

$$y_1 y_2 = e^{x_1 + x_2},$$

which establishes Eq. (10).

Again, we have

$$\boxed{e^{-x} = 1/e^{x}} \tag{11}$$

for any real number x. For, if

$$y = e^{-x}$$

then, by definition,

$$-x = \ln y$$

or, from Eq. (6), Article 6–6,

$$x = -\ln y = \ln (1/y).$$

Therefore, by definition,

$$1/y = e^x \quad \text{or} \quad y = 1/e^x,$$

which establishes Eq. (11).

Powers of e are tabulated in many mathematical tables, such as Burington's. They may also be read directly from the LL-scales of a log-log slide rule. For example, if the number x on the D-scale in Fig. 6–14 is $x = 2$, then the corresponding readings on the LL-scales are:

$$e^2 = 7.4 \quad \text{on LL 3,}$$
$$e^{0.2} = 1.2215 \text{ on LL 2,}$$
$$e^{0.02} = 1.0202 \text{ on LL 1.}$$

The value of e^{-2} can be read from the

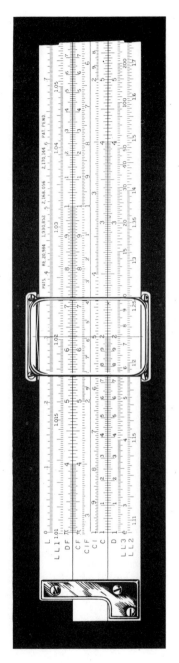

FIGURE 6–14

LL00-scale on the reverse side of the slide rule opposite the 2 on the right half of the A-scale (the reading gives $e^{-2} = 0.135$). It is also possible to use

$$e^{-2} = \frac{1}{e^2} = \frac{1}{7.4} = 0.135$$

to arrive at the same result. The use of the LL-scales is described in the manual of instructions that comes with the log-log slide rule.

A table of e^x and e^{-x} is included at the end of the book for convenience and to give an appreciation of the rapid rate of increase of the exponential function for positive values of x.

PROBLEMS

1. Simplify each of the following expressions:

(a) $e^{\ln x}$, (b) $\ln (e^x)$, (c) $e^{-\ln (x^2)}$, (d) $\ln (e^{-x^2})$,

(e) $\ln (e^{1/x})$, (f) $\ln (1/e^x)$, (g) $e^{\ln (1/x)}$, (h) $e^{-\ln (1/x)}$,

(i) $e^{\ln 2 + \ln x}$, (j) $e^{2 \ln x}$, (k) $\ln (e^{x-x^2})$, (l) $\ln (x^2 e^{-2x})$,

(m) $e^{x + \ln x}$, (n) $e^{\ln x - 2 \ln y}$.

Find dy/dx in each of the following problems (2 through 19).

2. $y = x^2 e^x$

3. $y = e^{2x}(2 \cos 3x + 3 \sin 3x)$

4. $y = \ln \dfrac{e^x}{1 + e^x}$

5. $y = \frac{1}{2}(e^x - e^{-x})$

6. $y = \frac{1}{2}(e^x + e^{-x})$

7. $y = \dfrac{e^x - e^{-x}}{e^x + e^{-x}}$

8. $y = e^{\sin^{-1} x}$

9. $y = (1 + 2x)e^{-2x}$

10. $y = (9x^2 - 6x + 2)e^{3x}$

11. $y = \dfrac{ax - 1}{a^2} e^{ax}$

12. $y = e^{-x^2}$

13. $y = x^2 e^{-x^2}$

14. $y = e^x \ln x$

15. $y = \tan^{-1} (e^x)$

16. $y = \sec^{-1} (e^{2x})$

17. $e^{2x} = \sin (x + 3y)$

18. $y = e^{1/x}$

19. $\tan y = e^x + \ln x$

20. (a) Show that $y = Ce^{ax}$ is a solution of the differential equation $dy/dx = ay$ for any choice of the constant C. (b) Using the result of (a), find a solution of the differential equation $dy/dt = -2y$ satisfying the initial condition $y = 3$ when $t = 0$.

21. Show that $y = e^{-ax} u$ is a solution of the differential equation

$$\frac{d^2y}{dx^2} + 2a \frac{dy}{dx} + (a^2 + b^2) y = 0$$

if and only if u satisfies the equation

$$\frac{d^2u}{dx^2} + b^2u = 0,$$

provided a and b are constants.

Evaluate the following integrals:

22. $\displaystyle\int e^{2x}\, dx$ 23. $\displaystyle\int xe^{x^2}\, dx$ 24. $\displaystyle\int e^{\sin x}\cos x\, dx$

25. $\displaystyle\int e^{x/3}\, dx$ 26. $\displaystyle\int \frac{4dx}{e^{3x}}$ 27. $\displaystyle\int \frac{e^x\, dx}{1 + 2e^x}$

28. $\displaystyle\int_e^{e^2} \frac{dx}{x\ln x}$ 29. $\displaystyle\int \frac{(e^x - e^{-x})\, dx}{(e^x + e^{-x})}$

30. If a particle moves along the x-axis so that its position at time t is given by $x = ae^{\omega t} + be^{-\omega t}$, where a, b, ω, are constants, show that it is repelled from the origin with a force proportional to the displacement. [Assume that force = mass $\times$ acceleration.]

6–9 The function a^u. If a is any positive real number and

$$b = \ln a, \tag{1a}$$

then

$$a = e^b. \tag{1b}$$

The two equations (1a, b) may be combined to give the result

$$a = e^{\ln a}. \tag{2}$$

In words, **ln a is the power to which the base e may be raised to give a.**

Suppose we now raise both sides of Eq. (2) to the power u, where u is any real number. We would like to have the law of exponents

$$(e^{\ln a})^u = e^{u\ln a}$$

be true. Hence we now make the following *definition:*

$$\boxed{a^u = e^{u\ln a}.} \tag{3}$$

This definition is equivalent to saying that

$$\boxed{\ln a^u = u\ln a,} \tag{3'}$$

since both Eqs. (3) and (3′) say that $u \ln a$ is the power to which e may be raised to produce a^u. But (3′) is the same as Eq. (3), Article 6–6, in case $u = n$ is a rational number. What we are now considering is the case where u may be any real number, rational or irrational, $-\infty < u < +\infty$. Our new definition of a^u includes the old case but goes beyond and extends it.

Properties of a^u. By making use of the law of exponents, Eq. (10), Article 6–8,

$$e^{x_1} \cdot e^{x_2} = e^{x_1 + x_2}, \tag{4}$$

and the law of logarithms, Eq. (1), Article 6–6,

$$\ln ab = \ln a + \ln b, \tag{5}$$

together with the definition (3) and Eq. (2) above, the following laws may be established.

$$\left.\begin{array}{l} \text{(a)} \ a^0 = 1 \\[4pt] \text{(b)} \ a^1 = a \\[4pt] \text{(c)} \ a^u \cdot a^v = a^{u+v} \\[4pt] \text{(d)} \ a^{-u} = \dfrac{1}{a^u} \\[4pt] \text{(e)} \ (a^u)^v = a^{uv} \\[4pt] \text{(f)} \ (ab)^u = a^u b^u \end{array}\right\} \tag{6}$$

The first two properties, $a^0 = 1$ and $a^1 = a$, are trivial consequences of Eqs. (2) and (3). To prove (6c), we use the definition

$$a^u \cdot a^v = e^{u \ln a} \cdot e^{v \ln a},$$

then Eq. (4),

$$e^{u \ln a} \cdot e^{v \ln a} = e^{(u+v) \ln a},$$

and then the definition

$$a^{u+v} = e^{(u+v) \ln a},$$

and combine the results into the following:

$$a^u \cdot a^v = e^{u \ln a} \cdot e^{v \ln a} = e^{(u+v) \ln a} = a^{u+v},$$

which establishes the result

$$a^u \cdot a^v = a^{u+v}.$$

Equation (6d) is a consequence of (6a) and (6b):

$$a^{-u} \cdot a^u = a^{-u+u} = a^0 = 1.$$

Equation (6e) is established as follows. Let

$$b = a^u = e^{u \ln a}, \tag{7a}$$

so that

$$(a^u)^v = b^v = e^{v \ln b}. \tag{7b}$$

But

$$\ln b = u \ln a, \tag{7c}$$

since $u \ln a$ is the power to which e may be raised to produce b, Eq. (7a). Now substitute from (7c) into (7b),

$$(a^u)^v = e^{v \ln b} = e^{vu \ln a}, \tag{7d}$$

and make use of the definition, Eq. (3),

$$a^{uv} = e^{uv \ln a}. \tag{7e}$$

When we compare Eqs. (7d, e), we see that we have

$$(a^u)^v = a^{uv},$$

since both expressions are equal to

$$e^{uv \ln a}.$$

The proof of (6f) is left as a problem.

With the definition of a^u now clarified, we are ready to calculate its derivative in case u is a differentiable function of x. We apply formula XX, Article 6–8, and remembering that $\ln a$ is constant when a is, we obtain

$$\frac{da^u}{dx} = \frac{de^{u \ln a}}{dx}$$

$$= e^{u \ln a} \cdot \frac{du}{dx} \cdot \ln a,$$

$$\boxed{\frac{da^u}{dx} = a^u \cdot \frac{du}{dx} \cdot \ln a.} \tag{8}$$

This gives us a formula for the derivative of any positive constant a raised to a variable power. There is very little reason to memorize the result, since it may always be derived very quickly by the method of logarithmic differentiation, which will presently be discussed. It illustrates the fact that the base e is the most desirable one to encounter, since $\ln e = 1$ and Eq. (8) is the same as formula XX in case $a = e$. It also enables us to write down a formula for the integral of $a^u \, du$. For, if we multiply both sides of Eq. (8) by dx to change it to differential form,

$$da^u = \ln a \cdot a^u \, du,$$

and then divide by $\ln a$, provided $a \neq 1$, we see that

$$\int a^u \, du = \int \frac{1}{\ln a} \, da^u = \frac{a^u}{\ln a} + C, \qquad (a > 0, \, a \neq 1). \qquad (9)$$

Logarithmic differentiation. The properties

$$
\left.
\begin{aligned}
&\text{(a)} \ \ln uv = \ln u + \ln v \\
&\text{(b)} \ \ln \frac{u}{v} = \ln u - \ln v \\
&\text{(c)} \ \ln u^n = n \ln u \\
&\text{(d)} \ \ln a^u = u \ln a
\end{aligned}
\right\} \qquad (10)
$$

can be used to advantage in calculating derivatives of products, quotients, roots, and powers, as illustrated in the examples that follow. The method, known as logarithmic differentiation, is to take the natural logarithm of both sides of an equation

$$y = f(x),$$
$$\ln y = \ln f(x),$$

simplify $\ln f(x)$ as much as possible by making use of the properties in Eq. (10), and then differentiate implicitly with respect to x:

$$\frac{d}{dx} \ln y = \frac{1}{y} \frac{dy}{dx}.$$

EXAMPLE 1. Derive Eq. (8).

Solution. Let $y = a^u$. Then

$$\ln y = \ln a^u = u \ln a,$$

$$\frac{1}{y} \frac{dy}{dx} = \frac{du}{dx} \ln a,$$

$$\frac{dy}{dx} = y \frac{du}{dx} \ln a,$$

or, since $y = a^u$,

$$\frac{da^u}{dx} = a^u \frac{du}{dx} \ln a.$$

EXAMPLE 2. If n is a real constant and u is a positive differentiable function of x, show that

$$\frac{du^n}{dx} = nu^{n-1}\frac{du}{dx}.$$

Solution. Let $y = u^n$. Then

$$\ln y = \ln u^n = n \ln u,$$

$$\frac{1}{y}\frac{dy}{dx} = n\frac{1}{u}\frac{du}{dx},$$

$$\frac{dy}{dx} = n\frac{y}{u}\frac{du}{dx} = n\frac{u^n}{u}\frac{du}{dx}$$

$$= nu^{n-1}\frac{du}{dx}. \qquad \text{Q.E.D.}$$

EXAMPLE 3. Find dy/dx if $y = x^x$, $x > 0$.

Solution. $\ln y = \ln x^x = x \ln x$,

$$\frac{1}{y}\frac{dy}{dx} = x \cdot \frac{1}{x} + \ln x = 1 + \ln x,$$

$$\frac{dy}{dx} = y(1 + \ln x) = x^x(1 + \ln x).$$

EXAMPLE 4. Find dy/dx if

$$y^{2/3} = \frac{(x^2 + 1)(3x + 4)^{1/2}}{\sqrt[5]{(2x - 3)(x^2 - 4)}}, \qquad (x > 2).$$

Solution.

$\ln y^{2/3} = \frac{2}{3}\ln y$

$$= \ln (x^2 + 1) + \tfrac{1}{2}\ln (3x + 4) - \tfrac{1}{5}\ln (2x - 3) - \tfrac{1}{5}\ln (x^2 - 4) \qquad \text{(a)}$$

and

$$\frac{2}{3} \cdot \frac{1}{y}\frac{dy}{dx} = \frac{2x}{x^2 + 1} + \frac{1}{2} \cdot \frac{3}{3x + 4} - \frac{1}{5} \cdot \frac{2}{2x - 3} - \frac{1}{5} \cdot \frac{2x}{x^2 - 4},$$

so that

$$\frac{dy}{dx} = \frac{3y}{2}\left[\frac{2x}{x^2 + 1} + \frac{\frac{3}{2}}{3x + 4} - \frac{\frac{2}{5}}{2x - 3} - \frac{2x/5}{x^2 - 4}\right].$$

Remark. The restriction $x > 2$ ensures that all the quantities whose logarithms are indicated in (a) above are positive. If we want dy/dx at a point where y is negative, we may multiply our equation by -1 before taking logarithms; for if y is negative, then $-y$ is positive and $\ln(-y)$ is well defined.

Economists define the ratio of "marginal cost" to "average cost" as the "elasticity of total cost." That is, if the total cost of producing x units of a given product is $y = f(x)$ dollars, then the "average cost" is y/x dollars per unit. The "marginal cost," which is, roughly speaking, the additional cost of producing one more unit, is dy/dx. Then, by definition,

$$\text{elasticity of total cost} = \frac{dy/dx}{y/x} = \frac{dy/y}{dx/x} = \frac{d(\ln y)}{d(\ln x)}.$$

When the elasticity of total cost equals one, then marginal cost equals average cost (that is, $dy/dx = y/x$) and average cost has a stationary value [that is, $d(y/x)/dx = 0$]. [For further discussion, see R. G. D. Allen, *Mathematical Analysis for Economists* (Macmillan, 1939), p. 260 ff.]

Problems

Use the method of logarithmic differentiation to find dy/dx in each of the following problems (1 through 8).

1. $y^2 = x(x+1)$ $(x > 0)$

2. $y = \sqrt[3]{\dfrac{x+1}{x-1}}$ $(x > 1)$

3. $y = \dfrac{x\sqrt{x^2+1}}{(x+1)^{2/3}}$ $(x > 0)$

4. $y = \sqrt[3]{\dfrac{x(x+1)(x-2)}{(x^2+1)(2x+3)}}$ $(x > 2)$

5. $y = x^{\sin x}$ $(x > 0)$

6. $y = (\sin x)^{\tan x}$ $(\sin x > 0)$

7. $y = 2^{\sec x}$

8. $y = x^{\ln x}$ $(x > 0)$

9. Show that $(ab)^u = a^u b^u$ if a and b are any positive numbers and u is any real number.

10. Show that the derivative of average cost is zero when marginal cost and average cost are equal.

Evaluate the following integrals (11–15):

11. $\displaystyle\int_0^{\ln 2} e^{-2x}\, dx$

12. $\displaystyle\int_0^{1.2} 3^x\, dx$

13. $\displaystyle\int_1^{\sqrt{2}} x\, 2^{-x^2}\, dx$

14. $\displaystyle\int_0^1 5^{2t-2}\, dt$

15. $\displaystyle\int_0^{\pi/6} (\cos\theta) 4^{-\sin\theta}\, d\theta$

16. Let a be a number greater than one. Prove that the graph of $y = a^x$ has the following characteristics:

(a) If $x_1 > x_2$, then $a^{x_1} > a^{x_2}$.

(b) The graph is everywhere concave upward.

(c) The graph lies entirely above the x-axis.

(d) The slope at any point is proportional to the ordinate there, and the proportionality factor is the slope at the y-intercept of the graph.

(e) The curve approaches the negative x-axis as $x \to -\infty$.

6–10 The function $\log_a u$. We know that $\ln u$ is the power to which e may be raised to give u. For that reason, we say that e is the base of the system of natural logarithms in keeping with the following definition.

DEFINITION. *If u is positive and a is a positive number different from 1, we say that y is the logarithm of u to the base a, and write*

$$y = \log_a u, \tag{1a}$$

provided y is the power to which a may be raised to give u:

$$a^y = u. \tag{1b}$$

For example,

$$\log_5 25 = 2 \quad \text{since} \quad 5^2 = 25,$$

$$\log_2 \tfrac{1}{4} = -2 \quad \text{since} \quad 2^{-2} = \tfrac{1}{4}.$$

To find $x = \log_4 8$, we rewrite the equation as

$$4^x = 2^{2x} = 8 = 2^3,$$

from which we read $2x = 3$, $x = \tfrac{3}{2}$. In other words,

$$\log_4 8 = \tfrac{3}{2} \quad \text{since} \quad 4^{3/2} = (\sqrt{4})^3 = 8.$$

We may solve Eq. (1b) for y, and thereby obtain an expression for $\log_a u$, by taking natural logarithms and applying Eq. (3′) of Article 6–9:

$$\ln u = \ln a^y = y \ln a.$$

If $\ln a \neq 0$ (which is the case when a is different from 1), we may solve for y. The result is that

$$y = \frac{\ln u}{\ln a}$$

is the power to which a may be raised to produce u. In other words,

$$\boxed{\log_a u = \frac{\ln u}{\ln a}.} \tag{2}$$

Properties of $\log_a u$. The following properties follow readily from Eq. (2) above and the analogous properties of $\ln u$.

$$
\begin{array}{ll}
\text{(a) } \log_a uv = \log_a u + \log_a v \\[2mm]
\text{(b) } \log_a \dfrac{u}{v} = \log_a u - \log_a v \\[2mm]
\text{(c) } \log_a u^v = v \log_a u
\end{array}
\tag{3}
$$

Equation (3c), for example, is derived as follows:

$$
\log_a u^v = \frac{\ln u^v}{\ln a} = \frac{v \ln u}{\ln a} = v \log_a u,
$$

where we make use of Eq. (2), then Eq. (3′) of Article 6–9, and then Eq. (2) again.

If u is a differentiable positive function of x, we may differentiate both sides of Eq. (2) and thus obtain

$$
\frac{d \log_a u}{dx} = \frac{1}{u \ln a} \frac{du}{dx}.
\tag{4}
$$

It is clear that this formula is simpler for logarithms to the base e than for any other base. The only bases of practical importance are $a = e$ (natural logarithms) and $a = 10$ (common logarithms). Since $\ln 10 = 2.30259\ldots$, Eq. (4) is certainly less attractive for the case $a = 10$ than it is for the case $a = e$. This is the primary reason why natural logarithms are to be preferred over common logarithms in applications of the calculus.

Logarithms to the base 10 are used primarily as aids in performing arithmetical calculations such as multiplication, division, and raising numbers to powers. The use of slide rules, desk calculators, and new high-speed computing machinery is rapidly making this use of logarithms less and less important. Natural logarithms, on the other hand, are not in any immediate danger of becoming obsolete, since they occur naturally when some common kinds of differential equations are solved. [See Examples 1 and 2, Article 6–11.]

PROBLEMS

Determine the following logarithms:

1. (a) $\log_4 16$, (b) $\log_8 32$, (c) $\log_5 0.04$, (d) $\log_{0.5} 4$.
2. (a) $\log_2 4$, (b) $\log_4 2$, (c) $\log_8 16$, (d) $\log_{32} 4$.
3. Find x if $3^x = 2^{x+1}$.
4. Find x if $3^{\log_3 7} + 2^{\log_2 5} = 5^{\log_5 x}$.
5. Show that $\log_b u = \log_a u \cdot \log_b a$ if a, b, and u are positive numbers, $a \neq 1$, $b \neq 1$.

6. Given $\ln 2 = 0.69315$, $\ln 10 = 2.30259$, $\log_{10} 2 = 0.30103$. Find
(a) $\log_{10} 20$, $\log_{10} 200$, $\log_{10} 0.2$, $\log_{10} 0.02$,
(b) $\ln 20$, $\ln 200$, $\ln 0.2$, $\ln 0.02$.

7. Use the table of natural logarithms at the end of the book to evaluate the following logarithms to two significant figures:

(a) $\log_3 5$,   (b) $\log_5 3$,   (c) $\log_{1.4} 2.3$.

8. Use the tables at the end of the book to evaluate the following to two significant figures:

(a) $(1.6)^{1.5}$,   (b) $\dfrac{\ln 0.7}{\ln 1.3}$.

9. Find the derivatives of the following:
(a) $y = 3^{\tan x}$,   (b) $y = (x^2 + 1)^{\ln x}$,
(c) $s = 2^{-t^2}$,   (d) $r = \theta e^{-2\theta}$.

6–11 Differential equations. Suppose a quantity x changes at a rate that at any instant of time t is proportional to the amount of x present at that instant. This is expressed by the differential equation

$$\frac{dx}{dt} = kx, \tag{1}$$

where k is the proportionality constant. If the amount of x present at time $t = 0$ is x_0, the initial condition

$$x = x_0 \qquad \text{when} \qquad t = 0 \tag{2}$$

enables us to evaluate the constant of integration that enters when we integrate Eq. (1). The method of solution will be illustrated by an example.

EXAMPLE 1. As a result of leakage, an electrical condenser discharges at a rate proportional to the charge. If the charge Q has the value Q_0 at the time $t = 0$, find Q as a function of t.

Solution. The mathematical statement of the problem consists of the differential equation $dQ/dt = -kQ$ and the initial condition $t = 0$, $Q = Q_0$. Then

$$\frac{dQ}{Q} = -k\,dt,$$

$$\int \frac{dQ}{Q} = -k \int dt,$$

$$\ln Q = -kt + C. \tag{3}$$

The constant of integration C is evaluated by using the initial conditions:

$$t = 0, \quad Q = Q_0; \qquad \ln Q_0 = C.$$

Substituting this value of C back into (3) and transposing it to the left of the equation, we get

$$\ln Q - \ln Q_0 = -kt$$

or

$$\ln \frac{Q}{Q_0} = -kt.$$

Hence, $-kt$ is the power to which e must be raised to give Q/Q_0, that is,

$$\frac{Q}{Q_0} = e^{-kt} \qquad \text{or} \qquad Q = Q_0 e^{-kt}.$$

According to this equation, Q is never zero; that is, some charge would always remain. But when $kt = 10$, say, then $Q = Q_0 e^{-10}$ so that the charge Q has by then diminished to less than $5/1000$ of 1 percent of its original value Q_0.

Remark. In this example, the function integrated was positive, so that we were able to omit the absolute value symbols and write simply $\ln Q$ in place of $\ln |Q|$. Occasionally we encounter a problem where the quantity whose logarithm we require is an unknown function which presumably could be either positive or negative. To change sign from one to the other, however, would mean that the quantity would become zero at the transition point, provided it is a *continuous* function (Fig. 6–15). An integral of the form

$$\int \frac{du}{u} \tag{4}$$

between points where u changes continuously from positive to negative or from negative to positive is a so-called *improper integral*, because the integrand $1/u$ becomes infinite at $u = 0$. We shall discuss improper integrals in more detail in a later chapter. At present we shall assume that any physical problems we encounter that lead to integrals of the form of (4) arise from physical situations in which infinities are excluded. Then if we know the sign of u at one point of the interval of integration, we shall assume that it always has the same sign throughout the whole interval.

EXAMPLE 2. Ohm's law, $E = Ri$, requires modification in a circuit containing self-inductance, as in a coil. The modified form is

$$L \frac{di}{dt} + Ri = E \tag{5}$$

for the series circuit shown in Fig. 6–16, where R denotes the resistance of the circuit in ohms, L is the self-inductance in henries, E is the impressed electro-

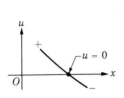

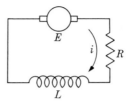

FIGURE 6–15   FIGURE 6–16

motive force (emf) in volts, i is the current in amperes, and t is the time in seconds. (See Sears, *Electricity and Magnetism*, Chapter 13.) We shall solve the differential equation (5) under the assumption that E is constant and

$$i = 0 \quad \text{when} \quad t = 0. \tag{6}$$

To integrate (5), we first separate the variables in order to have the terms involving the variable current i combined with di for purposes of integration. Thus

$$L \, di = (E - Ri) \, dt$$

and

$$\int \frac{L \, di}{E - Ri} = \int dt. \tag{7}$$

We let

$$u = E - Ri, \tag{8}$$

then

$$du = -R \, di, \qquad di = -\frac{1}{R} \, du,$$

so that (7) becomes

$$-\frac{L}{R} \int \frac{du}{u} = \int dt. \tag{9}$$

From (8) and the initial conditions (6) we see that $u = E - Ri$ has the positive value $u_0 = E$ at $t = 0$. We therefore assume that it remains positive, so that $|u| = u$ and the integral in (9) then gives

$$-\frac{L}{R} \ln u = t + C$$

or

$$-\frac{L}{R} \ln (E - Ri) = t + C. \tag{10}$$

The initial conditions $t = 0$, $i = 0$ enable us to evaluate the constant of integration:

$$C = -\frac{L}{R} \ln E.$$

When we substitute this back into (10) and transpose it to the left side of the equation, we obtain

$$\frac{L}{R}\left[\ln E - \ln (E - Ri)\right] = t,$$

$$\ln \frac{E}{E - Ri} = \frac{Rt}{L},$$

$$\frac{E}{E - Ri} = e^{(Rt)/L},$$

$$\frac{E - Ri}{E} = e^{-(Rt)/L},$$

$$1 - \frac{R}{E}i = e^{-(Rt)/L},$$

$$i = \frac{E}{R}\left(1 - e^{-(Rt)/L}\right). \tag{11}$$

We see from this that the current (for $t > 0$) is always less than, but increases toward, the steady state value

$$i_{\text{s.s.}} = \frac{E}{R}, \tag{12}$$

which is the current that would flow in the circuit if either $L = 0$ (no inductance) or $di/dt = 0$ (steady current, $i = $ constant) in Eq. (5). Indeed, if $L \to 0$, then for all $t > 0$ the exponent [in (11)]

$$-\frac{Rt}{L} \to -\infty \quad \text{and} \quad i \to \frac{E}{R}.$$

A graph of the current versus time relation (11) is shown in Fig. 6–17.

Incidentally, in problems involving electrical circuits, the letter e is usually used to denote an emf and the letter ϵ is then used to denote the constant which we have called (and shall continue to call) e. Mathematicians have become accustomed to the use of ϵ to denote an arbitrarily small positive number, so they are not likely to change their notation; nor are the electrical engineers likely to change theirs. However, this lack of uniformity should not cause confusion, since the meaning of the symbols will usually be clear from the context.

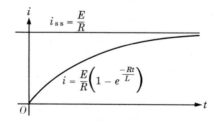

FIGURE 6–17

Problems

1. Suppose a body of mass m moving in a straight line with velocity v encounters a resistance proportional to the velocity and this is the only force acting on the body. If the body starts with velocity v_0, how far does it travel in time t? Assume $F = d(mv)/dt$.

2. A radioactive substance disintegrates at a rate proportional to the amount present. How much of the substance remains at time t if the initial amount is Q_0?

3. If the bacteria in a culture increase continuously at a rate proportional to the number present, and the initial number is N_0, find the number at time t.

In Problems 4–7, substitute $y = e^{rx}$ and find values of the constant r for which $y = e^{rx}$ is a solution of the given differential equation.

4. $\dfrac{d^2y}{dx^2} - 4\dfrac{dy}{dx} + 3y = 0$

5. $\dfrac{d^2y}{dx^2} - \dfrac{dy}{dx} - 2y = 0$

6. $\dfrac{d^3y}{dx^3} + 6\dfrac{d^2y}{dx^2} + 5\dfrac{dy}{dx} = 0$

7. $\dfrac{d^4y}{dx^4} - 13\dfrac{d^2y}{dx^2} + 36y = 0$

8. By substitution, verify that

$$y = (c_1 + c_2 x)e^{r_1 x}$$

satisfies the differential equation

$$\frac{d^2y}{dx^2} - 2r_1\frac{dy}{dx} + r_1^2 y = 0$$

for all values of the constants c_1, c_2, and r_1.

9. By substitution, verify that $y = e^{ax}(c_1 \cos bx + c_2 \sin bx)$ satisfies the differential equation

$$\frac{d^2y}{dx^2} - 2a\frac{dy}{dx} + (a^2 + b^2)y = 0$$

for all values of the constants c_1, c_2, a, and b.

10. Sketch the curve $y = e^{-x}\cos 2x$ for $x \geq 0$. Show that it is tangent to the curves $y = \pm e^{-x}$ when $\cos 2x = \pm 1$.

REVIEW QUESTIONS AND EXERCISES FOR CHAPTER 6

1. Review the formulas for derivatives of sums, products, quotients, powers, sines, and cosines. Using these, develop formulas for derivatives of the other trigonometric functions.

2. Define the inverse sine, inverse cosine, inverse tangent, and inverse secant functions. What is the *domain* of each? What is its *range*? What is the derivative of each? Sketch the graph of each.

3. Define the natural logarithm function. What is its domain? What is its range? What is its derivative? Sketch its graph.

4. What is the inverse function of the natural logarithm called? What is the domain of this function? What is its range? What is its derivative? Sketch its graph.

5. Define the term "algebraic function." Define "transcendental function." To which class (algebraic or transcendental) do you think the "greatest integer" step-function (Fig. 1–21) belongs?

[It is often difficult to prove that a particular function belongs to one class or the other. Numbers are also classified as algebraic and transcendental. *References:* (1) W. J. Le Veque, *Topics in Number Theory*, Addison-Wesley, Vol. II, Chap. 5, pp. 161–200; (2) I. M. Niven, *Irrational Numbers*, Carus monograph number 11 of the Mathematical Association of America, (1956). Both π and e are transcendental numbers, and proofs may be found in the references cited. That π is transcendental was first proved by Ferdinand Lindemann in 1882. One result that follows from the transcendence of π is that it is impossible to construct, with unmarked straightedge and compass alone, a square whose area is equal to the area of a given circle. The first proof that e is transcendental was published by Charles Hermite in 1873. You may also enjoy reading about an interesting related feature of the graph of $y = \ln x$ in the article on logarithms on p. 301 of Vol. 14 of the *Encyclopedia Britannica* (1956 edition).]

6. Let n be an integer greater than 1. Divide the interval $1 \leq x \leq n$ into n equal subintervals and write an expression for the trapezoidal approximation to the area under the graph of $y = 1/x$, $1 \leq x \leq n$, based on this subdivision. Is this approximation less than, equal to, or greater than $\ln n$? Give a reason for your answer.

7. Prove that $\lim_{x \to \infty} (\ln x)/x = 0$, starting with the definition of $\ln x$ as an integral.

8. The *Encyclopedia Britannica* article on logarithms begins with the statement: "By shortening processes of computation, logarithms have doubled the working speed of astronomers and engineers." What property or properties of logarithms do you think the author of the article had in mind when he made that statement?

9. What is the meaning of the differential equation $dy/dt = ky$? What is the solution of this equation that satisfies the initial condition $y = y_0$ when $t = 0$?

MISCELLANEOUS PROBLEMS FOR CHAPTER 6

In each of the following problems (1 through 25), (a) find dy/dx, and (b) sketch the curve.

1. $y = \sin 2x$

2. $y = 4 \cos (2x + \pi/4)$

3. $y = 2 \sin x + \sin 2x$

4. $y = \dfrac{\sin x}{1 + \cos x}$

5. $x = \cos y$

6. $x = \tan y$

7. $y = 4 \sin \left(\dfrac{x}{2} + \pi\right)$

8. $y = 1 - \sin x$

9. $y = x - \sin x$

10. $y = \dfrac{\sin x}{x}$ (What happens as $x \to 0$? As $x \to \infty$?)

11. $y = \dfrac{\sin x}{x^2}$ (What happens as $x \to 0$? As $x \to \infty$?)

12. $y = x \sin \dfrac{1}{x}$ (What happens as $x \to \infty$? As $x \to 0$?)

13. $y = x^2 \sin \dfrac{1}{x}$ (What happens as $x \to \infty$? As $x \to 0$?)

14. $x = \tan \dfrac{\pi y}{2}$

15. (a) $y = \frac{1}{2}(e^x + e^{-x})$,   (b) $y = \frac{1}{2}(e^x - e^{-x})$,   (c) $y = \dfrac{e^x - e^{-x}}{e^x + e^{-x}}$

16. $y = xe^{-x}$

17. (a) $y = x \ln x$,   (b) $y = \sqrt{x} \ln x$

18. (a) $y = \dfrac{\ln x}{x}$,   (b) $y = \dfrac{\ln x}{\sqrt{x}}$,   (c) $y = \dfrac{\ln x}{x^2}$

19. $y = e^{-x} \sin 2x$

20. (a) $y = 2x - \frac{1}{2}e^{2x}$,   (b) $y = e^{(2x - \frac{1}{2}e^{2x})}$

21. (a) $y = x - e^x$,   (b) $y = e^{(x - e^x)}$

22. $y = \ln (x + \sqrt{x^2 + 1})$

23. $y = \dfrac{1}{2} \ln \dfrac{1 + x}{1 - x}$

24. $y = \ln (x^2 + 4)$

25. $y = x \tan^{-1} \dfrac{x}{2}$

Find dy/dx in Problems 26–42.

26. $y = \dfrac{e^{2x} - e^{-2x}}{e^{2x} + e^{-2x}}$

27. $y = \ln \dfrac{\sec x + \tan x}{\sec x - \tan x}$

28. $y = x^2 e^{2x} \sin 3x$

29. $y = \sin^{-1}(x^2) - xe^{x^2}$

30. $y = \ln \left(\dfrac{x^4}{1 + x^3}\right) + 7^{x^{2/3}}$

31. $y = (x^2 + 2)^{2-x}$

32. $y = \dfrac{\ln x}{e^x}$

33. $y = \ln \dfrac{x}{\sqrt{x^2 + 1}}$

34. $y = \ln (4 - 3x)$

35. $y = \ln (3x^2 + 4x)$

36. $y = x (\ln x)^3$ 37. $y = x \ln (x^3)$

38. $y = x^3 \ln x$ 39. $y = \ln e^x$

40. $y = x^2 e^x$ 41. $x = \ln y$

42. $y = \ln (\ln x)$

43. Find dy/dx by logarithmic differentiation for

(a) $y = \dfrac{x}{x^2 + 1}$, $x > 0$;   (b) $y = \sqrt[3]{\dfrac{x(x - 2)}{x^2 + 1}}$, $x > 2$.

44. If $f(x) = x + e^{4x}$, find $f(0)$ and $f'(0)$, and find an approximation for $f(0.01)$.

45. Find dy/dx for each of the following:

(a) $y = a^{x^2 - x}$,   (b) $y = \ln \dfrac{e^x}{1 + e^x}$,   (c) $y = x^x$,   (d) $y = x^{1/x}$.

46. Sketch the graphs of $y = \ln (1 - x)$ and $y = \ln (1/x)$.

47. Sketch (in a common figure) the graphs of $y = e^{-x}$ and $y = -e^{-x}$.

48. Solve for x: $\tan^{-1} x - \cot^{-1} x = \pi/4$.

49. If $\dfrac{dy}{dx} = \dfrac{e^x - e^{-x}}{e^x + e^{-x}}$, find $\dfrac{d^2y}{dx^2}$ and y.

50. If $dy/dx = 2/e^y$ and $y = 0$ when $x = 5$, find y as a function of x.

51. $P(x_1, y_1)$ and $Q(x_2, y_2)$ are any two points (in the first quadrant) lying on the hyperbola $xy = R$ (R positive). Show that the area bounded by the arc PQ, the lines $x = x_1$, $x = x_2$, and the x-axis is equal to the area bounded by the arc PQ, the lines $y = y_1$, $y = y_2$, and the y-axis.

52. By the trapezoidal rule, find $\int_0^2 e^{-x^2} dx$, using $n = 4$.

53. In a condenser discharging electricity the rate of change of the voltage in volts per second is proportional to the voltage, being numerically equal to minus one-fortieth of the voltage. Express the voltage as a function of the time. In how many seconds will the voltage decrease to 10 percent of its original value?

54. (a) Sketch the graph $2y = (e^x + e^{-x})$. Observe that whenever $P_1(x_1, y_1)$ is on the graph, so is the point $P'_1(-x_1, y_1)$. This implies a certain symmetry property of the graph. What is it? (b) Find the length of the curve from its lowest point to an arbitrary point $P_1(x_1, y_1)$ on it.

55. The area bounded by the x-axis and one arch of the curve $y = \sin x$ is revolved around the x-axis. Find the volume of the solid of revolution thus generated. Compare its volume with that of two inscribed cones.

56. A curve $y = f(x)$ goes through the points $(0, 0)$ and (x_1, y_1). It divides the rectangle $0 \le x \le x_1$, $0 \le y \le y_1$ into two regions: A above the curve and B below. Find the curve if the area of A is twice the area of B for all choices of $x_1 > 0$ and $y_1 > 0$.

57. Find a curve passing through the origin and such that the length s of the curve between the origin and any point (x, y) of the curve is given by

$$s = e^x + y - 1.$$

58. A particle starts at the origin and moves along the x-axis in such a way that its velocity at the point $(x, 0)$ is given by the formula $dx/dt = \cos^2 \pi x$. How long will it take to cover the distance from the origin to the point $x = \frac{1}{4}$? Will it ever reach the point $x = \frac{1}{2}$? Why?

59. A particle moves in a straight line with acceleration $a = 4/(4 - t)^2$. If when $t = 0$ the velocity is equal to 2, find how far the particle moves between $t = 1$ and $t = 2$.

60. The velocity of a certain particle moving along the x-axis is proportional to x. At time $t = 0$ the particle is located at $x = 2$ and at time $t = 10$ it is at $x = 4$. Find its position at $t = 5$.

61. Solve the differential equation $dy/dx = y^2 e^{-x}$ if $y = 2$ when $x = 0$.

62. It is estimated that the population of a certain country is now increasing at a rate of 2% per year. Assuming that this (instantaneous) rate will continue indefinitely, estimate what the population N will be t years from now, if the population now is N_0. How many years will it take for the population to double?

63. If $y = (e^{2x} - 1)/(e^{2x} + 1)$, show that $dy/dx = 1 - y^2$.

64. Determine the inflection points of the curve $y = e^{-(x/a)^2}$, where a is a positive constant. Sketch the curve. (This is closely related to the normal curve used in statistics.)

65. Find the volume generated when the area bounded by $y = e^{-x}$, $x = 0$, $x = \ln 2$, $y = 0$ is rotated about the x-axis.

66. Find the volume generated when the area bounded by $x = \sec y$, $x = 0$, $y = 0$, $y = \pi/3$ is rotated about the y-axis.

67. (a) Find dy/dx if $y = \ln (\sec x + \tan x)$. (b) Find the length of arc of the curve $y = \ln \sec x$ from $x = 0$ to $\pi/4$, using, at some stage, the result of part (a).

68. Find the length of the curve $x/a = (y/b)^2 - \frac{1}{8}(b^2/a^2) \ln (y/b)$ from $y = b$ to $y = 3b$, assuming a and b to be positive constants.

69. Find the volume generated by rotating about the x-axis the area bounded by $y = e^x$, $y = 0$, $x = 0$, $x = 2$.

70. Find the area bounded by the curve $y = (a/2)(e^{x/a} + e^{-x/a})$, the x-axis, and the lines $x = -a$ and $x = +a$.

71. The portion of a tangent to a curve included between the x-axis and the point of tangency is bisected by the y-axis. If the curve passes through $(1, 2)$, find its equation.

72. Use the trapezoidal rule with $n = 5$ to approximate the value of (a) $\ln 0.5$, (b) $\ln 3$.

73. (a) If $y = x \ln x - x$, find y'. (b) Use the results of 73(a) and 72(b) to evaluate $\int_1^3 \ln x \, dx$ approximately.

Evaluate the integrals in Problems 74–76.

74. (a) $\displaystyle \int \frac{dx}{4 - 3x}$,

(b) $\displaystyle \int \frac{5 \, dx}{x - 3}$.

75. (a) $\displaystyle \int_0^2 \frac{x \, dx}{x^2 + 2}$,

(b) $\displaystyle \int_0^2 \frac{x \, dx}{(x^2 + 2)^2}$.

76. (a) $\int \frac{x+1}{x}\,dx,$ (b) $\int \frac{x}{2x+1}\,dx.$

77. Given $\ln 2 = 0.6932$ and $\ln 5 = 1.6094$. Use the properties of logarithms to find numerical values for $\ln 0.1$, $\ln 0.25$, $\ln 10$, and $\ln 20$.

78. Find the volume generated by rotating about the x-axis the area in the first quadrant bounded by the curve $xy^2 = 1$, the x-axis, the line $x = 1$, and the line $x = 4$.

79. Find the volume generated if the area in Problem 78 is rotated about the y-axis.

80. Evaluate:

(a) $\int_0^1 \frac{x^2\,dx}{2-x^3},$ (b) $\int_0^3 x(e^{x^2-1})\,dx,$

(c) $\int_1^3 \frac{dx}{x},$ (d) $\int_0^5 \frac{x\,dx}{x^2+1}.$

(e) $\int_0^1 (e^x + 1)\,dx.$

81. In the inversion of raw sugar the time rate of change of the amount of raw sugar present varies as the amount of raw sugar remaining. If after 10 hr 1000 lb of raw sugar has been reduced to 800 lb, how much raw sugar will remain after 24 hr?

82. A cylindrical tank of radius 10 ft and height 20 ft, with its axis vertical, is full of water but has a leak at the bottom. Assuming that water escapes at a rate proportional to the depth of water in the tank and that 10% escapes during the first hour, find a formula for the volume of water left in the tank after t hr.

83. Let p be a positive integer ≥ 2. Show that

$$\lim_{n\to\infty} \left(\frac{1}{n+1} + \frac{1}{n+2} + \cdots + \frac{1}{p\cdot n}\right) = \ln p.$$

84. (a) If $(\ln x)/x = (\ln 2)/2$, does it necessarily follow that $x = 2$? (b) If $(\ln x)/x = -2\ln 2$, does it necessarily follow that $x = \frac{1}{2}$? Give reasons for your answers.

85. Given that $\lim_{x\to\infty}(\ln x)/x = 0$ (see Article 6–7, Problem 4). Prove that (a) $\lim_{x\to\infty}(\ln x)/x^h = 0$ if h is any positive constant, (b) $\lim_{x\to+\infty} x^n/e^x = 0$ if n is any constant.

86. Show that $\lim_{h\to0}(e^h - 1)/h = 1$, by considering the definition of the derivative of e^x at $x = 0$.

87. Prove that if x is any positive number, $\lim_{n\to\infty} n(\sqrt[n]{x} - 1) = \ln x$. [*Hint:* Take $x = e^{nh}$ and apply Problem 86.] *Remark:* This result provides a method for finding $\ln x$ (to any desired finite number of decimal places) using nothing fancier than repeated use of the operation of extracting square roots. For we may take $n = 2^k$, and then $\sqrt[n]{x}$ is obtained from x by taking k successive square roots.

88. Show that $(x^2/4) < x - \ln(1 + x) < (x^2/2)$ if $0 < x < 1$. [*Hint:* Let $f(x) = x - \ln(1 + x)$ and show that $(x/2) < f'(x) < x$.]

89. Prove that the area under the graph of $y = 1/x$ over the interval $a \leq x \leq b$ $(a > 0)$ is the same as the area over the interval $ka \leq x \leq kb$, for any $k > 0$.

90. Find the limit, as $n \to \infty$, of

$$\frac{e^{1/n} + e^{2/n} + \cdots + e^{(n-1)/n} + e^{n/n}}{n}.$$

CHAPTER 7

METHODS OF INTEGRATION

7-1 Basic formulas. Since indefinite integration is defined as the inverse of differentiation, the problem of evaluating an integral

$$\int f(x)\,dx \tag{1}$$

is equivalent to finding a function F such that

$$dF(x) = f(x)\,dx. \tag{2}$$

At first sight, this may seem like a hopeless task when we think of adopting a "trial-and-error" approach, and realize that it is simply impossible to try *all functions* as F in Eq. (2) hoping that we find one that does the job.* In fact, it is even possible to write down fairly simple integrals, such as

$$\int e^{-x^2}\,dx, \tag{3}$$

which cannot be expressed in terms of finite combinations of the so-called "elementary functions" which we have studied thus far. We shall leave a discussion of such integrals as (3) to a later time, and say simply that the words "finite combinations" must give way and an integral like (3) may then be expressed in terms of an infinite series.

In order to cut down on the amount of trial-and-error involved in integration, it is useful to build up a table of standard types of integral formulas by inverting formulas for differentials as we have done in the previous chapters. Then we try to match any integral that confronts us against one of the standard types. This usually involves a certain amount of algebraic manipulation.

A table of integrals, more extensive than the list of basic formulas given here, probably is, or will be, a part of the reader's library. In order to use such a table intelligently, it is necessary to become familiar with

---

* If f is continuous, then an integral function F satisfying Eq. (2) always exists. For example, for $F(x)$ we could take the area A_a^x discussed in Article 4–8. Theoretically, this, together with the fact that such an area can be calculated as a limit of sums of areas of rectangles, gives us a rule for computing $F(x)$. However, we are interested in avoiding these arithmetical calculations, if possible. Hence we prefer to find simple closed-form expressions for the integral whenever possible.

certain basic techniques which one can apply to reduce a given integral to a form that matches an entry in the tables. The examples and problems in this book should serve to develop our skill with these techniques. In order to concentrate on the techniques without becoming entangled in a mass of algebra, these problems and examples have been kept fairly simple. This in turn means that *these particular* problems can frequently be solved immediately by consulting an integral table. But the reader should realize that if he adopts such a course he will defeat the intended purpose of developing his own power. And it is this power which is important, rather than the specific answer to any given problem.

Perhaps a good way to develop the skill we are aiming for is for each student to build his own table of integrals. He may, for example, make a notebook in which the various sections are headed by the standard forms such as $\int u^n \, du$, $\int du/u$, $\int e^u \, du$, etc., and then under each heading he may include several examples to illustrate the range of application of the particular formula.

Making such a notebook probably has educational value. But once it is made, it should rarely be necessary to refer to it!

Success in integration hinges on the ability to spot what part of the integrand should be called u in order that one will also have du so that a known formula can be applied. This means that the *first requirement* for skill in integration is a thorough mastery of the formulas for differentiation. We therefore list certain formulas for differentials that have been derived in previous chapters, together with their integral counterparts.

1. $du = \dfrac{du}{dx} \, dx$ 1. $\displaystyle\int du = u + C$

2. $d(au) = a \, du$ 2. $\displaystyle\int a \, du = a \int du$

3. $d(u + v) = du + dv$ 3. $\displaystyle\int (du + dv) = \int du + \int dv$

4. $d(u^n) = nu^{n-1} \, du$ 4. $\displaystyle\int u^n \, du = \dfrac{u^{n+1}}{n+1} + C, \quad n \neq -1$

5. $d(\ln u) = \dfrac{du}{u}$ 5. $\displaystyle\int \dfrac{du}{u} = \ln |u| + C$

6. (a) $d(e^u) = e^u \, du$ 6. (a) $\displaystyle\int e^u \, du = e^u + C$

   (b) $d(a^u) = a^u \ln a \, du$ (b) $\displaystyle\int a^u \, du = \dfrac{a^u}{\ln a} + C = \int e^{u \ln a}$

7. $d (\sin u) = \cos u \, du$

7. $\int \cos u \, du = \sin u + C$

8. $d (\cos u) = -\sin u \, du$

8. $\int \sin u \, du = -\cos u + C$

9. $d (\tan u) = \sec^2 u \, du$

9. $\int \sec^2 u \, du = \tan u + C$

10. $d (\cot u) = -\csc^2 u \, du$

10. $\int \csc^2 u \, du = -\cot u + C$

11. $d (\sec u) = \sec u \tan u \, du$

11. $\int \sec u \tan u \, du = \sec u + C$

12. $d (\csc u) = -\csc u \cot u \, du$

12. $\int \csc u \cot u \, du = -\csc u + C$

13. $d (\sin^{-1} u) = \dfrac{du}{\sqrt{1 - u^2}}$

14. $d (\cos^{-1} u) = \dfrac{-du}{\sqrt{1 - u^2}}$

13. and 14. $\int \dfrac{du}{\sqrt{1 - u^2}} = \begin{cases} \sin^{-1} u + C \\ -\cos^{-1} u + C' \end{cases}$

15. $d (\tan^{-1} u) = \dfrac{du}{1 + u^2}$

16. $d (\cot^{-1} u) = \dfrac{-du}{1 + u^2}$

15. and 16. $\int \dfrac{du}{1 + u^2} = \begin{cases} \tan^{-1} u + C \\ -\cot^{-1} u + C' \end{cases}$

17. $d (\sec^{-1} u) = \dfrac{du}{|u|\sqrt{u^2 - 1}}$

18. $d (\csc^{-1} u) = \dfrac{-du}{|u|\sqrt{u^2 - 1}}$

17. and 18. $\int \dfrac{du}{u\sqrt{u^2 - 1}} = \begin{cases} \sec^{-1} |u| + C \\ -\csc^{-1} |u| + C \end{cases}$

At present, let us just consider this list a handy reference and *not* a challenge to our memories! A bit of examination will probably convince us that we are already rather familiar with the first twelve formulas for *differentials* and, so far as *integration* is concerned, part of our training in technique will show how we can get the *integrals* in the last six cases without memorizing the formulas for the differentials of the inverse trigonometric functions.

Just what types of functions can we integrate directly by use of this short table of integrals?

Powers. $\int u^n \, du, \quad \int \dfrac{du}{u}.$

Exponentials. $\int e^u \, du, \quad \int a^u \, du.$

Trigonometric functions. $\displaystyle\int \sin u \, du, \quad \int \cos u \, du.$

Algebraic functions.

$$\int \frac{du}{\sqrt{1 - u^2}}, \quad \int \frac{du}{1 + u^2}, \quad \int \frac{du}{u\sqrt{u^2 - 1}}.$$

Of course, there are additional combinations of trigonometric functions such as $\int \sec^2 u \, du$, etc., which are integrable accidentally, so to speak. What common types of functions are *not* included in the table?

Logarithms. $\displaystyle\int \ln u \, du, \quad \int \log_a u \, du.$

Trigonometric functions. $\displaystyle\int \tan u \, du, \quad \int \cot u \, du, \quad \int \sec u \, du, \quad \int \csc u \, du.$

Algebraic functions. $\displaystyle\int \frac{du}{a^2 + u^2},$ etc. with $a^2 \neq 1.$

$$\int \sqrt{a^2 \pm u^2} \, du, \quad \int \sqrt{u^2 - a^2} \, du, \quad \text{etc.}$$

Inverse functions. $\displaystyle\int \sin^{-1} u \, du, \quad \int \tan^{-1} u \, du, \quad \text{etc.}$

We shall eventually see how to handle all of these and some others, but there are no methods which will solve *all* integration problems in terms of elementary functions.

PROBLEMS

Evaluate each of the following integrals by reducing the integrand to one of the standard forms (1 through 18). In each case, indicate what you have called u and refer by number to the standard formula used.

1. $\displaystyle\int \sqrt{2x + 3} \, dx$

2. $\displaystyle\int \frac{dx}{3x + 5}$

3. $\displaystyle\int \frac{dx}{(2x - 7)^2}$

4. $\displaystyle\int \frac{(x + 1) \, dx}{x^2 + 2x + 3}$

5. $\displaystyle\int \frac{\sin x \, dx}{2 + \cos x}$

6. $\displaystyle\int \tan^3 2x \sec^2 2x \, dx$

7. $\displaystyle\int \frac{x \, dx}{\sqrt{1 - 4x^2}}$

8. $\displaystyle\int x^{1/3}\sqrt{x^{4/3} - 1} \, dx$

9. $\displaystyle\int \frac{x\,dx}{(3x^2+4)^3}$

10. $\displaystyle\int x^2\sqrt{x^3+5}\,dx$

11. $\displaystyle\int \frac{x^2\,dx}{\sqrt{x^3+5}}$

12. $\displaystyle\int \frac{x\,dx}{4x^2+1}$

13. $\displaystyle\int e^{2x}\,dx$

14. $\displaystyle\int \sin x\, e^{\cos x}\,dx$

15. $\displaystyle\int \frac{dx}{e^{3x}}$

16. $\displaystyle\int \frac{e^{\sqrt{x+1}}}{\sqrt{x+1}}\,dx$

17. $\displaystyle\int \cos^2 x \sin x\,dx$

18. $\displaystyle\int \frac{\cos x\,dx}{\sin^3 x}$

19. $\displaystyle\int \cot^3 x \csc^2 x\,dx$

20. $\displaystyle\int \tan 3x \sec^2 3x\,dx$

21. $\displaystyle\int \frac{e^{2x}+e^{-2x}}{e^{2x}-e^{-2x}}\,dx$

22. $\displaystyle\int \sin 2x \cos^2 2x\,dx$

23. $\displaystyle\int (1+\cos\theta)^3 \sin\theta\,d\theta$

24. $\displaystyle\int te^{-t^2}\,dt$

25. $\displaystyle\int \frac{\cos x\,dx}{\sin x}$

26. $\displaystyle\int \frac{\cos x\,dx}{1+\sin x}$

27. $\displaystyle\int \sec^3 x \tan x\,dx$

28. $\displaystyle\int \frac{\sin\theta\,d\theta}{\sqrt{1+\cos\theta}}$

29. $\displaystyle\int \sec^2 3x\, e^{\tan 3x}\,dx$

30. $\displaystyle\int \cos 2t \sqrt{4-\sin 2t}\,dt$

31. $\displaystyle\int \frac{1+\cos 2x}{\sin^2 2x}\,dx$

32. $\displaystyle\int \frac{\sin^2 2x}{1+\cos 2x}\,dx$

33. $\displaystyle\int \frac{\csc^2 2t}{\sqrt{1+\cot 2t}}\,dt$

34. $\displaystyle\int e^{3x}\,dx$

35. $\displaystyle\int \frac{e^{\tan^{-1}2t}}{1+4t^2}\,dt$

36. $\displaystyle\int xe^{-x^2}\,dx$

37. $\displaystyle\int 3^x\,dx$

38. $\displaystyle\int 10^{2x}\,dx$

39. Each of the following integrals may be easily evaluated for a particular numerical value of n. Choose this value and integrate. For example,

$$\int x^n \cos(x^2)\,dx$$

is easily evaluated for $n = 1$:

$$\int x \cos(x^2)\,dx = \tfrac{1}{2}\sin(x^2) + C.$$

(a) $\int x^n \ln x \, dx,$ (b) $\int x^n e^{x^3} \, dx,$ (c) $\int x^n \sin \sqrt{x} \, dx.$

40. The integral $\int_a^\infty e^{-x^2} \, dx$ arises in statistics and elsewhere. It is defined to mean the same thing as

$$\lim_{b \to +\infty} \int_a^b e^{-x^2} \, dx.$$

Show that if $x > a \geq 1$, then $e^{-x^2} < e^{-ax}$. Hence, by comparing the integral from a to ∞ of e^{-x^2} with the integral of e^{-ax} and evaluating the latter integral, show that

$$\int_a^\infty e^{-x^2} \, dx < \frac{1}{a} e^{-a^2}, \qquad \text{if} \quad a \geq 1.$$

7–2 Powers of trigonometric functions. The formula

$$\int u^n \, du = \begin{cases} \dfrac{u^{n+1}}{n+1} + C, & n \neq -1 \\ \ln |u| + C, & n = -1 \end{cases}$$

may be used to evaluate certain integrals involving powers of the trigonometric functions, as illustrated by the examples that follow. The same methods work for powers of other functions. The reader should pay attention to the *methods* rather than trying to remember specific results.

EXAMPLE 1. $\int \sin^n ax \cos ax \, dx.$

Solution. If we let $u = \sin ax$, then

$$du = \cos ax \, d(ax) = a \cos ax \, dx,$$

so that we need only multiply the integral by unity in the form of a times $1/a$. Since a and $1/a$ are constants, we may write a inside the integral sign and $1/a$ in front of the integral sign to have

$$\int \sin^n ax \cos ax \, dx = \frac{1}{a} \int (\sin ax)^n (a \cos ax \, dx)$$

$$= \frac{1}{a} \int u^n \, du$$

$$= \begin{cases} \dfrac{1}{a} \dfrac{u^{n+1}}{n+1} + C, & n \neq -1 \\ \dfrac{1}{a} \ln |u| + C, & n = -1; \end{cases}$$

that is,

$$\int \sin^n ax \cos ax \, dx = \frac{\sin^{n+1} ax}{(n+1)a} + C, \quad n \neq -1 \qquad (1a)$$

and if $n = -1$, we get

$$\int \cot ax \, dx = \frac{1}{a} \ln |\sin ax| + C. \qquad (1b)$$

Note that the success of the method depended upon having $\cos ax$ to go with the dx as part of du.

EXAMPLE 2. $\qquad\qquad \int \sin^3 x \, dx.$

Solution. The method of the previous example does not work because there is no $\cos x$ to go with dx to give du if we try letting $u = \sin x$. But if we write

$$\sin^3 x = \sin^2 x \cdot \sin x = (1 - \cos^2 x) \cdot \sin x$$

and let

$$u = \cos x, \qquad du = -\sin x \, dx,$$

we have

$$\int \sin^3 x \, dx = \int (1 - \cos^2 x) \cdot \sin x \, dx = \int (1 - u^2) \cdot (-du)$$

$$= \int (u^2 - 1) \, du = \tfrac{1}{3} u^3 - u + C = \tfrac{1}{3} \cos^3 x - \cos x + C.$$

This *method* may be applied whenever an *odd* power of $\sin x$ or $\cos x$ is to be integrated. For example, any positive odd power of $\cos x$ has the form

$$\cos^{2n+1} x = \cos^{2n} x \cdot \cos x = (\cos^2 x)^n \cdot \cos x = (1 - \sin^2 x)^n \cdot \cos x,$$

with n an integer ≥ 0. Then if we let $u = \sin x$, $du = \cos x \, dx$, we have

$$\int \cos^{2n+1} x \, dx = \int (1 - \sin^2 x)^n \cdot \cos x \, dx = \int (1 - u^2)^n \cdot du.$$

The expression $(1 - u^2)^n$ may now be expanded by the binomial theorem and the result evaluated as a sum of individual integrals of the type $\int u^m \, du$.

EXAMPLE 3. $\qquad\qquad \int \sec x \tan x \, dx.$

Solution. Of course this is a standard form already, so there is no real problem in finding an answer. But in trigonometry we often express all trigonometric functions in terms of sines and cosines, and we now investigate what this does to the integral in question.

$$\int \sec x \tan x \, dx = \int \frac{1}{\cos x} \frac{\sin x}{\cos x} \, dx = \int \frac{\sin x \, dx}{\cos^2 x}.$$

Taking a clue from the previous examples (keeping in mind du as well as u), we let

$$u = \cos x, \qquad du = -\sin x \, dx,$$

and then

$$\int \frac{\sin x \, dx}{\cos^2 x} = \int \frac{-du}{u^2} = -\int u^{-2} \, du = \frac{-u^{-1}}{-1} + C = \frac{1}{u} + C$$

$$= \frac{1}{\cos x} + C = \sec x + C.$$

EXAMPLE 4. $\qquad\qquad \int \tan^4 x \, dx.$

Solution. This does not lend itself readily to the use of sines and cosines, since both of them occur to even powers. We say: $u = \tan x$ would require $du = \sec^2 x \, dx$. Is there some way to include $\sec^2 x$? Yes; there is an identity involving tangents and secants. How does it go? Since

$$\sin^2 x + \cos^2 x = 1,$$

if we divide through by $\cos^2 x$ we get

$$\tan^2 x + 1 = \sec^2 x \qquad \text{or} \qquad \tan^2 x = \sec^2 x - 1.$$

Then

$$\int \tan^4 x \, dx = \int \tan^2 x \cdot \tan^2 x \, dx = \int \tan^2 x \cdot (\sec^2 x - 1) \, dx$$

$$= \int \tan^2 x \sec^2 x \, dx - \int \tan^2 x \, dx.$$

The first of these is all set. But how about the $\tan^2 x$? Oh, yes,

$$\tan^2 x = \sec^2 x - 1,$$

so

$$\int \tan^4 x \, dx = \int \tan^2 x \sec^2 x \, dx - \int \tan^2 x \, dx$$

$$= \int \tan^2 x \sec^2 x \, dx - \int (\sec^2 x - 1) \, dx$$

$$= \int \tan^2 x \sec^2 x \, dx - \int \sec^2 x \, dx + \int dx.$$

In the first two of these, let

$$u = \tan x, \qquad du = \sec^2 x \, dx$$

and have

$$\int u^2 \, du - \int du = \tfrac{1}{3}u^3 - u + C'.$$

The other is a standard form, so

$$\int \tan^4 x \, dx = \tfrac{1}{3} \tan^3 x - \tan x + x + C.$$

The *method* works for any *even* power of tan x, but what is still better is a *reduction formula* derived as follows:

$$
\begin{aligned}
\int \tan^n x \, dx &= \int \tan^{n-2}x \, (\sec^2 x - 1) \, dx \\
&= \int \tan^{n-2} x \sec^2 x \, dx - \int \tan^{n-2} x \, dx \\
&= \frac{\tan^{n-1} x}{n-1} - \int \tan^{n-2} x \, dx.
\end{aligned}
$$

This reduces the problem of integrating $\tan^n x \, dx$ to the problem of integrating $\tan^{n-2} x \, dx$. Since this decreases the exponent on tan x by 2, a repetition with the same formula will reduce the exponent by 2 again, and so on. Applying this to the problem above, we have

$$n = 4: \quad \int \tan^4 x \, dx = \frac{\tan^3 x}{3} - \int \tan^2 x \, dx,$$

$$n = 2: \quad \int \tan^2 x \, dx = \frac{\tan x}{1} - \int \tan^0 x \, dx,$$

$$\int \tan^0 x \, dx = \int 1 \, dx = x + C.$$

Therefore,

$$\int \tan^4 x \, dx = \tfrac{1}{3} \tan^3 x - [\tan x - x + C]$$

$$= \tfrac{1}{3} \tan^3 x - \tan x + x + C'.$$

This reduction formula works whether the original exponent n is even or odd, but if the exponent is odd, say $2m + 1$, after m steps it will be reduced by $2m$, leaving

$$\int \tan x \, dx = \int \frac{\sin x}{\cos x} \, dx = -\int \frac{d\,(\cos x)}{\cos x} = -\ln |\cos x| + C \qquad (2)$$

as the final integral to be evaluated.

These examples illustrate how it is possible, by using the trigonometric identities

$$\sin^2 x + \cos^2 x = 1, \qquad \tan^2 x + 1 = \sec^2 x,$$

and others readily derived from these, to evaluate the integrals of

(a) *odd* powers of sin x or cos x,
(b) *any* integral powers of tan x (or cot x), and
(c) *even* powers of sec x (or csc x).

The even powers of sec x, say $\sec^{2n} x$, can all be reduced to powers of tan x by employing the substitution $\sec^2 x = 1 + \tan^2 x$, and then using the reduction formula for integrating powers of tan x after expanding $\sec^{2n} x = (1 + \tan^2 x)^n$ by the binomial theorem. But it is even simpler to use the method below:

$$\int \sec^{2n} x \, dx = \int \sec^{2n-2} x \sec^2 x \, dx = \int (\sec^2 x)^{n-1} \sec^2 x \, dx$$

$$= \int (1 + \tan^2 x)^{n-1} \sec^2 x \, dx$$

$$= \int (1 + u^2)^{n-1} \, du, \qquad (u = \tan x).$$

When $(1 + u^2)^{n-1}$ is expanded by the binomial theorem, the resulting polynomial in u may be integrated term by term.

For example,

$$\int \sec^6 x \, dx = \int \sec^4 x \cdot \sec^2 x \, dx = \int (1 + \tan^2 x)^2 \cdot \sec^2 x \, dx$$

$$= \int (1 + 2u^2 + u^4) \, du \qquad (u = \tan x)$$

$$= u + \frac{2u^3}{3} + \frac{u^5}{5} + C$$

$$= \tan x + 2 \frac{\tan^3 x}{3} + \frac{\tan^5 x}{5} + C.$$

EXAMPLE 5. $\qquad \int \sec x \, dx.$

Solution. This is hard to evaluate unless one has seen the following trick!

$$\sec x = \frac{\sec x \, (\tan x + \sec x)}{\sec x + \tan x} = \frac{\sec x \tan x + \sec^2 x}{\sec x + \tan x}.$$

In this form the numerator is the derivative of the denominator. Therefore

$$\int \sec x \, dx = \int \frac{\sec x \tan x + \sec^2 x}{\sec x + \tan x} \, dx$$

$$= \int \frac{du}{u} \qquad (u = \sec x + \tan x)$$

$$= \ln |u| + C.$$

That is,

$$\boxed{\int \sec x \, dx = \ln |\sec x + \tan x| + C.} \tag{3}$$

PROBLEMS

1. $\int \sin t \sqrt{1 + \cos t} \, dt$

22. $\int \frac{\sin \theta \, d\theta}{2 - \cos \theta}$

3. $\int \frac{\sec^2 2x \, dx}{1 + \tan 2x}$

4. $\int \tan 3x \, dx$

5. $\int \cos^3 x \, dx$

6. $\int \tan^2 4\theta \, d\theta$

7. (a) $\int \sin^3 x \cos^2 x \, dx$

8. $\int \sec^n x \tan x \, dx$

(b) $\int \frac{\sin^3 x \, dx}{\cos^2 x}$

9. $\int \tan^n x \sec^2 x \, dx$

10. $\int \sin^n x \cos x \, dx$

11. $\int \cos^n x \sin x \, dx$

12. $\int \sin^2 3x \cos 3x \, dx$

13. $\int \cos^3 2x \sin 2x \, dx$

14. $\int \sec^4 3x \tan 3x \, dx$

15. $\int \sec^4 3x \, dx$

16. $\int \cos^3 2x \, dx$

17. $\int \tan^3 2x \, dx$

18. $\int \tan^3 x \sec x \, dx$

19. $\int \sin^3 x \, dx$

20. $\int \frac{\cos x \, dx}{(1 + \sin x)^2}$

21. $\int \frac{\sec^2 x \, dx}{2 + \tan x}$

22. $\int \frac{\cos^3 t \, dt}{\sin^2 t}$

23. $\displaystyle\int \frac{e^x\,dx}{1+e^x}$ 24. $\displaystyle\int (\ln ax)^n\,\frac{dx}{x}$

25. $\displaystyle\int \frac{dx}{x\ln 3x}$ 26. $\displaystyle\int \cot^3 x\,dx$

27. $\displaystyle\int \csc^3 2t\cot 2t\,dt$ 28. $\displaystyle\int \csc^4 x\,dx$

29. Derive a reduction formula for $\int \cot^n ax\,dx$ and use the result to evaluate $\int \cot^4 3x\,dx$.

7-3 Even powers of sines and cosines.   In Article 7-2 we saw how we could evaluate integrals of odd powers of sines and cosines. Indeed, any integral of the form

$$\int \sin^m x\cos^n x\,dx \tag{1}$$

in which at least one of the exponents m and n is a positive odd integer may be evaluated by these methods.

EXAMPLE 1. $\displaystyle\int \cos^{2/3} x\sin^5 x\,dx.$

Solution.   Here we have $\sin x$ to an *odd* power. So we put one factor of $\sin x$ with dx and the remaining sine factors, namely $\sin^4 x$, can be expressed in terms of $\cos x$ without introducing any square roots, as follows:

$$\sin^4 x = (\sin^2 x)^2 = (1 - \cos^2 x)^2.$$

The $\sin x$ goes well with dx when we take

$$u = \cos x, \qquad du = -\sin x\,dx$$

and evaluate the integral as follows:

$$\int \cos^{2/3} x\sin^5 x\,dx = \int \cos^{2/3} x\,(1-\cos^2 x)^2\sin x\,dx$$

$$= \int u^{2/3}(1-u^2)^2(-du)$$

$$= -\int (u^{2/3} - 2u^{8/3} + u^{14/3})\,du$$

$$= -[\tfrac{3}{5}u^{5/3} - \tfrac{6}{11}u^{11/3} + \tfrac{3}{17}u^{17/3}] + C$$

$$= -\cos^{5/3} x[\tfrac{3}{5} - \tfrac{6}{11}\cos^2 x + \tfrac{3}{17}\cos^4 x] + C.$$

If both the exponents m and n in the integral (1) are even integers, the method illustrated above won't work. So we use one or both of the following trigonometric identities:

$$\sin^2 A = \tfrac{1}{2}(1 - \cos 2A), \tag{2a}$$

$$\cos^2 A = \tfrac{1}{2}(1 + \cos 2A). \tag{2b}$$

These identities may be derived very quickly by adding or subtracting the equations

$$\cos^2 A + \sin^2 A = 1, \qquad \cos^2 A - \sin^2 A = \cos 2A,$$

and dividing by two.

EXAMPLE 2.

$$\int \cos^4 x \, dx = \int (\cos^2 x)^2 \, dx = \int \tfrac{1}{4}(1 + \cos 2x)^2 \, dx \tag{a}$$

$$= \tfrac{1}{4} \int (1 + 2 \cos 2x + \cos^2 2x) \, dx \tag{b}$$

$$= \tfrac{1}{4} \int [1 + 2 \cos 2x + \tfrac{1}{2}(1 + \cos 4x)] \, dx$$

$$= \tfrac{3}{8} x + \tfrac{1}{4} \sin 2x + \tfrac{1}{32} \sin 4x + C.$$

In (a), we used Eq. (2b) with $A = x$, and in (b), we used Eq. (2b) with $A = 2x$. The final integrations involve

$$\int \cos ax \, dx = \frac{1}{a} \int \cos ax \, d(ax) = \frac{1}{a} \sin ax + C'.$$

Remark. An integral such as

$$\int \sin^2 x \cos^4 x \, dx,$$

which involves even powers of both $\sin x$ and $\cos x$, can be changed to a sum of integrals each of which involves only powers of one of them. Then these may be handled by the method illustrated above.

EXAMPLE 3.

$$\int \sin^2 x \cos^4 x \, dx = \int (1 - \cos^2 x) \cos^4 x \, dx$$

$$= \int \cos^4 x \, dx - \int \cos^6 x \, dx.$$

We evaluated $\int \cos^4 x \, dx$ above, and

$$\int \cos^6 x \, dx = \int (\cos^2 x)^3 \, dx = \tfrac{1}{8} \int (1 + \cos 2x)^3 \, dx$$

$$= \tfrac{1}{8} \int (1 + 3 \cos 2x + 3 \cos^2 2x + \cos^3 2x) \, dx.$$

We now know how to handle each term of this integral. The reader may supply the details and show that the result is

$$\int \cos^6 x \, dx = \tfrac{5}{16}x + \tfrac{1}{4} \sin 2x + \tfrac{3}{64} \sin 4x - \tfrac{1}{48} \sin^3 2x + C.$$

PROBLEMS

Evaluate the following integrals:

1. $\int \sin^2 x \cos^3 x \, dx$

2. $\int \dfrac{\sin^3 x \, dx}{\cos^2 x}$

3. $\int \sin^2 2t \, dt$

4. $\int \cos^2 3\theta \, d\theta$

5. $\int \sin^4 ax \, dx$

6. $\int \sin^2 y \cos^2 y \, dy$

7. $\int \dfrac{dx}{\cos^2 x}$

8. $\int \dfrac{dx}{\sin^4 x}$

9. $\int \dfrac{\cos 2t \, dt}{\sin^4 2t}$

10. $\int \sin^6 x \, dx$

7–4 Integrals involving $\sqrt{a^2 - u^2}$, $\sqrt{a^2 + u^2}$, $\sqrt{u^2 - a^2}$, $a^2 + u^2$, and $a^2 - u^2$. Some of these follow directly from the corresponding integral formulas with $a = 1$ listed in Article 7–1. For example, we have

$$\int \frac{du}{1 + u^2} = \tan^{-1} u + C, \tag{1}$$

and to evaluate

$$\int \frac{du}{a^2 + u^2} \tag{2}$$

we factor a^2 out of the denominator and proceed as follows:

$$\int \frac{du}{a^2 + u^2} = \int \frac{du}{a^2 \left[1 + \left(\frac{u}{a}\right)^2 \right]} = \frac{1}{a^2} \int \frac{a d \left(\frac{u}{a}\right)}{1 + \left(\frac{u}{a}\right)^2} = \frac{1}{a} \int \frac{dz}{1 + z^2}$$

$$= \frac{1}{a} \tan^{-1} z + C = \frac{1}{a} \tan^{-1} \frac{u}{a} + C. \qquad \left[z = \frac{u}{a} \right].$$

That is,

$$\int \frac{du}{a^2 + u^2} = \frac{1}{a} \tan^{-1} \frac{u}{a} + C. \qquad (3)$$

The essential feature here was the introduction of a new variable by means of the substitution

$$z = \frac{u}{a} \qquad \text{or} \qquad u = az.$$

Such a substitution allows the a terms to be brought outside the integral sign, and the resulting integral may then match one of the inverse trigonometric formulas.

An alternative approach will show, however, that one may bypass the job of learning these formulas. In addition, this method, which we shall soon illustrate, permits the evaluation of many additional integrals.

The method leans primarily upon the following identities.

$$\begin{aligned} 1 - \sin^2 \theta &= \cos^2 \theta, \\ 1 + \tan^2 \theta &= \sec^2 \theta, \\ \sec^2 \theta - 1 &= \tan^2 \theta. \end{aligned} \qquad (4)$$

These identities may be multiplied by a^2, with the result that the substitutions listed below have the following effects:

(a) $u = a \sin \theta$ replaces $a^2 - u^2$ by $a^2 \cos^2 \theta.$
(b) $u = a \tan \theta$ replaces $a^2 + u^2$ by $a^2 \sec^2 \theta.$ (5)
(c) $u = a \sec \theta$ replaces $u^2 - a^2$ by $a^2 \tan^2 \theta.$

It is thus seen that corresponding to each of the *binomial* expressions $a^2 - u^2$, $a^2 + u^2$, and $u^2 - a^2$, we have a substitution which replaces the binomial by a single squared term. The particular substitution to use will depend upon the form of the integrand. In the examples that follow, a is a positive constant.

EXAMPLE 1. $\displaystyle \int \frac{du}{\sqrt{a^2 - u^2}}, \qquad a > 0.$

Solution. We try the substitution (5a):

$$u = a \sin \theta, \qquad du = a \cos \theta \, d\theta,$$

$$a^2 - u^2 = a^2(1 - \sin^2 \theta) = a^2 \cos^2 \theta.$$

Then

$$\int \frac{du}{\sqrt{a^2 - u^2}} = \int \frac{a \cos \theta \, d\theta}{\sqrt{a^2 \cos^2 \theta}} = \int \frac{a \cos \theta \, d\theta}{\pm a \cos \theta} \quad (\pm \text{ depends on sign of } \cos \theta)$$

$$= \pm \int d\theta = \pm(\theta + C).$$

Since $\sin \theta = u/a$,

$$\theta = \sin^{-1} \frac{u}{a}$$

and

$$\int \frac{du}{\sqrt{a^2 - u^2}} = \pm \left(\sin^{-1} \frac{u}{a} + C \right).$$

Using only the *principal value* of $\sin^{-1} u/a$ means that θ will lie between $-\pi/2$ and $\pi/2$, hence $\cos \theta \geq 0$ and the ambiguous sign is $+$; that is,

$$\int \frac{du}{\sqrt{a^2 - u^2}} = \sin^{-1} \frac{u}{a} + C. \tag{6}$$

EXAMPLE 2. $\qquad \int \frac{du}{\sqrt{a^2 + u^2}}, \qquad a > 0.$

Solution. This time we try

$$u = a \tan \theta,$$

$$du = a \sec^2 \theta \, d\theta,$$

$$a^2 + u^2 = a^2(1 + \tan^2 \theta) = a^2 \sec^2 \theta.$$

Then

$$\int \frac{du}{\sqrt{a^2 + u^2}} = \int \frac{a \sec^2 \theta \, d\theta}{\sqrt{a^2 \sec^2 \theta}}$$

$$= \pm \int \sec \theta \, d\theta \quad (\pm \text{ depends on sign of } \sec \theta).$$

By Eq. (3), Article 7–2, we know that

$$\int \sec \theta \, d\theta = \ln |\sec \theta + \tan \theta| + C.$$

If we take

$$\theta = \tan^{-1} \frac{u}{a}, \qquad -\frac{\pi}{2} < \theta < \frac{\pi}{2},$$

then sec θ is positive, and

$$\int \frac{du}{\sqrt{a^2 + u^2}} = \int \sec \theta \, d\theta$$
$$= \ln |\sec \theta + \tan \theta| + C$$
$$= \ln \left| \frac{\sqrt{a^2 + u^2}}{a} + \frac{u}{a} \right| + C$$
$$= \ln |\sqrt{a^2 + u^2} + u| + C',$$

(7)

where

$$C' = C - \ln a.$$

EXAMPLE 3. $$\int \frac{du}{\sqrt{u^2 - a^2}}, \qquad |u| > a > 0.$$

Solution. We try the substitution

$$u = a \sec \theta,$$
$$du = a \sec \theta \tan \theta \, d\theta,$$
$$u^2 - a^2 = a^2 (\sec^2 \theta - 1) = a^2 \tan^2 \theta.$$

Then

$$\int \frac{du}{\sqrt{u^2 - a^2}} = \int \frac{a \sec \theta \tan \theta \, d\theta}{\sqrt{a^2 \tan^2 \theta}} = \pm \int \sec \theta \, d\theta \quad (\pm \text{ depends on sign of } \tan \theta).$$

If we take

$$\theta = \sec^{-1} \frac{u}{a}, \qquad 0 \le \theta \le \pi,$$

then

$$\tan \theta \text{ is positive if } 0 < \theta < \pi/2,$$
$$\tan \theta \text{ is negative if } \pi/2 < \theta < \pi,$$

and, from Eq. (3) of Article 7–2,

$$\pm \int \sec \theta \, d\theta = \pm \ln |\sec \theta + \tan \theta| + C.$$

When $\tan \theta$ is positive, we must use the plus sign; when $\tan \theta$ is negative, the minus sign. Moreover,

$$\sec \theta = \frac{u}{a}, \qquad \tan \theta = \pm \frac{\sqrt{u^2 - a^2}}{a}.$$

So we have

$$\int \frac{du}{\sqrt{u^2 - a^2}} = \pm\ln \left| \frac{u}{a} \pm \frac{\sqrt{u^2 - a^2}}{a} \right| + C$$

$$= \begin{cases} \ln \left| \dfrac{u}{a} + \dfrac{\sqrt{u^2 - a^2}}{a} \right| + C \\ \text{or} \\ -\ln \left| \dfrac{u}{a} - \dfrac{\sqrt{u^2 - a^2}}{a} \right| + C. \end{cases}$$

But the two forms are actually equal, because

$$-\ln \left| \frac{u}{a} - \frac{\sqrt{u^2 - a^2}}{a} \right| = \ln \left| \frac{a}{u - \sqrt{u^2 - a^2}} \right|$$

$$= \ln \left| \frac{a(u + \sqrt{u^2 - a^2})}{(u - \sqrt{u^2 - a^2})(u + \sqrt{u^2 - a^2})} \right|$$

$$= \ln \left| \frac{a(u + \sqrt{u^2 - a^2})}{a^2} \right|$$

$$= \ln \left| \frac{u + \sqrt{u^2 - a^2}}{a} \right|.$$

Therefore

$$\int \frac{du}{\sqrt{u^2 - a^2}} = \ln |u + \sqrt{u^2 - a^2}| + C', \tag{8}$$

where we have replaced $C - \ln a$ by C' in this final form.

EXAMPLE 4. $\displaystyle \int \frac{du}{a^2 + u^2}, \quad a > 0.$

Solution. We try

$$u = a \tan \theta, \quad du = a \sec^2 \theta \, d\theta,$$

$$a^2 + u^2 = a^2(1 + \tan^2 \theta) = a^2 \sec^2 \theta.$$

Then

$$\int \frac{du}{a^2 + u^2} = \int \frac{a \sec^2 \theta \, d\theta}{a^2 \sec^2 \theta}$$

$$= \frac{1}{a} \int d\theta = \frac{1}{a} \theta + C.$$

Since $u = a \tan \theta,$

$$\tan \theta = \frac{u}{a}, \quad \theta = \tan^{-1} \frac{u}{a},$$

and

$$\int \frac{du}{a^2 + u^2} = \frac{1}{a} \tan^{-1} \frac{u}{a} + C. \tag{9}$$

EXAMPLE 5. $\displaystyle\int \frac{x^2 \, dx}{\sqrt{9 - x^2}}$.

Solution. If we substitute

$$x = 3 \sin \theta, \qquad \frac{-\pi}{2} < \theta < \frac{\pi}{2},$$

$$dx = 3 \cos \theta \, d\theta,$$

$$9 - x^2 = 9(1 - \sin^2 \theta) = 9 \cos^2 \theta,$$

then we find

$$\int \frac{x^2 \, dx}{\sqrt{9 - x^2}} = \int \frac{9 \sin^2 \theta \cdot 3 \cos \theta \, d\theta}{3 \cos \theta} = 9 \int \sin^2 \theta \, d\theta.$$

This is considerably simpler than the integral we started with. To evaluate it, we make use of the identity

$$\sin^2 \theta = \tfrac{1}{2}(1 - \cos 2\theta).$$

Then

$$\int \sin^2 \theta \, d\theta = \tfrac{1}{2} \int (1 - \cos 2\theta) \, d\theta = \tfrac{1}{2}[\theta - \tfrac{1}{2} \sin 2\theta] + C$$

$$= \tfrac{1}{2}[\theta - \sin \theta \cos \theta] + C.$$

Substituting this above, we get

$$\int \frac{x^2 \, dx}{\sqrt{9 - x^2}} = \frac{9}{2} [\theta - \sin \theta \cos \theta] + C$$

$$= \frac{9}{2} \left[\sin^{-1} \frac{x}{3} - \frac{x\sqrt{9 - x^2}}{9} \right] + C.$$

The trigonometric substitutions (a), (b), and (c) of Eq. (5) can be easily remembered by thinking of the theorem of Pythagoras and taking a and u as two of the sides and θ as an angle in a right triangle. Thus $\sqrt{a^2 - u^2}$ suggests a as hypotenuse and u as a leg, $\sqrt{a^2 + u^2}$ suggests a and u as the legs, and $\sqrt{u^2 - a^2}$ suggests u as hypotenuse and a as a leg. These situations are shown in Fig. 7–1.

The trigonometric identities, Eqs. (4), are simply equivalent expres-

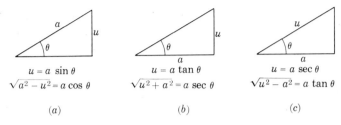

$$u = a\,\sin\theta \qquad\qquad u = a\,\tan\theta \qquad\qquad u = a\,\sec\theta$$
$$\sqrt{a^2 - u^2} = a\,\cos\theta \qquad \sqrt{u^2 + a^2} = a\,\sec\theta \qquad \sqrt{u^2 - a^2} = a\,\tan\theta$$

(a) $\qquad\qquad\qquad$ (b) $\qquad\qquad\qquad$ (c)

FIGURE 7–1

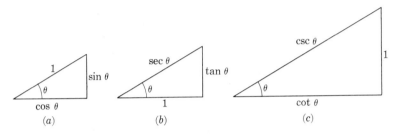

(a) $\qquad\qquad\qquad$ (b) $\qquad\qquad\qquad$ (c)

FIGURE 7–2

sions of the theorem of Pythagoras applied to the right triangles in Fig. 7–2. The triangles in Figs. 7–2(b) and (c) are obtained from the basic triangle in Fig. 7–2(a) by dividing its sides all by $\cos\theta$ or $\sin\theta$ respectively to obtain similar triangles.

PROBLEMS

Evaluate the following integrals:

1. $\displaystyle\int_0^a \frac{x\,dx}{\sqrt{a^2 - x^2}}$

2. $\displaystyle\int \frac{dx}{\sqrt{1 - 4x^2}}$

3. $\displaystyle\int_0^a \sqrt{a^2 - x^2}\,dx$

4. $\displaystyle\int \frac{dx}{\sqrt{4 - (x - 1)^2}}$

5. $\displaystyle\int \sec 2t\,dt$

6. $\displaystyle\int_0^2 \frac{dx}{\sqrt{4 + x^2}}$

7. $\displaystyle\int_0^1 \frac{dx}{\sqrt{4 - x^2}}$

8. $\displaystyle\int \frac{x\,dx}{\sqrt{4 + x^2}}$

9. $\displaystyle\int_0^2 \frac{x\,dx}{4 + x^2}$

10. $\displaystyle\int_0^2 \frac{dx}{4 + x^2}$

11. $\displaystyle\int_0^1 \frac{dx}{4 - x^2}$

12. $\displaystyle\int \csc u \, du$

13. $\displaystyle\int \frac{dx}{x\sqrt{a^2 + x^2}}$

14. $\displaystyle\int \frac{x + 1}{\sqrt{4 - x^2}} \, dx$

15. $\displaystyle\int \frac{dx}{\sqrt{2 - 5x^2}}$

16. $\displaystyle\int \frac{\sin\theta \, d\theta}{\sqrt{2 - \cos^2\theta}}$

17. $\displaystyle\int \frac{dx}{x\sqrt{x^2 - a^2}}$

18. $\displaystyle\int \frac{dx}{x\sqrt{a^2 - x^2}}$

19. $\displaystyle\int \frac{dx}{(a^2 - x^2)^{3/2}}$

20. $\displaystyle\int \frac{dx}{(a^2 + x^2)^2}$

7–5 Integrals involving $ax^2 + bx + c$. The general quadratic

$$f(x) = ax^2 + bx + c, \qquad a \neq 0 \tag{1}$$

can be reduced to the form $a(u^2 + B)$ by completing the square as follows:

$$ax^2 + bx + c = a\left(x^2 + \frac{b}{a}x\right) + c$$

$$= a\left(x^2 + \frac{b}{a}x + \frac{b^2}{4a^2}\right) + c - \frac{b^2}{4a}$$

$$= a\left(x + \frac{b}{2a}\right)^2 + \frac{4ac - b^2}{4a},$$

and then substituting

$$u = x + \frac{b}{2a}, \qquad B = \frac{4ac - b^2}{4a^2}. \tag{2}$$

When the integrand involves the square root of $f(x) = ax^2 + bx + c$, we restrict attention to the case where $f(x)$ is not negative. If a is negative and B is positive, the square root is imaginary. We disregard this case and consider

$$\sqrt{a(u^2 + B)}$$

1. when a is positive, and
2. when a and B are both negative.

In the first case the relation

$$\sqrt{a(u^2 + B)} = \sqrt{a}\sqrt{u^2 + B}$$

allows us to reduce the problem to a consideration of $\sqrt{u^2 + B}$, which we handle by the methods of Article 7–4. In the second case, when a and B are both negative, then $-a$ and $-B$ are positive and

$$\sqrt{a(u^2 + B)} = \sqrt{-a(-B - u^2)}$$

$$= \sqrt{-a}\sqrt{-B - u^2} \qquad (-a > 0, -B > 0),$$

and taking $-B = A^2$, say, we consider $\sqrt{A^2 - u^2}$ as in Article 7–4.

When the integrand does not involve an even root of $f(x)$, there need be no restriction on the signs of a and B. In these cases also, we try to make use of the trigonometric substitutions of the previous section, or we simply apply the integration formulas derived there.

EXAMPLE 1.
$$\int \frac{dx}{\sqrt{2x - x^2}}.$$

Solution. The algebraic transformations proceed as follows:

$$\sqrt{2x - x^2} = \sqrt{-(x^2 - 2x)} = \sqrt{-(x^2 - 2x + 1) + 1}$$

$$= \sqrt{1 - u^2}, \qquad (u = x - 1).$$

Then, with $u = x - 1$,

$$du = dx$$

and

$$\int \frac{dx}{\sqrt{2x - x^2}} = \int \frac{du}{\sqrt{1 - u^2}} = \sin^{-1} u + C;$$

that is,

$$\int \frac{dx}{\sqrt{2x - x^2}} = \sin^{-1} (x - 1) + C.$$

EXAMPLE 2.
$$\int \frac{dx}{4x^2 + 4x + 2}.$$

Solution. Again we start with the algebraic transformations:

$$4x^2 + 4x + 2 = 4(x^2 + x) + 2$$

$$= 4(x^2 + x + \tfrac{1}{4}) + (2 - \tfrac{4}{4}) = 4u^2 + 1, \qquad (u = x + \tfrac{1}{2}).$$

Then we let

$$u = x + \tfrac{1}{2}, \qquad du = dx,$$

and

$$\int \frac{dx}{4x^2 + 4x + 2} = \int \frac{du}{4u^2 + 1}$$

$$= \frac{1}{4} \int \frac{du}{u^2 + \frac{1}{4}}$$

$$= \frac{1}{4} \int \frac{du}{u^2 + a^2} \quad (a = \tfrac{1}{2})$$

$$= \frac{1}{4} \frac{1}{a} \tan^{-1} \frac{u}{a} + C$$

$$= \frac{1}{2} \tan^{-1} (2x + 1) + C.$$

EXAMPLE 3. $\displaystyle \int \frac{(x + 1)\, dx}{\sqrt{2x^2 - 6x + 4}}.$

Solution. The quadratic part may be reduced as follows:

$$2x^2 - 6x + 4 = 2(x^2 - 3x) + 4 = 2(x^2 - 3x + \tfrac{9}{4}) + 4 - \tfrac{9}{2} = 2(u^2 - a^2)$$

with

$$u = x - \tfrac{3}{2}, \qquad a = \tfrac{1}{2}.$$

Then

$$x = u + \tfrac{3}{2}, \qquad dx = du, \qquad x + 1 = u + \tfrac{5}{2},$$

and

$$\int \frac{(x + 1)\, dx}{\sqrt{2x^2 - 6x + 4}} = \int \frac{(u + \tfrac{5}{2})\, du}{\sqrt{2(u^2 - a^2)}}$$

$$= \frac{1}{\sqrt{2}} \int \frac{u\, du}{\sqrt{u^2 - a^2}} + \frac{5}{2\sqrt{2}} \int \frac{du}{\sqrt{u^2 - a^2}}.$$

In the former of these, we let

$$z = u^2 - a^2, \qquad dz = 2u\, du, \qquad u\, du = \tfrac{1}{2} dz,$$

and to the latter we apply Eq. (8), Article 7-4. That is,

$$\frac{1}{\sqrt{2}} \int \frac{u\, du}{\sqrt{u^2 - a^2}} = \frac{1}{2\sqrt{2}} \int \frac{dz}{\sqrt{z}} = \frac{1}{2\sqrt{2}} \int z^{-(1/2)}\, dz = \frac{1}{2\sqrt{2}} \frac{z^{1/2}}{\frac{1}{2}} + C_1$$

$$= \sqrt{\frac{u^2 - a^2}{2}} + C_1$$

and

$$\frac{5}{2\sqrt{2}} \int \frac{du}{\sqrt{u^2 - a^2}} = \frac{5}{2\sqrt{2}} \ln |u + \sqrt{u^2 - a^2}| + C_2,$$

so that

$$\int \frac{(x+1)\,dx}{\sqrt{2x^2 - 6x + 4}} = \sqrt{\frac{u^2 - a^2}{2}} + \frac{5}{2\sqrt{2}} \ln |u + \sqrt{u^2 - a^2}| + C$$

$$= \sqrt{\frac{x^2 - 3x + 2}{2}} + \frac{5}{2\sqrt{2}} \ln |x - \frac{3}{2} + \sqrt{x^2 - 3x + 2}| + C.$$

PROBLEMS

1. $\displaystyle\int_1^3 \frac{dx}{x^2 - 2x + 5}$
2. $\displaystyle\int \frac{x\,dx}{\sqrt{x^2 - 2x + 5}}$

3. $\displaystyle\int \frac{(x+1)\,dx}{\sqrt{2x - x^2}}$
4. $\displaystyle\int \frac{(x-1)\,dx}{\sqrt{x^2 - 4x + 3}}$

5. $\displaystyle\int \frac{x\,dx}{\sqrt{5 + 4x - x^2}}$
6. $\displaystyle\int \frac{dx}{\sqrt{x^2 - 2x - 8}}$

7. $\displaystyle\int \frac{(1-x)\,dx}{\sqrt{8 + 2x - x^2}}$
8. $\displaystyle\int \frac{x\,dx}{\sqrt{x^2 + 4x + 5}}$

9. $\displaystyle\int \frac{x\,dx}{x^2 + 4x + 5}$
10. $\displaystyle\int \frac{(2x + 3)\,dx}{4x^2 + 4x + 5}$

7–6 Integration by the method of partial fractions.   In algebra we learned how to combine fractions over a common denominator. In integration, it is desirable to reverse the process and split a fraction into a sum of fractions having simpler denominators. The technique of doing this is known as the *method of partial fractions*.

EXAMPLE 1.

$$\frac{2}{x+1} + \frac{3}{x-3} = \frac{2(x-3) + 3(x+1)}{(x+1)(x-3)} = \frac{5x - 3}{(x+1)(x-3)}.$$

The reverse process consists in finding constants A and B such that

$$\frac{5x - 3}{(x+1)(x-3)} = \frac{A}{x+1} + \frac{B}{x-3}.$$

(Pretend, for a moment, that we don't know that $A = 2$, $B = 3$ will work.

We call A and B *undetermined coefficients*.) Clearing of fractions, we have

$$5x - 3 = A(x - 3) + B(x + 1)$$
$$= (A + B)x - 3A + B.$$

This will be an identity in x if and only if coefficients of like powers of x on the two sides of the equation are equal:

$$A + B = 5, \qquad -3A + B = -3.$$

These two equations in two unknowns determine

$$A = 2, \qquad B = 3.$$

More generally, suppose we wish to separate a rational function

$$\frac{f(x)}{g(x)} \tag{1}$$

into a sum of partial fractions. Success in doing so hinges upon two things:

1. The degree of $f(x)$ should be less than the degree of $g(x)$. If this is not the case, we first perform a long division, then work with the remainder term. This remainder can always be put into the required form.

2. The factors of $g(x)$ should be known. Theoretically, any polynomial $g(x)$ with real coefficients can be expressed as a product of real linear and quadratic factors. In practice, it may be difficult to perform the factorization.

Let us assume that these two conditions prevail. Let $x - r$ be a linear factor of $g(x)$. Suppose $(x - r)^m$ is the highest power of $x - r$ that divides $g(x)$. Then, to this factor, assign the sum of m partial fractions, as follows:

$$\frac{A_1}{x - r} + \frac{A_2}{(x - r)^2} + \cdots + \frac{A_m}{(x - r)^m}.$$

Next, let $x^2 + px + q$ be a quadratic factor of $g(x)$. Suppose

$$(x^2 + px + q)^n$$

is the highest power of this factor that divides $g(x)$. Then, to this factor, assign the sum of n partial fractions:

$$\frac{B_1 x + C_1}{x^2 + px + q} + \frac{B_2 x + C_2}{(x^2 + px + q)^2} + \cdots + \frac{B_n x + C_n}{(x^2 + px + q)^n}.$$

Do this for each of the distinct linear and quadratic factors of $g(x)$. Then set the original fraction $f(x)/g(x)$ equal to the sum of all these partial fractions. Clear the resulting equation of fractions and arrange the terms in decreasing powers of x. Equate the coefficients of corresponding powers of x, and solve the resulting equations for the undetermined coefficients.

EXAMPLE 2. Express $\dfrac{4 - 2x}{(x^2 + 1)(x - 1)^2}$ as a sum of partial fractions.

Solution. Let

$$\frac{-2x + 4}{(x^2 + 1)(x - 1)^2} = \frac{Ax + B}{x^2 + 1} + \frac{C}{x - 1} + \frac{D}{(x - 1)^2}.$$

Then

$$-2x + 4 = (Ax + B)(x - 1)^2 + C(x - 1)(x^2 + 1) + D(x^2 + 1)$$
$$= (A + C)x^3 + (-2A + B - C + D)x^2 + (A - 2B + C)x$$
$$+ (B - C + D).$$

In order that this shall be an identity in x, it is both necessary and sufficient that the coefficient of each power of x which occurs should be the same on the left side of the equation as it is on the right side. Imposing this condition successively upon the coefficients of x^3, x^2, x, and x^0 respectively, we have

$$0 = A + C,$$
$$0 = -2A + B - C + D,$$
$$-2 = A - 2B + C,$$
$$4 = B - C + D.$$

If we subtract the second equation from the fourth, we can solve for A:

$$2A = 4, \qquad A = 2.$$

Then from the first equation, we have

$$C = -A = -2.$$

Knowing A and C, we find B from the third equation,

$$B = 1.$$

Finally, from the fourth equation, we have

$$D = 4 - B + C = 1.$$

Hence

$$\frac{-2x + 4}{(x^2 + 1)(x - 1)^2} = \frac{2x + 1}{x^2 + 1} - \frac{2}{x - 1} + \frac{1}{(x - 1)^2}.$$

EXAMPLE 3. Evaluate

$$\int \frac{x^5 - x^4 - 3x + 5}{x^4 - 2x^3 + 2x^2 - 2x + 1} \, dx.$$

Solution. The integrand is a fraction, but not a proper fraction. Hence we divide first, thus obtaining

$$\frac{x^5 - x^4 - 3x + 5}{x^4 - 2x^3 + 2x^2 - 2x + 1} = x + 1 + \frac{-2x + 4}{x^4 - 2x^3 + 2x^2 - 2x + 1}. \quad (2)$$

The denominator factors as follows:

$$x^4 - 2x^3 + 2x^2 - 2x + 1 = (x^2 + 1)(x - 1)^2.$$

By the result of Example 2, we have for the remainder term

$$\frac{-2x + 4}{(x^2 + 1)(x - 1)^2} = \frac{2x + 1}{x^2 + 1} - \frac{2}{x - 1} + \frac{1}{(x - 1)^2}. \quad (3)$$

Hence, substituting from (3) into (2), multiplying by dx, and integrating, we have

$$\int \frac{x^5 - x^4 - 3x + 5}{x^4 - 2x^3 + 2x^2 - 2x + 1} \, dx$$

$$= \int \left[x + 1 + \frac{2x + 1}{x^2 + 1} - \frac{2}{x - 1} + \frac{1}{(x - 1)^2} \right] dx$$

$$= \frac{x^2}{2} + x + \ln (x^2 + 1) + \tan^{-1} x - 2 \ln |x - 1|$$

$$- \frac{1}{x - 1} + K.$$

In theory, any rational function of x can be integrated by the method of partial fractions. Once the necessary algebra has been done, the problem reduces to that of evaluating integrals of the following two types:

$$\int \frac{dx}{(x - r)^h}, \quad (4a)$$

$$\int \frac{(ax + b) \, dx}{(x^2 + px + q)^k}. \quad (4b)$$

The first of these becomes simply $\int u^{-h} \, du$ when we let $u = x - r$. In the second type it is preferable to complete the square in the denominator:

$$x^2 + px + q = \left(x + \frac{p}{2}\right)^2 + q - \frac{p^2}{4},$$

and then let

$$u = x + \frac{p}{2}, \qquad c^2 = q - \frac{p^2}{4}.$$

Then

$$ax + b = a\left(u - \frac{p}{2}\right) + b = au + b', \qquad b' = b - a\,\frac{p}{2},$$

and we consider

$$\int \frac{au + b'}{(u^2 + c^2)^k}\, du = \frac{a}{2} \int (u^2 + c^2)^{-k}(2u\, du) + b' \int \frac{du}{(u^2 + c^2)^k}. \tag{5}$$

The first integral on the right in (5) readily yields to the substitution $z = u^2 + c^2$. In the second integral, we let

$$u = c \tan \theta, \qquad du = c \sec^2 \theta\, d\theta, \qquad u^2 + c^2 = c^2 \sec^2 \theta,$$

and obtain

$$\int \frac{du}{(u^2 + c^2)^k} = c^{1-2k} \int \cos^{2k-2} \theta\, d\theta \qquad \left(\theta = \tan^{-1} \frac{u}{c}\right). \tag{6}$$

In the next article we shall obtain a reduction formula for $\int \cos^n \theta\, d\theta$, which may be used to evaluate the integral in (6). The trigonometric identity

$$\cos^2 \theta = \frac{1 + \cos 2\theta}{2} \tag{7}$$

may also be used to advantage.

EXAMPLE 4. Evaluate

$$\int \frac{dx}{1 - x^2}.$$

Solution. By partial fractions,

$$\frac{1}{1 - x^2} = \frac{A}{1 - x} + \frac{B}{1 + x},$$

$$1 = A(1 + x) + B(1 - x)$$

$$= A + B + (A - B)x,$$

$$A + B = 1, \qquad A - B = 0,$$

$$A = B = \tfrac{1}{2}.$$

Therefore,

$$\int \frac{1}{1-x^2} \, dx = \int \left(\frac{\frac{1}{2}}{1-x} + \frac{\frac{1}{2}}{1+x} \right) dx$$

$$= -\tfrac{1}{2} \ln |1 - x| + \tfrac{1}{2} \ln |1 + x| + C$$

$$= \frac{1}{2} \ln \left| \frac{1+x}{1-x} \right| + C. \qquad (8)$$

EXAMPLE 5. Evaluate $\int \sec \theta \, d\theta$.

Solution. We did this in Example 5, Article 7–2, by a trick. We can now do it in a more straight-forward manner by writing $\sec \theta$ as $1/\cos \theta$ and proceeding as follows:

$$\int \sec \theta \, d\theta = \int \frac{d\theta}{\cos \theta}$$

$$= \int \frac{\cos \theta \, d\theta}{\cos^2 \theta}$$

$$= \int \frac{dx}{1 - x^2} \qquad [x = \sin \theta]$$

$$= \tfrac{1}{2} \ln \left| \frac{1+x}{1-x} \right| + C \qquad [\text{Eq. (8)}]$$

$$= \ln \sqrt{\frac{1 + \sin \theta}{1 - \sin \theta}} + C. \qquad (9)$$

This answer is equivalent to Eq. (3), Article 7–2, as may be seen by multiplying numerator and denominator by $1 + \sin \theta$:

$$\sqrt{\frac{1 + \sin \theta}{1 - \sin \theta}} = \sqrt{\frac{(1 + \sin \theta)^2}{1 - \sin^2 \theta}} = \left| \frac{1 + \sin \theta}{\cos \theta} \right|$$

$$= |\sec \theta + \tan \theta|.$$

PROBLEMS

1. $\displaystyle \int \frac{x \, dx}{x^2 + 4x - 5}$

2. $\displaystyle \int \frac{x \, dx}{x^2 - 2x - 3}$

3. $\displaystyle \int \frac{(x+1) \, dx}{x^2 + 4x - 5}$

4. $\displaystyle \int \frac{x^2 \, dx}{x^2 + 2x + 1}$

5. $\displaystyle \int \frac{dx}{x(x+1)^2}$

6. $\displaystyle \int \frac{dx}{(x+1)(x^2+1)}$

7. $\displaystyle \int \frac{dx}{x(x^2 + x + 1)}$

8. $\displaystyle \int \frac{\sin \theta \, d\theta}{\cos^2 \theta + \cos \theta - 2}$

9. $\int \dfrac{e^t \, dt}{e^{2t} + 3e^t + 2}$ 10. $\int \dfrac{dx}{(x^2 + 1)^2}$

11. $\int \dfrac{x^4 \, dx}{(x^2 + 1)^2}$

7-7 Integration by parts. There are really just two general methods of integration. One of these is the method of substitution, which we have illustrated in Articles 7-2 through 7-5. The method of partial fractions is really not a method of *integration* so much as it is a method of *algebraic transformation* of a rational function into an integrable form. The second general method of integration, called *integration by parts*, depends upon the formula for the differential of a product:

$$d(uv) = u \, dv + v \, du$$

or

$$u \, dv = d(uv) - v \, du.$$

When this is integrated, we have

$$\boxed{\int u \, dv = uv - \int v \, du + C.} \qquad (1)$$

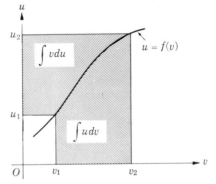

FIGURE 7-3

By way of comment on the formula (1) for integration by parts, we observe that it expresses one integral, $\int u \, dv$, in terms of a second integral, $\int v \, du$. If by proper choice of u and dv the second integral is simpler than the first, we may be able to evaluate it quite simply and thus arrive at an answer.

In a definite integral, appropriate limits must be supplied. We may then interpret the formula for integration by parts,

$$\int_{(1)}^{(2)} u \, dv = uv \bigg]_{(1)}^{(2)} - \int_{(1)}^{(2)} v \, du,$$

geometrically in terms of areas (see Fig. 7-3).

EXAMPLE 1. $\int \ln x \, dx.$

Solution. If we try to match $\ln x \, dx$ with $u \, dv$, we may take $u = \ln x$ and $dv = dx$. Then, to use (1), we see that we also require

$$du = d \, (\ln x) = \frac{dx}{x}$$

and

$$v = \int dv = \int dx = x + C_1,$$

so that

$$\int \ln x \, dx = (\ln x)(x + C_1) - \int (x + C_1) \frac{dx}{x} + C_2$$

$$= x \ln x + C_1 \ln x - \int dx - \int C_1 \frac{dx}{x} + C_2$$

$$= x \ln x + C_1 \ln x - x - C_1 \ln x + C_2 = x \ln x - x + C_2.$$

Note that the first constant of integration C_1 does not appear in the final answer. This is generally true, for if we write $v + C_1$ in place of v in the right side of (1), we obtain

$$u(v + C_1) - \int (v + C_1) \, du = uv + C_1 u - \int v \, du - \int C_1 \, du = uv - \int v \, du,$$

where it is understood that a constant of integration must still be added in the final result. It is therefore customary to drop the first constant of integration when determining v as $\int dv$. On the other hand, there is occasionally an advantage in taking C_1 equal to some specific constant. For instance, if we consider

$$\int \ln (x + 1) \, dx$$

and let

$$u = \ln (x + 1) \quad \text{and} \quad dv = dx,$$

then

$$du = \frac{dx}{x + 1} \quad \text{and} \quad v = x + C_1.$$

Equation (1) then gives

$$\int \ln (x + 1) \, dx = (x + C_1) \ln (x + 1) - \int \frac{x + C_1}{x + 1} \, dx.$$

Now taking $C_1 = 1$ greatly simplifies the second integral and leads to the result

$$\int \ln (x + 1) \, dx = (x + 1) \ln (x + 1) - x + C_2.$$

EXAMPLE 2. $$\int \tan^{-1} x \, dx.$$

Solution. This is typical of the inverse trigonometric functions. Let

$$u = \tan^{-1} x \quad \text{and} \quad dv = dx;$$

then

$$du = \frac{dx}{1 + x^2} \quad \text{and} \quad v = x,$$

so that

$$\int \tan^{-1} x \, dx = x \tan^{-1} x - \int \frac{x \, dx}{1 + x^2} = x \tan^{-1} x - \tfrac{1}{2} \ln (1 + x^2) + C.$$

Sometimes an integration by parts must be repeated to obtain an answer, as in the following example.

EXAMPLE 3. $\int x^2 e^x \, dx.$

Solution. Let

$$u = x^2 \quad \text{and} \quad dv = e^x \, dx.$$

Then

$$du = 2x \, dx \quad \text{and} \quad v = e^x,$$

so that

$$\int x^2 e^x \, dx = x^2 e^x - 2 \int x e^x \, dx.$$

The integral on the right is similar to the original integral, except that we have reduced the power of x from 2 to 1. If we could now reduce it from 1 to 0, we could see success ahead. In $\int x e^x \, dx$, we therefore let

$$U = x \quad \text{and} \quad dV = e^x \, dx,$$

so that

$$dU = dx \quad \text{and} \quad V = e^x.$$

Then

$$\int x e^x \, dx = x e^x - \int e^x \, dx = x e^x - e^x + c,$$

and

$$\int x^2 e^x \, dx = x^2 e^x - 2 x e^x + 2 e^x + C.$$

EXAMPLE 4. Obtain a reduction formula for $J_n \equiv \int \cos^n x \, dx.$

Solution. We may think of $\cos^n x$ as $\cos^{n-1} x \cdot \cos x$. Then we let

$$u = \cos^{n-1} x \quad \text{and} \quad dv = \cos x \, dx,$$

so that

$$du = (n - 1) \cos^{n-2} x \, (-\sin x \, dx) \quad \text{and} \quad v = \sin x.$$

Hence

$$J_n = \cos^{n-1} x \sin x + (n - 1) \int \sin^2 x \cos^{n-2} x \, dx$$

$$= \cos^{n-1} x \sin x + (n - 1) \int (1 - \cos^2 x) \cos^{n-2} x \, dx,$$

or

$$\int \cos^n x \, dx = \cos^{n-1} x \sin x + (n-1) \int \cos^{n-2} x \, dx - (n-1) \int \cos^n x \, dx.$$

The last integral on the right may now be transposed to the left to give

$$[1 + (n-1)]J_n = nJ_n.$$

We then divide by n, and the final result is

$$\int \cos^n x \, dx = \frac{\cos^{n-1} x \sin x}{n} + \frac{n-1}{n} \int \cos^{n-2} x \, dx. \qquad (2)$$

This allows us to reduce the exponent on $\cos x$ by 2 and is a very useful formula. When n is a positive integer, we may apply the formula repeatedly until the remaining integral is either

$$\int \cos x \, dx = \sin x + C \qquad \text{or} \qquad \int \cos^0 x \, dx = \int dx = x + C.$$

For example, with $n = 4$, we get

$$\int \cos^4 x \, dx = \frac{\cos^3 x \sin x}{4} + \frac{3}{4} \int \cos^2 x \, dx,$$

and with $n = 2$,

$$\int \cos^2 x \, dx = \frac{\cos x \sin x}{2} + \frac{1}{2} \int dx.$$

Therefore,

$$\int \cos^4 x \, dx = \frac{\cos^3 x \sin x}{4} + \frac{3}{4} \left(\frac{\cos x \sin x}{2} + \frac{1}{2} x \right) + C.$$

The reader may find it instructive to derive the companion formula:

$$\int \sin^n x \, dx = -\frac{\sin^{n-1} x \cos x}{n} + \frac{n-1}{n} \int \sin^{n-2} x \, dx. \qquad (3)$$

The integral in the following example occurs in electrical engineering problems. Its evaluation requires two integrations by parts, followed by solving for the unknown integral in a method analogous to that used above in finding reduction formulas.

EXAMPLE 5. $\qquad \int e^{ax} \cos bx \, dx.$

Solution. Let

$$u = e^{ax} \quad \text{and} \quad dv = \cos bx \, dx.$$

Then

$$du = ae^{ax} \, dx \quad \text{and} \quad v = \frac{1}{b} \sin bx,$$

so that

$$\int e^{ax} \cos bx \, dx = \frac{e^{ax} \sin bx}{b} - \frac{a}{b} \int e^{ax} \sin bx \, dx.$$

The second integral is like the first except that it has $\sin bx$ in place of $\cos bx$. If we apply integration by parts to it, letting

$$U = e^{ax} \quad \text{and} \quad dV = \sin bx \, dx,$$

then

$$dU = ae^{ax} \, dx \quad \text{and} \quad V = -\frac{1}{b} \cos bx,$$

so that

$$\int e^{ax} \cos bx \, dx = \frac{e^{ax} \sin bx}{b} - \frac{a}{b} \left[-\frac{e^{ax} \cos bx}{b} + \frac{a}{b} \int e^{ax} \cos bx \, dx \right].$$

Now the unknown integral appears on the left with a coefficient of unity and on the right with a coefficient of $-a^2/b^2$. Transposing this term to the left and dividing by the new coefficient

$$1 + \frac{a^2}{b^2} = \frac{a^2 + b^2}{b^2},$$

we have

$$\boxed{\int e^{ax} \cos bx \, dx = e^{ax} \left(\frac{b \sin bx + a \cos bx}{a^2 + b^2} \right) + C.} \tag{4}$$

PROBLEMS

1. $\int x \ln x \, dx$

2. $\int x^n \ln ax \, dx \quad (n \neq -1)$

3. $\int x \tan^{-1} x \, dx$

4. $\int \sin^{-1} ax \, dx$

5. $\int x \sin ax \, dx$

6. $\int x^2 \cos ax \, dx$

7. $\int x \sec^2 ax \, dx$

8. $\int e^{ax} \sin bx \, dx$

9. $\int \sin (\ln x) \, dx$

10. $\int \cos (\ln x) \, dx$

11. $\int \ln (a^2 + x^2) \, dx$

12. $\int x \cos (2x + 1) \, dx$

13. $\int x \sin^{-1} x \, dx$ 14. $\int_1^2 x \sec^{-1} x \, dx$

15. $\int_1^4 \sec^{-1} \sqrt{x} \, dx$ 16. $\int x^2 \tan^{-1} x \, dx$

Derive the following reduction formulas and apply each one to the specific problem given:

17. (a) $\int x^m (\ln x)^n \, dx = \dfrac{x^{m+1} (\ln x)^n}{m+1} - \dfrac{n}{m+1} \int x^m (\ln x)^{n-1} \, dx$

(b) $\int x^3 (\ln x)^2 \, dx$

18. (a) $\int \sin^n x \, dx = -\dfrac{\sin^{n-1} x \cos x}{n} + \dfrac{n-1}{n} \int \sin^{n-2} x \, dx$

(b) $\int_0^{\pi/6} \sin^4 3x \, dx$

19. (a) $\int x^n e^x \, dx = x^n e^x - n \int x^{n-1} e^x \, dx$,   (b) $\int x^3 e^x \, dx$

20. (a) $\int \sec^n x \, dx = \dfrac{\sec^{n-2} x \tan x}{(n-1)} + \dfrac{n-2}{n-1} \int \sec^{n-2} x \, dx$

(b) $\int \sec^3 x \, dx$ [See Eq. (3), Article 7–2.]

(c) $\int \sqrt{a^2 + x^2} \, dx$ [*Hint*: Let $x = a \tan \theta$.]

21. Find the second degree polynomial $P(x)$ that has the following properties: (a) $P(0) = 1$, (b) $P'(0) = 0$, and (c) the indefinite integral

$$\int \frac{P(x) \, dx}{x^3 (x-1)^2}$$

is a rational function. (That is, no logarithmic terms occur in the answer.)

7–8 Integration of rational functions of sin x and cos x, and other trigonometric integrals.

It has been discovered that the substitution

$$z = \tan \frac{x}{2} \tag{1}$$

enables one to reduce the problem of integrating any rational function of $\sin x$ and $\cos x$ to a problem involving a rational function of z. This in turn can be integrated by the method of partial fractions discussed in Article 7–6. Thus the substitution (1) is a very powerful tool. This method is cumbersome, however, and is used only when the simpler methods outlined previously have failed.

To see the effect of the substitution, we calculate

$$\cos x = 2 \cos^2 \frac{x}{2} - 1 = \frac{2}{\sec^2 \frac{x}{2}} - 1$$

$$= \frac{2}{1 + \tan^2 \frac{x}{2}} - 1 = \frac{2}{1 + z^2} - 1$$

or

$$\boxed{\cos x = \frac{1 - z^2}{1 + z^2},} \qquad (2a)$$

and

$$\sin x = 2 \sin \frac{x}{2} \cos \frac{x}{2} = 2 \frac{\sin \frac{x}{2}}{\cos \frac{x}{2}} \cdot \cos^2 \frac{x}{2} = 2 \tan \frac{x}{2} \cdot \frac{1}{\sec^2 \frac{x}{2}} = \frac{2 \tan \frac{x}{2}}{1 + \tan^2 \frac{x}{2}}$$

or

$$\boxed{\sin x = \frac{2z}{1 + z^2}.} \qquad (2b)$$

Finally,

$$x = 2 \tan^{-1} z,$$

so that

$$\boxed{dx = \frac{2 \, dz}{1 + z^2}.} \qquad (2c)$$

EXAMPLE 1.

$$\int \sec x \, dx = \int \frac{dx}{\cos x} \quad \text{becomes} \quad \int \frac{2 \, dz}{1 + z^2} \cdot \frac{1 + z^2}{1 - z^2} = \int \frac{2 \, dz}{1 - z^2}.$$

To this we apply the method of partial fractions:

$$\frac{2}{1 - z^2} = \frac{A}{1 - z} + \frac{B}{1 + z},$$

$$2 = A(1 + z) + B(1 - z)$$

$$= (A + B) + (A - B)z,$$

which requires

$$A + B = 2, \qquad A - B = 0.$$

Hence

$$A = B = 1$$

and

$$\int \frac{2\,dz}{1-z^2} = \int \frac{dz}{1-z} + \int \frac{dz}{1+z} = -\ln|1-z| + \ln|1+z| + C$$

$$= \ln\left|\frac{1+z}{1-z}\right| + C$$

$$= \ln\left|\frac{1+\tan\frac{x}{2}}{1-\tan\frac{x}{2}}\right| + C = \ln\left|\frac{\tan\frac{\pi}{4}+\tan\frac{x}{2}}{1-\tan\frac{\pi}{4}\tan\frac{x}{2}}\right| + C = \ln\left|\tan\left(\frac{\pi}{4}+\frac{x}{2}\right)\right| + C.$$

That is,

$$\int \sec x\,dx = \ln\left|\tan\left(\frac{\pi}{4}+\frac{x}{2}\right)\right| + C \qquad (3)$$

is an alternative form, which may be used in place of Eq. (3), Article 7–2, or Eq. (9), Article 7–6.

EXAMPLE 2.

$$\int \frac{dx}{1+\cos x} = \int \frac{2\,dz}{1+z^2}\,\frac{1+z^2}{2} = \int dz = z + C = \tan\frac{x}{2} + C.$$

EXAMPLE 3.

$$\int \frac{dx}{2+\sin x} = \int \frac{2\,dz}{1+z^2}\left[\frac{1+z^2}{2+2z+2z^2}\right] = \int \frac{dz}{z^2+z+1} = \int \frac{dz}{(z+\frac{1}{2})^2+\frac{3}{4}}$$

$$= \int \frac{du}{u^2+a^2} \qquad [u = z+\tfrac{1}{2}, \quad a = \sqrt{3}/2]$$

$$= \frac{1}{a}\tan^{-1}\frac{u}{a} + C = \frac{2}{\sqrt{3}}\tan^{-1}\frac{2z+1}{\sqrt{3}} + C$$

$$= \frac{2}{\sqrt{3}}\tan^{-1}\frac{1+2\tan\frac{x}{2}}{\sqrt{3}} + C.$$

We have already made repeated use of trigonometric identities to aid us in evaluating integrals. The following types of integrals:

$$\int \sin mx \sin nx\,dx, \qquad \int \sin mx \cos nx\,dx, \qquad \int \cos mx \cos nx\,dx, \qquad (4)$$

arise in connection with alternating-current theory, heat transfer problems, bending of beams, cable stress analysis in suspension bridges, and many other places where trigonometric series (or Fourier series) are applied to problems in mathematics, science, and engineering. The integrals in (4) can be evaluated by the method of integration by parts, but two such integrations are required in each case. A simpler way to evaluate them is to exploit the trigonometric identities

$$\text{(a)} \quad \sin mx \sin nx = \tfrac{1}{2}[\cos (m - n)x - \cos (m + n)x],$$

$$\text{(b)} \quad \sin mx \cos nx = \tfrac{1}{2}[\sin (m - n)x + \sin (m + n)x], \tag{5}$$

$$\text{(c)} \quad \cos mx \cos nx = \tfrac{1}{2}[\cos (m - n)x + \cos (m + n)x].$$

These identities follow at once from

$$\cos (A + B) = \cos A \cos B - \sin A \sin B,$$
$$\cos (A - B) = \cos A \cos B + \sin A \sin B, \tag{6a}$$

and

$$\sin (A + B) = \sin A \cos B + \cos A \sin B,$$
$$\sin (A - B) = \sin A \cos B - \cos A \sin B. \tag{6b}$$

For example, if we add the two equations in (6a) and then divide by 2, we obtain (5c) by taking $A = mx$ and $B = nx$. The identity in (5a) is obtained in a similar fashion by subtracting the first equation in (6a) from the second equation. Finally, if we add the two equations in (6b) we are led to the identity in (5b).

EXAMPLE 4. $\displaystyle\int \sin 3x \cos 5x \, dx = \tfrac{1}{2}\int [\sin (-2x) + \sin 8x] \, dx$

$$= \tfrac{1}{2}\int (\sin 8x - \sin 2x) \, dx$$

$$= -\frac{\cos 8x}{16} + \frac{\cos 2x}{4} + C.$$

PROBLEMS

1. $\displaystyle\int_0^{\pi} \frac{dx}{1 + \sin x}$

2. $\displaystyle\int_{\pi/2}^{\pi} \frac{dx}{1 - \cos x}$

3. $\displaystyle\int \frac{dx}{1 - \sin x}$

4. $\displaystyle\int_0^{\pi/2} \frac{dx}{2 + \cos x}$

5. $\displaystyle\int \frac{\cos x \, dx}{2 - \cos x}$

6. $\displaystyle\int_0^{\pi/2} \cos 3x \sin 2x \, dx$

7. $\displaystyle\int_{-\pi}^{\pi} \sin 3x \sin 2x \, dx$

8. $\displaystyle\int_{-\pi}^{\pi} \sin^2 3x \, dx$

9. Two functions f and g are said to be *orthogonal* on an interval $a \le x \le b$ if $\int_a^b f(x) \, g(x) \, dx = 0$. (a) Prove that $\sin mx$ and $\sin nx$ are orthogonal on any interval of length 2π provided m and n are integers such that $m^2 \ne n^2$. (b) Prove the same for $\sin mx$ and $\cos nx$. (c) Prove the same for $\cos mx$ and $\cos nx$.

7–9 Further substitutions. Some integrals involving fractional powers of the variable x may be simplified by substituting $x = z^n$, where n is the least common multiple of the denominators of the exponents.

For example

$$\int \frac{\sqrt{x}\, dx}{1 + \sqrt[4]{x}}$$

may be simplified by taking

$$x = z^4, \qquad dx = 4z^3\, dz.$$

This leads to

$$\int \frac{\sqrt{x}\, dx}{1 + \sqrt[4]{x}} = \int \frac{z^2 \cdot 4z^3\, dz}{1 + z}$$

$$= 4\int \left(z^4 - z^3 + z^2 - z + 1 - \frac{1}{z+1} \right) dz$$

$$= 4\left[\frac{z^5}{5} - \frac{z^4}{4} + \frac{z^3}{3} - \frac{z^2}{2} + z - \ln|z + 1| \right] + C$$

$$= \tfrac{4}{5}x^{5/4} - x + \tfrac{4}{3}x^{3/4} - 2x^{1/2} + 4x^{1/4} - 4\ln|1 + \sqrt[4]{x}| + C.$$

In $\int x^3\sqrt{x^2 + a^2}\, dx$, on the other hand, the substitution

$$z^2 = x^2 + a^2$$

or

$$x^2 = z^2 - a^2$$

and

$$2x\, dx = 2z\, dz$$

leads to

$$\int x^3\sqrt{x^2 + a^2}\, dx = \int x^2\sqrt{x^2 + a^2} \cdot x\, dx = \int (z^2 - a^2) \cdot z^2 \cdot dz$$

$$= \int (z^4 - a^2 z^2)\, dz$$

$$= \tfrac{1}{5}(x^2 + a^2)^{5/2} - \tfrac{1}{3}a^2(x^2 + a^2)^{3/2} + C$$

$$= \frac{3x^2 - 2a^2}{15} (x^2 + a^2)^{3/2} + C.$$

Even when it is not clear at the start that a substitution will work, it is advisable to try one that seems reasonable and pursue it until it either gives results or appears to make matters worse. In the latter case, try something else! Sometimes a chain of substitutions $u = f(x)$, $v = g(u)$,

$z = h(v)$, etc., will produce results when it is by no means obvious that this will work. The criterion of success is whether the new integrals so obtained appear to be simpler than the original integral. In this regard, it is handy to remember that any rational function of x can be integrated by the method of partial fractions and that any rational function of $\sin x$ and $\cos x$ can be integrated by using the substitution $z = \tan x/2$. If we can reduce a given integral to one of these types, we then know how to finish the job.

Even in these cases, however, it is frequently simpler to use special methods suggested by the particular integrand rather than to use the general methods. For instance, one would hardly let $z = \tan x/2$ in order to evaluate $\int \sin x\, dx = -\cos x + C$. And reference to Eqs. (5) and (6), Article 7–6, and the accompanying discussion shows that a trigonometric substitution is used to evaluate certain of the integrals that arise in the method of partial fractions. It may be more convenient to use the same substitution *before* going through the algebraic reductions instead of *after* doing so.

For example, consider the integral

$$\int_{-1}^{+1} \sqrt{\frac{1+x}{1-x}}\, dx, \tag{1}$$

which appears in the so-called "lifting line theory" in aerodynamics. If we let

$$\frac{1+x}{1-x} = z^2, \tag{2}$$

we shall, of course, get rid of the radical. Whether this is really a good substitution or not depends upon how complicated the expression is for dx in terms of z and dz. To settle this question, we solve for x as follows:

$$1 + x = z^2 - xz^2,$$

$$x(z^2 + 1) = z^2 - 1,$$

$$x = \frac{z^2 - 1}{z^2 + 1}. \tag{3}$$

Hence

$$dx = \frac{4z\, dz}{(z^2 + 1)^2}$$

and the integral becomes

$$\int \sqrt{\frac{1+x}{1-x}}\, dx = \int \frac{4z^2\, dz}{(z^2 + 1)^2}.$$

Now the integrand on the right is a rational function of z and we could proceed by the method of partial fractions. But the $z^2 + 1$ in the denominator also lends itself to the substitution

$$z = \tan \theta. \tag{4}$$

We try this, and have

$$dz = \sec^2 \theta \, d\theta, \qquad z^2 + 1 = \tan^2 \theta + 1 = \sec^2 \theta,$$

so that

$$\int \frac{4z^2 \, dz}{(z^2 + 1)^2} = \int \frac{4 \tan^2 \theta \cdot \sec^2 \theta \, d\theta}{\sec^4 \theta} = 4 \int \frac{\sin^2 \theta}{\cos^2 \theta} \cdot \frac{1}{\sec^2 \theta} \, d\theta = 4 \int \sin^2 \theta \, d\theta,$$

and the last integral can now be evaluated at once to give

$$4 \int \sin^2 \theta \, d\theta = 2 \left[\theta - \frac{\sin 2\theta}{2} \right] + C. \tag{5}$$

We now have two alternative courses of action for evaluating the *definite integral*, (1): namely,

(a) we may reverse the substitutions (3) and (4) and replace (5) by its equivalent in terms of x. Then the definite integral (1) could be evaluated by substituting the limits of integration. Or,

(b) we may determine new limits of integration corresponding to the new variable of integration.

We illustrate the second line of attack. In the original integral, (1), x varies from -1 to $+1$. As this happens, the left side of (2) varies from 0 to $+\infty$, and since we have tacitly taken

$$z = \sqrt{\frac{1 + x}{1 - x}}$$

as the *positive* square root, we see that then z varies from 0 to $+\infty$. Finally, from (4) we have $\theta = \tan^{-1} z$, so that θ varies from 0 to $\pi/2$ as z varies from 0 to $+\infty$. Combining these results, we have

$$\int_{-1}^{+1} \sqrt{\frac{1 + x}{1 - x}} \, dx = \int_{0}^{\infty} \frac{4z^2 \, dz}{(z^2 + 1)^2} \qquad \left[z = \sqrt{\frac{1 + x}{1 - x}} \right]$$

$$= 4 \int_{0}^{\pi/2} \sin^2 \theta \, d\theta \qquad [\theta = \tan^{-1} z]$$

$$= 2 \left[\theta - \frac{\sin 2\theta}{2} \right]_{0}^{\pi/2} = \pi.$$

The reader will find it instructive to evaluate the integral in (1) by making the alternative substitution

$$x = \cos 2t, \qquad dx = -2 \sin 2t \, dt = -4 \sin t \cos t \, dt,$$

which is particularly well adapted to the integrand in question, since

$$1 + \cos 2t = 2 \cos^2 t$$

and

$$1 - \cos 2t = 2 \sin^2 t.$$

But the shortest way of all is to notice that for $-1 < x < 1$ we have

$$\sqrt{\frac{1+x}{1-x}} = \frac{1+x}{\sqrt{1-x^2}},$$

and hence

$$\int \sqrt{\frac{1+x}{1-x}} \, dx = \int \frac{1+x}{\sqrt{1-x^2}} \, dx$$

$$= \sin^{-1} x - \sqrt{1-x^2} + C. \tag{6}$$

PROBLEMS

1. $\displaystyle\int \frac{1 - \sqrt{x}}{1 + \sqrt{x}} \, dx$

2. $\displaystyle\int \frac{dx}{a + b\sqrt{x}}$ (a and b constants)

3. $\displaystyle\int x^2 \sqrt{x + a} \, dx$

4. $\displaystyle\int \frac{\sqrt{x + a} \, dx}{x + b}$ $(b > a)$

5. $\displaystyle\int \sqrt{\frac{a + x}{b + x}} \, dx$ $(b \neq a)$

6. $\displaystyle\int \frac{dx}{x + \sqrt{x^2 + a^2}}$ $(a > 0)$

7. $\displaystyle\int_0^1 \frac{x^3 \, dx}{(x^2 + 1)^{3/2}}$

8. $\displaystyle\int \frac{dx}{x(ax^n + c)}$ $(anc \neq 0)$

9. $\displaystyle\int_3^8 \frac{(t + 2) \, dt}{t\sqrt{t + 1}}$

10. $\displaystyle\int \frac{dx}{x - x^{2/3}}$

11. $\displaystyle\int_0^3 \frac{\sqrt{x + 1} - 1}{\sqrt{x + 1} + 1} \, dx$

12. $\displaystyle\int \frac{dx}{x(1 - \sqrt[4]{x})}$

13. $\displaystyle\int \frac{y^{2/3} \, dy}{y + 1}$

14. $\displaystyle\int \frac{z^5 \, dz}{\sqrt{1 + z^3}}$

15. $\displaystyle\int \frac{\sqrt{t^3 - 1}}{t} \, dt$

16. $\displaystyle\int_0^{\ln 2} \frac{dw}{(1 + e^w)}$

17. $\displaystyle\int_0^{\pi/2} \frac{\sin 2\theta \, d\theta}{2 + \cos \theta}$

18. $\displaystyle\int \frac{\sin x \, dx}{\tan x + \cos x}$

19. $\displaystyle\int \frac{dx}{x^3 + 1}$

20. $\displaystyle\int \frac{dy}{y^{1/3} - y^{1/2}}$

7–10 Improper integrals. An integral of the type discussed in the previous article,

$$\int_{-1}^{+1} \sqrt{\frac{1 + x}{1 - x}} \, dx,$$

is called an *improper* integral because the function

$$f(x) = \sqrt{\frac{1 + x}{1 - x}}$$

which appears after the integral sign becomes infinite at one of the limits of integration, in this case at $x = +1$. More generally, integrals of the following two types are called improper integrals:

(a) $\int_a^b f(x) \, dx$, where $f(x)$ becomes infinite at a value of x between a and b inclusive,

(b) $\int_a^\infty f(x) \, dx$ or $\int_{-\infty}^b f(x) \, dx$, where one or both of the limits of integration are infinite.

In the example above, we had

$$\int_{-1}^1 \sqrt{\frac{1 + x}{1 - x}} \, dx = \int_0^\infty \frac{4z^2 \, dz}{(z^2 + 1)^2}, \qquad \left[z = \sqrt{\frac{1 + x}{1 - x}} \right]$$

where the integral on the left is an improper integral of the first type and the integral on the right is an improper integral of the second type.

Figure 7–4 illustrates the case where the function becomes infinite at one of the limits of integration. If we interpret the integral in terms of area under the curve $y = f(x)$, say from -1 to $+1$ as in the figure, we see that the curve extends to infinity as x approaches 1 and the area from -1 to $+1$ is not well defined. Nevertheless, we can certainly define the area from $x = -1$ to $x = b$, where b is any positive number *less* than one; for example, we can take $b = 0.999$. This defines a function of b:

$$g(b) = \int_{-1}^b f(x) \, dx.$$

If this function has a finite limit as b approaches $+1$ from the left, we

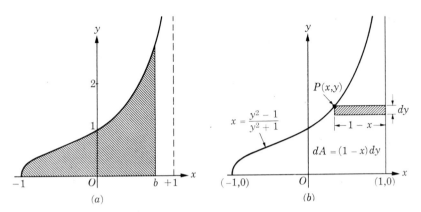

FIGURE 7–4

define this limit to be the value of the improper integral

$$\int_{-1}^{+1} f(x)\,dx = \lim_{b\to 1-} \int_{-1}^{b} f(x)\,dx.$$

In this case we also say that the improper integral *converges*. On the other hand, we say that the integral *diverges* if the function g has no definite finite limit as $b \to 1-$.

In the particular example above, we find, from Eq. (6) of Article 7–9, that

$$\int_{-1}^{b} \sqrt{\frac{1+x}{1-x}}\,dx = \sin^{-1} x - \sqrt{1-x^2}\,\bigg]_{-1}^{b}$$

$$= \sin^{-1} b - \sqrt{1-b^2} + \frac{\pi}{2}.$$

This is the number denoted above by $g(b)$. When b is slightly less than $+1$, $\sin^{-1} b$ is slightly less than $\pi/2$ and $\sqrt{1-b^2}$ is nearly zero. Hence

$$\lim_{b\to 1-} \int_{-1}^{b} \sqrt{\frac{1+x}{1-x}}\,dx = \lim_{b\to 1-} \left[\sin^{-1} b - \sqrt{1-b^2} + \frac{\pi}{2} \right]$$

$$= \frac{\pi}{2} - 0 + \frac{\pi}{2} = \pi.$$

The given integral therefore converges and its value is π.

The same result is obtained if, instead of finding the area by summing vertical elements (Fig. 7–4a), we sum horizontal elements (Fig. 7–4b). Then we find

$$A = \int_{y=0}^{\infty} (1-x)\,dy = \int_{0}^{\infty} \frac{2}{y^2+1}\,dy.$$

This time, the integral to be evaluated is an improper integral of the second type because the range of integration extends to infinity. In this case we investigate the integral from $y = 0$ to $y = c$ for large values of c:

$$\int_0^c \frac{2\,dy}{y^2 + 1} = 2 \tan^{-1} c,$$

and we *define* the integral from 0 to ∞ as the limit of this as $c \to \infty$ (if the limit exists). That is,

$$\int_0^\infty \frac{2\,dy}{y^2 + 1} = \lim_{c \to \infty} \int_0^c \frac{2\,dy}{y^2 + 1} = \lim_{c \to \infty} (2 \tan^{-1} c) = \pi.$$

The limit does exist, since $\tan^{-1} c$ approaches $\pi/2$ as c increases indefinitely.

As a second example, we consider

$$\int_0^1 \frac{dx}{x}.$$

The function f in this case is defined by

$$f(x) = \frac{1}{x},$$

which becomes infinite at $x = 0$. We cut off the point $x = 0$ and start our integration at some positive number $b < 1$. (See Fig. 7–5.) That is, we consider the integral

$$\int_b^1 \frac{dx}{x} = \ln x \bigg]_b^1 = \ln 1 - \ln b = \ln \frac{1}{b},$$

and investigate its behavior as b approaches zero from the right. Since

$$\lim_{b \to 0+} \int_b^1 \frac{dx}{x} = \lim_{b \to 0+} \left(\ln \frac{1}{b} \right) = +\infty,$$

we say that the integral from $x = 0$ to $x = 1$ *diverges*.

The method to be used when the function f becomes infinite at an interior point of the range of integration is illustrated in the following example.

Consider

$$\int_0^3 \frac{dx}{(x - 1)^{2/3}}.$$

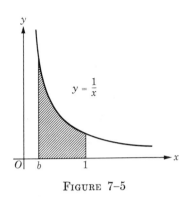

FIGURE 7–5

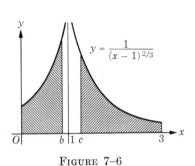

FIGURE 7–6

The function

$$f(x) = \frac{1}{(x-1)^{2/3}}$$

becomes infinite at $x = 1$, which lies between the limits of integration 0 and 3. In such a case, we again cut out the point where $f(x)$ becomes infinite. This time we integrate from 0 to b, where b is slightly less than 1, and start again on the other side of 1 at c and integrate from c to 3 (Fig. 7–6). Then we get the two integrals

$$\int_0^b \frac{dx}{(x-1)^{2/3}} \quad \text{and} \quad \int_c^3 \frac{dx}{(x-1)^{2/3}}$$

to investigate. If the first of these has a definite limit as $b \to 1-$ and if the second also has a definite limit as $c \to 1+$, then we say that the improper integral converges and that its value is given by

$$\int_0^3 \frac{dx}{(x-1)^{2/3}} = \lim_{b \to 1-} \int_0^b \frac{dx}{(x-1)^{2/3}} + \lim_{c \to 1+} \int_c^3 \frac{dx}{(x-1)^{2/3}}.$$

If either limit fails to exist, we say that the given improper integral *diverges*. For this example,

$$\lim_{b \to 1-} \int_0^b (x-1)^{-2/3}\, dx = \lim_{b \to 1-} [3(b-1)^{1/3} - 3(0-1)^{1/3}] = +3$$

and

$$\lim_{c \to 1+} \int_c^3 (x-1)^{-2/3}\, dx = \lim_{c \to 1+} [3(3-1)^{1/3} - 3(c-1)^{1/3}] = 3\sqrt[3]{2}.$$

Since both limits exist and are finite, the original integral is said to converge and its value is $3 + 3\sqrt[3]{2}$.

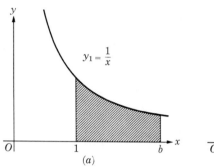
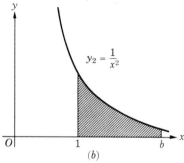

(a)   (b)

FIGURE 7-7

As further examples of the second type of improper integral, we consider

$$\int_1^\infty \frac{dx}{x} \quad \text{and} \quad \int_1^\infty \frac{dx}{x^2}.$$

The two curves

$$y_1 = \frac{1}{x} \quad \text{and} \quad y_2 = \frac{1}{x^2}$$

both approach the x-axis as $x \to \infty$ (Fig. 7-7). In the first case,

$$\int_1^b \frac{dx}{x} = \ln x \Big]_1^b = \ln b.$$

If we now let b take on larger and larger positive values, the logarithm of b increases indefinitely and

$$\lim_{b \to \infty} \int_1^b \frac{dx}{x} = \infty.$$

We therefore say that

$$\int_1^\infty \frac{dx}{x} = \infty$$

and that the integral *diverges*.

In the second case,

$$\int_1^b \frac{dx}{x^2} = -\frac{1}{x} \Big]_1^b = 1 - \frac{1}{b}.$$

This does have a definite limit, namely 1, as b increases indefinitely, and we say that the integral from 1 to ∞ converges and that its value is 1. That is,

$$\int_1^\infty \frac{dx}{x^2} = \lim_{b \to \infty} \int_1^b \frac{dx}{x^2} = \lim_{b \to \infty} \left(1 - \frac{1}{b}\right) = 1.$$

Sometimes we can determine whether a given integral converges or diverges by comparing it with a simpler integral.

For example, even though we cannot find any simpler expression for

$$I(b) \equiv \int_1^b e^{-x^2}\, dx,$$

we can show that

$$\lim_{b \to \infty} I(b)$$

exists and is finite. For the function $I(b)$ represents the area between the x-axis and the curve

$$y = e^{-x^2}$$

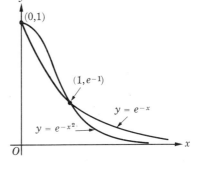

FIGURE 7–8

between $x = 1$ and $x = b$. Clearly, this is an increasing function of b, so that there are two alternatives: either

(a) $I(b)$ becomes infinite as $b \to \infty$,

or

(b) $I(b)$ has a finite limit as $b \to \infty$.

We show that the first alternative cannot be the true one. We do this by comparing the area under the given curve $y = e^{-x^2}$ with the area under the curve $y = e^{-x}$ (Fig. 7–8). The latter area, from $x = 1$ to $x = b$, is given by the integral

$$\int_1^b e^{-x}\, dx = -e^{-x}\Big]_1^b = e^{-1} - e^{-b},$$

which approaches the finite limit e^{-1} as $b \to \infty$. Since e^{-x^2} is less than e^{-x} for all x greater than one, the area under the given curve is certainly no greater than e^{-1} no matter how large b is.

The discussion above is summarized in the following inequalities:

$$I(b) = \int_1^b e^{-x^2}\, dx \le \int_1^b e^{-x}\, dx = e^{-1} - e^{-b} \le e^{-1},$$

that is,

$$I(b) \le e^{-1} < 0.37.$$

Therefore $I(b)$ does not become infinite as $b \to \infty$, so alternative (a) is ruled out and alternative (b) must hold; that is,

$$\int_1^\infty e^{-x^2}\, dx = \lim_{b \to \infty} \int_1^b e^{-x^2}\, dx$$

converges to a definite finite value. We have not calculated what this limit is, but we know that it exists and is less than 0.37.

It should be pointed out that an improper integral may diverge without becoming infinite.

For example, the integral

$$\int_0^b \cos x \, dx = \sin b$$

takes all values between -1 and $+1$ as b varies between $2n\pi - \pi/2$ and $2n\pi + \pi/2$, where n is any integer. Hence,

$$\lim_{b \to \infty} \int_0^b \cos x \, dx$$

does not exist. We might say that this integral "diverges by oscillation."

PROBLEMS

Show that the following improper integrals converge and evaluate them.

1. $\int_0^\infty \dfrac{dx}{x^2 + 1}$

2. $\int_0^1 \dfrac{dx}{\sqrt{x}}$

3. $\int_{-1}^1 \dfrac{dx}{x^{2/3}}$

4. $\int_1^\infty \dfrac{dx}{x^{1.001}}$

5. $\int_0^4 \dfrac{dx}{\sqrt{4 - x}}$

6. $\int_0^1 \dfrac{dx}{\sqrt{1 - x^2}}$

7. $\int_0^\infty e^{-x} \cos x \, dx$

8. $\int_0^1 \dfrac{dx}{x^{0.999}}$

Determine whether each of the following improper integrals converges or diverges.

9. $\int_1^\infty \dfrac{dx}{\sqrt{x}}$

10. $\int_1^\infty \dfrac{dx}{x^3}$

11. $\int_1^\infty \dfrac{dx}{x^3 + 1}$

12. $\int_0^\infty \dfrac{dx}{x^3}$

13. $\int_0^\infty \dfrac{dx}{x^3 + 1}$

14. $\int_0^\infty \dfrac{dx}{1 + e^x}$

15. $\int_0^{\pi/2} \tan x \, dx$

16. $\int_{-1}^1 \dfrac{dx}{x^2}$

17. $\displaystyle\int_{-1}^{1} \frac{dx}{x^{2/5}}$

18. $\displaystyle\int_{0}^{\infty} \frac{dx}{\sqrt{x}}$

19. $\displaystyle\int_{0}^{\infty} \frac{dx}{\sqrt{x + x^4}}$ [*Hint:* Compare the integral with $\int dx/\sqrt{x}$ for x near zero and with $\int dx/x^2$ for large x.]

7–11 Numerical methods for approximating definite integrals. Certain important integrals which arise in physical and mathematical problems cannot be expressed in terms of the so-called elementary functions. For example, the length of one arch of the curve $y = \sin x$, Fig. 7–9, is given by

$$L = \int_{0}^{\pi} \sqrt{1 + \cos^2 x}\, dx.$$

The integral cannot be evaluated by any of the methods we have studied thus far. Nevertheless it can be evaluated numerically to any required number of decimal places by several methods. The trapezoidal rule is one. We indicate another below.

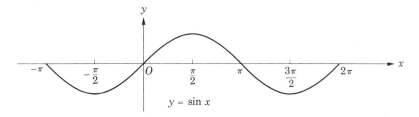

FIG. 7–9. Graph of $y = \sin x$.

Any definite integral $\int_{a}^{b} f(x)\, dx$ can be interpreted as an area or as a combination of areas, some added and some subtracted. Such an integral can therefore be approximated by any method of approximating these areas. Instruments called *planimeters* are useful in this connection, but they have two drawbacks: (a) the curve $y = f(x)$ must be drawn with some care, and (b) the accuracy of the planimeter is limited to approximately the order of 1%. Simpson's method, which we shall now study, avoids both of these drawbacks.

This method is based on the simple formula

$$A_p = \frac{h}{3}\, [y_0 + 4y_1 + y_2]$$

for the area under the arc of the parabola

$$y = Ax^2 + Bx + C$$

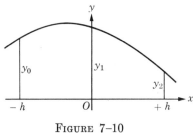

FIGURE 7–10

between $x = -h$ and $x = +h$, as in Fig. 7–10.

This result is readily established as follows: in the first place, we have

$$A_p = \int_{-h}^{h} (Ax^2 + Bx + C)\, dx$$

$$= \frac{2Ah^3}{3} + 2Ch.$$

Since the curve passes through the three points $(-h, y_0)$, $(0, y_1)$, and (h, y_2), we also have

$$y_0 = Ah^2 - Bh + C,$$
$$y_1 = C,$$
$$y_2 = Ah^2 + Bh + C,$$

from which there follows

$$C = y_1,$$
$$Ah^2 - Bh = y_0 - y_1,$$
$$Ah^2 + Bh = y_2 - y_1,$$
$$2Ah^2 = y_0 + y_2 - 2y_1.$$

Hence, expressing the area A_p in terms of the ordinates y_0, y_1, and y_2, we have

$$A_p = \frac{h}{3}[2Ah^2 + 6C] = \frac{h}{3}[(y_0 + y_2 - 2y_1) + 6y_1]$$

or

$$A_p = \frac{h}{3}[y_0 + 4y_1 + y_2]. \qquad (1)$$

Simpson's rule follows from applying this result to successive pieces of the curve $y = f(x)$ between $x = a$ and $x = b$. Each separate piece of the curve, covering an x-subinterval of width $2h$, is approximated by an arc of a parabola through its ends and its mid-point. The area under each parabolic arc is then given by an expression like Eq. (1) and the results are added to give

$$A_S = \frac{h}{3}[y_0 + 4y_1 + 2y_2 + 4y_3 + 2y_4 + \cdots + 2y_{n-2} + 4y_{n-1} + y_n],$$

$$(2)$$

which is taken as the approximate value of $\int_a^b f(x)\, dx$. In Eq. (2), $y_0, y_1, y_2, \ldots, y_n$ are the ordinates of the curve $y = f(x)$ at the points of abscissas $x_0 = a$, $x_1 = a + h$, $x_2 = a + 2h$, ..., $x_n = a + nh = b$ corresponding to a subdivision of the interval $a \leq x \leq b$ into n equal subintervals each of width $h = (b - a)/n$. (See Fig. 7–11.) The number n of subdivisions must be an *even* integer in order to apply the method. The application of the rule, Eq. (2), does not require a graph of the curve $y = f(x)$ nor a

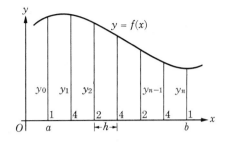

FIGURE 7–11

determination of the approximating parabolic arcs. All of the work is strictly arithmetical. Furthermore, it is clear on geometrical grounds that the smaller the value of h that is taken, the greater will be the accuracy of the approximation, since a parabola that passes through three points of the given curve that are close to one another will usually remain close to the curve throughout the entire strip of width $2h$. (For a detailed analytical discussion of the accuracy of the method, see Martin and Reissner, *Elementary Differential Equations*. Addison-Wesley, pp. 175–176.)

EXAMPLE 1. Use Simpson's rule with four subdivisions to find the approximate value of

$$\ln 2 = \int_1^2 \frac{1}{x}\, dx.$$

Solution. We arrange the work in tabular form as follows:

x	$y = 1/x$	Weighting factor	Product
1.00	1.00000	1	1.00000
1.25	0.80000	4	3.20000
1.50	0.66667	2	1.33333
1.75	0.57143	4	2.28572
2.00	0.50000	1	0.50000
			Sum = 8.31905

Since $h = \frac{1}{4}$, we must multiply the last sum by $h/3 = \frac{1}{12}$. Hence

$$A_S = \tfrac{1}{12}(8.31905) = 0.69325.$$

The approximation

$$\ln 2 \approx 0.69325$$

is in error by 1 part in 6900 or about one-seventieth of one percent. Greater accuracy may be obtained by taking twice as many subdivisions.

PROBLEMS

Find approximate numerical values for the following definite integrals by using Simpson's rule (a) with $n = 2$, and (b) with $n = 4$. Where possible, compare your answer with (c), the exact value.

1. $\displaystyle\int_0^2 x^2 \, dx$ 2. $\displaystyle\int_0^\pi \sin x \, dx$

3. $\displaystyle\int_0^\pi \sqrt{\sin x} \, dx$ 4. $\displaystyle\int_0^\pi \frac{dx}{2 + \cos x}$

5. $\displaystyle\int_0^\pi \frac{\sin x}{x} \, dx$ 6. $\displaystyle\int_0^1 \frac{dx}{x^2 + 1}$

7. Show that $\int_3^\infty e^{-3x} \, dx = \frac{1}{3} e^{-9} = 0.000041$, and hence that $\int_3^\infty e^{-x^2} \, dx < 0.000041$. Therefore, $\int_0^\infty e^{-x^2} \, dx$ can be replaced by $\int_0^3 e^{-x^2} \, dx$ without introducing any errors in the first three decimal places of the answer. Evaluate this last integral by Simpson's rule with $n = 6$. (This illustrates one method by which a convergent improper integral may be approximated numerically.)

REVIEW QUESTIONS AND EXERCISES FOR CHAPTER 7

1. What are some of the general methods presented in this chapter for finding an indefinite integral?

2. What substitution(s) would you consider trying if the integrand contained the following:

(a) $\sqrt{x^2 + 9}$,   (b) $\sqrt{x^2 - 9}$,   (c) $\sqrt{9 - x^2}$,

(d) $\sin^3 x \cos^2 x$,   (e) $\sin^2 x \cos^2 x$,   (f) $\dfrac{1 + \sin \theta}{2 + \cos \theta}$?

3. What method(s) would you try if the integrand contained:

(a) $\sin^{-1} x$,   (b) $\ln x$,   (c) $\sqrt{1 + 2x - x^2}$,

(d) $x \sin x$,   (e) $\dfrac{2x + 3}{x^2 - 5x + 6}$,   (f) $\sin 5x \cos 3x$,

(g) $\dfrac{1 - \sqrt{x}}{1 + \sqrt[4]{x}}$,   (h) $x\sqrt{2x + 3}$?

4. What numerical methods do you know for approximating a definite integral? How can an approximation usually be improved upon to give greater accuracy?

5. Discuss two types of improper integral. Define convergence and divergence of each type. Give examples of convergent and divergent integrals of each type.

MISCELLANEOUS PROBLEMS FOR CHAPTER 7

Evaluate the following integrals:

1. $\displaystyle\int \frac{\cos x\, dx}{\sqrt{1 + \sin x}}$

2. $\displaystyle\int \frac{\sin^{-1} x\, dx}{\sqrt{1 - x^2}}$

3. $\displaystyle\int \frac{\tan x\, dx}{\cos^2 x}$

4. $\displaystyle\int \frac{dx}{1 - \sin x}$

5. $\displaystyle\int e^{\ln \sqrt{x}}\, dx$

6. $\displaystyle\int \frac{\cos \sqrt{x}}{\sqrt{x}}\, dx$

7. $\displaystyle\int \frac{dx}{\sqrt{x^2 + 2x + 2}}$

8. $\displaystyle\int \frac{(3x - 7)\, dx}{(x - 1)(x - 2)(x - 3)}$

9. $\displaystyle\int x^2 e^x\, dx$

10. $\displaystyle\int \sqrt{x^2 + 1}\, dx$

11. $\displaystyle\int \frac{e^t\, dt}{1 + e^{2t}}$

12. $\displaystyle\int \frac{dx}{e^x + e^{-x}}$

13. $\displaystyle\int \frac{dx}{1 + \sqrt{x}}$

14. $\displaystyle\int \frac{dx}{\sqrt{1 + \sqrt{x}}}$

15. $\displaystyle\int t^{2/3}(t^{5/3} + 1)^{2/3}\, dt$

16. $\displaystyle\int \frac{\cot x\, dx}{\ln (\sin x)}$

17. $\displaystyle\int \frac{dt}{\sqrt{e^t + 1}}$

18. $\displaystyle\int \frac{dt}{\sqrt{1 - e^{-t}}}$

19. $\displaystyle\int \frac{\sin x\, e^{\sec x}}{\cos^2 x}\, dx$

20. $\displaystyle\int \frac{\cos x\, dx}{1 + \sin^2 x}$

21. $\displaystyle\int \frac{dx}{\sqrt{2x - x^2}}$

22. $\displaystyle\int \frac{\sin x\, dx}{1 + \cos^2 x}$

23. $\displaystyle\int \frac{\cos 2t}{1 + \sin 2t}\, dt$

24. $\displaystyle\int \frac{dx}{\sin x \cos x}$

25. $\displaystyle\int \sqrt{1 + \sin x}\, dx$

26. $\displaystyle\int \sqrt{1 - \sin x}\, dx$

27. $\displaystyle\int \frac{dx}{\sqrt{(a^2 - x^2)^3}}$

28. $\displaystyle\int \frac{dx}{\sqrt{(a^2 + x^2)^3}}$

29. $\displaystyle\int \frac{\sin x\, dx}{\cos^2 x - 5 \cos x + 4}$

30. $\displaystyle\int \frac{e^{2x}\, dx}{\sqrt[3]{1 + e^x}}$

31. $\displaystyle\int \frac{dx}{x(x+1)(x+2)\cdots(x+m)}$

32. $\displaystyle\int \frac{dx}{x^6-1}$

33. $\displaystyle\int \frac{dy}{y(2y^3+1)^2}$

34. $\displaystyle\int \frac{x\,dx}{1+\sqrt{x}}$

35. $\displaystyle\int \frac{dx}{x(x^2+1)^2}$

36. $\displaystyle\int \ln\sqrt{x-1}\,dx$

37. $\displaystyle\int \frac{dx}{e^x-1}$

38. $\displaystyle\int \frac{d\theta}{1-\tan^2\theta}$

39. $\displaystyle\int \frac{(x+1)\,dx}{x^2(x-1)}$

40. $\displaystyle\int \frac{x\,dx}{x^2+4x+3}$

41. $\displaystyle\int \frac{du}{(e^u-e^{-u})^2}$

42. $\displaystyle\int \frac{4dx}{x^3+4x}$

43. $\displaystyle\int \frac{dx}{5x^2+8x+5}$

44. $\displaystyle\int \frac{\sqrt{x^2-a^2}}{x}\,dx$

45. $\displaystyle\int e^x\cos 2x\,dx$

46. $\displaystyle\int \frac{dx}{x(3\sqrt{x}+1)}$

47. $\displaystyle\int \frac{dx}{x(1+\sqrt[3]{x})}$

48. $\displaystyle\int \frac{\cot\theta\,d\theta}{1+\sin^2\theta}$

49. $\displaystyle\int \frac{z^5\,dz}{\sqrt{1+z^2}}$

50. $\displaystyle\int \frac{e^{4t}\,dt}{(1+e^{2t})^{2/3}}$

51. $\displaystyle\int \frac{dx}{x^{1/5}\sqrt{1+x^{4/5}}}$

52. $\displaystyle\int x\sec^2 x\,dx$

53. $\displaystyle\int x\sin^{-1} x\,dx$

54. $\displaystyle\int \frac{(x^3+x^2)\,dx}{x^2+x-2}$

55. $\displaystyle\int \frac{x^3+1}{x^3-x}\,dx$

56. $\displaystyle\int \frac{x\,dx}{(x-1)^2}$

57. $\displaystyle\int \frac{(2e^{2x}-e^x)\,dx}{\sqrt{3e^{2x}-6e^x-1}}$

58. $\displaystyle\int \frac{(x+1)\,dx}{(x^2+2x-3)^{2/3}}$

59. $\displaystyle\int \frac{dy}{(2y+1)\sqrt{y^2+y}}$

60. $\displaystyle\int \frac{dx}{x^2\sqrt{a^2-x^2}}$

61. $\displaystyle\int (1-x^2)^{3/2}\,dx$

62. $\displaystyle\int \ln(x+\sqrt{1+x^2})\,dx$

63. $\displaystyle\int x\tan^2 x\,dx$

64. $\displaystyle\int \frac{\tan^{-1} x}{x^2}\,dx$

65. $\int x \cos^2 x \, dx$

66. $\int x^2 \sin x \, dx$

67. $\int x \sin^2 x \, dx$

68. $\int \frac{dt}{t^4 + 4t^2 + 3}$

69. $\int \frac{du}{e^{4u} + 4e^{2u} + 3}$

70. $\int x \ln \sqrt{x + 2} \, dx$

71. $\int (x + 1)^2 e^x \, dx$

72. $\int \sec^{-1} x \, dx$

73. $\int \frac{8 \, dx}{x^4 + 2x^3}$

74. $\int \frac{x \, dx}{x^4 - 16}$

75. $\int_0^{\pi/2} \frac{\cos x \, dx}{\sqrt{1 + \cos x}}$

76. $\int \frac{\cos x \, dx}{\sin^3 x - \sin x}$

77. $\int \frac{du}{(e^u + e^{-u})^2}$

78. $\int \frac{x \, dx}{1 + \sqrt{x} + x}$

79. $\int \frac{\sec^2 t \, dt}{\sec^2 t - 3 \tan t + 1}$

80. $\int \frac{dt}{\sec^2 t + \tan^2 t}$

81. $\int \frac{dx}{1 + \cos^2 x}$

82. $\int e^{2t} \cos(e^t) \, dt$

83. $\int \ln \sqrt{x^2 + 1} \, dx$

84. $\int x \ln (x^3 + x) \, dx$

85. $\int x^3 e^{x^2} \, dx$

86. $\int \frac{\cos x \, dx}{\sqrt{4 - \cos^2 x}}$

87. $\int \frac{\sec^2 x \, dx}{\sqrt{4 - \sec^2 x}}$

88. $\int x^2 \sin (1 - x) \, dx$

89. $\int \frac{dx}{1 + \sin x}$

90. $\int \frac{dx}{1 + 2 \sin x}$

91. $\int \frac{dx}{\sin^3 x}$

92. $\int \frac{dx}{\cot^3 x}$

93. $\int (\sin^{-1} x)^2 \, dx$

94. $\int x \ln \sqrt[3]{3x + 1} \, dx$

95. $\int \frac{x^3 \, dx}{(x^2 + 1)^2}$

96. $\int \frac{x \, dx}{\sqrt{1 - x}}$

97. $\int x\sqrt{2x + 1} \, dx$

98. $\int \ln (x + \sqrt{x^2 - 1}) \, dx$

99. $\int \ln (x - \sqrt{x^2 - 1}) \, dx$

100. $\int \dfrac{dt}{t - \sqrt{1 - t^2}}$

101. $\int e^{-x} \tan^{-1} (e^x) \, dx$

102. $\int \sin^{-1} \sqrt{x} \, dx$

103. $\int \ln (x + \sqrt{x}) \, dx$

104. $\int \tan^{-1} \sqrt{x} \, dx$

105. $\int \ln (x^2 + x) \, dx$

106. $\int \ln (\sqrt{x} + \sqrt{1 + x}) \, dx$

107. $\int \cos \sqrt{x} \, dx$

108. $\int \sin \sqrt{x} \, dx$

109. $\int \tan^{-1} \sqrt{x + 1} \, dx$

110. $\int \sqrt{1 - x^2} \sin^{-1} x \, dx$

111. $\int x \sin^2 (2x) \, dx$

112. $\int \dfrac{\tan x \, dx}{\tan x + \sec x}$

113. $\int \dfrac{dt}{\sqrt{e^{2t} + 1}}$

114. $\int \dfrac{dx}{(\cos^2 x + 4 \sin x - 5) \cos x}$

115. $\int \dfrac{dt}{a + be^{ct}}, \quad abc \neq 0$

116. $\int \sqrt{\dfrac{1 - \cos x}{\cos \alpha - \cos x}} \, dx, \quad \alpha \text{ constant}, \quad 0 < \alpha < x < \pi$

117. $\int \dfrac{dx}{\sin x - \cos x}$

118. $\int \ln \sqrt{1 + x^2} \, dx$

119. $\int \ln (2x^2 + 4) \, dx$

120. $\int \dfrac{x^3}{\sqrt{1 - x^2}} \, dx$

121. $\int \dfrac{dx}{x(2 + \ln x)}$

122. $\int \dfrac{\cos 2x - 1}{\cos 2x + 1} \, dx$

123. $\int \dfrac{dx}{x^3 + 1}$

124. $\int \dfrac{e^{2x} \, dx}{\sqrt[4]{e^x + 1}}$

125. $\int \dfrac{e^x \, dx}{1 + e^{2x}}$

126. $\int e^{\sqrt{t}} \, dt$

127. $\int \sin \sqrt{x + 1} \, dx$

128. $\int \cos \sqrt{1 - x} \, dx$

Evaluate each of the following limits, Problems 129–135, by identifying it with an appropriate definite integral and evaluating the latter.

129. $\lim\limits_{n\to\infty}\left(\dfrac{1}{n+1}+\dfrac{1}{n+2}+\cdots+\dfrac{1}{2n}\right)$

130. $\lim\limits_{n\to\infty}\left(\dfrac{1}{\sqrt{n^2}}+\dfrac{1}{\sqrt{n^2+n}}+\dfrac{1}{\sqrt{n^2+2n}}+\cdots+\dfrac{1}{\sqrt{n^2+(n-1)n}}\right)$

131. $\lim\limits_{n\to\infty}\left(\dfrac{\sin 0+\sin\dfrac{\pi}{n}+\sin\dfrac{2\pi}{n}+\cdots+\sin\dfrac{(n-1)\pi}{n}}{n}\right)$

132. $\lim\limits_{n\to\infty}\left(\dfrac{1+\sqrt[n]{e}+\sqrt[n]{e^2}+\sqrt[n]{e^3}+\cdots+\sqrt[n]{e^{n-1}}}{n}\right)$

133. $\lim\limits_{n\to\infty}\left(\dfrac{n}{n^2+0^2}+\dfrac{n}{n^2+1^2}+\dfrac{n}{n^2+2^2}+\cdots+\dfrac{n}{n^2+(n-1)^2}\right)$

134. $\lim\limits_{n\to\infty}\sum\limits_{k=1}^{n}\ln\sqrt[n]{1+\dfrac{k}{n}}$

135. $\lim\limits_{n\to\infty}\sum\limits_{k=0}^{n-1}\dfrac{1}{\sqrt{n^2-k^2}}$

136. Show that $\int_0^\infty x^3 e^{-x^2}\,dx$ is a convergent integral, and evaluate it.

137. Show that $\int_0^1 \ln x\,dx$ is a convergent integral and find its value. Sketch the integrand $y=\ln x$ for $0<x\le 1$.

138. Assuming that $|\alpha|\ne|\beta|$, prove that

$$\lim_{T\to\infty}\frac{1}{T}\int_0^T \sin\alpha x\sin\beta x\,dx=0.$$

139. Evaluate: $\lim\limits_{h\to 0}\dfrac{1}{h}\displaystyle\int_2^{2+h} e^{-x^2}\,dx.$

140. At points of the curve $y^2=4px$ lines of length $h=y$ are drawn perpendicular to its plane. Find the area of the surface formed by these lines at points of the curve between $(0,0)$ and $(p,2p)$.

141. A plane figure is bounded by a 90° arc of a circle of radius r and a straight line. Find its area and its centroid.

142. Find the coordinates of the center of gravity of the area bounded by the curves $y=e^x$, $x=1$, and $y=1$.

143. At points of a circle of radius r, perpendiculars to its plane are erected, the perpendicular at each point P being of length ks, where s is the arc of the circle from a fixed point A to P. Find the area of the surface formed by the perpendiculars along the arc beginning at A and extending once around the circle.

144. A plate in the first quadrant, bounded by the curves $y=e^x$, $y=1$, and $x=4$, is submerged vertically in water with its upper corner on the sur-

face. The surface of the water is given by the line $y = e^4$. Find the total force on one side of the plate if the weight of water is 62.5 lb/ft^3, and if the units of x and y are also measured in feet.

145. The area under the curve $xy = 1$, for $x \geq 1$, is rotated about the x-axis. If A is the area under the curve, V is the volume generated, and S is the surface area of this volume: (a) is A finite? (b) is V finite? (c) is S finite? Give reasons for your answers.

146. Answer the questions of Problem 145 if the curve given there is replaced by the curve $y = e^{-x}$. Give reasons for your answers.

147. Find the centroid of the area bounded by $y = e^x$, $y = 0$, $x = 0$, $x = 1$.

148. Find the centroid of the area bounded by $y = \ln x$, $x = 1$, $y = 1$.

149. Find the length of arc of $y = \ln x$ from $x = 1$ to $x = e$.

150. The arc of Problem 149 is rotated about the y-axis. Find the surface area generated. Check your answer by comparing it with the area of a frustum of a suitably related cone.

151. Find the length of arc of the curve $y = e^x$ from $x = 0$ to $x = 2$.

152. The arc of Problem 151 is rotated about the x-axis. Find the surface area generated. Compare this area with the area of a suitably related frustum of a cone to check your answer.

153. One arch of the curve $y = \cos x$ is rotated about the x-axis. Find the surface area generated.

154. Use Simpson's rule to compute, approximately, the length of arc of $y = \cos x$ from $x = -\pi/2$ to $x = \pi/2$. Check your answer by consulting a table of elliptic integrals if one is available.

155. A thin wire is bent into the shape of one arch of the curve $y = \cos x$. Find its center of mass (see Problems 153, 154).

156. The area between the graph of $y = \ln (1/x)$, the x-axis, and the y-axis is revolved around the x-axis. Find the volume of the solid it generates.

157. Find the total perimeter of the curve $x^{2/3} + y^{2/3} = a^{2/3}$.

158. Find the length of arc of the curve $y = \ln (\cos x)$ from $x = 0$ to $x = \pi/3$.

159. Find the area of the surface generated by rotating the curve $x^{2/3} + y^{2/3} = a^{2/3}$ about the x-axis.

160. A thin homogeneous wire is bent into the shape of one arch of the curve $x^{2/3} + y^{2/3} = a^{2/3}$. Find its center of mass (see Problems 157, 159).

161. Determine whether the integral $\int_1^\infty \ln x (dx/x^2)$ converges or diverges.

162. Sketch the curves:

(a) $y = x - e^x$, show behavior for large $|x|$;

(b) $y = e^{(x-e^x)}$, show behavior for large $|x|$.

Show that the following integrals converge and compute their values:

(c) $\displaystyle\int_{-\infty}^b e^{(x-e^x)} \, dx,$ (d) $\displaystyle\int_{-\infty}^\infty e^{(x-e^x)} \, dx.$

163. The gamma function $\Gamma(x)$ is defined, for $x > 0$, by the definite integral

$$\Gamma(x) = \int_0^\infty t^{x-1} e^{-t} \, dt.$$

(a) Sketch graphs of the integrand $y = t^{x-1} e^{-t}$ vs. t, $t > 0$, for the three typical cases $x = \frac{1}{2}, 1, 3$. Find maxima, minima, and points of inflection (if they exist).

(b) Show that the integral converges if $x > 0$.

(c) Show that the integral diverges if $x \leq 0$.

(d) Using integration by parts, show that $\Gamma(x + 1) = x\Gamma(x)$, for $x > 0$.

(e) Using the result of part (b), show that, if n is a positive integer, $\Gamma(n) = (n - 1)!$ where $0! = 1$ (by definition) and if m is a positive integer, $m!$ is the product of the positive integers from 1 through m inclusive.

(f) Discuss how one might compute a table of values of $\Gamma(x)$ for the domain $1 \leq x \leq 2$, say. Consult such a table, if available, and sketch the graph of $y = \Gamma(x)$ for $0 < x \leq 3$.

164. Determine whether the integral $\int_0^\infty t^{x-1} (\ln t) e^{-t} dt$ converges or diverges for fixed $x > 0$. Sketch the integrand $y = t^{x-1} \ln t \, e^{-t}$ vs. t, $t > 0$, for the two cases $x = \frac{1}{2}$ and $x = 3$.

165. Solve the differential equation $d^2x/dt^2 = -k^2x$, subject to the initial conditions $x = a$, $dx/dt = 0$ when $t = 0$. [*Hint:* Let $dx/dt = v$, $d^2x/dt^2 = dv/dt = v \, dv/dx$.]

166. Find $\displaystyle\lim_{n\to\infty} \int_0^1 \frac{ny^{n-1}}{1+y} \, dy$.

167. Prove that if n is a positive integer, or zero, then

$$\int_{-1}^1 (1 - x^2)^n \, dx = \frac{2^{2n+1}(n!)^2}{(2n + 1)!},$$

with $0! = 1$; $n! = 1 \cdot 2 \cdots n$ for $n \geq 1$.

CHAPTER 8

DETERMINANTS AND LINEAR EQUATIONS

8–1 Introduction. Determinants have their origin in connection with the problem of solving simultaneous linear equations. For example, if we wish to find the point of intersection of two straight lines

$$a_1 x + b_1 y = c_1, \qquad a_2 x + b_2 y = c_2, \tag{1}$$

we seek a pair of numbers x and y which satisfy both equations simultaneously. There are several methods of doing this, but one fairly common method is to find equations equivalent to the given equations but having the property that the unknowns (x and y) are separated. This may be achieved, for example, by multiplying the first equation by b_2, the second equation by $-b_1$, and adding, to obtain the equation

$$(a_1 b_2 - a_2 b_1)x = c_1 b_2 - c_2 b_1; \tag{2a}$$

and by multiplying the first equation by $-a_2$, the second by a_1, and adding, to obtain the equation

$$(a_1 b_2 - a_2 b_1)y = a_1 c_2 - a_2 c_1. \tag{2b}$$

Equations (2a) and (2b) must be satisfied by any pair of numbers x and y which satisfy the original equations, (1). They have the added merit of being easy to solve, since each equation contains only one of the unknowns. Thus, we find that the only pair of numbers which can satisfy Eqs. (1) is

$$x = \frac{c_1 b_2 - c_2 b_1}{a_1 b_2 - a_2 b_1}, \qquad y = \frac{a_1 c_2 - a_2 c_1}{a_1 b_2 - a_2 b_1}, \tag{3}$$

provided

$$a_1 b_2 - a_2 b_1 \neq 0. \tag{4}$$

By direct substitution from (3) back into (1) we find, conversely, that these values of x and y do indeed satisfy both of the original equations.

We shall verify that this is so for the first equation and leave to the reader the computation for the second. Substituting for x and y from (3) into (1_1), we find

$$a_1 x + b_1 y = a_1 \left(\frac{c_1 b_2 - c_2 b_1}{a_1 b_2 - a_2 b_1} \right) + b_1 \left(\frac{a_1 c_2 - a_2 c_1}{a_1 b_2 - a_2 b_1} \right)$$

$$= \frac{a_1 c_1 b_2 - a_1 c_2 b_1 + b_1 a_1 c_2 - b_1 a_2 c_1}{a_1 b_2 - a_2 b_1}$$

$$= \frac{c_1 (a_1 b_2 - a_2 b_1)}{a_1 b_2 - a_2 b_1} = c_1.$$

In the exceptional case where $a_1b_2 - a_2b_1$ vanishes, the left sides of Eqs. (2a) and (2b) are both zero and the Eqs. (1) are inconsistent unless

$$c_1b_2 - c_2b_1 = a_1c_2 - a_2c_1 = 0$$

as well. In this case, we have a pair of straight lines having equal slopes and one of two things happens:

(a) The straight lines coincide and there are infinitely many number-pairs (x, y) which satisfy the equations, or else
(b) the lines are parallel and there are no number-pairs (x, y) which satisfy the equations simultaneously.

For example, if the equations are

$$2x + 3y = 5, \qquad 4x + 6y = 10,$$

then x may have any value, and provided $y = (5 - 2x)/3$, the point (x, y) will lie on both lines, since they are really not distinct. But if the equations are

$$2x + 3y = 5, \qquad 4x + 6y = 11,$$

then the lines are parallel and we say that the equations are inconsistent, because no pair of numbers x and y can satisfy both equations simultaneously.

Let us, then, rule out the case of parallel or coincident lines and discuss the results obtained in (3) when condition (4) is satisfied. The expression $a_1b_2 - a_2b_1$ is defined to be the expanded value of the *determinant*

$$D_2 = \begin{vmatrix} a_1 & b_1 \\ a_2 & b_2 \end{vmatrix} = a_1b_2 - a_2b_1, \tag{5}$$

which we get by writing the coefficients of x and y from Eqs. (1) in the order indicated in (5). Such an expression is called a determinant of order two, since it contains two rows and two columns. To evaluate such a determinant, multiply the diagonal elements in the upper-left and lower-right corners to get a_1b_2, then multiply the elements on the other diagonal and subtract this product, a_2b_1, from the former.

For example,

$$\begin{vmatrix} 3 & 2 \\ 7 & 5 \end{vmatrix} = 3 \cdot 5 - 7 \cdot 2 = 15 - 14 = 1$$

and

$$\begin{vmatrix} 4 & -3 \\ 2 & -6 \end{vmatrix} = 4 \cdot (-6) - 2 \cdot (-3) = -24 + 6 = -18.$$

Now the equations

$$a_1x + b_1y = c_1, \qquad a_2x + b_2y = c_2$$

have the solutions (3), which may be expressed by determinants as

$$x = \frac{\begin{vmatrix} c_1 & b_1 \\ c_2 & b_2 \end{vmatrix}}{\begin{vmatrix} a_1 & b_1 \\ a_2 & b_2 \end{vmatrix}}, \qquad y = \frac{\begin{vmatrix} a_1 & c_1 \\ a_2 & c_2 \end{vmatrix}}{\begin{vmatrix} a_1 & b_1 \\ a_2 & b_2 \end{vmatrix}}. \tag{6}$$

In the equations for both x and y, the denominator is the determinant of the coefficients, arranged in order, from the given equations. The numerator for x is a determinant which may be obtained from the denominator determinant by suppressing from the latter the coefficients of x and writing the constants c_1 and c_2 in their places. The numerator for y may similarly be obtained from the denominator determinant by suppressing from the latter the coefficients of y and writing the constants c_1 and c_2 in their places. In applying this rule, it is assumed that the denominator determinant is not zero. If it is zero, one has the case where there is no solution if the equations are inconsistent, or there are infinitely many solutions if the straight lines coincide. If the denominator determinant is zero, Eqs. (6) are not to be used.

EXAMPLE. $2x - 3y = 8, \qquad 3x + y = 1.$

Then

$$x = \frac{\begin{vmatrix} 8 & -3 \\ 1 & 1 \end{vmatrix}}{\begin{vmatrix} 2 & -3 \\ 3 & 1 \end{vmatrix}} = \frac{8 \cdot 1 - 1 \cdot (-3)}{2 \cdot 1 - 3 \cdot (-3)} = \frac{8 + 3}{2 + 9} = 1,$$

$$y = \frac{\begin{vmatrix} 2 & 8 \\ 3 & 1 \end{vmatrix}}{\begin{vmatrix} 2 & -3 \\ 3 & 1 \end{vmatrix}} = \frac{2 \cdot 1 - 3 \cdot 8}{2 \cdot 1 - 3 \cdot (-3)} = \frac{-22}{11} = -2.$$

PROBLEMS

Expand the following second order determinants:

1. $\begin{vmatrix} 3 & 4 \\ 2 & 5 \end{vmatrix}$ 2. $\begin{vmatrix} 0 & 3 \\ -1 & 7 \end{vmatrix}$ 3. $\begin{vmatrix} 5 & 7 \\ 6 & 2 \end{vmatrix}$ 4. $\begin{vmatrix} a & b \\ 2a & 2b \end{vmatrix}$

Solve the following sets of simultaneous equations by means of determinants. In every case, check your answers by substituting them back into the original equations.

5. $2x + 3y = 5, \quad 3x - y = 2$
6. $4x - 3y = 6, \quad 3x - 2y = 5$

7. Show that the two lines

$$a_1x + b_1y = c_1 \qquad \text{and} \qquad a_2x + b_2y = c_2$$

are parallel if and only if the determinant D_2, Eq. (5), is zero.

8. Show that all the determinants appearing in Eq. (6) are zero if the equation $a_2x + b_2y = c_2$ is a multiple of the equation $a_1x + b_1y = c_1$, that is, if there is a constant k such that $a_2 = ka_1$, $b_2 = kb_1$, and $c_2 = kc_1$.

9. Suppose the elements of the determinant

$$F = \begin{vmatrix} u_1 & v_1 \\ u_2 & v_2 \end{vmatrix}$$

are differentiable functions of x. Show that

$$\frac{dF}{dx} = \begin{vmatrix} \dfrac{du_1}{dx} & \dfrac{dv_1}{dx} \\ u_2 & v_2 \end{vmatrix} + \begin{vmatrix} u_1 & v_1 \\ \dfrac{du_2}{dx} & \dfrac{dv_2}{dx} \end{vmatrix}.$$

In particular, verify the result for the case

$$F = \begin{vmatrix} \cos x & -\sin x \\ \sin x & \cos x \end{vmatrix}.$$

10. Solve the equations

$$x' \cos \alpha - y' \sin \alpha = x, \qquad x' \sin \alpha + y' \cos \alpha = y$$

for x' and y' in terms of x and y by means of determinants.

8-2 Determinants of order 3. A third order determinant,

$$D_3 = \begin{vmatrix} a_1 & b_1 & c_1 \\ a_2 & b_2 & c_2 \\ a_3 & b_3 & c_3 \end{vmatrix}, \tag{1}$$

contains nine elements arranged in three horizontal rows and three vertical columns. Each element has an "address" in the determinant given by its row number r and its column number s. Thus in (1) the element b_3

is in the third row and second column; that is, $r = 3$, $s = 2$ for b_3. Similarly, for the element c_1, $r = 1$ and $s = 3$. We have used different letters a, b, and c to denote the different columns in (1) and subscripts 1, 2, and 3 on these letters to denote the rows.

To obtain the expanded value of the determinant of the third order as in (1), one forms *all possible products* $a_i b_j c_k$, where the subscripts i, j, and k form some permutation of the numbers 1, 2, and 3. There are precisely six possible products of this kind, namely, $a_1 b_2 c_3$, $a_1 b_3 c_2$, $a_2 b_1 c_3$, $a_2 b_3 c_1$, $a_3 b_1 c_2$, and $a_3 b_2 c_1$. One must next attach an algebraic sign to each of these six products according to the rule that the sign is to be plus if the subscripts i, j, and k in $a_i b_j c_k$ form an *even permutation* of the integers 1, 2, 3; and the sign is to be minus if i, j, k is an *odd permutation* of 1, 2, 3. This terminology will now be explained.

When the numbers 1, 2, 3 are arranged in their normal order, we say there are no inversions among them. If, on the other hand, they are arranged in some other order, such as 3, 1, 2, we say that we now have a *permutation* of them and the permutation is called "even" or "odd" according as the number of *inversions* (defined below) is an even integer (0, 2, 4, . . .) or an odd integer (1, 3, 5, 7, . . .) respectively.

The number of inversions in any permutation is determined as follows. If in a given permutation i is any integer which is followed by a smaller integer, we say that there is an *inversion* relative to i and the smaller integer. The number of integers following i and smaller than i gives the total number of inversions relative to i. The total number of inversions relative to all the integers of a permutation may be called the *index* of that permutation. In the permutation

$$5 \quad 2 \quad 1 \quad 4 \quad 3,$$

for example, we may count the following:

	relative to		*the number of inversions is*
5	. . . .	4
2	. . . .	1
1	. . . .	0
4	. . . .	1
3	. . . .	0

Thus the index of the given permutation is

$$4 + 1 + 1 = 6,$$

and the permutation is said to be *even* because 6 is an even integer.

Let us now examine in turn each of the six products in the expansion of D_3, count the inversions in its subscripts, and then affix a plus sign if this number is even and a minus sign if the number is odd.

Product	Subscripts	Index	Signed product
$a_1b_2c_3$	1 2 3	0	$+a_1b_2c_3$
$a_1b_3c_2$	1 3 2	1	$-a_1b_3c_2$
$a_2b_1c_3$	2 1 3	1	$-a_2b_1c_3$
$a_2b_3c_1$	2 3 1	2	$+a_2b_3c_1$
$a_3b_1c_2$	3 1 2	2	$+a_3b_1c_2$
$a_3b_2c_1$	3 2 1	3	$-a_3b_2c_1$

We are now in a position to complete the definition of a third order determinant. Form all possible signed products $(\pm)$ $a_ib_jc_k$, where i, j, k is a permutation of 1, 2, 3 in some order and the sign is plus or minus according as the number of inversions in i, j, k is even or odd. The expanded value of the determinant is the algebraic sum of these signed products:

$$D_3 = \begin{vmatrix} a_1 & b_1 & c_1 \\ a_2 & b_2 & c_2 \\ a_3 & b_3 & c_3 \end{vmatrix} = a_1b_2c_3 + a_2b_3c_1 + a_3b_1c_2 - a_3b_2c_1 - a_2b_1c_3 - a_1b_3c_2. \tag{2}$$

The expansion (2) can also be expressed in several ways as the sum of three second order minor determinants each multiplied by an element of a row or column of D_3. For example, it is a simple matter to verify by direct computation that the expanded value in (2) is precisely the same as

$$D_3 = \begin{vmatrix} a_1 & b_1 & c_1 \\ a_2 & b_2 & c_2 \\ a_3 & b_3 & c_3 \end{vmatrix} = a_1 \begin{vmatrix} b_2 & c_2 \\ b_3 & c_3 \end{vmatrix} - b_1 \begin{vmatrix} a_2 & c_2 \\ a_3 & c_3 \end{vmatrix} + c_1 \begin{vmatrix} a_2 & b_2 \\ a_3 & b_3 \end{vmatrix}. \tag{3}$$

Here, we say that we have expanded D_3 by minors according to elements of its first row. The *minor* of the element in the rth row and sth column of a determinant of any order n is the determinant of order $n - 1$ obtained by suppressing all the elements in the rth row and sth column in the original array. The minor of a_1 is found by covering up the first row and first column in D_3, and the result, which we shall call A_1, is

$$A_1 = \begin{vmatrix} b_2 & c_2 \\ b_3 & c_3 \end{vmatrix} = b_2c_3 - b_3c_2.$$

Similarly, the minor of b_1 is found by covering up the first row and second column of D_3, and the result, denoted by $-B_1$, is

$$-B_1 = \begin{vmatrix} a_2 & c_2 \\ a_3 & c_3 \end{vmatrix} = a_2c_3 - a_3c_2.$$

The *negative* of this minor is called the cofactor of b_1 in D_3 and that is why we call the minor $-B_1$ so that the cofactor is $+B_1$. In general, the *cofactor* of the element in the rth row and sth column of a determinant is related to its minor according to the law

$$\text{cofactor} = (-1)^{r+s} \text{ minor.} \tag{4}$$

Using cofactors instead of minors in the expansion (3), with A_1, B_1, and C_1 denoting the cofactors of a_1, b_1, and c_1 respectively, we have

$$D_3 = a_1A_1 + b_1B_1 + c_1C_1; \tag{5}$$

that is, *the determinant is the sum of the products of the elements of the first row by their corresponding cofactors.*

It may also be verified by comparison with the expansion in (2) that the determinant is the sum of the products of the elements of *any* row (or column) by their corresponding cofactors. The cofactor of an element is simply its *signed minor*, the sign being $+$ or $-$ according to the law in Eq. (4). The sign may also be obtained from a checkerboard arrangement of $+$ and $-$ signs. One starts with $+$ in the upper left corner and changes sign in going from any square to an adjacent square as follows:

$$\begin{vmatrix} + & - & + \\ - & + & - \\ + & - & + \end{vmatrix}.$$

EXAMPLE 1.   Evaluate:

$$D = \begin{vmatrix} 2 & 2 & 1 \\ -1 & 0 & -1 \\ 3 & -1 & 3 \end{vmatrix}.$$

Solution. We exploit the presence of small numbers and the zero in the second row and expand the determinant by cofactors of the elements of this row.

$$D = -(-1) \begin{vmatrix} 2 & 1 \\ -1 & 3 \end{vmatrix} + 0 \begin{vmatrix} 2 & 1 \\ 3 & 3 \end{vmatrix} -(-1) \begin{vmatrix} 2 & 2 \\ 3 & -1 \end{vmatrix}$$

$$= +(6 + 1) + 0 + (-2 - 6) = -1.$$

Actually, we need not have written the cofactor of 0, since it contributes nothing to the answer.

EXAMPLE 2. Show that the equation

$$\begin{vmatrix} x & y & 1 \\ -1 & 2 & 1 \\ 1 & 0 & 1 \end{vmatrix} = 0$$

represents a straight line which passes through the points $(-1, 2)$ and $(1, 0)$.

Solution. Expanding the determinant by cofactors of the elements of its first row and equating the result to zero, we get

$$x\begin{vmatrix} 2 & 1 \\ 0 & 1 \end{vmatrix} - y\begin{vmatrix} -1 & 1 \\ 1 & 1 \end{vmatrix} + 1\begin{vmatrix} -1 & 2 \\ 1 & 0 \end{vmatrix} = 0,$$

or

$$2x + 2y - 2 = 0,$$

or

$$x + y = 1.$$

This is the equation of a straight line. Clearly, by substitution, the given points satisfy the equation.

Another fairly convenient device for evaluating a third order determinant consists in repeating the first two columns of the determinant to the right of it, and then taking the sum of the products along diagonals parallel to the main diagonal minus the products along the diagonals which run up from left to right. This is illustrated schematically in the accompanying diagram. A word of caution: The method does not work for determinants of order 4 or higher!

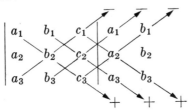

EXAMPLE.

$$\begin{vmatrix} 3 & 2 & 1 \\ 2 & 3 & 1 \\ 1 & 2 & 3 \end{vmatrix}\begin{matrix} 3 & 2 \\ 2 & 3 \\ 1 & 2 \end{matrix} = (27 + 2 + 4) - (3 + 6 + 12) = 12.$$

PROBLEMS

1. Find the index of the permutation 4 1 3 2.

2. Verify Eq. (3) by expanding the second order determinants on the right and comparing the result with Eq. (2).

3. Find the *cofactor* of the element in the second row and first column of the determinant

$$\begin{vmatrix} 2 & 3 & 4 \\ 3 & 2 & -1 \\ 4 & 3 & 7 \end{vmatrix}$$

4. Show that the third order determinant, Eq. (2), is equal to the sum of the products of the elements of the second column by their corresponding cofactors.

5. Evaluate the determinant

$$\begin{vmatrix} 2 & 2 & 1 \\ 1 & 3 & 2 \\ 3 & 1 & -1 \end{vmatrix}$$

by two different methods.

Evaluate each of the following third order determinants:

6. $\begin{vmatrix} 1 & 3 & -2 \\ 2 & -1 & 1 \\ -2 & 2 & 3 \end{vmatrix}$ 7. $\begin{vmatrix} 2 & 0 & 2 \\ 0 & 3 & -3 \\ -3 & -2 & 0 \end{vmatrix}$

8–3 Determinants of order n. To denote a determinant of order n, it is advantageous to use a slightly different notation from that introduced above. Namely, we shall not use different letters of the alphabet to represent the elements in the different columns, but shall instead use double subscripts and write a_{ij} to denote the element in the ith row, jth column of the determinant:

$$D_n = \begin{vmatrix} a_{11} & a_{12} & a_{13} & \ldots & a_{1n} \\ a_{21} & a_{22} & a_{23} & \ldots & a_{2n} \\ \ldots & \ldots & \ldots & \ldots & \ldots \\ a_{n1} & a_{n2} & a_{n3} & \ldots & a_{nn} \end{vmatrix} \qquad (1)$$

The expanded value of D_n is the sum of all signed products:

$$(\pm) a_{1i_1} a_{2i_2} a_{3i_3} \ldots a_{ni_n}, \qquad (2)$$

where $i_1, i_2, \ldots, i_n$ is a permutation of the integers $1, 2, 3, \ldots, n$ in some order and the sign is $+$ or $-$ according as the permutation is even or odd.

For a determinant of order 4, for example, we shall have

$$D_4 = \sum(\pm) a_{1i_1} a_{2i_2} a_{3i_3} a_{4i_4},$$

where i_1, i_2, i_3, i_4 is to range over all permutations of 1, 2, 3, 4. There are $4! = 24$ such permutations and accordingly the determinant D_4 will be the sum of 24 signed products.

In general, a determinant of order n is the sum of $n!$ signed products. Since this number increases rapidly with n, it is desirable to develop equivalent ways of expanding determinants, but ways which will be less laborious than the direct application of the definition. This is the purpose behind the discussion which follows.

PROBLEM

Write out the 24 permutations of the numbers 1, 2, 3, 4. What is the index of the permutation 4 3 2 1? In the expansion of the determinant D_4, what sign is to be attached to the product $a_{14}a_{23}a_{32}a_{41}$?

8–4 Properties of determinants of order n.

THEOREM 1. *If all elements of any row of D_n are zero, the expanded value of the determinant is zero.*

Proof. Each of the signed products contains one factor from each row (because the first subscripts include all the integers $1, 2, \ldots, n$), so that each product is zero under the given hypothesis. Hence their sum is also zero; that is, $D_n = 0$.

THEOREM 2. *If D_n and D'_n are two determinants of the nth order which differ only in that the elements in some one row of D'_n are k times the corresponding elements in D_n, then the expanded value of D'_n is k times the value of D_n.*

The proof is similar to the proof of Theorem 1 and is omitted. The result permits us to factor out any common factor from a row of a determinant and write the factor in front of the new determinant. For example:

$$\begin{vmatrix} a_{11} & a_{12} & a_{13} \\ ka_{21} & ka_{22} & ka_{23} \\ a_{31} & a_{32} & a_{33} \end{vmatrix} = k \begin{vmatrix} a_{11} & a_{12} & a_{13} \\ a_{21} & a_{22} & a_{23} \\ a_{31} & a_{32} & a_{33} \end{vmatrix}.$$

THEOREM 3. *If D'_n is obtained from D_n by interchanging two adjacent rows of D_n, then $D'_n = -D_n$.*

Proof. Suppose D'_n is obtained from D_n by interchanging its kth and $(k + 1)$th rows. Then, denoting the elements by a'_{ij} and a_{ij} respectively, we have

$$a'_{ij} = a_{ij} \quad \text{if} \quad i \neq k, \quad i \neq k+1,$$

while

$$a'_{kj} = a_{k+1,j}, \quad a'_{k+1,j} = a_{kj}, \quad j = 1, 2, \ldots, n.$$

By definition, D_n is the sum of signed products:

$$\pm a_{1i_1} a_{2i_2} a_{3i_3} \ldots a_{ni_n}, \tag{1}$$

while D'_n is the sum of similar products with primes throughout. Let P be a typical product in the expansion of D_n:

$$P = \pm a_{1i_1} a_{2i_2} \ldots a_{ki_k} a_{k+1,i_{k+1}} \ldots a_{ni_n}, \tag{2}$$

where the sign is determined by the number of inversions in the permutation $i_1, i_2, \ldots, i_n$. If we interchange a_{ki_k} and $a_{k+1,i_{k+1}}$ in (2), we obtain a typical product in the expansion of D'_n except that the sign is now to be determined by the number of inversions in the permutation

$$\underbrace{i_1, i_2, \ldots, i_{k-1},}_{Q'} \quad \underbrace{i_{k+1}, i_k,}_{R'} \quad \underbrace{i_{k+2}, \ldots, i_n.}_{S'} \tag{3}$$

Next, we shall show that the number of inversions in (3) differs by unity from the number of inversions in

$$\underbrace{i_1, i_2, \ldots, i_{k-1},}_{Q} \quad \underbrace{i_k, i_{k+1},}_{R} \quad \underbrace{i_{k+2}, \ldots, i_n,}_{S} \tag{4}$$

which determines the sign in (2).

We have indicated the permutations in (3) and (4) as composed of three segments. Suppose we examine the number of inversions in (3), term by term, and record the total number q' relative to elements in Q' which are followed by smaller elements in Q', R', and S'. Similarly, we record the numbers of inversions r' and s' from the segments R' and S', so that the total number of inversions in (3) is

$$I' = q' + r' + s'.$$

We repeat the process for the permutation (4) and obtain the total number of inversions:

$$I = q + r + s,$$

where the letters have meanings which are clear by analogy. But $q = q'$ and $s = s'$, and we need only look more closely at the relation between

r and r'. The number r' consists of two parts:

$$r' = r'_1 + r'_2,$$

where r'_1 is the number of inversions caused by the occurrence in R' of numbers which are greater than numbers in S', and r'_2 is 0 or 1, depending upon whether $i_{k+1} < i_k$ or $i_{k+1} > i_k$. Defining r_1 analogously, we write

$$r = r_1 + r_2$$

and observe that $r_1 = r'_1$, since the segments R and S contain the same integers as do the segments R' and S'. But r_2 is not equal to r'_2, but rather $r_2 = 1$ if $i_k > i_{k+1}$ and $r_2 = 0$ if $i_k < i_{k+1}$. That is,

$$r_2 = r'_2 \pm 1.$$

This leads to the end result that

$$I = I' \pm 1,$$

so that one of the permutations (3) or (4) is even and the other is odd. Therefore every product P in D_n undergoes a change in sign in becoming a product P' in D'_n. The sum of all the products P is therefore the negative of the sum of the products P'; that is, $D_n = -D'_n$ or $D'_n = -D_n$.

To illustrate the relationship $I' = I \pm 1$, let us consider an example. For instance, suppose we interchange the 3 and the 7 in the permutation

$$\underbrace{8, 1, 4,}_{Q} \quad \underbrace{3, 7,}_{R} \quad \underbrace{6, 2, 5}_{S}$$

and thus obtain

$$\underbrace{8, 1, 4,}_{Q'} \quad \underbrace{7, 3,}_{R'} \quad \underbrace{6, 2, 5.}_{S'}$$

We may record the number of inversions relative to a given number directly beneath it as follows:

$\overbrace{Q}$	$\overbrace{R}$	$\overbrace{S}$	$\overbrace{Q'}$	$\overbrace{R'}$	$\overbrace{S'}$
8, 1, 4,	3, 7,	6, 2, 5	8, 1, 4,	7, 3,	6, 2, 5

$$7 + 0 + 2 + 1 + 3 + 2 + 0 + 0 \qquad 7 + 0 + 2 + 4 + 1 + 2 + 0 + 0$$

$$I = q \quad + \quad r \quad + \quad s \qquad I' = \quad q' \quad + r' \quad + \quad s'$$

Thus

$$q = q' = 7 + 0 + 2 = 9,$$
$$s = s' = 2 + 0 + 0 = 2,$$

but

$$r = 1 + 3 = 4 \quad \text{while} \quad r' = 4 + 1 = 5; \quad \text{hence} \quad I' = I + 1.$$

When we interchanged the 3 and the 7 we added one inversion to the total, namely, the inversion caused by having 7 ahead of 3. All other inversions were unaltered; hence we increased the index of the permutation by one, from $I = 15$ to $I' = 16$.

THEOREM 4. *If D_n' is obtained from D_n by interchanging any pair of rows, then $D_n' = -D_n$.*

Proof. By Theorem 3, the theorem is true if the two rows in question are adjacent. Suppose, then, in the general case, that the two rows are not adjacent but that there are m intervening rows. Call the two rows to be interchanged α and β. By successively interchanging α and an *adjacent* row, m times, we may bring α adjacent to β. This changes the sign of the determinant m times. Next, interchange α and β and then continue to move β one row at a time, interchanging it with the m rows mentioned above, until it comes into the position originally occupied by α. This changes the sign $(m + 1)$ times and results in the determinant D_n' in which the rows α and β of D_n have been interchanged. Altogether, the sign has been changed $m + (m + 1) = 2m + 1$ times; that is

$$D_n' = (-1)^{2m+1} D_n.$$

But $2m + 1$ is odd for any integer m; hence

$$D_n' = -D_n.$$

THEOREM 5. *If two rows of D_n are identical, then $D_n = 0$.*

Proof. Interchange the two identical rows and call the result D_n'. Then $D_n' = -D_n$ by Theorem 4. But the interchange of two *identical* rows leaves D_n unaltered; that is, $D_n' = D_n$. Therefore $D_n = -D_n$, $2D_n = 0$; hence $D_n = 0$.

COROLLARY. *If two rows of D_n are proportional, then $D_n = 0$.*

Proof. Suppose the elements of row α are all k times the corresponding elements of row β. Then, by Theorem 2, the determinant is k times a determinant whose α and β rows are identical, and this is zero by Theorem 5.

EXAMPLE.

$$\begin{vmatrix} 1 & 3 & -2 \\ 2 & 4 & 5 \\ -4 & -12 & 8 \end{vmatrix} = -4 \begin{vmatrix} 1 & 3 & -2 \\ 2 & 4 & 5 \\ 1 & 3 & -2 \end{vmatrix} = 0.$$

The -4 may be factored out of the third row. Then the first and third rows are identical and the result is zero by Theorem 5.

THEOREM 6. *Suppose each element a_{kj} in the kth row of D_n is a sum*

$$a_{kj} = b_{kj} + c_{kj}, \qquad j = 1, 2, \ldots, n.$$

Let D_n' be obtained from D_n by replacing the elements a_{kj} of the kth row by b_{kj}, and let D_n'' be obtained from D_n by replacing the elements of the kth row by c_{kj}. Then

$$D_n = D_n' + D_n''.$$

Proof. Each product in the expansion of D_n contains a term

$$a_{ki_k} = b_{ki_k} + c_{ki_k}$$

as a factor and leads to a product in the expansion of D_n' plus a product in the expansion of D_n''. Adding these (signed) products leads to the result stated.

EXAMPLE.

$$\begin{vmatrix} a_{11} & a_{12} & a_{13} \\ b_{21}+c_{21} & b_{22}+c_{22} & b_{23}+c_{23} \\ a_{31} & a_{32} & a_{33} \end{vmatrix} = \begin{vmatrix} a_{11} & a_{12} & a_{13} \\ b_{21} & b_{22} & b_{23} \\ a_{31} & a_{32} & a_{33} \end{vmatrix} + \begin{vmatrix} a_{11} & a_{12} & a_{13} \\ c_{21} & c_{22} & c_{23} \\ a_{31} & a_{32} & a_{33} \end{vmatrix}$$

THEOREM 7. *The value of a determinant of order n is unaltered if to each element of any row is added k times the corresponding element of some other row, where k is any constant.*

Proof. Let D_n be the given determinant and let D_n' be the result of adding k times the rth row of D_n to its tth row ($r \neq t$). Then, by Theorem 6, D_n' is the sum of two determinants, one of which is D_n and the other is zero by the corollary to Theorem 5.

EXAMPLE.

$$\begin{vmatrix} a_1 & b_1 & c_1 \\ a_2 & b_2 & c_2 \\ a_3+ka_1 & b_3+kb_1 & c_3+kc_1 \end{vmatrix} = \begin{vmatrix} a_1 & b_1 & c_1 \\ a_2 & b_2 & c_2 \\ a_3 & b_3 & c_3 \end{vmatrix} + \begin{vmatrix} a_1 & b_1 & c_1 \\ a_2 & b_2 & c_2 \\ ka_1 & kb_1 & kc_1 \end{vmatrix}$$

The second determinant on the right is zero, since its third row is proportional to its first row.

THEOREM 8. *Let D_n be a determinant of order n and let D_n' be obtained by taking the 1st, 2nd, $\ldots$, nth rows respectively of D_n as the 1st, 2nd, $\ldots$, nth columns respectively of D_n'. Then*

$$D_n' = D_n.$$

Proof. If we denote the elements in the ith row and jth column of D_n and D'_n respectively by a_{ij} and a'_{ij}, the relation between D'_n and D_n is expressed by the equations

$$a'_{ij} = a_{ji}, \qquad i, j = 1, 2, \ldots, n.$$

By definition,

$$D'_n = \sum \pm a'_{1j_1} a'_{2j_2} \ldots a'_{nj_n},$$

where $j_1, j_2, \ldots, j_n$ is a permutation of $1, 2, \ldots, n$. In terms of the elements a_{ij} of D_n, this is the same as

$$D'_n = \sum \pm a_{j_1 1} a_{j_2 2} \ldots a_{j_n n},$$

and each signed product

$$\pm a_{j_1 1} a_{j_2 2} \ldots a_{j_n n} \tag{5}$$

corresponds to one and only one signed product

$$\pm a_{1 i_1} a_{2 i_2} \ldots a_{n i_n} \tag{6}$$

in the expansion of D_n in the following manner. Since $j_1, j_2, \ldots, j_n$ is a permutation of $1, 2, \ldots, n$, we may rearrange the factors in the product (5) so as to have the first subscripts appearing in the natural order $1, 2, 3, \ldots, n$. This induces a permutation $i_1, i_2, \ldots, i_n$ in the second subscripts and gives the product (6), except that there is at least a possibility that the signs in (5) and in (6) may not agree. The fact is, however, that the signs do agree, since the permutation $j_1, j_2, \ldots, j_n$ in (5) and the related permutation $i_1, i_2, \ldots, i_n$ in (6) are both even or both odd, as we shall prove below. Let us accept this as true for the present; then D'_n is the sum of all signed products (5) and D_n is the sum of the equal signed products (6), that is,

$$D'_n = D_n.$$

Let us now prove the statement that the permutations $j_1, \ldots, j_n$ and $i_1, \ldots, i_n$ above are both even or both odd. To this end, we consider the two sequences of double subscripts

$$P': \quad (j_1 1), (j_2 2), \ldots, (j_n n) \tag{7}$$

and

$$P: \quad (1 i_1), (2 i_2), \ldots, (n i_n). \tag{8}$$

In P' the second subscripts are in their natural order $1, 2, \ldots, n$, so that there are no inversions in their order. Hence the total number T' of inversions in P', counting inversions in the first subscripts $j_1, j_2, \ldots, j_n$ plus inversions in the second subscripts, is the same as the index I' of the permutation $j_1, j_2, \ldots, j_n$. Similarly, the total number T of inversions in P, counting inversions in the first subscripts $1, 2, \ldots, n$ plus inversions in the second subscripts $i_1, i_2, \ldots, i_n$, is equal to the index I of the permutation $i_1, i_2, \ldots, i_n$. Now (8) may be obtained from (7) by a sequence of transpositions of adjacent terms. Each such transposition changes the number of inversions in the first subscripts by ± 1 and also changes the number of inversions in the second subscripts by ± 1, hence changes the sum total of inversions by 2, 0, or -2, but always by an *even* number. Thus T and T' differ by an even integer, so that I and I' also differ by an even integer. Thus the permutations are both even or both odd as was asserted.

EXAMPLE. The term $a_{21}a_{32}a_{13}$ has its second subscripts arranged in natural order. The index of the permutation 2, 3, 1 of its first subscripts is 2. If we rearrange the factors so as to put the first subscripts in natural order, we have $a_{13}a_{21}a_{32}$. Then the second subscripts form the permutation 3, 1, 2, which also has index 2.

Remark. The import of Theorem 8 is that each theorem about determinants which contains the word "row" in its statement is true when the word "column" is substituted everywhere for the word row. For example, Theorem 5 is true if stated for columns instead of rows: "If two columns of a determinant are identical, the determinant is zero." For we may, by Theorem 8, interchange rows and columns in the original determinant. (In some theorems a second interchange of rows and columns may be required to establish the end result.)

THEOREM 9. *If D has the special form*

$$D = \begin{vmatrix} a_{11} & 0 & 0 & \ldots & 0 \\ a_{21} & a_{22} & a_{23} & \ldots & a_{2n} \\ \ldots & \ldots & \ldots & \ldots & \ldots \\ a_{n1} & a_{n2} & a_{n3} & \ldots & a_{nn} \end{vmatrix}, \tag{9}$$

in which all elements after the first in its first row are zero, then D is a_{11} times its minor; that is,

$$D = a_{11} \begin{vmatrix} a_{22} & a_{23} & \ldots & a_{2n} \\ \ldots & \ldots & \ldots & \ldots \\ a_{n2} & a_{n3} & \ldots & a_{nn} \end{vmatrix}. \tag{10}$$

Proof. In the expansion for D,

$$D = \sum \pm\, a_{1i_1}a_{2i_2}\ldots a_{ni_n},$$

each product is zero except possibly those in which $i_1 = 1$. Hence

$$D = a_{11}(\sum \pm a_{2i_2} \ldots a_{ni_n})$$

and the signed products in the sum are precisely the same as the signed products in the expansion of the minor of a_{11}.

COROLLARY. *The value of a triangular determinant*

$$D = \begin{vmatrix} a_{11} & 0 & 0 & \ldots & 0 \\ a_{21} & a_{22} & 0 & \ldots & 0 \\ \ldots & \ldots & \ldots & \ldots & \ldots \\ a_{n1} & a_{n2} & a_{n3} & \ldots & a_{nn} \end{vmatrix}, \tag{11}$$

in which all elements above the main diagonal are zero, is simply the product of the elements on this diagonal; that is,

$$D = a_{11}a_{22} \ldots a_{nn}.$$

It should, of course, be noted that Theorem 9 has a companion theorem or the case where the elements below a_{11} in the first column are zero. Also, the value of a triangular determinant which is zero everywhere *below* the main diagonal is just the product of the diagonal elements.

THEOREM 10. *If D has the special form*

$$D = \begin{vmatrix} a_{11} & a_{12} & \ldots & a_{1n} \\ \ldots & \ldots & \ldots & \ldots \\ 0 & 0 & a_{ij} & 0 \\ \ldots & \ldots & \ldots & \ldots \\ a_{n1} & a_{n2} & \ldots & a_{nn} \end{vmatrix}, \tag{12}$$

in which all elements of the ith row are zero except for the element a_{ij} in the jth column, then

$$D = (-1)^{i+j}a_{ij}D_{ij}, \tag{13}$$

where D_{ij} is the minor of a_{ij} obtained by covering up the ith row and jth column in D.

Proof. By $(i-1)$ successive row transpositions followed by $(j-1)$ column transpositions, the element a_{ij} of D may be brought into the upper left corner of a determinant D' having the special form described in Theorem 9. The minor of this element in D' is the same as the minor D_{ij}

of the element a_{ij} in D. Hence

$$D' = a_{ij}D_{ij}.$$

But, by Theorem 4 and its analog for columns,

$$D' = (-1)^{(i-1)+(j-1)}D$$

or

$$D = (-1)^{i+j}D',$$

so that

$$D = (-1)^{i+j}a_{ij}D_{ij}.$$

Of course, a companion theorem for columns is also true. The results may be summarized by saying that whenever all but one of the elements of a row or column of a determinant are zero, the order of the determinant may be reduced by unity by simply multiplying the element times its signed minor, the sign being given by $(-1)^{i+j}$, where i and j are the row and column numbers of the element in question.

EXAMPLE 1. Exploiting the first row of the fourth order determinant below, we have

$$\begin{vmatrix} 0 & 2 & 0 & 0 \\ 3 & 4 & 0 & 0 \\ -2 & -7 & 4 & 0 \\ 6 & 8 & -1 & 5 \end{vmatrix} = -2 \begin{vmatrix} 3 & 0 & 0 \\ -2 & 4 & 0 \\ 6 & -1 & 5 \end{vmatrix} = -120.$$

The 2 in the first row and second column must be multiplied by $(-1)^{1+2}$ times its minor. The minor is a triangular determinant whose value is simply $(3)(4)(5) = 60$.

In the next example, we illustrate how Theorem 7 and the corresponding theorem for columns are used to transform a given determinant into the special form where all but one of the elements of a row or column are zero. The order of the determinant is then reduced by one and the process repeated if desired. Note that several applications of Theorem 7 may be combined in one step provided the same base row (or column) is used to modify several other rows (or columns). In every case, the base row itself is *not* changed. That is, if we multiply the first row by 3 and add it to the second row, we thereby get a new second row, but we do not change the first row when we do this. Of course we may now, if we wish, use a new base row to alter the first row.

EXAMPLE 2. In the following fourth order determinant we use the first row to obtain zeros in all but one place in the fourth column. We denote the second row by R_2, and so forth, and replace

$$
\begin{aligned}
R_2 &\quad\text{by}\quad R_2 + R_1, \\
R_3 &\quad\text{by}\quad R_3 + R_1, \\
R_4 &\quad\text{by}\quad R_4 + 3R_1,
\end{aligned}
$$

and do not change R_1.

$$
D = \begin{vmatrix} 1 & 3 & 2 & -1 \\ 2 & -1 & 3 & 1 \\ -1 & 2 & 1 & 1 \\ -2 & -5 & 2 & 3 \end{vmatrix} = \begin{vmatrix} 1 & 3 & 2 & -1 \\ 3 & 2 & 5 & 0 \\ 0 & 5 & 3 & 0 \\ 1 & 4 & 8 & 0 \end{vmatrix}.
$$

This determinant is equal to the element -1 in its first row and fourth column times $(-1)^{4+1}$ times the minor obtained by deleting the first row and fourth column; that is,

$$
D = (-1)(-1)^{4+1} \begin{vmatrix} 3 & 2 & 5 \\ 0 & 5 & 3 \\ 1 & 4 & 8 \end{vmatrix}.
$$

This third order determinant can be evaluated at once, or we may further transform it to get another zero in its first column by adding -3 times its third row to its first row. Thus

$$
D = \begin{vmatrix} 0 & -10 & -19 \\ 0 & 5 & 3 \\ 1 & 4 & 8 \end{vmatrix} = (1)(-1)^{3+1} \begin{vmatrix} -10 & -19 \\ 5 & 3 \end{vmatrix} = +(-30 + 95) = 65.
$$

Problems

1. Following the notation used in the proof of Theorem 3, calculate the numbers q, r, s and q', r', s' relative to the permutations

$$
\underbrace{5, 1,}_{Q} \ \underbrace{3, 6,}_{R} \ \underbrace{2, 4}_{S} \quad\text{and}\quad \underbrace{5, 1,}_{Q'} \ \underbrace{6, 3,}_{R'} \ \underbrace{2, 4.}_{S'}
$$

Apply Theorem 5 to the following problems (2 and 3):

2. Show that the determinantal equation

$$
\begin{vmatrix} x^2 & x & 1 \\ 4 & 2 & 1 \\ 9 & -3 & 1 \end{vmatrix} = 0
$$

has roots $x = 2$, $x = -3$.

3. Let $P_1(x_1, y_1)$, $P_2(x_2, y_2)$, and $P_3(x_3, y_3)$ be the vertices of a triangle.

Show that the area of the triangle is the absolute value of

$$\frac{1}{2} \begin{vmatrix} x_1 & y_1 & 1 \\ x_2 & y_2 & 1 \\ x_3 & y_3 & 1 \end{vmatrix} .$$

[*Hint:* Write the coordinates of P_2 and P_3 as

$$x_2 = x_1 + a \cos \alpha, \qquad y_2 = y_1 + a \sin \alpha,$$
$$x_3 = x_1 + b \cos \beta, \qquad y_3 = y_1 + b \sin \beta,$$

where $a = \overline{P_1 P_2}$, $b = \overline{P_1 P_3}$, while α and β are angles from the horizontal to $P_1 P_2$ and $P_1 P_3$ respectively. Sketch.]

4. Evaluate:

$$\begin{vmatrix} 1 & 3 & -1 & 2 \\ 2 & 1 & 3 & 1 \\ -1 & 2 & -1 & 3 \\ -2 & 1 & 2 & -3 \end{vmatrix} .$$

5. Evaluate:

$$\begin{vmatrix} 4 & 3 & -2 & 7 \\ 8 & 1 & -4 & 6 \\ 6 & 2 & -3 & 11 \\ 10 & 4 & -5 & -8 \end{vmatrix} .$$

6. Show that the determinant

$$\begin{vmatrix} 1 & x_1 & x_1^2 \\ 1 & x_2 & x_2^2 \\ 1 & x_3 & x_3^2 \end{vmatrix}$$

is equal to the product

$$(x_3 - x_1)(x_3 - x_2)(x_2 - x_1). \qquad [\textit{Hint:} \text{ Use Theorem 5.}]$$

7. Generalize the result of Problem 6, and show that

$$\begin{vmatrix} 1 & x_1 & x_1^2 & \cdots & x_1^{n-1} \\ 1 & x_2 & x_2^2 & \cdots & x_2^{n-1} \\ 1 & x_3 & x_3^2 & \cdots & x_3^{n-1} \\ \cdots & \cdots & \cdots & & \cdots \\ 1 & x_n & x_n^2 & \cdots & x_n^{n-1} \end{vmatrix} = \underset{i>j}{\Pi} (x_i - x_j),$$

where the II symbol denotes the product of all factors of the form $(x_i - x_j)$ that can be formed with $i > j$, i and j ranging between 1 and n inclusive; i.e., $n \geq i > j \geq 1$. There are $[n(n - 1)]/2$ such factors.

8–5 Expansion by cofactors. In the expansion of a determinant

$$D = \begin{vmatrix} a_{11} & a_{12} & \ldots & a_{1n} \\ a_{21} & a_{22} & \ldots & a_{2n} \\ \ldots & \ldots & \ldots & \ldots \\ a_{n1} & a_{n2} & \ldots & a_{nn} \end{vmatrix} \tag{1}$$

as the sum of all signed products

$$D = \sum \pm a_{1i_1} a_{2i_2} \ldots a_{ni_n}, \tag{2}$$

we may arrange the products in blocks from which common factors may be removed. Thus, for example, we may collect all those products for which $i_1 = 1$ in (2), then all terms in which $i_1 = 2$, and so forth. The result may be written in the form

$$D = a_{11}A_{11} + a_{12}A_{12} + \cdots + a_{1n}A_{1n}, \tag{3}$$

where A_{1j} is called the cofactor of $a_{1j}; j = 1, \ldots, n$. More generally, we could single out the kth row of D instead of its first row, and write the expression in the form

$$D = a_{k1}A_{k1} + a_{k2}A_{k2} + \cdots + a_{kn}A_{kn}, \tag{4}$$

which is called the expansion of D by cofactors of the elements of the kth row.

We may interpret Eq. (4) as follows. If we were to take all elements $a_{k2}, a_{k3}, \ldots, a_{kn}$ after the first, in the kth row of D, to be zero, then by (4) the resulting determinant D' would have the value

$$D' = a_{k1}A_{k1};$$

that is,

$$D' = \begin{vmatrix} a_{11} & a_{12} & \ldots & a_{1n} \\ \ldots & \ldots & \ldots & \ldots \\ a_{k1} & 0 & \ldots & 0 \\ \ldots & \ldots & \ldots & \ldots \\ a_{n1} & a_{n2} & \ldots & a_{nn} \end{vmatrix} = a_{k1}A_{k1}. \tag{5}$$

In general, the right side of (4) may be interpreted as the sum of n determinants of the type exhibited in (5), in which all elements of the kth row are replaced by zeros except for one element a_{kj}; that is,

$$
D = \begin{vmatrix} a_{11} & a_{12} & a_{13} & \cdots & a_{1n} \\ \cdots & \cdots & \cdots & \cdots & \cdots \\ a_{k1} & a_{k2} & a_{k3} & \cdots & a_{kn} \\ \cdots & \cdots & \cdots & \cdots & \cdots \\ a_{n1} & a_{n2} & a_{n3} & \cdots & a_{nn} \end{vmatrix} = \begin{vmatrix} a_{11} & a_{12} & \cdots & a_{1n} \\ \cdots & \cdots & \cdots & \cdots \\ a_{k1} & 0 & \cdots & 0 \\ \cdots & \cdots & \cdots & \cdots \\ a_{n1} & a_{n2} & \cdots & a_{nn} \end{vmatrix}
$$

$$
+ \begin{vmatrix} a_{11} & a_{12} & \cdots & a_{1n} \\ \cdots & \cdots & \cdots & \cdots \\ 0 & a_{k2} & \cdots & 0 \\ \cdots & \cdots & \cdots & \cdots \\ a_{n1} & a_{n2} & \cdots & a_{nn} \end{vmatrix} + \cdots + \begin{vmatrix} a_{11} & a_{12} & \cdots & a_{1n} \\ \cdots & \cdots & \cdots & \cdots \\ 0 & 0 & \cdots & a_{kn} \\ \cdots & \cdots & \cdots & \cdots \\ a_{n1} & a_{n2} & \cdots & a_{nn} \end{vmatrix} . \quad (6)
$$

This may also be interpreted as a generalization of Theorem 6 of the preceding article and may in fact be obtained by repeated application of that theorem.

Now each of the determinants in (6) which has all but one element zero in its kth row may be evaluated by means of Theorem 10 of the preceding article. The results are summarized in the following theorem.

THEOREM 1. *The sum of the products of the elements of any row (or column) by their respective cofactors is equal to the determinant. The cofactor of the element in the kth row and jth column is $(-1)^{k+j}$ times its minor.*

In expanding a determinant by cofactors, it may be convenient first to transform the determinant into a form in which all elements, except one, of some row (or column) are zero. This method was illustrated in the preceding article in connection with Theorem 10.

On the other hand, if we wish to avoid these preliminary transformations, we may do so at the expense of using all the elements of a row times their respective cofactors. Thus a fourth order determinant reduces to four third order determinants, in general.

EXAMPLE 1. Show that

$$
\begin{vmatrix} x & y & 1 \\ x_1 & y_1 & 1 \\ x_2 & y_2 & 1 \end{vmatrix} = 0
$$

is the equation of the straight line through the points (x_1, y_1) and (x_2, y_2) provided the two points are distinct.

Solution. If the determinant is expanded by elements of its first row, the result is a linear equation of the form $Ax + By + C = 0$, which represents a straight line since one, at least, of A and B is not zero. Furthermore, if one substitutes (x_1, y_1) for (x, y) in the determinant, the first two rows are identical and the equation is satisfied. Hence (x_1, y_1) does lie on the line. The same is true of (x_2, y_2).

THEOREM 2. *If the elements of any row (or column) are multiplied by the cofactors of the corresponding elements of some other row (or column) and the products added, the result is zero.*

Proof. The result may be interpreted as the expansion of a determinant having two identical rows (or columns) and hence is zero by a previous theorem. We shall illustrate this interpretation for a third order determinant. Start with any determinant

$$D = \begin{vmatrix} a_{11} & a_{12} & a_{13} \\ a_{21} & a_{22} & a_{23} \\ a_{31} & a_{32} & a_{33} \end{vmatrix}$$

and expand it by cofactors of any row, say the second to be specific. Then

$$D = a_{21}A_{21} + a_{22}A_{22} + a_{23}A_{23}. \tag{7}$$

Suppose one now replaces a_{21}, a_{22}, and a_{23} by other numbers, say c_1, c_2, and c_3 respectively in (7), with a result

$$D' = c_1A_{21} + c_2A_{22} + c_3A_{23}. \tag{8}$$

This may be interpreted as the expansion by cofactors relative to the second row in

$$D' = \begin{vmatrix} a_{11} & a_{12} & a_{13} \\ c_1 & c_2 & c_3 \\ a_{31} & a_{32} & a_{33} \end{vmatrix}, \tag{9}$$

since the cofactors of c_1, c_2, and c_3 in D' are precisely the original cofactors A_{21}, A_{22}, A_{23} respectively. In particular, if c_1, c_2, and c_3 are taken to be the elements of either the first or the third row of D, then (8) is the sum of products of elements of that row by the cofactors of corresponding elements of a different row, while simultaneously the determinant D' in (9) then has two identical rows, and hence $D' = 0$ as stated in the theorem.

These two theorems form the basis for the solution, by determinants, of n simultaneous linear equations in n unknowns, which we shall discuss in the next article.

PROBLEMS

1. Suppose the elements of the determinant

$$F = \begin{vmatrix} u_1 & v_1 & w_1 \\ u_2 & v_2 & w_2 \\ u_3 & v_3 & w_3 \end{vmatrix}$$

are differentiable functions of x. Prove that

$$\frac{dF}{dx} = \begin{vmatrix} \dfrac{du_1}{dx} & \dfrac{dv_1}{dx} & \dfrac{dw_1}{dx} \\ u_2 & v_2 & w_2 \\ u_3 & v_3 & w_3 \end{vmatrix} + \begin{vmatrix} u_1 & v_1 & w_1 \\ \dfrac{du_2}{dx} & \dfrac{dv_2}{dx} & \dfrac{dw_2}{dx} \\ u_3 & v_3 & w_3 \end{vmatrix} + \begin{vmatrix} u_1 & v_1 & w_1 \\ u_2 & v_2 & w_2 \\ \dfrac{du_3}{dx} & \dfrac{dv_3}{dx} & \dfrac{dw_3}{dx} \end{vmatrix}.$$

State the result in words as a rule for differentiating a determinant of order 3. Can you generalize the result to a determinant of any order n?

2. Write out the sum of the products of the elements of the second row times the cofactors of the corresponding elements of the third row in the determinant

$$\begin{vmatrix} 2 & 3 & -1 \\ -2 & -3 & 2 \\ 3 & 2 & 1 \end{vmatrix}.$$

8–6 Solution of simultaneous linear equations. In the discussion to follow we shall work with three equations in three unknowns in order to simplify the writing, but the argument used may be applied to n equations in n unknowns. We shall accordingly denote the unknowns by x_1, x_2, and x_3, since such a notation lends itself to generalization. The equations may then be represented by

$$a_{11}x_1 + a_{12}x_2 + a_{13}x_3 = c_1,$$
$$a_{21}x_1 + a_{22}x_2 + a_{23}x_3 = c_2, \tag{1}$$
$$a_{31}x_1 + a_{32}x_2 + a_{33}x_3 = c_3.$$

The coefficients of the unknowns may be used to form the determinant

$$D = \begin{vmatrix} a_{11} & a_{12} & a_{13} \\ a_{21} & a_{22} & a_{23} \\ a_{31} & a_{32} & a_{33} \end{vmatrix}, \tag{2}$$

which is called the determinant of the system. In forming this determinant, the first row contains the coefficients, in order, of the unknowns x_1, x_2, x_3 in the first equation. Similarly, each row in D corresponds to one equation of the system, and each column of D corresponds to one of the unknowns.

The solution of the equations (1) by determinants is given by the following theorem, which is known as "Cramer's rule":

THEOREM. *If the determinant D of the coefficients in a system of n linear equations in n unknowns is not zero, then the equations have a unique solution. In the solution, each unknown may be expressed as a fraction of two determinants with denominator D and with numerator obtained from D by replacing the column of coefficients of the unknown in question by the constants $c_1, c_2, \ldots, c_n$.*

Proof. Suppose x_1, x_2, x_3 are three numbers which satisfy the system (1). Then if we multiply these equations by constants and add to get new equations, the same three numbers must satisfy these equations also. Now we choose multipliers in the following way.

Suppose, first, that we wish to find x_1. We calculate the cofactors A_{11}, A_{21}, and A_{31} of the elements in the first column of D. Then we multiply the first equation by A_{11}, the second by A_{21}, and the third by A_{31}, and add. The resulting new equation is

$$(a_{11}A_{11} + a_{21}A_{21} + a_{31}A_{31})x_1 + (a_{12}A_{11} + a_{22}A_{21} + a_{32}A_{31})x_2$$

$$+ (a_{13}A_{11} + a_{23}A_{21} + a_{33}A_{31})x_3 = c_1A_{11} + c_2A_{21} + c_3A_{31}. \tag{3}$$

In this equation, the coefficient which multiplies x_1 is the sum of products of the elements of the first column of D by their cofactors, which by Theorem 1 of the previous article is just D. But the coefficient which multiplies x_2 is the sum of products of the elements of the second column of D by the cofactors of the corresponding elements of the first column of D, and this is zero by Theorem 2 above. Similarly, the coefficient of x_3 is zero. Hence (3) contains only x_1 and has the form

$$x_1 \begin{vmatrix} a_{11} & a_{12} & a_{13} \\ a_{21} & a_{22} & a_{23} \\ a_{31} & a_{32} & a_{33} \end{vmatrix} = \begin{vmatrix} c_1 & a_{12} & a_{13} \\ c_2 & a_{22} & a_{23} \\ c_3 & a_{32} & a_{33} \end{vmatrix}, \tag{4}$$

where we have simply written out the determinant D on the left, while the right sides of (4) and (3) are equal, as can be seen at once if the determinant in (4) is expanded by cofactors according to the elements of its first column. Hence, if the determinant D is not zero, the value that x_1 must have, if x_1, x_2, x_3 are to satisfy the system (1), may be found by division:

$$
x_1 = \frac{\begin{vmatrix} c_1 & a_{12} & a_{13} \\ c_2 & a_{22} & a_{23} \\ c_3 & a_{32} & a_{33} \end{vmatrix}}{\begin{vmatrix} a_{11} & a_{12} & a_{13} \\ a_{21} & a_{22} & a_{23} \\ a_{31} & a_{32} & a_{33} \end{vmatrix}}.
$$

The same argument may be repeated for each of the other unknowns; we simply multiply the equations of the system (1) by the cofactors in D of the elements in the column of D which corresponds to the unknown in question, and then add the results to obtain a new equation. In the equation thus obtained all terms drop out except for the one unknown, and the value of the unknown is then found to be precisely the kind of a fraction described in the theorem.

EXAMPLE 1.
$$
\begin{aligned}
x + y + z &= 1, \\
2x - y + z &= 0, \\
x + 2y - z &= 4.
\end{aligned}
$$

Solution. The determinant of the system is

$$
D = \begin{vmatrix} 1 & 1 & 1 \\ 2 & -1 & 1 \\ 1 & 2 & -1 \end{vmatrix}.
$$

Suppose we are interested in finding z. We then calculate the cofactors of the elements of the third column of D, namely,

$$
\begin{vmatrix} 2 & -1 \\ 1 & 2 \end{vmatrix} = 5, \qquad - \begin{vmatrix} 1 & 1 \\ 1 & 2 \end{vmatrix} = -1, \qquad \begin{vmatrix} 1 & 1 \\ 2 & -1 \end{vmatrix} = -3.
$$

Multiplying the first equation by 5, the second by -1, and the third by -3, and adding, we obtain

$$
(5 - 2 - 3)x + (5 + 1 - 6)y + (5 - 1 + 3)z = 5 - 12,
$$

or

$$
7z = -7, \qquad z = -1.
$$

The method described shows that if the original equations have a solution, then it must be given by Cramer's rule. It does not, however, show that these values of the unknowns actually do satisfy the original equations. This may be done by substituting the answers back into the original equations.

For the first equation in (1), written in the form

$$a_{11}x_1 + a_{12}x_2 + a_{13}x_3 - c_1 = 0,$$

when we substitute the expressions for x_1, x_2, and x_3 in terms of determinants, and clear of fractions, the left side becomes

$$a_{11} \begin{vmatrix} c_1 & a_{12} & a_{13} \\ c_2 & a_{22} & a_{23} \\ c_3 & a_{32} & a_{33} \end{vmatrix} + a_{12} \begin{vmatrix} a_{11} & c_1 & a_{13} \\ a_{21} & c_2 & a_{23} \\ a_{31} & c_3 & a_{33} \end{vmatrix}$$

$$+ a_{13} \begin{vmatrix} a_{11} & a_{12} & c_1 \\ a_{21} & a_{22} & c_2 \\ a_{31} & a_{32} & c_3 \end{vmatrix} - c_1 \begin{vmatrix} a_{11} & a_{12} & a_{13} \\ a_{21} & a_{22} & a_{23} \\ a_{31} & a_{32} & a_{33} \end{vmatrix} . \quad (5)$$

In each of the first two determinants, move the column of constants c_1, c_2, c_3 to the right, changing signs twice in the first determinant and once in the second. The result may then be identified as the expansion, by cofactors relative to the first row, of the fourth order determinant

$$\begin{vmatrix} a_{11} & a_{12} & a_{13} & c_1 \\ a_{11} & a_{12} & a_{13} & c_1 \\ a_{21} & a_{22} & a_{23} & c_2 \\ a_{31} & a_{32} & a_{33} & c_3 \end{vmatrix} \quad (6)$$

This is zero, since its first two rows are identical. A determinant similar to the one in (6) also results when the expressions for the unknowns are substituted into the remaining equations in (1), except that the first row becomes the same as the third or fourth row respectively. Thus the expressions given by Cramer's rule give the unique solution of the system of equations, when D is not zero.

EXAMPLE 2. To illustrate Cramer's rule, we solve the following system by determinants.

$$2x + y - z = 0,$$

$$x - y + z = 6,$$

$$x + 2y + z = 3.$$

The determinant of the coefficients is

$$D = \begin{vmatrix} 2 & 1 & -1 \\ 1 & -1 & 1 \\ 1 & 2 & 1 \end{vmatrix} = \begin{vmatrix} 2 & 1 & -1 \\ 3 & 0 & 0 \\ 3 & 3 & 0 \end{vmatrix} = -9.$$

Since $D \neq 0$, we may solve by determinants. Thus

$$x = \frac{\begin{vmatrix} 0 & 1 & -1 \\ 6 & -1 & 1 \\ 3 & 2 & 1 \end{vmatrix}}{D} = \frac{-18}{-9} = 2,$$

$$y = \frac{\begin{vmatrix} 2 & 0 & -1 \\ 1 & 6 & 1 \\ 1 & 3 & 1 \end{vmatrix}}{D} = \frac{9}{-9} = -1,$$

$$z = \frac{\begin{vmatrix} 2 & 1 & 0 \\ 1 & -1 & 6 \\ 1 & 2 & 3 \end{vmatrix}}{D} = \frac{-27}{-9} = 3.$$

As a check, we quickly verify that $x = 2$, $y = -1$, $z = 3$ actually do satisfy the original three equations.

The question naturally arises as to what the situation is regarding the solvability of the original equations when the determinant of coefficients is zero. A complete answer will not be given here, but is given in more advanced algebra courses where the subject of matrices is studied. Some idea of the complications which may arise may be gained from considering the case of three equations in three unknowns. Each such equation represents a plane in space, as we shall show in a later chapter, and the determinant of coefficients vanishes if

(a) any two of the planes are parallel or coincident, or
(b) the line of intersection of two of the planes is parallel to, or lies in, the third plane.

A solution of the system of simultaneous equations corresponds to a point on all three planes. If the cases (a) or (b) occur, there may be no point at all which lies on all three planes, or there may [for example, if the two planes in (a) are identical] be infinitely many points on all three planes. (See Fig. 8–1.) In particular, there are infinitely many solutions if the three planes all intersect along one straight line.

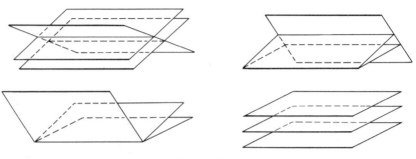

FIGURE 8–1

In any case where $D = 0$, one should attempt to solve the system of equations by the method of "successive elimination" illustrated below. In fact, this method is usually more economical than the solution by determinants, even in those cases where D does not vanish.

EXAMPLE 3.
$$2x - y + z = 4,$$
$$x + 3y + 2z = 12,$$
$$3x + 2y + 3z = 16.$$

Solution. The determinant of coefficients is

$$D = \begin{vmatrix} 2 & -1 & 1 \\ 1 & 3 & 2 \\ 3 & 2 & 3 \end{vmatrix} = \begin{vmatrix} 2 & -1 & 1 \\ 3 & 2 & 3 \\ 3 & 2 & 3 \end{vmatrix} = 0.$$

Multiply the second equation by 2 and by 3 respectively and subtract from the first and third equations to eliminate x from them. The three new equations are

$$x + 3y + 2z = 12,$$
$$-7y - 3z = -20,$$
$$-7y - 3z = -20.$$

Here the third equation is superfluous, since it contains no information not already given by the second equation. Thus we need only solve

$$x + 3y = 12 - 2z,$$
$$7y = 20 - 3z.$$

In these, let z have any value whatever. Then we have a solution, provided we take

$$y = \frac{20 - 3z}{7}$$

and

$$x = 12 - 2z - 3y \quad \text{or} \quad x = \frac{24 - 5z}{7}.$$

It is easily verified, by substitution into the original equations, that

$$x = \frac{24 - 5z}{7}, \quad y = \frac{20 - 3z}{7}, \quad z \text{ arbitrary}$$

do satisfy the equations. For example,

$$z = -5, \quad x = 7, \quad y = 5 \quad \text{and} \quad z = 2, \quad x = 2, \quad y = 2$$

are particular solutions.

PROBLEMS

Solve the following systems of simultaneous equations by Cramer's rule:

1. $x + y + z = 2,$
   $2x - y + z = 0,$
   $x + 2y - z = 4$

2. $2x + y - z = 2,$
   $x - y + z = 7,$
   $x + 2y + z = 4$

3. By multiplying the following equations by appropriate factors and adding, eliminate x, y, and t:

$$x + y + z + t = 6,$$
$$x - 2y + 3z + t = 2,$$
$$3x + y - z + 2t = 6,$$
$$2x + 3y + 2z - t = 2.$$

4. For what value of k may the following set of equations fail to have a unique solution?

$$x + y - z = 3,$$
$$kx - y + 2z = 5,$$
$$x + 2y - z = 4.$$

8-7 Homogeneous linear equations. There is one case in particular where one rather hopes that the determinant of the coefficients will be zero. That is in the case of homogeneous equations:

$$a_{11}x_1 + a_{12}x_2 + a_{13}x_3 = 0,$$
$$a_{21}x_1 + a_{22}x_2 + a_{23}x_3 = 0, \qquad (1)$$
$$a_{31}x_1 + a_{32}x_2 + a_{33}x_3 = 0,$$

where $x_1 = x_2 = x_3 = 0$ always gives a solution regardless of the coefficients a_{ij}. Since this solution contains no distinguishing information which is characteristic of the particular system of equations, it is referred to as the *trivial solution*. The question of interest in such a case is whether or not a *nontrivial* solution can be found. By Cramer's rule, it follows that the answer is in the negative if $D \neq 0$. On the other hand, if $D = 0$, it is true that nontrivial solutions do exist, as we shall prove in the next theorem.

THEOREM. *A necessary and sufficient condition for existence of nontrivial solutions of a system of n homogeneous linear equations in n unknowns is that the determinant of coefficients be zero.*

Proof (by induction on n). If $n = 1$, the system of equations is just $a_{11}x_1 = 0$ and this implies that $a_{11} = 0$ or $x_1 = 0$. Therefore, if the "determinant" a_{11} is not zero, only the trivial solution $x_1 = 0$ exists. But if the determinant a_{11} is zero, then x_1 may have any value; in particular, $x_1 = 1$ gives a nontrivial solution.

Suppose now that n is a positive integer and the theorem is known to be true for the smaller integer $n - 1$. We then proceed as follows to reduce the problem to the case of $n - 1$ equations in $n - 1$ unknowns. Let the given system of n equations in n unknowns be

$$
\begin{aligned}
a_{11}x_1 + a_{12}x_2 + \cdots + a_{1n}x_n &= 0, \\
a_{21}x_1 + a_{22}x_2 + \cdots + a_{2n}x_n &= 0, \\
&\vdots \\
a_{n1}x_1 + a_{n2}x_2 + \cdots + a_{nn}x_n &= 0.
\end{aligned}
\tag{E}
$$

Case 1. If it happens that $a_{11} = a_{21} = \cdots = a_{n1} = 0$, so that x_1 doesn't actually appear in any of equations (E), we may take $x_1 = 1$, $x_2 = x_3 = \cdots = x_n = 0$ and have a nontrivial solution of (E).

Case 2. Suppose that x_1 does appear in (E) with a nonzero coefficient. If necessary, we could rearrange the equations to have a nonzero coefficient of x_1 in the first equation. So, with no loss in generality, suppose

$$a_{11} \neq 0.$$

Then we replace (E) by the equivalent set of equations (E'):

$$
\begin{aligned}
x_1 + b_{12}x_2 + b_{13}x_3 + \cdots + b_{1n}x_n &= 0, \\
b_{22}x_2 + b_{23}x_3 + \cdots + b_{2n}x_n &= 0, \\
&\vdots \\
b_{n2}x_2 + b_{n3}x_3 + \cdots + b_{nn}x_n &= 0.
\end{aligned}
\tag{E'}
$$

We divide the first equation of (E) by a_{11}, thus getting the first equation of (E') with leading coefficient one. This equation is multiplied by a_{k1} and the result subtracted from the kth equation of (E), thus giving the kth equation of (E'); $k = 2, 3, \ldots, n$. These operations are reversible. Hence any solution of the system (E) is a solution of (E'), and conversely. The determinant D' of the coefficients of the system (E') may be obtained from the determinant D of the system (E) by dividing the first row by a_{11}, then subtracting a_{k1} times the new first row from the kth row; $k = 2, 3, \ldots, n$. Hence

$$D' = \frac{D}{a_{11}}.$$

Therefore $D' = 0$ if and only if $D = 0$.

But if

$$D' = \begin{vmatrix} 1 & b_{12} & b_{13} & \ldots & b_{1n} \\ 0 & b_{22} & b_{23} & \ldots & b_{2n} \\ 0 & b_{32} & b_{33} & \ldots & b_{3n} \\ \vdots & & & & \\ 0 & b_{n2} & b_{n3} & \ldots & b_{nn} \end{vmatrix}$$

is expanded by cofactors of its first column, we see it is equal to B_{11}, the cofactor of the element in its upper left corner:

$$B_{11} = \begin{vmatrix} b_{22} & b_{23} & \ldots & b_{2n} \\ b_{32} & b_{33} & \ldots & b_{3n} \\ \ldots & \ldots & \ldots & \ldots \\ b_{n2} & b_{n3} & \ldots & b_{nn} \end{vmatrix}.$$

This is also the determinant of the $n - 1$ equations in $n - 1$ unknowns that we get by temporarily ignoring the first equation of the system (E').

We now apply our inductive hypothesis to this system of $n - 1$ equations. By our assumption, the theorem is true for $n - 1$ equations in $n - 1$ unknowns. Therefore if $D = 0$, then $B_{11} = 0$, and the last $n - 1$ equations have a solution in which $x_2, x_3, \ldots, x_n$ are not all zero. From this we get a nontrivial solution of the full system (E'), and hence of (E), by solving the first equation for x_1 in terms of the numbers $x_2, x_3, \ldots x_n$:

$$x_1 = -b_{12}x_2 - b_{13}x_3 - \cdots - b_{1n}x_n.$$

So, if $D = 0$, the system has a nontrivial solution.

Conversely, if $D \neq 0$, then $B_{11} \neq 0$, and the only solution of the last

$n - 1$ equations of (E′) is $x_2 = x_3 = \cdots = x_n = 0$. To satisfy the first equation of (E′), we must then also take $x_1 = 0$. That is, if $D \neq 0$, the system has only the trivial solution. Q.E.D.

COROLLARY. *m homogeneous linear equations in n unknowns always have nontrivial solutions if* $m < n$.

Proof. Augment the given set of equations by adjoining $n - m$ equations of the form

$$0 \cdot x_1 + 0 \cdot x_2 + \cdots + 0 \cdot x_n = 0.$$

The determinant of coefficients of the new set of n equations in n unknowns has one or more rows of zeros; hence its value is zero. Therefore it has nontrivial solutions. Q.E.D.

EXAMPLE 1.

$$x + 3y + 2z = 0,$$
$$2x - y + z = 0,$$
$$3x + 2y + 3z = 0.$$

Solution. The coefficient of x in the first equation is already 1. We subtract twice the first equation from the second, and three times the first from the third. The new system is

$$x + 3y + 2z = 0,$$
$$-7y - 3z = 0,$$
$$-7y - 3z = 0.$$

The last two equations are identical:

$$7y + 3z = 0.$$

Infinitely many numbers satisfy this equation. We may, for example, let

$$z = a \qquad (a \text{ arbitrary})$$

so long as we then take

$$y = \frac{-3a}{7}.$$

The original system requires that

$$x = -3y - 2z = \frac{9a}{7} - 2a = \frac{-5a}{7}.$$

In particular, if we take $a = 1$, we have a solution

$$x = -\tfrac{5}{7}, \qquad y = -\tfrac{3}{7}, \qquad z = 1.$$

Another solution, with $a = 7$, is

$$x = -5, \qquad y = -3, \qquad z = 7.$$

Every solution in this case is proportional to this solution; that is,

$$x = -5k, \qquad y = -3k, \qquad z = 7k$$

represents the general solution of the system. Assigning different values to k, $-\infty < k < +\infty$, corresponds to letting the point (x, y, z) trace out the line of intersection of the three given planes.

EXAMPLE 2.
$$x + 2y - 3z + 4t = 0,$$
$$2x - y + z - 2t = 0.$$

Solution. Subtract twice the first equation from the second:

$$x + 2y - 3z + 4t = 0,$$
$$-5y + 7z - 10t = 0.$$

In this system, or an augmented system with two more equations of the form

$$0 \cdot z + 0 \cdot t = 0, \qquad 0 \cdot t = 0,$$

we may take

$$t = a, \qquad (a \text{ arbitrary})$$

$$z = b, \qquad (b \text{ arbitrary})$$

$$y = \frac{7z - 10t}{5} = -2a + \tfrac{7}{5}b,$$

$$x = -2y + 3z - 4t = \frac{b}{5}.$$

Here we have four equations and only two unknowns, so it is not surprising that there are two "degrees of freedom" evidenced by the two arbitrary numbers a and b. If we take $a = 0$, $b = 5$, we get a solution $x_1 = 1$, $y_1 = 7$, $z_1 = 5$, $t_1 = 0$. If we take $a = 1$, $b = 0$, we get another solution $x_2 = 0$, $y_2 = -2$, $z_2 = 0$, $t_2 = 1$. The solution corresponding to $a = 1$, $b = 5$ is $x_3 = x_2 + x_1$, $y_3 = y_2 + y_1$, and so on.

EXAMPLE 3. For what values of r is $x = Ae^{rt}$, $y = Be^{rt}$ a nontrivial solution of the pair of differential equations

$$\frac{dx}{dt} = x - 2y, \qquad \frac{dy}{dt} = y - 2x?$$

Solution. Substituting the expressions given for x and y into the differential equations produces

$$Are^{rt} = Ae^{rt} - 2Be^{rt},$$

$$Bre^{rt} = Be^{rt} - 2Ae^{rt}.$$

Dividing by e^{rt} and collecting terms, we get

$$(r - 1)A + 2B = 0,$$
$$2A + (r - 1)B = 0.$$

These are two homogeneous linear equations for A and B. The determinant is

$$D = \begin{vmatrix} r - 1 & 2 \\ 2 & r - 1 \end{vmatrix} = (r - 1)^2 - 4.$$

The equations have only the trivial solution $A = B = 0$ if $D \neq 0$. To get a nontrivial solution, it is necessary that $D = 0$, or

$$r = 1 \pm 2 = 3 \quad \text{or} \quad -1.$$

Case 1. $r = 3$. Then the two equations for A and B are identical:

$$2A + 2B = 0, \quad \text{or} \quad B = -A.$$

So one solution is

$$x = Ae^{3t}, \quad y = -Ae^{3t}.$$

Case 2. $r = -1$. Then the equations for A and B become

$$-2A + 2B = 0, \quad 2A - 2B = 0,$$

or

$$B = A.$$

So another solution is

$$x = Ae^{-t}, \quad y = Ae^{-t}.$$

PROBLEMS

1. For what value of k do the following equations possess a nontrivial solution?

$$2x + 3y - 4z = 0,$$
$$x + ky + 3z = 0,$$
$$3x + ky - 2z = 0.$$

2. Find at least one nontrivial solution of the equations

$$x + y - z = 0,$$
$$3x - y - z = 0,$$
$$x - 3y + z = 0,$$

or else show that there is no nontrivial solution.

3. Suppose the determinant of the coefficients of the system of equations (1) is zero. Show that

$$x_1 = kA_{11}, \qquad x_2 = kA_{12}, \qquad x_3 = kA_{13}$$

is a solution of the system, for any k, where A_{11} is the cofactor of a_{11}, and so on. Could cofactors of elements of other rows than the first be used? Give a reason for your answer.

4. Verify that the system of equations

$$2x - y + z = 0,$$

$$x + 2y - z = 0,$$

$$4x + 3y - z = 0$$

has nontrivial solutions. Find some of them by using the results of Problem 3 above.

The following sets of simultaneous differential equations, Problems 5–12, possess nonzero solutions of the form $x = Ae^{rt}$, $y = Be^{rt}$ for certain values of the constants A, B, and r. Find them.

5. $\dfrac{dx}{dt} = 2x + 2y, \qquad \dfrac{dy}{dt} = x + y$

6. $\dfrac{dx}{dt} = 3x + y, \qquad \dfrac{dy}{dt} = -x + y$

7. $\dfrac{dx}{dt} = x + y, \qquad \dfrac{dy}{dt} = x + y$

8. $\dfrac{dx}{dt} = 2x + 3y, \qquad \dfrac{dy}{dt} = -x - 2y$

9. $\dfrac{dx}{dt} + x - 2y = 0, \qquad \dfrac{dy}{dt} - 2x + y = 0$

10. $\dfrac{dx}{dt} + 2x - y = 0, \qquad \dfrac{dy}{dt} - x + 2y = 0$

11. $\dfrac{dx}{dt} + 2x = 0, \qquad \dfrac{dy}{dt} - 4x - 2y = 0$

12. $\dfrac{dx}{dt} = 3x + 4y, \qquad \dfrac{dy}{dt} + x + 2y = 0$

13. If $x = A_1 e^{r_1 t}$, $y = B_1 e^{r_1 t}$ is one solution of any of the sets of differential equations of Problems 3–10 above, and $x = A_2 e^{r_2 t}$, $y = B_2 e^{r_2 t}$ is another solution, prove that

$$x = A_1 e^{r_1 t} + A_2 e^{r_2 t},$$

$$y = B_1 e^{r_1 t} + B_2 e^{r_2 t}$$

is also a solution.

REVIEW QUESTIONS AND EXERCISES FOR CHAPTER 8

1. What methods are available for evaluating a determinant?
2. What is the effect on a determinant if:

(a) Two rows are interchanged?

(b) Three rows are permuted cyclically (the first one to be moved goes to the position of the second, the second to the position of the third, the third back to the position of the first)?

(c) Each element of a row is divided by 3?

(d) Each element of a column is subtracted from the corresponding element of a different column?

3. Under what conditions do n linear equations in n unknowns have a unique solution? When they fail to have a unique solution, they may have no solution or more than one solution. Discuss the possibilities for $n = 3$.

4. Define "homogeneous linear equations." When does a system of n homogeneous linear equations in n unknowns have nontrivial solutions? When do they have a unique solution, and what is that solution?

5. State Cramer's rule. Illustrate for three equations in three unknowns.

MISCELLANEOUS PROBLEMS FOR CHAPTER 8

In each of the following problems (1–10), solve by Cramer's rule, or by the method of elimination, or show that the system of equations has no solution.

1. $2x + 3y = 5,$
   $4x - y = 3$

2. $3x + y - z = 2,$
   $x - 2y + z = 0,$
   $4x - y + z = 3$

3. $x - y + 2z = 2,$
   $x + 3y + z = 1,$
   $-7x + y + 4z = 0$

4. $x + y + z = 1,$
   $x - y = 4,$
   $x + y - 2z = 4$

5. $x + 2y + 3z = 0,$
   $x - 5y + 3z = 0,$
   $3x - z = 0$

6. $2x + y = 0,$
   $-x + 2y + z = 2,$
   $x - 2y + 5z = 5$

7. $x - y + 2z = 2,$
   $3x - 2y + 4z = 5,$
   $2y - 3z + 2 = 0$

8. $2x - y + 3z = 6,$
   $4x + y = 9,$
   $7x + 2y - z = 15$

9. $x + y + 3z = 6,$
   $x - 3y - 3z = -4,$
   $5x - 3y + 3z = 8$

10. $x - y - 3z - t = 1,$
    $2x + 4y - 2t = 2,$
    $3x + 4y - 2z = 0,$
    $x + 2z - 3t = 3$

11. Show that the three points $P_1(x_1, y_1)$, $P_2(x_2, y_2)$, $P_3(x_3, y_3)$ are collinear if and only if

$$\begin{vmatrix} x_1 & y_1 & 1 \\ x_2 & y_2 & 1 \\ x_3 & y_3 & 1 \end{vmatrix} = 0.$$

12. Let $P_1(x_1, y_1)$, $P_2(x_2, y_2)$, $P_3(x_3, y_3)$ be vertices of a triangle. Let

$$\begin{vmatrix} x & y & 1 \\ x_2 & y_2 & 1 \\ x_3 & y_3 & 1 \end{vmatrix} \equiv Ax + By + C.$$

Let $b = \overline{P_2P_3}$ and let h be the length of the altitude from P_1 to the base P_2P_3.
(a) Show that $b = \sqrt{A^2 + B^2}$. (b) Show that

$$h = \left| \frac{1}{b} D \right|,$$

where
$$D = \begin{vmatrix} x_1 & y_1 & 1 \\ x_2 & y_2 & 1 \\ x_3 & y_3 & 1 \end{vmatrix}.$$

(c) Hence deduce that the area of the triangle is $\frac{1}{2}|D|$. [Compare "Area of a Triangle and the Determinant" by G. M. Petersen, *Amer. Math. Monthly*, Vol. 62 (1955), p. 249.] (d) Find the area of the triangle with vertices $P_1(1, -1)$, $P_2(3, 1)$, $P_3(2, 4)$.

13. Show that
$$\begin{vmatrix} 1 & 1 & 1 \\ a & b & c \\ a^3 & b^3 & c^3 \end{vmatrix} = (b - a)(c - a)(c - b)(a + b + c).$$

14. Let u, v, and w be functions of x with $u' = du/dx$, $u'' = d^2u/dx^2$, $v' = dv/dx$, etc. If
$$A = \begin{vmatrix} u & v & w \\ u' & v' & w' \\ u'' & v'' & w'' \end{vmatrix},$$
show that
$$\frac{dA}{dx} = \begin{vmatrix} u & v & w \\ u' & v' & w' \\ u''' & v''' & w''' \end{vmatrix}.$$

15. Show, without expanding, that
$$\begin{vmatrix} b + c & a & 1 \\ c + a & b & 1 \\ b + a & c & 1 \end{vmatrix} = 0.$$

16. Reduce the following to an array with only four nonzero entries and thus evaluate the determinant
$$\begin{vmatrix} -1 & 1 & 1 & 1 \\ 1 & -1 & 1 & 1 \\ 1 & 1 & -1 & 1 \\ 1 & 1 & 1 & -1 \end{vmatrix}.$$

17. Solve the following system of equations:
$$x + y + z = a + b + c,$$

$$bx + cy + az = ab + bc + ca,$$

$$b^2x + c^2y + a^2z = ca^2 + ab^2 + bc^2,$$

where a, b, c are three given numbers, different from each other.

18. Show that

$$F(x) = \begin{vmatrix} A+x & a+x & a+x \\ b+x & B+x & a+x \\ b+x & b+x & C+x \end{vmatrix}$$

defines a linear function of x, and that

$$F(0) = \frac{af(b) - bf(a)}{a - b},$$

where

$$f(x) = (A - x)(B - x)(C - x).$$

19. If

$$\Delta_1 = \begin{vmatrix} a_{11} & a_{12} \\ a_{21} & a_{22} \end{vmatrix} \quad \text{and} \quad \Delta_2 = \begin{vmatrix} b_{11} & b_{12} \\ b_{21} & b_{22} \end{vmatrix},$$

show that

$$\begin{vmatrix} c_{11} & c_{12} \\ c_{21} & c_{22} \end{vmatrix} = \Delta_1\Delta_2,$$

where $c_{ij} = a_{i1}b_{1j} + a_{i2}b_{2j}$

20. (a) If three lines

$$a_1x + b_1y + c_1 = 0,$$

$$a_2x + b_2y + c_2 = 0,$$

$$a_3x + b_3y + c_3 = 0$$

pass through a point, show that $\Delta = 0$, where

$$\Delta = \begin{vmatrix} a_1 & b_1 & c_1 \\ a_2 & b_2 & c_2 \\ a_3 & b_3 & c_3 \end{vmatrix}.$$

(b) If $\Delta = 0$, do the lines necessarily pass through a point? [*Hint:* Consider the case of three parallel lines.]

21. If the equations

$$a_1x + b_1y + c_1 = 0,$$

$$a_2x + b_2y + c_2 = 0,$$

$$a_3x + b_3y + c_3 = 0$$

have a simultaneous solution, show that constants K_1, K_2, and K_3 not all zero exist such that

$$K_1(a_1x + b_1y + c_1) + K_2(a_2x + b_2y + c_2)$$
$$+ K_3(a_3x + b_3y + c_3) \equiv 0, \qquad \text{for all } x \text{ and } y.$$

Is the converse true? [*Hint:* For the converse, consider the equations

$$x + y - 1 = 0, \qquad x + y - 2 = 0, \qquad x + y - 3 = 0.]$$

CHAPTER 9

PLANE ANALYTIC GEOMETRY

9-1 Curves and equations. Analytic geometry combines algebra and calculus with geometry in the following typical problems:

(a) to study the geometric properties of a curve when its equation is given, or

(b) to find an equation of the curve when its geometric properties are known.

The cardinal principle of analytic geometry is that an equation

$$F(x, y) = 0 \tag{1}$$

determines a curve which is the locus of all and only those points $P(x, y)$ whose coordinates satisfy the given equation. Thus every point on the curve must satisfy the equation and every point which satisfies the equation is on the curve. We have already had some experience in analyzing a given equation to find the turning points and points of inflection of the curve it represents. We shall now consider certain other important characteristics which we may find by investigating a given equation.

In this chapter we shall assume that the scales on the x- and y-axes are the same, unless we specifically note otherwise.

Symmetry. If the equation of the curve is unaltered when x is replaced by $-x$, that is, if

$$F(x, y) = F(-x, y),$$

then the points (x_1, y_1) and $(-x_1, y_1)$ are both on the curve when either of them is. Then the curve is symmetric with respect to the y-axis. (See Fig. 9–1a.) In particular, an equation which contains only even powers of x represents such a curve.

Other symmetries which are easily detected are:

Symmetry about the x-axis if the equation is unaltered when y is replaced by $-y$; in particular if only even powers of y occur.

Symmetry about the origin if the equation is unaltered when x and y are replaced by $-x$ and $-y$ respectively (Fig. 9–1c).

Symmetry about the 45° line $y = x$ if the equation is unaltered when x and y are interchanged (Fig. 9–1d).

EXAMPLE 1. $x^2 + y^2 = 1$.
Symmetric about both axes, about the origin, and about the line $y = x$.

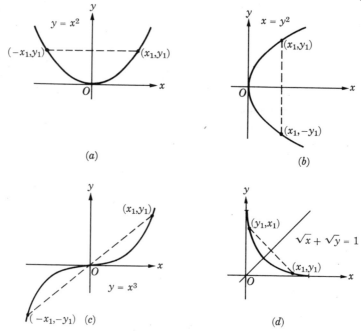

FIGURE 9–1

EXAMPLE 2. $x^2 - y^2 = 1$.
Symmetric about both axes and the origin. Not symmetric about the line $y = x$.

EXAMPLE 3. $xy = 1$.
Not symmetric about either axis. Symmetric about the origin and about the line $y = x$.

Extent. Only real values of x and y are considered in determining the points (x, y) whose coordinates satisfy a given equation. When even powers of a variable appear in the equation, the solution for that variable may involve square roots (or other even roots). The *extent* of the curve may then be limited by the condition that negative numbers do not have real square roots.

EXAMPLE 4. $x^2 + y^2 = 1$.
When this equation is solved for y, we get

$$y = \pm\sqrt{1 - x^2}.$$

The quantity under the radical is negative if $|x| > 1$. The extent of the curve in the x-direction is therefore limited to the interval $-1 \leq x \leq 1$. By symmetry about the line $y = x$, the curve is also limited in the y-direction to $-1 \leq y \leq 1$.

EXAMPLE 5. $x^2 - y^2 = 1$.
Solving for y, we get

$$y = \pm\sqrt{x^2 - 1}.$$

In this case, y is imaginary unless $|x| \geq 1$. There is no curve between the two lines $x = -1$ and $x = +1$. Solving for x, we get

$$x = \pm\sqrt{1 + y^2}.$$

The quantity under the radical is positive (actually it is greater than or equal to one) for all real values of y, $-\infty < y < +\infty$. The extent of this curve is not limited in the y-direction.

Intercepts. The point or points where a given curve crosses the x-axis can be found by setting $y = 0$ in the equation and solving for x. These points are called the *x-intercepts.* The y-intercepts are found in an analogous way by setting $x = 0$. If the labor involved in finding the intercepts is not excessive, they may be determined and will give specific points on the curve.

EXAMPLE 6. $x^2 + y^2 = 1$.
Setting $y = 0$, we have $x^2 = 1$. Therefore $(1, 0)$ and $(-1, 0)$ are the x-intercepts. By symmetry, $(0, 1)$ and $(0, -1)$ are the y-intercepts.

EXAMPLE 7. $x^2 - y^2 = 1$.
Setting $y = 0$, we find the x-intercepts are $(1, 0)$ and $(-1, 0)$. Setting $x = 0$, we obtain $y^2 = -1$, which has no real solutions. The curve does not have intercepts on the y-axis (see Example 5).

EXAMPLE 8. $xy = 1$.
Setting either $x = 0$ or $y = 0$ leads to the equation $0 = 1$, which has no solutions. There are no x- or y-intercepts.

Asymptotes. As the point $P(x, y)$ on a given curve moves farther and farther away from the vicinity of the origin, it may happen that the distance between P and some fixed line tends to zero. In such a case the line is called an *asymptote* of the curve. For example, if the equation of the curve has the form

$$y = \frac{N(x)}{D(x)}, \tag{2}$$

where $N(x)$ and $D(x)$ are polynomials without any factors in common, and if $x = c$ is a root of the equation

$$D(x) = 0, \tag{3}$$

then as the x-coordinate of the tracing point $P(x, y)$ approaches c, two things will occur:

1. $y \to \infty$, hence the distance $OP \to \infty$, and

2. $(x - c) \to 0$; that is, the horizontal distance $P'P$ between the curve and the vertical line $x = c$ tends to zero (see Fig. 9–2). In other words, *the line $x = c$ is an asymptote of the curve in Eq. (2) if $x = c$ makes the denominator, $D(x)$, vanish.* Such asymptotes are thus found by solving the equation explicitly for y in terms of x; then, if the result is a fraction, we set the denominator of the fraction equal to zero and solve for the numerical values of x. A similar procedure with the roles of x and y reversed shows that values of y which cause the denominator to vanish in the expression

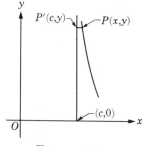

FIGURE 9–2

$$x = \frac{f(y)}{g(y)} \tag{4}$$

may give horizontal asymptotes of the curve. An alternate method for finding such asymptotes is to let $x \to \pm\infty$ (provided the extent of the curve does not prohibit this) in Eq. (2) and find the limiting values of y.

EXAMPLE 9. (Fig. 9–3) $y^2(x^2 - x) = x^2 + 1$. $\tag{5}$
Solving for y, we obtain

$$y = \pm\sqrt{\frac{x^2 + 1}{x(x - 1)}}. \tag{6}$$

The expression under the radical must not be negative, so no portion of the curve lies between the lines $x = 0$ and $x = 1$. But all values of $x > 1$ and all negative values of x, that is, $x < 0$, are permissible. As x approaches zero *from the left*, $y \to \pm\infty$ and as x approaches one *from the right*, $y \to \pm\infty$. The lines $x = 0$ and $x = 1$ are asymptotes of the curve. Since arbitrarily large values of $|x|$ are permitted, we also investigate the behavior of the curve as $x \to -\infty$ and again as $x \to +\infty$. The expression

$$\frac{\infty^2 + 1}{\infty(\infty - 1)},$$

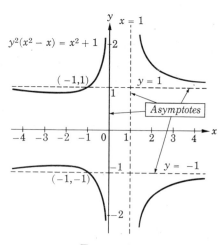

FIGURE 9–3

which appears if we substitute $x = \infty$ directly into (6), is meaningless, but if we write the equation of the curve in the equivalent form

$$y^2 = \frac{x^2 + 1}{x^2 - x} = \frac{1 + \dfrac{1}{x^2}}{1 - \dfrac{1}{x}}, \tag{7}$$

we readily see that $y^2 \to 1$ as $x \to \infty$ or as $x \to -\infty$. Thus the lines $y = 1$ and $y = -1$ are also asymptotes of the curve. We now scrutinize Eq. (7) more closely to see whether or not y^2 is necessarily always greater than one, or always less than one, or may be equal to one. Certainly when x tends to $+\infty$, the numerator in (7) is greater than one, while the denominator is less than one, hence the fraction is larger than one; that is,

$$y^2 > 1, \qquad y^2 \to 1 \quad \text{as} \quad x \to +\infty. \tag{8}$$

On the other hand, when x tends to $-\infty$, both $1/x^2$ and $-1/x$ are positive, so that both the numerator and denominator in (7) are greater than one. However, $1/x^2$ will be less than $-1/x$, so that the numerator is less than the denominator; that is,

$$y^2 < 1, \qquad y^2 \to 1 \quad \text{as} \quad x \to -\infty. \tag{9}$$

To determine whether or not we may ever have $y^2 = 1$, we try it, say in (5), and find

$$y^2 = 1 \qquad \text{when} \qquad x = -1. \tag{10}$$

We now have quite a bit of information about the curve represented by Eq. (5). It is immediately evident that the curve is symmetric about the x-axis, because y may be replaced by $-y$ without changing the equation. There is no curve between $x = 0$ and $x = 1$. The lines $x = 0$, $x = 1$, $y = 1$, $y = -1$ are asymptotes of the curve. It crosses $y = 1$ and $y = -1$ at $x = -1$. There is no x-intercept, because putting $y = 0$ in Eq. (5) requires $0 = x^2 + 1$, which has only imaginary roots. Using this information, we may sketch the curve with a fair degree of accuracy (see Fig. 9–3). In fact, it becomes apparent that the curve has a minimum (and a symmetrically located maximum) somewhat to the left of $x = -1$, and that there is also a point of inflection to the left of this turning point. To find these points accurately requires that we determine dy/dx and d^2y/dx^2. The turning points will be found to occur at $(-1 - \sqrt{2}, \pm\sqrt{2\sqrt{2} - 2})$. The algebra involved in finding the points of inflection is excessive.

Direction at a point. The three curves

(a) $y = x$, $dy/dx = 1$,

(b) $y = x^2$, $dy/dx = 2x$,

(c) $y = \sqrt{x}$, $dy/dx = 1/(2\sqrt{x})$

all pass through the origin and the point $(1, 1)$. But their behavior for small values of x is radically different. The individual nature of any one of them in the vicinity of $(0, 0)$ is better indicated if the *direction* of the curve at that point is also given. This, of course, means that it is desirable to find the slope of each of them at $(0, 0)$. We find the inclination angles are respectively $45°$, $0°$, and $90°$ (see Fig. 9–4).

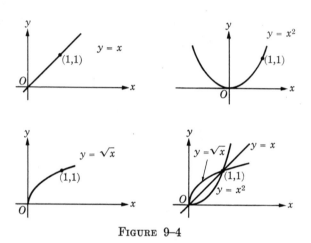

FIGURE 9–4

EXAMPLE 10. (Fig. 9–5) $y^2 = x^2(1 - x^2)$.

This curve has symmetry with respect to both axes and the origin. Its extent in the x-direction is limited to $|x| \le 1$. Differentiating implicitly, we find

$$y' = \frac{x - 2x^3}{y}.$$

At one x-intercept, $(1, 0)$, the slope is infinite. At the origin, which is another intercept, the expression we have for y' becomes $0/0$, which is meaningless. However, if we replace y in the denominator by its equivalent expression in terms of x, we obtain

$$y' = \frac{x(1 - 2x^2)}{\pm x\sqrt{1 - x^2}} = \pm \frac{1 - 2x^2}{\sqrt{1 - x^2}}.$$

At $x = 0$, this gives $y' = \pm 1$. The same result can be obtained by considering the limit, as P approaches the origin O, of the slope of the secant line through O and a second point $P(x, y)$ on the curve. Denoting this slope by m_{sec}, we have

$$m_{\text{sec}} = \frac{\text{rise}}{\text{run}} = \frac{y - 0}{x - 0} = \pm\sqrt{1 - x^2}.$$

When $P \to O$, $x \to 0$, and $m_{\text{sec}} \to \pm 1$. The double sign means, of course, that if P approaches O along the branch of the curve given by

$$y = x\sqrt{1 - x^2},$$

the limit of the slope of the secant is $+1$, while the branch given by

$$y = -x\sqrt{1 - x^2}$$

has slope -1 at the origin (Fig. 9–5). We also find turning points at $x = \pm\sqrt{\frac{1}{2}}$, $y = \pm\frac{1}{2}$. It is worth noting that we may determine the extent of the curve in the y-direction by comparing the equation of the curve in the form

$$x^4 - x^2 + y^2 = 0$$

with the quadratic equation

$$az^2 + bz + c = 0,$$

whose solutions are

$$z = \frac{-b \pm \sqrt{b^2 - 4ac}}{2a}.$$

Taking $z = x^2$, $a = 1$, $b = -1$, and $c = y^2$, this leads to

$$x^2 = \frac{1 \pm \sqrt{1 - 4y^2}}{2},$$

and it is seen that there is no portion of the curve above the line $y = \frac{1}{2}$ or below the line $y = -\frac{1}{2}$. The curve is sketched in Fig. 9–5.

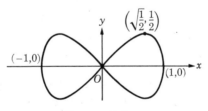

FIGURE 9–5

We observe in Example 10 that the equation is of the second degree in y and of the fourth degree in x. A line parallel to the y-axis has the equation $x = $ constant. Solving the equation of the curve and the equation of the line simultaneously will therefore produce at most two values of y, that is, such a line will cut the curve in at most two points. Similarly, because $y^2 = x^2(1 - x^2)$ is of the fourth degree in x, a line parallel to the x-axis will cut the curve in at most four points. The line $y = c$ and the curve will, in fact, have

(a) no intersections if $|c| > \frac{1}{2}$,

(b) two intersections if $|c| = \frac{1}{2}$,

(c) four intersections if $0 < |c| < \frac{1}{2}$,

(d) three intersections if $c = 0$.

In cases (b) and (d), the results may be interpreted as limiting cases of (c) with some of the intersections coinciding.

PROBLEMS

Analyze each of the equations below to investigate the following properties of the curve: (a) symmetry, (b) extent, (c) intercepts, (d) asymptotes, (e) slope at the intercepts. Locate a few points, and sketch the curve, taking into account the information discovered above.

1. $y^2 = x(x - 2)$

2. $y^2 = \dfrac{x}{x - 2}$

3. $x^4 + y^4 = 1$

4. $x^2 = \dfrac{1 + y^2}{1 - y^2}$

5. $x^2 = \dfrac{y^2 + 1}{y^2 - 1}$

6. $y = x + \dfrac{1}{x}$

7. $y = x^2 + 1$

8. $y = \dfrac{1}{x^2 + 1}$

9. $y = x^2 - 1$

10. $y = \dfrac{1}{x^2 - 1}$

9–2 Tangents and normals. In Chapter 1 we learned that a straight line of slope m which passes through the point (x_1, y_1) is represented by an equation

$$y - y_1 = m(x - x_1). \tag{1}$$

The equation of a line *tangent* to a given curve $y = f(x)$ at a given point (x_1, y_1) on the curve can be found at once by taking

$$m = \left(\frac{dy}{dx}\right)_{(x_1, y_1)} = f'(x_1)$$

in Eq. (1), which then becomes

$$\boxed{y - y_1 = f'(x_1)(x - x_1).} \tag{2}$$

In this equation x_1, y_1, and $f'(x_1)$ are all *constants*; the variables x and y appear only linearly.

The line through $P_1(x_1, y_1)$ and perpendicular to the tangent line is called

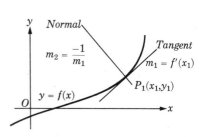

FIGURE 9–6

the *normal* to the curve at P_1. Its slope is the negative reciprocal of the slope of the tangent, that is,

$$m_2 = -\frac{1}{m_1} = \frac{-1}{f'(x_1)},$$

and the equation of the *normal* is

$$y - y_1 = \frac{-1}{f'(x_1)}(x - x_1). \tag{3}$$

EXAMPLE 1. The tangent to the curve

$$y^2 = 4px \tag{4}$$

at the point $P_1(x_1, y_1)$ intersects the x-axis at M and the y-axis at N. Show that N is the mid-point of the segment MP_1.

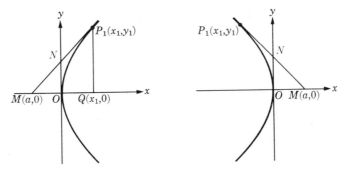

FIGURE 9–7

Solution. The curve is symmetric about the x-axis and lies entirely to the right of the y-axis if p is positive, or entirely to the left of the y-axis if p is negative (Fig. 9–7).

Its slope at any point is found from

$$\frac{dy}{dx} = \frac{2p}{y}.$$

The tangent to the curve at the origin is vertical and for this point the problem becomes meaningless. But if P_1 is any point on the curve (4) other than the origin, then the equation of the line tangent to the curve at P_1 is

$$y - y_1 = \frac{2p}{y_1}(x - x_1).$$

The point $M(a, 0)$ where this line cuts the x-axis *lies on the line*, and hence

$$-y_1 = \frac{2p}{y_1}(a - x_1),$$

which gives

$$a = x_1 - \frac{y_1^2}{2p}. \tag{5}$$

The point (x_1, y_1) is *on the curve*, and hence

$$y_1^2 = 4px_1,$$

so that

$$\frac{y_1^2}{2p} = 2x_1,$$

which reduces (5) to

$$a = -x_1. \tag{6}$$

Equation (6) tells us that the origin bisects the line segment MQ joining $M(-x_1, 0)$ and $Q(x_1, 0)$. Hence, by similar triangles, point N bisects the segment MP_1.

EXAMPLE 2. Show that the normal to the curve

$$x^2 + y^2 = a^2 \tag{7}$$

at any point (x_1, y_1) on it passes through the origin.

Solution. Differentiating (7) implicitly and solving for dy/dx, we find

$$\frac{dy}{dx} = -\frac{x}{y}$$

as the slope of the *tangent* at (x, y). The slope of the *normal* at (x_1, y_1) is therefore

$$m = \frac{y_1}{x_1},$$

and the equation of the normal is

$$y - y_1 = \frac{y_1}{x_1}(x - x_1). \tag{8}$$

When we clear of fractions, (8) reduces to

$$x_1 y = y_1 x.$$

Clearly, the origin lies on this line, since the coordinates $x = 0$, $y = 0$ satisfy the equation.

EXAMPLE 3. Show that the number of tangent lines that can be drawn from the point $Q(h, k)$ to the curve

$$y = x^2 \tag{9}$$

is two, one, or zero according as k is less than h^2, equal to h^2, or greater than h^2, respectively.

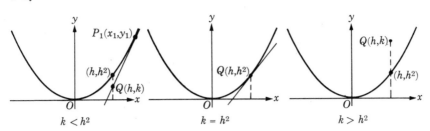

FIGURE 9–8

Solution. Figure 9–8 represents the curve and the three cases $k < h^2$, $k = h^2$, $k > h^2$. From the fact that $d^2y/dx^2 = 2$ is always positive, so that the curve is concave upward, we see that the results stated are equivalent to saying that two tangents can be drawn from a point on the convex side of the curve, no tangents from a point on the concave side of the curve, and only one tangent from a point on the curve. This is geometrically evident, but we shall adopt an analytical approach as follows.

Suppose that a tangent *can* be drawn to the curve from Q touching the curve at some point $P_1(x_1, y_1)$ which is at present not known. Then, using Eq. (2), we find the equation of this tangent line to be

$$y - y_1 = 2x_1(x - x_1).$$

Since $Q(h, k)$ is *on this line*, its coordinates must satisfy the equation

$$k - y_1 = 2x_1(h - x_1). \tag{10a}$$

Also, since (x_1, y_1) is *on the curve*, its coordinates must satisfy the equation

$$y_1 = x_1^2. \tag{10b}$$

Now in reality, h and k are known to us but x_1 and y_1 are not. We therefore have two equations, (10a) and (10b), for two unknowns, x_1 and y_1. We eliminate y_1 between them and obtain

$$k - x_1^2 = 2hx_1 - 2x_1^2$$

or

$$x_1^2 - 2hx_1 + k = 0.$$

If we solve this for x_1 by means of the quadratic formula, we obtain

$$x_1 = h \pm \sqrt{h^2 - k}. \tag{10c}$$

Only real values of x_1 correspond to points P_1 on the curve; hence no tangent may be drawn if $h^2 - k$ is negative, which is the same condition as saying k is greater than h^2. If $h^2 = k$, then the two roots in (10c) coincide and give only one point, namely $x_1 = h$, $y_1 = k = h^2$, to which the tangent can be

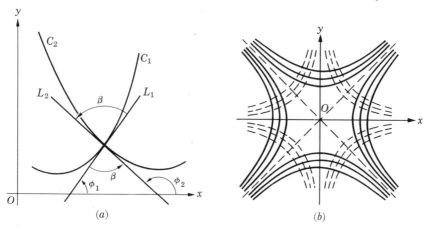

FIGURE 9–9

drawn. But if $k < h^2$, the two roots in (10c) are distinct and each root gives a value of x_1 which with $y_1 = x_1^2$ determines a point P_1 such that the line QP_1 is tangent to the curve, so that two tangents may be drawn.

Angle between two curves. Let C_1 and C_2 be two curves which intersect at a point P. Then the angle between C_1 and C_2 at P is, by definition, the angle β between their tangents at P (Fig. 9–9a). If these tangents are, respectively, L_1 and L_2, they have slopes

$$m_1 = \tan \phi_1, \qquad m_2 = \tan \phi_2.$$

Then $\tan \beta$ can be found from m_1 and m_2 as follows. Since

$$\beta = \phi_2 - \phi_1,$$

we have

$$\boxed{\tan \beta = \tan (\phi_2 - \phi_1) = \frac{\tan \phi_2 - \tan \phi_1}{1 + \tan \phi_2 \tan \phi_1} = \frac{m_2 - m_1}{1 + m_2 m_1}.} \qquad (11)$$

Here β is measured in the counterclockwise direction from L_1 to L_2.

We recall that the lines L_1 and L_2 are perpendicular if $m_2 = -1/m_1$. In this case we say that the curves C_1 and C_2 are *orthogonal*.

EXAMPLE 4. Show that every curve of the family

$$xy = a, \qquad a \neq 0 \qquad (12a)$$

is orthogonal to every curve of the family

$$x^2 - y^2 = b, \qquad b \neq 0. \tag{12b}$$

Solution. The two families of curves are sketched in Fig. 9–9(b). At a point $P(x, y)$ on any curve of (12a), the slope is

$$\frac{dy}{dx} = -\frac{y}{x}, \tag{13a}$$

and on any curve of (12b) the slope is

$$\frac{dy}{dx} = \frac{x}{y}. \tag{13b}$$

At a point of intersection, the values of x and y in (13b) are the same as in (13a), and the two curves are orthogonal because these slopes are negative reciprocals of each other. The cases $x = 0$ or $y = 0$ cannot occur in Eqs. (13) if (x, y) is a point of intersection of any curve (12a) and a curve (12b), since a and b are restricted to be constants different from zero. That every curve in (12a) does in fact intersect every curve in (12b) follows from the fact that the equation

$$x^2 - \frac{a^2}{x^2} = b,$$

which results from eliminating y between (12a) and (12b), has real roots for every pair of nonzero real constants a and b.

The curves in (12b) are called *orthogonal trajectories* of the curves in (12a). Such mutually orthogonal systems of curves are of particular importance in physical problems related to electrical potential, where the curves in one family correspond to lines of flow and those in the other family correspond to lines of constant potential. They also occur in hydrodynamics and in heat flow problems.

Problems

1. Find the equation of the line that is tangent to the curve $y^2 - 2x - 4y - 1 = 0$ at the point $(-2, 1)$.

2. Find the equation of the line that is normal to the curve $xy + 2x - 5y - 2 = 0$ at the point $(3, 2)$.

3. Find the equations of the lines that are tangent to the curve $y = x^3 - 6x + 2$ and are parallel to the line $y = 6x - 2$.

4. Find the equations of the lines that are normal to the curve $xy + 2x - y = 0$ and parallel to the line $2x + y = 0$.

5. Show that the two lines that are drawn from $(\frac{3}{2}, 0)$ tangent to the curve $x^2 - 4y + 4 = 0$ are perpendicular.

6. Show that the two lines that are drawn from any point on the line $x = -p$ tangent to the curve $y^2 = 4px$ are perpendicular (p = constant).

7. Does the line that is tangent to the curve $y = x^3$ at the point $(1, 1)$ intersect the curve at any other point? If so, find the point.

8. A line is drawn from the point $P_0(1, 5)$ tangent to the curve $y = x^3$ at a point $P_1(x_1, y_1)$ on it. Find the coordinates of P_1. Is there more than one possibility for the point P_1? Why?

9. Find all lines that can be drawn normal to the curve $x^2 - y^2 = 5$ and parallel to the line $2x + 3y = 10$. Sketch the curve and the lines.

10. Find all lines that can be drawn tangent to the curve $4xy = 1$ from the point $P(-1, 2)$. Sketch the curve and the lines.

11. The line that is normal to the curve $y = x^2 + 2x - 3$ at $(1, 0)$ intersects the curve at what other point?

12. If l represents the distance from a fixed point $P_1(x_1, y_1)$ to a variable point $P(x, y)$ on a curve $y = f(x)$ (Fig. 9-10), then

$$l^2 = (x - x_1)^2 + [f(x) - y_1]^2.$$

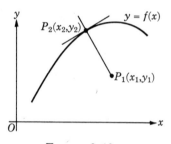

Figure 9-10

Show that the derivative $d(l^2)/dx$ is equal to zero when $x = x_2$ if and only if the line P_1P_2 is normal to the curve at $P_2[x_2, f(x_2)]$.

13. Show that the curve $2x^2 + 3y^2 = 5$ and the curve $y^2 = x^3$ intersect at right angles.

14. Let $P_1(x_1, y_1)$ and $P_2(x_2, y_2)$ be any two points on the curve $y = ax^2 + bx + c$, $a \neq 0$. If a line is drawn tangent to the curve at (x_0, y_0) and is parallel to the chord P_1P_2, show that $x_0 = (x_1 + x_2)/2$.

15. For what values of b is the line $y = 12x + b$ tangent to the curve $y = x^3$?

16. For what values of m is the line $y = mx$ tangent to the curve $y^2 + x^2 - 4x + 3 = 0$?

17. Find the interior angles of the triangle whose vertices are $A(1, 1)$, $B(3, -1)$, and $C(5, 2)$.

18. Find the slope of the line that bisects the angle ACB in the previous problem.

19. Let A, B, C be the interior angles of a triangle in which no angle is a right angle. By calculating $\tan(A + B + C)$ and observing that $A + B + C = 180°$, show that the equation

$$\tan A + \tan B + \tan C = \tan A \tan B \tan C$$

must be satisfied.

20. Calculate the interior angles of the triangle whose vertices are $A(1, 2)$, $B(2, -1)$, and $C(-1, 1)$, and check your results by showing that they satisfy the equation

$$\tan A + \tan B + \tan C = \tan A \tan B \tan C.$$

(See Problem 19, above.)

21. Find the angles between the following pairs of curves:

(a) $3x + y = 5$, $2x - y = 4$,   (b) $y = x^2$, $xy = 1$,

(c) $x^2 + y^2 = 16$, $y^2 = 6x$,   (d) $x^2 + xy + y^2 = 7$, $y = 2x$.

9–3 Newton's method for approximating roots of equations. Suppose we want to find a real root of the equation $f(x) = 0$. If the equation is linear or quadratic, we know simple rules to use. There are formulas for solving third and fourth degree equations, too, though they are less familiar. But there are no algebraic formulas for solving equations of the fifth degree or higher. Moreover, even the quadratic formula doesn't immediately give the answer in decimal form. Often we must look up the square root in a table or compute it. Newton's method, however, has these advantages:

    (a) It applies to an equation of any degree. Indeed, it even applies to nonpolynomial equations such as $2 \sin x - x = 0$.

    (b) It gives the answer in numerical form. We continue the computations until we have the degree of accuracy we want.

Its disadvantage is that the arithmetic becomes involved unless a calculating machine is used.

Newton's method proceeds as follows. If the equation we want to solve is $f(x) = 0$, we make a rough graph of $y = f(x)$. We estimate the root r, where the curve crosses the x-axis. This estimate is our first approximation; call it x_1. The next approximation, x_2, is the place where the *tangent*

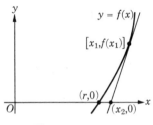

FIGURE 9–11

to the curve at $(x_1, f(x_1))$ crosses the x-axis, Fig. 9–11. The equation of this tangent line is

$$y - f(x_1) = f'(x_1)(x - x_1). \tag{1}$$

We assume that this line is not parallel to the x-axis, that is, $f'(x_1) \neq 0$. (If we started at a place where the slope is zero, we must start over again at a nearby place where the slope isn't zero.) Then the line crosses the x-axis at a point with coordinates $x = x_2$, $y = 0$ which satisfy (1). Hence

$$0 - f(x_1) = f'(x_1)(x_2 - x_1)$$

and

$$\boxed{x_2 = x_1 - \frac{f(x_1)}{f'(x_1)}.} \tag{2}$$

Equation (2) provides the basis for an iterative process, since we may now replace x_1 by x_2 on the right side and call the new result x_3 instead of x_2. More generally, having arrived at an approximation x_n, we replace

x_1 by x_n on the right side of (2) and x_2 by x_{n+1}, thus:

$$x_{n+1} = x_n - \frac{f(x_n)}{f'(x_n)}. \qquad (3)$$

A computing machine can be programmed with feedback to keep repeating the process of Eq. (3) automatically, as indicated in Fig. 9–12.

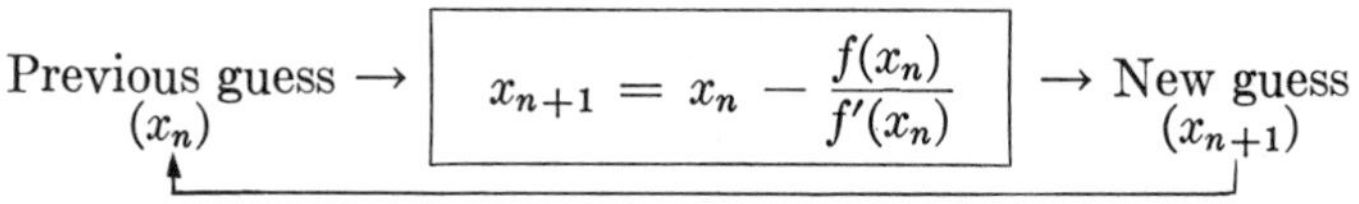

Previous guess $\rightarrow$ $\qquad x_{n+1} = x_n - \dfrac{f(x_n)}{f'(x_n)} \qquad \rightarrow$ New guess
$\qquad (x_n) \qquad\qquad\qquad\qquad\qquad\qquad\qquad\qquad (x_{n+1})$

FIG. 9–12. Feedback for iterating Newton's method.

EXAMPLE 1. Use Newton's method to solve $x^2 = 5$ to two decimals.

Solution. We take $f(x) = x^2 - 5$, and sketch the curve

$$y = f(x) = x^2 - 5.$$

A root of the equation $x^2 = 5$ corresponds to a place where this curve crosses the x-axis. From the graph (Fig. 9–13) we see that one crossing is between 2 and 3, and is closer to 2 than to 3. We therefore take $x_1 = 2$ as our first approximation. Then we compute x_2 from Eq. (2). Here we have

$$f(x) = x^2 - 5, \qquad f(2) = -1,$$
$$f'(x) = 2x, \qquad f'(2) = 4.$$

Hence

$$x_2 = 2 - (-\tfrac{1}{4}) = \tfrac{9}{4} = 2.25.$$

To get the next approximation, we use Eq. (3) with $n = 2$:

$$x_3 = x_2 - \frac{f(x_2)}{f'(x_2)}$$

with

$$f(x_2) = f(\tfrac{9}{4}) = (\tfrac{9}{4})^2 - 5 = \tfrac{1}{16}$$
$$f'(x_2) = f'(\tfrac{9}{4}) = 2(\tfrac{9}{4}) = \tfrac{9}{2}.$$

Hence

$$x_3 = \frac{9}{4} - \frac{\frac{1}{16}}{\frac{9}{2}} = \frac{161}{72} = 2.236^+.$$

Since $(2.236)^2 = 4.999696$ and $(2.237)^2 = 5.004169$, it is clear that the positive root is between 2.236 and 2.237, hence is 2.24 to two decimal places.

EXAMPLE 2. Newton's method may be used to find cube roots, fourth roots, and so on. We illustrate the method for finding the cube root of 2. That is, we try to find a root of the equation $x = \sqrt[3]{2}$ or $x^3 = 2$. We put $f(x) = x^3 - 2$

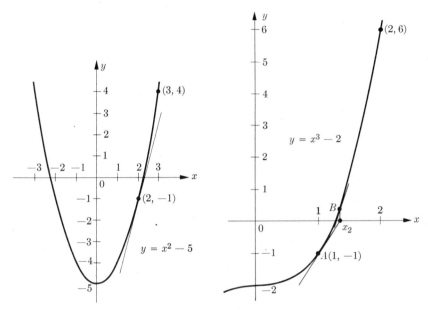

FIG. 9–13. Graph of $y = x^2 - 5$.   FIG. 9–14. Graph of $y = x^3 - 2$.

and sketch the graph of $y = f(x)$, Fig. 9–14. Since $f(1) = -1$ and $f(2) = 6$, we let our first approximation be $x_1 = 1$. Then Eq. (2) becomes

$$x_2 = x_1 - \frac{f(x_1)}{f'(x_1)}$$

$$= x_1 - \frac{(x_1^3 - 2)}{3x_1^2}$$

$$= \tfrac{2}{3}x_1 + \tfrac{1}{3}(2/x_1^2). \qquad (4)$$

We have written Eq. (4) in a form that shows x_2 is a "weighted average" of x_1 (with coefficient $\tfrac{2}{3}$) and of $2/x_1^2$ (with coefficient $\tfrac{1}{3}$). The sum of these coefficients is 1, but we "weight" x_1 in our average twice as heavily as we do $2/x_1^2$. This same procedure may of course be repeated with x_2 in place of x_1 on the right side of (4) and x_3 on the left. In general we have

$$x_{n+1} = \tfrac{2}{3}x_n + \tfrac{1}{3}(2/x_n^2). \qquad (5)$$

If at any stage the numbers x_n and $2/x_n^2$ are equal, then x_{n+1} is also equal to this common value, and it is $\sqrt[3]{2}$, since

$$x_n = 2/x_n^2$$

implies

$$x_n^3 = 2.$$

Starting with $x_1 = 1$, we find the first three approximations are

$$x_1 = 1, \qquad x_2 = \tfrac{4}{3} = 1.33^+, \qquad x_3 = \tfrac{91}{72} = 1.264^-.$$

A table of cube roots gives $\sqrt[3]{2} = 1.259921$ to six decimal places. Our third approximation is too large by about 0.004, but 1.26 is correct to two decimal places.

Remark 1. The accuracy of Newton's method for functions f which possess continuous first and second derivatives can be estimated by applying the Mean Value Theorem. One estimate, obtainable that way, is

$$|x_2 - r| \le (x_1 - r)^2(M/m), \tag{6}$$

where M is the maximum absolute value of the second derivative and m the minimum absolute value of the first derivative in an interval that contains the root r and the estimates x_1 and x_2. The error decreases if the first guess is accurate enough to make

$$\left|(x_1 - r)\,\frac{M}{m}\right| < 1. \tag{7}$$

In Example 1, for instance, we had $f(x) = x^2 - 5, f'(x) = 2x, f''(x) = 2$, $r = \sqrt{5}$, $x_1 = 2$, and all other approximations x_n between 2 and $\tfrac{9}{4}$. Hence in (6) we could take $M = 2$, $m = 4$ and have

$$|x_2 - \sqrt{5}| \le \tfrac{1}{2}(x_1 - \sqrt{5})^2.$$

The same inequality applies to any two successive approximations x_{n+1} and x_n,

$$|x_{n+1} - \sqrt{5}| \le \tfrac{1}{2}(x_n - \sqrt{5})^2.$$

This inequality shows that the number of decimal places of accuracy doubles with each successive iteration.

In Example 2, $f(x) = x^3 - 2, f'(x) = 3x^2, f''(x) = 6x, r = \sqrt[3]{2} = 1.26^-$, $x_1 = 1, x_2 = \tfrac{4}{3}$, and all other approximations lie between x_1 and x_2. Hence in (6) we may take $M = 6(\tfrac{4}{3}) = 8$, $m = 3$, and get

$$|x_2 - \sqrt[3]{2}| \le (\tfrac{8}{3})(x_1 - \sqrt[3]{2})^2.$$

The condition (7) is satisfied since the left side of the inequality (7) is actually less than 0.7.

Remark 2. We can get a good picture of how the Newton process converges in a favorable situation like that shown in Fig. 9–15. Here x_1 is to the left of r. The tangent to the curve at $A(x_1, f(x_1))$ crosses the x-axis at x_2 to the right of r. The second tangent line, through $B(x_2, f(x_2))$ crosses at x_3, much nearer r. And the third tangent line, through $C(x_3, f(x_3))$,

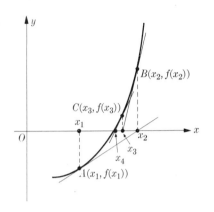

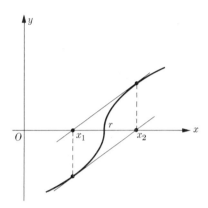

FIG. 9–15. Successive approximations to root of equation $f(x) = 0$ by
Newton's method.

FIG. 9–16. Graph of example where
Newton's method fails to converge.

is practically indistinguishable from the curve itself in the vicinity of the
root r.

Remark 3. In some cases, Newton's method may not converge. For
instance, if the graph of $y = f(x)$ is like Fig. 9–16, we may have

$$x_1 = r - h, \qquad x_2 = r + h,$$

and successive approximations go back and forth between these two
values alternately. A function such as

$$f(x) = \begin{cases} \sqrt{x - r} & \text{for} \quad x \geq r \\ -\sqrt{r - x} & \text{for} \quad x \leq r \end{cases} \tag{8}$$

has this property. No amount of iteration of the process will bring us
any closer to the root r than our initial guess.

PROBLEMS

Sketch the graph of $y = f(x)$ in each of the following problems (1 through 6).
Show that $f(a)$ and $f(b)$ have opposite signs and use Newton's method to estimate the root of the equation $f(x) = 0$ between a and b. One might use
$x_1 = (a + b)/2$ as first approximation.

1. $f(x) = x^2 + x - 1, \quad a = 0, \quad b = 1$
2. $f(x) = x^3 + x - 1, \quad a = 0, \quad b = 1$
3. $f(x) = x^4 + x - 3, \quad a = 1, \quad b = 2$
4. $f(x) = x^4 - 2, \quad a = 1, \quad b = 2$
5. $f(x) = 2 - x^4, \quad a = -1, \quad b = -2$
6. $f(x) = \sqrt{2x + 1} - \sqrt{x + 4}, \quad a = 2, \quad b = 4$

7. Suppose our first guess is lucky, in the sense that x_1 is a root of $f(x) = 0$. What happens to x_2 and later approximations?

8. In Example 2, take $x_3 = 1.26$ and compute x_4 to five decimal places. Compare with the six-place $\sqrt[3]{2}$ given in the text. How does your result check with the statement that "when one approximation is good to two decimal places, the next Newton's-method approximation will be good to about four decimals"?

9. To find $x = \sqrt[q]{a}$, we apply Newton's method to $f(x) = x^q - a$. Here we assume that a is a positive real number and q is a positive integer. Show that x_2 is a "weighted average" of x_1 and a/x_1^{q-1}, and find the coefficients m_1, m_2 such that

$$x_2 = m_1 x_1 + m_2(a/x_1^{q-1}), \qquad m_1 > 0, \quad m_2 > 0, \quad m_1 + m_2 = 1.$$

What conclusion would you reach if x_1 and a/x_1^{q-1} were equal? What would be the value of x_2 in that case? [You may also wish to read the article by J. P. Ballantine, "An Averaging Method of Extracting Roots," *American Mathematical Monthly*, Vol. 63, 1956, pp. 249–252, where more efficient ways of averaging are discussed. Also see J. S. Frame, "The Solution of Equations by Continued Fractions," ibid., Vol. 60, 1953, pp. 293–305.]

10. In Example 2, let $e_1 = x_1 - r$ and $e_2 = x_2 - r$ be the errors in our first two approximations of $r = \sqrt[3]{2}$. Show algebraically that $e_2 = e_1^2(2x_1 + r)/(3x_1^2)$. Similar equations relate the errors in any two successive approximations. All our approximations in Example 2 lie between $x_1 = 1$ and $x_2 = \frac{4}{3}$, inclusive. Deduce that the factor $(2x_n + r)/(3x_n^2)$ is not greater than $(\frac{8}{3} + r)/3$, which in turn is less than $(2.67 + 1.26)/3 = 1.31$. Therefore, $e_{n+1} \leq 1.31 e_n^2$.

11. Show that Newton's method applied to $f(x)$ in Eq. (8) leads to $x_2 = r + h$ if $x_1 = r - h$, and to $x_2 = r - h$ if $x_1 = r + h$, $h > 0$. Interpret the result geometrically.

12. (See Remark 3.) Is it possible that successive approximations actually get "worse," in that x_{n+1} is farther away from the root r than x_n is? Can you find such a "pathological" example? [*Hint:* Try cube roots in place of square roots in Eq. (8).]

13. Using the following hints, derive the inequality (6).

   (1) By the Mean Value Theorem there is a number a between x_1 and r such that

   $$f(x_1) - f(r) = f'(a)(x_1 - r).$$

   If the minimum of the absolute value of $f'(x)$ in an interval containing x_1 and r is m, and $m \neq 0$, then $f'(a) \neq 0$. We assume that r is a root of $f(r) = 0$. Hence

   $$x_1 - r = \frac{f(x_1)}{f'(a)}. \tag{a}$$

   (2) By Eq. (2),

   $$x_2 - x_1 = -\frac{f(x_1)}{f'(x_1)}. \tag{b}$$

(3) Add (a) and (b) to get

$$x_2 - r = \frac{f(x_1)}{f'(a)f'(x_1)}[f'(x_1) - f'(a)]$$

$$= \frac{x_1 - r}{f'(x_1)}[f'(x_1) - f'(a)]. \tag{c}$$

(4) By the Mean Value Theorem there is a number b between x_1 and a such that

$$f'(x_1) - f'(a) = f''(b)(x_1 - a). \tag{d}$$

(5) From (c) and (d), deduce that

$$x_2 - r = (x_1 - r)(x_1 - a)\frac{f''(b)}{f'(x_1)}, \tag{e}$$

where a and b are numbers between x_1 and r. In particular, therefore,

$$|x_1 - a| < |x_1 - r|. \tag{f}$$

Now deduce (6) from (e) and (f).

9–4 Distance between two points. Equations of loci. It is at once apparent from Fig. 9–17 and the theorem of Pythagoras that the distance d between the two points $P_1(x_1, y_1)$ and $P_2(x_2, y_2)$ is given by

$$d = \sqrt{(x_2 - x_1)^2 + (y_2 - y_1)^2}. \tag{1}$$

This formula is particularly useful in finding the equation of a curve when its geometric character depends upon one or more distances, as in the example below.

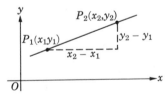

FIGURE 9–17

EXAMPLE 1. Find the locus of $P(x, y)$ if the distance from P to the origin is equal to the distance from P to the line $L: x = 4$.

Solution. The distance from P to L is the perpendicular distance PQ from P to $Q(4, y)$, where Q has the same ordinate as P, Fig. 9–18. Thus

$$PQ = \sqrt{(4 - x)^2 + (y - y)^2} = |4 - x|.$$

The distance OP is

$$OP = \sqrt{x^2 + y^2}.$$

The condition of the locus is $OP = PQ$, or

$$\sqrt{x^2 + y^2} = |4 - x|. \tag{1}$$

If (1) holds, so does the equation we get by squaring:

$$x^2 + y^2 = 16 - 8x + x^2$$

or

$$y^2 = 16 - 8x. \tag{2}$$

That is, if a point belongs to the locus, then its coordinates must satisfy Eq. (2). The converse is also true, for if Eq. (2) holds, then

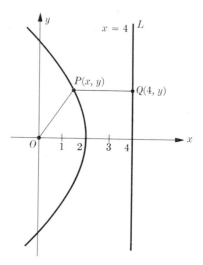

$$\begin{aligned}
\sqrt{x^2 + y^2} &= \sqrt{x^2 + (16 - 8x)} \\
&= \sqrt{(x - 4)^2} \\
&= |x - 4| \\
&= |4 - x|,
\end{aligned}$$

and hence

$$OP = PQ.$$

Therefore Eq. (2) expresses both the necessary and the sufficient condition on the coordinates of $P(x, y)$ for P to belong to the locus.

Fig. 9–18. Locus of P when P is equidistant from point O and from line L.

PROBLEMS

In Problems 1–8, use the distance formula to derive the equation of the locus of points $P(x, y)$ that satisfy the specified conditions. Analyze the equation and sketch its graph.

1. P is equidistant from the two points $A(-2, 1)$ and $B(2, -3)$.
2. The distance from P to $F_1(-1, 0)$ is twice its distance to $F_2(2, 0)$.
3. The product of its distances from $F_1(-2, 0)$ and $F_2(2, 0)$ is 4.
4. The sum of the distances from P to $F_1(1, 0)$ and $F_2(0, 1)$ is constant and the curve passes through the origin.
5. The distance of P from the line $x = -2$ is 2 times its distance from the point $(2, 0)$.
6. The distance of P from the point $(-3, 0)$ is 4 more than its distance from the point $(3, 0)$.
7. The distance of P from the line $y = 1$ is 3 less than its distance from the origin.

8. P is 3 units from the point $(2, 3)$.

9. Find a point that is equidistant from the three points $A(0, 1)$, $B(1, 0)$, $C(4, 3)$. What is the radius of the circle through A, B, and C?

10. Find the distance from the point $P_1(x_1, y_1)$ to the straight line $Ax + By + C = 0$.

9–5 The circle.

DEFINITION. *A circle is the locus of points in a plane at a given distance from a given point.*

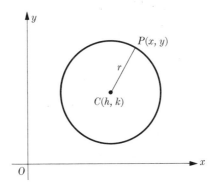

FIGURE 9–19

Equation of a circle. Let $C(h, k)$ be the given point, the center of the circle. Let r be the given distance, the radius of the circle. Let $P(x, y)$ be a point on the circle. Then

$$\overline{CP} = r, \tag{1}$$

or

$$\sqrt{(x - h)^2 + (y - k)^2} = r,$$

or

$$\boxed{(x - h)^2 + (y - k)^2 = r^2.} \tag{2}$$

If (1) is satisfied so is (2), and conversely. Therefore (2) is the equation of the locus.

EXAMPLE 1. Find the equation of the circle with center at the origin and with radius r.

Solution. If $h = k = 0$, Eq. (2) becomes

$$x^2 + y^2 = r^2. \tag{3}$$

EXAMPLE 2. Find the circle through the origin with center at $C(2, -1)$.

Solution. Its equation, (2), is of the form

$$(x - 2)^2 + (y + 1)^2 = r^2.$$

Since it goes through the origin, $x = y = 0$ must satisfy the equation. Hence

$$(0 - 2)^2 + (0 + 1)^2 = r^2$$

or

$$r^2 = 5.$$

The equation is

$$(x - 2)^2 + (y + 1)^2 = 5.$$

EXAMPLE 3. What is the locus of points $P(x, y)$ whose coordinates satisfy the inequality

$$(x - h)^2 + (y - k)^2 < r^2? \quad (4)$$

Solution. The left side of (4) is the square of the distance CP from $C(h, k)$ to $P(x, y)$. The inequality is satisfied if and only if

$$\overline{CP} < r,$$

that is, P lies inside the circle of radius r with center at $C(h, k)$, Fig. 9–20.

EXAMPLE 4. Analyze the equation

$$x^2 + y^2 + 4x - 6y = 12.$$

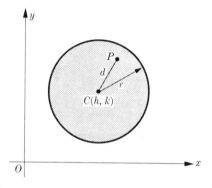

FIG. 9–20. $(x - h)^2 + (y - k)^2 < r^2$, the interior of a circle with center $C(h, k)$, radius r.

Solution. We complete the squares in the x terms and y terms and get

$$(x^2 + 4x + 4) + (y^2 - 6y + 9) = 12 + 4 + 9$$

or

$$(x + 2)^2 + (y - 3)^2 = 25.$$

This is of the same form as Eq. (2); therefore it represents a circle with center $C(-2, 3)$ and radius $r = 5$. Its graph is shown in Fig. 9–21.

Remark 1. An equation of the form

$$\boxed{Ax^2 + Ay^2 + Dx + Ey + F = 0, \quad A \neq 0,} \quad (5)$$

can often be reduced to the form of Eq. (2) by completing the squares as we did in Example 4. More specifically, we may divide (5) by A and

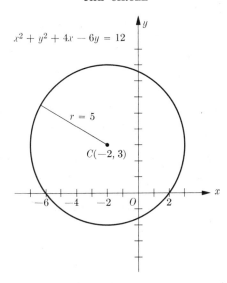

$x^2 + y^2 + 4x - 6y = 12$

$r = 5$

$C(-2, 3)$

Fig. 9–21. Graph of $x^2 + y^2 + 4x - 6y = 12$.

write

$$\left(x^2 + \frac{D}{A}x\right) + \left(y^2 + \frac{E}{A}y\right) = -\frac{F}{A}. \tag{6}$$

To complete the squares for x, we must add $(D/2A)^2 = D^2/(4A^2)$; and for y we add $(E/2A)^2 = E^2/(4A^2)$. Of course we must add to both sides of Eq. (6), thus obtaining

$$\left(x + \frac{D}{2A}\right)^2 + \left(y + \frac{E}{2A}\right)^2 = -\frac{F}{A} + \frac{D^2 + E^2}{4A^2}$$

$$= \frac{D^2 + E^2 - 4AF}{4A^2}. \tag{7}$$

Equation (7) is like Eq. (2), with

$$r^2 = \frac{D^2 + E^2 - 4AF}{4A^2}, \tag{8}$$

provided this expression is positive. Then (5) represents a circle with center at $(-D/2A, -E/2A)$ and radius $r = \sqrt{(D^2 + E^2 - 4AF)/(4A^2)}$.

If (8) is equal to zero, the locus reduces to a single point, and if it is negative, there are no points (with real coordinates) that satisfy Eq. (7) or Eq. (5).

It is recommended that the reader apply the method of Example 4, rather than using formulas, to handle problems of this type. The thing to remember is that an equation like (5), which is *quadratic in x and in y, with equal coefficients of x^2 and y^2, and with no xy term, represents a circle* (or a single point, or no real locus).

Remark 2. Equation (5) can be divided by A and be replaced by an equation of the form

$$\boxed{x^2 + y^2 + C_1 x + C_2 y + C_3 = 0,} \qquad (9)$$

where C_1, C_2, C_3 are three constants. The three coefficients in (9) can often be determined so as to satisfy three prescribed conditions: for example, that the circle go through three given (noncollinear) points; or be tangent to three given nonconcurrent lines; or be tangent to two lines and pass through a given point not on either line.

EXAMPLE 5. Find the circle through the three points $A(1, 0)$, $B(0, 1)$, and $C(2, 2)$.

Solution 1. Let Eq. (9) be the equation of the circle. Then substitute for x and y the coordinates of A, B, and C, since these points are to be on the circle.

$$
\begin{array}{lccccc}
\text{Point} & x^2 + y^2 + & C_1 x + & C_2 y + & C_3 = 0 & \\
A(1, 0) & 1 & + C_1 & & + C_3 = 0 & \left.\vphantom{\begin{array}{c}1\\1\\4\end{array}}\right\} \\
B(0, 1) & 1 & & + C_2 & + C_3 = 0 & \\
C(2, 2) & 4 + 4 & + 2C_1 & + 2C_2 & + C_3 = 0 &
\end{array} \qquad (10)
$$

Equations (10) are three equations for the three unknowns. Subtracting the second equation from the first, we get

$$C_2 = C_1.$$

Substitute C_1 for C_2 in the third equation:

$$8 + 4C_1 + C_3 = 0.$$

Subtract the first equation from this:

$$7 + 3C_1 = 0.$$

Hence

$$C_2 = C_1 = -\tfrac{7}{3}$$

and

$$C_3 = -1 - C_1 = \tfrac{4}{3}.$$

Therefore, the equation is

$$x^2 + y^2 - \tfrac{7}{3}x - \tfrac{7}{3}y + \tfrac{4}{3} = 0$$

or

$$3x^2 + 3y^2 - 7x - 7y + 4 = 0.$$

Of course this example could equally well have been solved starting with Eq. (2), which contains the three unknowns h, k, and r. Or we could have found the center Q of the circle by locating the point of intersection of the perpendicular bisectors of the segments AB and BC. The radius is the distance from the center Q to any one of the three points A, B, or C.

Solution 2 (using determinants). The determinantal equation

$$\begin{vmatrix} x^2 + y^2 & x & y & 1 \\ x_1^2 + y_1^2 & x_1 & y_1 & 1 \\ x_2^2 + y_2^2 & x_2 & y_2 & 1 \\ x_3^2 + y_3^2 & x_3 & y_3 & 1 \end{vmatrix} = 0 \qquad (11)$$

has the form of Eq. (5) when expanded by cofactors of elements of its first row. In addition, if x is replaced by x_1 and y by y_1, the first row becomes identical with the second and the equation is satisfied. The equation is also satisfied if x and y are replaced by x_2 and y_2 or by x_3 and y_3. Hence (11) represents a circle through the three points $P_1(x_1, y_1)$, $P_2(x_2, y_2)$, and $P_3(x_3, y_3)$, provided the cofactor of $x^2 + y^2$,

$$A_{11} = \begin{vmatrix} x_1 & y_1 & 1 \\ x_2 & y_2 & 1 \\ x_3 & y_3 & 1 \end{vmatrix},$$

is not zero. This 3×3 determinant vanishes if and only if the three points are collinear (see Problem 11, Miscellaneous Problems for Chapter 8), in which case there is no circle through the three points if they are distinct.

In the present example, Eq. (11) is

$$\begin{vmatrix} x^2 + y^2 & x & y & 1 \\ 1 & 1 & 0 & 1 \\ 1 & 0 & 1 & 1 \\ 8 & 2 & 2 & 1 \end{vmatrix} = 0.$$

The expanded value of the determinant is

$$-3(x^2 + y^2) + 7x + 7y - 4,$$

which gives the same result as found above.

Problems

In each of the following problems (1 through 6), find the equation of the circle having the given center $C(h, k)$ and radius r.

1. $C(0, 2)$, $r = 2$ 2. $C(-2, 0)$, $r = 3$

3. $C(3, -4)$, $r = 5$ 4. $C(1, 1)$, $r = \sqrt{2}$
5. $C(-2, -1)$, $r = \sqrt{6}$ 6. $C(-4, 2)$, $r = 4$

In each of the following problems (7 through 12), find the center and radius of the given circle.

7. $x^2 + y^2 - 2y = 3$ 8. $x^2 + y^2 + 2x = 8$
9. $3x^2 + 3y^2 + 6x = 1$ 10. $2x^2 + 2y^2 + x + y = 0$
11. $x^2 + y^2 + 2x - 4y + 5 = 0$ 12. $x^2 + y^2 + 4x + 4y + 9 = 0$

13. The center of a circle is $C(2, 2)$. The circle goes through the point $A(4, 5)$. Find its equation.

14. The center of a circle is $C(-1, 1)$. The circle is tangent to the line $x + 2y = 4$. Find its equation.

15. A circle passes through the points $A(2, -2)$ and $B(3, 4)$. Its center is on the line $x + y = 2$. Find its equation.

16. Show geometrically that the lines that are drawn from the exterior point $P_1(x_1, y_1)$ tangent to the circle $(x - h)^2 + (y - k)^2 = r^2$ have length l given by

$$l^2 = (x_1 - h)^2 + (y_1 - k)^2 - r^2.$$

17. Find the equation of the circle that passes through the three points, $A(2, 3)$, $B(3, 2)$, and $C(-4, 3)$.

18. Find the locus of the point $P(x, y)$ if the sum of the squares of its distances from the two points $(-5, 2)$ and $(1, 4)$ is always 52. Identify and sketch the curve.

19. Is the point $(0.1, 3.1)$ inside, outside, or on the circle $x^2 + y^2 - 2x - 4y + 3 = 0$? Why?

20. If the distance from $P(x, y)$ to the point $(6, 0)$ is twice its distance from the point $(0, 3)$, show that the locus is a circle and find the center and radius.

21. Find the circle inscribed in the triangle whose sides are the lines $4x + 3y = 24$, $3x - 4y = 18$, $4x - 3y + 32 = 0$. [*Hint:* The distance from the point (h, k) to the line $ax + by = c$ is

$$\frac{|ah + bk - c|}{\sqrt{a^2 + b^2}}$$

by the answer to Problem 10, Article 9–4.]

22. Let P be a point outside a given circle C. Let PT be tangent to C at T. Let the line PN from P through the center of C intersect C at M and N. Prove that $PM \cdot PN = (PT)^2$.

23. It is known that any angle inscribed in a semicircle is a right angle. Prove the converse: i.e., if for every choice of the point $P(x, y)$ on a curve C joining O and A, the angle OPA is a right angle, then the curve is a circle or a semicircle having OA as diameter.

24. Suppose that Eqs. (2) and (9) represent the same circle. (a) Express C_1, C_2, and C_3 in terms of h, k, and r. (b) Express h, k, and r in terms of C_1, C_2, and C_3.

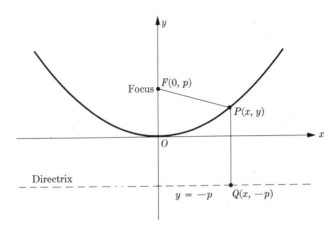

Fɪɢ. 9–22. Parabola with focus $F(0, p)$ and directrix $y = -p$.

9–6 The parabola.

DEFINITION. *A parabola is the locus of points in a plane equidistant from a given point and a given line. The given point is called the* focus *of the parabola and the given line the* directrix.

Equation. We choose the y-axis through the focus F and perpendicular to the directrix L, and take the origin halfway between F and L. If the distance between F and L is $2p$, we may assign F coordinates $(0, p)$ and the equation of L is $y = -p$, as in Fig. 9–22. Then $P(x, y)$ is on the parabola if and only if the distances PF and PQ are equal:

$$PF = PQ, \tag{1}$$

where $Q(x, -p)$ is the foot of the perpendicular from P to L. From the distance formula,

$$PF = \sqrt{x^2 + (y - p)^2} \quad \text{and} \quad PQ = \sqrt{(y + p)^2}.$$

When we equate these two expressions, square, and simplify, we get

$$\boxed{x^2 = 4py.} \tag{2}$$

This equation must be satisfied by any point on the locus. Conversely, if (2) is satisfied, then

$$
\begin{aligned}
PF &= \sqrt{x^2 + (y - p)^2} \\
&= \sqrt{4py + (y^2 - 2py + p^2)} \\
&= \sqrt{(y + p)^2} \\
&= PQ
\end{aligned}
$$

and $P(x, y)$ is on the locus. In other words, Eq. (2) is both a necessary and a sufficient condition on the coordinates x and y of points on the parabola.

Discussion. In Eq. (2) assume p is positive. Then y cannot be negative, for real x, and the curve lies above the x-axis. It is symmetric about the y-axis, since x appears only to an even power.

The axis of symmetry of the parabola is also called the "axis of the parabola." The point on this axis midway between the focus and the directrix is on the parabola, since it is equidistant from the focus and the directrix. It is called the *vertex* of the parabola. The origin is the vertex of the parabola in Fig. 9–22. The tangent to a parabola at its vertex is parallel to the directrix. From Eq. (2) we find the slope of the tangent at any point is $dy/dx = x/2p$, and this is zero at the origin. The second derivative is $d^2y/dx^2 = 1/2p$, which is positive, so the curve is concave upward. A geometric method for constructing points on a parabola (in contrast to using its equation to locate points) is described in Problem 24, p. 472.

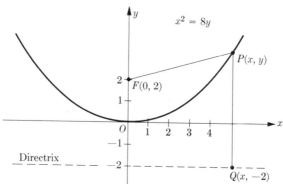

FIG. 9–23. Parabola $x^2 = 8y$.

EXAMPLE 1. Find the focus and directrix of the parabola

$$x^2 = 8y. \qquad (3)$$

Solution. Equation (3) matches (2) if we take $4p = 8$, $p = 2$. The focus is on the axis of symmetry (the y-axis), p units from the vertex, that is, at $F(0, 2)$. The directrix is the line $y = -2$. Every point on the graph of (3) is equidistant from $F(0, 2)$ and the line $y = -2$.

Remark 1. Suppose the parabola opens downward, as in Fig. 9–24, with its focus $F(0, -p)$ and directrix the line $y = p$. The effect is to change the sign of p in Eq. (2), which now becomes

$$\boxed{x^2 = -4py.} \qquad (4)$$

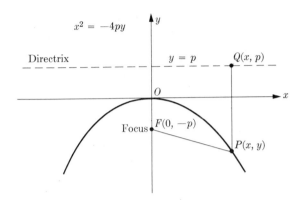

Fig. 9–24. Parabola $x^2 = -4py$.

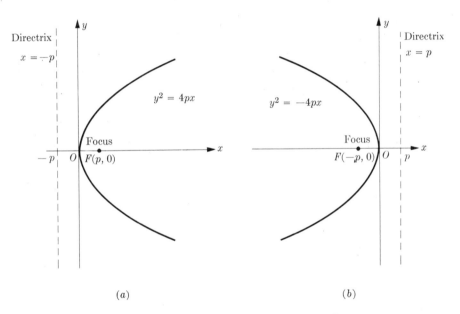

(a) (b)

Fig. 9–25. (a) Parabola $y^2 = 4px$. (b) Parabola $y^2 = -4px$.

We may also interchange the roles of x and y in Eqs. (2) and (4). The resulting equations

$$y^2 = 4px \qquad (5a)$$

and

$$y^2 = -4px \qquad (5b)$$

also represent parabolas, but now they are symmetric about the x-axis because y appears only to an even power. The *vertex* is still at the origin. The directrix is perpendicular to the axis of symmetry, and p units from the vertex. The focus is on the axis of symmetry, also p units from the vertex, and "inside" the curve. If we assume p is positive in Eqs. (5), then (5a) opens toward the right, because x must be greater than or equal to zero, while (5b) opens toward the left. Figure 9–25 shows graphs of parabolas of these two types.

Translation of axes. If the vertex of the parabola is at the point $V(h, k)$, Eqs. (2), (4), and (5) no longer apply in those forms. However, it is easy to determine what the appropriate equation is, by considering a new coordinate system, with its origin O' at V, and axes parallel to the original axes. Every point P in the plane then has two sets of coordinates, say x and y in the original system, and x', y' in the new. To go from O to P, we have a horizontal displacement x and a vertical displacement y.

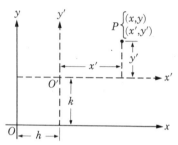

Fig. 9–26. Diagram for translation of axes.

The abscissa may be resolved into two horizontal displacements: h from O to O' and x' from O' to P. Similarly, the ordinate is the resultant of two vertical displacements: k from O to O' and y' from O' to P. Thus the two sets of coordinates are related as follows:

$$\begin{cases} x = x' + h \\ y = y' + k \end{cases} \quad (6a)$$

or

$$\begin{cases} x' = x - h \\ y' = y - k \end{cases}. \quad (6b)$$

Equations (6) are called the equations for *translation of axes*, because the new coordinate axes may be obtained by moving the old axes to the position of the new ones in a motion known as a pure translation without rotation.

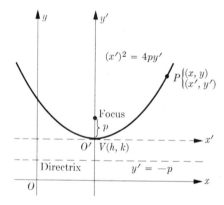

Fig. 9–27. Parabola with vertex at $V(h, k)$; $(x')^2 = 4py'$.

Suppose, now, we consider a parabola, with vertex $V(h, k)$ and opening upward as in Fig. 9–27. In terms of $x'y'$-coordinates, Eq. (2) provides us with the equation of the parabola in the form

$$(x')^2 = 4py'. \tag{7}$$

By using Eqs. (6), we may express this in xy-coordinates by the equation

$$\boxed{(x - h)^2 = 4p(y - k).} \tag{8a}$$

The axis of symmetry of the parabola in (8a) is the line $x = h$. Observe that this corresponds to setting the quadratic term $(x - h)^2$ in (8a) equal to zero. When p is positive, $y - k$ must be greater than or equal to zero in (8a), for real $x - h$, and therefore the graph opens upward. The focus is on the axis of symmetry, p units above the vertex at $x = h$, $y = k + p$. The directrix is p units below the vertex and perpendicular to the axis of symmetry.

Other forms of equations of parabolas are:

$$\boxed{\begin{aligned} (x - h)^2 &= -4p(y - k), \\ (y - k)^2 &= 4p(x - h), \\ (y - k)^2 &= -4p(x - h). \end{aligned}} \tag{8b} \tag{8c} \tag{8d}$$

Equation (8b) has a graph symmetric about $x = h$, opening downward; (8c) symmetric about $y = k$ and opening to the right ($x \geq h$); (8d) symmetric about $y = k$ and opening to the left ($x \leq h$).

EXAMPLE 2. Discuss the parabola

$$y = x^2 + 4x. \tag{9}$$

Solution. We complete the square in the x terms by adding 4 to both sides of Eq. (9):

$$\begin{aligned} y + 4 &= x^2 + 4x + 4 \\ &= (x + 2)^2. \end{aligned}$$

This is of the form

$$(x - h)^2 = 4p(y - k)$$

with

$$h = -2, \quad k = -4,$$
$$4p = 1, \quad p = \tfrac{1}{4}.$$

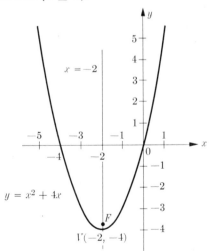

FIG. 9–28. Parabola $y = x^2 + 4x$.

The vertex of the parabola is $V(-2, -4)$; its axis of symmetry $(x + 2)^2 = 0$; and it opens upward because $y \geq -4$ for real x. The graph is shown in Fig. 9–28. The focus is on the axis of symmetry, $\frac{1}{4}$ unit above the vertex, at $F(-2, -3\frac{3}{4})$. The directrix is parallel to the x-axis, $\frac{1}{4}$ unit below the vertex. Its equation is $y = -4\frac{1}{4}$.

Remark 2. The clue to an equation of a parabola is that it is quadratic in one of the coordinates and linear in the other. Whenever we have such an equation we may reduce it to one of the standard forms (8a, b, c, d) by completing the square in the coordinate which appears quadratically. We then put the linear terms in the form $\pm 4p(x - h)$ or $\pm 4p(y - k)$. Then the information about vertex, distance from vertex to focus, axis of symmetry, and direction the curve opens can all be read from the equation in this standard form.

EXAMPLE 3. Discuss the equation

$$2x^2 + 5y - 3x + 4 = 0.$$

Solution. This equation is quadratic in x, linear in y. We divide by 2, the coefficient of x^2, and collect all the x terms on one side of the equation:

$$x^2 - \tfrac{3}{2}x = -\tfrac{5}{2}y - 2.$$

Now we complete the square by adding $(-\tfrac{3}{4})^2 = \tfrac{9}{16}$ to both sides:

$$(x - \tfrac{3}{4})^2 = -\tfrac{5}{2}y - 2 + \tfrac{9}{16}$$
$$= -\tfrac{5}{2}y - \tfrac{23}{16}.$$

To get the y terms in the form $-4p(y - k)$, we factor out $-\tfrac{5}{2}$, and write

$$(x - \tfrac{3}{4})^2 = -\tfrac{5}{2}(y + \tfrac{23}{40}).$$

This has the form

$$(x - h)^2 = -4p(y - k)$$

with

$$h = \tfrac{3}{4}, \qquad k = -\tfrac{23}{40}, \qquad 4p = \tfrac{5}{2}.$$

Hence the vertex is $V(\tfrac{3}{4}, -\tfrac{23}{40})$. The axis of symmetry is $(x - \tfrac{3}{4})^2 = 0$, or $x = \tfrac{3}{4}$; and the distance from the vertex to the focus is

$$p = \tfrac{5}{8}.$$

Since $y - k$ must here be ≤ 0 for real x, the curve opens downward, and the focus is p units below the vertex at $F(\tfrac{3}{4}, -\tfrac{6}{5})$. The graph is shown in Fig. 9–29.

Remark 3. In Fig. 9–30, $T'PT$ is tangent to the parabola, F is the focus, and PL is parallel to the axis of the parabola. The angles $\alpha = \angle LPT$

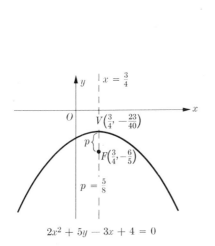

FIG. 9–29.   Parabola
$2x^2 + 5y - 3x + 4 = 0$.

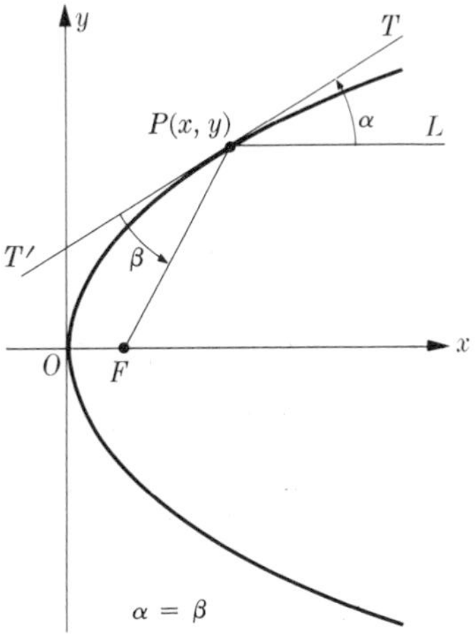

FIG. 9–30.   Parabolic reflector; $\alpha = \beta$.

and $\beta = \angle T'PF$ are equal (see Problem 31). This accounts for the property of a parabolic reflector that rays originating from the focus are reflected parallel to the axis. Or, rays coming into the reflector parallel to the axis are reflected to the focus. These properties are used in parabolic mirrors of telescopes and in parabolic radar antennas.

PROBLEMS

In each of the following problems (1 through 6), the vertex V and focus F of a parabola are given. Find the equation of the parabola and of its directrix. Sketch the graph showing the focus, vertex, and directrix.

1. $V(0, 0)$, $F(0, 2)$ 2. $V(0, 0)$, $F(-2, 0)$
3. $V(-2, 3)$, $F(-2, 4)$ 4. $V(0, 3)$, $F(-1, 3)$
5. $V(-3, 1)$, $F(0, 1)$ 6. $V(1, -3)$, $F(1, 0)$

In each of the following problems (7 through 12), the vertex V and directrix L of a parabola are given. Find the equation of the parabola and its focus. Sketch the graph showing the focus, vertex, and directrix.

7. $V(2, 0)$; L is the y-axis.
8. $V(1, -2)$; L is the x-axis.
9. $V(-3, 1)$; L is the line $x = 1$.
10. $V(-2, -2)$; L is the line $y = -3$.
11. $V(0, 1)$; L is the line $x = -1$.
12. $V(0, 1)$; L is the line $y = 2$.

In each of the following problems (13 through 22), find the vertex, axis of symmetry, focus, and directrix of the given parabola. Sketch the curve, showing these features.

13. $x^2 + 8y - 2x = 7$

14. $x^2 - 2y + 8x + 10 = 0$

15. $y^2 + 4x = 8$

16. $x^2 - 8y = 4$

17. $x^2 + 2x - 4y - 3 = 0$

18. $y^2 + x + y = 0$

19. $4y^2 - 8y + 3x - 2 = 0$

20. $y^2 + 6y + 2x + 5 = 0$

21. $3x^2 - 8y - 12x = 4$

22. $3x - 2y^2 - 4y + 7 = 0$

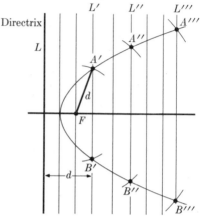

Fig. 9–31. Construction of points on parabola with focus F, directrix L.

23. What is the locus of points whose coordinates satisfy the inequality $x^2 < 8y$? Sketch.

24. Explain why the following method of locating points on the graph of a parabola is valid.

(a) Construct a family of lines parallel to the directrix.

(b) Set a compass to measure the distance d from the directrix to one of these lines L'. With the focus as center, construct an arc of radius d intersecting L' in points A' and B', as in Fig. 9–31.

(c) Repeat the process with other lines L'', L''', and so on, constructing points A'', B'', A''', B''', and so on. The points so constructed lie on a parabola with focus F, directrix L.

25. Use the method of Problem 24 to construct the graph of the parabola with focus $F(2, 2)$ and directrix the line $x + y = 0$.

26. Find the equation of the parabola of Problem 25. [*Hint:* The distance from a point (x, y) to the line $Ax + By + C = 0$ is $|Ax + By + C|/\sqrt{A^2 + B^2}$ by the answer to Problem 10, Article 9–4.]

27. Find the equation of the parabolic arch of base b and altitude h in Fig. 9–32.

28. Given the three points $(-1, 2)$, $(1, -1)$, and $(2, 1)$. (a) Find a parabola passing through the given points and having its axis parallel to the x-axis. (b) Find a parabola passing through the given points and having its axis parallel to the y-axis.

29. Suppose a and b are positive numbers. Sketch the parabolas $y^2 = 4a^2 - 4ax$ and $y^2 = 4b^2 + 4bx$ in the same diagram. Show that they have a common focus, the same for any a and b. Show that they intersect at $(a - b, \pm 2\sqrt{ab})$, and that each "a-parabola" is orthogonal to every "b-parabola." (Using different values of a and b, we obtain families of confocal parabolas. Each family is a set of orthogonal trajectories of the other family. See Article 9–2.)

30. What is the locus of the equation

$$(2x + y - 3)(x^2 + y^2 - 4)(x^2 - 8y) = 0?$$

Give a reason for your answer.

31. Prove that the angles α and β in Fig. 9–30 are equal.

32. Prove that the tangent to the parabola $y^2 = 4px$ at $P_1(x_1, y_1)$ intersects the axis of symmetry x_1 units to the left of the vertex. (This provides a simple method for constructing the tangent to a parabola at any point on it.)

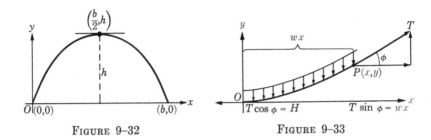

FIGURE 9–32 FIGURE 9–33

33. Show that the area of a parabolic segment of altitude h and base b is $\frac{2}{3}bh$ (see Problem 27).

34. Show that the volume generated by rotating the area bounded by the parabola $y = (4h/b^2)x^2$ and the line $y = h$ about the y-axis is equal to one and one-half times the volume of the corresponding inscribed cone.

35. The condition for equilibrium of the section OP of a cable that supports a weight of w pounds per foot measured along the horizontal (Fig. 9–33) is

$$\frac{dy}{dx} = \frac{wx}{H} \left(= \frac{T \sin \phi}{T \cos \phi} \right),$$

where the origin O is taken at the low point of the cable and H is the horizontal tension at O. Show that the curve in which the cable hangs is a parabola.

36. Assume, from optics, that when a ray of light is reflected by a mirror the angle of incidence is equal to the angle of reflection. If a mirror is formed by rotating a parabola about its axis and silvering the resulting surface, show that a ray of light emanating from the focus of the parabola is reflected parallel to the axis.

9–7 The ellipse.

DEFINITION. *An ellipse is the locus of points $P(x, y)$ the sum of whose distances from two fixed points is constant.*

If the two fixed points, called *foci*, are taken at $F_1(-c, 0)$ and $F_2(c, 0)$

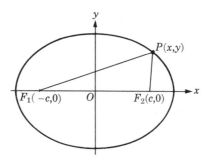

FIGURE 9–34. Ellipse.

(Fig. 9–34), and the sum of the distances $PF_1 + PF_2$ is denoted by $2a$, then the coordinates of P must satisfy the equation

$$\sqrt{(x + c)^2 + y^2} + \sqrt{(x - c)^2 + y^2} = 2a.$$

To simplify this expression, we transpose the second radical to the right side of the equation, square, and simplify, to obtain

$$a - \frac{c}{a} x = \sqrt{(x - c)^2 + y^2}.$$

Again we square and simplify, and obtain

$$\frac{x^2}{a^2} + \frac{y^2}{a^2 - c^2} = 1. \tag{1}$$

Since the sum $PF_1 + PF_2 = 2a$ of two sides of the triangle F_1F_2P is greater than the third side $F_1F_2 = 2c$, the term $(a^2 - c^2)$ in (1) is positive and has a real positive square root which we denote by b:

$$b = \sqrt{a^2 - c^2}. \tag{2}$$

Then (1) takes the more compact form

$$\boxed{\frac{x^2}{a^2} + \frac{y^2}{b^2} = 1,} \tag{3}$$

from which it is readily seen that the curve is symmetric about both axes and lies inside the rectangle bounded by the lines $x = a$, $x = -a$, $y = b$, $y = -b$. The intercepts of the curve are at $(\pm a, 0)$ and $(0, \pm b)$. The curve intersects each axis at an angle of $90°$, since

$$\frac{dy}{dx} = \frac{-b^2 x}{a^2 y}$$

is zero at $x = 0$, $y = \pm b$ and is infinite at $y = 0$, $x = \pm a$.

We have shown that the coordinates of P must satisfy (1) if P satisfies the geometric condition $PF_1 + PF_2 = 2a$. Conversely, if x and y satisfy the algebraic equation (1) with $0 < c < a$, then

$$y^2 = (a^2 - c^2)\frac{a^2 - x^2}{a^2},$$

and substituting this in the radicals below, we find that

$$PF_1 = \sqrt{(x + c)^2 + y^2} = \left| a + \frac{c}{a}x \right| \qquad (4a)$$

and

$$PF_2 = \sqrt{(x - c)^2 + y^2} = \left| a - \frac{c}{a}x \right|. \qquad (4b)$$

Since x is restricted to the range $-a \le x \le a$, the value of $(c/a)x$ lies between $-c$ and c, so that both $a + (c/a)x$ and $a - (c/a)x$ are positive, both being between $a + c$ and $a - c$. Hence the absolute values in (4a) and (4b) yield

$$PF_1 = a + \frac{c}{a}x, \qquad PF_2 = a - \frac{c}{a}x, \qquad (5)$$

and, adding these, we see that $PF_1 + PF_2$ has a value $2a$ independent of the position of P on the curve. Thus the *geometric property* and *algebraic equation* are equivalent.

In Eq. (3), $b^2 = a^2 - c^2$ is less than a^2. The *major axis* of the ellipse is the segment of length $2a$ between the x-intercepts $(\pm a, 0)$. The *minor axis* is the segment of length $2b$ between the y-intercepts $(0, \pm b)$. The numbers a and b are also referred to respectively as semimajor axis and semiminor axis. If these semiaxes are $a = 4$, $b = 3$, then Eq. (3) is

$$\frac{x^2}{16} + \frac{y^2}{9} = 1. \qquad (6a)$$

On the other hand, if we interchange the roles of x and y in (6a), we get the equation

$$\frac{x^2}{9} + \frac{y^2}{16} = 1, \qquad (6b)$$

which must also represent an ellipse, but one with its major axis vertical rather than horizontal. Graphs of Eqs. (6a) and (6b) are given in Fig. 9–35 (a) and (b).

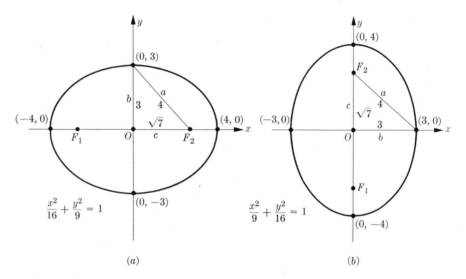

Fig. 9–35. Ellipses with major axes (a) horizontal and (b) vertical.

There is never any need for confusion in analyzing equations like (6a) and (6b). We simply find the intercepts on the axes of symmetry; then we know which way the major axis runs. The foci are always on the major axis. And if we use the letters a, b, and c to represent the lengths of semi-major axis, semiminor axis, and half-distance between foci, then Eq. (2) tells us that

$$b^2 = a^2 - c^2$$

or

$$a^2 = b^2 + c^2. \qquad (7)$$

Hence a is the hypotenuse of a right triangle of sides b and c, as in Fig. 9–35. When we start with an equation like (6a) or (6b), we can read off a^2 and b^2 from it at once. Then Eq. (7) determines c^2 as their difference. So in either of Eqs. (6a) and (6b) we have

$$c^2 = 16 - 9 = 7.$$

Therefore the foci are $\sqrt{7}$ units from the center of the ellipse as shown.

Center not at the origin. The *center* of an ellipse is defined as the point of intersection of its axes of symmetry. If the center is at $C(h, k)$, and the axes of the ellipse are parallel to the x- and y-axes, then we may introduce new coordinates

$$x' = x - h, \qquad y' = y - k, \qquad (8)$$

using C as origin O' of $x'y'$-coordinates. The equation of the ellipse in the new coordinates is either

$$\frac{x'^2}{a^2} + \frac{y'^2}{b^2} = 1 \qquad\qquad (9a)$$

or

$$\frac{x'^2}{b^2} + \frac{y'^2}{a^2} = 1, \qquad\qquad (9b)$$

depending upon which way the major axis runs.

EXAMPLE 1. Analyze the equation $9x^2 + 4y^2 + 36x - 8y + 4 = 0$.

Solution. In order to complete the squares, we collect the x terms and the y terms separately, thus

$$9(x^2 + 4x) + 4(y^2 - 2y) = -4,$$

and then complete the square in each set of parentheses to obtain

$$9(x^2 + 4x + 4) + 4(y^2 - 2y + 1) = -4 + 36 + 4.$$

We now divide both sides by 36 and write

$$\frac{(x + 2)^2}{4} + \frac{(y - 1)^2}{9} = 1.$$

Setting

$$x' = x + 2, \qquad y' = y - 1,$$

we see that the new origin $x' = 0$, $y' = 0$ is the same as the point $x = -2$, $y = 1$. In terms of the new coordinates, the equation is

$$\frac{x'^2}{4} + \frac{y'^2}{9} = 1,$$

which represents an ellipse with intercepts at $(0, \pm 3)$ on the y'-axis and $(\pm 2, 0)$ on the x'-axis. To locate the foci, we use the relation

$$b = \sqrt{a^2 - c^2}$$

to find

$$c = \sqrt{a^2 - b^2}.$$

Here

$$a^2 = 9, \qquad b^2 = 4,$$

so

$$c = \sqrt{5}.$$

The foci are at the points $(0, \pm\sqrt{5})$ on the y'-axis or at $(-2, 1\pm \sqrt{5})$ in terms of the original coordinates.

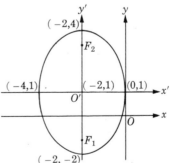

FIGURE 9–36

We recall (Fig. 9–34) that the essential *geometric* property of an ellipse is that the sum of the distances from any point on it to the two foci is a constant, namely,

$$PF_1 + PF_2 = 2a.$$

The essential *algebraic* property of its equation when written in the form of a quadratic without a cross-product term is that the x^2 and y^2 terms have the same sign.

In order to discuss the properties of the ellipse in more detail, we shall assume that its equation has been reduced to the form

$$\frac{x^2}{a^2} + \frac{y^2}{b^2} = 1, \qquad a > b > 0. \tag{10}$$

Although the distance c from the center of the ellipse to a focus does not appear in its equation, we may still determine c as in the examples above from the equation

$$c^2 = a^2 - b^2, \tag{11}$$

which is another way of writing Eq. (7).

A simple geometric method of finding c is shown by Fig. 9–37 and is based on the following considerations. Since the sum of the distances

$$PF_1 + PF_2 = 2a$$

for *every point* P on the ellipse, then certainly this must hold when P is taken to be at the y-intercept B. But the y-axis is the perpendicular

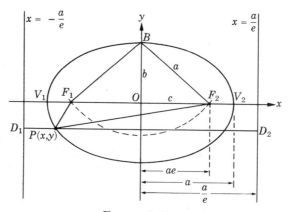

FIGURE 9–37

bisector of the line segment F_1F_2, so every point on it is equidistant from F_1 and F_2. We therefore have

$$BF_1 + BF_2 = 2a \quad \text{and} \quad BF_1 = BF_2;$$

hence

$$BF_1 = BF_2 = a.$$

We may therefore use B as the center of a circular arc of radius a. It will cut the x-axis in the two foci F_1 and F_2. Equation (11) then follows at once from applying the Theorem of Pythagoras to the right triangle OBF_2 in the figure.

Eccentricity. If we keep a fixed and vary c over the range $0 \le c \le a$, the resulting ellipses will vary in shape, being circular when $c = 0$ and becoming flatter as c increases, until in the extreme case $c = a$, the "ellipse" reduces to the line segment F_1F_2 joining the two foci (Fig. 9–38). The ratio

$$e = c/a, \tag{12}$$

called the *eccentricity* of the ellipse, varies from 0 to 1 and indicates the degree of departure from circularity.

We recall that a parabola has one focus and one directrix. Each ellipse has two foci and two directrices. The directrices are lines perpendicular to the major axis of the ellipse at distances $\pm a/e$ from its center. The *parabola* has the property that

$$PF = 1 \cdot PD \tag{13}$$

for any point P on it, where F is the focus and D is the point nearest P on the directrix.

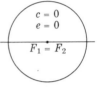

FIGURE 9–38

For an *ellipse*, it is not difficult to show that the equations which take the place of (13) are

$$PF_1 = e \cdot PD_1, \qquad PF_2 = e \cdot PD_2. \tag{14}$$

Here e is the eccentricity, P is any point on the ellipse, F_1 and F_2 are the foci, and D_1 and D_2 are the points nearest P on the two directrices. In Eq. (14), the corresponding directrix and focus must be used; that is, if one uses the distance from P to the focus F_1, one must also use the distance from P to the directrix at the same end of the ellipse (see Fig. 9–37). We thus associate the directrix $x = -a/e$ with the focus $F_1(-c, 0)$, and the directrix $x = a/e$ with the focus $F_2(c, 0)$. In terms of the semimajor axis a and eccentricity $e < 1$, as one goes away from the center along the major axis, one finds successively

　　　a *focus* at distance ae from the center,

　　　a *vertex* at distance a from the center,

　　　a *directrix* at distance a/e from the center.

An interesting feature of the "focus-and-directrix" property is that it furnishes a common bond uniting the parabola, ellipse, and hyperbola. Namely, if a point $P(x, y)$ is such that its distance PF from a fixed point (the focus) is proportional to its distance PD from a fixed line (the directrix), that is, so that

$$\boxed{PF = e \cdot PD,} \tag{15}$$

where e is a constant of proportionality, then the locus of P is

　　(a) a *parabola* if $e = 1$,

　　(b) an *ellipse* of eccentricity e if $e < 1$, and

　　(c) a *hyperbola* of eccentricity e if $e > 1$.

Constructions. There are several methods of constructing an ellipse. One of these simply uses the definition directly. The two ends of a string of length $2a$ are held fixed at the foci F_1 and F_2 and a pencil traces the curve as it is held taut against the string (see Fig. 9–39).

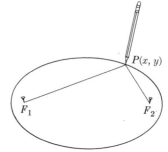

FIG. 9–39. Construction of an ellipse using the definition $PF_1 + PF_2 = 2a$.

A second method makes use of a straight edge AB of length $a + b$. Place point A on the y-axis and B on the x-axis, and on the graph paper, make a dot at $P(x, y)$ at distance a from A (see Fig. 9–40). In terms of the angle θ that line AB makes with the (negative) x-axis, we have

$$x = a \cos \theta, \qquad y = b \sin \theta, \tag{16}$$

and hence

$$\frac{x^2}{a^2} + \frac{y^2}{b^2} = \cos^2\theta + \sin^2\theta = 1.$$

Therefore $P(x, y)$ is on the ellipse, Eq. (10).

A third method is to construct two concentric circles of radii a and b (Fig. 9–41). A line making an angle θ with the horizontal is drawn from

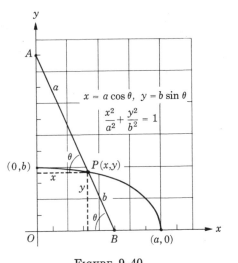

$$x = a \cos \theta, \quad y = b \sin \theta$$

$$\frac{x^2}{a^2} + \frac{y^2}{b^2} = 1$$

FIGURE 9–40　　　　　　　　　　　FIGURE 9–41

the center cutting the two circles in points A and B respectively. The vertical line through A and the horizontal line through B intersect in a point P whose coordinates also satisfy (16). By varying the angle θ from 0 to 360°, as many points as desired may be obtained on the ellipse.

PROBLEMS

In each of the following problems (1 through 5), find the equation of an ellipse having the given center C, focus F, and semimajor axis a. Sketch the graph and give the eccentricity of each ellipse.

1. $C(0, 0)$, $\quad F(0, 2)$, $\quad a = 4$　　　　2. $C(0, 0)$, $\quad F(-3, 0)$, $\quad a = 5$

3. $C(0, 2)$, $\quad F(0, 0)$, $\quad a = 3$　　　　4. $C(-3, 0)$, $\quad F(-3, -2)$, $\quad a = 4$

5. $C(2, 2)$, $\quad F(-1, 2)$, $\quad a = \sqrt{10}$

6. The end points of the major and minor axes of an ellipse are $(1, 1)$, $(3, 4)$, $(1, 7)$, and $(-1, 4)$. Sketch the ellipse, give its equation, and find its foci.

7. Find the center, vertices, and foci of the ellipse $25x^2 + 9y^2 - 100x + 54y - 44 = 0$. Sketch the curve.

8. Sketch each of the following ellipses:

(a) $9x^2 + 4y^2 = 36$,　　　　　　　(b) $4x^2 + 9y^2 = 144$,

(c) $\dfrac{(x - 1)^2}{16} + \dfrac{(y + 2)^2}{4} = 1$,　　　(d) $4x^2 + y^2 = 1$,

(e) $16(x - 2)^2 + 9(y + 3)^2 = 144$.

9. Find the equation of the ellipse that passes through the origin and has foci at $(-1, 1)$ and $(1, 1)$.

10. Find the eccentricity and the directrices of the ellipse $x^2/7 + y^2/16 = 1$.

11. Find the volume generated by rotating an ellipse of semi-axes a and b ($a > b$) about its major axis.

12. Set up the integrals that give (a) the area of a quadrant of the circle $x^2 + y^2 = a^2$, (b) the area of a quadrant of the ellipse $b^2x^2 + a^2y^2 = a^2b^2$. Show that the integral in (b) is b/a times the integral in (a) and deduce the area of the ellipse from the known area of the circle.

13. An ellipsoid is generated by rotating an ellipse about its major axis. The inside surface of the ellipsoid is silvered to produce a mirror. Show that a ray of light emanating from one focus will be reflected to the other focus. (Sound waves also follow such paths and this property of ellipsoids accounts for phenomena in certain "whispering galleries.")

14. Find the length of the chord perpendicular to the major axis of the ellipse $b^2x^2 + a^2y^2 = a^2b^2$ and passing through a focus. (This chord is called the "latus rectum" of the ellipse.)

15. Find the equation of an ellipse of eccentricity $\frac{2}{3}$ if the line $x = 9$ is one directrix and the corresponding focus is at $(4, 0)$.

16. Find the values of the constants A, B, and C if the ellipse $4x^2 + y^2 + Ax + By + C = 0$ is to be tangent to the x-axis at the origin and to pass through the point $(-1, 2)$.

17. Show that the line tangent to the ellipse $(x^2/a^2) + (y^2/b^2) = 1$ at the point $P_1(x_1, y_1)$ on it is

$$\frac{xx_1}{a^2} + \frac{yy_1}{b^2} = 1.$$

18. Graph the locus of $P(x, y)$ if $9x^2 + 16y^2 < 144$.

19. Graph the locus of $P(x, y)$ if

$$(x^2 + 4y)(2x - y - 3)(x^2 + y^2 - 25)(x^2 + 4y^2 - 4) = 0.$$

20. Graph the locus of $P(x, y)$ if $(x^2 + y^2 - 1)(9x^2 + 4y^2 - 36) < 0$.

9–8 The hyperbola.

DEFINITION. *A hyperbola is the locus of $P(x, y)$ if the difference of its distances from two fixed points is constant.*

Taking the fixed points at $F_1(-c, 0)$ and $F_2(c, 0)$ and the constant equal to $2a$ (see Fig. 9–42, p. 484), we have the condition

$$\sqrt{(x + c)^2 + y^2} - \sqrt{(x - c)^2 + y^2} = 2a$$

or

$$\sqrt{(x - c)^2 + y^2} - \sqrt{(x + c)^2 + y^2} = 2a.$$

The second equation is like the first, with $2a$ replaced by $-2a$. Hence we write the first one with $\pm 2a$, transpose one radical to the right side of

the equation, square, and simplify. One radical still remains. We isolate
it and square again. We then obtain the equation

$$\frac{x^2}{a^2} + \frac{y^2}{a^2 - c^2} = 1. \tag{1}$$

So far, this is just like the equation for an ellipse. But now $a^2 - c^2$ is
negative, because the *difference* in two sides of the triangle F_1F_2P is less
than the third side:

$$2a < 2c.$$

So in this case $c^2 - a^2$ is positive and has a real positive square root which
we call b:

$$b = \sqrt{c^2 - a^2}, \tag{2a}$$

or

$$a^2 - c^2 = -b^2. \tag{2b}$$

The equation of the hyperbola now becomes

$$\boxed{\frac{x^2}{a^2} - \frac{y^2}{b^2} = 1,} \tag{3}$$

which is analogous to the equation of an ellipse; the only differences are
the minus sign in the equation of the hyperbola, and the new relation
among a, b, and c given by Eq. (2b). The hyperbola, like the ellipse, is
symmetric with respect to both axes and the origin, but it has no real
y-intercepts and in fact no portion of the curve lies between the lines
$x = a$ and $x = -a$.

If we start with a point $P(x, y)$ whose coordinates satisfy Eq. (3),
the distances PF_1 and PF_2 will be given by

$$PF_1 = \sqrt{(x + c)^2 + y^2} = \left| a + \frac{c}{a} x \right|, \tag{4a}$$

$$PF_2 = \sqrt{(x - c)^2 + y^2} = \left| a - \frac{c}{a} x \right|, \tag{4b}$$

as for the ellipse. But now c is greater than a, and P is either to the right
of the line $x = a$, that is

$$x > a,$$

or else P is to the left of the line $x = -a$, and then

$$x < -a.$$

The absolute values in Eqs. (4) work out to be

$$\left.\begin{array}{l} PF_1 = a + \dfrac{c}{a}x \\[2mm] PF_2 = \dfrac{c}{a}x - a \end{array}\right\} \text{if } x > a \qquad (5a)$$

and

$$\left.\begin{array}{l} PF_1 = -\left(a + \dfrac{c}{a}x\right) \\[2mm] PF_2 = a - \dfrac{c}{a}x \end{array}\right\} \text{if } x < -a. \qquad (5b)$$

Thus, when P is to the right of the line $x = a$, the condition $PF_1 - PF_2 = 2a$ is satisfied, while if P is to the left of $x = -a$, the condition $PF_2 - PF_1 = 2a$ is fulfilled (Fig. 9–42). In either case, *any point P that satisfies the geometric conditions must satisfy the algebraic equation and, conversely, any point that satisfies the algebraic equation does also satisfy the geometric conditions.*

The left side of (3) can be factored and the equation written in the form

$$\left(\frac{x}{a} - \frac{y}{b}\right)\left(\frac{x}{a} + \frac{y}{b}\right) = 1$$

or

$$\frac{x}{a} - \frac{y}{b} = \frac{ab}{bx + ay}. \qquad (6a)$$

Analysis of (3) shows that one branch of the curve lies in the first quadrant and has infinite extent. If the point P moves along this branch so that x and y both become infinite, then the right side of (6a) tends to zero; hence the left side must do likewise. That is

$$\lim_{\substack{x \to \infty \\ y \to \infty}} \left(\frac{x}{a} - \frac{y}{b}\right) = 0, \qquad (6b)$$

which leads us to speculate that the straight line

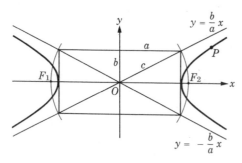

FIGURE 9–42

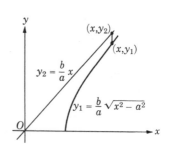

FIGURE 9–43

$$\frac{x}{a} - \frac{y}{b} = 0 \qquad (7a)$$

may be an asymptote of the curve. To see that this is definitely so, we investigate the vertical distance $(y_2 - y_1)$ between the curve and the line where we take

$$y_2 = \frac{b}{a} x$$

on the line, and

$$y_1 = \frac{b}{a} \sqrt{x^2 - a^2}$$

on the curve (Fig. 9–43). We then multiply both sides of Eq. (6b) by b, and see that

$$\lim_{x \to \infty} (y_2 - y_1) = 0.$$

Since this vertical distance tends to zero, certainly the perpendicular distance from the line to the curve also approaches zero, and the line in Eq. (7a) is an asymptote of the hyperbola.

By symmetry, the line

$$\frac{x}{a} + \frac{y}{b} = 0 \qquad (7b)$$

is also an asymptote of the hyperbola. Both asymptotes may be obtained by simply replacing the "one" on the right side of (3) by a zero and then factoring. In sketching a hyperbola (Fig. 9–42), it is convenient to mark off distances a to the right and to the left of the origin along the x-axis and distances b above and below the origin along the y-axis, and to construct a rectangle with sides passing through these points, parallel to the coordinate axes. The diagonals of this rectangle, extended, are then the asymptotes of the hyperbola. The semidiagonal

$$c = \sqrt{a^2 + b^2}$$

can also be used as the radius of a circle that will cut the x-axis in two points, $F_1(-c, 0)$ and $F_2(c, 0)$, which are the foci of the hyperbola.

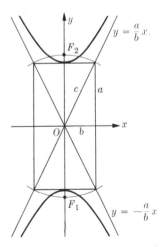

Fig. 9–44. Hyperbola $(y^2/a^2) - (x^2/b^2) = 1$.

If we interchange x and y in Eq. (3), the new equation

$$\frac{y^2}{a^2} - \frac{x^2}{b^2} = 1 \qquad (8)$$

represents a hyperbola with foci on the y-axis. Its graph is shown in Fig. 9–44.

Center not at the origin. The *center* of a hyperbola is the point of intersection of its axes of symmetry. If the center is $C(h, k)$, we may introduce a translation to new coordinates

$$x' = x - h, \qquad y' = y - k \qquad (9)$$

with origin O' at the center. In terms of the new coordinates, the equation of the hyperbola is either

$$\frac{x'^2}{a^2} - \frac{y'^2}{b^2} = 1 \qquad (10a)$$

or

$$\frac{y'^2}{a^2} - \frac{x'^2}{b^2} = 1. \qquad (10b)$$

EXAMPLE 1. Analyze the equation $x^2 - 4y^2 + 2x + 8y - 7 = 0$.

Solution. We complete the squares in the x and y terms separately and reduce to standard form:

$$(x^2 + 2x) - 4(y^2 - 2y) = 7,$$
$$(x^2 + 2x + 1) - 4(y^2 - 2y + 1) = 7 + 1 - 4,$$
$$\frac{(x + 1)^2}{4} - (y - 1)^2 = 1.$$

The translation of axes

$$x' = x + 1, \qquad y' = y - 1$$

reduces the equation to

$$\frac{x'^2}{4} - \frac{y'^2}{1} = 1,$$

which represents a hyperbola with center at $x' = 0$, $y' = 0$ or $x = -1$, $y = 1$, having

$$a^2 = 4, \qquad b^2 = 1, \qquad c^2 = a^2 + b^2 = 5$$

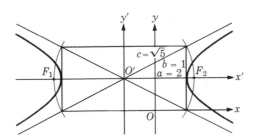

FIGURE 9–45

and asymptotes

$$\frac{x'}{2} - y' = 0, \qquad \frac{x'}{2} + y' = 0.$$

The foci have coordinates $(\pm\sqrt{5}, 0)$ relative to the new axes or, since

$$x = x' - 1, \qquad y = y' + 1,$$

the coordinates relative to the original axes are $(-1 \pm \sqrt{5}, 1)$. The curve is sketched in Fig. 9–45.

EXAMPLE 2. $x^2 - 4y^2 - 2x + 8y - 2 = 0.$

Proceeding as before, we obtain

$$(x - 1)^2 - 4(y - 1)^2 = 2 + 1 - 4 = -1.$$

The standard form requires a plus one on the right side of the equation, so we change signs and have

$$4(y - 1)^2 - (x - 1)^2 = 1.$$

Comparison with (10) indicates that we should write the first term of this equation as $(y - 1)^2$ divided by 0.25:

$$\frac{(y - 1)^2}{0.25} - \frac{(x - 1)^2}{1} = 1.$$

The translation $x' = x - 1$, $y' = y - 1$ replaces this by

$$\frac{y'^2}{0.25} - \frac{x'^2}{1} = 1,$$

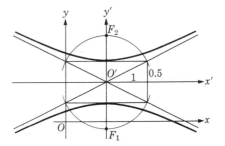

FIGURE 9–46

which represents a hyperbola with center at $x' = y' = 0$, or $x = y = 1$. The curve has intercepts at $(0, \pm 0.5)$ on the y'-axis but does not cross the x'-axis.

Here (10b) applies, with

$$a^2 = 0.25, \qquad b^2 = 1, \qquad c^2 = a^2 + b^2 = 1.25.$$

The lines (Fig. 9–46)

$$\frac{y'}{0.5} - x' = 0, \qquad \frac{y'}{0.5} + x' = 0$$

are the asymptotes, while the foci are at $(0, \pm\sqrt{1.25})$ on the y'-axis.

It is worth noting that there is no restriction $a > b$ for the hyperbola as there is for the ellipse, and the direction in which the hyperbola opens is controlled by the *signs* rather than by the relative *sizes* of the coefficients of the quadratic terms.

In our further discussion of the hyperbola, we shall assume that it has been referred to axes through its center and that its equation has the form

$$\frac{x^2}{a^2} - \frac{y^2}{b^2} = 1. \tag{11}$$

Then

$$b = \sqrt{c^2 - a^2}$$

and

$$\boxed{c^2 = a^2 + b^2.} \tag{12}$$

As for the ellipse, we define the *eccentricity* e to be

$$\boxed{e = \frac{c}{a},}$$

and since $c \geq a$, the eccentricity of a hyperbola is never less than unity. The lines

$$x = \frac{a}{e}, \qquad x = -\frac{a}{e}$$

are the *directrices*.

We shall now verify that a point $P(x, y)$ whose coordinates satisfy Eq. (11) also has the property that

$$PF_1 = e \cdot PD_1 \tag{13a}$$

and

$$PF_2 = e \cdot PD_2, \tag{13b}$$

where $F_1(-c, 0)$ and $F_2(c, 0)$ are the foci while $D_1(-a/e, y)$ and $D_2(a/e, y)$ are the points nearest P on the directrices.

We shall content ourselves with establishing the results (13a, b) for any point P on the right branch of the hyperbola; the method is the same

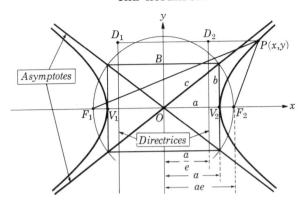

FIGURE 9–47

when P is on the left branch. Reference to Eqs. (5a) then shows that

$$PF_1 = \frac{c}{a}x + a = e\left(x + \frac{a}{e}\right),$$
$$PF_2 = \frac{c}{a}x - a = e\left(x - \frac{a}{e}\right),$$

(14a)

while we see from Fig. 9–47 that

$$PD_1 = x + \frac{a}{e}, \qquad PD_2 = x - \frac{a}{e}.$$

(14b)

These results combine to establish the "focus-and-directrix" properties of the hyperbola expressed in Eqs. (13a, b). Conversely, if Eqs. (14a) are satisfied, it is also true that

$$\boxed{PF_1 - PF_2 = 2a;}$$

that is, P satisfies the requirement that the difference of its distances from the two foci is constant.

It is possible to devise various schemes for sketching a hyperbola. In one method (see Fig. 9–48) we exploit the equation

$$PF_1 = 2a + PF_2$$

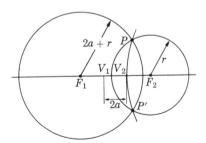

FIGURE 9–48

by constructing a circle of radius r with center at F_2 and another circle of radius $2a + r$ with center at F_1. The points P, P' where the two circles intersect are points on the hyperbola.

By varying r, as many points on the hyperbola as desired may be obtained. Interchanging the roles of the two foci F_1 and F_2 will give points on the other branch of the hyperbola.

PROBLEMS

1. Sketch each of the following hyperbolas:

(a) $\dfrac{x^2}{9} - \dfrac{y^2}{16} = 1,$ (b) $\dfrac{x^2}{16} - \dfrac{y^2}{9} = 1,$

(c) $\dfrac{y^2}{9} - \dfrac{x^2}{16} = 1,$ (d) $\dfrac{x^2}{9} - \dfrac{y^2}{16} = -1.$

In each of the following problems (2 through 8), find the center, vertices, foci, and asymptotes of the given hyperbola. Sketch the curve.

2. $9(x - 2)^2 - 4(y + 3)^2 = 36$ 3. $4(x - 2)^2 - 9(y + 3)^2 = 36$
4. $4(y + 3)^2 - 9(x - 2)^2 = 1$ 5. $5x^2 - 4y^2 + 20x + 8y = 4$
6. $4x^2 = y^2 - 4y + 8$ 7. $4y^2 = x^2 - 4x$
8. $4x^2 - 5y^2 - 16x + 10y + 31 = 0$

9. Show that the line tangent to the hyperbola $b^2x^2 - a^2y^2 = a^2b^2$ at a point $P(x_1, y_1)$ on it has an equation which may be written in the form $b^2xx_1 - a^2yy_1 = a^2b^2$.

10. Find the volume generated when the area bounded by the hyperbola $b^2x^2 - a^2y^2 = a^2b^2$ and the line $x = c$, through its focus $(c, 0)$, is rotated about the y-axis.

11. Show that the equation

$$\frac{x^2}{9 - C} + \frac{y^2}{5 - C} = 1$$

represents (a) an ellipse if C is any constant less than 5, (b) a hyperbola if C is any constant between 5 and 9, (c) no real locus if C is greater than 9. Show that each ellipse in (a) and each hyperbola in (b) has foci at the two points $(\pm 2, 0)$, independent of the value of C.

12. Find the equation of the hyperbola with foci at $(0, 0)$ and $(0, 4)$ if it is required to pass through the point $(12, 9)$.

13. One focus of a hyperbola is located at the point $(1, -3)$ and the corresponding directrix is the line $y = 2$. Find the equation of the hyperbola if its eccentricity is $\frac{3}{2}$.

14. Find out what you can about the DECCA system of air navigation. [See *Time*, Feb. 23, 1959, p. 87.]

9–9 Second degree curves. The circle, parabola, ellipse, and hyperbola are curves whose equations are all special cases of the following general equation of the second degree:

$$Ax^2 + Bxy + Cy^2 + Dx + Ey + F = 0. \qquad (1)$$

For example, the circle

$$(x - h)^2 + (y - k)^2 = r^2$$

may be obtained from Eq. (1) by taking

$$A = C = 1, \quad B = 0, \quad D = -2h,$$
$$E = -2k, \qquad F = h^2 + k^2 - r^2,$$

and the parabóla

$$x^2 = 4py$$

is obtained by taking

$$A = 1, \qquad E = -4p, \qquad B = C = D = F = 0.$$

In fact, even the straight line is a special case of (1) with $A = B = C = 0$, but this reduces (1) to a *linear* equation instead of maintaining its status as a second degree equation. The terms Ax^2, Bxy, and Cy^2 are the second degree, or quadratic terms, and we shall presently investigate the nature of the curve represented by Eq. (1) when at least one of these quadratic terms is present.

The so-called "cross-product" term, Bxy, has not appeared in the equations we found in Articles 9–5 to 9–8. This is a consequence of the way in which we chose coordinate axes, namely, such that at least one of them is parallel to an axis of symmetry of the curve in question. However, suppose we seek to find the equation of a hyperbola with

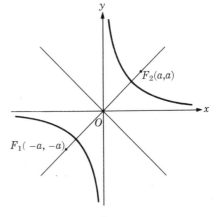

FIGURE 9–49

foci at $F_1(-a, -a)$ and $F_2(a, a)$ for example, and with $|PF_1 - PF_2| = 2a$ (Fig. 9–49). Then

$$\sqrt{(x + a)^2 + (y + a)^2} - \sqrt{(x - a)^2 + (y - a)^2} = \pm 2a,$$

and when we transpose one radical, square, solve for the radical that still appears, and square again, this reduces to

$$2xy = a^2, \tag{2}$$

which is a special case of Eq. (1) in which the cross-product term is present. The asymptotes of the hyperbola in Eq. (2) are the x- and y-axes, and the transverse axis of the hyperbola (which is the axis of symmetry on which the foci lie) makes an angle of 45° with the co-ordinate axes. In fact, the cross-product term is present only in some similar circumstance, where the axes have been "tilted."

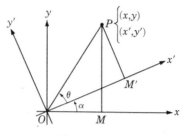

FIGURE 9–50

We shall now see how the equation of a curve is modified if it is referred to $x'y'$-axes by a rotation through an angle α in the counterclockwise direction. Referring to Fig. 9–50, we have

$$x = OM = OP \cos (\theta + \alpha),$$
$$y = MP = OP \sin (\theta + \alpha),$$

(3a)

while

$$x' = OM' = OP \cos \theta,$$
$$y' = M'P = OP \sin \theta.$$

(3b)

Using the relationships

$$\cos (\theta + \alpha) = \cos \theta \cos \alpha - \sin \theta \sin \alpha,$$
$$\sin (\theta + \alpha) = \sin \theta \cos \alpha + \cos \theta \sin \alpha,$$

in (3a) and taking account of (3b), we find

$$\boxed{\begin{aligned} x &= x' \cos \alpha - y' \sin \alpha, \\ y &= x' \sin \alpha + y' \cos \alpha, \end{aligned}}$$

(4)

which are known as the equations for *rotation of axes*.

To illustrate their application, suppose that we take $\alpha = 45°$ and find the equation of the hyperbola of (2) in terms of the new coordinates. Since $\cos 45° = \sin 45° = \sqrt{\frac{1}{2}}$, we substitute

$$x = \frac{x' - y'}{\sqrt{2}}, \qquad y = \frac{x' + y'}{\sqrt{2}}$$

into Eq. (2) and obtain

$$(x')^2 - (y')^2 = a^2,$$

which is like Eq. (3), Article 9–8, with $b = a$.

If we apply the general rotation of axes of equations (4) to the general quadratic equation (1), we obtain a new quadratic equation of the form

$$A'x'^2 + B'x'y' + C'y'^2 + D'x' + E'y' + F' = 0, \qquad (5)$$

with new coefficients related to the old as follows:

$$\left.\begin{aligned}
A' &= A\cos^2\alpha + B\cos\alpha\sin\alpha + C\sin^2\alpha, \\
B' &= B(\cos^2\alpha - \sin^2\alpha) + 2(C - A)\sin\alpha\cos\alpha, \\
C' &= A\sin^2\alpha - B\sin\alpha\cos\alpha + C\cos^2\alpha, \\
D' &= D\cos\alpha + E\sin\alpha, \\
E' &= -D\sin\alpha + E\cos\alpha, \\
F' &= F.
\end{aligned}\right\} \qquad (6)$$

If we start with an equation in which the cross-product term is present, $B \neq 0$, we can always find an angle of rotation α such that the new cross-product term is eliminated. To find the angle α that does this, we simply put $B' = 0$ in (6_2) and solve for α. It is easier to do this if we note that

$$\cos^2\alpha - \sin^2\alpha = \cos 2\alpha,$$

$$2\sin\alpha\cos\alpha = \sin 2\alpha,$$

so that

$$B' = B\cos 2\alpha + (C - A)\sin 2\alpha.$$

Hence B' will vanish if we choose α so that

$$\boxed{\cot 2\alpha = \frac{A - C}{B}.} \qquad (7)$$

For example, the curve whose equation is

$$x^2 + xy + y^2 = 3$$

has $A = B = C = 1$. Choosing α according to Eq. (7),

$$\cot 2\alpha = 0, \qquad 2\alpha = 90°, \qquad \alpha = 45°,$$

and substituting

$$x = \frac{x' - y'}{\sqrt{2}}, \qquad y = \frac{x' + y'}{\sqrt{2}}$$

according to (4), we obtain

$$3(x')^2 + (y')^2 = 6.$$

This may be identified as an ellipse with its foci on the new y'-axis.

Since axes may be rotated to eliminate the cross-product term, there is no loss in generality in assuming that this has been done. Then the quadratic equation (5), with $B' = 0$, will look like Eq. (1), with $B = 0$:

$$Ax^2 + Cy^2 + Dx + Ey + F = 0. \tag{8}$$

Eq. (8) represents:

(a) A straight line if $A = C = 0$, and not both D and E vanish.

(b) A circle if $A = C \neq 0$. In special cases the locus may reduce to a single point, or no real locus.

(c) A parabola if (8) is quadratic in one variable, linear in the other.

(d) An ellipse if A and C are both positive or both negative. In special cases the locus may reduce to a single point, or no real locus.

(e) A hyperbola if A and C are of opposite signs, both different from zero. In special cases the locus may reduce to a pair of inter-secting straight lines. (For example: $x^2 - y^2 = 0$.)

We have already seen how to reduce (8) to the standard form for the equation of a circle, parabola, ellipse, or hyperbola by completing the squares (as needed) and translating to new axes.

Summary. Any second degree equation in x and y represents a circle, parabola, ellipse, or hyperbola (except for certain special cases in which the locus may reduce to a point, a line, a pair of lines, or fail to exist, as noted above). Conversely, any of these curves has an equation of the second degree. To find the curve, given its equation, we

first, rotate axes (if necessary)
to eliminate the cross-product term,

and

second, translate axes (if desired) to reduce the
equation to a standard form which we recognize.

PROBLEMS

1. Show that the equation $x^4 + 6x^2y^2 + y^4 = 32$ becomes $x'^4 + y'^4 = 16$ under a 45° rotation of axes. Sketch the curve and the two sets of axes.

2. Use the definition of an ellipse to find the equation of an ellipse with foci at $F_1(-1, 0)$ and $F_2(0, \sqrt{3})$ if it passes through the point $(1, 0)$. Through

what angle α should the axes be rotated to eliminate the cross-product term from the equation found?

3. Show that the equation $x^2 + y^2 = r^2$ becomes $x'^2 + y'^2 = r^2$ for every choice of the angle α in the equations for rotation of axes.

4. Show that $A' + C' = A + C$ for every choice of the angle α in Eqs. (6).

5. Show that $B'^2 - 4A'C' = B^2 - 4AC$ for every choice of the angle α in Eqs. (6).

6. Show that a rotation of the axes through $45°$ will eliminate the cross-product term from Eq. (1) whenever $A = C$.

7. Find the equation of the curve $x^2 + 2xy + y^2 = 1$ after a rotation of axes which makes $A' = 0$ in Eq. (6).

By means of a rotation of axes, transform each of the following equations into an equation that has no cross-product term.

8. $3x^2 + 2xy + 3y^2 = 19$ 9. $x^2 - 3xy + y^2 = 5$

10. $3x^2 + 4\sqrt{3}xy - y^2 = 7$

9-10 Invariants and the discriminant. It is sometimes useful to apply directly to the equation

$$Ax^2 + Bxy + Cy^2 + Dx + Ey + F = 0 \tag{1}$$

a criterion that will tell whether the curve is a parabola, an ellipse, or a hyperbola, without first performing a rotation of axes to eliminate the cross-product term. Our discussion has shown that a rotation of axes through an angle α determined by

$$\cot 2\alpha = \frac{A - C}{B} \tag{2}$$

will transform the equation to the equivalent form

$$A'x'^2 + B'x'y' + C'y'^2 + D'x' + E'y' + F' = 0 \tag{3}$$

with new coefficients $A', \ldots, F'$ related to the old as in Eq. (6), Article 9-9, and with $B' = 0$ for the particular choice of α satisfying Eq. (2) above.

Now the nature of the curve whose equation is (3) with cross-product term removed is determined as follows:

(a) a *parabola* if A' or $C' = 0$, that is, if $A'C' = 0$,

(b) an *ellipse* if A' and C' have the same sign, that is, if $A'C' > 0$, and

(c) a *hyperbola* if A' and C' have opposite signs, that is, if $A'C' < 0$.

But it has been discovered and can easily be verified by use of Eq. (6), Article 9–9, that the coefficients A, B, C and A', B', C' satisfy the following condition:

$$B^2 - 4AC = B'^2 - 4A'C' \qquad (4)$$

for *any* rotation of axes. That is, the quantity $B^2 - 4AC$ is *invariant* under a rotation of axes. But when the particular rotation is performed that makes $B' = 0$, the right side of (4) becomes simply $-4A'C'$. The criteria above, expressed in terms of A' and C', can now be expressed in terms of the *discriminant:*

$$\text{discriminant} = B^2 - 4AC. \qquad (5)$$

Namely, the curve is

(a) a *parabola* if $B^2 - 4AC = 0$,
(b) an *ellipse* if $B^2 - 4AC < 0$,
(c) a *hyperbola* if $B^2 - 4AC > 0$,

with the understanding that certain degenerate cases may arise.

Another invariant associated with Eqs. (1) and (3) is the sum of the coefficients of the squared terms. For it is evident from Eq. (6), Article 9–9, that

$$A' + C' = A\,(\cos^2\alpha + \sin^2\alpha) + C\,(\sin^2\alpha + \cos^2\alpha)$$

or

$$A' + C' = A + C, \qquad (6)$$

since

$$\sin^2\alpha + \cos^2\alpha = 1$$

for any angle α.

The two invariants (4) and (6) may be used as a check against numerical errors in performing a rotation of axes of a quadratic equation. They may also be used to find the new coefficients of the quadratic terms

$$A'x'^2 + B'x'y' + C'y'^2,$$

with

$$B' = 0,$$

as in the following example.

EXAMPLE. Determine the equation to which

$$x^2 + xy + y^2 = 1$$

reduces when the axes are rotated to eliminate the cross-product term.

Solution. From the original equation we find

$$B^2 - 4AC = -3, \qquad A + C = 2.$$

Then, taking $B' = 0$, we have from (4) and (6),

$$-4A'C' = -3, \qquad A' + C' = 2.$$

Substituting $C' = 2 - A'$ from the second of these into the first, we obtain the quadratic equation

$$4A'^2 - 8A' + 3 = 0,$$

which factors into

$$(2A' - 3)(2A' - 1) = 0$$

and gives

$$A' = \tfrac{3}{2} \qquad \text{or} \qquad A' = \tfrac{1}{2}.$$

The corresponding values of C' are

$$C' = \tfrac{1}{2} \qquad \text{or} \qquad C' = \tfrac{3}{2}.$$

The equation therefore is

$$\tfrac{3}{2}x'^2 + \tfrac{1}{2}y'^2 = 1$$

or

$$\tfrac{1}{2}x'^2 + \tfrac{3}{2}y'^2 = 1$$

in the new coordinates. Hence the curve is an ellipse.

It should be noted that when no first power terms are present in the original equation, they will also be absent in the new equation. This is due to the fact that a rotation of axes preserves the algebraic degree of each term of the equation; or we may refer to Eq. (6), Article 9–9, which shows that D' and E' are both zero if D and E vanish.

PROBLEMS

Use the discriminant and classify each of the following second degree equations as representing a circle, an ellipse, a parabola, or a hyperbola.

1. $x^2 + y^2 + xy + x - y = 3$
2. $2x^2 - y^2 + 4xy - 2x + 3y = 6$
3. $x^2 + 4xy + 4y^2 - 3x = 6$
4. $x^2 + y^2 + 3x - 2y = 10$
5. $xy + y^2 - 3x = 5$
6. $3x^2 + 6xy + 3y^2 - 4x + 5y = 12$
7. $x^2 - y^2 = 1$
8. $2x^2 + 3y^2 - 4x = 7$
9. $x^2 - 3xy + 3y^2 + 6y = 7$

10. When $B^2 - 4AC$ is negative, the equation $Ax^2 + Bxy + Cy^2 = 1$ represents an ellipse. If the semiaxes have lengths a and b, the area of the ellipse is πab. Show that the area of the ellipse given above is $2\pi/\sqrt{4AC - B^2}$.

11. Show, by reference to Eq. (6), Article 9–9, that $D'^2 + E'^2 = D^2 + E^2$ for every angle of rotation α.

12. If $C = -A$ in Eq. (1), show that there is a rotation of axes for which $A' = C' = 0$ in the resulting Eq. (3). Find the angle α that makes $A' = C' = 0$ in this case. [*Hint:* Since $A' + C' = 0$, one need only make the further requirement that $A' = 0$ in Eq. (3).]

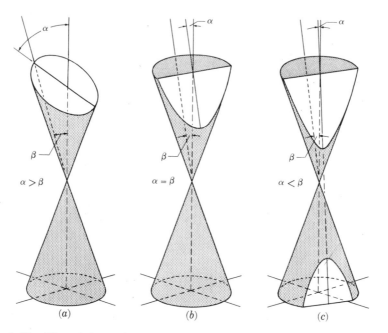

FIG. 9–51. Plane intersecting cone in (a) ellipse, (b) parabola, (c) hyperbola.

9–11 Sections of a cone. The circle, parabola, ellipse, and hyperbola are known as *conic* sections because each may be obtained by cutting a cone by a plane. If the cutting plane is perpendicular to the axis of the cone, the section is a circle.

More generally, suppose the cutting plane makes an angle α with the axis of the cone and let the generating angle of the cone be β. Then the section is:

(a) a circle if $\alpha = 90°$,   (b) an ellipse if $\beta < \alpha < 90°$,

(c) a parabola if $\alpha = \beta$,   (d) a hyperbola if $0 \leq \alpha < \beta$.

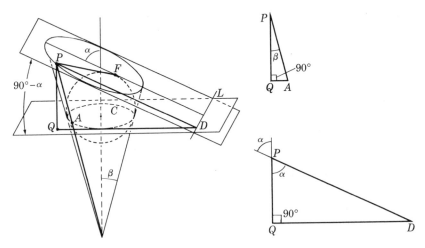

FIGURE 9–52

The connection between these curves as we have defined them and the sections from a cone is readily made by reference to Fig. 9–52. The figure is drawn to illustrate the case of an ellipse, but the argument holds for the other cases as well.

A sphere is inscribed tangent to the cone along a circle C, and tangent to the cutting plane at a point F. Point P is any point on the conic section, and we shall see that F is a focus and the line L in which the cutting plane and the plane of the circle C intersect is a directrix of the curve. To this end let Q be the point where the line through P parallel to the axis of the cone intersects the plane of C, let A be the point where the line joining P to the vertex of the cone touches C, and let PD be perpendicular to line L at D. Then PA and PF are two lines tangent to the same sphere from a common point P and hence have the same length;

$$PA = PF.$$

Also, from the right triangle PQA, we have

$$PQ = PA \cos \beta$$

and from the right triangle PQD, we find

$$PQ = PD \cos \alpha.$$

Hence

$$PA \cos \beta = PD \cos \alpha$$

or

$$\frac{PA}{PD} = \frac{\cos \alpha}{\cos \beta}.$$

But since $PA = PF$, this means that

$$\frac{PF}{PD} = \frac{\cos \alpha}{\cos \beta}. \tag{1}$$

Since α and β are constant for a given cone and a given cutting plane, Eq. (1) has the form

$$PF = e \cdot PD.$$

This characterizes P as belonging to a parabola, an ellipse, or a hyperbola, with focus at F and directrix L, according as $e = 1$, $e < 1$, or $e > 1$ respectively, where

$$e = \frac{\cos \alpha}{\cos \beta}$$

is thus identified with the eccentricity.

PROBLEMS

1. Sketch a figure similar to Fig. 9–52 when the conic section is a parabola, and carry through the argument of Article 9–11 on the basis of such a figure.

2. Sketch a figure similar to Fig. 9–52 when the conic section is a hyperbola and carry through the argument of Article 9–11 on the basis of such a figure.

3. Which parts of the construction described in Article 9–11 become impossible when the conic section is a circle?

4. Let one directrix be the line $x = -p$ and take the corresponding focus at the origin. Using Eq. (15) of Article 9–7, derive the equation of the general conic section of eccentricity e. If e is neither 0 nor 1, show that the center of the conic section has coordinates

$$\left(\frac{pe^2}{1 - e^2}, \ 0 \right).$$

*9–12 Curve fitting using determinants. It is often of interest to see if a curve of given type can be made to pass through certain given points. When it can be done, we want to know the equation of the curve. Of course the given points do not uniquely determine the equation of the curve, since other curves of different types might also go through the same points. For example, a circle or a parabola might be made to go through three noncollinear points. But if it is to be a circle, that circle is unique.

Determinants may often be used to advantage in writing down an equation for a curve, as in the following examples.

EXAMPLE 1.

$$\begin{vmatrix} x & y & 1 \\ x_1 & y_1 & 1 \\ x_2 & y_2 & 1 \end{vmatrix} = 0$$

is the equation of a straight line through $P_1(x_1, y_1)$ and $P_2(x_2, y_2)$.

EXAMPLE 2.

$$\begin{vmatrix} x^2 + y^2 & x & y & 1 \\ x_1^2 + y_1^2 & x_1 & y_1 & 1 \\ x_2^2 + y_2^2 & x_2 & y_2 & 1 \\ x_3^2 + y_3^2 & x_3 & y_3 & 1 \end{vmatrix} = 0$$

is the equation of a circle through $P_1(x_1, y_1)$, $P_2(x_2, y_2)$, and $P_3(x_3, y_3)$, provided the cofactor

$$A_{11} = \begin{vmatrix} x_1 & y_1 & 1 \\ x_2 & y_2 & 1 \\ x_3 & y_3 & 1 \end{vmatrix}$$

is not zero. This is the same as requiring that the three points be noncollinear, from Example 1.

EXAMPLE 3.

$$\begin{vmatrix} y & x^2 & x & 1 \\ y_1 & x_1^2 & x_1 & 1 \\ y_2 & x_2^2 & x_2 & 1 \\ y_3 & x_3^2 & x_3 & 1 \end{vmatrix} = 0$$

is an equation of the form

$$Ay + Bx^2 + Cx + D = 0$$

and hence represents a parabola through $P_1(x_1, y_1)$, $P_2(x_2, y_2)$, and $P_3(x_3, y_3)$, provided $AB \neq 0$, where

$$A = \begin{vmatrix} x_1^2 & x_1 & 1 \\ x_2^2 & x_2 & 1 \\ x_3^2 & x_3 & 1 \end{vmatrix} = (x_1 - x_2)(x_1 - x_3)(x_2 - x_3)$$

and

$$B = - \begin{vmatrix} y_1 & x_1 & 1 \\ y_2 & x_2 & 1 \\ y_3 & x_3 & 1 \end{vmatrix} = \begin{vmatrix} x_1 & y_1 & 1 \\ x_2 & y_2 & 1 \\ x_3 & y_3 & 1 \end{vmatrix}.$$

The condition $A \neq 0$ is the same as x_1, x_2, x_3 all different; while $B \neq 0$ is the condition that P_1, P_2, P_3 be noncollinear.

EXAMPLE 4.

$$\begin{vmatrix} x^2 & xy & y^2 & x & y & 1 \\ x_1^2 & x_1 y_1 & y_1^2 & x_1 & y_1 & 1 \\ x_2^2 & x_2 y_2 & y_2^2 & x_2 & y_2 & 1 \\ x_3^2 & x_3 y_3 & y_3^2 & x_3 & y_3 & 1 \\ x_4^2 & x_4 y_4 & y_4^2 & x_4 & y_4 & 1 \\ x_5^2 & x_5 y_5 & y_5^2 & x_5 & y_5 & 1 \end{vmatrix} = 0$$

is the general equation of a conic section

$$Ax^2 + Bxy + Cy^2 + Dx + Ey + F = 0$$

through the five points $P_i(x_i, y_i)$; $i = 1, 2, 3, 4, 5$.

PROBLEMS

1. Write a determinantal equation for a curve of the form

$$by = a_0x^n + a_1x^{n-1} + a_2x^{n-2} + \cdots + a_{n-1}x + a_n$$

through $n + 1$ points $P_i(x_i, y_i)$; $i = 1, 2, \ldots, n + 1$. When the x_i's are all different, prove that there is such a curve with $b \neq 0$.

2. Find a parabola of the form

$$Ax + By^2 + Cy + D = 0$$

through the three points $P_1(-1, 0)$, $P_2(2, 1)$, $P_3(1, -1)$. Find the vertex and axis of the parabola, and sketch.

3. Find a conic of the form

$$Ax^2 + Bxy + Cy^2 = D$$

through the three points $P_1(3, 0)$, $P_2(1, 2)$, $P_3(-1, -1)$.

REVIEW QUESTIONS AND EXERCISES FOR CHAPTER 9

1. Discuss criteria for symmetry of a curve with respect to: (a) the x-axis, (b) the y-axis, (c) the origin, (d) the line $y = x$.

2. Define *asymptote*. How do you find vertical and horizontal asymptotes of a curve if its equation is given in the form $y = f(x)/g(x)$?

3. How do you find the extent of a curve (or, alternatively, strips of the plane from which the curve is excluded)?

4. Name the conic sections.

5. What kind of equation characterizes the conic sections?

6. If the equation of a conic section is given, and it contains no xy-term, how can you tell by inspection whether it is a parabola, circle, ellipse, or hyperbola? How can you tell what the curve is if there is an xy-term in the equation?

7. What are the equations of transformation of coordinates:

(a) for a translation of axes? (b) for a rotation of axes?

Illustrate with diagrams.

8. What two quantities that are associated with the equation of a conic section remain invariant under a rotation of axes?

9. Sketch a parabola and label its vertex, focus, axis, and directrix. What is the definition of a parabola? What is the equation of your parabola?

10. Sketch an ellipse and label its vertices, foci, axes, and directrices. What is the definition of an ellipse? What is the equation of your ellipse?

11. Sketch a hyperbola and label its vertices, foci, axes, asymptotes, and directrices. What is the definition of a hyperbola? What is the equation of your hyperbola?

12. A ripple tank is made by bending a strip of tin around the perimeter of an ellipse for the wall of the tank and soldering a flat bottom onto this. An inch or two of water is put in the tank and the experimenter pokes a finger into it, right at one focus of the ellipse. Ripples radiate outward through the water, reflect from the strip around the edge of the tank, and (in a short time) a drop of water spurts up at the second focus. Why?

MISCELLANEOUS PROBLEMS FOR CHAPTER 9

In Problems 1 through 9 determine the following properties of the curves whose equations are given: (A) symmetry, (B) extent, (C) intercepts, (D) asymptotes, (E) slope at intercepts. Use this information in sketching the curves.

1. (a) $y^2 = x(4 - x)$; (b) $y^2 = x(x - 4)$; (c) $y^2 = \dfrac{x}{4 - x}$

2. (a) $y = x + \dfrac{1}{x^2}$; (b) $y^2 = x + \dfrac{1}{x^2}$; (c) $y = x^2 + \dfrac{1}{x}$

3. (a) $y = x(x + 1)(x - 2)$; (b) $y^2 = x(x + 1)(x - 2)$

4. (a) $y = \dfrac{8}{4 + x^2}$; (b) $y = \dfrac{8}{4 - x^2}$; (c) $y = \dfrac{8x}{4 + x^2}$

5. (a) $xy = x^2 + 1$; (b) $y = \dfrac{x^2}{x - 1}$

6. (a) $y^2 = x^4 - x^2$; (b) $y^2 = \dfrac{x - 1}{x - 2}$

7. $x^2y - y = 4(x - 2)$

8. $y = \dfrac{x^2 + 1}{x^2 - 1}$

9. $x^2 + xy + y^2 = 3$

10. Let C be the curve in Problem 9. Let $P(x, y)$ be a point on C. Let $P'(kx, ky)$ be a point on the line OP from the origin to P. If k is held constant, what is the equation of the locus described by P' as P traces out the curve C?

11. Sketch the graph whose equation is $(y - x + 2)(2y + x - 4) = 0$.

12. A certain graph has an equation of the form

$$ay^2 + by = \frac{cx + d}{ex^2 + fx + g},$$

where a, b, c, d, e, f, and g are constants whose value in each case is either 0 or 1. From the following information about the graph, determine the constants and give a reason for your choice in each case:

Extent. The curve does not exist for $x < -1$. All values of y are permissible.

Symmetry. The curve is symmetric about the x-axis.

Intercepts. No y-intercept; x-intercept at $(-1, 0)$.

Asymptotes. Both axes; no others.

Sketch the graph.

13. Each of the following inequalities describes one or more regions of the xy-plane. Sketch first the locus obtained by replacing the inequality sign by an equal sign, then indicate the region that contains the points whose coordinates satisfy the given inequality.

(a) $x < 3$, (b) $x < y$, (c) $x^2 < y$, (d) $x^2 + y^2 > 4$, (e) $x^2 + xy + y^2 < 3$,

(f) $x^2 + xy + y^2 > 3$, (g) $y^2 < \dfrac{x}{4 - x}$.

14. Write an equation of the tangent, at $(2, 2)$, to the curve

$$x^2 - 2xy + y^2 + 2x + y - 6 = 0.$$

15. Sketch the curves $xy = 2$ and $x^2 - y^2 = 3$ in one diagram, and show that they intersect orthogonally.

16. Find equations of the lines that are tangent to the curve $y = x^3 - 6x + 2$ and are parallel to the line $y = 6x - 2$.

17. Prove that if a line is drawn tangent to the curve $y^2 = kx$ at a point $P(x, y)$ not at the origin, then the portion of the tangent that lies between the x-axis and P is bisected by the y-axis.

18. Through the point $P(x, y)$ on the curve $y^2 = kx$, lines are drawn parallel to the axes. The rectangular area bounded by these two lines and the axes is divided into two portions by the given curve. (a) If these two areas are rotated about the y-axis, show that they generate two solids whose volumes are in the ratio of four to one. (b) What is the ratio of the volumes of the solids generated when these areas are rotated about the x-axis?

19. Show that the curves $2x^2 + 3y^2 = a^2$ and $ky^2 = x^3$ are orthogonal for all values of the constants a and k $(a \neq 0, k \neq 0)$. Sketch the four curves corresponding to $a = 2$, $a = 4$, $k = \frac{1}{2}$, $k = -2$ in one diagram.

20. Show, analytically, that an angle inscribed in a semicircle is a right angle.

21. Two points P, Q are called symmetric with respect to a circle if P and Q lie on the same ray through the center and if the product of their distances from the center is equal to the square of the radius. Given that Q describes the straight line $x + 2y - 5 = 0$, find the locus of the point P that is symmetric to Q with respect to the circle $x^2 + y^2 = 4$.

22. A point $P(x, y)$ moves so that the ratio of its distances from two fixed points is a constant k. Show that the locus is a circle if $k \neq 1$, and is a straight line if $k = 1$.

23. Show that the centers of all chords of the parabola $x^2 = 4py$ with slope m lie on a straight line and find its equation.

24. The line through the focus F and the point $P(x_1, y_1)$ on the parabola $y^2 = 4px$ intersects the parabola in a second point $Q(x_2, y_2)$. Find the coordinates of Q in terms of y_1 and p. If O is the vertex and PO cuts the directrix at R, prove that QR is parallel to the axis of the parabola.

25. Find the point (or points) on the curve $x^2 = y^3$ nearest the point $P(0, 4)$. Sketch the curve and the shortest line from P to the curve.

26. Prove that every line through the center of the circle $(x - h)^2 + (y - k)^2 = r^2$ is orthogonal to the circle.

27. Find all points on the curve $x^2 + 2xy + 3y^2 = 3$, where the tangent line is perpendicular to the line $x + y = 1$.

28. A line PT is drawn tangent to the curve $xy = x + y$ at the point $P(-2, \frac{2}{3})$. Find equations of two lines that are normal to the curve and perpendicular to PT.

29. Sketch the loci described by each of the following equations:

(a) $(x + y)(x^2 + y^2 - 1) = 0$; (b) $(x + y)(x^2 + y^2 - 1) = 1$.

[*Hint:* In part (b), consider intersections of the locus with the line $x + y = k$ for different values of the constant k.]

30. Find the center and radius of the circle through the two points $A(2, 0)$ and $B(6, 0)$ and tangent to the curve $y = x^2$.

31. Find the center of the circle that passes through the point $(0, 1)$ and is tangent to the curve $y = x^2$ at $(2, 4)$.

32. Let L_1, L_2, L_3 be three straight lines, no two of which are parallel. Let $L_i = a_i x + b_i y + c_i = 0$, $i = 1, 2, 3$, be the equation of the line L_i.

(a) Describe the locus whose equation is $L_1 L_2 + h L_2 L_3 + k L_1 L_3 = 0$, assuming h and k are constants.

(b) Use the method of part (a) and determine h and k so that the equation represents a circle through the points of intersection of the lines

$$x + y - 2 = 0, \qquad x - y + 2 = 0, \qquad y - 2x = 0.$$

(c) Find a parabola, axis vertical, through the points of intersection of the lines in (b).

33. A comet moves in a parabolic orbit with the sun at the focus. When the comet is 4×10^7 miles from the sun, the line from the sun to it makes an angle of $60°$ with the axis of the orbit (drawn in the direction in which the orbit opens). Find how near the comet comes to the sun.

34. Sketch in one diagram the curves $y^2 = 4x + 4$, $y^2 = 64 - 16x$, and find the angles at which they intersect.

35. Find an equation of the curve such that the distance from any point $P(x, y)$ on the curve to the line $x = 3$ is the same as its distance to the point $(4, 0)$. Sketch the curve.

36. Two radar stations lying along an east-west line are separated by 20 mi. Choose a coordinate system such that their positions are $(-10, 0)$ and $(10, 0)$. A low-flying plane traveling from west to east is known to have a speed of v_0 mi/sec. At $t = 0$ a signal is sent from the station at $(-10, 0)$, bounces off the plane, and is received at $(10, 0)$ $30/c$ sec later (c is the velocity of the signal). When $t = 10/v_0$, another signal is sent out from the station at $(-10, 0)$, reflects off the plane, and is once again received $30/c$ sec later by the other station. What is the position of the plane when it reflects the second signal, providing that one assumes $v_0 \ll c$ (that is, v_0 is much less than c)?

37. A line is drawn tangent to the parabola $y^2 = 4px$ at a point $P(x, y)$ on the curve. Let A be the point where this tangent line crosses the axis of the parabola, let F be the focus, and let PD be the line parallel to the axis of the parabola and intersecting the directrix at D. Prove that $AFPD$ is a rhombus.

38. Find the equation of the locus of a point $P(x, y)$ if the distance from P to the vertex is twice the distance from P to the focus of the parabola $x^2 = 8y$. Name the locus.

39. Prove that the tangent to a parabola at a point P cuts the axis of the parabola at a point whose distance from the vertex equals the distance from P to the tangent at the vertex.

40. Discuss the locus of the equation $x^4 - (y^2 - 9)^2 = 0$ and sketch its graph.

41. Show that the curve $C: x^4 - (y^2 - 9)^2 = 1$ approaches part of the curve $x^4 - (y^2 - 9)^2 = 0$ as the point $P(x, y)$ moves farther and farther away from the origin. Sketch. Do any points of C lie inside the circle $x^2 + y^2 = 9$? Give a reason for your answer.

42. The ellipse $(x^2/a^2) + (y^2/b^2) = 1$ divides the plane into two regions; one inside the ellipse, the other outside. Show that points in one of these regions have coordinates that satisfy the inequality $(x^2/a^2) + (y^2/b^2) < 1$, while in the other, $(x^2/a^2) + (y^2/b^2) > 1$. (Consider the effect of replacing x, y in the given equation by $x' = kx$, $y' = ky$, with $k < 1$ in one case and $k > 1$ in the other.)

43. Find an equation of an ellipse with foci at $(1, 0)$ and $(5, 0)$, and one vertex at the origin.

44. Let $F_1 = (3, 0)$, $F_2 = (0, 5)$, $P = (-1, 3)$. (a) Find the distances F_1P and F_2P. (b) Does the origin O lie inside or outside the ellipse that has F_1 and F_2 as its foci and that passes through the point P? Why?

45. Find the greatest area of a rectangle inscribed in the ellipse $(x^2/a^2) + (y^2/b^2) = 1$, with sides parallel to the coordinate axes.

46. Show that the line $y = mx + c$ is tangent to the conic section $Ax^2 + y^2 = 1$ if and only if the constants A, m, and c satisfy the condition $A(c^2 - 1) = m^2$.

47. Starting from the general equation for the conic, find the equation of the conic with the following properties: (a) it is symmetric with respect to the origin, (b) it passes through the point $(1, 0)$, (c) the tangent to it at the point $(-2, 1)$ on it is the line $y = 1$.

48. Find an ellipse with one vertex at the point $(3, 1)$, the nearer focus at the point $(1, 1)$, and eccentricity $\frac{2}{3}$.

49. By a suitable rotation of axes, show that the equation $xy - x - y = 1$ represents a hyperbola. Sketch.

50. Find an equation of a hyperbola with eccentricity equal to $\sqrt{2}$ and with vertices at the points $(2, 0)$ and $(-2, 0)$.

51. Sketch the conic $\sqrt{2}y - 2xy = 3$. Locate its center and find its eccentricity.

52. If c is a fixed positive constant, then

$$\frac{x^2}{t^2} + \frac{y^2}{t^2 - c^2} = 1 \qquad (c^2 < t^2)$$

defines a family of ellipses, any member of which is characterized by a particular value of t. Show that every member of the family

$$\frac{x^2}{t^2} - \frac{y^2}{c^2 - t^2} = 1 \qquad (t^2 < c^2)$$

intersects any member of the first family at right angles.

53. Sketch the locus $|x| + |y| = 1$ and find the area it encloses.

54. Show that if the tangent to a curve at a point $P(x, y)$ passes through the origin, then $dy/dx = y/x$ at the point. Hence show that no tangent can be drawn from the origin to the hyperbola $x^2 - y^2 = 1$.

55. (a) Find the coordinates of the center and the foci, the lengths of the axes, and the eccentricity of the ellipse $x^2 + 4y^2 - 4x + 8y - 1 = 0$. (b) Do likewise with the hyperbola $3x^2 - y^2 + 12x - 3y = 0$, and in addition find equations of its asymptotes.

56. If the ends of a line segment of constant length move along perpendicular lines, show that a point P on the segment, at distances a and b from the ends, describes an ellipse.

57. Sketch the loci:

(a) $(9x^2 + 4y^2 - 36)(4x^2 + 9y^2 - 36) = 0$,

(b) $(9x^2 + 4y^2 - 36)(4x^2 + 9y^2 - 36) = 1$.

Is the curve in (b) bounded or does it extend to points arbitrarily far from the origin? Give a reason for your answer.

58. Let p, q be positive numbers such that $q < p$. If r is a third number, prove that the equation $[x^2/(p - r)] + [y^2/(q - r)] = 1$ represents (a) an ellipse if $r < q$, (b) a hyperbola if $q < r < p$, (c) nothing if $p < r$. Prove that all these ellipses and hyperbolas have the same foci, and find these foci.

59. Find the eccentricity of the hyperbola $xy = 1$.

60. On a level plane the sound of a rifle and that of the bullet striking the target are heard at the same instant. What is the locus of the hearer?

61. Show that any tangent to the hyperbola $xy = a^2$ determines with its asymptotes a triangle of area $2a^2$.

62. Given the hyperbola $9x^2 - 4y^2 - 18x - 16y + 29 = 0$. Find the coordinates of the center and foci, and the equations of the asymptotes. Sketch.

63. By an appropriate rotation, eliminate the xy-term from the equation,

$$7x^2 - 8xy + y^2 = 9.$$

64. Show that the tangent to the conic section

$$Ax^2 + Bxy + Cy^2 + Dx + Ey + F = 0$$

at a point (x_1, y_1) on it has an equation that may be written in the form

$$Axx_1 + B\left(\frac{x_1 y + xy_1}{2}\right) + Cyy_1$$
$$+ D\left(\frac{x + x_1}{2}\right) + E\left(\frac{y + y_1}{2}\right) + F = 0.$$

65. (a) Find the eccentricity and center of the conic

$$x^2 + 12y^2 - 6x - 48y + 9 = 0.$$

(b) Find the vertex of the conic

$$x^2 - 6x - 12y + 9 = 0.$$

(c) Sketch the conics in one diagram.

66. Find an equation of the circle passing through the three points common to the conics of Problem 65.

67. Two vertices A, B of a triangle are fixed and the vertex $C(x, y)$ moves in such a way that $\angle A = 2(\angle B)$. Find the locus of C.

68. Find the equation into which $x^{1/2} + y^{1/2} = a^{1/2}$ is transformed by a rotation of axes through 45°, and elimination of radicals.

69. Show that $dx^2 + dy^2$ is invariant under any rotation of axes about the origin.

70. Show that $x \, dy - y \, dx$ is invariant under any rotation of axes about the origin.

71. Graph the locus $x^{2n} + y^{2n} = a^{2n}$ for the following values of n: (a) 1, (b) 2, (c) 100. In each instance find where the curve cuts the line $y = x$.

CHAPTER 10

HYPERBOLIC FUNCTIONS

10–1 Introduction. In this chapter we shall consider certain combinations of the exponentials e^x and e^{-x} which are called "hyperbolic functions." There are two reasons why we study these functions. One reason is that they are used in solving certain engineering problems. For example, the tension at any point in a cable suspended by its ends and hanging under its own weight, such as an electric transmission line, may be computed in terms of hyperbolic functions. We shall investigate the hanging cable in some detail in Article 10–6. A second reason for studying the hyperbolic functions is that they are useful in connection with differential equations.

10–2 Definitions and identities. The combinations $\frac{1}{2}(e^u + e^{-u})$ and $\frac{1}{2}(e^u - e^{-u})$ occur with sufficient frequency that it has been found convenient to give special names to them. It may not be clear at this particular time why the names about to be introduced are especially appropriate. But it will become more apparent as we proceed that these functions have many properties analogous, respectively, to cos u and sin u. And just as cos u and sin u are easily identified with the point (x, y) on the unit circle $x^2 + y^2 = 1$, where by properly defining u we may take $x = \cos u$ and $y = \sin u$, so it is also possible to identify

$$\boxed{\begin{aligned} \cosh u &= \tfrac{1}{2}(e^u + e^{-u}), \\ \sinh u &= \tfrac{1}{2}(e^u - e^{-u}), \end{aligned}} \tag{1}$$

with the coordinates of the point (x, y) on the "unit hyperbola" $x^2 - y^2 = 1$.

Equations (1) are the *definitions* of the *hyperbolic cosine* of u (cosh u, which is often pronounced to rhyme with "gosh you") and of the *hyperbolic sine* of u (sinh u, which is pronounced as though it were spelled "cinch u").

Suppose we check the statement that the point (x, y) with $x = \cosh u$ and $y = \sinh u$ lies on the unit hyperbola. We simply substitute the defining relations (1) into the equation of the hyperbola, and see whether or not these coordinates do satisfy the equation:

$$x^2 - y^2 = 1,$$
$$\cosh^2 u - \sinh^2 u \overset{?}{=} 1,$$
$$\tfrac{1}{4}(e^{2u} + 2 + e^{-2u}) - \tfrac{1}{4}(e^{2u} - 2 + e^{-2u}) \overset{?}{=} 1,$$

$$\tfrac{1}{4}(e^{2u} + 2 + e^{-2u} \cdot - e^{2u} + 2 - e^{-2u}) \overset{?}{=} 1,$$

$$\tfrac{1}{4}(4) \overset{?}{=} 1. \quad \text{(Yes!)}$$

Actually, if we let

$$x = \cosh u = \tfrac{1}{2}(e^u + e^{-u}),$$
$$y = \sinh u = \tfrac{1}{2}(e^u - e^{-u}),$$

(2)

then when u varies from $-\infty$ to $+\infty$, the point $P(x, y)$ describes the right-hand branch of the hyperbola $x^2 - y^2 = 1$. The sense in which the curve is described is indicated by the arrows in Fig. 10–1. Since e^u is always positive and $e^{-u} = 1/e^u$ is also positive, it follows that $x = \cosh u = \tfrac{1}{2}(e^u + e^{-u})$ is positive for all real values of u, $-\infty < u < +\infty$. Hence the point (x, y) remains always to the right of the y-axis.

The first bit of hyperbolic trigonometry that we have just established is the basic identity

$$\boxed{\cosh^2 u - \sinh^2 u = 1.}$$

(3)

This is analogous to, but not the same as, the ordinary trigonometric identity, $\cos^2 u + \sin^2 u = 1$. We shall now investigate additional points of analogy between these two types of functions.

The remaining hyperbolic functions are *defined* in terms of $\sinh u$ and $\cosh u$ as follows:

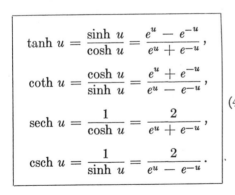

$$\tanh u = \frac{\sinh u}{\cosh u} = \frac{e^u - e^{-u}}{e^u + e^{-u}},$$

$$\coth u = \frac{\cosh u}{\sinh u} = \frac{e^u + e^{-u}}{e^u - e^{-u}},$$

(4)

$$\operatorname{sech} u = \frac{1}{\cosh u} = \frac{2}{e^u + e^{-u}},$$

$$\operatorname{csch} u = \frac{1}{\sinh u} = \frac{2}{e^u - e^{-u}}.$$

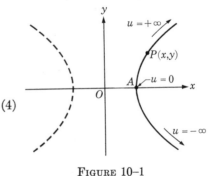

FIGURE 10–1

If we divide the identity (3) by $\cosh^2 u$, we get

$$1 - \tanh^2 u = \operatorname{sech}^2 u,$$

(5a)

and if we divide it by $\sinh^2 u$, we get

$$\coth^2 u - 1 = \operatorname{csch}^2 u.$$

(5b)

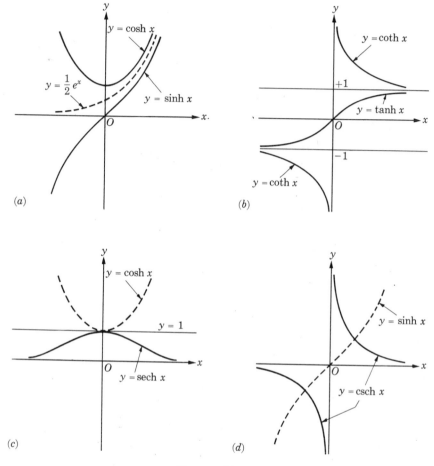

FIGURE 10–2

Since from (1) we find

$$\cosh u + \sinh u = e^u, \tag{6a}$$

$$\cosh u - \sinh u = e^{-u}, \tag{6b}$$

it is apparent that *any* combination of the exponentials e^u and e^{-u} can be replaced by a combination of $\sinh u$ and $\cosh u$, and conversely. Also, since e^{-u} is positive, (6b) shows that $\cosh u$ is always greater than $\sinh u$. But for large values of u, e^{-u} is small, and $\cosh u \approx \sinh u$.

The graphs of the hyperbolic functions are shown in Fig. 10–2(a—d).

At $x = 0$, $\cosh x = 1$ and $\sinh x = 0$, so the hyperbolic functions all have the same values at 0 that the corresponding trigonometric functions have. The hyperbolic cosine is an *even function*, that is,

$$\boxed{\cosh{(-x)} = \cosh{x},} \tag{7}$$

and the hyperbolic sine is an *odd function*, that is,

$$\boxed{\sinh{(-x)} = -\sinh{x};} \tag{8}$$

so one curve is symmetric about the y-axis and the other is symmetric with respect to the origin. Here again the hyperbolic functions behave like the ordinary trigonometric (or circular) functions.

The hyperbolic functions are so important and useful that their numerical values have been calculated and tabulated just as have the circular functions, at least for $\sinh{x}$, $\cosh{x}$, and $\tanh{x}$. The values of the other functions can be readily expressed in terms of these, and hence it is unnecessary to tabulate them also. Some slide rules also have $\sinh{x}$ and $\cosh{x}$ scales, and the values of these functions may be read directly in the same way that e^x may be read from the LL-scales.

Certain major differences between the hyperbolic and the circular functions should be noted. For example, the circular functions are periodic: $\sin{(x + 2\pi)} = \sin{x}$, $\tan{(x + \pi)} = \tan{x}$, etc. But *the hyperbolic functions are not periodic.* Again, they differ greatly in the range of values they assume:

$\sin{x}$ varies between -1 and $+1$, oscillates;
$\sinh{x}$ varies from $-\infty$ to $+\infty$, steadily increases;

$\cos{x}$ varies between -1 and $+1$, oscillates;
$\cosh{x}$ varies from $+\infty$ to $+1$ to $+\infty$;

$|\sec{x}|$ is never less than unity;
$\operatorname{sech}{x}$ is never greater than unity, is always positive;

$\tan{x}$ varies from $-\infty$ to $+\infty$;
$\tanh{x}$ varies from -1 to $+1$.

Another difference is exhibited in the behavior of the functions as $x \to \pm\infty$. In the case of the circular functions, $\sin{x}$, $\cos{x}$, $\tan{x}$, etc., we can say nothing very specific about their behavior for large values of x. On the other hand, the hyperbolic functions behave very much like $e^x/2$, $e^{-x}/2$, unity, or zero as follows:

For x large and positive:	*For x negative, $|x|$ large:*
$\cosh{x} \approx \sinh{x} \approx \frac{1}{2}e^x$	$\cosh{x} \approx -\sinh{x} \approx \frac{1}{2}e^{-x}$
$\tanh{x} \approx \coth{x} \approx 1$	$\tanh{x} \approx \coth{x} \approx -1 \qquad (9)$
$\operatorname{sech}{x} \approx \operatorname{csch}{x} \approx 2e^{-x} \approx 0$	$\operatorname{sech}{x} \approx -\operatorname{csch}{x} \approx 2e^{x} \approx 0$

Additional analogies will be apparent when we study the calculus of hyperbolic functions in the next article. We conclude this article with certain formulas which the reader may readily verify. The following identities require only some algebraic calculations combined with the definitions (1), namely,

$$\sinh (x + y) = \sinh x \cosh y + \cosh x \sinh y,$$
$$\cosh (x + y) = \cosh x \cosh y + \sinh x \sinh y. \tag{10}$$

These in turn give

$$\sinh 2x = 2 \sinh x \cosh x, \tag{11a}$$

$$\cosh 2x = \cosh^2 x + \sinh^2 x, \tag{11b}$$

when we take $y = x$. The second of these leads to certain useful "half-angle" formulas when we combine it with the basic identity

$$1 = \cosh^2 x - \sinh^2 x. \tag{3}$$

For if we add (11b) and (3), we have

$$\cosh 2x + 1 = 2 \cosh^2 x, \tag{12a}$$

while if we subtract (3) from (11b), we get

$$\cosh 2x - 1 = 2 \sinh^2 x. \tag{12b}$$

Thus practically all the circular trigonometric identities have hyperbolic analogies. The formulas (3) and (10) are easily verified in terms of the definitions (1). The others follow from these by straightforward algebraic manipulations.

PROBLEMS

1. Show that $x = -\cosh u$, $y = \sinh u$ represents a point on the left branch of the hyperbola $x^2 - y^2 = 1$.

2. Using the definitions of $\cosh u$ and $\sinh u$ given by Eq. (1), show that $\cosh (-u) = \cosh u$ and $\sinh (-u) = -\sinh u$.

3. Verify Eqs. (10) for $\sinh (x + y)$ and $\cosh (x + y)$.

4. Show that $(\cosh x + \sinh x)^n = \cosh nx + \sinh nx$.

5. Let L be the line tangent to the hyperbola $x^2 - y^2 = 1$ at the point $P_1(x_1, y_1)$, where $x_1 = \cosh u$, $y_1 = \sinh u$. Show that L cuts the x-axis at the point (sech u, 0) and the y-axis at (0, $-$csch u).

6. In each of the following problems, one of the six hyperbolic functions of u is given; determine the remaining five.

(a) $\sinh u = -\frac{3}{4}$,   (b) $\cosh u = \frac{17}{15}$,   (c) $\tanh u = -\frac{7}{25}$,
(d) $\coth u = \frac{13}{12}$,   (e) $\operatorname{sech} u = \frac{3}{5}$,   (f) $\operatorname{csch} u = \frac{5}{12}$.

7. Show that the distance r from the origin O to the point $P(\cosh u, \sinh u)$ on the hyperbola $x^2 - y^2 = 1$ is $r = \sqrt{\cosh 2u}$.

8. Show that the line tangent to the hyperbola at its vertex A in Fig. 10–1 intersects the line OP in the point $(1, \tanh u)$. This gives a geometric representation of $\tanh u$.

9. If θ lies in the interval $-\pi/2 < \theta < \pi/2$ and $\sinh x = \tan \theta$, show that $\cosh x = \sec \theta$, $\tanh x = \sin \theta$, $\coth x = \csc \theta$, $\operatorname{csch} x = \cot \theta$, and $\operatorname{sech} x = \cos \theta$.

10–3 Derivatives and integrals. Let u be a differentiable function of x and differentiate

$$\sinh u = \tfrac{1}{2}(e^u - e^{-u}), \qquad \cosh u = \tfrac{1}{2}(e^u + e^{-u}), \tag{1}$$

with respect to x. Applying the formulas

$$\frac{de^u}{dx} = e^u \frac{du}{dx}, \qquad \frac{de^{-u}}{dx} = e^{-u} \frac{d(-u)}{dx} = -e^{-u} \frac{du}{dx},$$

we get

$$\frac{d(\sinh u)}{dx} = \cosh u \frac{du}{dx}, \qquad\qquad \text{XXI}$$

$$\frac{d(\cosh u)}{dx} = \sinh u \frac{du}{dx}. \qquad\qquad \text{XXII}$$

Then, if we let

$$y = \tanh u = \frac{\sinh u}{\cosh u}$$

and differentiate as a fraction, we get

$$\frac{d(\tanh u)}{dx} = \frac{\cosh u \dfrac{d(\sinh u)}{dx} - \sinh u \dfrac{d(\cosh u)}{dx}}{\cosh^2 u}$$

$$= \frac{\cosh^2 u \dfrac{du}{dx} - \sinh^2 u \dfrac{du}{dx}}{\cosh^2 u}$$

$$= \frac{(\cosh^2 u - \sinh^2 u) \dfrac{du}{dx}}{\cosh^2 u} = \frac{1}{\cosh^2 u} \frac{du}{dx}$$

$$= \operatorname{sech}^2 u \frac{du}{dx}.$$

In a similar manner, we may establish the rest of the formulas in the following list:

$$\frac{d(\tanh u)}{dx} = \operatorname{sech}^2 u \frac{du}{dx},$$ XXIII

$$\frac{d(\coth u)}{dx} = -\operatorname{csch}^2 u \frac{du}{dx},$$ XXIV

$$\frac{d(\operatorname{sech} u)}{dx} = -\operatorname{sech} u \tanh u \frac{du}{dx},$$ XXV

$$\frac{d(\operatorname{csch} u)}{dx} = -\operatorname{csch} u \coth u \frac{du}{dx}.$$ XXVI

Note that aside from the pattern of algebraic signs, these formulas are the exact analogs of the formulas for the corresponding circular functions. Again, exactly half of them have minus signs, but we no longer attach the minus signs to the derivatives of the cofunctions, but rather notice that the first three, sinh u, cosh u, tanh u, have positive derivatives and the last three have negative derivatives.

Each of these derivative formulas has a matching differential formula. These in turn may be integrated at once to produce the following integration formulas:

$$(1) \int \sinh u\, du = \cosh u + C.$$

$$(2) \int \cosh u\, du = \sinh u + C.$$

$$(3) \int \operatorname{sech}^2 u\, du = \tanh u + C.$$

$$(4) \int \operatorname{csch}^2 u\, du = -\coth u + C.$$

$$(5) \int \operatorname{sech} u \tanh u\, du = -\operatorname{sech} u + C.$$

$$(6) \int \operatorname{csch} u \coth u\, du = -\operatorname{csch} u + C.$$

(2)

EXAMPLE 1. Show that $y = a \cosh (x/a)$ satisfies the differential equation

$$\frac{d^2y}{dx^2} = \frac{w}{H} \sqrt{1 + \left(\frac{dy}{dx}\right)^2},$$ (3)

provided $a = H/w$, where H and w are constants.

Solution. By differentiating $y = a \cosh (x/a)$, we find

$$\frac{dy}{dx} = a \sinh \frac{x}{a} \cdot \frac{1}{a} = \sinh \frac{x}{a}, \qquad \frac{d^2y}{dx^2} = \cosh \frac{x}{a} \cdot \frac{1}{a}.$$

We substitute these into (3) and obtain

$$\frac{1}{a} \cosh \frac{x}{a} \stackrel{?}{=} \frac{w}{H} \sqrt{1 + \sinh^2 \frac{x}{a}} \tag{a}$$

$$= \frac{w}{H} \sqrt{\cosh^2 \frac{x}{a}} \tag{b}$$

$$= \frac{w}{H} \cosh \frac{x}{a}, \tag{c}$$

which is a true equation provided $a = H/w$.

Remark 1. In going from (a) to (b) above, we used the fundamental identity

$$\cosh^2 u - \sinh^2 u = 1$$

in the form

$$1 + \sinh^2 u = \cosh^2 u.$$

In going from (b) to (c), we used the fact that $\cosh u$ is always positive, and hence

$$\sqrt{\cosh^2 u} = |\cosh u| = \cosh u.$$

Remark 2. The differential equation (3) expresses the condition for equilibrium of forces acting on a section AP of a hanging cable (Fig. 10–3). We imagine the rest of the cable as having been removed and the section AP from the lowest point A to the representative point $P(x, y)$ as being in equilibrium under the forces

(1) H = horizontal tension pulling on the cable at A,
(2) T = tangential tension pulling on the cable at P,
(3) $W = ws$ = weight of s feet of the cable at w pounds per foot of length from A to P.

Then equilibrium of the cable requires that the horizontal and vertical components of T balance H and W respectively:

$$T \cos \phi = H, \qquad T \sin \phi = W = ws. \tag{4}$$

By division, we get

$$\frac{T \sin \phi}{T \cos \phi} = \tan \phi = \frac{W}{H}$$

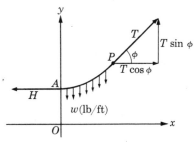

FIGURE 10–3

or
$$\frac{dy}{dx} = \frac{ws}{H},$$
(5)

since $\tan \phi = dy/dx$. The arc length s in Eq. (5) would be found by integrating

$$ds = \sqrt{1 + \left(\frac{dy}{dx}\right)^2}\, dx$$

from A to P. But instead of doing so, we may differentiate Eq. (5) with respect to x:

$$\frac{d^2y}{dx^2} = \frac{w}{H}\frac{ds}{dx},$$

and then substitute $\sqrt{1 + (dy/dx)^2}$ in place of ds/dx to obtain Eq. (3) above.

Remark 3. In Example 1, above, we pulled the equation $y = a \cosh(x/a)$ out of the hat, so to speak, and showed by substitution that it satisfies the differential equation (3). In Article 10–6, we shall adopt the more straightforward approach of simply solving Eq. (3) subject to the initial conditions

$$\frac{dy}{dx} = 0 \quad \text{and} \quad y = y_0 \quad \text{when} \quad x = 0.$$

By choosing the origin so that $y_0 = a = H/w$, we shall find that the solution is indeed the one given above, namely,

$$y = a \cosh \frac{x}{a} \quad \text{with} \quad a = \frac{H}{w}.$$
(6)

EXAMPLE 2. Show that the tension in the cable at $P(x, y)$ in Fig. 10–3 is

$$T = wy.$$

Solution. We make use of the fact that

$$\frac{dy}{dx} = \tan \phi,$$

since T acts along the tangent, and

$$T = \frac{H}{\cos \phi} = H \sec \phi,$$

by Eq. (4a). Then, differentiating (6), we have

$$\tan \phi = \frac{dy}{dx} = \sinh \frac{x}{a}$$

and

$$\sec \phi = \sqrt{\sec^2 \phi} = \sqrt{1 + \tan^2 \phi} = \sqrt{1 + \left(\frac{dy}{dx}\right)^2}$$

$$= \sqrt{1 + \sinh^2 \frac{x}{a}} = \sqrt{\cosh^2 \frac{x}{a}} = \cosh \frac{x}{a}.$$

Therefore

$$T = H \sec \phi = H \cosh \frac{x}{a}, \quad (7a)$$

where

$$a = \frac{H}{w} \quad \text{or} \quad H = wa. \quad (7b)$$

Combining (7a) and (7b), we have

$$T = wa \cosh \frac{x}{a}$$

or, when we take account of Eq. (6),

$$T = wy.$$

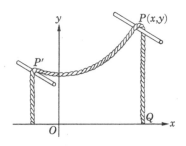

FIGURE 10–4

This means that the tension at P is equal to the weight of y feet of the cable. Thus if the end of the cable to the right of P is allowed to hang down over a smooth peg while the cable is held at P so that it does not slip, and if the cable is then cut off at the point Q where it crosses the x-axis (Fig. 10–4), it may then be released at P and the weight wy of the section of cable PQ will be just sufficient to prevent the cable from slipping. If this is carried out at two different points P and P', the cable may be draped over two smooth pegs without slipping, provided the free ends reach just to the x-axis. The curve, $y = a \cosh (x/a)$, is called a *catenary* from the Latin word *catena*, meaning chain. The x-axis is called the directrix of the catenary.

Problems

1. Establish the validity of the formulas XXIV–XXVI.

Find dy/dx in each of the following:

2. $y = \sinh 3x$ 3. $y = \cosh^2 5x$

4. $y = \cosh^2 5x - \sinh^2 5x$ 5. $y = \tanh 2x$

6. $y = \coth (\tan x)$ 7. $y = \operatorname{sech}^3 x$

8. $y = 4 \operatorname{csch} (x/4)$ 9. $\sinh y = \tan x$

Integrate each of the following:

10. $\displaystyle\int \cosh (2x + 1) \, dx$ 11. $\displaystyle\int \tanh x \, dx$ 12. $\displaystyle\int \frac{\sinh x}{\cosh^4 x} \, dx$

13. $\displaystyle\int \frac{4 \, dx}{(e^x + e^{-x})^2}$ 14. $\displaystyle\int \frac{e^x - e^{-x}}{e^x + e^{-x}} \, dx$ 15. $\displaystyle\int \tanh^2 x \, dx$

16. $\displaystyle\int \frac{\sinh \sqrt{x}}{\sqrt{x}} \, dx$ 17. $\displaystyle\int \cosh^2 3x \, dx$ 18. $\displaystyle\int \sqrt{\cosh x - 1} \, dx$

19. Find the area of the hyperbolic sector AOP bounded by the arc AP and the lines OA, OP through the origin, in Fig. 10–1.

20. Show that the straight line $y = x/2 + 1$ and the catenary $y = \cosh x$ intersect at the two points $(0, 1)$ and $(0.930, 1.465)$. (Consult tables for $\cosh x$.)

21. Two successive poles supporting an electric power line are 100 feet apart, the supporting members being at the same level. If the wire dips 25 feet at the center, (a) find the length of the wire between supports, and (b) find the tension in the wire at its lowest point if its weight is $w = 0.3$ lb/ft. [*Hint:* First find a from the equation $25/a + 1 = \cosh 50/a$, which can be related to Problem 20 with $x = 50/a$.]

22. The equation $\sinh x = \tan \theta$, $-\pi/2 < \theta < \pi/2$, defines θ as a function of x:

$$\theta = \tan^{-1}(\sinh x),$$

to which the name "gudermannian of x" has been attached, written

$$\theta = \text{gd } x.$$

Show that

$$\frac{d\theta}{dx} = \frac{1}{\cosh x} = \frac{1}{\sec \theta},$$

so that $\sec \theta \, d\theta = dx$ and

$$\int \sec \theta \, d\theta = \text{gd}^{-1} \theta + C = \sinh^{-1}(\tan \theta) + C.$$

23. Sketch the curve $\theta = \text{gd } x$ (see Problem 22) by the following procedure. First sketch the curves $y = \sinh x$ and $y = \tan \theta$ $(-\pi/2 < \theta < \pi/2)$ on separate xy- and θy-planes. Starting in the xy-plane with any value of x, $-\infty < x < +\infty$, determine the corresponding value of y from the curve $y = \sinh x$. Transfer this y reading to the y-axis in the θy-plane and determine the corresponding value of θ from the curve $y = \tan \theta$. Use this value of θ as ordinate and the original value of x as abscissa to plot a point on the curve $\theta = \text{gd } x$.

24. Show that the curve $\theta = \text{gd } x$ (see Problems 22 and 23) has the lines $\theta = \pm\pi/2$ as horizontal asymptotes, is always rising (from left to right), has a point of inflection at the origin, and is symmetric with respect to the origin.

*10–4 Geometric significance of the hyperbolic radian. We are now in a position to illustrate the meaning of the variable u in the equations

$$x = \cosh u, \qquad y = \sinh u \tag{1}$$

as they relate to the point $P(x, y)$ on the unit hyperbola

$$x^2 - y^2 = 1. \tag{2}$$

Before we do so, however, we shall find the analogous meaning of the variable θ in the equations

$$x = \cos \theta, \qquad y = \sin \theta \tag{3}$$

---

* Starred sections may be omitted without loss of continuity.

as they relate to the point $P(x, y)$ on the unit circle

$$x^2 + y^2 = 1. \qquad (4)$$

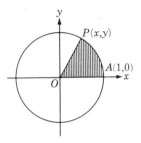

The most familiar interpretation of θ is, of course, that it is the radian measure of the angle AOP in Fig. 10–5, that is

$$\theta = \frac{\text{arc } AP}{\text{radius } OA}.$$

FIGURE 10–5

But we also recall that the area of a circular sector of radius r and central angle θ (radians) is given by $(\frac{1}{2})r^2\theta$. Since we are here dealing with a unit circle, this says that

$$\text{area of sector } AOP = \tfrac{1}{2}\theta$$

or, if we solve this for θ,

$$\boxed{\theta = \text{twice the area of the sector } AOP.} \qquad (5)$$

Of course we must realize that θ is a pure (dimensionless) number and Eq. (5) really says that the value of θ which Eqs. (3) associate with the point $P(x, y)$ on the unit circle is twice the *number* of square units of area that the radius vector OP sweeps out as P moves along the circle from A to its final position P. Thus when the area of the sector AOP is one-half the area of a square having OA as a side, then $\theta = 1$ and the coordinates of P represent cos 1 and sin 1. Negative values of θ would be interpreted as corresponding to areas swept over in a clockwise rotation of OA.

Now for the unit hyperbola,

$$x^2 - y^2 = 1,$$

we shall find an analogous interpretation for the variable u in the equations

$$x = \cosh u, \qquad y = \sinh u.$$

To see that this is indeed the case, we shall calculate the area of the sector AOP in Fig. 10–6. This area is clearly equal to the area of the triangle OQP minus the area AQP bounded above by the curve, below

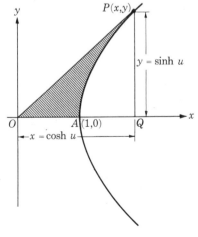

FIGURE 10–6

by the x-axis, and on the right by the vertical line QP. But this area is simply

$$\text{area } AQP = \int_A^P y \, dx = \int_A^P \sinh u \, d(\cosh u)$$

$$= \int_A^P \sinh^2 u \, du = \tfrac{1}{2} \int_A^P (\cosh 2u - 1) \, du \quad \text{[Eq. (12b),}$$
$$\text{Article 10–2]}$$

$$= \tfrac{1}{2} \Big[\tfrac{1}{2} \sinh 2u - u \Big]_{A\,(u=0)}^{P\,(u=u)}$$

$$= \tfrac{1}{4} \sinh 2u - \tfrac{1}{2}u = \tfrac{1}{2} \sinh u \cosh u - \tfrac{1}{2}u.$$

Hence,

$$\text{area of sector } AOP = \text{area of } OQP - \text{area of } AQP$$

$$= \tfrac{1}{2} \sinh u \cosh u - (\tfrac{1}{2} \sinh u \cosh u - \tfrac{1}{2}u)$$

$$= \tfrac{1}{2}u,$$

or solving for u,

$$\boxed{u = \text{twice the area of the sector } AOP.} \tag{6}$$

As for the circle, a positive value of u is associated with an area above the x-axis and a negative value with an area below the x-axis, and areas are to be measured in terms of the unit square having OA as side. The term *hyperbolic radian* is sometimes used in connection with the variable u in Eq. (6), but here again, u is just a dimensionless real number. For example, $\cosh 2$ and $\sinh 2$ may be interpreted as the coordinates of P when the area of the sector AOP is just equal to the area of a square having OA as side.

10–5 The inverse hyperbolic functions. If we start with

$$x = \sinh y, \tag{1}$$

then as y varies continuously from $-\infty$ to $+\infty$, x does likewise. Graphically, this means that we may start with any real value on the y-axis in Fig. 10–7 and draw a horizontal line to the curve. Then a vertical line to the x-axis locates exactly one value of x such that the point (x, y) is on the curve. On the other hand, we could equally well reverse these steps and start with any real value x on the x-axis, go along a vertical line to the curve, then on a horizontal line to the y-axis. This latter procedure gives us y as a function of x, and the notation we use is

$$y = \sinh^{-1} x. \tag{2}$$

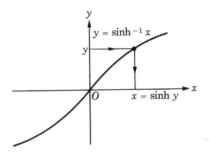

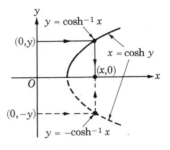

FIGURE 10–7   FIGURE 10–8

Here we have no problem about principal values, as we did in the case of the inverses of the circular functions, since the correspondence between the real numbers x and the real numbers y in Eq. (1) is one-to-one. Equation (1) says exactly the same thing as Eq. (2).

$$y = \sinh^{-1} x \qquad \text{means} \qquad x = \sinh y.$$

The inverse hyperbolic cosine, however, is double-valued and it is desirable to prescribe a principal branch. For if we start with the equation

$$x = \cosh y, \tag{3}$$

then y and $-y$ both give the same value of x; that is, the correspondence between y-values and x-values is two-to-one, so that if x is considered the independent variable, there are *two* corresponding values of y. This is analogous to the situation surrounding the equation $x = y^2$, which defines x as a single-valued function of y; but when x is given and we ask for y, the result is $y = \pm\sqrt{x}$. In the case of the inverse hyperbolic cosine, we take the positive values of y as the principal branch:

$$\boxed{y = \cosh^{-1} x \qquad \text{means} \qquad x = \cosh y, \quad y \geq 0, \quad x \geq 1.} \tag{4}$$

Thus in Fig. 10–8 the equation $x = \cosh y$ represents the entire curve, but $y = \cosh^{-1} x$ represents only that portion above the x-axis, while the portion below the x-axis is given by $y = -\cosh^{-1} x$.

Reference to Fig. 10–2 shows that the only other double-valued inverse is the inverse hyperbolic secant, and again we select the positive branch. That is,

$$y = \text{sech}^{-1} x, \qquad y > 0, \qquad 0 < x \leq 1 \tag{5}$$

defines the principal branch and the numbers x and y satisfy

$$x = \text{sech } y. \tag{6}$$

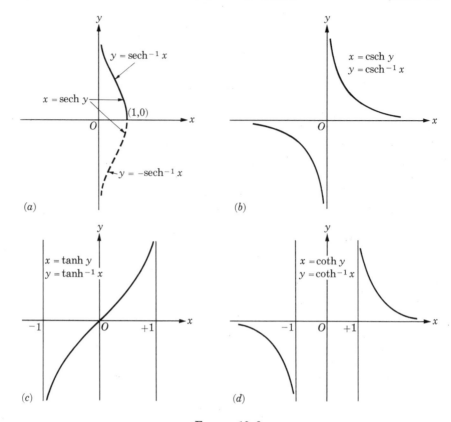

FIGURE 10–9

Since

$$\operatorname{sech} y = \frac{1}{\cosh y},$$

Eq. (6) is equivalent to

$$\cosh y = \frac{1}{x}$$

and the restriction $y > 0$ defines the same branch as in (5), so that

$$y = \cosh^{-1} \frac{1}{x}.$$

That is,

$$\operatorname{sech}^{-1} x = \cosh^{-1} \frac{1}{x}.$$

Similarly, we see that

$$y = \operatorname{csch}^{-1} x = \sinh^{-1} \frac{1}{x} \qquad \text{means} \qquad \operatorname{csch} y = x. \qquad (7)$$

Also,

$$y = \tanh^{-1} x \qquad \text{means} \qquad x = \tanh y, \qquad (8a)$$

and

$$y = \coth^{-1} x \qquad \text{means} \qquad x = \coth y. \qquad (8b)$$

The graphs of the various inverse hyperbolic functions are given in Figs. 10–7, 10–8, 10–9. Numerical values of $\sinh^{-1} x$, $\cosh^{-1} x$, and $\tanh^{-1} x$ may be read from the tables of $\sinh x$, $\cosh x$, and $\tanh x$ respectively in the same way that antilogarithms are read from tables of logarithms.

For example, suppose it is required to find $\tanh^{-1} 0.25$. If we let

$$x = \tanh^{-1} 0.25,$$

then

$$\tanh x = 0.25.$$

We consult a table of hyperbolic tangents and we find the following entries:

x	$\tanh x$	$\tanh x$ (rounded off)
0.25	0.24492	0.24
0.26	0.25430	0.25

Since we want the entry which corresponds to $\tanh x = 0.25$, we may simply round off the tabular entries to two significant figures and read $x = 0.26$. Or else we may take $\tanh x = 0.25000$ and interpolate between the readings listed above. Using ordinary proportional parts, we have

$$x_1 = 0.25, \qquad \tanh x_1 = 0.24492,$$
$$x = (?), \qquad \tanh x = 0.25000,$$
$$x_2 = 0.26, \qquad \tanh x_2 = 0.25430,$$

$$\frac{x - x_1}{x_2 - x_1} = \frac{\tanh x - \tanh x_1}{\tanh x_2 - \tanh x_b},$$

$$\frac{x - x_1}{0.01} = \frac{508}{938} = 0.54,$$

$$x = 0.2554 = \tanh^{-1} 0.25000.$$

An alternative method for evaluating the inverse hyperbolic functions is to express each of them in terms of logarithms, as illustrated below for $\tanh^{-1} x$. Let $y = \tanh^{-1} x$, then $\tanh y = x$ or

$$x = \frac{\sinh y}{\cosh y} = \frac{\frac{1}{2}(e^y - e^{-y})}{\frac{1}{2}(e^y + e^{-y})} = \frac{e^y - \dfrac{1}{e^y}}{e^y + \dfrac{1}{e^y}} = \frac{e^{2y} - 1}{e^{2y} + 1}.$$

We now solve this equation for e^{2y}:

$$xe^{2y} + x = e^{2y} - 1$$

or

$$1 + x = e^{2y}(1 - x),$$

and

$$e^{2y} = \frac{1 + x}{1 - x}.$$

Hence

$$\boxed{y = \tanh^{-1} x = \frac{1}{2}\ln\frac{1 + x}{1 - x}, \qquad |x| < 1.} \tag{9}$$

The variable x in Eq. (9) is restricted to the domain $|x| < 1$, since $x = \tanh y$ lies in this interval for all real values of y, $-\infty < y < +\infty$.

For example,

$$\tanh^{-1} 0.25 = \frac{1}{2}\ln\frac{1.25}{0.75} = \frac{1}{2}\ln\frac{5}{3}$$

$$= \tfrac{1}{2}(\ln 5 - \ln 3) = 0.25542.$$

The expressions for the other inverse hyperbolic functions in terms of logarithms are found in a similar manner. They are:

$$\boxed{\begin{aligned}
\sinh^{-1} x &= \ln(x + \sqrt{x^2 + 1}), \quad -\infty < x < \infty, \\
\cosh^{-1} x &= \ln(x + \sqrt{x^2 - 1}), \quad x \geq 1, \\
\operatorname{sech}^{-1} x &= \ln\left(\frac{1 + \sqrt{1 - x^2}}{x}\right) = \cosh^{-1}\left(\frac{1}{x}\right), \quad 0 < x \leq 1, \\
\operatorname{csch}^{-1} x &= \ln\left(\frac{1}{x} + \frac{\sqrt{1 + x^2}}{|x|}\right) = \sinh^{-1}\left(\frac{1}{x}\right), \quad x \neq 0, \\
\coth^{-1} x &= \frac{1}{2}\ln\frac{x + 1}{x - 1} = \tanh^{-1}\left(\frac{1}{x}\right), \quad |x| > 1.
\end{aligned}} \tag{10}$$

It should be evident that the logarithmic expressions are, on the whole, rather cumbersome, and that the inverse hyperbolic functions do provide a useful shorthand wherever these expressions arise.

The chief merit of the inverse hyperbolic functions lies in their usefulness in integration. This will easily be understood after we have derived the following formulas for their derivatives:

$$\frac{d(\sinh^{-1} u)}{dx} = \frac{1}{\sqrt{1 + u^2}} \frac{du}{dx},$$
XXVII

$$\frac{d(\cosh^{-1} u)}{dx} = \frac{1}{\sqrt{u^2 - 1}} \frac{du}{dx},$$
XXVIII

$$\frac{d(\tanh^{-1} u)}{dx} = \frac{1}{1 - u^2} \frac{du}{dx}, \quad |u| < 1,$$
XXIX

$$\frac{d(\coth^{-1} u)}{dx} = \frac{1}{1 - u^2} \frac{du}{dx}, \quad |u| > 1,$$
XXX

$$\frac{d(\operatorname{sech}^{-1} u)}{dx} = \frac{-du/dx}{u\sqrt{1 - u^2}},$$
XXXI

$$\frac{d(\operatorname{csch}^{-1} u)}{dx} = \frac{-du/dx}{|u|\sqrt{1 + u^2}}.$$
XXXII

The proofs of these all follow the same method. We illustrate for the case of $\cosh^{-1} u$. To this end, let

$$y = \cosh^{-1} u;$$

then

$$\cosh y = u,$$

$$\sinh y \frac{dy}{dx} = \frac{du}{dx},$$

and

$$\frac{dy}{dx} = \frac{1}{\sinh y} \frac{dy}{dx}.$$

But

$$\cosh^2 y - \sinh^2 y = 1,$$

$$\cosh y = u,$$

so that

$$\sinh y = \pm\sqrt{\cosh^2 y - 1}$$

$$= \pm\sqrt{u^2 - 1}$$

and
$$\frac{dy}{dx} = \frac{1}{\pm\sqrt{u^2 - 1}} \frac{du}{dx}.$$

The ambiguous sign will be $+$ if we restrict attention to the principal value, $y = \cosh^{-1} u$, $y \geq 0$, for then $\sinh y \geq 0$ and the ambiguous sign is the same as the sign of $\sinh y$. Thus XXVIII is established. The identities (5a) and (5b) of Article 10–2, with y in place of u, will be found to be useful in proving formulas XXIX to XXXII. The reader should have no difficulty in deriving these results.

The restrictions $|u| < 1$ and $|u| > 1$ in XXIX and XXX respectively are due to the fact that if

$$y = \tanh^{-1} u,$$

then

$$u = \tanh y,$$

and since

$$-1 < \tanh y < 1,$$

this means $|u| < 1$. Similarly,

$$y = \coth^{-1} u, \qquad u = \coth y$$

requires $|u| > 1$. The distinction becomes important when we invert the formulas to get integration formulas, since otherwise we would be unable to tell whether we should write $\tanh^{-1} u$ or $\coth^{-1} u$ for

$$\int \frac{du}{1 - u^2}.$$

The following integration formulas follow at once from the differential formulas XXVII' to XXXII', that are obtained by multiplying both sides of XXVII to XXXII by dx:

$$
\begin{aligned}
&(1) \quad \int \frac{du}{\sqrt{1 + u^2}} = \sinh^{-1} u + C, \\[2ex]
&(2) \quad \int \frac{du}{\sqrt{u^2 - 1}} = \cosh^{-1} u + C, \\[2ex]
&(3) \quad \int \frac{du}{1 - u^2} = \begin{cases} \tanh^{-1} u + C & \text{if } |u| < 1 \\ \coth^{-1} u + C & \text{if } |u| > 1 \end{cases} = \frac{1}{2} \ln \left| \frac{1 + u}{1 - u} \right| + C, \quad (11) \\[2ex]
&(4) \quad \int \frac{du}{u\sqrt{1 - u^2}} = -\operatorname{sech}^{-1} |u| + C = -\cosh^{-1}\left(\frac{1}{|u|}\right) + C, \\[2ex]
&(5) \quad \int \frac{du}{u\sqrt{1 + u^2}} = -\operatorname{csch}^{-1} |u| + C = -\sinh^{-1}\left(\frac{1}{|u|}\right) + C.
\end{aligned}
$$

Problems

1. Solve the equation $x = \sinh y = \frac{1}{2}(e^y - e^{-y})$ for e^y in terms of x, and thus show that $y = \ln(x + \sqrt{1 + x^2})$. (This equation expresses $\sinh^{-1} x$ as a logarithm.)

2. Express $\cosh^{-1} x$ in terms of logarithms by using the method of Problem 1.

3. Establish formula XXVII.

4. Establish formula XXIX.

5. Establish formula XXXI.

Find dy/dx in each of the following:

6. $y = \sinh^{-1}(2x)$
7. $y = \tanh^{-1}(\cos x)$

8. $y = \cosh^{-1}(\sec x)$
9. $y = \coth^{-1}(\sec x)$

10. $y = \text{sech}^{-1}(\sin 2x)$

Evaluate each of the following integrals:

11. $\displaystyle\int \frac{dx}{\sqrt{1 + 4x^2}}$
12. $\displaystyle\int \frac{dx}{\sqrt{4 + x^2}}$
13. $\displaystyle\int_0^{0.5} \frac{dx}{1 - x^2}$

14. $\displaystyle\int_{5/4}^{2} \frac{dx}{1 - x^2}$
15. $\displaystyle\int \frac{dx}{x\sqrt{4 + x^2}}$

16. If a body of mass m falling from rest under the action of gravity encounters an air resistance proportional to the square of the velocity, then the velocity v at time t satisfies the differential equation $m(dv/dt) = mg - kv^2$, where k is a constant of proportionality and $v = 0$ when $t = 0$. Show that $v = \sqrt{mg/k} \tanh(\sqrt{gk/m}\, t)$, and hence deduce that the body approaches a "limiting velocity" $= \sqrt{mg/k}$ as $t \to \infty$.

*10–6 The hanging cable. We conclude this chapter by deriving the solution of the differential equation

$$\frac{d^2 y}{dx^2} = \frac{w}{H}\sqrt{1 + \left(\frac{dy}{dx}\right)^2}, \tag{1}$$

which is the equation of equilibrium of forces on a hanging cable discussed in Article 10–3, Example 1. Since Eq. (1) involves the second derivative, we shall require two conditions to determine the constants of integration. By choosing the y-axis to be the vertical line through the lowest point of the cable, one condition becomes

$$\frac{dy}{dx} = 0 \qquad \text{when} \qquad x = 0. \tag{2a}$$

Then we may still move the x-axis up or down to suit our convenience. That is, we let

$$y = y_0 \qquad \text{when} \qquad x = 0, \tag{2b}$$

and we may choose y_0 so as to give us the simplest form in our final answer.

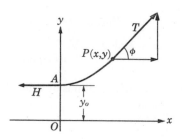

FIGURE 10–10

It is customary, when solving an equation such as (1), to introduce a single letter to represent dy/dx. The letter p is most often used. Thus we let

$$\frac{dy}{dx} = p, \tag{3a}$$

and then we may write

$$\frac{d^2y}{dx^2} = \frac{dp}{dx}, \tag{3b}$$

so that Eq. (1) takes the form

$$\frac{dp}{dx} = \frac{w}{H} \sqrt{1 + p^2}.$$

We may now separate the variables to get

$$\frac{dp}{\sqrt{1 + p^2}} = \frac{w}{H} dx$$

or

$$\int \frac{dp}{\sqrt{1 + p^2}} = \frac{w}{H} x + C_1. \tag{4a}$$

The integral on the left is of the same form, with p in place of u, as (11_1), Article 10–5. Hence (4a) becomes

$$\sinh^{-1} p = \frac{w}{H} x + C_1. \tag{4b}$$

Since $p = dy/dx = 0$ when $x = 0$, we determine the constant of integration

$$\sinh^{-1} 0 = C_1,$$

from which (see Fig. 10–7)

$$C_1 = 0.$$

Hence

$$\sinh^{-1} p = \frac{w}{H} x$$

or
$$p = \sinh\left(\frac{w}{H}x\right).$$ (5a)

We substitute $p = dy/dx$, multiply by dx, and have

$$dy = \sinh\left(\frac{w}{H}x\right)dx$$

or

$$
\begin{aligned}
y &= \int \sinh\left(\frac{w}{H}x\right)dx \\
&= \frac{H}{w}\int \sinh\left(\frac{w}{H}x\right)d\left(\frac{w}{H}x\right) \\
&= \frac{H}{w}\cosh\left(\frac{w}{H}x\right) + C_2.
\end{aligned}
$$ (5b)

The condition $y = y_0$ when $x = 0$ determines C_2:

$$y_0 = \frac{H}{w}\cosh 0 + C_2,$$

$$C_2 = y_0 - \frac{H}{w},$$ (5c)

and hence

$$y = \frac{H}{w}\cosh\left(\frac{w}{H}x\right) + y_0 - \frac{H}{w}.$$ (5d)

Clearly, this equation will have a simpler form if we choose y_0 so that

$$y_0 = \frac{H}{w}.$$

We do so. The answer then takes the form

$$y = \frac{H}{w}\cosh\left(\frac{w}{H}x\right)$$

or

$$y = a\cosh\frac{x}{a} \quad \text{with} \quad a = \frac{H}{w}.$$ (6)

PROBLEMS

1. Find the length of arc of the catenary $y = a\cosh x/a$ from $A(0, a)$ to $P_1(x_1, y_1)$, $x_1 > 0$.

2. Show that the area bounded by the x-axis, the catenary $y = a\cosh x/a$, the y-axis, and the vertical line through $P_1(x_1, y_1)$, $x_1 > 0$, is the same as the

area of a rectangle of altitude a and base s, where s is the length of the arc from $A(0, a)$ to P_1. (See Problem 1.)

3. The catenary $y = a \cosh x/a$ is revolved about the x-axis. Find the surface area generated by the portion of the curve between the points $A(0, a)$ and $P_1(x_1, y_1)$, $x_1 > 0$.

4. Find the center of gravity of the arc of the catenary $y = a \cosh x/a$ between two symmetrically located points $P_0(-x_1, y_1)$ and $P_1(x_1, y_1)$.

5. Find the volume generated when the area of Problem 2 is revolved about the x-axis.

6. (a) The length of the arc AP (Fig. 10–10) is $s = a \sinh x/a$. (See Problem 1.) Show that the coordinates of $P(x, y)$ may be expressed as functions of the arc length s as follows:

$$x = a \sinh^{-1} \frac{s}{a}, \qquad y = \sqrt{s^2 + a^2}.$$

(b) Calculate dx/ds and dy/ds from part (a) above and verify that $(dx/ds)^2 + (dy/ds)^2 = 1$.

7. A cable 32 feet long and weighing 2 pounds per foot has its ends fastened at the same level to two posts 30 feet apart.

(a) Show that the constant a in Eq. (6) must satisfy the equation

$$\sinh u = \frac{16}{15} u, \qquad u = \frac{15}{a}. \qquad \text{(See Problem 6a.)}$$

(b) Sketch graphs of the curves $y_1 = \sinh u$, $y_2 = \frac{16}{15} u$ and show (by consulting tables) that they intersect at $u = 0$ and $u = \pm 0.6$ (approximately).

(c) Using the results of part (b), find the dip in the cable at its center.

(d) Using the results of part (b), find the tension in the cable at its lowest point.

REVIEW QUESTIONS AND EXERCISES FOR CHAPTER 10

1. Define each of the hyperbolic functions.

2. State three trigonometric identities [such as formulas for $\sin (A + B)$, $\cos (A - B)$, $\cos^2 A + \sin^2 A = 1$, etc.]. What are the corresponding hyperbolic identities? Verify them.

3. Develop formulas for derivatives of the six hyperbolic functions.

4. What is the domain of the hyperbolic sine? What is its range?

5. What are the domain and range of the hyperbolic cosine? Of the hyperbolic tangent?

6. State some differences between the graphs of the trigonometric functions and their hyperbolic counterparts (for example, sine and sinh, cosine and cosh, tangent and tanh).

7. If $y = A \sin (at) + B \cos (at)$, then $y'' = -a^2 y$. What is the corresponding differential equation satisfied by $y = A \sinh (at) + B \cosh (at)$?

8. Define $\sinh^{-1}$ and $\cosh^{-1}$ functions. What are their domains? What are their ranges? What are their derivatives?

MISCELLANEOUS PROBLEMS FOR CHAPTER 10

1. Prove the hyperbolic identity $\cosh 2x = \cosh^2 x + \sinh^2 x$.

2. Verify that $\tanh x = \sinh 2x/(1 + \cosh 2x)$.

3. Sketch the curves $y = \cosh x$ and $y = \sinh x$ in one diagram. To each positive value of x corresponds a point P on $y = \sinh x$ and a point Q on $y = \cosh x$. Calculate the limit of the distance PQ as x becomes infinitely large.

4. If $\cosh x = \frac{5}{4}$, find $\sinh x$ and $\tanh x$.

5. If $\operatorname{csch} x = -\frac{9}{40}$, find $\cosh x$ and $\tanh x$.

6. If $\tanh x > \frac{5}{13}$, show that $\sinh x > 0.4$ and $\operatorname{sech} x < 0.95$.

7. Let $P(x, y)$ be a point on the curve $y = \tanh x$ (Fig. 10–2b). Let AB be the vertical line segment through P with A and B on the asymptotes of the curve. Let C be a semicircle with AB as diameter. Let L be a line through P perpendicular to AB and cutting C in a point Q. Show that $PQ = \operatorname{sech} x$.

8. Prove that $\sinh 3u = 3 \sinh u + 4 \sinh^3 u$.

9. Find equations of the asymptotes of the hyperbola represented by the equation $y = \tanh (\frac{1}{2} \ln x)$.

10. A particle moves along the x-axis according to one of the following laws: (a) $x = a \cos kt + b \sin kt$, (b) $x = a \cosh kt + b \sinh kt$. In both cases, show that the acceleration is proportional to x, but that in the first case it is always directed toward the origin while in the second case it is directed away from the origin.

11. Show that $y = \cosh x$, $\sinh x$, $\cos x$, and $\sin x$ all satisfy the relationship $d^4y/dx^4 = y$.

Find dy/dx in each of Problems 12–21.

12. $y = \sinh^2 3x$

13. $\tan x = \tanh^2 y$

14. $\sin^{-1} x = \operatorname{sech} y$

15. $\sinh y = \sec x$

16. $\tan^{-1} y = \tanh^{-1} x$

17. $y = \tanh (\ln x)$

18. $x = \cosh (\ln y)$

19. $y = \sinh (\tan^{-1} e^{3x})$

20. $y = \sinh^{-1} (\tan x)$

21. $y^2 + x \cosh y + \sinh^2 x = 50$

Evaluate each of the following integrals, Problems 22–31:

22. $\displaystyle\int \frac{d\theta}{\sinh \theta + \cosh \theta}$

23. $\displaystyle\int \frac{\cosh \theta \, d\theta}{\sinh \theta + \cosh \theta}$

24. $\displaystyle\int \sinh^3 x \, dx$

25. $\displaystyle\int e^x \sinh 2x \, dx$

26. $\displaystyle\int \frac{e^{2x} - 1}{e^{2x} + 1} \, dx$

27. $\displaystyle\int_0^1 \frac{dx}{4 - x^2}$

28. $\displaystyle\int_3^5 \frac{dx}{4 - x^2}$

29. $\displaystyle\int \frac{e^t \, dt}{\sqrt{1 + e^{2t}}}$

30. $\displaystyle\int \frac{\sin x \, dx}{1 - \cos^2 x}$

31. $\displaystyle\int \frac{\sec^2 \theta \, d\theta}{\sqrt{\tan^2 \theta - 1}}$

Sketch the following loci, Problems 32–34:

32. $y = \dfrac{1}{2} \ln \dfrac{1 + \tanh x}{1 - \tanh x}$ 33. $y = \tan \left(\dfrac{\pi}{2} \tanh x \right)$

34. $\cosh y = 1 + \dfrac{x^2}{2}$

35. If the arc s of the catenary $y = \cosh (x/a)$ is measured from the lowest point, show that $dy/dx = s/a$.

36. A body starting from rest falls under the attraction of gravity but encounters resistance proportional to the square of its velocity. Show that if the body could continue to fall indefinitely under these same conditions, its velocity would approach a limiting value and find the distance it would fall in time t.

37. Evaluate the limit, as $x \to \infty$, of $\cosh^{-1} x - \ln x$.

38. Evaluate $\displaystyle \lim_{x \to \infty} \int_1^x \left(\dfrac{1}{\sqrt{1 + t^2}} - \dfrac{1}{t} \right) dt$.

CHAPTER 11

POLAR COORDINATES

11–1 The polar coordinate system. We know that a point can be located in a plane by giving its abscissa and ordinate relative to a given coordinate system. Such x- and y-coordinates are called *Cartesian* coordinates, in honor of the French mathematician-philosopher René Descartes* (1596–1650), who is credited with discovering this method of fixing the position of a point in a plane.

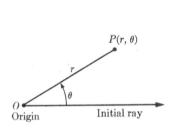

FIG. 11–1. Polar coordinates.

FIG. 11–2. The ray $\theta = 30°$ is the same as the ray $\theta = -330°$.

Another useful way to locate a point in a plane is by *polar coordinates*, Fig. 11–1. First, we fix an *origin O* and an *initial ray* † from O. The point P has polar coordinates r, θ, with

$$r = \text{directed distance from } O \text{ to } P, \qquad (1a)$$

and

$$\theta = \text{directed angle from initial ray to } OP. \qquad (1b)$$

As in trigonometry, the angle θ is *positive* when measured counterclockwise and negative when measured clockwise (Fig. 11–1). But the angle associated with a given point is not unique (Fig. 11–2). For instance, the point 2 units from the origin, along the ray $\theta = 30°$, has polar co-

---

* For an interesting biographical account together with an excerpt from Descartes' own writings, see *World of Mathematics*, Vol. 1, pp. 235–253.

† A *ray* is a half-line consisting of a vertex and points of a line on one side of the vertex. For example, the origin and positive x-axis is a ray. The points on the line $y = 2x + 3$ with $x \geq 1$ is another ray; its vertex is (1, 5).

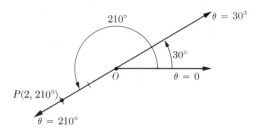

FIG. 11–3. The rays $\theta = 30°$ and $\theta = 210°$ make a line.

ordinates $r = 2$, $\theta = 30°$. It also has coordinates $r = 2$, $\theta = -330°$, or $r = 2$, $\theta = 390°$.

There are occasions when we wish to allow r to be negative. That's why we say "directed distance" in Eq. (1a). The ray $\theta = 30°$ and the ray $\theta = 210°$ together make up a complete line through O (Fig. 11–3). The point $P(2, 210°)$ 2 units from O on the ray $\theta = 210°$ has polar coordinates $r = 2$, $\theta = 210°$. It can be reached by a person standing at O and facing out along the initial ray, if he first turns 210° counterclockwise, and then goes forward 2 units. He would reach the same point by turning only 30° counterclockwise from the initial ray and then going *backward* 2 units. So we say that the point also has polar coordinates $r = -2$, $\theta = 30°$.

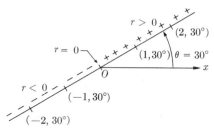

FIG. 11–4. The ray $\theta = \pi/6$ and its negative.

Whenever the angle between two rays is 180°, the rays actually make a straight line. We then say that either ray is the negative of the other. Points on the ray $\theta = \alpha$ have polar coordinates (r, α) with $r \geq 0$. Points on the negative ray, $\theta = \alpha + 180°$, have coordinates (r, α) with $r \leq 0$. The origin is $r = 0$. (See Fig. 11–4 for the ray $\theta = 30°$ and its negative. Caution: the "negative" of the ray $\theta = 30°$ is the ray $\theta = 30° + 180° = 210°$ and *not* the ray $\theta = -30°$. "Negative" refers to the directed distance r.)

There is a great advantage in being able to use both polar and Cartesian coordinates. To do this, we use a common origin and take the ini-

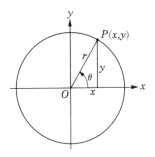

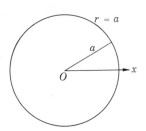

Fig. 11–5. Polar and Cartesian co-ordinates.

Fig. 11–6. The circle $r = a$.

tial ray as the positive x-axis, the ray $\theta = 90°$ as the positive y-axis. The coordinates (Fig. 11–5) are then related by the equations

$$x = r \cos \theta, \qquad y = r \sin \theta. \tag{2}$$

These are the equations that define $\sin \theta$ and $\cos \theta$ when r is positive. They are also valid if r is negative, because $\cos (\theta + 180°) = -\cos \theta$, $\sin (\theta + 180°) = -\sin \theta$, so positive r's on the ray $\theta + 180°$ correspond to negative r's associated with the ray θ. When $r = 0$, then $x = y = 0$, and P is the origin.

If we impose the condition

$$r = a \qquad (a \text{ constant}), \tag{3}$$

then the locus of P is a circle with center O, radius a, and P describes the circle once as θ varies from 0 to 360° (Fig. 11–6). On the other hand, if we let r vary and hold θ fixed, say

$$\theta = 30°, \tag{4}$$

the locus of P is the straight line shown in Fig. 11–4.

We adopt the convention that r may be any real number, $-\infty < r < \infty$. Then $r = 0$ corresponds to $x = 0$, $y = 0$ in Eqs. (2), regardless of θ. That is,

$$r = 0, \qquad \theta \text{ any value} \tag{5}$$

is the origin. Positive values of r with θ fixed give points on the terminal side of the angle θ; *negative* values of r give points on the negative ray.

The same point may be represented in several different ways in polar coordinates. For example, the point $(2, 30°)$, or $(2, \pi/6)$, has the following representations: $(2, 30°)$, $(2, -330°)$, $(-2, 210°)$, $(-2, -150°)$.

These and all others are summarized in the two formulas

$$(2, 30° + n\ 360°),\quad (-2, 210° + n\ 360°)\qquad [n = 0, \pm 1, \pm 2, \ldots]$$

or, if we represent the angles in radians,

$$\left(2, \frac{\pi}{6} + 2n\pi\right),\qquad \left(-2, \frac{7\pi}{6} + 2n\pi\right)\qquad [n = 0, \pm 1, \pm 2, \ldots].$$

The fact that the same point may be represented in several different ways in polar coordinates makes added care necessary in certain situations. For example, the point $(2a, \pi)$ is on the curve

$$r^2 = 4a^2 \cos\theta \tag{6}$$

even though its coordinates as given do not satisfy the equation, because the same point is represented by $(-2a, 0)$ and these coordinates do satisfy the equation. The same point $(2a, \pi)$ is on the curve

$$r = a(1 - \cos\theta), \tag{7}$$

and hence this point should be included among the points of intersection of the two curves represented by Eqs. (6) and (7). But if we solve the equations simultaneously by substituting $\cos\theta = r^2/4a^2$ from (6) into (7) and then solving the resulting quadratic equation

$$\left(\frac{r}{a}\right)^2 + 4\left(\frac{r}{a}\right) - 4 = 0$$

for

$$\frac{r}{a} = -2 \pm 2\sqrt{2}, \tag{8}$$

we do *not* obtain the point $(2a, \pi)$ as a point of intersection. The reason is simple enough; namely, the point is not on the curves "simultaneously" in the sense of being reached at the "same time," since it is reached in the one case when $\theta = 0$ and in the other case when $\theta = \pi$. It is as though two ships describe paths which intersect at a point, but the ships do not collide because they reach the point of intersection at different times! The curves represented by Eqs. (6) and (7) are shown in Fig. 11–9(c), p. 541, and they are seen to intersect at the four points

$$(0, 0),\quad (2a, \pi),\quad (r_1, \theta_1),\quad (r_1, -\theta_1), \tag{9a}$$

where

$$r_1 = (-2 + 2\sqrt{2})a,$$
$$\cos\theta_1 = 1 - \frac{r_1}{a} = 3 - 2\sqrt{2}. \tag{9b}$$

Only the last two of these points are found from the simultaneous solution; the first two are disclosed only by the graphs of the curves.

PROBLEMS

1. Plot the following points, given in polar form, and find *all* polar coordinates of each point:

(a) $(3, \pi/4)$,   (b) $(-3, \pi/4)$,   (c) $(3, -\pi/4)$,   (d) $(-3, -\pi/4)$.

2. Graph the locus of points $P(r, \theta)$ whose polar coordinates satisfy the given equation, inequality, or inequalities:

(a) $r = 2$,   (b) $r < 2$,   (c) $r > 1$,   (d) $1 < r < 2$,
(e) $0° \leq \theta \leq 30°, r \geq 0$,   (f) $\theta = 120°, r \leq -2$,
(g) $\theta = 60°, -1 \leq r \leq 3$,   (h) $\theta = 495°, r \geq -1$.

3. Find Cartesian coordinates of the points in Problem 1.
4. Graph the loci:

(a) $r \cos \theta = 2$,   (b) $r \sin \theta = -1$,
(c) $r \cos (\theta - 60°) = 3$, [*Hint:* rotate axes so that $\theta' = \theta - 60°$.]
(d) $r \sin (\theta + 45°) = 4$,   (e) $r \cos (30° - \theta) = 0$.

5. Show that $(2, \frac{3}{4}\pi)$ is on the curve $r = 2 \sin 2\theta$.
6. Show that $(\frac{1}{2}, \frac{3}{2}\pi)$ is on the curve $r = -\sin (\theta/3)$.
7. Show that the equations $r = \cos \theta + 1$, $r = \cos \theta - 1$, represent the same curve.

Find some intersections of the following pairs of curves ($a = $ constant):

8. $r^2 = 2a^2 \sin 2\theta$, $r = a$ 9. $r = a \sin \theta$, $r = a \cos \theta$
10. $r = a(1 + \cos \theta)$, $r = a(1 - \sin \theta)$
11. $r = a(1 + \sin \theta)$, $r = 2a \cos \theta$ 12. $r = a \cos 2\theta$, $r = a(1 + \cos \theta)$

11–2 Graphs of polar equations. The graph of an equation

$$F(r, \theta) = 0$$

consists of all those points whose coordinates (in some form) satisfy the equation. Frequently the equation gives r explicitly in terms of θ, as

$$r = f(\theta).$$

As many points as desired may then be obtained by substituting values of θ and calculating the corresponding values of r. In particular, it is desirable to plot the points where r is a maximum or a minimum and to find the values of θ when the curve passes through the origin, if that occurs.

Certain types of *symmetry* are readily detected. For example, the curve is:

(a) symmetric about the origin if the equation is unchanged when r is replaced by $-r$,

(b) symmetric about the x-axis if the equation is unchanged when θ is replaced by $-\theta$,

(c) symmetric about the y-axis if the equation is unchanged when θ is replaced by $\pi - \theta$.

These and certain other tests for symmetry are readily verified by considering the symmetrically located points in Fig. 11–7. [*Question:* What kind of symmetry occurs if the equation is unaltered when r and θ are replaced by $-r$ and $-\theta$ respectively?]

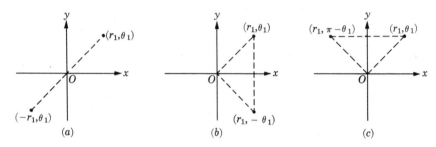

Fig. 11–7. Symmetries.

EXAMPLE 1. As an illustration of the method to be used, we shall discuss and sketch the curve

$$r = a(1 - \cos \theta),$$

where a is a positive constant.

Discussion. Since

$$\cos (-\theta) = \cos \theta,$$

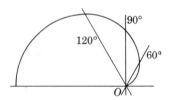

FIGURE 11–8

the equation is unaltered when θ is replaced by $-\theta$; hence the curve is symmetric about the x-axis (Fig. 11–7b). Also, since

$$-1 \le \cos \theta \le 1,$$

the values of r vary between 0 and $2a$. The minimum value, $r = 0$, occurs at $\theta = 0$, and the maximum value, $r = 2a$, occurs at $\theta = \pi$. Moreover, as θ varies from 0 to π, $\cos \theta$ decreases from 1 to -1, hence $1 - \cos \theta$ increases from 0 to 2; that is, r increases from 0 to $2a$ as the radius vector OP swings from $\theta = 0$ to $\theta = \pi$. We mark the points from the following table:

θ:	0	60°	90°	120°	180°
r:	0	$a/2$	a	$3a/2$	$2a$

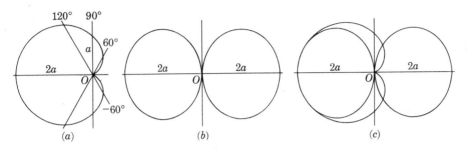

FIGURE 11–9

and sketch a smooth curve through them (Fig. 11–8) in such a way that r increases as θ increases, since

$$\frac{dr}{d\theta} = a \sin \theta$$

is positive for $0 < \theta < \pi$. Then we exploit the symmetry of the curve and reflect this portion across the x-axis. The result is the curve shown in Fig. 11–9(a), which is called a *cardioid* because of its heart-shaped appearance. Its behavior at the origin and the angles between its tangents and the coordinate axes at the other intercepts are more easily discussed at a later time. However, we may investigate the slope of the cardioid at the origin as follows. Let P be a point on the curve in the first quadrant, where P is destined to approach O along the curve.

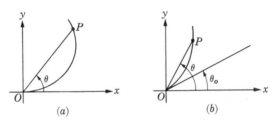

FIGURE 11–10

Then

$$\text{the slope of } OP = \tan \theta$$

approaches

$$\text{the slope of the tangent at } O$$

as $P \to O$. But $P \to O$ as $\theta \to 0$, and hence

$$\lim_{\theta \to 0} (\text{slope of } OP) = \lim_{\theta \to 0} \tan \theta = 0.$$

That is, the slope of the tangent to the curve at the origin is zero.

In fact, if any curve passes through the origin, say when $\theta = \theta_0$, then the discussion above would be modified only to the extent of saying that $P \to O$ along the curve as $\theta \to \theta_0$, and hence

$$\left(\frac{dy}{dx}\right)_{\theta=\theta_0} = \lim_{\theta \to \theta_0} (\tan \theta) = \tan \theta_0.$$

But $(dy/dx)_{\theta=\theta_0}$ is also the tangent of the angle between the x-axis and the curve at this point. Hence the line $\theta = \theta_0$ is tangent to the curve at the origin. In other words, whenever a curve passes through the origin for a value θ_0 of θ, it does so *tangent* to the line $\theta = \theta_0$. See Fig. 11–10(b).

EXAMPLE 2. $r^2 = 4a^2 \cos \theta$. This curve is symmetric about the origin. Two values,

$$r = \pm 2a\sqrt{\cos \theta},$$

correspond to each value of θ for which $\cos \theta > 0$, namely,

$$-\frac{\pi}{2} < \theta < \frac{\pi}{2}.$$

Furthermore, the curve is symmetric about the x-axis, since θ may be replaced by $-\theta$ without altering the value of $\cos \theta$. The curve passes through the origin at $\theta = \pi/2$ and is tangent to the y-axis at this point. Since $\cos \theta$ never exceeds unity, the maximum value of r is $2a$, which occurs at $\theta = 0$. As θ increases from 0 to $\pi/2$, $|r|$ decreases from $2a$ to 0. The curve is sketched in Fig. 11–9(b).

EXAMPLE 3. $r\theta = a$, where a is a positive constant. When $\theta = 0$ the equation becomes $0 = a$, which is not true. That is, there is no point on the curve for $\theta = 0$. However, suppose θ is a *small* positive angle. Then from $r = a/\theta$, we see that r is large and positive. Consider the situation in Fig.

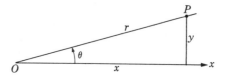

FIGURE 11–11

11–11. No matter how small the positive angle θ may be, if r is sufficiently large the point P may be far above the x-axis. In fact, we need to see what happens to

$$y = r \sin \theta = \frac{a}{\theta} \sin \theta$$

for small positive values of θ. We know, of course, that

$$\lim_{\theta \to 0} \frac{\sin \theta}{\theta} = 1,$$

hence

$$\lim_{\theta \to 0} y = \lim_{\theta \to 0} a \frac{\sin \theta}{\theta} = a.$$

This shows that the line $y = a$ is an asymptote of this curve. So we think of the

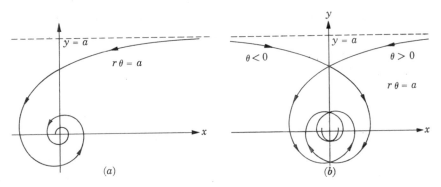

FIG. 11–12. Hyperbolic spiral $r\theta = a$.

curve being traced by a point P that starts far out near the line $y = a$ for $\theta = 0 +$ and moves in the direction indicated by the arrows in Fig. 11–12(a) as θ increases and r decreases. As the radius vector OP continues to rotate about the origin, it shrinks in length, and P describes a spiral which coils around the origin with r tending to zero as θ increases indefinitely.

When r and θ are replaced by $-r$ and $-\theta$ respectively, the equation is unaltered. Hence for every point (r_1, θ_1) on the curve in Fig. 11–12(a), there is a point $(-r_1, -\theta_1)$ symmetrically located with respect to the y-axis also on the curve $r\theta = a$. We therefore reflect the curve in Fig. 11–12(a) in the y-axis, obtaining another spiral which coils around the origin in the clockwise sense as θ approaches minus infinity. The complete curve is indicated in Fig. 11–12(b). It is called a *hyperbolic spiral*, the adjective "hyperbolic" being used because the equation $r\theta = a$ is analogous to the equation $xy = a$, which represents a hyperbola in Cartesian coordinates.

PROBLEMS

1. Find the polar form of the equation of the line $3x + 4y = 5$.

2. If the polar coordinates (r, θ) of a point P satisfy the equation $r = 2a \cos \theta$, what equation is satisfied by the Cartesian coordinates (x, y) of P? Discuss and sketch each of the following curves:

3. $r = a(1 + \cos \theta)$ 4. $r = a(1 - \sin \theta)$

5. $r = a \sin 2\theta$ 6. $r^2 = 2a^2 \cos 2\theta$

7. $r = a(2 + \sin \theta)$ 8. $r = a(1 + 2 \sin \theta)$

9. $r = \theta$ 10. $r = a \sin \theta/2$

11. Find the points on the curve $r = a(1 + \cos \theta)$, where the tangent is (a) parallel to the x-axis, (b) parallel to the y-axis. [*Hint.* Express x and y in terms of θ. Then calculate dy/dx.]

12. Sketch the curves $r = a(1 + \cos \theta)$ and $r = 3a \cos \theta$ in one diagram and find the angle between their tangents at the point of intersection that lies in the first quadrant.

11–3 Polar equations of the conic sections and other curves. The relationships given in Article 11–1 between Cartesian and polar coordinates enable us to change any Cartesian equation into a polar equation for the same curve.

For example, the circle

$$x^2 + y^2 - 2ax = 0, \tag{1}$$

with center at $(a, 0)$ and radius a, becomes

$$(r \cos \theta)^2 + (r \sin \theta)^2 - 2a(r \cos \theta) = 0,$$

which reduces to

$$r(r - 2a \cos \theta) = 0.$$

The locus obtained by putting the first factor equal to zero, $r = 0$, is just one point, the origin. The other factor vanishes when

$$r = 2a \cos \theta. \tag{2}$$

This includes the origin among its points and hence represents the entire locus given by Eq. (1).

The example illustrates one method of finding the polar equation for a curve, namely by transforming its Cartesian equation into polar form. An alternative method is to derive the polar equation directly from some geometric property. For example, take the circle in Fig. 11–13(b) and let $P(r, \theta)$ be a representative point on the circle. Then angle OPA is a right angle (why?) and from the right triangle OPA, we read

$$\frac{r}{2a} = \cos \theta \qquad \text{or} \qquad r = 2a \cos \theta,$$

which is the same equation obtained above.

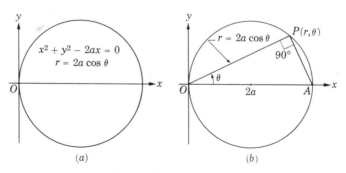

Fig. 11–13. Circle $r = 2a \cos \theta$.

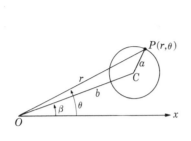

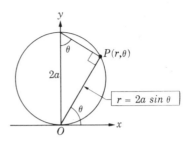

FIGURE 11–14   FIGURE 11–15

We shall apply this second method to obtain equations of various curves in the following examples.

EXAMPLE 1. Find the polar equation of the circle of radius a with center at (b, β).

Solution. We let $P\ (r, \theta)$ be a representative point on the circle and apply the law of cosines to the triangle OCP (Fig. 11–14) to obtain

$$a^2 = b^2 + r^2 - 2br \cos (\theta - \beta). \tag{3}$$

If the circle passes through the origin, then $b = a$ and the equation takes the simpler form

$$r[r - 2a \cos (\theta - \beta)] = 0$$

or

$$r = 2a \cos (\theta - \beta). \tag{4}$$

In particular, if $\beta = 0$, Eq. (4) reduces to the result we have obtained before, while if $\beta = 90°$, so that the center of the circle lies on the y-axis, Eq. (4) reduces to

$$r = 2a \sin \theta. \tag{5}$$

EXAMPLE 2. The normal from the origin to the line L intersects L at the point $N(p, \beta)$. Find the polar equation of L.

Solution. We let $P(r, \theta)$ be a representative point on the line L in Fig. 11–16 and from the right triangle ONP read the result

$$r \cos (\theta - \beta) = p. \tag{6}$$

This equation is simply a more general form of the equation

$$r \cos \theta = p, \tag{7}$$

which is the polar form of the line

$$x = p.$$

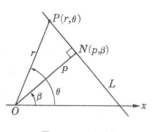

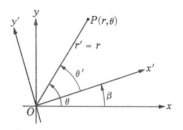

FIGURE 11–16   FIGURE 11–17

In fact, if we perform a rotation of axes as in Fig. 11–17, the new polar coordinates (r', θ') are related to the old polar coordinates as follows:

$$r' = r, \qquad \theta' = \theta - \beta. \tag{8}$$

If we apply this rotation to Eq. (6), we get

$$r' \cos \theta' = p.$$

But

$$r' \cos \theta' = x',$$

so the equation is the same as

$$x' = p,$$

which represents a straight line p units from and parallel to the y'-axis.

EXAMPLE 3. Find the polar locus of P if the product of its distances to the two points $F_1(a, \pi)$ and $F_2(a, 0)$ is a constant, say b^2.

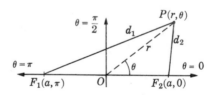

FIGURE 11–18

Solution. We let $P(r, \theta)$ be a representative point on the locus and determine the equation satisfied by the coordinates r and θ in order to fulfill the requirement

$$d_1 d_2 = b^2, \tag{9}$$

where $d_1 = PF_1$ and $d_2 = PF_2$ (Fig. 11–18). We apply the law of cosines twice: once to the triangle OPF_2,

$$d_2^2 = r^2 + a^2 - 2ar \cos \theta,$$

and again to the triangle OPF_1,

$$d_1^2 = r^2 + a^2 - 2ar \cos (\pi - \theta).$$

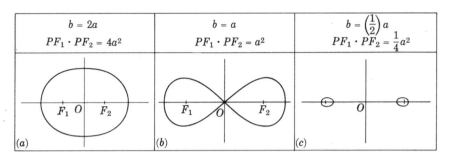

| $b = 2a$ | $b = a$ | $b = \left(\frac{1}{2}\right)a$ |
| $PF_1 \cdot PF_2 = 4a^2$ | $PF_1 \cdot PF_2 = a^2$ | $PF_1 \cdot PF_2 = \frac{1}{4}a^2$ |

FIGURE 11–19

But

$$\cos(\pi - \theta) = -\cos\theta,$$

so that

$$d_1^2 = r^2 + a^2 + 2ar\cos\theta.$$

Hence

$$d_1^2 d_2^2 = (r^2 + a^2)^2 - (2ar\cos\theta)^2$$

or

$$b^4 = a^4 + r^4 + 2a^2r^2(1 - 2\cos^2\theta).$$

The trigonometric identity $\cos 2\theta = 2\cos^2\theta - 1$ enables us to put our equation in the form

$$b^4 = a^4 + r^4 - 2a^2r^2\cos 2\theta. \tag{10}$$

One special case allows the locus to pass through the origin, namely, if $b = a$. Then the equation simplifies still further to the form

$$r^2 = 2a^2\cos 2\theta. \tag{11}$$

The graphs of the curves represented by (10) for different values of the ratio b/a are shown in Fig. 11–19(a)–(c). The curves in both (a) and (b) are called lemniscates, and the curve in (c) consists of two separate closed portions known as "ovals of Cassini."

EXAMPLE 4. Find the polar equation of the conic section of eccentricity e if the focus is at the origin and the associated directrix is the line $x = -k$.

Solution. We adopt the notation of Fig. 11–20 and use the focus-and-directrix property

$$PF = e \cdot PD, \tag{12}$$

which allows us to handle the parabola, ellipse, and hyperbola all at the same time.

By taking the origin at the focus F, we have

$$PF = r,$$

while

$$PD = AB$$

and

$$AB = AF + FB = k + r \cos \theta.$$

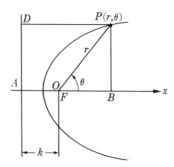

Then Eq. (12) is the same as

$$r = e(k + r \cos \theta).$$

If we solve this equation for r, we get

$$r = \frac{ke}{1 - e \cos \theta}. \qquad (13)$$

FIGURE 11-20

Typical special cases of (13) are obtained by taking

$$e = 1, \qquad r = \frac{k}{1 - \cos \theta} = \frac{k}{2} \csc^2 \frac{\theta}{2}, \qquad (14a)$$

which represents a *parabola;*

$$e = \tfrac{1}{2}, \qquad r = \frac{k}{2 - \cos \theta}, \qquad (14b)$$

which represents an *ellipse;*

$$e = 2, \qquad r = \frac{2k}{1 - 2 \cos \theta}, \qquad (14c)$$

which represents a *hyperbola.*

It is worth noting that the denominator in Eq. (14b) for the ellipse can never vanish, so that r remains finite for all values of θ. But r becomes infinite as θ approaches 0 in (14a) and as θ approaches $\pi/3$ in (14c).

By replacing the constant ke in Eq. (13) by its equivalent value

$$ke = a(1 - e^2)$$

when $e < 1$, we may let $e \to 0$ and get

$$r = a$$

in the limit. That is, the circle of radius a and center at O is a limiting case of the curves represented by Eq. (13).

PROBLEMS

1. A line segment of length $2a$ slides with its ends on the x- and y-axes. Find the polar equation of the locus described by the point $P(r, \theta)$ in which the perpendicular from the origin intersects the moving line. Sketch the curve.

2. OA is a diameter of a circle of radius a, AC is tangent to the circle, and OC intersects the circle at B. On OC the point $P(r, \theta)$ is found such that $OP = BC$. With O as origin, OA as x-axis, and angle AOP as θ, find the polar equation of

the locus of P and sketch the curve. Show that the line $x = 2a$ is an asymptote. The curve is called a "cissoid," meaning "ivy-like."

In Problems 3–7 determine the polar equation and sketch the given curve.

3. $x^2 + y^2 - 2ay = 0$

4. $(x^2 + y^2)^2 + 2ax(x^2 + y^2) - a^2y^2 = 0$

5. $x \cos \alpha + y \sin \alpha = p$ (α, p constants)

6. $y^2 = 4ax + 4a^2$ 7. $(x^2 + y^2)^2 = x^2 - y^2$

In Problems 8–13 determine the Cartesian equation and sketch the given curve.

8. $r = 4 \cos \theta$ 9. $r = 6 \sin \theta$

10. $r = \sin 2\theta$ 11. $r^2 = 2a^2 \cos 2\theta$

12. $r = 8/(1 - 2 \cos \theta)$ 13. $r = a(1 + \sin \theta)$

14. Sketch the following loci:

(a) $r = 2 \cos (\theta + 45°)$,   (b) $r = 4 \csc (\theta - 30°)$,

(c) $r = 5 \sec (60° - \theta)$,   (d) $r = 3 \sin (\theta + 30°)$,

(e) $r = a + a \cos (\theta - 30°)$,   (f) $0 \le r \le 2 - 2 \cos \theta$.

15. (a) How can the angle β and the distance p [see Fig. 11–16 and Eq. (6)] be determined from the Cartesian equation $ax + by = c$ for a straight line? (b) Specifically, find p, β, and the polar equation for the straight line $\sqrt{3}x + y = 6$.

16. The focus of a parabola is at the origin and its directrix is the line $4 = r \cos (\theta + \pi/3)$. Find the polar equation of the parabola.

17. One focus of a hyperbola of eccentricity $\frac{5}{4}$ is at the origin and the corresponding directrix is the line $r \cos \theta = 9$. Find the polar coordinates of the second focus. Also determine the polar equation of the hyperbola and sketch.

18. From the origin a line is drawn perpendicular to a tangent of the circle $r = 2a \cos \theta$. Find the locus of the point of intersection and sketch the curve.

19. Find the maximum and minimum values of r that satisfy Eq. (10), first in terms of a and b, and then specifically for the cases $b = 2a$, $b = a$, and $b = a/2$.

20. Determine the slopes of the lines that are tangent to the lemniscate $r^2 = 2a^2 \cos 2\theta$ at the origin.

21. Equation (14b), $r = k/(2 - \cos \theta)$, represents an ellipse with one focus at the origin. Sketch the curve and its directrices for the case $k = 2$ and locate the center of the ellipse.

22. In the case $e > 1$, Eq. (13) represents a hyperbola. From the polar form of the equation, determine the slopes of the asymptotes of the hyperbola of eccentricity e.

23. Show, by reference to a figure, that the distance from the line

$$r \cos (\theta - \beta) = p$$

to the point $P_1(r_1, \theta_1)$ is $|r_1 \cos (\theta_1 - \beta) - p|$.

11–4 The angle ψ between the radius vector and the tangent line. In Cartesian coordinates, when we want to discuss the direction of a curve at a point, we use the angle ϕ from the positive x-axis to the tangent line. In polar coordinates, it is more convenient to make use of the angle ψ (psi) from the *radius vector* to the tangent line. Then the relationship

$$\phi = \theta + \psi, \tag{1}$$

which can be read from Fig. 11–21, makes it a simple matter to find ϕ if that angle is desired instead of ψ.

Suppose the equation of the curve is given in the form $r = f(\theta)$, where $f(\theta)$ is a differentiable function of θ. Then from

$$x = r \cos \theta, \qquad y = r \sin \theta, \tag{2}$$

we see that x and y are differentiable functions of θ with

$$\frac{dx}{d\theta} = -r \sin \theta + \cos \theta \, \frac{dr}{d\theta},$$

$$\frac{dy}{d\theta} = r \cos \theta + \sin \theta \, \frac{dr}{d\theta}. \tag{3}$$

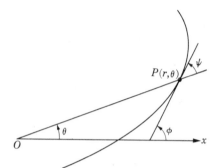

FIG. 11–21. Angle ψ between tangent and radius vector.

Since $\psi = \phi - \theta$ from (1),

$$\tan \psi = \tan (\phi - \theta) = \frac{\tan \phi - \tan \theta}{1 + \tan \phi \tan \theta},$$

while

$$\tan \phi = \frac{dy/d\theta}{dx/d\theta}, \qquad \tan \theta = \frac{y}{x}.$$

Hence

$$\tan \psi = \frac{\dfrac{dy/d\theta}{dx/d\theta} - \dfrac{y}{x}}{1 + \dfrac{y}{x} \dfrac{dy/d\theta}{dx/d\theta}} = \frac{x \dfrac{dy}{d\theta} - y \dfrac{dx}{d\theta}}{x \dfrac{dx}{d\theta} + y \dfrac{dy}{d\theta}}. \tag{4}$$

The numerator in the last expression in Eq. (4) is found by substitution from Eqs. (2) and (3) to be

$$x \frac{dy}{d\theta} - y \frac{dx}{d\theta} = r^2.$$

Similarly, the denominator is

$$x \frac{dx}{d\theta} + y \frac{dy}{d\theta} = r \frac{dr}{d\theta}.$$

When we substitute these into Eq. (4), we obtain the very simple final result

$$\boxed{\tan \psi = \frac{r}{dr/d\theta} \cdot}$$

(5)

This formula for $\tan \psi$ is much simpler than the formula

$$\tan \phi = \frac{r \cos \theta + (\sin \theta)\, dr/d\theta}{-r \sin \theta + (\cos \theta)\, dr/d\theta},$$

(6)

that one obtains by calculating

$$\frac{dy}{dx} = \frac{dy/d\theta}{dx/d\theta}$$

from (3). This is why it is usually preferable to work with the angle ψ rather than with ϕ in the case of polar coordinates.

One may also obtain a simple expression for the differential element of arc length ds by squaring and adding the differentials

$$dx = -r \sin \theta\, d\theta + \cos \theta\, dr,$$

$$dy = r \cos \theta\, d\theta + \sin \theta\, dr.$$

We find that

$$ds^2 = dx^2 + dy^2 = r^2\, d\theta^2 + dr^2.$$

This result and the result for $\tan \psi$ are both easily remembered in the form

$$\boxed{\begin{array}{ll} (1) & \tan \psi = \dfrac{r\, d\theta}{dr}, \\[2mm] (2) & ds^2 = r^2\, d\theta^2 + dr^2 \end{array}}$$

(7)

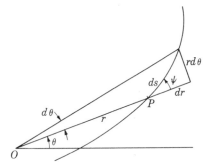

FIG. 11–22. Arc length.

if we refer to the "differential triangle" shown in Fig. 11–22. We simply treat dr and $r\, d\theta$ as the two legs and ds as the hypotenuse of an ordinary right triangle with the angle ψ opposite the side $r\, d\theta$. If we realize that certain terms of higher order are being neglected, we may think of dr as the component of displacement along the radius vector and $r\, d\theta$ as the component at right angles to this produced by the displacement ds along the curve. The relationships (7) may be read at once from this triangle. We should realize, of course, that the *proof* of these equations did not depend upon any such "differential triangle" and that the latter represents only a mnemonic device.

To find the angle ψ, we use (7_1); and to find the length of a polar curve, we find ds from (7_2) and integrate between appropriate limits as illustrated in the following examples.

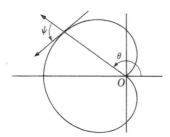

Fig. 11–23. Cardioid.

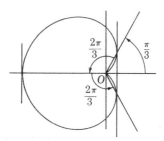

Fig. 11–24. Vertical tangents to cardioid.

EXAMPLE 1. Find the angle ψ for the cardioid (Fig. 11–23)

$$r = a(1 - \cos \theta). \tag{8a}$$

Solution. From the equation of the curve, we get

$$dr = a \sin \theta \, d\theta, \tag{8b}$$

so that

$$\tan \psi = \frac{r \, d\theta}{dr} = \frac{a(1 - \cos \theta) \, d\theta}{a \sin \theta \, d\theta} = \tan \frac{\theta}{2}.$$

As θ varies from 0 to 2π, the angle ψ varies from 0 to π according to the equation $\psi = \theta/2$. Thus at the y-intercepts the tangent line makes an angle of 45° with the vertical, at the origin the curve is tangent to the x-axis, and at $(2a, \pi)$ the tangent line makes an angle of 90° with the negative x-axis.

Suppose we ask for the points on the cardioid where the tangent line is vertical. Denoting the inclination angle of the tangent line by ϕ and recalling that

$$\phi = \psi + \theta$$

and

$$\psi = \tfrac{1}{2}\theta,$$

we get

$$\phi = \tfrac{3}{2}\theta.$$

Since the tangent is vertical when

$$\phi = \frac{\pi}{2} + n\pi,$$

the values of θ satisfy

$$\theta = \frac{2}{3}\phi = \frac{\pi}{3} + \frac{2}{3}n\pi.$$

Taking $n = 0, -1, 1, -2, 2, \ldots$, we obtain

$$\theta = \frac{\pi}{3}, \quad \frac{-\pi}{3}, \quad \pi, \quad -\pi, \quad \frac{5}{3}\pi, \ldots$$

These lead to three distinct points, namely,

$$\left(\frac{a}{2}, \pm\frac{\pi}{3}\right) \quad \text{and} \quad (2a, \pi),$$

whose radius vectors are evenly spaced 120° apart. (See Fig. 11–24.)

EXAMPLE 2. Find the length of the cardioid $r = a(1 - \cos\theta)$.

Solution. Substituting dr and r from (8b, a) into (7_2), we have

$$ds^2 = a^2\, d\theta^2\, [\sin^2\theta + (1 - \cos\theta)^2]$$
$$= 2a^2\, d\theta^2 (1 - \cos\theta)$$

and

$$ds = a\sqrt{2}\,\sqrt{1 - \cos\theta}\, d\theta.$$

In order to integrate the expression on the right, we recall the trigonometric identity

$$1 - \cos\theta = 2\sin^2\frac{\theta}{2}$$

and have

$$ds = 2a\left|\sin\frac{\theta}{2}\right|d\theta.$$

Since $\sin\theta/2$ is not negative when θ varies from 0 to 2π, we obtain

$$s = \int_0^{2\pi} 2a\sin\frac{\theta}{2}\, d\theta$$

$$= -4a\cos\frac{\theta}{2}\Big]_0^{2\pi} = 8a.$$

We observe in passing that in letting θ range from 0 to 2π, we start at the cusp at the origin, go once around the smooth portion of the cardioid and return to the cusp. In doing this we do not pass *across* the cusp (Fig. 11–23). If, on the other hand, we take the cardioid $r = a(1 + \cos\theta)$, the appropriate procedure for avoiding the cusp (Fig. 11–25) is to let θ increase from $-\pi$ to π, or we may use the symmetry of the curve and calculate half of the total length by letting θ vary from 0 to π.

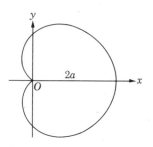

FIG. 11–25. Cardioid.

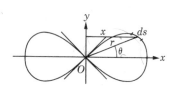

FIG. 11–26. Lemniscate.

EXAMPLE 3. The lemniscate

$$r^2 = 2a^2 \cos 2\theta$$

is revolved about the y-axis. Find the area of the surface generated.

Solution. An element of arc length ds (Fig. 11–26) generates a portion of surface area

$$dS = 2\pi x \, ds,$$

where

$$x = r \cos \theta, \qquad ds = \sqrt{dr^2 + r^2 \, d\theta^2}.$$

That is,

$$dS = 2\pi r \cos \theta \sqrt{dr^2 + r^2 \, d\theta^2} = 2\pi \cos \theta \sqrt{r^2 \, dr^2 + r^4 \, d\theta^2}.$$

From the equation of the curve, we get

$$r \, dr = -2a^2 \sin 2\theta \, d\theta.$$

Then

and

$$(r^2 \, dr^2 + r^4 \, d\theta^2) = (2a^2 \, d\theta)^2 (\sin^2 2\theta + \cos^2 2\theta)$$

$$dS = 4\pi a^2 \cos \theta \, d\theta.$$

The total surface area is generated by the loop of the lemniscate to the right of the y-axis between $\theta = -\pi/4$ and $\theta = +\pi/4$, so that

$$S = \int_{-\pi/4}^{\pi/4} 4\pi a^2 \cos \theta \, d\theta = 4\pi a^2 \sqrt{2}.$$

PROBLEMS

1. For the hyperbolic spiral $r\theta = a$ show that $\psi = 135°$ when $\theta = 1$ radian, and that $\psi \to 90°$ as the spiral winds around the origin. Sketch the curve and indicate ψ for $\theta = 1$ radian.

2. Show, by reference to a figure, that the angle β between the tangents to two curves at a point of intersection may be found from the formula

$$\tan \beta = \frac{\tan \psi_2 - \tan \psi_1}{1 + \tan \psi_2 \tan \psi_1}.$$

When will the two curves intersect orthogonally?

3. Find a point of intersection of the parabolas

$$r = \frac{1}{1 - \cos \theta} \quad \text{and} \quad r = \frac{3}{1 + \cos \theta}$$

and find the angle between the tangents to these curves at this point.

4. Find points on the cardioid $r = a(1 + \cos \theta)$ where the tangent line is horizontal.

5. Find the length of the cardioid $r = a(1 + \cos \theta)$. [*Hint:* $\int \sqrt{1 + \cos \theta}\, d\theta = \int \sqrt{2}\, |\cos \theta/2|\, d\theta.$]

6. A thin, uniform wire is bent into the shape of the cardioid $r = a(1 + \cos \theta)$. Find its center of gravity $(\bar{x}, \bar{y})$.   [*Hint:* $\int \cos \theta \cos \theta/2\, d\theta$ can be evaluated by substituting $\cos \theta = 1 - 2 \sin^2 \theta/2$ and then letting $u = \sin \theta/2$.]

7. The lemniscate $r^2 = 2a^2 \cos 2\theta$ is rotated about the x-axis. Find the area of the surface generated.

8. Find the length of the curve $r = a \sin^2 \theta/2$ from $\theta = 0$ to $\theta = \pi$. Sketch the curve.

9. Find the length of the parabolic spiral $r = a\theta^2$ between $\theta = 0$ and $\theta = \pi$. Sketch the curve.

10. Find the length of the curve $r = a \sin^3 \theta/3$ between $\theta = 0$ and $\theta = \pi$. Sketch the curve.

11. Find the surface area generated by rotating the curve $r = 2a \cos \theta$ about the line $\theta = \pi/2$. Sketch.

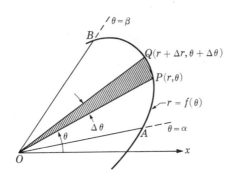

FIGURE 11–27

11–5 Plane areas in polar coordinates. The area AOB in Fig. 11–27 is bounded by the rays $\theta = \alpha$, $\theta = \beta$, and the curve $r = f(\theta)$. We imagine the angle AOB as being divided into n parts

$$\Delta \theta = \frac{\beta - \alpha}{n},$$

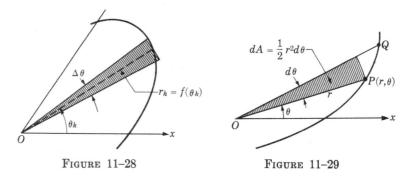

FIGURE 11–28   FIGURE 11–29

and we approximate the area in a typical sector POQ by the area of a *circular* sector of radius r and central angle $\Delta\theta$, that is,

$$\text{area of } POQ \approx \tfrac{1}{2}r^2\,\Delta\theta,$$

and hence the entire area AOB is approximately

$$\sum_{\theta=\alpha}^{\beta}\tfrac{1}{2}r^2\,\Delta\theta.$$

In fact, if the function $r = f(\theta)$ which represents the polar curve is a continuous function of θ for $\alpha \le \theta \le \beta$, then there is a θ_k between θ and $\theta + \Delta\theta$ such that the circular sector of radius

$$r_k = f(\theta_k)$$

and central angle $\Delta\theta$ gives the *exact* area of POQ (Fig. 11–28). Then the entire area is given exactly by

$$A = \sum\tfrac{1}{2}r_k^2\,\Delta\theta = \sum\tfrac{1}{2}[f(\theta_k)]^2\,\Delta\theta.$$

If we let $\Delta\theta \to 0$, we may apply the Fundamental Theorem of the integral calculus and obtain

$$A = \lim_{\Delta\theta\to 0}\sum\tfrac{1}{2}[f(\theta_k)]^2\,\Delta\theta = \tfrac{1}{2}\int_{\alpha}^{\beta}[f(\theta)]^2\,d\theta,$$

or

$$\boxed{A = \int_{\alpha}^{\beta}\tfrac{1}{2}r^2\,d\theta.}\tag{1}$$

This result may also be remembered as the integral of the differential element of area (Fig. 11–29):

$$dA = \tfrac{1}{2}r^2\,d\theta,$$

taken between the appropriate limits on θ.

EXAMPLE. Find the area that is inside the circle $r = a$ and outside the cardioid $r = a(1 - \cos \theta)$. (See Fig. 11–30.)

Solution. We take a representative element of area

$$dA = dA_1 - dA_2,$$

where

$$dA_1 = \tfrac{1}{2}r_1^2 \, d\theta, \qquad dA_2 = \tfrac{1}{2}r_2^2 \, d\theta$$

with

$$r_1 = a, \qquad r_2 = a(1 - \cos \theta).$$

Such elements of area belong to the region inside the circle and outside the cardioid provided θ lies between

$$-\frac{\pi}{2} \quad \text{and} \quad +\frac{\pi}{2},$$

where the curves intersect. Hence

$$A = \int_{-\pi/2}^{\pi/2} \tfrac{1}{2}(r_1^2 - r_2^2) \, d\theta$$

$$= \int_{-\pi/2}^{\pi/2} \frac{a^2}{2} (2 \cos \theta - \cos^2 \theta) \, d\theta$$

$$= a^2 \int_{-\pi/2}^{\pi/2} \cos \theta \, d\theta - \frac{a^2}{2} \int_{-\pi/2}^{\pi/2} \frac{1 + \cos 2\theta}{2} \, d\theta$$

$$= a^2 \left(2 - \frac{\pi}{4}\right).$$

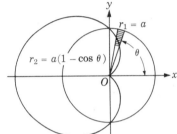

FIGURE 11–30

As a check against gross errors, we observe that this is roughly 80% of the area of a semicircle of radius a and this seems reasonable when we look at the area in Fig. 11–30.

PROBLEMS

[*Note:* The trigonometric identities

$$\sin^2 \theta = \tfrac{1}{2}(1 - \cos 2\theta), \qquad \cos^2 \theta = \tfrac{1}{2}(1 + \cos 2\theta)$$

should be used to evaluate $\int \sin^2 \theta \, d\theta$ and $\int \cos^2 \theta \, d\theta$ in certain of the problems that follow.]

1. Find the total area inside the cardioid $r = a(1 + \cos \theta)$.
2. Find the total area inside the circle $r = 2a \sin \theta$.
3. Find the total area inside the lemniscate $r^2 = 2a^2 \cos 2\theta$.
4. Find that portion of the area inside the lemniscate $r^2 = 2a^2 \cos 2\theta$ that is not included in the circle $r = a$. Sketch.

5. Find the area inside the curve $r = a(2 + \cos \theta)$.

6. Find the area common to the circles $r = 2a \cos \theta$ and $r = 2a \sin \theta$. Sketch.

7. Find the area inside the circle $r = 3a \cos \theta$ and outside the cardioid $r = a(1 + \cos \theta)$.

8. Since the center of gravity of a triangle is located on a median at a distance $\frac{2}{3}$ of the way from a vertex to the opposite base, the lever arm for the moment about the x-axis of the area of triangle POQ in Fig. 11–27 is $\frac{2}{3}r \sin \theta + \epsilon$, where $\epsilon \to 0$ as $\Delta\theta \to 0$. Deduce that the center of gravity of the area AOB in the figure is given by

$$\bar{y} = \frac{\int \frac{2}{3}r \sin \theta \cdot \frac{1}{2}r^2 \, d\theta}{\int \frac{1}{2}r^2 \, d\theta}$$

and similarly,

$$\bar{x} = \frac{\int \frac{2}{3}r \cos \theta \cdot \frac{1}{2}r^2 \, d\theta}{\int \frac{1}{2}r^2 \, d\theta},$$

with limits $\theta = \alpha$ to $\theta = \beta$ on all integrals.

9. Use the results of Problem 8 to find the center of gravity of the area bounded by the cardioid $r = a(1 + \cos \theta)$.

10. Use the results of Problem 8 to find the center of gravity of the area of a semicircle of radius a.

REVIEW QUESTIONS AND EXERCISES FOR CHAPTER 11

1. Make a diagram to show the standard relations between Cartesian coordinates (x, y) and polar coordinates (r, θ). Express each set of coordinates in terms of the other kind.

2. If a point has polar coordinates (r_1, θ_1), what other polar coordinates represent the same point?

3. What is the expression for area between curves in polar coordinates?

4. What is the expression for length of arc of a curve in polar coordinates? For area of a surface of revolution?

5. What are some criteria for symmetry of a curve if its polar coordinates satisfy the equation $r = f(\theta)$? Illustrate your discussion with specific examples.

6. An artificial satellite is in an orbit that passes over the North and South Poles of the earth. When it is over the North Pole it is at the highest point of its orbit, 1000 miles above the earth's surface. Above the South Pole it is at the lowest point of its orbit, 300 miles above the earth's surface. (a) Assuming that the orbit (with reference to the earth) is an ellipse with one focus at the center of the earth, find its eccentricity. (Take the diameter of the earth to be 8000 miles.) (b) Using the north-south axis of the earth as polar axis, and the center of the earth as origin, find a polar equation of the orbit.

MISCELLANEOUS PROBLEMS FOR CHAPTER 11

Discuss and sketch each of the curves in Problems 1–13 (where a is a positive constant).

1. $r = a\theta$

2. $r = a(1 + \cos 2\theta)$

3. (a) $r = a \sec \theta$;　　(b) $r = a \csc \theta$;　　(c) $r = a \sec \theta + a \csc \theta$

4. $r = a \sin \left(\theta + \dfrac{\pi}{3} \right)$

5. $r^2 + 2r (\cos \theta + \sin \theta) = 7$

6. $r = a \cos \theta - a \sin \theta$

7. $r \cos \dfrac{\theta}{2} = a$

8. $r^2 = a^2 \sin \theta$

9. $r^2 = 2a^2 \sin 2\theta$

10. $r = a(1 - 2 \sin 3\theta)$

11. (a) $r = \cos 2\theta$
    (b) $r^2 = \cos 2\theta$

12. (a) $r = 1 + \cos \theta$

(b) $r = \dfrac{1}{1 + \cos \theta}$

13. (a) $r = \dfrac{2}{1 - \cos \theta}$

(b) $r = \dfrac{2}{1 + \sin \theta}$

14. Sketch and discuss the graph whose equation in polar coordinates is

$$r = 1 - \tan^2\theta.$$

Show that it has no vertical asymptotes.

Sketch each of the pairs of curves in Problems 15–20, and find all points of intersection and the angle between their tangents at each point of intersection.

15. $r = a$,　$r = 2a \sin \theta$

16. $r = a$,　$r = a(1 - \sin \theta)$

17. $r = a \sec \theta$,　$r = 2a \sin \theta$

18. $r = a \cos \theta$,

19. $r = a(1 + \cos 2\theta)$,

$r = a \cos 2\theta$

$r = a(1 + \cos \theta)$

20. $r^2 = 4 \cos 2\theta$,　$r^2 = \sec 2\theta$

21. Find the equation, in polar coordinates, of a parabola whose focus is at $r = 0$ and whose vertex is at $r = 1$, $\theta = 0$.

22. Find the polar equation of the straight line with intercepts a and b on the lines $\theta = 0$, $\theta = \pi/2$.

23. Find the equation of a circle with center on the line $\theta = \pi$, of radius a, and passing through the origin.

24. Find the polar equation of a parabola with focus at the origin and vertex at $(a, \pi/4)$.

25. Find the polar equation of an ellipse with one focus at the origin, the other at $(2, 0)$, and a vertex at $(4, 0)$.

26. Find the polar equation of a hyperbola with one focus at the origin, center at $(2, \pi/2)$, and vertex at $(1, \pi/2)$.

27. Three loran stations are located (in polar coordinates) at $(a, 0)$, $(0, 0)$, and $(a, \pi/4)$. Radio signals are sent out from the three stations simultaneously.

A plane receiving the signals notes that the signals from the second and third stations arrive $a/2\nu$ sec later than that from the first. If ν is the velocity of a radio signal, what is the location of the plane in polar coordinates?

28. Show that the parabolas $r = a/(1 + \cos\theta)$, $r = b/(1 - \cos\theta)$ are orthogonal at each point of intersection ($ab \neq 0$).

29. Find the angle between the line $\theta = \pi/2$ and the cardioid $r = a(1 - \cos\theta)$ at their intersection.

30. Find the angle between the line $r = 3\sec\theta$ and the curve $r = 4(1 + \cos\theta)$ at one of their intersections.

31. Find the slope of the tangent line to the curve $r = a\tan(\theta/2)$ at $\theta = \pi/2$.

32. Check that the two curves $r = 1/(1 - \cos\theta)$ and $r = 3/(1 + \cos\theta)$ intersect at the point $(2, \pi/3)$. Find the angle between the tangents to these curves at this point.

33. The equation $r^2 = 2\csc 2\theta$ represents a curve in polar coordinates. (a) Sketch the curve. (b) Find the equation of the curve in rectangular coordinates. (c) Find the angle at which the curve intersects the line $\theta = \pi/4$.

34. A given curve cuts all rays $\theta = $ constant at the constant angle α. (a) Show that the area bounded by the curve and two rays $\theta = \theta_1$, $\theta = \theta_2$, is proportional to $r_2^2 - r_1^2$, where (r_1, θ_1) and (r_2, θ_2) are polar coordinates of the ends of the arc of the curve between these rays. Find the factor of proportionality. (b) Show that the length of the arc of the curve in part (a) is proportional to $r_2 - r_1$ and find the proportionality constant.

35. The cardioid $r = a(1 - \cos\theta)$ is rotated about the initial line. (a) Find the area of the surface generated. [*Hint:* You may use the fact that $\sin\theta = 2\sin(\theta/2)\cos(\theta/2)$, and $1 - \cos\theta = 2\sin^2(\theta/2)$ to evaluate your integral.] (b) Set up the definite integral (or integrals) that would be used to find the centroid of the area in part (a). (c) Find the centroid of the area in part (a).

36. Let P be a point on the hyperbola $r^2\sin 2\theta = 2a^2$. Show that the triangle formed by OP, the tangent at P, and the initial line is isosceles.

37. Verify that the formula for finding the length of a curve in polar form gives the correct result for the circumference of the circles (a) $r = a$, (b) $r = a\cos\theta$, (c) $r = a\sin\theta$.

38. If $r = a\cos^3(\theta/3)$, show that $ds = a\cos^2(\theta/3)\,d\theta$ and determine the perimeter of the curve.

39. Find the area that lies inside the curve $r = 2a\cos 2\theta$ and outside the curve $r = a\sqrt{2}$.

40. Sketch the curves $r = 2a\cos^2(\theta/2)$ and $r = 2a\sin^2(\theta/2)$, and find the area they have in common.

Find the total area enclosed by each of the curves in Problems 41–47.

41. $r^2 = a^2\cos 2\theta$ 42. $r = a(2 - \cos\theta)$

43. $r = a(1 + \cos 2\theta)$ 44. $r = 2a\cos\theta$

45. $r = 2a\sin 3\theta$ 46. $r^2 = 2a^2\sin 3\theta$

47. $r^2 = 2a^2\cos^2(\theta/2)$

48. Find the area that is inside the cardioid $r = a(1 + \sin\theta)$ and outside the circle $r = a\sin\theta$.

CHAPTER 12

VECTORS AND PARAMETRIC EQUATIONS

12-1 Parametric equations in kinematics. In Newtonian mechanics, the motion of a particle in a plane is usually described by means of a pair of differential equations expressing Newton's second law of motion*

$$\mathbf{F} = \frac{d(m\mathbf{v})}{dt}. \tag{1}$$

Here $\mathbf{F}$ is the vector force acting on the particle of mass m at time t and $\mathbf{v}$ is its vector velocity at time t. When the x- and y-components of Eq. (1) are separated, the equivalent equations are

$$F_x = \frac{d(mv_x)}{dt}, \qquad F_y = \frac{d(mv_y)}{dt}. \tag{2}$$

In addition to these laws of motion, we require a knowledge of the position and velocity of the particle at some given instant. Then the position of the particle at all later instants is determined by the prescribed forces. The result of integrating the second-order differential equations (2) subject to the given initial conditions usually yields equations that determine the x- and y-coordinates of the particle as functions of t:

$$x = f(t), \qquad y = g(t). \tag{3}$$

These equations are called *parametric equations* of the path of the particle and t is called the *parameter*. Equations (3) contain more information about the motion of the particle than does the *Cartesian equation*

$$y = F(x), \tag{4}$$

that one obtains from (3) by eliminating t. The parametric equations tell *where* the particle goes and *when* it gets to any given place, whereas the Cartesian equation tells only the curve along which the particle travels.

We shall illustrate these ideas by determining the path of a projectile. Suppose the projectile is fired with an initial velocity v_0 at an angle of elevation α. Assuming that gravity is the only force acting on the projectile, we shall find its motion.

---

* Vectors are indicated by bold-faced Roman letters. In handwritten work, it is customary to indicate them by a small arrow over each letter which represents a vector.

561

We introduce coordinate axes with origin at the point where the projectile begins its motion, as in Fig. 12–1. The initial conditions may then be taken to be

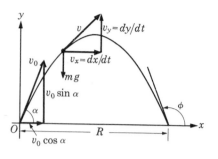

$$t = 0: \quad \begin{aligned} v_x \left(= \frac{dx}{dt} \right) &= v_0 \cos \alpha, \\[2mm] v_y \left(= \frac{dy}{dt} \right) &= v_0 \sin \alpha, \end{aligned} \qquad (5)$$

$$x = 0, \qquad y = 0.$$

FIGURE 12–1

The force components at time t, with appropriate sign, are

$$F_x = 0, \qquad F_y = -mg,$$

so that the differential equations (2) become

$$0 = m \frac{d^2 x}{dt^2}, \qquad -mg = m \frac{d^2 y}{dt^2}. \qquad (6)$$

Each of Eqs. (6) requires two integrations. This introduces a total of four constants of integration. These may be evaluated by using the initial conditions (5). Thus by integration one obtains from (6_1):

$$\frac{d^2 x}{dt^2} = 0, \qquad \frac{dx}{dt} = c_1, \qquad x = c_1 t + c_2, \qquad (7a)$$

and from (6_2):

$$\frac{d^2 y}{dt^2} = -g, \qquad \frac{dy}{dt} = -gt + c_3, \qquad y = -\tfrac{1}{2} g t^2 + c_3 t + c_4. \qquad (7b)$$

From the initial conditions, we find

$$c_1 = v_0 \cos \alpha, \qquad c_2 = 0, \qquad c_3 = v_0 \sin \alpha, \qquad c_4 = 0. \qquad (7c)$$

The position of the projectile at time t (seconds, say, after firing) is given by

$$x = (v_0 \cos \alpha)t, \qquad y = -\tfrac{1}{2} g t^2 + (v_0 \sin \alpha)t. \qquad (8)$$

For a given angle of elevation α and a given muzzle velocity v_0, the position of the projectile at any time may be determined from the parametric equations, (8). The equations may be used to answer such questions as the following:

1. How high does the projectile rise vertically?
2. How far does the projectile travel horizontally?

3. What is the range of the projectile (horizontally) in terms of the angle of elevation? What angle produces the maximum range?

The projectile will attain maximum height when its y velocity component is zero, that is, when

$$\frac{dy}{dt} = -gt + v_0 \sin \alpha = 0$$

or when

$$t = t_m = \frac{v_0 \sin \alpha}{g}.$$

Then

$$y_{max} = -\tfrac{1}{2}g(t_m)^2 + (v_0 \sin \alpha)t_m = \frac{(v_0 \sin \alpha)^2}{2g}.$$

To find the horizontal range of the projectile, we find the time when it strikes the ground, that is, when $y = 0$. From (8_2), we have

$$y = t(-\tfrac{1}{2}gt + v_0 \sin \alpha) = 0$$

when

$$t = 0 \quad \text{or} \quad t = \frac{2v_0 \sin \alpha}{g} = 2t_m.$$

Clearly, $t = 0$ corresponds to the instant when the projectile is fired, so that $t = 2t_m$ gives the range $x = R$:

$$R = v_0 \cos \alpha \frac{2v_0 \sin \alpha}{g} = \frac{v_0^2}{g} \sin 2\alpha.$$

For a given muzzle velocity, this shows that the maximum range is obtained when $\sin 2\alpha = 1$, that is, when $\alpha = 45°$.

The slope of the path of the projectile at any point may also be found directly from (8), namely,

$$\frac{dy}{dx} = \frac{dy/dt}{dx/dt} = \frac{-gt + v_0 \sin \alpha}{v_0 \cos \alpha}.$$

At $y = 0$, $x = R$, we found

$$t = \frac{2v_0 \sin \alpha}{g},$$

and hence

$$\frac{dy}{dx} = \frac{-2v_0 \sin \alpha + v_0 \sin \alpha}{v_0 \cos \alpha} = -\tan \alpha.$$

This shows that the angle ϕ (Fig. 12–1) is $\pi - \alpha$, so that the projectile returns to the earth at the same angle as that at which it was fired.

Finally, the Cartesian equation of the path is readily obtained from (8); for we need only substitute

$$t = \frac{x}{v_0 \cos \alpha}$$

from (8_1) into (8_2) to eliminate t and obtain

$$y = - \left(\frac{g}{2v_0^2 \cos^2 \alpha} \right) x^2 + (\tan \alpha)x. \tag{9}$$

Since this equation is linear in y and quadratic in x, it represents a *parabola*. Thus the path of a projectile (in vacuo, that is, neglecting air resistance) is a parabola.

When air resistance is taken into account, the differential equations obtained are too complicated for straightforward integration. The M.I.T. differential analyzers were used to solve such problems during World War II in order to build up "range tables." Against a moving target, in particular, the *time* is also of great importance, so that equations or tables which give x and y in terms of t are preferred over the Cartesian form.

Problems

In Problems 1–4, the projectile is assumed to obey the laws of motion discussed above, in which air resistance is neglected.

1. Find two values of the angle of elevation that will enable a projectile to reach a target on the same level as the gun and 25,000 feet distant from it if the initial velocity is 1000 ft/sec. Determine the times of flight corresponding to these two angles.

2. Show that doubling of the initial velocity of a projectile multiplies both the maximum height and the range by a factor of four.

3. Show that a projectile attains three-quarters of its maximum height in one-half the time required to reach that maximum.

4. Suppose a target moving at the constant rate of a ft/sec is level with and b ft away from a gun at the instant the gun is fired. If the target moves in a horizontal line directly away from the gun, show that the muzzle velocity v_0 and angle of elevation α must satisfy the equation.

$$v_0^2 \sin 2\alpha - 2a \, v_0 \sin \alpha - bg = 0$$

if the projectile is to strike the target.

In Problems 5–7, find parametric equations and sketch the curve described by the point $P(x, y)$ for $t \geq 0$ if its coordinates satisfy the given differential equations and initial conditions.

5. $\dfrac{dx}{dt} = x, \quad \dfrac{dy}{dt} = -x^2; \quad t = 0, \quad x = 1, \quad y = -4.$

6. $\dfrac{dx}{dt} = y,\quad \dfrac{dy}{dt} = y^2;\quad t = 0,\quad x = 0,\quad y = 1.$

7. $\dfrac{dx}{dt} = \sqrt{1 - x^2},\quad \dfrac{dy}{dt} = x^2;\quad t = 0,\quad x = 0,\quad y = 1.$

12–2 Parametric equations in analytic geometry. The solutions of differential equations of motion are not the only ways in which parametric equations arise. For example, we have frequently had occasion to use equations such as

$$x = a \cos \theta, \qquad y = a \sin \theta \tag{1}$$

to represent a circle. Here θ is the parameter and Eqs. (1) are parametric equations of the circle (Fig. 12–2). Similarly,

$$x = a \cos \phi, \qquad y = b \sin \phi \tag{2}$$

are parametric equations of an ellipse whose Cartesian equation is

$$\frac{x^2}{a^2} + \frac{y^2}{b^2} = 1.$$

The parabola

$$y^2 = 4px \tag{3}$$

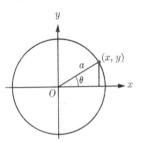

FIGURE 12–2

can be parametrized in several ways. One method is to use as parameter the slope

$$t = \frac{dy}{dx}$$

of the tangent to the curve at (x, y) (Fig. 12–3a). Since

$$2y \frac{dy}{dx} = 4p \qquad \text{or} \qquad \frac{dy}{dx} = \frac{2p}{y},$$

the parametric equations in this case are

$$y = \frac{2p}{t}, \qquad x = \frac{p}{t^2}. \tag{4}$$

If we use the parameter defined (Fig. 12–3b) by

$$m = \frac{y}{x},$$

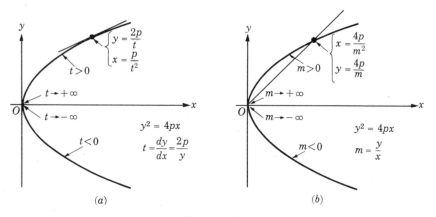

FIGURE 12–3

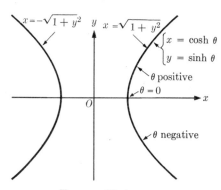

FIGURE 12–4

we have

$$y^2 = m^2 x^2 \quad \text{and} \quad y^2 = 4px,$$

which lead to

$$x = \frac{4p}{m^2}, \quad y = \frac{4p}{m} \tag{5}$$

as the parametric equations.

Sometimes the parametric equations of a locus and the Cartesian equation are not coextensive.

For example, suppose the parametric equations of a curve are

$$x = \cosh \theta, \quad y = \sinh \theta. \tag{6}$$

Then the hyperbolic identity

$$\cosh^2 \theta - \sinh^2 \theta = 1$$

enables us to eliminate θ and write

$$x^2 - y^2 = 1 \tag{7}$$

as the Cartesian equation of the curve. Closer scrutiny, however, shows that Eq. (7) *includes too much*. For $x = \cosh \theta$ is never less than unity, so the parametric equations represent a curve lying wholly to the right of the y-axis, whereas the Cartesian equation (7) represents both the right- and left-hand branches of the hyperbola (Fig. 12–4). The left-hand branch could be excluded by taking only positive values of x. That is,

$$x = \sqrt{1 + y^2} \tag{8}$$

does represent the same curve as (6).

As a second example, consider the curve whose parametric equations are

$$x = \cos 2\theta, \qquad y = \cos \theta. \tag{9}$$

It is certainly restricted to lie within the square $-1 \le x \le 1$, $-1 \le y \le 1$. But we eliminate θ as follows:

$$x = \cos 2\theta = 2 \cos^2 \theta - 1 = 2y^2 - 1.$$

Thus every point on the locus of (9) also lies on the curve

$$x = 2y^2 - 1 \tag{10}$$

and, in addition, is restricted by

$$|x| \le 1, \qquad |y| \le 1.$$

If we omit these restrictions, Eq. (10) represents the complete parabola

$$y^2 = \tfrac{1}{2}(x + 1)$$

with vertex at $(-1, 0)$ and opening to the right, as shown in Fig. 12–5. The parametric equations, on the other hand, represent only the arc ABC. Referring to Eqs. (9), we readily see that the point starts at $A(1, 1)$ when $\theta = 0$, moves along AB to $B(-1, 0)$ as θ varies from 0 to $\pi/2$,

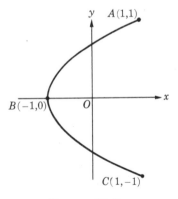

FIGURE 12–5

and continues to $C(1, -1)$ as θ increases to π. As θ varies from π to 2π, the point traverses the arc CBA back to A. Since both x and y are periodic functions of θ of period 2π, further variations in θ result in retracing the same portion of the parabola.

The following example illustrates further how parametric equations may be derived from geometric properties of a curve. A wheel of radius

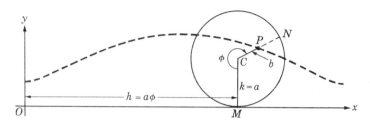

FIGURE 12–6

a rolls along a horizontal straight line without slipping. Find the locus described by a point on a spoke of the wheel at distance b from its center. Such a curve is called a *trochoid*. When $b = a$ the tracing point is on the circumference of the wheel and the trochoid in this case is called a *cycloid*.

In Fig. 12–6, we take the x-axis as the line the wheel rolls along, with the y-axis through a low point of the trochoid. Point P describes the curve in question. It is customary to use the angle ϕ through which CP has rotated as the parameter. We introduce $x'y'$-axes parallel to the xy-axes but having their origin at the center of the circle C (Fig. 12–7). If (h, k) are the coordinates of C relative to the xy-axes, then the xy-coordinates of P are related to its $x'y'$-coordinates as follows:

$$x = h + x', \qquad y = k + y'. \tag{11}$$

From the fact that the circle rolls along the x-axis without slipping, we see that the distance OM that the wheel has moved horizontally is just equal to the arc $MN = a\phi$. (Roll the wheel back; then N will fall at the origin O.) The xy-coordinates of C are therefore

$$h = a\phi, \qquad k = a. \tag{12}$$

From Fig. 12–7 we may immediately read

$$x' = b \cos \theta, \qquad y' = b \sin \theta,$$

or, since

$$\theta = \frac{3\pi}{2} - \phi,$$

$$x' = -b \sin \phi, \qquad y' = -b \cos \phi. \tag{13}$$

We substitute these results and Eqs. (12) into (11) and obtain

$$x = a\phi - b \sin \phi,$$
$$\tag{14}$$
$$y = a - b \cos \phi$$

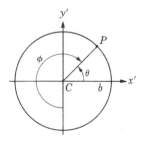

FIGURE 12–7

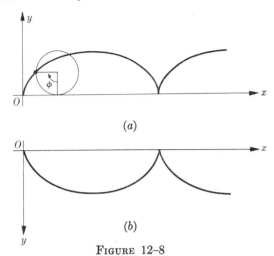

(a)

(b)

FIGURE 12–8

as parametric equations of the trochoid. The cycloid (Fig. 12–8a),

$$x = a(\phi - \sin\phi), \qquad y = a(1 - \cos\phi), \qquad (15)$$

obtained from (14) by taking $b = a$, is the most important special case of a trochoid.

If we reflect both the cycloid and the y-axis across the x-axis, Eqs. (15) still apply and the resulting curve (Fig. 12–8b) has several interesting properties, one of which we shall now discuss without proof. The proofs belong to a branch of mathematics known as the calculus of variations. Much of the fundamental theory of this subject is attributable to the Bernoulli brothers, John and James, who were friendly rivals and stimulated each other with mathematical problems in the form of challenges. One of these, the brachistochrone problem, was: Among all smooth curves joining two given points, to find that one along which a bead might slide, subject only to the force of gravity, *in the shortest time.*

The two points, labeled P_0 and P_1 in Fig. 12–9, may be taken to lie at the origin and at (x_1, y_1) respectively in a vertical plane. We can formulate the problem in mathematical terms as follows. The kinetic energy of the bead at the start is zero, since its velocity is zero. The work done by gravity in moving the particle from $(0, 0)$ to any point (x, y) is mgy and this must be equal to the change in kinetic energy; that is,

$$mgy = \tfrac{1}{2}mv^2 - \tfrac{1}{2}m(0)^2.$$

Thus the velocity

$$v = ds/dt$$

that the particle has when it reaches $P(x,y)$ is

$$v = \sqrt{2gy}.$$

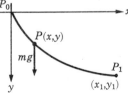

FIGURE 12–9

That is,

$$\frac{ds}{dt} = \sqrt{2gy}$$

or

$$dt = \frac{ds}{\sqrt{2gy}} = \frac{\sqrt{1 + \left(\frac{dy}{dx}\right)^2}\, dx}{\sqrt{2gy}}.$$

The time t_1 required for the bead to slide from P_0 to P_1 depends upon the particular curve $y = f(x)$ along which it moves and is given by

$$t_1 = \int_0^{x_1} \sqrt{\frac{1 + (f'(x))^2}{2gf(x)}}\, dx. \tag{16}$$

The problem is *to find the curve* $y = f(x)$ that passes through the points $P_0(0, 0)$ and $P_1(x_1, y_1)$ and minimizes the value of the integral in Eq. (16). (*Brachistochrone* is derived from two Greek words that together mean "shortest time.")

At first sight, one might guess that the straight line joining P_0 and P_1 would also yield the shortest time, but a moment's reflection will cast some doubt on this conjecture. For there may be some gain in time by having the particle start to fall vertically at first, thereby building up its velocity more quickly than if it were to slide along an inclined path. With this increased velocity, one may be able to afford to travel over a longer path and still reach P_1 in a shorter time. The solution of the problem is beyond the present book, but the brachistochrone curve is actually an arc of a cycloid through P_0 and P_1, having a cusp at the origin. [The interested reader is referred to the book *Calculus of Variations* by G. A. Bliss, The Mathematical Association of America (1925), for a discussion of this problem and others belonging to this branch of mathematics.]

If we write Eq. (16) in the equivalent form

$$t_1 = \int \sqrt{\frac{dx^2 + dy^2}{2gy}}$$

and then substitute Eqs. (15) into this, we obtain

$$t_1 = \int_{\phi=0}^{\phi_1} \sqrt{\frac{a^2(2 - 2\cos\phi)}{2ga(1 - \cos\phi)}}\, d\phi = \phi_1 \sqrt{\frac{a}{g}}$$

as the time required for the particle to slide from P_0 to P_1. The time required to reach the bottom of the arc is obtained by taking $\phi_1 = \pi$. Now it is a remarkable fact, which we shall soon demonstrate, that the time required to slide along the cycloid from $(0, 0)$ to the lowest point $(a\pi, 2a)$ is the same as the time required for the particle, starting from rest, to slide from *any intermediate point* of the arc, say (x_0, y_0), to $(a\pi, 2a)$. For the latter case, one has

$$v = \sqrt{2g(y - y_0)}$$

as the velocity at $P(x, y)$, and the time required is

$$T = \int_{\phi_0}^{\pi} \sqrt{\frac{a^2(2 - 2\cos\phi)}{2ag(\cos\phi_0 - \cos\phi)}}\, d\phi = \sqrt{\frac{a}{g}} \int_{\phi_0}^{\pi} \sqrt{\frac{1 - \cos\phi}{\cos\phi_0 - \cos\phi}}\, d\phi$$

$$= \sqrt{\frac{a}{g}} \int_{\phi_0}^{\pi} \sqrt{\frac{2\sin^2\dfrac{\phi}{2}}{\left(2\cos^2\dfrac{\phi_0}{2} - 1\right) - \left(2\cos^2\dfrac{\phi}{2} - 1\right)}}\, d\phi$$

$$= 2\sqrt{\frac{a}{g}} \left[-\sin^{-1}\frac{\cos\dfrac{\phi}{2}}{\cos\dfrac{\phi_0}{2}}\right]_{\phi_0}^{\pi} = 2\sqrt{\frac{a}{g}}(-\sin^{-1}0 + \sin^{-1}1) = \pi\sqrt{\frac{a}{g}}.$$

Since this answer is independent of the value of ϕ_0, it follows that the same length of time is required to reach the lowest point on the cycloid no matter where on the arc the particle is released from rest. Thus, in Fig. 12–10, three particles which start at the same time from O, A, and B will reach C simultaneously. In this sense, the cycloid is also a tautochrone (meaning "the same time") as well as being a brachistochrone.

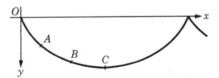

FIGURE 12–10

PROBLEMS

In each of Problems 1–10, sketch the graph of the curve described by the point $P(x, y)$ as the parameter t varies over the domain given. Also determine the Cartesian equation of the curve in each case.

1. $x = \cos t$, $y = \sin t$, $0 \le t \le 2\pi$
2. $x = \cos 2t$, $y = \sin t$, $0 \le t \le 2\pi$
3. $x = \sec t$, $y = \tan t$, $-\pi/2 < t < \pi/2$
4. $x = 2 + 4\sin t$, $y = 3 - 2\cos t$, $0 \le t \le 2\pi$
5. $x = 2t + 3$, $y = 4t^2 - 9$, $-\infty < t < \infty$
6. $x = \cosh t$, $y = 2\sinh t$, $0 \le t < \infty$
7. $x = 2 + 1/t$, $y = 2 - t$, $0 < t < \infty$
8. $x = t + 1$, $y = t^2 + 4$, $0 \le t < \infty$
9. $x = t^2 + t$, $y = t^2 - t$, $-\infty < t < \infty$

10. $x = 3 + 2 \operatorname{sech} t,\quad y = 4 - 3 \tanh t,\quad -\infty < t < \infty$

11. Find parametric equations of the semicircle

$$x^2 + y^2 = a^2, \qquad y > 0,$$

using as parameter the slope $t = dy/dx$ of the tangent to the curve at (x, y).

12. Find parametric equations of the semicircle

$$x^2 + y^2 = a^2, \qquad y > 0,$$

using as parameter the variable θ defined by the equation $x = a \tanh \theta$.

13. Find parametric equations of the circle

$$x^2 + y^2 = a^2,$$

using as parameter the arc length s measured counterclockwise from the point $(a, 0)$ to the point (x, y).

14. Find parametric equations of the catenary $y = a \cosh x/a$, using as parameter the length of arc s from the point $(0, a)$ to the point (x, y), with the sign of s taken to be the same as the sign of x.

15. If a string wound around a fixed circle is unwound while held taut in the plane of the circle, its end traces an *involute* of the circle. Let the fixed circle be located with its center at the origin O and have radius a. Let the initial position of the tracing point P be $A(a, 0)$ and let the unwound portion of the string PT be tangent to the circle at T. Derive parametric equations of the involute, using the angle AOT as the parameter ϕ.

16. When a circle rolls externally on the circumference of a second, fixed circle, any point P on the circumference of the rolling circle describes an *epicycloid*. Let the fixed circle have its center at the origin O and have radius a. Let the radius of the rolling circle be b and let the initial position of the tracing point P be $A(a, 0)$. Determine parametric equations of the epicycloid, using as parameter the angle θ from the positive x-axis to the line of centers.

17. When a circle rolls on the inside of a fixed circle any point P on the circumference of the rolling circle describes a *hypocycloid*. Let the fixed circle be $x^2 + y^2 = a^2$, let the radius of the rolling circle be b, and let the initial position of the tracing point P be $A(a, 0)$. Use the angle θ from the positive x-axis to the line of centers as parameter and determine parametric equations of the hypocycloid. In particular, if $b = a/4$, show that

$$x = a \cos^3 \theta, \qquad y = a \sin^3 \theta.$$

18. Find the length of one arch of the cycloid

$$x = a(\phi - \sin \phi), \qquad y = a(1 - \cos \phi).$$

19. Show that the slope of the cycloid

$$x = a(\phi - \sin \phi), \qquad y = a(1 - \cos \phi)$$

is $dy/dx = \cot \phi/2$. In particular, the tangent to the cycloid is vertical when ϕ is 0 or 2π.

20. Show that the slope of the trochoid

$$x = a\phi - b \sin \phi, \quad y = a - b \cos \phi$$

is always finite if $b < a$.

21. The *witch* is a bell-shaped curve that may be constructed as follows: Let C be a circle of radius a having its center at $(0, a)$ on the y-axis. The variable line OA through the origin O intersects the line $y = 2a$ in the point A and intersects the circle in the point B. A point P on the witch is now located by taking the intersection of lines through A and B parallel to the y- and x-axes respectively. Find parametric equations of the witch, using as parameter the angle θ from the x-axis to the line OA. Also find the Cartesian equation.

12–3 Vector components and the unit vectors i and j.

Some physical quantities are completely determined when their magnitudes, in terms of specific units, are given. Such quantities are called *scalars* and are exemplified by mass and length. Other quantities, like forces and velocities, in which the direction as well as the magnitude is important, are called *vectors*. It is customary to represent a vector by a directed line segment whose direction represents the direction of the vector and whose length (in terms of some chosen unit of length) represents the magnitude.

The most satisfactory algebra of vectors is based on a representation of each vector in terms of its components parallel to the axes of a Cartesian coordinate system. This is accomplished by using the same unit of length on both the x- and y-axes with unit vectors along these axes used as basic components in terms of which every vector in the plane may be expressed. Thus, in Fig. 12–11, the vector from $(0, 0)$ to $(1, 0)$ is the unit vector i, while j is the unit vector from $(0, 0)$ to $(0, 1)$. Then ai, a being a scalar, represents a vector parallel to the x-axis, having magnitude $|a|$ and pointing to the right if a is positive, to the left if a is negative. Similarly, bj is a vector parallel to the y-axis and having the same sense as j or the opposite sense, according as b is positive or negative.

We shall ordinarily deal with "free vectors," meaning that a vector is free to move about under parallel displacements. We say that two vectors are *equal* provided they have the same direction and the same magnitude. The same condition may be expressed algebraically by saying that

$$a\mathbf{i} + b\mathbf{j} = a'\mathbf{i} + b'\mathbf{j} \quad \text{if and only if} \quad a = a' \text{ and } b = b'.$$

That is, two vectors are equal if and only if their corresponding components are equal. Thus, in Fig. 12–11, the vector $\overrightarrow{AB} = a\mathbf{i}$ and the vector $\overrightarrow{OP}$ from $(0, 0)$ to the point $(a, 0)$ on the x-axis is also equal to $a\mathbf{i}$.

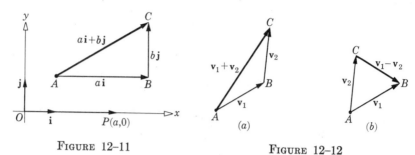

FIGURE 12-11   FIGURE 12-12

Addition. Two vectors, $\mathbf{v}_1$ and $\mathbf{v}_2$ are *added* by drawing a vector $\mathbf{v}_1$, say from A to B in Fig. 12-12(a), and then a vector equal to $\mathbf{v}_2$ starting from the terminal point of $\mathbf{v}_1$; thus $\mathbf{v}_2 = \overrightarrow{BC}$ in Fig. 12-12(a). The sum $\mathbf{v}_1 + \mathbf{v}_2$ is then the vector from the starting point A of $\mathbf{v}_1$ to the terminal point C of $\mathbf{v}_2$:

$$\mathbf{v}_1 = \overrightarrow{AB}, \qquad \mathbf{v}_2 = \overrightarrow{BC},$$

$$\mathbf{v}_1 + \mathbf{v}_2 = \overrightarrow{AB} + \overrightarrow{BC} = \overrightarrow{AC}.$$

If we apply this principle to the vectors $a\mathbf{i}$ and $b\mathbf{j}$ in Fig. 12-11, we see that $a\mathbf{i} + b\mathbf{j}$ is the vector hypotenuse of a right triangle whose vector sides are $a\mathbf{i}$ and $b\mathbf{j}$ respectively. If the vectors $\mathbf{v}_1$ and $\mathbf{v}_2$ are given in terms of components

$$\mathbf{v}_1 = a_1\mathbf{i} + b_1\mathbf{j},$$

$$\mathbf{v}_2 = a_2\mathbf{i} + b_2\mathbf{j},$$

then

$$\boxed{\mathbf{v}_1 + \mathbf{v}_2 = (a_1 + a_2)\mathbf{i} + (b_1 + b_2)\mathbf{j}} \qquad (1)$$

has x- and y-components obtained by adding the x- and y-components of $\mathbf{v}_1$ and $\mathbf{v}_2$.

Subtraction. To *subtract* one vector $\mathbf{v}_2$ from another vector $\mathbf{v}_1$ geometrically, we draw them both from a common initial point and then draw the vector from the tip of $\mathbf{v}_2$ to the tip of $\mathbf{v}_1$. Thus in Fig. 12-12(b), we have

$$\mathbf{v}_1 = \overrightarrow{AB}, \qquad \mathbf{v}_2 = \overrightarrow{AC},$$

and

$$\mathbf{v}_1 - \mathbf{v}_2 = -\mathbf{v}_2 + \mathbf{v}_1 = \overrightarrow{CA} + \overrightarrow{AB} = \overrightarrow{CB}.$$

In terms of components, vector subtraction follows the simple algebraic law

$$\mathbf{v}_1 - \mathbf{v}_2 = (a_1 - a_2)\mathbf{i} + (b_1 - b_2)\mathbf{j},$$

which says that corresponding components are subtracted.

Multiplication by scalars. The algebraic operation of multiplying a vector $\mathbf{v} = a\mathbf{i} + b\mathbf{j}$ by a scalar c is also simple, namely,

$$c(a\mathbf{i} + b\mathbf{j}) = (ca)\mathbf{i} + (cb)\mathbf{j}.$$

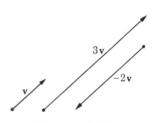

FIGURE 12–13

Geometrically, $c\mathbf{v}$ is a vector whose length is $|c|$ times the length of $\mathbf{v}$ and whose direction is the same as, or opposite to, that of $\mathbf{v}$ respectively according as c is positive or negative. Thus $3\mathbf{v}$ has the same sense as $\mathbf{v}$ and is three times as long; while $-2\mathbf{v}$ is twice as long as $\mathbf{v}$ but is directed in the opposite sense (Fig. 12–13).

The unit vectors **i** and **j** serve the useful purpose of allowing us to keep the components separated from one another when we operate on the vectors algebraically.

The length of the vector $\mathbf{v}$ is usually denoted by $|\mathbf{v}|$, which is read "magnitude of v." Reference to Fig. 12–11 shows that $\mathbf{v} = a\mathbf{i} + b\mathbf{j}$ is the hypotenuse of a right triangle whose legs have lengths $|a|$ and $|b|$ respectively. Hence we may apply the theorem of Pythagoras to obtain

$$|a\mathbf{i} + b\mathbf{j}| = \sqrt{a^2 + b^2}. \qquad (2)$$

Zero vector. Any vector whose length is zero is called the *zero vector*, **0**. The vector

$$a\mathbf{i} + b\mathbf{j} = \mathbf{0}, \qquad \text{if and only if} \qquad a = b = 0.$$

Unit vector. Any vector $\mathbf{u}$ whose length is equal to the unit of length used along the coordinate axes is called a *unit vector*. If $\mathbf{u}$ is a unit vector obtained by rotating the unit vector **i** through an angle θ in the positive direction, then (see Fig. 12–14) $\mathbf{u}$ has a horizontal component

$$u_x = \cos \theta$$

and a vertical component

$$u_y = \sin \theta,$$

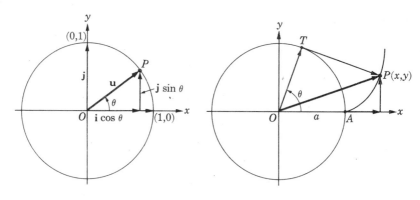

FIGURE 12–14   FIGURE 12–15

so that

$$\mathbf{u} = \mathbf{i} \cos \theta + \mathbf{j} \sin \theta. \qquad (3)$$

If we allow the angle θ in Eq. (3) to vary from 0 to 2π, say, then the point P traces out the unit circle $x^2 + y^2 = 1$ precisely once in the counterclockwise direction.

As an illustration of how vector methods may be applied to problems in geometry, we shall derive parametric equations of the involute of a circle. This is the locus described by the end point P of a string that is held taut as it is unwound from the circle. In Fig. 12–15, the origin is taken at the center of the circle whose radius is a. The x-axis passes through the point A where P started when the string was all wound onto the circle. The figure illustrates the position of P after a length of string

$$TP = \text{arc } AT = a\theta$$

has been unwound. The line TP is drawn tangent to the circle, since the string is held taut as it is unwound. Now the vector from the origin O to the point P is simply

$$\overrightarrow{OP} = \mathbf{i}x + \mathbf{j}y. \qquad (4)$$

On the other hand, the same vector is also given by

$$\overrightarrow{OP} = \overrightarrow{OT} + \overrightarrow{TP}, \qquad (5)$$

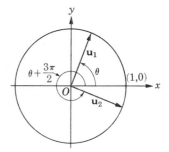

FIGURE 12–16

and if we express the right side in terms of the parameter θ, we may equate the two right sides of (4) and (5) and separate the components to obtain x and y

in terms of θ. Now

$$\overrightarrow{OT} = a\mathbf{u}_1$$

and

$$\overrightarrow{TP} = (a\theta)\mathbf{u}_2,$$

where $\mathbf{u}_1$ and $\mathbf{u}_2$ are unit vectors making angles θ and $\theta + 3\pi/2$ respectively with the x-axis. (See Fig. 12–16.) Then, applying (3), we have

$$\mathbf{u}_1 = \mathbf{i} \cos \theta + \mathbf{j} \sin \theta$$

and

$$\mathbf{u}_2 = \mathbf{i} \cos \left(\theta + \frac{3\pi}{2}\right) + \mathbf{j} \sin \left(\theta + \frac{3\pi}{2}\right)$$

$$= \mathbf{i} \sin \theta - \mathbf{j} \cos \theta.$$

Therefore

$$\overrightarrow{OP} = a\mathbf{u}_1 + (a\theta)\, \mathbf{u}_2$$

$$= a\,(\mathbf{i} \cos \theta + \mathbf{j} \sin \theta) + a\theta(\mathbf{i} \sin \theta - \mathbf{j} \cos \theta)$$

$$= a\,(\cos \theta + \theta \sin \theta)\, \mathbf{i} + a\,(\sin \theta - \theta \cos \theta)\, \mathbf{j}.$$

We equate this to $x\mathbf{i} + y\mathbf{j}$ and, since corresponding components must be equal, we obtain the parametric equations

$$x = a\,(\cos \theta + \theta \sin \theta), \qquad y = a\,(\sin \theta - \theta \cos \theta). \tag{6}$$

Problems

In Problems 1–10 express each of the vectors in the form $a\mathbf{i} + b\mathbf{j}$. Indicate all quantities graphically.

1. $\overrightarrow{P_1P_2}$ if P_1 is the point $(1, 3)$ and P_2 is the point $(2, -1)$.

2. $\overrightarrow{OP_3}$ if O is the origin and P_3 is the mid-point of the vector $\overrightarrow{P_1P_2}$ joining $P_1(2, -1)$ and $P_2(-4, 3)$.

3. The vector from the point $A(2, 3)$ to the origin.

4. The sum of the vectors $\overrightarrow{AB}$ and $\overrightarrow{CD}$, given the four points $A(1, -1)$, $B(2, 0)$, $C(-1, 3)$, and $D(-2, 2)$.

5. A unit vector making an angle of $30°$ with the positive x-axis.

6. The unit vector obtained by rotating $\mathbf{j}$ through $120°$ in the clockwise direction.

7. A unit vector having the same direction as the vector $3\mathbf{i} - 4\mathbf{j}$.

8. A unit vector tangent to the curve $y = x^2$ at the point $(2, 4)$.

9. A unit vector normal to the curve $y = x^2$ at the point $P(2, 4)$ and pointing from P toward the concave side of the curve (that is, an "inner" normal).

10. A unit vector tangent to the involute of a circle whose parametric equations are given in Eq. (6).

Find the lengths of each of the following vectors and the angle that each makes with the positive x-axis.

11. $\mathbf{i} + \mathbf{j}$ 12. $2\mathbf{i} - 3\mathbf{j}$ 13. $\sqrt{3}\,\mathbf{i} + \mathbf{j}$

14. $-2\mathbf{i} + 3\mathbf{j}$ 15. $5\mathbf{i} + 12\mathbf{j}$ 16. $-5\mathbf{i} - 12\mathbf{j}$

17. Use vector methods and determine parametric equations for the trochoid of Fig. 12–6, by taking

$$\mathbf{R} = \overrightarrow{OP} = \overrightarrow{OM} + \overrightarrow{MC} + \overrightarrow{CP}.$$

18. Let A, B, C, D be the vertices, in order, of a quadrilateral. Let A', B', C', D' be the mid-points of the sides AB, BC, CD, and DA, in order. Prove that $A'B'C'D'$ is a parallelogram. [*Hint:* First show that $\overrightarrow{A'B'} = \overrightarrow{D'C'} = \frac{1}{2}\overrightarrow{AC}$.]

19. Using vectors, show that the diagonals of a parallelogram bisect each other. [*Method:* Let A be one vertex and let M and N be the mid-points of the diagonals. Then show that $\overrightarrow{AM} = \overrightarrow{AN}$.]

12–4 Differentiation of vectors. We shall be interested in applications of vectors to problems in physics. For applications to *statics*, we need only a knowledge of the *algebra* of vectors. But for applications to *dynamics*, we also require a knowledge of the *calculus* of vectors.

Position vector. Suppose the point P moves along a curve in the xy-plane and suppose we know its position at any time t. This means that the motion of P is described by a pair of functions f and g:

$$x = f(t), \qquad y = g(t). \tag{1}$$

The vector from the origin to P is customarily called the *position vector* of P, although it might be appropriate to call it the "radar" vector. This vector is a function of t given by

$$\boxed{\mathbf{R} = \mathbf{i}x + \mathbf{j}y} \tag{2a}$$

or

$$\mathbf{R} = \mathbf{i}f(t) + \mathbf{j}g(t). \tag{2b}$$

Velocity vector. We now raise the question as to what we might mean by the *derivative* of $\mathbf{R}$ with respect to t, both mathematically and physically. Mathematically, we would simply *define* the derivative as

$$\frac{d\mathbf{R}}{dt} = \lim_{\Delta t \to 0} \frac{\Delta \mathbf{R}}{\Delta t}, \tag{3}$$

where $\mathbf{R}$ is given by (2a) and

$$\mathbf{R} + \Delta \mathbf{R} = \mathbf{i}(x + \Delta x) + \mathbf{j}(y + \Delta y). \tag{4}$$

Here, $P(x, y)$ represents the position of the particle at time t, while $Q(x + \Delta x, y + \Delta y)$ gives its position at time $t + \Delta t$. By subtracting (2a) from (4), we obtain

$$\Delta \mathbf{R} = \mathbf{i}\, \Delta x + \mathbf{j}\, \Delta y, \tag{5}$$

which is the vector $\overrightarrow{PQ}$ in Fig. 12–17. The remaining calculations needed to give $d\mathbf{R}/dt$ proceed as follows:

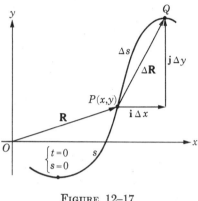

FIGURE 12–17

$$\frac{\Delta \mathbf{R}}{\Delta t} = \mathbf{i}\, \frac{\Delta x}{\Delta t} + \mathbf{j}\, \frac{\Delta y}{\Delta t},$$

$$\lim_{\Delta t \to 0} \frac{\Delta \mathbf{R}}{\Delta t} = \lim_{\Delta t \to 0} \left(\mathbf{i}\, \frac{\Delta x}{\Delta t} + \mathbf{j}\, \frac{\Delta y}{\Delta t} \right)$$

$$= \mathbf{i} \lim_{\Delta t \to 0} \frac{\Delta x}{\Delta t} + \mathbf{j} \lim_{\Delta t \to 0} \frac{\Delta y}{\Delta t},$$

$$\boxed{\frac{d\mathbf{R}}{dt} = \mathbf{i}\, \frac{dx}{dt} + \mathbf{j}\, \frac{dy}{dt}.} \tag{6}$$

The result (6) is equivalent to what would be obtained by differentiating both sides of (2a) with respect to t, holding $\mathbf{i}$ and $\mathbf{j}$ constant. The geometric significance of (6) may be learned by calculating the direction and the magnitude as follows:

$$\text{slope of } \frac{d\mathbf{R}}{dt} = \frac{\text{rise}}{\text{run}} = \frac{dy/dt}{dx/dt} = \frac{dy}{dx},$$

$$\text{magnitude} = \left| \frac{d\mathbf{R}}{dt} \right| = \left| \mathbf{i}\, \frac{dx}{dt} + \mathbf{j}\, \frac{dy}{dt} \right| = \sqrt{\left(\frac{dx}{dt} \right)^2 + \left(\frac{dy}{dt} \right)^2} = \left| \frac{ds}{dt} \right|. \tag{7}$$

Here s represents arc length along the curve measured from some starting point (x_0, y_0).

If we draw a vector equal to $d\mathbf{R}/dt$, placing its initial point at P, the resulting vector will

(a) be tangent to the curve at P, since its slope equals dy/dx, which is the same as the slope of the curve at P, and

(b) have magnitude $= |ds/dt|$, which gives the instantaneous speed of the particle at P.

Thus, physically, the vector $d\mathbf{R}/dt$, when drawn from P, is a suitable representation of the *velocity vector* which has the same two properties (a) and (b).

We may now summarize by saying that if we differentiate the position vector

$$\boxed{\mathbf{R} = \mathbf{i}x + \mathbf{j}y}$$

with respect to time, the result gives the *velocity vector*

$$\boxed{\mathbf{v} = \frac{d\mathbf{R}}{dt} = \mathbf{i}\frac{dx}{dt} + \mathbf{j}\frac{dy}{dt}\,.}$$

It is customary to think of the velocity vector as being drawn at the point P.

Acceleration. The acceleration vector $\mathbf{a}$ is obtained from $\mathbf{v}$ by a further differentiation:

$$\boxed{\mathbf{a} = \frac{d\mathbf{v}}{dt} = \mathbf{i}\frac{d^2x}{dt^2} + \mathbf{j}\frac{d^2y}{dt^2}\,.} \tag{8}$$

For a particle of constant mass m moving under the action of an applied force $\mathbf{F}$, Newton's second law of motion states that

$$\mathbf{F} = m\mathbf{a}. \tag{9}$$

Since one ordinarily visualizes the force vector as being *applied at P*, it is customary to adopt the same viewpoint about the acceleration vector $\mathbf{a}$.

EXAMPLE 1. A particle $P(x, y)$ moves on the hyperbola

$$x = r\cosh \omega t, \quad y = r\sinh \omega t, \tag{10}$$

where r and ω are positive constants. Then

$$\mathbf{R} = \mathbf{i}(r\cosh \omega t) + \mathbf{j}(r\sinh \omega t),$$

$$\mathbf{v} = \frac{d\mathbf{R}}{dt} = \mathbf{i}(\omega r\sinh \omega t) + \mathbf{j}(\omega r\cosh \omega t)$$

and

$$\mathbf{a} = \mathbf{i}(\omega^2 r\cosh \omega t) + \mathbf{j}(\omega^2 r\sinh \omega t)$$

$$= \omega^2\mathbf{R}.$$

This means that the force $\mathbf{F} = m\mathbf{a} = m\omega^2\mathbf{R}$ has a magnitude $m\omega^2|\mathbf{R}| = m\omega^2|\overrightarrow{OP}|$ which is directly proportional to the distance OP, and that its direction is the same as the direction of $\mathbf{R}$. Thus the force is directed away from O (Fig. 12–18).

The next example illustrates how we obtain the path of motion by integrating Eq. (9) when the force $\mathbf{F}$ is a given function of time and the

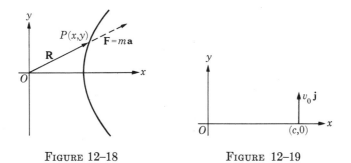

FIGURE 12–18   FIGURE 12–19

initial position and initial velocity of the particle are given. In general, the force **F** may depend upon the position of P as well as upon the time and the problem of integrating the differential equations so obtained is usually discussed in textbooks on that subject. [For example, see Martin and Reissner, *Elementary Differential Equations*, Addison-Wesley Publishing Company (1956).]

EXAMPLE 2. (Fig. 12–19.) The force acting on a particle P of mass m is given as a function of t by

$$\mathbf{F} = \mathbf{i}\cos t + \mathbf{j}\sin t.$$

If the particle starts at the point $(c, 0)$ with initial velocity $v_0\mathbf{j}$ perpendicular to the x-axis, find the curve it describes.

Solution. If we denote the position vector by

$$\mathbf{R} = \mathbf{i}x + \mathbf{j}y,$$

we may restate the problem as follows. Find **R** if

$$\mathbf{F} = m\frac{d^2\mathbf{R}}{dt^2} = \mathbf{i}\cos t + \mathbf{j}\sin t \tag{11}$$

and

$$\text{at } t = 0: \quad \mathbf{R} = \mathbf{i}c, \quad \frac{d\mathbf{R}}{dt} = \mathbf{j}v_0. \tag{12}$$

In (11) we let $\mathbf{v} = d\mathbf{R}/dt$, and separate the variables to obtain

$$m\,d\mathbf{v} = (\mathbf{i}\cos t + \mathbf{j}\sin t)\,dt.$$

Integrating this, we have

$$m\mathbf{v} = m\frac{d\mathbf{R}}{dt} = \mathbf{i}\sin t - \mathbf{j}\cos t + \mathbf{C}_1, \tag{13}$$

where the constant of integration is a *vector* denoted by $\mathbf{C}_1$. The value of $\mathbf{C}_1$

may be found by using the initial velocity, (12_2), in (13) with $t = 0$:

$$m\mathbf{j}v_0 = -\mathbf{j} + \mathbf{C}_1,$$

$$\mathbf{C}_1 = (mv_0 + 1)\mathbf{j}.$$

Substituting this into (13), we have

$$m\frac{d\mathbf{R}}{dt} = \mathbf{i}\sin t + (mv_0 + 1 - \cos t)\mathbf{j}.$$

Another integration gives

$$m\mathbf{R} = -\mathbf{i}\cos t + \mathbf{j}(mv_0t + t - \sin t) + \mathbf{C}_2.$$

The initial condition (12_1) enables us to evaluate $\mathbf{C}_2$:

$$mc\mathbf{i} = -\mathbf{i} + \mathbf{C}_2, \qquad \mathbf{C}_2 = \mathbf{i}(mc + 1),$$

so that the position vector $\mathbf{R}$ is given by

$$\mathbf{R} = \frac{1}{m}[\mathbf{i}(mc + 1 - \cos t) + \mathbf{j}(mv_0t + t - \sin t)].$$

The parametric equations of the curve are found by equating components of the above equation and

$$\mathbf{R} = \mathbf{i}x + \mathbf{j}y,$$

which gives

$$x = c + \frac{1 - \cos t}{m}, \qquad y = v_0t + \frac{t - \sin t}{m}.$$

PROBLEMS

In Problems 1–8, $\mathbf{R} = \mathbf{i}x + \mathbf{j}y$ is the vector from the origin to the moving point $P(x, y)$ at time t. Find the velocity and acceleration vectors for any t. Also find these vectors and the speed at the particular instant given.

1. $\mathbf{R} = (a \cos \omega t)\mathbf{i} + (a \sin \omega t)\mathbf{j}$, a and ω being positive constants; $t = \pi/(3\omega)$.
2. $\mathbf{R} = (2 \cos t)\mathbf{i} + (3 \sin t)\mathbf{j}$, $\quad t = \pi/4$
3. $\mathbf{R} = (t + 1)\mathbf{i} + (t^2 - 1)\mathbf{j}$, $\quad t = 2$
4. $\mathbf{R} = (\cos 2t)\mathbf{i} + (2 \sin t)\mathbf{j}$, $\quad t = 0$
5. $\mathbf{R} = e^t\mathbf{i} + e^{-2t}\mathbf{j}$, $\quad t = \ln 3$
6. $\mathbf{R} = (\sec t)\mathbf{i} + (\tan t)\mathbf{j}$, $\quad t = \pi/6$
7. $\mathbf{R} = (\cosh 3t)\mathbf{i} + (2 \sinh t)\mathbf{j}$, $t = 0$
8. $\mathbf{R} = [\ln (t + 1)]\mathbf{i} + t^2\mathbf{j}$, $\quad t = 1$

9. If the force that acts on a particle P of mass m is

$$\mathbf{F} = -mg\mathbf{j},$$

where m and g are constants, and the particle starts from the origin with velocity

$$\mathbf{v_0} = (v_0 \cos \alpha)\mathbf{i} + (v_0 \sin \alpha)\mathbf{j}$$

at time $t = 0$, find the vector $\mathbf{R} = \mathbf{i}x + \mathbf{j}y$ from the origin to P at time t.

10. Problem 9 describes the motion of a projectile in vacuo. If the projectile encounters a resistance proportional to the velocity, the force is

$$\mathbf{F} = -mg\mathbf{j} - k\frac{d\mathbf{R}}{dt}.$$

Show that one integration of $\mathbf{F} = md^2\mathbf{R}/dt^2$ leads to the differential equation

$$\frac{d\mathbf{R}}{dt} + \frac{k}{m}\mathbf{R} = \mathbf{v_0} - gt\mathbf{j}.$$

(This differential equation can in turn be integrated by means of the following device: multiply both sides of the equation by $e^{(k/m)t}$. Then the left side is the derivative of the product $\mathbf{R}e^{(k/m)t}$ and both sides can be integrated.)

12–5 Tangential vectors. As the point P moves along a given curve in the xy-plane, we may imagine its position as being specified by the length of arc s from some arbitrarily chosen reference point P_0 on the curve. The vector

$$\mathbf{R} = \mathbf{i}x + \mathbf{j}y$$

from O to $P(x, y)$ is therefore a function of s and we shall now investigate the properties of $d\mathbf{R}/ds$. To this end, let P have coordinates (x, y) corresponding to the value s, while $Q(x + \Delta x, y + \Delta y)$ corresponds to $s + \Delta s$. Then

$$\frac{\Delta \mathbf{R}}{\Delta s} = \mathbf{i}\frac{\Delta x}{\Delta s} + \mathbf{j}\frac{\Delta y}{\Delta s} = \frac{\overrightarrow{PQ}}{\Delta s} \tag{1}$$

is a *vector* whose magnitude is chord PQ divided by arc PQ, and this approaches unity as $\Delta s \to 0$. Hence

$$\frac{d\mathbf{R}}{ds} = \lim_{\Delta s \to 0} \frac{\Delta \mathbf{R}}{\Delta s} \tag{2}$$

is a *unit* vector. The *direction* of this unit vector is the limiting direction approached by the direction of $\Delta \mathbf{R}/\Delta s$ as $\Delta s \to 0$. Now

$$\frac{\Delta \mathbf{R}}{\Delta s} = \frac{\overrightarrow{PQ}}{\Delta s}$$

has the same direction as $\overrightarrow{PQ}$ in case (a) when Δs is positive, or else it has the same direction as $\overrightarrow{QP}$ in case (b) when Δs is negative. Figures 12–20(a) and (b) illustrate these two cases and show that in *either* case,

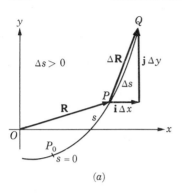

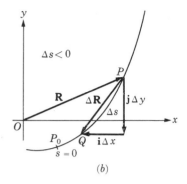

FIGURE 12-20

$\Delta R/\Delta s$ is directed along the chord through P and Q and points in the direction of increasing s (that is, upward to the right in both figures). As $\Delta s \to 0$ and $Q \to P$, the direction of the chord through P and Q approaches the direction of the *tangent* to the curve at P. Thus the limiting direction of $\Delta R/\Delta s$, in other words the *direction of* dR/ds, is along the *tangent to the curve at* P and its sense is that which points in the direction of increasing arc length s (that is, away from P_0 when s is positive, or toward P_0 when s is negative).

That is,

$$\boxed{\frac{dR}{ds} = T} \tag{3}$$

is a *unit vector, tangent to the curve at* P (Fig. 12–21).

If we let $\Delta s \to 0$ in Eq. (1), we find that

$$\boxed{\frac{dR}{ds} = i\,\frac{dx}{ds} + j\,\frac{dy}{ds}} \tag{4}$$

and this may be used to find T at any point of a curve whose equation is given.

EXAMPLE. (Fig. 12–22.) Find the unit vector T tangent to the circle

$$x = a \cos \theta,$$

$$y = a \sin \theta,$$

at any point $P(x, y)$.

Solution. From the equations of the curve,

$$dx = -a \sin \theta\, d\theta, \qquad dy = a \cos \theta\, d\theta,$$

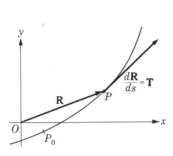

FIGURE 12–21

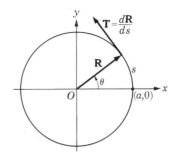

FIGURE 12–22

and

$$ds^2 = dx^2 + dy^2 = a^2 (\sin^2 \theta + \cos^2 \theta)\, d\theta^2 = a^2\, d\theta^2,$$

so that

$$ds = \pm a\, d\theta.$$

If we measure arc length in the counterclockwise direction, with $s = 0$ at $(a,\, 0)$, s will be an increasing function of θ, so that the $+$ sign should be taken:

$$ds = a\, d\theta.$$

Then

$$\mathbf{T} = \frac{d\mathbf{R}}{ds} = \mathbf{i}\, \frac{dx}{ds} + \mathbf{j}\, \frac{dy}{ds} = \mathbf{i} \left(\frac{-a \sin \theta\, d\theta}{a\, d\theta} \right) + \mathbf{j} \left(\frac{a \cos \theta\, d\theta}{a\, d\theta} \right)$$

$$= -\mathbf{i} \sin \theta + \mathbf{j} \cos \theta.$$

PROBLEMS

In each of the following problems (1 through 5), $\mathbf{R} = \mathbf{i}x + \mathbf{j}y$ is the vector from the origin O to $P(x,\, y)$. For each of these motions, find the unit tangent vector $\mathbf{T} = d\mathbf{R}/ds$.

1. $\mathbf{R} = 2\mathbf{i} \cos t + 2\mathbf{j} \sin t$ 2. $\mathbf{R} = e^t\mathbf{i} + t^2\mathbf{j}$

3. $\mathbf{R} = (\cos^3 t)\mathbf{i} + (\sin^3 t)\mathbf{j}$ 4. $\mathbf{R} = \mathbf{i}x + \mathbf{j}x^2$

5. $\mathbf{R} = (\cos 2t)\mathbf{i} + (2 \cos t)\mathbf{j}$

12–6 Curvature and normal vectors. Our next step is to consider the rate of change of the unit tangent vector $\mathbf{T}$ as P moves along the curve. Of course the length of $\mathbf{T}$ is constant, always being equal to unity. But the direction of $\mathbf{T}$ changes, since it is tangent to the curve and this tangent changes direction from point to point unless the curve is a straight line.

We may specify the direction of $\mathbf{T}$ by means of the angle ϕ from the x-axis to $\mathbf{T}$ (Fig. 12–23). The instantaneous rate of change of this slope

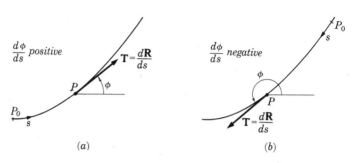

FIGURE 12–23

angle ϕ with respect to arc length s (measured in radians per unit of length) is taken as the mathematical *definition of the curvature* of the curve at P. The Greek letter κ (kappa) is used to denote curvature, and its definition is given by the equation

$$\kappa = \frac{d\phi}{ds}, \tag{1}$$

where

$$\tan \phi = \frac{dy}{dx}$$

and

$$ds = \pm\sqrt{dx^2 + dy^2}.$$

One may derive a formula for κ from the equations above in a straightforward manner. Namely,

$$\phi = \tan^{-1} \frac{dy}{dx},$$

$$\frac{d\phi}{dx} = \frac{\dfrac{d^2y}{dx^2}}{1 + \left(\dfrac{dy}{dx}\right)^2},$$

and

$$\frac{ds}{dx} = \pm \sqrt{1 + \left(\frac{dy}{dx}\right)^2},$$

so that

$$\kappa = \frac{d\phi}{ds} = \frac{d\phi/dx}{ds/dx} = \frac{\pm \dfrac{d^2y}{dx^2}}{\left[1 + \left(\dfrac{dy}{dx}\right)^2\right]^{3/2}}. \tag{2a}$$

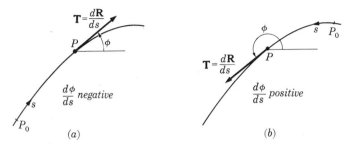

FIGURE 12–24

The ambiguous sign in (2a) is plus if ds/dx is positive, that is, if s increases as we move along the curve from left to right (as on the lower half of the circle in Fig. 12–22). But the ambiguous sign is minus if ds/dx is negative (as on the upper half of the circle in Fig. 12–22).

It is desirable for our purposes to have κ carry the same sign as $d\phi/ds$; hence we shall need to keep the ambiguous sign in Eq. (2a), subject to the discussion above. The sign of $d\phi/ds$ depends, of course, upon whether ϕ increases or decreases as s increases. Geometric considerations (Figs. 12–23 and 12–24) show that

κ is positive if the concave side of the curve lies on our left and

κ is negative if the concave side of the curve lies on our right,

as we "walk" along the curve in the direction of increasing s.

In Fig. 12–23(a), we indicate that s increases as we go from left to right along the curve. If we go from P to a nearby point P' to the right of P (corresponding to a positive Δs), we see that the tangent at P' is steeper than at P; hence $\Delta\phi$ is also positive, so that

$$d\phi/ds = \lim_{\Delta s \to 0} (\Delta\phi/\Delta s)$$

is positive at P. We also see that the concave side of the curve is on our left as we travel along the curve in the direction indicated.

A similar analysis of the situation illustrated by Fig. 12–23(b) leads to the conclusion that $d\phi/ds$ is negative at P, since a small increase in s causes a decrease in ϕ. In this case, κ is negative and the concave side of the curve is on our right as we go along the curve in the direction of increasing s.

Finally, the two cases illustrated in Fig. 12–24(a) and (b) show that the geometric interpretation of the sign of κ which was given above holds valid in every case. It should be pointed out that some writers take the sign of κ to be the same as the sign of d^2y/dx^2, which corresponds to assuming that ds/dx is positive.

We may arrive at a formula for κ in terms of dx/dy and d^2x/dy^2 if we use

$$\phi = \cot^{-1}\frac{dx}{dy}$$

and

$$\kappa = \frac{d\phi}{ds} = \frac{d\phi/dy}{ds/dy}.$$

The result, which corresponds to (2a), is

$$\kappa = \frac{\pm\dfrac{d^2x}{dy^2}}{\left[1+\left(\dfrac{dx}{dy}\right)^2\right]^{3/2}}. \tag{2b}$$

If the equation of the curve is given in parametric form,

$$x = f(t), \qquad y = g(t),$$

then

$$\phi = \tan^{-1}\left(\frac{dy/dt}{dx/dt}\right),$$

and if we use

$$\kappa = \frac{d\phi/dt}{ds/dt},$$

the calculations are as follows:

$$\frac{d\phi}{dt} = \frac{1}{1+\left(\dfrac{dy/dt}{dx/dt}\right)^2}\frac{\dfrac{dx}{dt}\dfrac{d^2y}{dt^2}-\dfrac{dy}{dt}\dfrac{d^2x}{dt^2}}{\left(\dfrac{dx}{dt}\right)^2} = \frac{\dot{x}\ddot{y}-\dot{y}\ddot{x}}{\dot{x}^2+\dot{y}^2}\left[\dot{x}=\frac{dx}{dt},\ \ddot{x}=\frac{d^2x}{dt^2}\right]$$

and

$$\frac{ds}{dt} = \pm\sqrt{\dot{x}^2+\dot{y}^2},$$

so that

$$\kappa = \pm\frac{\dot{x}\ddot{y}-\dot{y}\ddot{x}}{[\dot{x}^2+\dot{y}^2]^{3/2}}. \tag{2c}$$

On a straight line, ϕ is constant, so $d\phi/ds$ is zero and Eq. (2a) says that *the curvature of a straight line is zero.*

If we apply (2), or (1), to a circle of radius a, we find that the curvature

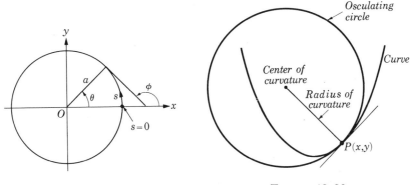

FIGURE 12–25 FIGURE 12–26

of a circle is constant in magnitude. In fact, we see from Fig. 12–25 that both s and ϕ may be expressed in terms of the angle θ as follows:

$$s = a\theta, \qquad \phi = \theta + \frac{\pi}{2}, \tag{3}$$

so that

$$\kappa = \frac{d\phi}{ds} = \frac{d\theta}{a\,d\theta} = \frac{1}{a}.$$

That is, the curvature of a circle traversed in the positive direction is equal to the reciprocal of its radius. The smaller the circle, the greater its curvature. "Turning around on a dime" indicates a more rapid change of direction per unit of arc length than does turning around on a silver dollar!

Circle and radius of curvature. The circle that is tangent to a given curve at P, whose center lies on the concave side of the curve and that has the same curvature as the curve has at P, is called the *circle of curvature.* Its radius is $1/|\kappa|$. We define the *radius of curvature* at P to be $|\rho|$, where

$$\rho = \frac{1}{\kappa} = \frac{\left[1 + \left(\dfrac{dy}{dx}\right)^2\right]^{3/2}}{\pm \dfrac{d^2y}{dx^2}}. \tag{4}$$

As we have defined it, ρ has the same sign as κ. The center of the circle of curvature is called the center of curvature. The circle of curvature has its first and second derivatives equal respectively to the first and second derivatives of the curve itself at this point. For this reason it has a higher degree of contact with the curve at P than has any other circle, so it is also called the *osculating* circle! (See Fig. 12–26.) Since velocity

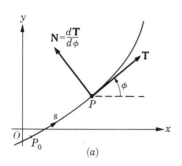
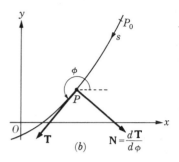

FIGURE 12–27

and acceleration involve only the first and second time derivatives of the coordinates of P, it is natural to anticipate that the instantaneous velocity and acceleration of a particle moving on any curve may be expressed in terms of instantaneous velocity and acceleration of an associated particle moving on the osculating circle. This will be investigated in the next article.

Unit normal vector. We return once more to the question of the rate of change of the unit vector $\mathbf{T}$ as P moves along the curve. In terms of the slope angle ϕ (Fig. 12–27), we may write

$$\mathbf{T} = \mathbf{i} \cos \phi + \mathbf{j} \sin \phi, \tag{5}$$

and then the derivative

$$\frac{d\mathbf{T}}{d\phi} = -\mathbf{i} \sin \phi + \mathbf{j} \cos \phi \tag{6}$$

has magnitude

$$\left|\frac{d\mathbf{T}}{d\phi}\right| = \sqrt{\sin^2 \phi + \cos^2 \phi} = 1.$$

Its slope is

$$\frac{\cos \phi}{-\sin \phi} = \frac{-1}{\tan \phi},$$

which is the negative reciprocal of the slope of $\mathbf{T}$. Therefore $d\mathbf{T}/d\phi$ is perpendicular to $\mathbf{T}$. In fact, we see from Eq. (6) that

$$\boxed{\frac{d\mathbf{T}}{d\phi} = \mathbf{N},} \tag{7}$$

where $\mathbf{N}$ is the *unit normal* vector obtained by rotating the unit tangent vector $\mathbf{T}$ through 90° in the counterclockwise direction, since

$$\mathbf{N} = \mathbf{i} \cos (\phi + 90°) + \mathbf{j} \sin (\phi + 90°) = -\mathbf{i} \sin \phi + \mathbf{j} \cos \phi.$$

If we combine Eqs. (7) and (1), we have

$$\frac{d\mathbf{T}}{ds} = \frac{d\mathbf{T}}{d\phi}\frac{d\phi}{ds} = \mathbf{N}\kappa. \tag{8}$$

We observe in passing that whether κ is positive or negative, $\mathbf{N}\kappa$ is always directed toward the concave side of the curve. (See Figs. 12–23, 12–24, 12–27.)

PROBLEMS

Find the curvature of each of the curves in the following problems (1 through 9).

1. $y = a \cosh (x/a)$ 2. $y = \ln (\cos x)$

3. $y = e^{2x}$ 4. $x = a \cos^3 t, \quad y = a \sin^3 t$

5. $x = a (\cos \theta + \theta \sin \theta),$ 6. $x = a(\theta - \sin \theta),$

   $y = a (\sin \theta - \theta \cos \theta)$ $y = a(1 - \cos \theta)$

7. $x = \ln \sec y$ 8. $x = \frac{1}{3}(y^2 + 2)^{3/2}$

9. $x = \dfrac{y^4}{4} + \dfrac{1}{8y^2}$

10. Find the equation of the osculating circle associated with the curve $y = e^x$ at the point $(0, 1)$. By calculating dy/dx and d^2y/dx^2 at the point $(0, 1)$ from the equation of this circle, verify that these derivatives have the same values there as do the corresponding derivatives for the curve $y = e^x$. Sketch the curve and the osculating circle.

11. Show that when x and y are considered as functions of arc length s, the unit vectors $\mathbf{T}$ and $\mathbf{N}$ may be expressed as follows:

$$\mathbf{T} = \mathbf{i}\frac{dx}{ds} + \mathbf{j}\frac{dy}{ds}, \qquad \mathbf{N} = -\mathbf{i}\frac{dy}{ds} + \mathbf{j}\frac{dx}{ds},$$

where $dx/ds = \cos \phi$, $dy/ds = \sin \phi$, and ϕ is the angle from the positive x-axis to the tangent line.

12–7 Tangential and normal components of the velocity and acceleration vectors.

In mechanics it is useful to be able to discuss the motion of a particle P in terms of its instantaneous speed ds/dt, acceleration along its path d^2s/dt^2, and the curvature of the path. This is easy if we refer the velocity and acceleration vectors to the unit vectors $\mathbf{T}$ and $\mathbf{N}$, rather than using horizontal and vertical components.

In Article 12–4 we found the velocity vector to be given by

$$\mathbf{v} = \frac{d\mathbf{R}}{dt}, \tag{1}$$

where $\mathbf{R} = \mathbf{i}x + \mathbf{j}y$ is the position vector $\overrightarrow{OP}$. We may also write this in the form

$$\mathbf{v} = \frac{d\mathbf{R}}{dt} = \frac{d\mathbf{R}}{ds}\frac{ds}{dt}$$

or

$$\mathbf{v} = \mathbf{T}\frac{ds}{dt} \qquad (2)$$

if we use the result of Eq. (3), Article 12–5. This is in keeping with our earlier remark that the velocity vector is tangent to the curve and has magnitude $|ds/dt|$. (See Fig. 12–28.)

To obtain the acceleration vector, we differentiate Eq. (2) with respect to t:

$$\mathbf{a} = \frac{d\mathbf{v}}{dt} = \mathbf{T}\frac{d^2s}{dt^2} + \frac{ds}{dt}\frac{d\mathbf{T}}{dt}.$$

By Eq. (8), Article 12–6,

$$\frac{d\mathbf{T}}{dt} = \frac{d\mathbf{T}}{ds}\frac{ds}{dt} = \mathbf{N}\kappa\frac{ds}{dt},$$

so that

$$\mathbf{a} = \mathbf{T}\frac{d^2s}{dt^2} + \mathbf{N}\kappa\left(\frac{ds}{dt}\right)^2. \qquad (3)$$

Equation (3) expresses the acceleration vector in terms of its tangential and normal components. The *tangential component*, d^2s/dt^2, is simply the derivative of the speed ds/dt of the particle in its path. The *normal component* is directed toward the concave side of the curve and has magnitude

$$|\kappa|\left(\frac{ds}{dt}\right)^2 = \frac{(ds/dt)^2}{|\rho|} = \frac{v^2}{|\rho|},$$

where v is the instantaneous speed of the particle and $|\rho|$ is the radius of curvature of the path at the point in question. This explains why a large normal force, which must be supplied by friction between the tires and the roadway, is required to hold an automobile on a level road if it makes a sharp turn (small $|\rho|$) or a moderate turn at high speed (large v^2). (See Sears: *Mechanics*, p. 187, for a discussion of the banking of curves.)

If the particle is moving in a circle with *constant* speed $v = ds/dt$, then d^2s/dt^2 is zero, and the only acceleration is the normal acceleration v^2/ρ toward the center of the circle. If the speed is not constant, the acceleration vector $\mathbf{a}$ is the resultant of the tangential and normal components, as in Fig. 12–29.

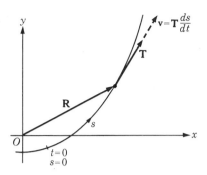

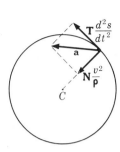

FIGURE 12–28   FIGURE 12–29

The following example illustrates how the tangential and normal components of velocity and acceleration may be computed when the equations of motion are known. In particular, it should be noted that the equation

$$|\mathbf{a}|^2 = a_x^2 + a_y^2 = a_T^2 + a_N^2 \tag{4}$$

is used to determine the normal component of acceleration

$$a_N = \sqrt{|\mathbf{a}|^2 - a_T^2}. \tag{5}$$

EXAMPLE. The coordinates of a moving particle at time t are given by

$$x = \cos t + t \sin t, \qquad y = \sin t - t \cos t.$$

Then

$$\mathbf{v} = \mathbf{i}\frac{dx}{dt} + \mathbf{j}\frac{dy}{dt} = \mathbf{i}[-\sin t + t \cos t + \sin t] + \mathbf{j}[\cos t + t \sin t - \cos t]$$

$$= \mathbf{i}t \cos t + \mathbf{j}t \sin t$$

and

$$\mathbf{a} = \frac{d\mathbf{v}}{dt} = \mathbf{i}[-t \sin t + \cos t] + \mathbf{j}[t \cos t + \sin t].$$

Now the tangential component of velocity is

$$\frac{ds}{dt} = |\mathbf{v}| = \sqrt{(t \cos t)^2 + (t \sin t)^2} = t$$

and the tangential component of acceleration is

$$a_T = \frac{d^2 s}{dt^2} = \frac{d}{dt}\left(\frac{ds}{dt}\right) = \frac{d}{dt}(t) = 1.$$

We use Eq. (5) to determine the normal component of acceleration:

$$a_N = \sqrt{|\mathbf{a}|^2 - a_T^2} = \sqrt{(-t \sin t + \cos t)^2 + (t \cos t + \sin t)^2 - 1} = t.$$

Here the tangential acceleration has constant magnitude and the normal acceleration starts with zero magnitude at $t = 0$ and increases with time. The equations of motion are the same as the parametric equations for the involute of a circle of unit radius with $\theta = t$. (See Figs. 12–15, 12–30.) We could also readily find the radius of curvature without any complicated calculations from the equation

$$a_N = \frac{v^2}{\rho},$$

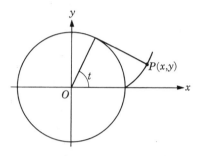

since $v^2 = |\mathbf{v}|^2 = t^2$ and $a_N = t$, hence

$$\rho = \frac{v^2}{a_N} = \frac{t^2}{t} = t.$$

FIGURE 12–30

PROBLEMS

1. With the book closed, derive vector expressions for the velocity and acceleration in terms of tangential and normal components. Check your derivations with those given in the text.

In each of the following problems (2 through 6), find the velocity and acceleration vectors, then find the speed ds/dt and the tangential and normal components of acceleration.

2. $\mathbf{R} = \mathbf{i} \cosh 2t + \mathbf{j} \sinh 2t$ 3. $\mathbf{R} = (2t + 3)\mathbf{i} + (t^2 - 1)\mathbf{j}$

4. $\mathbf{R} = a \cos \omega t \, \mathbf{i} + a \sin \omega t \, \mathbf{j}$,   5. $\mathbf{R} = \mathbf{i} \ln (t^2 + 1) + \mathbf{j}(t - 2 \tan^{-1} t)$
    a and ω positive constants   6. $\mathbf{R} = \mathbf{i} e^t \cos t + \mathbf{j} e^t \sin t$

7. Deduce from Eq. (3) that a particle will move in a straight line if the normal component of acceleration is zero.

8. Show that the radius of curvature is given by the formula

$$\rho = \frac{\pm(\dot{x}^2 + \dot{y}^2)}{\sqrt{\ddot{x}^2 + \ddot{y}^2 - \ddot{s}^2}},$$

where

$$\dot{x} = \frac{dx}{dt}, \quad \ddot{x} = \frac{d^2x}{dt^2}, \text{ etc.,} \quad \text{and} \quad \ddot{s} = \frac{d}{dt}\left(\sqrt{\dot{x}^2 + \dot{y}^2}\right).$$

9. If a particle moves in a curve with constant speed, show that the force is always directed along the normal.

10. If the force acting on a particle is at all times perpendicular to the direction of motion, show that the speed remains constant.

12–8 Polar coordinates. If the particle P moves on a curve whose equation is given in polar coordinates, it is convenient to express the velocity and acceleration vectors in terms of still a third set of unit vectors. We introduce **unit vectors**

$$\mathbf{u}_r = \mathbf{i} \cos \theta + \mathbf{j} \sin \theta, \qquad \mathbf{u}_\theta = -\mathbf{i} \sin \theta + \mathbf{j} \cos \theta, \tag{1}$$

that point respectively along the radius vector $\overrightarrow{OP}$ and at right angles to $\overrightarrow{OP}$ and in the direction of increasing θ, as shown in Fig. 12–31. Then, from (1), we find

$$\frac{d\mathbf{u}_r}{d\theta} = -\mathbf{i} \sin \theta + \mathbf{j} \cos \theta = \mathbf{u}_\theta,$$

$$\frac{d\mathbf{u}_\theta}{d\theta} = -\mathbf{i} \cos \theta - \mathbf{j} \sin \theta = -\mathbf{u}_r. \tag{2}$$

This says that the result of differentiating either one of the unit vectors $\mathbf{u}_r$ or $\mathbf{u}_\theta$ with respect to θ is equivalent to rotating that vector through 90° in the positive (counterclockwise) direction.

Since the vectors $\mathbf{R} = \overrightarrow{OP}$ and $r\mathbf{u}_r$ have the same direction, and the length of $\mathbf{R}$ is the absolute value of the polar coordinate r of $P(r, \theta)$, we have

$$\mathbf{R} = r\mathbf{u}_r. \tag{3}$$

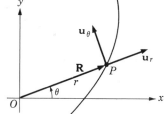

FIGURE 12–31

To obtain the velocity, we must differentiate this with respect to t, remembering that both r and $\mathbf{u}_r$ may be variables. From (2) it is clear that

$$\frac{d\mathbf{u}_r}{dt} = \frac{d\mathbf{u}_r}{d\theta}\frac{d\theta}{dt} = \mathbf{u}_\theta \frac{d\theta}{dt}, \qquad \frac{d\mathbf{u}_\theta}{dt} = \frac{d\mathbf{u}_\theta}{d\theta}\frac{d\theta}{dt} = -\mathbf{u}_r \frac{d\theta}{dt}. \tag{4}$$

Hence,

$$\mathbf{v} = \frac{d\mathbf{R}}{dt} = \mathbf{u}_r \frac{dr}{dt} + r \frac{d\mathbf{u}_r}{dt}$$

becomes

$$\mathbf{v} = \mathbf{u}_r \frac{dr}{dt} + \mathbf{u}_\theta r \frac{d\theta}{dt}. \tag{5}$$

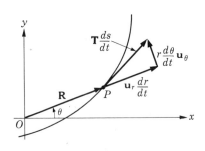

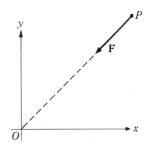

FIGURE 12–32   FIGURE 12–33

Of course this velocity vector is tangent to the curve at P and has magnitude

$$|\mathbf{v}| = \sqrt{(dr/dt)^2 + r^2(d\theta/dt)^2} = |ds/dt| .$$

In fact, if the three sides of the "differential triangle" of sides dr, $r\,d\theta$, and ds are all divided by dt (Fig. 12–32), the result will be a similar triangle having sides dr/dt, $r\,d\theta/dt$, and ds/dt, which illustrates the vector equation

$$\mathbf{v} = \mathbf{T}\,\frac{ds}{dt} = \mathbf{u}_r\,\frac{dr}{dt} + \mathbf{u}_\theta r\,\frac{d\theta}{dt}\,.$$

The acceleration vector is found by differentiating the velocity vector in (5) as follows:

$$\mathbf{a} = \frac{d\mathbf{v}}{dt} = \left(\mathbf{u}_r\,\frac{d^2r}{dt^2} + \frac{dr}{dt}\,\frac{d\mathbf{u}_r}{dt}\right) + \left(\mathbf{u}_\theta r\,\frac{d^2\theta}{dt^2} + \mathbf{u}_\theta\,\frac{dr}{dt}\,\frac{d\theta}{dt} + \frac{d\mathbf{u}_\theta}{dt}\,r\,\frac{d\theta}{dt}\right).$$

When Eqs. (4) are used to evaluate the derivatives of $\mathbf{u}_r$ and $\mathbf{u}_\theta$ and the components are separated, the result becomes

$$\mathbf{a} = \mathbf{u}_r\left[\frac{d^2r}{dt^2} - r\left(\frac{d\theta}{dt}\right)^2\right] + \mathbf{u}_\theta\left[r\,\frac{d^2\theta}{dt^2} + 2\,\frac{dr}{dt}\,\frac{d\theta}{dt}\right]. \tag{6}$$

The polar form is particularly convenient in discussing the motion of a particle in what is called a "central force field." By this we mean that the force acting on the particle is always directed toward a single point, the center of force, which we choose as origin (Fig. 12–33). Then from $\mathbf{F} = m\mathbf{a}$, we see that the $\mathbf{u}_\theta$ component of acceleration must vanish. That is, in any central force field

$$r\,\frac{d^2\theta}{dt^2} + 2\,\frac{dr}{dt}\,\frac{d\theta}{dt} = 0 \tag{7}$$

where the origin is at the center of force. (For instance, the sun would be chosen as the origin in discussing the gravitational attraction between the sun and a planet.) To integrate the differential equation (7), let

$$u = \frac{d\theta}{dt};$$

then

$$r \frac{du}{dt} + 2u \frac{dr}{dt} = 0$$

or

$$r \, du = -2u \, dr, \qquad \frac{du}{u} = -2 \frac{dr}{r},$$

$$\ln |u| = -2 \ln |r| + c_1,$$

$$\ln |ur^2| = c_1, \qquad |ur^2| = e^{c_1} = C,$$

or

$$r^2 \frac{d\theta}{dt} = \pm C. \tag{8}$$

We recognize the left side of this equation as $2 \, dA/dt$, where $dA = \frac{1}{2} r^2 \, d\theta$ is the area swept over as the radius vector $\overrightarrow{OP}$ rotates through a small angle $d\theta$. Hence, Eq. (8) says that the radius vector *sweeps over area at a constant rate* in a central force field. This is Kepler's second law of planetary motion, and it is thus seen to be a consequence of the fact that the field of gravitational attraction of the sun for the planets is a central force field.

Problems

1. With the book closed, derive vector expressions for the velocity and acceleration in terms of components along and at right angles to the radius vector. Check your derivations with those given in the text.

In Problems 2–6, find the velocity and acceleration vectors in terms of the unit vectors $\mathbf{u}_r$ and $\mathbf{u}_\theta$ if:

2. $r = a(1 - \cos \theta)$ and $\dfrac{d\theta}{dt} = 3$ 3. $r = a \sin 2\theta$ and $\dfrac{d\theta}{dt} = 2t$

4. $r = e^{a\theta}$ and $\dfrac{d\theta}{dt} = 2$ 5. $r = a(1 + \sin t)$ and $\theta = 1 - e^{-t}$

6. $r = 2 \cos 4t$ and $\theta = 2t$

7. If a particle moves in an ellipse whose polar equation is $r = c/(1 - e \cos \theta)$ and the force is directed toward the origin, show that the magnitude of the force is proportional to $1/r^2$.

REVIEW QUESTIONS AND EXERCISES FOR CHAPTER 12

1. When are two vectors equal?

2. How are two vectors added? Subtracted?

3. If a vector is multiplied by a scalar, how is the result related to the original vector? In your discussion include all possible values of the scalar: positive, negative, and zero.

4. Define the derivative of a vector function.

5. Develop formulas for the derivatives, with respect to θ, of the unit vectors $\mathbf{u}_r$ and $\mathbf{u}_\theta$.

6. Develop vector formulas for velocity and acceleration of a particle moving in a plane curve:

(a) in terms of Cartesian coordinates,

(b) in terms of polar coordinates,

(c) in terms of distance traveled along the curve and unit vectors tangent and normal to the curve.

7. (a) Define *curvature* of a plane curve. (b) Define radius of curvature. (c) Define center of curvature. (d) Define osculating circle.

8. Develop a formula for the curvature of a curve whose parametric equations are $x = f(t)$, $y = g(t)$.

9. In what way does the curvature of a curve affect the acceleration of a particle moving along the curve? In particular, discuss the case of constant-speed motion along a curve.

10. State and derive Kepler's second law concerning motion in a central force field.

11. Give examples of two ways in which parametric equations of a curve may arise.

12. What is the relation between a locus represented by parametric equations and the locus represented by the Cartesian equations that we may get when we eliminate the parameter? Illustrate with an example.

MISCELLANEOUS PROBLEMS FOR CHAPTER 12

In each of Problems 1–10, find parametric equations of the locus of $P(x, y)$ for the data given.

1. $\dfrac{dx}{dt} = x^2$, $\dfrac{dy}{dt} = x$; $t = 0$, $x = 1$, $y = 1$

2. $\dfrac{dx}{dt} = \cos^2 x$, $\dfrac{dy}{dt} = x$; $t = 0$, $x = \dfrac{\pi}{4}$, $y = 0$

3. $\dfrac{dx}{dt} = e^t$, $\dfrac{dy}{dt} = xe^x$; $t = 0$, $x = 1$, $y = 0$

4. $\dfrac{dx}{dt} = 6 \sin 2t$, $\dfrac{dy}{dt} = 4 \cos 2t$; $t = 0$, $x = 0$, $y = 4$

5. $\dfrac{dx}{dt} = 1 - \cos t$, $\dfrac{dy}{dt} = \sin t$; $t = 0$, $x = 0$, $y = 0$

6. $\dfrac{dx}{dt} = \sqrt{1 + y}$, $\dfrac{dy}{dt} = y$; $t = 0$, $x = 0$, $y = 1$

7. $\dfrac{dx}{dt} = \operatorname{sech} x$, $\dfrac{dy}{dt} = x$; $t = 0$, $x = 0$, $y = 0$

8. $\dfrac{dx}{dt} = \cosh \dfrac{t}{2}$, $\dfrac{dy}{dt} = x$; $t = 0$, $x = 2$, $y = 0$

9. $\dfrac{dx}{dt} = y$, $\dfrac{dy}{dt} = -x$; $t = 0$, $x = 0$, $y = 4$

10. $\dfrac{d^2 x}{dt^2} = -\dfrac{dx}{dt}$, $\dfrac{dy}{dt} = x$; $t = 0$, $x = 1$, $\dfrac{dx}{dt} = 1$, $y = 1$.

11. A particle is projected with velocity v at an angle α to the horizontal from a point that is at the foot of a hill inclined at an angle ϕ to the horizontal $[0 < \phi < \alpha < (\pi/2)]$. Show that it reaches the ground at a distance $[(2v^2 \cos \alpha)/(g \cos^2 \phi)] \sin (\alpha - \phi)$ measured up the face of the hill. Hence show that the greatest range achieved for a given v is when $\alpha = (\phi/2) + (\pi/4)$.

12. A wheel of radius 4 in. rolls along the x-axis with angular velocity 2 rad/sec. Find the locus described by a point on a spoke and 2 in. from the center of the wheel if it starts from the point $(0, 2)$ at time $t = 0$.

13. OA is the diameter of a circle of radius a. AN is tangent to the circle at A. A line through O making angle θ with diameter OA intersects the circle at M and tangent line at N. On ON a point P is located so that $OP = MN$. Taking O as origin, OA along the y-axis, and angle θ as parameter, find parametric equations of the locus described by P.

14. Let a line AB be the x-axis of a system of rectangular coordinates. Let the point C be the point $(0, 1)$. Let the line DE through C intersect AB at F. Let P and P' be the points on DE such that $PF = P'F = a$. Find parametric equations of the loci of P and P' in terms of the angle $\theta = \angle CFB$.

15. For the curve $x = a(t - \sin t)$, $y = a(1 - \cos t)$, find the following quantities: (a) The area bounded by the x-axis and one loop of the curve. (b) The length of one loop. (c) The radius of curvature. (d) The area of the surface of revolution obtained by rotating one loop about the x-axis. (e) The coordinates of the center of gravity of the area in part (a).

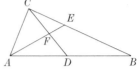

16. In the accompanying figure, D is the mid-point of side AB and E is one-third of the way between C and B. *Using vectors*, prove that F is the mid-point of the line CD.

17. The vectors $2\mathbf{i} + 3\mathbf{j}$, $4\mathbf{i} + \mathbf{j}$, and $5\mathbf{i} + y\mathbf{j}$ have their initial points at the origin. Find the value of y so that the vectors terminate on one straight line.

18. **A** and **B** are vectors from the origin to the two points A and B. The point P is determined by the vector $\overrightarrow{OP} = x\mathbf{A} + y\mathbf{B}$ where x and y are positive quantities, neither of which is zero, and whose sum is equal to one. Prove that P lies on the line segment AB.

19. Using vector methods, prove that the line joining the mid-points of two sides of a triangle is parallel to, and half the length of, the third side.

20. Let ABC be a triangle and let M be the mid-point of AB. Let P be the point on CM that is two-thirds of the way from C to M. Let O be any point in space. (a) Show that

$$\overrightarrow{OP} = \left(\frac{\overrightarrow{OA} + \overrightarrow{OB} + \overrightarrow{OC}}{3}\right).$$

(b) Show how the result in part (a) leads to the conclusion that the medians of a triangle meet in a point.

21. A, B, C are the vertices of a triangle and a, b, c are the mid-points of the opposite sides. Show that $\overrightarrow{Aa} + \overrightarrow{Bb} + \overrightarrow{Cc} = 0$. Interpret the result geometrically.

22. Vectors are drawn from the center of a regular polygon to its vertices. Show that their sum is zero.

23. Let **A**, **B**, **C** be vectors from a common point O to points A, B, C. (a) If A, B, C are collinear, show that three constants x, y, z (not all zero) exist such that $x + y + z = 0$ and $x\mathbf{A} + y\mathbf{B} + z\mathbf{C} = 0$. (b) Conversely, if three constants x, y, z (not all zero) exist such that $x + y + z = 0$ and $x\mathbf{A} + y\mathbf{B} + z\mathbf{C} = 0$, show that A, B, C are collinear.

24. A particle moves in the xy-plane, according to the time law: $x = 1/\sqrt{1 + t^2}$, $y = t/\sqrt{1 + t^2}$. (a) Compute the velocity vector and acceleration vector, when $t = 1$. (b) At what time is the speed of the particle a maximum?

25. A circular wheel with unit radius rolls along the x-axis uniformly, rotating one half turn per second. The position of a point P on the circumference is given by the formula $\overrightarrow{OP} = \mathbf{R} = \mathbf{i}(\pi t - \sin \pi t) + \mathbf{j}(1 - \cos \pi t)$. (a) Determine the velocity (*vector*) **v** and the acceleration (*vector*) **a** at time t. (b) Determine the slopes (as functions of t) of the two straight lines PC and PQ joining P to

the center C of the wheel and to the point
Q that is topmost at the instant. (c) Show
that the directions of the vectors $\mathbf{v}$ and $\mathbf{a}$
can be expressed in terms of the straight
lines described in (b).

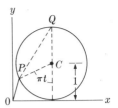

26. The motion of a particle in the xy-
plane is given by

$$\mathbf{R} = \mathbf{i}at \cos t + \mathbf{j}at \sin t.$$

Find the speed, and the tangential and normal components of the acceleration.

27. A particle moves in such a manner that the derivative of the position
vector is always perpendicular to the position vector. Show that the particle
moves on a circle with center at the origin.

28. The position of a point at time t is given by the formulas $x = e^t \cos t$,
$y = e^t \sin t$. (a) Show that $\mathbf{a} = 2\mathbf{v} - 2\mathbf{r}$. (b) Show that the angle between
the radius vector $\mathbf{r}$ and the acceleration vector $\mathbf{a}$ is constant, and find this angle.

29. Given the instantaneous velocity $\mathbf{v} = a\mathbf{i} + b\mathbf{j}$ and acceleration $\mathbf{a} = c\mathbf{i} + d\mathbf{j}$
of a particle at a point P on its path of motion, determine the curvature of the
path at P.

30. Find the parametric equations, in terms of the parameter θ, of the locus
of the center of curvature of the cycloid $x = a(\theta - \sin \theta)$, $y = a(1 - \cos \theta)$.

31. Find the point on the curve $y = e^x$ for which the radius of curvature is
a minimum.

32. (a) Given a closed curve having the property that every line parallel to the
x-axis or the y-axis has at most two points in common with the curve. Let

$$x = x(t), \qquad y = y(t), \qquad \alpha \le t \le \beta$$

be equations of the curve. Prove that if dx/dt and dy/dt are continuous, then
the area bounded by the curve is

$$\frac{1}{2}\left| \int_\alpha^\beta \left\{ x(t)\,\frac{dy}{dt} - y(t)\,\frac{dx}{dt} \right\} dt \right| .$$

(b) Use the result of part (a) to find the area inside the ellipse $x = a \cos \phi$,
$y = b \sin \phi$, $0 \le \phi \le 2\pi$. What does the answer become when $a = b$?

33. For the curve defined by the equations

$$x = \int_0^\theta \cos\left(\tfrac{1}{2}\pi t^2\right) dt, \qquad y = \int_0^\theta \sin\left(\tfrac{1}{2}\pi t^2\right) dt,$$

calculate the curvature κ as a function of the length of arc s, where s is measured
from $(0, 0)$.

34. The curve for which the length of the tangent intercepted between the
point of contact and the y-axis is always equal to 1 is called the *tractrix*. Find
its equation. Show that the radius of curvature at each point of the curve is
inversely proportional to the length of the normal intercepted between the
point on the curve and the y-axis. Calculate the length of arc of the tractrix,
and find the parametric equations in terms of the length of arc.

35. Let $x = x(t), y = y(t)$ be a closed curve. A constant length p is measured

off along the normal to the curve. The extremity of this segment describes a curve which is called a *parallel curve* to the original curve. Find the area, the length of arc, and the radius of curvature of the parallel curve.

36. Given the curve represented by the parametric equations $x = 32t$, $y = 16t^2 - 4$. (a) Calculate the radius of curvature of the curve at the point where $t = 3$. (b) Find the length of the curve between the points where $t = 0$ and $t = 1$.

37. Find the velocity, acceleration, and speed of a particle whose position at time t is $x = 3 \sin t$, $y = 2 \cos t$. Also find the tangential and normal components of the acceleration.

38. The position of a particle at time t is given by the equations $x = 1 + \cos 2t$, $y = \sin 2t$. Find (a) the normal and tangential components of acceleration at time t; (b) the radius of curvature of the path; (c) the equation of the path in polar coordinates, using the x-axis as the line $\theta = 0$ and the y-axis as the line $\theta = \pi/2$.

39. A particle moves so that its position at time t has the polar coordinates $r = t$, $\theta = t$. Find the velocity $\mathbf{v}$, the acceleration $\mathbf{a}$, and the curvature κ at any time t.

40. Find an expression for the curvature of the curve whose equation in polar coordinates is $r = f(\theta)$.

41. (a) Find the equation in *polar coordinates* of the curve $x = e^{2t} \cos t$, $y = e^{2t} \sin t$. (b) Find the length of this curve from $t = 0$ to $t = 2\pi$.

42. Express the velocity vector in terms of $\mathbf{u}_r$ and $\mathbf{u}_\theta$ for a point moving in the xy-plane according to the law $\mathbf{r} = (t + 1)\mathbf{i} + (t - 1)\mathbf{j}$.

43. The polar coordinates of a particle at time t are $r = e^{\omega t} + e^{-\omega t}$, $\theta = t$, where ω is a constant. Find the acceleration vector when $t = 0$.

44. A slender rod, passing through the fixed point O, is rotating about O in a plane at the constant rate of 3 rad/min. An insect is crawling along the rod toward O at the constant rate of 1 in/min. Use polar coordinates in the plane, with point O as the origin, and assume that the insect starts at the point $r = 2$, $\theta = 0$. (a) Find, in polar form, the vector velocity and vector acceleration of the insect when it is halfway to the origin. (b) What will be the length of the path, in the plane, that the insect has traveled when it reaches the origin?

45. A smooth ball rolls inside a long hollow tube while the tube rotates with constant angular velocity ω about an axis perpendicular to the axis of the tube. Assuming no friction between the ball and the sides of the tube, show that the distance r from the axis of rotation to the ball satisfies the differential equation $d^2r/dt^2 - \omega^2 r = 0$. If at time $t = 0$ the ball is at rest (relative to the tube) at $r = a > 0$, find r as a function of t.

46. Find the orbit of a planet relative to the sun, assuming the sun to be fixed at the origin and the force acting on the planet to be directed toward the sun with magnitude $\gamma mM/r^2$ where γ is the universal gravitational constant, M is the mass of the sun, m is the mass of the planet, and r is its distance from the sun. Choose the initial line to pass through the perihelion point of the orbit, and assume the velocity at perihelion is v_0. Show that the path is a circle, ellipse, parabola, or hyperbola according as $v_0^2 r_0/\gamma M$ equals one, lies between one and two, equals two, or is greater than two.

CHAPTER 13

SOLID GEOMETRY AND VECTORS

13–1 Space coordinates. A. *Cartesian coordinates.* In Fig. 13–1, a system of mutually orthogonal coordinate axes, Ox, Oy, and Oz, is indicated. The system is called *right-handed* if a right-threaded screw pointing along Oz will advance when the blade of the screw driver is twisted from Ox to Oy through an angle of 90°. In the right-handed system shown, the y- and z-axes lie in the plane of the paper and the x-axis points straight out from the paper. The Cartesian coordinates of a point $P(x, y, z)$ in space may be read from the scales along the coordinate axes by passing planes through P perpendicular to each axis. All points on the x-axis have their y- and z-coordinates both zero; that is, they have the form $(x, 0, 0)$. Points in a plane perpendicular to the z-axis, say, all have the same value of their z-coordinates. Thus, for example, $z = 5$ is an equation satisfied by every point $(x, y, 5)$ lying in a plane perpendicular to the z-axis and 5 units above the xy-plane. The three planes

$$x = 2, \qquad y = 3, \qquad z = 5$$

intersect in the point $P(2, 3, 5)$. The yz-plane is characterized by $x = 0$. The three coordinate planes $x = 0$, $y = 0$, $z = 0$ divide the space into eight cells, called *octants*. That octant in which the points (x, y, z) have all three coordinates positive is called the *first octant*, but there is no conventional numbering of the remaining seven octants.

B. *Cylindrical coordinates.* It is frequently convenient to use cylindrical coordinates (r, θ, z) to locate a point in space. Essentially, these are

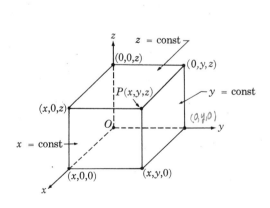

FIGURE 13–1

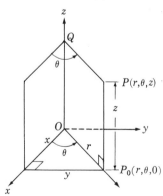

FIGURE 13–2

603

just the polar coordinates (r, θ) used instead of (x, y) in the plane $z = 0$ coupled with the z-coordinate. Cylindrical and Cartesian coordinates are related by the familiar equations (Fig. 13–2)

$$
\begin{aligned}
x &= r \cos \theta, & r^2 &= x^2 + y^2, \\
y &= r \sin \theta, & \tan \theta &= y/x, \\
z &= z.
\end{aligned}
\tag{1}
$$

If we hold $r = $ constant and let θ and z vary, the locus of $P(r, \theta, z)$ is then a right circular cylinder of radius r and axis along Oz. The locus $r = 0$ is just the z-axis itself. The locus $\theta = $ constant is a plane containing the z-axis and making an angle θ with the xz-plane (Fig. 13–3).

C. *Spherical coordinates.* Just as cylindrical coordinates are convenient to use when there is an axis of symmetry in a physical problem, so are spherical coordinates useful when there is a point which is a center of sym-

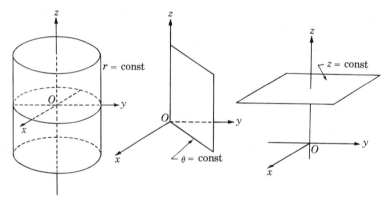

FIGURE 13–3

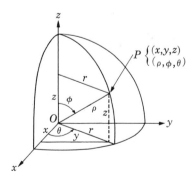

FIGURE 13–4

metry. In this case, we would take this center as the origin. The *spherical coordinates* (ρ, ϕ, θ) are illustrated in Fig. 13-4. In the first place,

$$\rho = |OP|$$

is simply the distance from the origin to the point P and is always taken to be greater than or equal to zero. The locus of points $\rho =$ constant (Fig. 13-5) is the surface of a sphere of radius ρ with center at O. The second spherical coordinate, ϕ, is the angle measured down from the z-axis to the line OP. The locus of points $\phi =$ constant is a cone with vertex at O, axis Oz, and generating angle ϕ, provided we are willing to broaden our interpretation of the word "cone" in this case to include the xy-plane for which $\phi = \pi/2$ as well as cones with generating angles greater than $\pi/2$. The third spherical coordinate θ is the same as the angle θ in cylindrical coordinates, namely, the angle from the xz-plane to the plane through P and the z-axis.

We may read (Fig. 13-4) the following relationships between the Cartesian, cylindrical, and spherical coordinate systems:

$$
\begin{array}{lll}
r = \rho \sin \phi, & x = r \cos \theta, & x = \rho \sin \phi \cos \theta, \\
z = \rho \cos \phi, & y = r \sin \theta, & y = \rho \sin \phi \sin \theta, \\
\theta = \theta, & z = z, & z = \rho \cos \phi.
\end{array}
\tag{2}
$$

Every point in the whole space can be given spherical coordinates restricted to the ranges

$$\rho \geq 0, \quad 0 \leq \phi \leq \pi, \quad 0 \leq \theta < 2\pi. \tag{3}$$

Because of the analogy between the surface of a sphere and the earth's surface, the z-axis is sometimes called the *polar axis*, while ϕ is referred to as *co-latitude* and θ as *longitude*. One also speaks of meridians, parallels, and the northern and southern hemispheres.

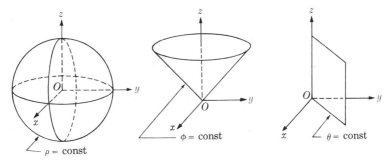

FIGURE 13-5

PROBLEMS

In Problems 1–4, describe the locus of points $P(x, y, z)$ that satisfy the given pairs of simultaneous equations. Sketch.

1. $x =$ constant, $\quad y =$ constant

2. $y = x, \quad z = 5$

3. $x^2 + y^2 = 4, \quad z = -2$

4. $x = 0, \quad \dfrac{y^2}{a^2} + \dfrac{z^2}{b^2} = 1$

In Problems 5–8, describe the locus of points $P(r, \theta, z)$ whose cylindrical coordinates satisfy the given pairs of simultaneous equations. Sketch.

5. $r = 2, \quad z = 3$

6. $\theta = \pi/6, \quad z = r$

7. $r = 3, \quad z = 2\theta$

8. $r = 2\theta, \quad z = 3\theta$

In Problems 9–12, describe the locus of points $P(\rho, \phi, \theta)$ whose spherical coordinates satisfy the given pairs of simultaneous equations. Sketch.

9. $\rho = 5, \quad \theta = \pi/4$

10. $\rho = 5, \quad \phi = \pi/4$

11. $\theta = \pi/4, \quad \phi = \pi/4$

12. $\theta = \pi/2, \quad \rho = 4 \cos \phi$

Translate each of the following equations from the given coordinate system (Cartesian, cylindrical, or spherical) into the forms that are appropriate to the other two systems.

13. $x^2 + y^2 + z^2 = 4$

14. $x^2 + y^2 + z^2 = 4z$

15. $z^2 = r^2$

16. $\rho = 6 \cos \phi$

Describe the following space loci.

17. $x \geq 0$

18. $3 \leq \rho \leq 5$

19. $r \geq 2, \quad \rho \leq 5$

20. $0 \leq \theta \leq \pi/4, \quad 0 \leq \phi \leq \pi/4, \quad \rho \geq 0$

21. $4x^2 + 9y^2 \leq 36$

13–2 Vectors. The study of solid analytic geometry is greatly facilitated by the use of vectors. The vectors from the origin to the points whose Cartesian coordinates are $(1, 0, 0)$, $(0, 1, 0)$, and $(0, 0, 1)$ respectively are the basic *unit* vectors which we denote by **i**, **j**, and **k**. Then the vector from the origin O to the point $P(x, y, z)$ is simply

$$\mathbf{R} = \overrightarrow{OP} = \mathbf{i}x + \mathbf{j}y + \mathbf{k}z. \tag{1}$$

If P moves along a curve in space, its position at time t being given by three twice-differentiable functions of time

$$x = f(t), \qquad y = g(t), \qquad z = h(t),$$

then its velocity vector is given by

$$\boxed{\mathbf{v} = \frac{d\mathbf{R}}{dt} = \mathbf{i}\frac{dx}{dt} + \mathbf{j}\frac{dy}{dt} + \mathbf{k}\frac{dz}{dt}} \tag{2}$$

and its acceleration by

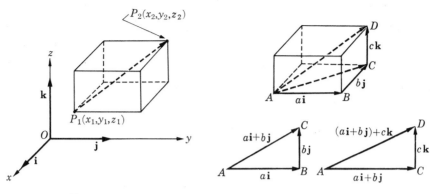

FIGURE 13–6　　　　　　　FIGURE 13–7

$$\mathbf{a} = \frac{d\mathbf{v}}{dt} = \mathbf{i}\frac{d^2x}{dt^2} + \mathbf{j}\frac{d^2y}{dt^2} + \mathbf{k}\frac{d^2z}{dt^2}. \tag{3}$$

If $P_1(x_1, y_1, z_1)$ and $P_2(x_2, y_2, z_2)$ are two points in space (Fig. 13–6), then the vector from P_1 to P_2 is the vector sum

$$\overrightarrow{P_1P_2} = \overrightarrow{P_1O} + \overrightarrow{OP_2}.$$

Since

$$\overrightarrow{P_1O} = -\overrightarrow{OP_1},$$

this is the same as

$$\overrightarrow{P_1P_2} = \overrightarrow{OP_2} - \overrightarrow{OP_1}$$

or

$$\overrightarrow{P_1P_2} = \mathbf{i}(x_2 - x_1) + \mathbf{j}(y_2 - y_1) + \mathbf{k}(z_2 - z_1). \tag{4}$$

The length of any vector

$$\mathbf{A} = a\mathbf{i} + b\mathbf{j} + c\mathbf{k}$$

is readily determined by applying the theorem of Pythagoras twice; once to the diagonal of a face of a rectangular box (Fig. 13–7) and then to the diagonal of the box. In the right triangle ABC, Fig. 13–7,

$$|\overrightarrow{AC}| = |a\mathbf{i} + b\mathbf{j}| = \sqrt{a^2 + b^2},$$

and in the right triangle ACD,

$$|\overrightarrow{AD}| = \sqrt{|\overrightarrow{AC}|^2 + |\overrightarrow{CD}|^2} = \sqrt{(a^2 + b^2) + c^2};$$

that is,

$$|a\mathbf{i} + b\mathbf{j} + c\mathbf{k}| = \sqrt{a^2 + b^2 + c^2}. \tag{5}$$

If we apply this result to the vector $\overrightarrow{P_1P_2}$ of Eq. (4), we obtain a formula for the distance between two points:

$$|\overrightarrow{P_1P_2}| = \sqrt{(x_2 - x_1)^2 + (y_2 - y_1)^2 + (z_2 - z_1)^2}. \qquad (6)$$

Since a sphere is the locus of points in space that are equidistant from one fixed point, the center, Eq. (6) may be used to determine the equation satisfied by every point P on a sphere of radius a with center at $P_0(x_0, y_0, z_0)$. P is on the sphere if and only if

$$|\overrightarrow{P_0P}| = a$$

or, what amounts to the same thing,

$$(x - x_0)^2 + (y - y_0)^2 + (z - z_0)^2 = a^2. \qquad (7)$$

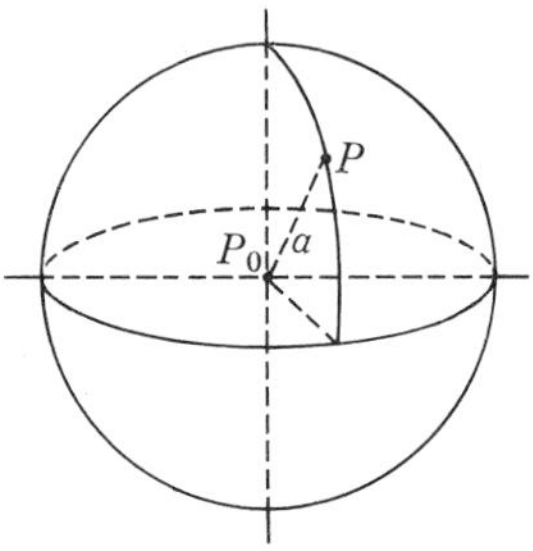

For example, if we complete the squares in the equation

$$x^2 + y^2 + z^2 + 2x - 4y = 0,$$

thus obtaining

$$(x + 1)^2 + (y - 2)^2 + z^2 = 5,$$

FIGURE 13-8

we may identify the locus of points that satisfy the equation as a sphere with center at $(-1, 2, 0)$ and radius $\sqrt{5}$.

PROBLEMS

Find the center and radius of each of the spheres in Problems 1–4.

1. $x^2 + y^2 + z^2 + 4x - 4z = 0$ 2. $2x^2 + 2y^2 + 2z^2 + x + y + z = 9$
3. $x^2 + y^2 + z^2 - 2az = 0$ 4. $3x^2 + 3y^2 + 3z^2 + 2y - 2z = 9$

5. What is the distance from the point $P(x, y, z)$ to (a) the x-axis, (b) the y-axis, (c) the z-axis, (d) the xy-plane?

6. The distance from $P(x, y, z)$ to the origin is d_1 and the distance from P to $A(0, 0, 3)$ is d_2. Find the locus of P if

(a) $d_1 = 2d_2$,   (b) $d_1 + d_2 = 6$,   (c) $|d_1 - d_2| = 2$.

Find the length of each of the following vectors.

7. $2\mathbf{i} + \mathbf{j} - 2\mathbf{k}$ 8. $3\mathbf{i} - 6\mathbf{j} + 2\mathbf{k}$
9. $\mathbf{i} + 4\mathbf{j} - 8\mathbf{k}$ 10. $9\mathbf{i} - 2\mathbf{j} + 6\mathbf{k}$

11. Find a unit vector having the same direction as $4\mathbf{i} + 3\mathbf{j} + 12\mathbf{k}$.

12. Find the vector from the origin O to the point of intersection of the medians of the triangle whose vertices are the three points $A(1, -1, 2)$, $B(2, 1, 3)$, and $C(-1, 2, -1)$.

13–3 The scalar product of two vectors. So far in our work with vectors we have not defined what meaning, if any, is to be attached to the product of two vectors **A** and **B**. There are three kinds of multiplication of two vectors which have been defined and found to have significance in physical applications. These are:

1. The *scalar product*, denoted by **A** · **B**. This product is also called "dot" product because of the dot symbol used to denote it. The result is a scalar.

2. The *vector product*, or cross product, denoted by **A** × **B**. The result is a vector.

3. The *dyadic product*, denoted simply by **AB** with no sign written between the factors. The result is a new mathematical quantity called a *dyad*. The study of dyads has largely been superseded by the subject of matrices. We shall not be concerned with either matrices or dyads in this book.

The *scalar*, or *dot*, product of two vectors **A** and **B** is defined by the equation

$$\mathbf{A} \cdot \mathbf{B} = |\mathbf{A}|\ |\mathbf{B}| \cos \theta, \qquad (1)$$

where θ measures the angle $(0 \leq \theta \leq \pi)$ determined by **A** and **B** when their initial points coincide (Fig. 13–9).

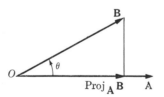

FIGURE 13–9

It is clear from Eq. (1) that the two factors **A** and **B** may be interchanged. That is,

$$\mathbf{A} \cdot \mathbf{B} = \mathbf{B} \cdot \mathbf{A}. \qquad (2)$$

When an operation, such as addition or multiplication of ordinary numbers, satisfies such an equation as $a + b = b + a$, or $ab = ba$, we call that operation *commutative*. Equation (2) says, therefore, that the operation of scalar multiplication of two vectors is commutative.

The vector that we get by projecting **B** onto **A** is called the *"vector projection"* of **B** onto **A**. We shall denote it by $\text{proj}_A \mathbf{B}$ (Fig. 13–9). The *"scalar* projection" of **B** onto **A** is plus or minus the length of this vector projection. The sign is to be plus if $\text{proj}_A \mathbf{B}$ has the same sense as $+\mathbf{A}$ and to be minus if it has the same sense as $-\mathbf{A}$. Then the scalar projection of **B** onto **A** is equal to $|\mathbf{B}| \cos \theta$. Hence the dot product, Eq. (1), may be interpreted geometrically as follows:

$$\mathbf{A} \cdot \mathbf{B} = |\mathbf{A}|(|\mathbf{B}| \cos \theta)$$

$$= \text{(length of } \mathbf{A}) \text{ times (scalar projection of } \mathbf{B} \text{ onto } \mathbf{A}).$$

Of course we may interchange the roles of $|\mathbf{A}|$ and $|\mathbf{B}|$ and write the dot product in the alternative form of

$$\mathbf{A} \cdot \mathbf{B} = |\mathbf{B}|(|\mathbf{A}| \cos \theta)$$

$$= \text{(length of } \mathbf{B}) \text{ times (scalar projection of } \mathbf{A} \text{ onto } \mathbf{B}).$$

In order to calculate the scalar product $\mathbf{A} \cdot \mathbf{B}$ in terms of the components of the vectors, we let

$$\mathbf{A} = a_1\mathbf{i} + a_2\mathbf{j} + a_3\mathbf{k},$$
$$\mathbf{B} = b_1\mathbf{i} + b_2\mathbf{j} + b_3\mathbf{k}, \tag{3}$$

and

$$\mathbf{C} = \mathbf{B} - \mathbf{A}$$
$$= (b_1 - a_1)\mathbf{i} + (b_2 - a_2)\mathbf{j} + (b_3 - a_3)\mathbf{k}.$$

Then we apply the law of cosines to the triangle whose sides represent the vectors **A**, **B**, and **C** (Fig. 13–10) and obtain

$$|\mathbf{C}|^2 = |\mathbf{A}|^2 + |\mathbf{B}|^2 - 2|\mathbf{A}| \, |\mathbf{B}| \cos \theta,$$

$$|\mathbf{A}| \, |\mathbf{B}| \cos \theta = \frac{|\mathbf{A}|^2 + |\mathbf{B}|^2 - |\mathbf{C}|^2}{2}. \tag{4}$$

The left side of this equation is the same as $\mathbf{A} \cdot \mathbf{B}$ and we may calculate all terms on the right side of (4) by applying Eq. (5) of Article 13–2 to find the lengths of the vectors **A**, **B**, and **C**. The result of this algebra is the formula

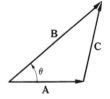

FIGURE 13–10

$$\boxed{\mathbf{A} \cdot \mathbf{B} = a_1b_1 + a_2b_2 + a_3b_3,} \tag{5}$$

which expresses the scalar product in terms of the components of the vectors. Thus, to find the scalar product of two given vectors, we simply multiply their *corresponding* components together and add the results.

EXAMPLE 1. Vectors are drawn from the origin to the two points $A(1, -2, -2)$ and $B(6, 3, -2)$. Find the angle AOB.

Solution. Let

$$\mathbf{A} = \overrightarrow{OA} = \mathbf{i} - 2\mathbf{j} - 2\mathbf{k},$$

$$\mathbf{B} = \overrightarrow{OB} = 6\mathbf{i} + 3\mathbf{j} - 2\mathbf{k},$$

and denote the angle AOB by θ. Then

$$\mathbf{A} \cdot \mathbf{B} = 6 - 6 + 4 = 4$$

from Eq. (5), while

$$\mathbf{A} \cdot \mathbf{B} = |\mathbf{A}|\,|\mathbf{B}| \cos \theta$$

from Eq. (1). Since $|\mathbf{A}| = \sqrt{1 + 4 + 4} = 3$ and $|\mathbf{B}| = \sqrt{36 + 9 + 4} = 7$, we have

$$\cos \theta = \frac{\mathbf{A} \cdot \mathbf{B}}{|\mathbf{A}|\,|\mathbf{B}|} = \frac{4}{21},$$

$$\theta = \cos^{-1} \frac{4}{21} \approx 79°.$$

From Eq. (5), it is readily seen that if

$$\mathbf{C} = c_1\mathbf{i} + c_2\mathbf{j} + c_3\mathbf{k}$$

is any third vector, then

$$\mathbf{A} \cdot (\mathbf{B} + \mathbf{C}) = a_1(b_1 + c_1) + a_2(b_2 + c_2) + a_3(b_3 + c_3)$$

$$= (a_1 b_1 + a_2 b_2 + a_3 b_3) + (a_1 c_1 + a_2 c_2 + a_3 c_3)$$

$$= \mathbf{A} \cdot \mathbf{B} + \mathbf{A} \cdot \mathbf{C}.$$

Hence scalar multiplication obeys the *distributive* law:

$$\mathbf{A} \cdot (\mathbf{B} + \mathbf{C}) = \mathbf{A} \cdot \mathbf{B} + \mathbf{A} \cdot \mathbf{C}. \qquad (6)$$

If we combine this with the commutative law, Eq. (2), it is also evident that

$$(\mathbf{A} + \mathbf{B}) \cdot \mathbf{C} = \mathbf{A} \cdot \mathbf{C} + \mathbf{B} \cdot \mathbf{C}. \qquad (7)$$

Equations (6) and (7) together permit us to multiply sums of vectors according to the familiar laws of elementary algebra. For example,

$$(\mathbf{A} + \mathbf{B}) \cdot (\mathbf{C} + \mathbf{D}) = \mathbf{A} \cdot \mathbf{C} + \mathbf{A} \cdot \mathbf{D} + \mathbf{B} \cdot \mathbf{C} + \mathbf{B} \cdot \mathbf{D}. \qquad (8)$$

Orthogonal vectors. It is clear from Eq. (1) that the dot product is zero when the vectors are perpendicular, since $\cos 90° = 0$. Conversely, if $\mathbf{A} \cdot \mathbf{B} = 0$ then one of the vectors is zero or else the vectors are perpendicular. The zero vector has no specified direction, and we might adopt the convention that it is perpendicular to any vector. Then we could say that $\mathbf{A} \cdot \mathbf{B} = 0$ if and only if the vectors $\mathbf{A}$ and $\mathbf{B}$ are perpendicular. Perpendicular vectors are also said to be *orthogonal*.

If the scalar product is negative, then $\cos \theta$ is negative and the angle between the vectors is greater than $90°$.

If $\mathbf{B} = \mathbf{A}$, then $\theta = 0$ and $\cos \theta = 1$, so that $\mathbf{A} \cdot \mathbf{A} = |\mathbf{A}|^2$.

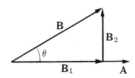

FIGURE 13–11

EXAMPLE 2. Resolve the vector $\mathbf{B}$ into components $\mathbf{B}_1$ and $\mathbf{B}_2$, where $\mathbf{B}_1$ is to be parallel to a given vector $\mathbf{A}$ while $\mathbf{B}_2$ is to be perpendicular to $\mathbf{A}$ (Fig. 13–11).

Solution. Let

$$\mathbf{B} = \mathbf{B}_1 + \mathbf{B}_2,$$

with $\mathbf{B}_1 = c\mathbf{A}$ and $\mathbf{B}_2 \cdot \mathbf{A} = 0$. Then, substituting for $\mathbf{B}_1$, we have

$$\mathbf{B} = c\mathbf{A} + \mathbf{B}_2$$

and the scalar c is determined by the equation

$$0 = \mathbf{B}_2 \cdot \mathbf{A} = (\mathbf{B} - c\mathbf{A}) \cdot \mathbf{A} = \mathbf{B} \cdot \mathbf{A} - c(\mathbf{A} \cdot \mathbf{A})$$

or

$$c = \frac{\mathbf{B} \cdot \mathbf{A}}{\mathbf{A} \cdot \mathbf{A}}.$$

Then

$$\mathbf{B}_2 = \mathbf{B} - \mathbf{B}_1 = \mathbf{B} - c\mathbf{A} = \mathbf{B} - \frac{\mathbf{B} \cdot \mathbf{A}}{\mathbf{A} \cdot \mathbf{A}} \mathbf{A}$$

is perpendicular to $\mathbf{A}$ by the way in which c was determined. For example, if

$$\mathbf{B} = 2\mathbf{i} + \mathbf{j} - 3\mathbf{k} \quad \text{and} \quad \mathbf{A} = 3\mathbf{i} - \mathbf{j},$$

then

$$c = \frac{\mathbf{B} \cdot \mathbf{A}}{\mathbf{A} \cdot \mathbf{A}} = \frac{6 - 1}{9 + 1} = \frac{1}{2},$$

and

$$\mathbf{B}_1 = \tfrac{1}{2}\mathbf{A} = \tfrac{3}{2}\mathbf{i} - \tfrac{1}{2}\mathbf{j}$$

is parallel to $\mathbf{A}$, while

$$\mathbf{B}_2 = \mathbf{B} - \mathbf{B}_1 = \tfrac{1}{2}\mathbf{i} + \tfrac{3}{2}\mathbf{j} - 3\mathbf{k}$$

is perpendicular to $\mathbf{A}$.

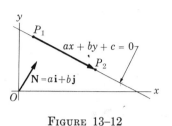

FIGURE 13-12

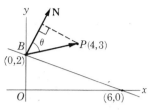

FIGURE 13-13

EXAMPLE 3. Show that the vector $\mathbf{N} = a\mathbf{i} + b\mathbf{j}$ is perpendicular to the line $ax + by + c = 0$ in the xy-plane (Fig. 13-12).

Solution. Let $P_1(x_1, y_1)$ and $P_2(x_2, y_2)$ be any two points on the line; that is,

$$ax_1 + by_1 + c = 0, \qquad ax_2 + by_2 + c = 0.$$

By subtraction, we eliminate c and obtain

$$a(x_2 - x_1) + b(y_2 - y_1) = 0,$$

or

$$(a\mathbf{i} + b\mathbf{j}) \cdot [(x_2 - x_1)\mathbf{i} + (y_2 - y_1)\mathbf{j}] = 0. \tag{9}$$

Now $(x_2 - x_1)\mathbf{i} + (y_2 - y_1)\mathbf{j} = \overrightarrow{P_1P_2}$ is a vector joining two points on the line, while $\mathbf{N} = a\mathbf{i} + b\mathbf{j}$ is the given vector. Equation (9) says that either $\mathbf{N} = 0$, or $\overrightarrow{P_1P_2} = 0$, or else $\mathbf{N} \perp \overrightarrow{P_1P_2}$. Now $ax + by + c = 0$ is assumed to be an honest equation of a straight line, so that not both a and b are zero, hence $\mathbf{N} \neq 0$. Furthermore, we may surely choose P_2 different from P_1 on the line, hence $\overrightarrow{P_1P_2} \neq 0$. Hence $\mathbf{N} \perp \overrightarrow{P_1P_2}$; that is, $\mathbf{N}$ is perpendicular to the line. For example, if the equation of the line is $2x - 3y - 5 = 0$, then the vector $\mathbf{N} = 2\mathbf{i} - 3\mathbf{j}$ is normal to the line.

EXAMPLE 4. Using vector methods, find the distance of the point $(4, 3)$ from the line $x + 3y - 6 = 0$ (Fig. 13-13).

Solution. The line cuts the y-axis at $B(0, 2)$. At B, draw the vector

$$\mathbf{N} = \mathbf{i} + 3\mathbf{j}$$

normal to the line (see Example 3). Then the distance from the line to P is $d = |\overrightarrow{BP}| \cos \theta$. This reminds one of the dot product

$$\mathbf{N} \cdot \overrightarrow{BP} = |\mathbf{N}| \, |\overrightarrow{BP}| \cos \theta = |\mathbf{N}| \, d,$$

so that

$$d = \frac{\mathbf{N} \cdot \overrightarrow{BP}}{|\mathbf{N}|}.$$

One readily finds $\overrightarrow{BP} = 4\mathbf{i} + \mathbf{j}$, hence

$$d = \frac{4 + 3}{\sqrt{1 + 9}} = \frac{7}{10}\sqrt{10}.$$

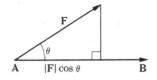

FIGURE 13–14

In addition to applications to geometry as indicated above, the scalar product is useful in mechanics, where it is used in calculating the work done by a force **F** when the point of application of **F** undergoes a displacement $\overrightarrow{AB}$. If the force remains constant in direction and magnitude, this work is given by (Fig. 13–14)

$$\text{work} = (|\mathbf{F}| \cos \theta) \, |\overrightarrow{AB}|$$
$$= \mathbf{F} \cdot \overrightarrow{AB}.$$

The concept of work also enters into the study of electricity and magnetism and the scalar product again plays a basic role. (See Sears, *Electricity and Magnetism*, Chapter 3.)

PROBLEMS

1. Suppose it is known that $\mathbf{A} \cdot \mathbf{B}_1 = \mathbf{A} \cdot \mathbf{B}_2$, and **A** is not zero, but nothing more is known about the vectors $\mathbf{B}_1$ and $\mathbf{B}_2$. Is it permissible to cancel **A** from both sides of the equation? Give a reason for your answer.

2. (a) Express the vector projection of **B** onto **A** in a vector form which is convenient for calculation. (b) Find the vector projection of $\mathbf{B} = \mathbf{i} + 3\mathbf{j} + 4\mathbf{k}$ onto the vector $\mathbf{A} = 10\mathbf{i} + 11\mathbf{j} - 2\mathbf{k}$.

3. Find the interior angles of the triangle ABC whose vertices are the points $A(-1, 0, 2)$, $B(2, 1, -1)$, and $C(1, -2, 2)$.

4. Find the point $A(a, a, 0)$ on the line $y = x$ in the xy-plane such that the vector $\overrightarrow{AB}$ is perpendicular to the line OA. Here O is the origin and B is the point $(2, 4, -3)$.

5. Find the scalar projection of the vector $\mathbf{A} = 2\mathbf{i} + 2\mathbf{j} + \mathbf{k}$ onto the vector $\mathbf{B} = 2\mathbf{i} + 10\mathbf{j} - 11\mathbf{k}$.

6. Find the angle between the diagonal of a cube and one of its edges.

7. Find the angle between the diagonal of a cube and a diagonal of one of its faces.

8. Find the angle between the vectors **A** and **B** of Problem 5.

9. How many lines through the origin make angles of 60° with both the y- and z-axes? What angles do they make with the positive x-axis?

10. If $a = |\mathbf{A}|$ and $b = |\mathbf{B}|$, show that the vector

$$\mathbf{C} = \frac{a\mathbf{B} + b\mathbf{A}}{a + b}$$

bisects the angle between **A** and **B**.

11. With the same notation as in Problem 10, show that the vectors $a\mathbf{B} + b\mathbf{A}$ and $\mathbf{A}b - \mathbf{B}a$ are perpendicular.

12. If $\mathbf{R}$ is the vector from the origin O to $P(x, y, z)$ and $\mathbf{k}$ is the unit vector along the z-axis, show geometrically that the equation

$$\frac{\mathbf{R} \cdot \mathbf{k}}{|\mathbf{R}|} = \cos 45°$$

represents a cone with vertex at the origin and generating angle of 45°. Express the equation in Cartesian form.

13. Find the work done by a force $\mathbf{F} = -w\mathbf{k}$ as its point of application moves from the point $P_1(x_1, y_1, z_1)$ to a second point $P_2(x_2, y_2, z_2)$ along the straight line P_1P_2.

14. Using vector methods, show that the distance d from the point (x_1, y_1) to the line $ax + by + c = 0$ is

$$d = \frac{|ax_1 + by_1 + c|}{\sqrt{a^2 + b^2}}.$$

15. *Direction cosines.* If the vector $\mathbf{A} = a\mathbf{i} + b\mathbf{j} + c\mathbf{k}$ makes angles α, β, and γ, respectively, with the positive x-, y-, and z-axes, then $\cos \alpha$, $\cos \beta$, $\cos \gamma$ are called its *direction cosines.* Show that

(a) $\cos \alpha = \dfrac{a}{\sqrt{a^2 + b^2 + c^2}}$, $\cos \beta = \dfrac{b}{\sqrt{a^2 + b^2 + c^2}}$,

$\cos \gamma = \dfrac{c}{\sqrt{a^2 + b^2 + c^2}}$,

(b) $\cos^2 \alpha + \cos^2 \beta + \cos^2 \gamma = 1$,

(c) $\mathbf{u} = \mathbf{i} \cos \alpha + \mathbf{j} \cos \beta + \mathbf{k} \cos \gamma$ is a unit vector having the same direction as $\mathbf{A}$.

16. In Article 12–4 we found the velocity vector of a particle moving in a plane to be

$$\mathbf{v} = \frac{d\mathbf{R}}{dt} = \mathbf{i}\frac{dx}{dt} + \mathbf{j}\frac{dy}{dt}$$

$$= \mathbf{u}_r \frac{dr}{dt} + \mathbf{u}_\theta \frac{r\,d\theta}{dt}.$$

(a) Express dx/dt and dy/dt in terms of dr/dt and $r\,d\theta/dt$ by computing $\mathbf{v} \cdot \mathbf{i}$ and $\mathbf{v} \cdot \mathbf{j}$. (b) Express dr/dt and $r\,d\theta/dt$ in terms of dx/dt and dy/dt by computing $\mathbf{v} \cdot \mathbf{u}_r$ and $\mathbf{v} \cdot \mathbf{u}_\theta$.

13–4 The vector product of two vectors. The two vectors $\mathbf{A}$ and $\mathbf{B}$ may be subjected to parallel displacements, if necessary, to bring their initial points into coincidence. Consider this as having been done and

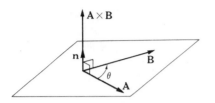

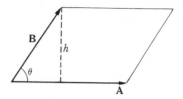

FIGURE 13–15   FIGURE 13–16

again let the angle from **A** to **B** be θ, with $0 \leq \theta \leq \pi$. Then, unless **A** and **B** are parallel, they now determine a plane. Let **n** be a unit vector perpendicular to this plane and pointing in the direction a right-threaded screw advances when its head is rotated from **A** to **B** through the angle θ. The *vector product*, or *cross product*, of **A** and **B**, in that order, is then defined by the equation (Fig. 13–15)

$$\mathbf{A} \times \mathbf{B} = \mathbf{n}|\mathbf{A}|\ |\mathbf{B}| \sin \theta. \tag{1}$$

(Applications of the cross product to electricity and magnetism are discussed in Sears, *Electricity and Magnetism*, Chapters 9 and 11.)

In case **A** and **B** are parallel, $\theta = 0$ or $180°$ and $\sin \theta = 0$, so that $\mathbf{A} \times \mathbf{B} = 0$. In this case, the direction of **n** is not determined, but this is immaterial, since the zero vector has no specific direction. In all other cases, however, **n** is determined and the cross product is a vector having the same direction as **n** and having magnitude equal to the area, $|\mathbf{A}|\ |\mathbf{B}| \sin \theta$, of the parallelogram determined by the vectors **A** and **B** (Fig. 13–16).

If the factors **A** and **B** are reversed in the above definition, the vector **n** is replaced by $-\mathbf{n}$ with the result that

$$\mathbf{B} \times \mathbf{A} = -\mathbf{A} \times \mathbf{B}. \tag{2}$$

This kind of multiplication is not commutative and we must pay attention to the order of the factors.

When the definition is applied to the unit vectors **i**, **j**, and **k**, one readily finds that

$$\mathbf{i} \times \mathbf{j} = -\mathbf{j} \times \mathbf{i} = \mathbf{k},$$
$$\mathbf{j} \times \mathbf{k} = -\mathbf{k} \times \mathbf{j} = \mathbf{i}, \tag{3}$$
$$\mathbf{k} \times \mathbf{i} = -\mathbf{i} \times \mathbf{k} = \mathbf{j},$$

while

$$\mathbf{i} \times \mathbf{i} = \mathbf{j} \times \mathbf{j} = \mathbf{k} \times \mathbf{k} = 0.$$

Our next objective is to obtain a formula which will express $\mathbf{A} \times \mathbf{B}$ in terms of the components of $\mathbf{A}$ and $\mathbf{B}$. First, we notice that the associative law

$$(r\mathbf{A}) \times (s\mathbf{B}) = rs(\mathbf{A} \times \mathbf{B}) \qquad (4)$$

follows immediately from the definition of the cross product. Secondly, we adopt a geometric argument to establish the distributive law

$$\mathbf{A} \times (\mathbf{B} + \mathbf{C}) = \mathbf{A} \times \mathbf{B} + \mathbf{A} \times \mathbf{C}. \qquad (5)$$

To see that Eq. (5) is valid, we interpret the cross product $\mathbf{A} \times \mathbf{B}$ in a slightly different way. The vectors $\mathbf{A}$ and $\mathbf{B}$ are drawn from the common point O and a plane M is constructed perpendicular to $\mathbf{A}$ at O (Fig. 13–17). Vector $\mathbf{B}$ is now projected orthogonally onto M, yielding a vector $\mathbf{B'}$ whose length is $|\mathbf{B}| \sin \theta$. The vector $\mathbf{B'}$ is then rotated 90° about $\mathbf{A}$ in the positive sense to produce a vector $\mathbf{B''}$. Finally, $\mathbf{B''}$ is multiplied by the length of $\mathbf{A}$. The resulting vector $|\mathbf{A}|\mathbf{B''}$ is equal to $\mathbf{A} \times \mathbf{B}$ since $\mathbf{B''}$ has the same direction as $\mathbf{n}$ by its construction (Fig. 13–17) and

$$|\mathbf{A}| \, |\mathbf{B''}| = |\mathbf{A}| \, |\mathbf{B'}| = |\mathbf{A}| \, |\mathbf{B}| \sin \theta = |\mathbf{A} \times \mathbf{B}|.$$

Now each of these three operations, namely,

(1) projection onto M,

(2) rotation about $\mathbf{A}$ through 90°,

(3) multiplication by the scalar $|\mathbf{A}|$,

when applied to a triangle will produce another triangle. If we start with the triangle whose sides are $\mathbf{B}$, $\mathbf{C}$, and $\mathbf{B} + \mathbf{C}$ (Fig. 13–18) and apply these three steps, we successively obtain:

(1) a triangle whose sides are $\mathbf{B'}$, $\mathbf{C'}$, and $(\mathbf{B} + \mathbf{C})'$ satisfying the vector equation

$$\mathbf{B'} + \mathbf{C'} = (\mathbf{B} + \mathbf{C})',$$

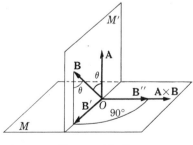

FIGURE 13–17

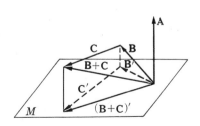

FIGURE 13–18

(2) a triangle whose sides are $\mathbf{B}''$, $\mathbf{C}''$, and $(\mathbf{B} + \mathbf{C})''$ satisfying the vector equation

$$\mathbf{B}'' + \mathbf{C}'' = (\mathbf{B} + \mathbf{C})'',$$

(the double-prime on each vector has the same meaning as in Fig. 13–17), and finally,

(3) a triangle whose sides are $|\mathbf{A}|\mathbf{B}''$, $|\mathbf{A}|\mathbf{C}''$, and $|\mathbf{A}|(\mathbf{B} + \mathbf{C})''$ satisfying the vector equation

$$|\mathbf{A}|\mathbf{B}'' + |\mathbf{A}|\mathbf{C}'' = |\mathbf{A}|(\mathbf{B} + \mathbf{C})''. \tag{6}$$

When we use the equations $|\mathbf{A}|\mathbf{B}'' = \mathbf{A} \times \mathbf{B}$, $|\mathbf{A}|\mathbf{C}'' = \mathbf{A} \times \mathbf{C}$ and $|\mathbf{A}|(\mathbf{B} + \mathbf{C})'' = \mathbf{A} \times (\mathbf{B} + \mathbf{C})$ which result from our discussion above, Eq. (6) becomes

$$\mathbf{A} \times \mathbf{B} + \mathbf{A} \times \mathbf{C} = \mathbf{A} \times (\mathbf{B} + \mathbf{C}),$$

which is the distributive law, (5), that we wanted to establish.

The companion law

$$\boxed{(\mathbf{B} + \mathbf{C}) \times \mathbf{A} = \mathbf{B} \times \mathbf{A} + \mathbf{C} \times \mathbf{A}} \tag{7}$$

now follows at once from Eq. (5) if we multiply both sides of it by minus one and take account of the fact that interchanging the two factors in a cross product changes the sign of the result.

From Eqs. (4), (5), and (7), we may conclude that multiplication of two vectors according to the cross product law follows the ordinary laws of algebra, *except that the order of the factors is not reversible.* If we apply these results to calculate $\mathbf{A} \times \mathbf{B}$ with

$$\mathbf{A} = a_1\mathbf{i} + a_2\mathbf{j} + a_3\mathbf{k},$$
$$\mathbf{B} = b_1\mathbf{i} + b_2\mathbf{j} + b_3\mathbf{k},$$

we obtain

$$\begin{aligned}
\mathbf{A} \times \mathbf{B} &= (a_1\mathbf{i} + a_2\mathbf{j} + a_3\mathbf{k}) \times (b_1\mathbf{i} + b_2\mathbf{j} + b_3\mathbf{k}) \\
&= a_1b_1\mathbf{i} \times \mathbf{i} + a_1b_2\mathbf{i} \times \mathbf{j} + a_1b_3\mathbf{i} \times \mathbf{k} \\
&\quad + a_2b_1\mathbf{j} \times \mathbf{i} + a_2b_2\mathbf{j} \times \mathbf{j} + a_2b_3\mathbf{j} \times \mathbf{k} \\
&\quad + a_3b_1\mathbf{k} \times \mathbf{i} + a_3b_2\mathbf{k} \times \mathbf{j} + a_3b_3\mathbf{k} \times \mathbf{k} \\
&= \mathbf{i}(a_2b_3 - a_3b_2) + \mathbf{j}(a_3b_1 - a_1b_3) \\
&\quad + \mathbf{k}(a_1b_2 - a_2b_1), \tag{8}
\end{aligned}$$

where Eqs. (3) have been used to evaluate the products $\mathbf{i} \times \mathbf{i} = 0$, $\mathbf{i} \times \mathbf{j} = \mathbf{k}$, etc. The six terms on the right side of Eq. (8) are precisely the same as the six terms in the expansion of the third order determinant below, so that the cross product may conveniently be calculated from the equation

$$\mathbf{A} \times \mathbf{B} = \begin{vmatrix} \mathbf{i} & \mathbf{j} & \mathbf{k} \\ a_1 & a_2 & a_3 \\ b_1 & b_2 & b_3 \end{vmatrix}. \tag{9}$$

EXAMPLE 1. Find the area of the triangle whose vertices are $A(1, -1, 0)$, $B(2, 1, -1)$, and $C(-1, 1, 2)$.

Solution. Two sides of the given triangle are represented by the vectors

$$\mathbf{a} = \overrightarrow{AB} = (2 - 1)\mathbf{i} + (1 + 1)\mathbf{j} + (-1 - 0)\mathbf{k} = \mathbf{i} + 2\mathbf{j} - \mathbf{k},$$
$$\mathbf{b} = \overrightarrow{AC} = (-1 - 1)\mathbf{i} + (1 + 1)\mathbf{j} + (2 - 0)\mathbf{k} = -2\mathbf{i} + 2\mathbf{j} + 2\mathbf{k}.$$

The vector

$$\mathbf{c} = \mathbf{a} \times \mathbf{b} = \begin{vmatrix} \mathbf{i} & \mathbf{j} & \mathbf{k} \\ 1 & 2 & -1 \\ -2 & 2 & 2 \end{vmatrix} = 6\mathbf{i} + 6\mathbf{k}$$

has magnitude $|\mathbf{c}| = \sqrt{36 + 36} = 6\sqrt{2}$, which is equal to the area of a parallelogram of which the given triangle is exactly one-half. Hence the area of the triangle is $\frac{1}{2}(|\mathbf{a} \times \mathbf{b}|) = 3\sqrt{2}$.

EXAMPLE 2. Find a unit vector perpendicular to both of the vectors $\mathbf{A} = 2\mathbf{i} + \mathbf{j} - \mathbf{k}$ and $\mathbf{B} = \mathbf{i} - \mathbf{j} + 2\mathbf{k}$.

Solution. The vector $\mathbf{N} = \mathbf{A} \times \mathbf{B}$ is perpendicular to both $\mathbf{A}$ and $\mathbf{B}$; hence $\mathbf{u} = c(\mathbf{A} \times \mathbf{B})$ is also such a vector for any scalar $c \neq 0$ and we may choose c so as to make $\mathbf{u}$ have unit length. We thus find

$$\mathbf{N} = \mathbf{A} \times \mathbf{B} = \mathbf{i} - 5\mathbf{j} - 3\mathbf{k},$$
$$\mathbf{u} \cdot \mathbf{u} = c^2 \mathbf{N} \cdot \mathbf{N} = 35c^2 = 1,$$
$$c = \pm 1/\sqrt{35},$$

and

$$\mathbf{u} = \pm \frac{\mathbf{i} - 5\mathbf{j} - 3\mathbf{k}}{\sqrt{35}}.$$

PROBLEMS

1. Find $\mathbf{A} \times \mathbf{B}$ if $\mathbf{A} = 2\mathbf{i} - 2\mathbf{j} - \mathbf{k}$, $\mathbf{B} = \mathbf{i} + \mathbf{j} + \mathbf{k}$.

2. Find a vector $\mathbf{N}$ perpendicular to the plane determined by the three points $A(1, -1, 2)$, $B(2, 0, -1)$, and $C(0, 2, 1)$.

3. Find the area of the triangle ABC of Problem 2.

4. Find the distance from the origin to the plane ABC of Problem 2 by projecting $\overrightarrow{OA}$ onto the normal vector **N**.

5. Find a vector that is perpendicular to both of the vectors $\mathbf{A} = \mathbf{i} + \mathbf{j} + \mathbf{k}$ and $\mathbf{B} = \mathbf{i} + \mathbf{j}$.

6. Vectors from the origin to the points A, B, C are given by $\mathbf{A} = \mathbf{i} - \mathbf{j} + \mathbf{k}$, $\mathbf{B} = 2\mathbf{i} + 3\mathbf{j} - \mathbf{k}$, $\mathbf{C} = -\mathbf{i} + 2\mathbf{j} + 2\mathbf{k}$. Find all points $P(x, y, z)$ which satisfy the following requirements: $\overrightarrow{OP}$ is a unit vector perpendicular to **C** and P lies in the plane determined by **A** and **B**.

7. Using vector methods, find the distance between the line L_1 determined by the two points $A(1, 0, -1)$, $B(-1, 1, 0)$ and the line L_2 determined by the points $C(3, 1, -1)$, $D(4, 5, -2)$. The distance is to be measured along a line perpendicular to both L_1 and L_2.

8. $\mathbf{A} = 3\mathbf{i} + \mathbf{j} - \mathbf{k}$ is normal to a plane M_1 and $\mathbf{B} = 2\mathbf{i} - \mathbf{j} + \mathbf{k}$ is normal to a second plane M_2. (a) Find the angle between the two normals. (b) Do the two planes necessarily intersect if they are both extended indefinitely? Give a reason for your answer. (c) If the two planes do intersect, find a vector which is parallel to their line of intersection.

13–5 Equations of lines and planes. *Lines.* Suppose L is a line in space that passes through a given point $P_1(x_1, y_1, z_1)$ and is parallel to a given nonzero vector

$$\mathbf{v} = A\mathbf{i} + B\mathbf{j} + C\mathbf{k}.$$

Then L is the locus of all points $P(x, y, z)$ such that the vector $\overrightarrow{P_1P}$ is parallel to the given vector **v** (Fig. 13–19).

That is, P is on the line L if and only if there is a scalar t such that

$$\boxed{\overrightarrow{P_1P} = t\mathbf{v}.} \tag{1}$$

When we separate the components in Eq. (1), we have

$$\boxed{x - x_1 = tA, \quad y - y_1 = tB, \quad z - z_1 = tC.} \tag{2}$$

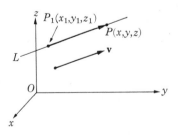

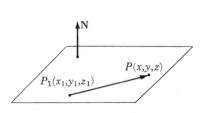

FIGURE 13–19   FIGURE 13–20

If we allow t to vary from $-\infty$ to $+\infty$, the point $P(x, y, z)$ given by Eq. (2) will traverse the infinite line L through P_1. These equations may be interpreted as parametric equations of the line. In order to obtain its Cartesian equations, we may eliminate t, thereby obtaining

$$\frac{x - x_1}{A} = \frac{y - y_1}{B} = \frac{z - z_1}{C}. \tag{3}$$

If any one of the constants A, B, or C is zero in a denominator in Eq. (3), the corresponding numerator must also be zero. This follows at once from the parametric form, Eq. (2), which shows, for example, that

$$x - x_1 = tA \quad \text{and} \quad A = 0$$

together imply that

$$x - x_1 = 0.$$

Thus, when one of the denominators in Eq. (3) vanishes, we interpret the equations to say that the corresponding numerator must vanish. With this interpretation, Eqs. (3) may always be used.

Planes. To obtain the equation of a *plane*, we suppose that a point $P_1(x_1, y_1, z_1)$ on the plane and a nonzero normal vector

$$\mathbf{N} = A\mathbf{i} + B\mathbf{j} + C\mathbf{k} \tag{4}$$

perpendicular to the plane are given (Fig. 13–20). Then the point $P(x, y, z)$ will lie in the plane if and only if the vector $\overrightarrow{P_1P}$ is perpendicular to $\mathbf{N}$; that is, if and only if

$$\mathbf{N} \cdot \overrightarrow{P_1P} = 0$$

or

$$A(x - x_1) + B(y - y_1) + C(z - z_1) = 0. \tag{5}$$

This equation may also be put in the form

$$Ax + By + Cz = D, \tag{6}$$

where D is the constant $Ax_1 + By_1 + Cz_1$. Conversely, if we start from any linear equation such as (6), we may find a point $P_1(x_1, y_1, z_1)$ whose coordinates do satisfy it, that is, such that

$$Ax_1 + By_1 + Cz_1 = D.$$

Then, by subtraction, we may put the given equation (6) into the form of Eq. (5) and factor it into the dot product

$$\mathbf{N} \cdot \overrightarrow{P_1 P} = 0,$$

with $\mathbf{N}$ as in Eq. (4). This says that the constant vector $\mathbf{N}$ is perpendicular to the vector $\overrightarrow{P_1 P}$ for every pair of points P_1 and P whose coordinates satisfy the equation. Hence the locus of points $P(x, y, z)$ whose coordinates satisfy such a linear equation is a plane and the vector $A\mathbf{i} + B\mathbf{j} + C\mathbf{k}$, having the same coefficients as x, y, and z have in the given equation, is normal to the plane.

EXAMPLE 1. Find the distance from the point $P(2, -3, 4)$ to the plane $x + 2y + 2z = 13$.

Solution (a). The vector $\mathbf{N} = \mathbf{i} + 2\mathbf{j} + 2\mathbf{k}$ is normal to the given plane, and the line L:

$$\frac{x - 2}{1} = \frac{y + 3}{2} = \frac{z - 4}{2}$$

goes through P and is parallel to $\mathbf{N}$. Hence L is normal to the plane. If we denote the common ratio in the equations for L by t,

$$\frac{x - 2}{1} = \frac{y + 3}{2} = \frac{z - 4}{2} = t,$$

we have

$$x = t + 2, \qquad y = 2t - 3, \qquad z = 2t + 4$$

as parametric equations of the line in terms of the parameter t. Substituting these into the equation of the plane, we obtain

$$(t + 2) + 2(2t - 3) + 2(2t + 4) = 13,$$

or $t = 1$ at the point of intersection of the plane and the line L. That is, $Q(3, -1, 6)$ is the point of intersection. Then the distance from the point to the plane is simply the distance between $P(2, -3, 4)$ and $Q(3, -1, 6)$, Fig. 13-21(a). Hence

$$d = \sqrt{(3 - 2)^2 + (-1 + 3)^2 + (6 - 4)^2} = 3.$$

Solution (b). Let R be any point of the plane and project the skew segment $\overrightarrow{RP}$ onto a line normal to the plane. This will give the distance d from the point P to the plane. (See Fig. 13-21b.) The plane intersects the x-axis at $(13, 0, 0)$ which we take as point R on the plane. Also $\mathbf{N} = \mathbf{i} + 2\mathbf{j} + 2\mathbf{k}$ is normal to the plane. Minus $\mathbf{N}$ is also normal to the plane. If we project the

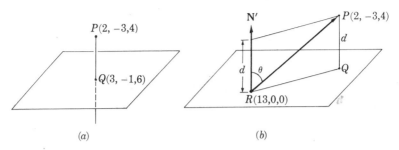

FIGURE 13–21

vector $\overrightarrow{RP}$ = $-11\mathbf{i}$ $-$ $3\mathbf{j}$ + $4\mathbf{k}$ onto that normal $\mathbf{N}'$ = $+\mathbf{N}$ or $-\mathbf{N}$ which makes an angle $\theta < 90°$ with RP, we may obtain the distance d from the equation

$$d = |\overrightarrow{RP}|\cos\theta = \frac{|\mathbf{N}'|\,|\overrightarrow{RP}|\cos\theta}{|\mathbf{N}'|}$$

$$= \frac{\mathbf{N}'\cdot\overrightarrow{RP}}{|\mathbf{N}'|}.$$

Taking $\mathbf{N}'$ = $\pm\mathbf{N}$ (the sign to be decided later), we find

$$\mathbf{N}'\cdot\overrightarrow{RP} = \pm(-11-6+8) = \pm(-9),$$

$$|\mathbf{N}'| = \sqrt{(\pm1)^2+(\pm2)^2+(\pm2)^2} = 3,$$

and

$$d = \frac{\pm(-9)}{3}.$$

Clearly, we should take the ambiguous sign to be $-$, that is, $\mathbf{N}'$ = $-\mathbf{N}$, and we then find $d = 3$.

EXAMPLE 2. Find the angle between the two planes $2x + y - 2z = 5$ and $3x - 6y - 2z = 7$.

Solution. Clearly the angle between two planes, Fig. 13–22, is the same as the angle between their normals. (Actually there are two angles in each case, namely θ and $180° - \theta$.) From the equations of the planes we may read off their normal vectors:

$$\mathbf{N}_1 = 2\mathbf{i} + \mathbf{j} - 2\mathbf{k}, \quad \mathbf{N}_2 = 3\mathbf{i} - 6\mathbf{j} - 2\mathbf{k}.$$

Then

$$\cos\theta = \frac{\mathbf{N}_1\cdot\mathbf{N}_2}{|\mathbf{N}_1|\,|\mathbf{N}_2|} = \frac{4}{21}, \quad \theta = \cos^{-1}\left(\frac{4}{21}\right) \approx 79°.$$

EXAMPLE 3. Find a vector parallel to the line of intersection of the two planes in the example above.

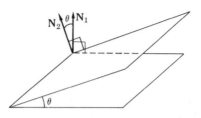

FIGURE 13–22

Solution. The requirements are met by the vector

$$\mathbf{v} = \mathbf{N}_1 \times \mathbf{N}_2 = \begin{vmatrix} \mathbf{i} & \mathbf{j} & \mathbf{k} \\ 2 & 1 & -2 \\ 3 & -6 & -2 \end{vmatrix} = -14\mathbf{i} - 2\mathbf{j} - 15\mathbf{k}.$$

In connection with the last two examples, it should be noted that any two intersecting planes determine a straight line in space. The equations of the two planes are satisfied simultaneously only by points on the line of intersection. Hence a pair of simultaneous linear equations may be interpreted as representing a line, namely, the line of intersection of the two planes represented by the individual equations. For example, recall the Eqs. (3),

$$\frac{x - x_1}{A} = \frac{y - y_1}{B} = \frac{z - z_1}{C}, \tag{3'}$$

which we found for the line L through the point $P_1(x_1, y_1, z_1)$ and parallel to the vector $\mathbf{v} = A\mathbf{i} + B\mathbf{j} + C\mathbf{k}$. This is equivalent to the three simultaneous equations

$$B(x - x_1) = A(y - y_1),$$
$$C(x - x_1) = A(z - z_1), \tag{7}$$
$$C(y - y_1) = B(z - z_1).$$

Each of these equations represents a plane. Any pair of them represents the line of intersection of the corresponding pair of planes. There are three such pairs of planes, namely 1st and 2nd, 1st and 3rd, 2nd and 3rd. But the three lines of intersection so determined are all identical; that is, there is just *one* line of intersection.

To see that this is so, we consider three separate cases.

Case 1. If any two of the three coefficients A, B, C are zero and the third one is different from zero, then one of the three equations in (7) reduces to $0 = 0$, which imposes no restriction on (x, y, z), while the other two equations represent two planes that intersect in a common line.

Case 2. If only one of the coefficients is zero, say $A = 0$ and $BC \neq 0$, then the first two of Eqs. (7) say simply that $x = x_1$. These two equations thus represent just one plane and the intersection of this plane with the plane

$$C(y - y_1) = B(z - z_1)$$

is the line L.

Case 3. If $A \neq 0$, we may multiply Eq. (7_1) by C/A and Eq. (7_2) by B/A and subtract one from the other to obtain Eq. (7_3). Thus we might just as well ignore the third equation, since it contains no new information.

In all cases, we see that the three Eqs. (7) reduce to just two independent equations, and the three planes intersect in one straight line.

The Eqs. (3) for a line are said to be in *standard form*. The line determined by the two planes in Example 2 may be given in standard form by finding any one point, for example $(9, 1, 7)$, on both planes and then A, B, and C may be read from the coefficients of $\mathbf{v} = \mathbf{N}_1 \times \mathbf{N}_2$ (or, from $-\mathbf{v}$). Thus one obtains

$$\frac{x - 9}{14} = \frac{y - 1}{2} = \frac{z - 7}{15}$$

as "standard form" equations of the line.

EXAMPLE 4. Find the equation of the plane that passes through the two points $P_1(1, 0, -1)$ and $P_2(-1, 2, 1)$ and is parallel to the line of intersection of the planes $3x + y - 2z = 6$ and $4x - y + 3z = 0$.

Solution. Our main problem is to find a vector $\mathbf{N}$, normal to the plane in question. The line of intersection of the two given planes is parallel to the vector

$$\mathbf{v} = \mathbf{N}_1 \times \mathbf{N}_2 = \begin{vmatrix} \mathbf{i} & \mathbf{j} & \mathbf{k} \\ 3 & 1 & -2 \\ 4 & -1 & 3 \end{vmatrix} = \mathbf{i} - 17\mathbf{j} - 7\mathbf{k},$$

where $\mathbf{N}_1$ and $\mathbf{N}_2$ are normals to the two given planes. The vector $\overrightarrow{P_1P_2} = -2\mathbf{i} + 2\mathbf{j} + 2\mathbf{k}$ is to lie in the required plane. Now we may also slide $\mathbf{v}$ parallel to itself until it also lies in the required plane (since the plane is to be parallel to $\mathbf{v}$). Hence we may take

$$\mathbf{N} = \overrightarrow{P_1P_2} \times \mathbf{v} = 20\mathbf{i} - 12\mathbf{j} + 32\mathbf{k}$$

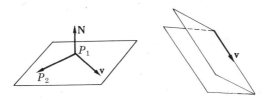

FIGURE 13–23

as a vector normal to the plane. Actually, $\frac{1}{4}\mathbf{N} = 5\mathbf{i} - 3\mathbf{j} + 8\mathbf{k}$ serves just as well. From this normal vector, we may substitute

$$A = 5, \quad B = -3, \quad C = 8$$

in Eq. (5), together with $x_1 = 1$, $y_1 = 0$, $z_1 = -1$, since $P_1(1, 0, -1)$ is to lie in the plane. The required plane is therefore

$$5(x - 1) - 3(y - 0) + 8(z + 1) = 0$$

or

$$5x - 3y + 8z + 3 = 0.$$

Problems

1. Find the coordinates of the point P in which the line

$$\frac{x - 1}{2} = \frac{y + 1}{-1} = \frac{z}{3}$$

intersects the plane $3x + 2y - z = 5$.

2. Find parametric and Cartesian equations of the line joining the points $A(1, 2, -1)$ and $B(-1, 0, 1)$.

3. Show, by vector methods, that the distance from the point $P_1(x_1, y_1, z_1)$ to the plane $Ax + By + Cz - D = 0$ is

$$\frac{|Ax_1 + By_1 + Cz_1 - D|}{\sqrt{A^2 + B^2 + C^2}}.$$

4. (a) Define what is meant by the angle between a line and a plane. (b) Find the acute angle between the line

$$\frac{x + 1}{2} = \frac{y}{3} = \frac{z - 3}{6}$$

and the plane $10x + 2y - 11z = 3$.

5. Find a plane that passes through the point $(1, -1, 3)$ and is parallel to the plane $3x + y + z = 7$.

6. Show that the equations obtained by substituting different values for the constant D in the equation

$$2x + 3y - 6z = D$$

represent a family of parallel planes. What is the distance between two of these planes, one corresponding, say, to $D = D_1$ and the other to $D = D_2$?

7. Prove that the line

$$\frac{x - 1}{2} = \frac{y + 1}{3} = \frac{z - 2}{4}$$

is parallel to the plane $x - 2y + z = 5$.

8. Find a plane through the points $A(1, 1, -1)$, $B(2, 0, 2)$, and $C(0, -2, 1)$.

9. Let $P_i(x_i, y_i, z_i)$, $i = 1, 2, 3$, be three points. What is the locus described by the equation

$$\begin{vmatrix} x & y & z & 1 \\ x_1 & y_1 & z_1 & 1 \\ x_2 & y_2 & z_2 & 1 \\ x_3 & y_3 & z_3 & 1 \end{vmatrix} = 0?$$

10. Find a plane through $A(1, -2, 1)$ and perpendicular to the vector from the origin to A.

11. Find a plane through $P_0(2, 1, -1)$ and perpendicular to the line of intersection of the planes $2x + y - z = 3$, $x + 2y + z = 2$.

12. Find a plane through the points $P_1(1, 2, 3)$, $P_2(3, 2, 1)$, and perpendicular to the plane $4x - y + 2z = 7$.

13. Find the distance from the origin to the line

$$\frac{x - 2}{3} = \frac{y - 1}{4} = \frac{2 - z}{5}.$$

14. (a) Prove that three points A, B, C are collinear if and only if $\overrightarrow{AC} \times \overrightarrow{AB} = 0$. (b) Are the points $A(1, 2, -3)$, $B(3, 1, 0)$, $C(-3, 4, -9)$ collinear?

15. Prove that four points A, B, C, D are coplanar if and only if $\overrightarrow{AD} \cdot (\overrightarrow{AB} \times \overrightarrow{BC}) = 0$.

16. Show that the line of intersection of the planes

$$x + 2y - 2z = 5 \quad \text{and} \quad 5x - 2y - z = 0$$

is parallel to the line

$$\frac{x + 3}{2} = \frac{y}{3} = \frac{z - 1}{4}.$$

Find the plane determined by these two lines.

17. Show that the lines

$$\frac{x - 2}{1} = \frac{y - 2}{3} = \frac{z - 3}{1} \quad \text{and} \quad \frac{x - 2}{1} = \frac{y - 3}{4} = \frac{z - 4}{2}$$

intersect. Find the plane determined by these two lines.

18. Find the direction cosines (Article 13-3, Problem 15) of the line

$$2x + y - z = 5, \qquad x - 3y + 2z = 2.$$

19. The equation $\mathbf{N} \cdot \overrightarrow{P_1P} = 0$ represents a plane through P_1 perpendicular to $\mathbf{N}$. What locus does the inequality $\mathbf{N} \cdot \overrightarrow{P_1P} > 0$ represent? Give a reason for your answer.

20. The unit vector $\mathbf{u}$ makes angles α, β, γ, respectively, with the positive x-, y-, z-axes. Find the plane that is normal to $\mathbf{u}$ and goes through $P_0(x_0, y_0, z_0)$.

13–6 Products of three or more vectors. Certain products involving three or more vectors arise in physical and engineering problems. For example (see Sears, *Electricity and Magnetism*, p. 286), the electromotive force $\overrightarrow{dE}$ induced in an element of a conducting wire $\overrightarrow{dl}$ moving with velocity **v** through a magnetic field at a point where the flux density is **B** is given by $\overrightarrow{dE} = (\mathbf{B} \times \overrightarrow{dl}) \cdot \mathbf{v}$. Here the factor in parentheses is a vector, and the result of forming the scalar product of this vector and **v** is a scalar. It is a real economy in thinking to represent the result in the compact vector form which removes the necessity of carrying factors such as the sine of the angle between **B** and $\overrightarrow{dl}$ and the cosine of the angle between the normal to their plane and the velocity vector **v**. All of these are automatically taken account of by the given product of three vectors.

Triple scalar product. The product $(\mathbf{A} \times \mathbf{B}) \cdot \mathbf{C}$, called the *triple scalar product*, has the following geometrical significance. The vector $\mathbf{N} = \mathbf{A} \times \mathbf{B}$ is normal to the base of the parallelepiped determined by the vectors **A**, **B**,

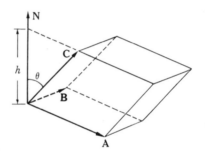

FIGURE 13–24

and **C** in Fig. 13–24. The magnitude of **N** equals the area of the base determined by **A** and **B**. Thus

$$(\mathbf{A} \times \mathbf{B}) \cdot \mathbf{C} = \mathbf{N} \cdot \mathbf{C} = |\mathbf{N}| \, |\mathbf{C}| \cos \theta$$

is, except perhaps for sign, the *volume of a box* of edges **A**, **B**, and **C**, since

$$|\mathbf{N}| = |\mathbf{A} \times \mathbf{B}| = \text{area of base}$$

and

$$|\mathbf{C}| \cos \theta = \pm h = \pm \text{ altitude of box.}$$

In case **C** and $\mathbf{A} \times \mathbf{B}$ lie on the same side of the plane determined by **A** and **B**, the triple scalar product will be positive. But if the vectors **A**, **B**, and **C** are so oriented as to form a left-handed system, then $(\mathbf{A} \times \mathbf{B}) \cdot \mathbf{C}$ is negative. By successively considering the plane of **B** and **C**, then the plane of **C** and **A**, as the base of the box, it is readily seen that

$$(\mathbf{A} \times \mathbf{B}) \cdot \mathbf{C} = (\mathbf{B} \times \mathbf{C}) \cdot \mathbf{A} = (\mathbf{C} \times \mathbf{A}) \cdot \mathbf{B}. \tag{1}$$

Since the dot product is commutative, we also have

$$(\mathbf{B} \times \mathbf{C}) \cdot \mathbf{A} = \mathbf{A} \cdot (\mathbf{B} \times \mathbf{C}),$$

so that Eq. (1) gives the result

$$(\mathbf{A} \times \mathbf{B}) \cdot \mathbf{C} = \mathbf{A} \cdot (\mathbf{B} \times \mathbf{C}). \tag{2}$$

Equation (2) says that the dot and the cross may be interchanged in the triple scalar product, provided only that the multiplications are performed in a way that "makes sense." Thus $(\mathbf{A} \cdot \mathbf{B}) \times \mathbf{C}$ is excluded on the ground that $(\mathbf{A} \cdot \mathbf{B})$ is a scalar and we never "cross" a scalar and a vector.

The triple scalar product in Eq. (2) is conveniently expressed in determinant form as follows:

$$\mathbf{A} \cdot (\mathbf{B} \times \mathbf{C}) = \begin{vmatrix} a_1 & a_2 & a_3 \\ b_1 & b_2 & b_3 \\ c_1 & c_2 & c_3 \end{vmatrix}, \tag{3}$$

as the reader may verify by first considering the determinant representation for $\mathbf{B} \times \mathbf{C}$. For if one interprets the dot product of $\mathbf{A} = a_1\mathbf{i} + a_2\mathbf{j} + a_3\mathbf{k}$ and this vector $\mathbf{B} \times \mathbf{C} = B_1\mathbf{i} + B_2\mathbf{j} + B_3\mathbf{k}$ as being formed by replacing the unit vectors $\mathbf{i}$, $\mathbf{j}$, and $\mathbf{k}$ in the latter equation by the coefficients a_1, a_2, and a_3 respectively, then this replacement may as well be carried out before the determinant for $\mathbf{B} \times \mathbf{C}$ is expanded. The result will be that given in Eq. (3).

A product which involves three vectors but is much simpler than the triple scalar product is $(\mathbf{A} \cdot \mathbf{B})\mathbf{C}$. Here the scalar, $s = \mathbf{A} \cdot \mathbf{B}$, multiplies $\mathbf{C}$ and we have simply the result $s\mathbf{C}$.

Triple vector product. The triple vector products $(\mathbf{A} \times \mathbf{B}) \times \mathbf{C}$ and $\mathbf{A} \times (\mathbf{B} \times \mathbf{C})$ are, in general, not equal. Each of them can be expressed rather simply in terms of the vectors involved, by formulas which we shall now derive.

To focus our attention, let us consider the vector product $(\mathbf{A} \times \mathbf{B}) \times \mathbf{C}$. We shall show that this is given by

$$(\mathbf{A} \times \mathbf{B}) \times \mathbf{C} = (\mathbf{A} \cdot \mathbf{C})\mathbf{B} - (\mathbf{B} \cdot \mathbf{C})\mathbf{A}. \tag{4}$$

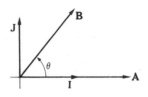

FIGURE 13–25

In the special case where any one of the vectors is the zero vector, Eq. (4) is certainly true, since both sides of it are then zero. Also, if none of the vectors is zero, but if $B = sA$ for some scalar s, then again both sides of Eq. (4) are zero. Now we consider the case where none of the vectors is zero and where A and B are not parallel. The vector on the left in Eq. (4) is parallel to the plane determined by A and B, so that it is possible to find scalars m and n such that

$$(A \times B) \times C = mA + nB. \tag{5}$$

To facilitate the calculation of m and n, we introduce orthogonal unit vectors I and J in the plane of A and B with $I = A/|A|$ (Fig. 13–25). We also introduce a third unit vector $K = I \times J$, and write all our vectors in terms of these unit vectors I, J, and K:

$$A = a_1 I,$$
$$B = b_1 I + b_2 J, \tag{6}$$
$$C = c_1 I + c_2 J + c_3 K.$$

Then

$$A \times B = a_1 b_2 K$$

and

$$(A \times B) \times C = a_1 b_2 c_1 J - a_1 b_2 c_2 I. \tag{7}$$

Comparing this with the right side of Eq. (5), we have

$$m(a_1 I) + n(b_1 I + b_2 J) = a_1 b_2 c_1 J - a_1 b_2 c_2 I.$$

This is equivalent to the pair of scalar equations

$$m a_1 + n b_1 = -a_1 b_2 c_2,$$
$$n b_2 = a_1 b_2 c_1.$$

If b_2 were equal to zero, A and B would be parallel, contrary to hypothesis. Hence b_2 is not zero and we may solve the last equation for n. We find

$$n = a_1 c_1 = A \cdot C.$$

Then, by substitution,

$$m a_1 = -n b_1 - a_1 b_2 c_2$$
$$= -a_1 c_1 b_1 - a_1 b_2 c_2,$$

and since $|\mathbf{A}| = a_1 \neq 0$, we may divide by a_1 and have

$$m = -(b_1 c_1 + b_2 c_2) = -(\mathbf{B} \cdot \mathbf{C}).$$

When these values are substituted for m and n in Eq. (5), we obtain the result given in Eq. (4).

The identity

$$(\mathbf{B} \times \mathbf{C}) \times \mathbf{A} = (\mathbf{B} \cdot \mathbf{A})\mathbf{C} - (\mathbf{C} \cdot \mathbf{A})\mathbf{B} \tag{8a}$$

follows from Eq. (4) by a simple interchange of the letters $\mathbf{A}$, $\mathbf{B}$, and $\mathbf{C}$. If we now interchange the factors $\mathbf{B} \times \mathbf{C}$ and $\mathbf{A}$ we must change the sign on the right side of the equation. This gives the following identity, which is a companion of Eq. (4):

$$\boxed{\mathbf{A} \times (\mathbf{B} \times \mathbf{C}) = (\mathbf{A} \cdot \mathbf{C})\mathbf{B} - (\mathbf{A} \cdot \mathbf{B})\mathbf{C}.} \tag{8b}$$

The identities in Eqs. (4) and (8b) make it possible to reduce expressions involving the multiplication of three or more vectors to at most scalars times cross products of two factors.

EXAMPLE 1. Verify the result of Eq. (4) by calculating $(\mathbf{A} \times \mathbf{B}) \times \mathbf{C}$ in two ways, where

$$\mathbf{A} = \mathbf{i} - \mathbf{j} + 2\mathbf{k},$$
$$\mathbf{B} = 2\mathbf{i} + \mathbf{j} + \mathbf{k},$$
$$\mathbf{C} = \mathbf{i} + 2\mathbf{j} - \mathbf{k}.$$

Solution. One method of calculation is to use Eq. (4). This way, we find

$$\mathbf{A} \cdot \mathbf{C} = -3, \quad \mathbf{B} \cdot \mathbf{C} = 3,$$

and hence

$$(\mathbf{A} \times \mathbf{B}) \times \mathbf{C} = (\mathbf{A} \cdot \mathbf{C})\mathbf{B} - (\mathbf{B} \cdot \mathbf{C})\mathbf{A} = -3\mathbf{B} - 3\mathbf{A}$$
$$= -9(\mathbf{i} + \mathbf{k}).$$

Another way is to calculate

$$\mathbf{A} \times \mathbf{B} = \begin{vmatrix} \mathbf{i} & \mathbf{j} & \mathbf{k} \\ 1 & -1 & 2 \\ 2 & 1 & 1 \end{vmatrix} = -3\mathbf{i} + 3\mathbf{j} + 3\mathbf{k}$$

and then

$$(\mathbf{A} \times \mathbf{B}) \times \mathbf{C} = \begin{vmatrix} \mathbf{i} & \mathbf{j} & \mathbf{k} \\ -3 & 3 & 3 \\ 1 & 2 & -1 \end{vmatrix} = -9\mathbf{i} - 9\mathbf{k}.$$

EXAMPLE 2. Use Eqs. (4) and (8b) to express

$$(\mathbf{A} \times \mathbf{B}) \times (\mathbf{C} \times \mathbf{D})$$

in terms involving at most multiplication by scalars and cross products involving no more than two factors.

Solution. Write, for convenience,

$$\mathbf{C} \times \mathbf{D} = \mathbf{V}.$$

Then we use Eq. (4) to evaluate

$$(\mathbf{A} \times \mathbf{B}) \times \mathbf{V} = (\mathbf{A} \cdot \mathbf{V})\mathbf{B} - (\mathbf{B} \cdot \mathbf{V})\mathbf{A}$$

or

$$(\mathbf{A} \times \mathbf{B}) \times (\mathbf{C} \times \mathbf{D}) = (\mathbf{A} \cdot \mathbf{C} \times \mathbf{D})\mathbf{B} - (\mathbf{B} \cdot \mathbf{C} \times \mathbf{D})\mathbf{A}.$$

The result, as written, expresses the answer as a scalar times **B** minus a scalar times **A**. One could also represent the answer as a scalar times **C** minus a scalar times **D**. Geometrically, the vector is parallel to the line of intersection of the **A**, **B**-plane and the **C**, **D**-plane.

EXAMPLE 3. (See Fig. 13–26.) Let

$$\mathbf{A} = \overrightarrow{PQ}, \qquad \mathbf{B} = \overrightarrow{PS}$$

$$\mathbf{A}' = \overrightarrow{P'Q'}, \qquad \mathbf{B}' = \overrightarrow{P'S'}$$

be sides of parallelograms $PQRS$ and $P'Q'R'S'$ that are related in such a way that PP', QQ', RR', and SS' are parallel to one another and to the unit vector **n**. Show that

$$(\mathbf{A} \times \mathbf{B}) \cdot \mathbf{n} = (\mathbf{A}' \times \mathbf{B}') \cdot \mathbf{n} \quad (9)$$

and discuss the geometrical meaning of this identity.

Solution. From the way the parallelograms are related, it follows that

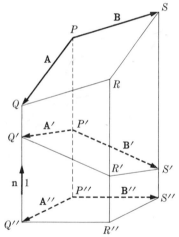

FIGURE 13–26

$$\mathbf{A} = \overrightarrow{PQ} = \overrightarrow{PP'} + \overrightarrow{P'Q'} + \overrightarrow{Q'Q}$$

$$= \overrightarrow{P'Q'} + (\overrightarrow{PP'} - \overrightarrow{QQ'})$$

$$= \mathbf{A}' + s\mathbf{n}$$

for some scalar s, since both $\overrightarrow{PP'}$ and $\overrightarrow{QQ'}$ are parallel to **n**. Similarly,

$$\mathbf{B} = \mathbf{B}' + t\mathbf{n}$$

for some scalar t. Hence

$$\mathbf{A} \times \mathbf{B} = (\mathbf{A}' + s\mathbf{n}) \times (\mathbf{B}' + t\mathbf{n})$$

$$= \mathbf{A}' \times \mathbf{B}' + t(\mathbf{A}' \times \mathbf{n}) + s(\mathbf{n} \times \mathbf{B}') + st(\mathbf{n} \times \mathbf{n}). \tag{10}$$

But $\mathbf{n} \times \mathbf{n} = 0$, while $\mathbf{A}' \times \mathbf{n}$ and $\mathbf{n} \times \mathbf{B}'$ are both perpendicular to $\mathbf{n}$. Therefore when we dot both sides of (10) with $\mathbf{n}$ we get Eq. (9).

Geometrical meaning of Eq. (9). The result (9) says that when the parallelograms $PQRS$ and $P'Q'R'S'$ are any two plane sections of a prism with sides parallel to $\mathbf{n}$, then the box determined by $\mathbf{A}$, $\mathbf{B}$, and $\mathbf{n}$ has the same volume as the box determined by $\mathbf{A}'$, $\mathbf{B}'$, and $\mathbf{n}$. Thus, in particular, we may replace the right side of (9) by $(\mathbf{A}'' \times \mathbf{B}'') \cdot \mathbf{n}$, where $\mathbf{A}''$ and $\mathbf{B}''$ are sides of a *right* section $P''Q''R''S''$ as in Fig. 13–26. Then $\mathbf{A}'' \times \mathbf{B}''$ is parallel to $\mathbf{n}$, and

$$\mathbf{A}'' \times \mathbf{B}'' = (\text{area right section})\,\mathbf{n}$$

and

$$(\mathbf{A}'' \times \mathbf{B}'') \cdot \mathbf{n} = \text{area right section}.$$

Therefore, by Eq. (9), we have the following interpretation:

$(\mathbf{A} \times \mathbf{B}) \cdot \mathbf{n}$ is the area of the orthogonal projection of the parallelogram determined by $\mathbf{A}$ and $\mathbf{B}$ onto a plane whose unit normal is $\mathbf{n}$.* $\qquad(11)$

In particular,

$$(\mathbf{A} \times \mathbf{B}) \cdot \mathbf{k} = \text{area of projection in the } xy\text{-plane}, \tag{12a}$$

$$(\mathbf{A} \times \mathbf{B}) \cdot \mathbf{j} = \text{area of projection in the } xz\text{-plane}, \tag{12b}$$

$$(\mathbf{A} \times \mathbf{B}) \cdot \mathbf{i} = \text{area of projection in the } yz\text{-plane}. \tag{12c}$$

PROBLEMS

In Problems 1–3, take

$$\mathbf{A} = 4\mathbf{i} - 8\mathbf{j} + \mathbf{k},$$
$$\mathbf{B} = 2\mathbf{i} + \mathbf{j} - 2\mathbf{k},$$
$$\mathbf{C} = 3\mathbf{i} - 4\mathbf{j} + 12\mathbf{k}.$$

---

* This assumes that $\mathbf{A} \times \mathbf{B}$ and $\mathbf{n}$ lie on the same side of the plane $PQRS$. If they are on opposite sides, take the absolute value to get the area.

1. Find $(\mathbf{A} \cdot \mathbf{B})\mathbf{C}$ and $\mathbf{A}(\mathbf{B} \cdot \mathbf{C})$.

2. Find the volume of the box having $\mathbf{A}$, $\mathbf{B}$, $\mathbf{C}$ as three co-terminous edges.

3. (a) Find $\mathbf{A} \times \mathbf{B}$ and use the result to find $(\mathbf{A} \times \mathbf{B}) \times \mathbf{C}$. (b) Find $(\mathbf{A} \times \mathbf{B}) \times \mathbf{C}$ by another method.

4. Prove that any vector $\mathbf{A}$ satisfies the identity

$$\mathbf{A} = \tfrac{1}{2}[\mathbf{i} \times (\mathbf{A} \times \mathbf{i}) + \mathbf{j} \times (\mathbf{A} \times \mathbf{j}) + \mathbf{k} \times (\mathbf{A} \times \mathbf{k})].$$

5. Express the product $\mathbf{R} = (\mathbf{A} \times \mathbf{B}) \times (\mathbf{C} \times \mathbf{D})$ in the form $a\mathbf{C} + b\mathbf{D}$ with scalars a and b.

6. Find the volume of the tetrahedron with vertices at $(0, 0, 0)$, $(1, -1, 1)$, $(2, 1, -2)$, and $(-1, 2, -1)$.

7. Use Eq. (3) to show that

(a) $\mathbf{A} \cdot (\mathbf{C} \times \mathbf{B}) = -\mathbf{A} \cdot (\mathbf{B} \times \mathbf{C})$,

(b) $\mathbf{A} \cdot (\mathbf{A} \times \mathbf{B}) = 0$,

(c) $(\mathbf{A} + \mathbf{D}) \cdot (\mathbf{B} \times \mathbf{C}) = \mathbf{A} \cdot (\mathbf{B} \times \mathbf{C}) + \mathbf{D} \cdot (\mathbf{B} \times \mathbf{C})$.

Interpret the results geometrically.

8. Explain the statement in the text that $(\mathbf{A} \times \mathbf{B}) \times \mathbf{C}$ is parallel to the plane determined by $\mathbf{A}$ and $\mathbf{B}$. Illustrate with a sketch.

9. Explain the statement, at the end of Example 2, that $(\mathbf{A} \times \mathbf{B}) \times (\mathbf{C} \times \mathbf{D})$ is parallel to the line of intersection of the $\mathbf{A}, \mathbf{B}$-plane and the $\mathbf{C}, \mathbf{D}$-plane. Illustrate with a sketch.

10. Find a line in the plane of $P_0(0, 0, 0)$, $P_1(2, 2, 0)$, $P_2(0, 1, -2)$, and perpendicular to the line

$$\frac{x + 1}{3} = \frac{y - 1}{2} = 2z.$$

11. Let $P(1, 2, -1)$, $Q(3, -1, 4)$, and $R(2, 6, 2)$ be three vertices of a parallelogram $PQRS$.

(a) Find the coordinates of S.

(b) Find the area of $PQRS$.

(c) Find the area of the projection of $PQRS$ in the xy-plane; in the yz-plane; in the xz-plane.

12. Show that the area of a parallelogram in space is the square root of the sum of the squares of the areas of its projections on any three mutually orthogonal planes.

13–7 Differentiation of vectors and of their products.

If the components of a vector are differentiable functions of a scalar variable t, then the vector is a differentiable function of t and its derivative is obtained by differentiating the components [see Article 13–2, Eqs. (1) and (2)].

It is also convenient to develop formulas for the derivative of the dot product or the cross product of two vectors each of which is a differentiable function of t. Suppose, for example, that

$$\mathbf{U} = \mathbf{i}f_1(t) + \mathbf{j}g_1(t) + \mathbf{k}h_1(t),$$
$$\mathbf{V} = \mathbf{i}f_2(t) + \mathbf{j}g_2(t) + \mathbf{k}h_2(t), \tag{1}$$

where f, g, and h are differentiable functions of t. Then by the ordinary formulas for differentiating products of scalar functions, it is easy to verify that

$$\boxed{\frac{d}{dt}(\mathbf{U}\cdot\mathbf{V}) = \frac{d\mathbf{U}}{dt}\cdot\mathbf{V} + \mathbf{U}\cdot\frac{d\mathbf{V}}{dt}} \tag{2}$$

and that

$$\boxed{\frac{d}{dt}(\mathbf{U}\times\mathbf{V}) = \frac{d\mathbf{U}}{dt}\times\mathbf{V} + \mathbf{U}\times\frac{d\mathbf{V}}{dt}.} \tag{3}$$

However, instead of appealing to the component-wise verification of the identities in Eqs. (2) and (3), it is instructive to think of how these equations might be established by direct appeal to the Δ-process for calculating derivatives. For example, let

$$\mathbf{W} = \mathbf{U}\times\mathbf{V},$$

where t has some specific value; then give t an increment Δt and denote the new values of the vectors by $\mathbf{U} + \Delta\mathbf{U}$, etc., and have

$$\mathbf{W} + \Delta\mathbf{W} = (\mathbf{U} + \Delta\mathbf{U})\times(\mathbf{V} + \Delta\mathbf{V})$$
$$= \mathbf{U}\times\mathbf{V} + \mathbf{U}\times\Delta\mathbf{V} + \Delta\mathbf{U}\times\mathbf{V} + \Delta\mathbf{U}\times\Delta\mathbf{V},$$

so that

$$\frac{\Delta\mathbf{W}}{\Delta t} = \mathbf{U}\times\frac{\Delta\mathbf{V}}{\Delta t} + \frac{\Delta\mathbf{U}}{\Delta t}\times\mathbf{V} + \frac{\Delta\mathbf{U}}{\Delta t}\times\Delta\mathbf{V}.$$

Now take limits as $\Delta t \to 0$, noting that

$$\lim\frac{\Delta\mathbf{W}}{\Delta t} = \frac{d\mathbf{W}}{dt}, \qquad \lim\frac{\Delta\mathbf{U}}{\Delta t} = \frac{d\mathbf{U}}{dt},$$

$$\lim\Delta\mathbf{V} = \lim\frac{\Delta\mathbf{V}}{\Delta t}\cdot\lim\Delta t = 0,$$

so that

$$\frac{d\mathbf{W}}{dt} = \mathbf{U}\times\frac{d\mathbf{V}}{dt} + \frac{d\mathbf{U}}{dt}\times\mathbf{V},$$

which is equivalent to Eq. (3).

Equations (2) and (3) are just like the equations one has for the derivatives of products of scalar functions u and v, and indeed the proofs by the

Δ-process are the same for vectors and for scalars. The only place we need to be careful is in a derivative involving a cross product; here it is essential that the relative order of the factors be preserved, since a reversal of order is equivalent to a change of sign.

The formula for the derivative of the triple scalar product leads to an interesting identity regarding the derivative of a determinant of order three. Let

$$\begin{aligned}
\mathbf{U} &= u_1\mathbf{i} + u_2\mathbf{j} + u_3\mathbf{k}, \\
\mathbf{V} &= v_1\mathbf{i} + v_2\mathbf{j} + v_3\mathbf{k}, \\
\mathbf{W} &= w_1\mathbf{i} + w_2\mathbf{j} + w_3\mathbf{k},
\end{aligned} \qquad (4)$$

where the components are differentiable functions of a scalar t. Then the identity

$$\frac{d}{dt}(\mathbf{U} \cdot \mathbf{V} \times \mathbf{W}) = \frac{d\mathbf{U}}{dt} \cdot \mathbf{V} \times \mathbf{W} + \mathbf{U} \cdot \frac{d\mathbf{V}}{dt} \times \mathbf{W} + \mathbf{U} \cdot \mathbf{V} \times \frac{d\mathbf{W}}{dt} \qquad (5)$$

is equivalent to

$$\frac{d}{dt}\begin{vmatrix} u_1 & u_2 & u_3 \\ v_1 & v_2 & v_3 \\ w_1 & w_2 & w_3 \end{vmatrix} = \begin{vmatrix} \frac{du_1}{dt} & \frac{du_2}{dt} & \frac{du_3}{dt} \\ v_1 & v_2 & v_3 \\ w_1 & w_2 & w_3 \end{vmatrix} + \begin{vmatrix} u_1 & u_2 & u_3 \\ \frac{dv_1}{dt} & \frac{dv_2}{dt} & \frac{dv_3}{dt} \\ w_1 & w_2 & w_3 \end{vmatrix} + \begin{vmatrix} u_1 & u_2 & u_3 \\ v_1 & v_2 & v_3 \\ \frac{dw_1}{dt} & \frac{dw_2}{dt} & \frac{dw_3}{dt} \end{vmatrix}, \qquad (6)$$

which says that the derivative of a determinant of order three is the sum of three determinants obtained from the original determinant by differentiating one row of it at a time. This result may also be extended to determinants of any order n.

An interesting geometrical result is obtained by differentiating the identity

$$\mathbf{V} \cdot \mathbf{V} = |\mathbf{V}|^2,$$

in the case where $\mathbf{V}$ is a vector of constant magnitude. For then $|\mathbf{V}|^2$ is a constant, so its derivative is zero, and one has

$$\mathbf{V} \cdot \frac{d\mathbf{V}}{dt} + \frac{d\mathbf{V}}{dt} \cdot \mathbf{V} = 0$$

or, since the scalar product is commutative,

$$2\mathbf{V} \cdot \frac{d\mathbf{V}}{dt} = 0.$$

Geometrically, this means that either $\mathbf{V}$ is zero, or $d\mathbf{V}/dt$ is zero and hence $\mathbf{V}$ is constant in direction as well as in magnitude, or else that $d\mathbf{V}/dt$ is

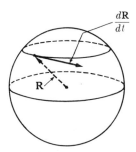

FIGURE 13–27

perpendicular to **V**. For example, if a point P moves about on the surface of a sphere, then the vector **R** from the center to P has constant magnitude and $d\mathbf{R}/dt$, which in this case is the velocity vector of P, is perpendicular to **R** (Fig. 13–27).

PROBLEMS

Find the velocity **v** and acceleration **a** for the motion in each of the following problems (1–3). Also, find the angle θ between **v** and **a** at time $t = 0$.

1. $x = e^t$, $y = e^t \sin t$, $z = e^t \cos t$
2. $x = \tan t$, $y = \sinh 2t$, $z = \operatorname{sech} 3t$
3. $x = \ln (t^2 + 1)$, $y = \tan^{-1} t$, $z = \sqrt{t^2 + 1}$
4. Derive Eq. (2) by the Δ-process.
5. Apply Eqs. (2) and (3) to $\mathbf{U} \cdot \mathbf{V}_1$ with $\mathbf{V}_1 = \mathbf{V} \times \mathbf{W}$ and thereby derive Eq. (5) for

$$\frac{d}{dt} [\mathbf{U} \cdot (\mathbf{V} \times \mathbf{W})].$$

6. If $\mathbf{F}(t) = \mathbf{i}f(t) + \mathbf{j}g(t) + \mathbf{k}h(t)$, where f, g, and h are functions of t which have derivatives of orders one, two, and three, show that

$$\frac{d}{dt} \left[\mathbf{F} \cdot \left(\frac{d\mathbf{F}}{dt} \times \frac{d^2\mathbf{F}}{dt^2} \right) \right] = \mathbf{F} \cdot \left(\frac{d\mathbf{F}}{dt} \times \frac{d^3\mathbf{F}}{dt^3} \right).$$

Explain why the answer contains just this one term rather than the three terms which one might expect.

13–8 Space curves, curvature, and arc length. Let $P(x, y, z)$ be a point whose position in space is given by the equations

$$x = f(t), \qquad y = g(t), \qquad z = h(t), \tag{1}$$

where f, g, and h are differentiable functions of t. As t varies continuously, the locus of P is a curve in space.

For example, the equations

$$x = a \cos \omega t, \qquad y = a \sin \omega t, \qquad z = bt, \tag{2}$$

where a, b, and ω are positive constants, represents a circular helix (Fig. 13–28).

If we let P_0 be any fixed point on the space curve, and adopt a positive direction for measuring distance along the curve from P_0 (for example, let P_0 be the position of P when $t = 0$ and let arc length be measured in the direction in which P first moves away from P_0 as t takes on positive values), then the position of P on the curve becomes a function of the arc length s from P_0 to P. Then the vector

$$\mathbf{R} = \mathbf{i}x + \mathbf{j}y + \mathbf{k}z \tag{3}$$

from the origin to P is also a function of s and we propose to discuss the geometrical significance of the derivative,

$$\frac{d\mathbf{R}}{ds} = \mathbf{i}\frac{dx}{ds} + \mathbf{j}\frac{dy}{ds} + \mathbf{k}\frac{dz}{ds}. \tag{4}$$

If we calculate the derivative from the definition

$$\frac{d\mathbf{R}}{ds} = \lim_{\Delta s \to 0} \frac{\Delta \mathbf{R}}{\Delta s},$$

we have (Fig. 13–29)

$$\frac{\Delta \mathbf{R}}{\Delta s} = \text{a vector} \left(\text{of magnitude } \frac{\text{chord } PQ}{\text{arc } PQ} \right) \text{ directed along the secant line } PQ.$$

As $Q \to P$ and $\Delta s \to 0$, the direction of the secant line approaches the

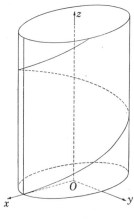

FIGURE 13–28

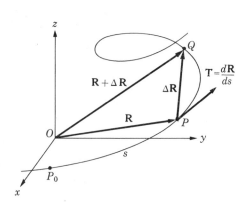

FIGURE 13–29

direction of the tangent to the curve at P, while the ratio of chord to arc approaches unity (for a "smooth" curve). Therefore the limit of $\Delta R/\Delta s$ is a unit vector tangent to the curve at P and pointing in the direction in which arc length increases along the curve. In other words, the vector $\mathbf{T}$, which is defined by the equation

$$\frac{d\mathbf{R}}{ds} = \mathbf{T},\qquad(5)$$

is a *unit* vector *tangent* to the space curve described by the end point P of the vector $\mathbf{R} = \overrightarrow{OP}$.

EXAMPLE 1. From Eqs. (2) and (4), we find

$$\mathbf{T} = \frac{d\mathbf{R}}{ds} = \mathbf{i}\frac{dx}{ds} + \mathbf{j}\frac{dy}{ds} + \mathbf{k}\frac{dz}{ds}$$

$$= \mathbf{i}\left(-a\omega \sin \omega t\,\frac{dt}{ds}\right) + \mathbf{j}\left(a\omega \cos \omega t\,\frac{dt}{ds}\right) + \mathbf{k}\left(b\,\frac{dt}{ds}\right)$$

as the unit vector tangent to the helix at any point P. To determine the magnitude of the scalar factor dt/ds, we use the fact that

$$|\mathbf{T}| = 1, \qquad \text{hence} \qquad \mathbf{T} \cdot \mathbf{T} = 1.$$

This leads to

$$\left(\frac{dt}{ds}\right)^2 (a^2\omega^2 + b^2) = 1,$$

so that

$$\frac{dt}{ds} = \pm \frac{1}{\sqrt{a^2\omega^2 + b^2}}.$$

Since dt/ds is a constant, we may as well agree to take it to be positive so that s is an increasing function of t. Then we have

$$\mathbf{T} = \frac{a\omega\,(-\mathbf{i} \sin \omega t + \mathbf{j} \cos \omega t) + b\mathbf{k}}{\sqrt{a^2\omega^2 + b^2}}.$$

If we combine the results of Eqs. (4) and (5), we have

$$\mathbf{T} = \mathbf{i}\frac{dx}{ds} + \mathbf{j}\frac{dy}{ds} + \mathbf{k}\frac{dz}{ds},\qquad(6)$$

and since

$$\mathbf{T} \cdot \mathbf{T} = 1,$$

this means that

$$ds = \pm\sqrt{dx^2 + dy^2 + dz^2}.\qquad(7)$$

The length of an arc of a curve may be calculated by computing ds from (7) and integrating between appropriate limits.

EXAMPLE 2. For the helix, Example 1, we have

$$ds = \sqrt{a^2\omega^2 + b^2}\, dt$$

and

$$s = \sqrt{a^2\omega^2 + b^2} \int dt,$$

where appropriate limits of integration are to be supplied.

The *curvature* of a space curve is defined by the same vector equation as for a plane curve, Eq. (8), Article 12–6. One considers the rate of change of the unit tangent vector $\mathbf{T}$ with respect to arc length s along the curve. Since $\mathbf{T}$ has constant length, its derivative $d\mathbf{T}/ds$ will either be zero (meaning $\mathbf{T}$ has constant direction, that is, the curve is a straight line which has zero curvature) or else it will be normal to $\mathbf{T}$. If we write

$$\boxed{\frac{d\mathbf{T}}{ds} = \kappa\mathbf{N}, \qquad |\mathbf{N}| = 1,} \qquad (8)$$

the scalar κ so defined, ($\kappa \geq 0$), is called the *curvature* of the space curve at P and the unit vector $\mathbf{N}$ is called a *principal normal* to the curve at P.

EXAMPLE 3. For the helix, Eq. (2), we have found

$$\mathbf{T} = \frac{a\omega(-\mathbf{i}\sin\omega t + \mathbf{j}\cos\omega t) + b\mathbf{k}}{\sqrt{a^2\omega^2 + b^2}}$$

and

$$\frac{ds}{dt} = \sqrt{a^2\omega^2 + b^2}.$$

Hence

$$\frac{d\mathbf{T}}{ds} = \frac{d\mathbf{T}/dt}{ds/dt} = \frac{-a\omega^2}{a^2\omega^2 + b^2}(\mathbf{i}\cos\omega t + \mathbf{j}\sin\omega t).$$

Comparing this with Eq. (8), we have

$$\kappa = \left|\frac{d\mathbf{T}}{ds}\right| = \frac{a\omega^2}{a^2\omega^2 + b^2}. \qquad (9)$$

Two limiting cases of Eq. (9) are readily checked. Namely, if $b = 0$, then $z = 0$ in Eq. (2) and the curve reduces to a circle of radius a in the xy-plane, while Eq. (9) reduces to $\kappa = 1/a$, which we recognize as the correct relationship between the curvature and radius of a circle. The other limiting case, $a = 0$, gives

$x = y = 0$ and $z = bt$ in Eq. (2); that is, the point moves along the z-axis, and again in this case, Eq. (9) gives us a correct answer, namely that $\kappa = 0$. In the general case, we note that the curvature of a circular helix is constant and less than the curvature of the circle which is the cross section of the cylinder. It is also worth noting that the principal normal in this case is the vector

$$\mathbf{N} = -(\mathbf{i}\cos\omega t + \mathbf{j}\sin\omega t)$$

$$= -\frac{\mathbf{i}x + \mathbf{j}y}{a},$$

which is parallel to the vector from the point $(0, 0, z)$ on the z-axis to the point $P(x, y, z)$ on the helix.

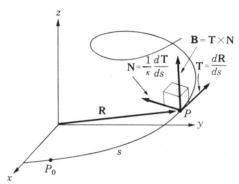

FIGURE 13–30

Once the unit vectors $\mathbf{T}$ and $\mathbf{N}$ have been determined, it is a simple matter to define a third unit vector, perpendicular to both $\mathbf{T}$ and $\mathbf{N}$, by the equation

$$\boxed{\mathbf{B} = \mathbf{T} \times \mathbf{N}.}$$

(10)

The vector $\mathbf{B}$ so defined may be thought of as lying in the plane normal to $\mathbf{T}$ at P and is called the *binormal* at P. These three unit vectors, $\mathbf{T}$, $\mathbf{N}$, and $\mathbf{B}$, form a right-handed system of mutually orthogonal unit vectors which are useful in more thorough investigations of space curves. (Struik, *Differential Geometry*, Chapter 1. Addison-Wesley, 1950.)

PROBLEMS

In Problems 1–4, $\mathbf{R} = \mathbf{i}x + \mathbf{j}y + \mathbf{k}z$. Find the unit vector $\mathbf{T} = d\mathbf{R}/ds$ that is tangent to the given space curve. Take $ds/dt \geq 0$.

1. $x = 6\sin 2t$, $\quad y = 6\cos 2t$, $\quad z = 5t$
2. $x = e^t\cos t$, $\quad y = e^t\sin t$, $\quad z = e^t$
3. $x = 3\cosh 2t$, $\quad y = 3\sinh 2t$, $\quad z = 6t$
4. $x = 3t\cos t$, $\quad y = 3t\sin t$, $\quad z = 4t$

Find the length of the curve, between $t = 0$ and $t = \pi$, for Problems 5-8.

5. The curve of Problem 1.   6. The curve of Problem 2.
7. The curve of Problem 3.   8. The curve of Problem 4.

Find the principal normal vector $\mathbf{N}$, the curvature κ, and the unit binormal vector $\mathbf{B}$ for Problems 9-11.

9. The curve of Problem 1.   10. The curve of Problem 2.
11. The curve of Problem 3.

12. Let $\mathbf{R} = \overrightarrow{OP}$ be the vector from the origin to a moving point P. Let $\mathbf{T}$ and $\mathbf{N}$ be the unit tangent and principal normal vectors, respectively, for the curve described by P. Express the velocity and acceleration vectors $d\mathbf{R}/dt$ and $d^2\mathbf{R}/dt^2$ in terms of their $\mathbf{T}$ and $\mathbf{N}$ components.

In Problems 13-16, r, θ, and z are cylindrical coordinates of a moving point P. The vectors $\mathbf{u}_r = \mathbf{i} \cos \theta + \mathbf{j} \sin \theta$ and $\mathbf{u}_\theta = -\mathbf{i} \sin \theta + \mathbf{j} \cos \theta$ are the usual unit vectors used with polar coordinates, as in Article 12-8.

13. Express the vector $\mathbf{R} = \overrightarrow{OP}$ in terms of cylindrical coordinates and the unit vectors $\mathbf{u}_r$, $\mathbf{u}_\theta$, and $\mathbf{k}$.

14. Derive formulas for the velocity $\mathbf{v} = d\mathbf{R}/dt$ and acceleration $\mathbf{a} = d\mathbf{v}/dt$ in terms of cylindrical coordinates and the unit vectors $\mathbf{u}_r$, $\mathbf{u}_\theta$, and $\mathbf{k}$.

15. A particle P slides without friction along a coil spring having the form of a right circular helix. If the positive z-axis is taken downward, the cylindrical coordinates of P at time t are $r = a$, $z = b\theta$, where a and b are positive constants. If the particle starts at $r = a$, $\theta = 0$ with zero velocity and falls under gravity, the law of conservation of energy then tells us that its speed after it has fallen a vertical distance z is $\sqrt{2gz}$. (a) Find the angular velocity $d\theta/dt$, when $\theta = 2\pi$. (b) Express θ and z as functions of the time t. (c) Determine the tangential and normal components of the velocity $d\mathbf{R}/dt$ and acceleration $d^2\mathbf{R}/dt^2$ as functions of t. Is there any component of acceleration in the direction of the binormal, $\mathbf{B}$?

16. Suppose the curve in Problem 15 is replaced by the conical helix $r = a\theta$, $z = b\theta$. (a) Express the angular velocity $d\theta/dt$ as a function of θ. (b) Express the distance that the particle travels along this helix as a function of θ.

17. Hold two of the three spherical coordinates ρ, ϕ, θ of point P in Fig. 13-4 constant while letting the other coordinate increase. Let $\mathbf{u}$, with subscript corresponding to the coordinate which is permitted to vary, denote the unit vector that points in the direction in which P starts to move under these conditions. (a) Express the three unit vectors $\mathbf{u}_\rho$, $\mathbf{u}_\phi$, $\mathbf{u}_\theta$, which are obtained in this manner, in terms of ρ, ϕ, θ and the unit vectors $\mathbf{i}$, $\mathbf{j}$, $\mathbf{k}$. (b) Show that $\mathbf{u}_\rho \cdot \mathbf{u}_\phi = 0$. (c) Show that $\mathbf{u}_\theta = \mathbf{u}_\rho \times \mathbf{u}_\phi$. (d) Do the vectors $\mathbf{u}_\rho$, $\mathbf{u}_\phi$, $\mathbf{u}_\theta$ form a system of mutually orthogonal vectors? Is the system, in the order given, a right-handed or a left-handed system?

18. If the spherical coordinates ρ, ϕ, θ of a moving point P are differentiable functions of the time t and $\mathbf{R} = \overrightarrow{OP}$ is the vector from the origin to P, express $\mathbf{R}$ and $d\mathbf{R}/dt$ in terms of ρ, ϕ, θ and their derivatives and the unit vectors $\mathbf{u}_\rho$, $\mathbf{u}_\phi$, $\mathbf{u}_\theta$ of Problem 17.

19. Express $ds^2 = dx^2 + dy^2 + dz^2$ in terms of (a) cylindrical coordinates r, θ, z (see Problem 14), (b) spherical coordinates ρ, ϕ, θ (see Problem 18). Interpret your results geometrically in terms of the sides and a diagonal of a rectangular box. Sketch.

20. Using the results of Problem 19, find the lengths of the following curves between $\theta = 0$ and $\theta = \ln 8$: (a) $z = r = ae^\theta$, (b) $\phi = \pi/6$, $\rho = 2e^\theta$.

21. Determine parametric equations giving x, y, z in terms of the parameter θ for the curve of intersection of the sphere $\rho = a$ and the plane $y + z = 0$.

13–9 Cylinders. The locus of points $P(x, y, z)$ that satisfy an equation

$$F(x, y, z) = 0 \tag{1}$$

may be interpreted in a broad sense as being a surface. The simplest surfaces are planes and we have already seen that the equation of a plane is a linear equation; that is, it involves only first powers of the variables x, y, and z.

Next after planes in order of simplicity are *cylinders*. In general, a *cylinder* is a surface generated by a straight line that moves parallel to a given line and passes through a given curve. For example, the given curve may be the curve

$$f(x, y) = 0 \tag{2}$$

in the xy-plane and the generator of the cylinder may always be parallel to the z-axis. Then if the point $P_0(x, y, 0)$ lies on the curve (2), the point $P(x, y, z)$ having the same values of x and y and any value of z also lies on the surface. That is, if its x- and y-coordinates satisfy the equation $f(x, y) = 0$, then the point P lies on the cylinder regardless of the value of its z-coordinate. Conversely, if the point $P(x, y, z)$ is on the cylinder, then the point $P_0(x, y, 0)$ is on the curve in the xy-plane, and hence the x- and y-coordinates of P satisfy Eq. (2). Thus, if we interpret the equation $f(x, y) = 0$ as the equation of a space locus (rather than the equation of a plane curve), the locus is a cylinder with elements parallel to the z-axis (the "missing letter" in the equation) and having the curve $f(x, y) = 0$ in the plane $z = 0$ as a typical cross section.

Example 1. The cylinder

$$y = x^2$$

has elements parallel to the z-axis and a parabolic cross section in the plane $z = 0$. It is called a *parabolic cylinder* (Fig. 13–31).

Clearly the discussion above could be carried through for cylinders with elements parallel to the other coordinate axes, and the result is summarized by saying that *an equation, in Cartesian coordinates, from which one letter is missing, represents, in space, a cylinder with elements parallel to the axis associated with the missing letter.*

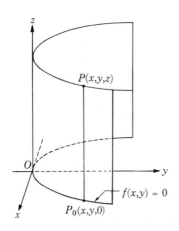

FIGURE 13–31

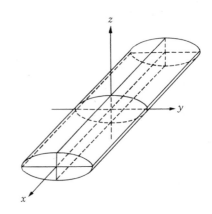

FIGURE 13–32

EXAMPLE 2. The surface
$$y^2 + 4z^2 = 4$$

is an elliptic cylinder with elements parallel to the x-axis. It extends indefinitely in both the negative and positive directions along the x-axis, which in this case is also called the axis of the cylinder, since it passes through the centers of the elliptical cross sections of the cylinder (Fig. 13–32).

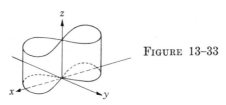

FIGURE 13–33

EXAMPLE 3. The surface
$$r^2 = 2a^2 \cos 2\theta$$

in cylindrical coordinates is a cylinder with elements parallel to the z-axis. Each section perpendicular to the z-axis is a lemniscate. The cylinder extends indefinitely in both the positive and negative directions along the z-axis (Fig. 13–33).

PROBLEMS

Describe and sketch each of the following surfaces [(r, θ, z) are cylindrical coordinates]:

1. $x^2 + y^2 = a^2$ 2. $x^2 - z^2 = 1$
3. $r = 2a \cos \theta$ 4. $r = a(1 + \cos \theta)$
5. $y^2 + z^2 - 4z = 0$ 6. $x^2 + 4z^2 - 4z = 0$

13–10 Quadric surfaces.   A surface whose equation is a quadratic in the variables x, y, and z is called a *quadric* surface. We shall not make an exhaustive study of such surfaces, but shall briefly indicate how the simpler ones which are most frequently encountered may be recognized from their equations. Just as we have plane curves which are parabolas, ellipses, and hyperbolas, we here have surfaces called paraboloids, ellipsoids, and hyperboloids. We often analyze an equation to determine the nature of the curves obtained by cutting the given surface by planes

$$x = \text{constant}, \quad y = \text{constant}, \quad z = \text{constant}$$

perpendicular to the coordinate axes. This is usually sufficient to enable us to visualize the surface.

The *sphere*

$$(x - h)^2 + (y - k)^2 + (z - m)^2 = a^2 \tag{1}$$

with center at (h, k, m) and radius a has already been mentioned in Article 13–2. Likewise, the various *cylinders*

$$Ax^2 + Bxy + Cy^2 + Dx + Ey + F = 0 \tag{2}$$

with elements parallel to the z-axis, and others with elements parallel to the other coordinate axes, are familiar and will not be further discussed. In the examples that follow, we shall refer the surfaces discussed to coordinate axes that yield simple forms of the equations. For example, we take the origin to be at the center of the ellipsoid in Example 1 below. If the center were at (h, k, m) instead, the equation would simply have $x - h$, $y - k$, and $z - m$ in place of x, y, z respectively. We take a, b, and c to be positive constants in every case.

Example 1. The ellipsoid

$$\frac{x^2}{a^2} + \frac{y^2}{b^2} + \frac{z^2}{c^2} = 1 \tag{3}$$

cuts the coordinate axes at $(\pm a, 0, 0)$, $(0, \pm b, 0)$, and $(0, 0, \pm c)$. It is limited in extent to lie inside the rectangular box where

$$|x| \le a, \quad |y| \le b, \quad |z| \le c.$$

Since only even powers of x, y, and z occur in the equation, this surface is symmetric with respect to each of the coordinate planes. The sections cut out by the coordinate planes are ellipses; for example, we have

$$\frac{x^2}{a^2} + \frac{y^2}{b^2} = 1 \quad \text{when} \quad z = 0.$$

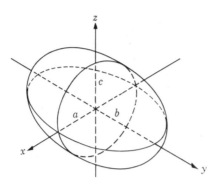

FIGURE 13–34   FIGURE 13–35

Each section cut out by a plane

$$z = z_1, \qquad |z_1| < c$$

is an ellipse

$$\frac{x^2}{a^2\left(1 - \dfrac{z_1^2}{c^2}\right)} + \frac{y^2}{b^2\left(1 - \dfrac{z_1^2}{c^2}\right)} = 1$$

with center on the z-axis and having semiaxes

$$\frac{a}{c}\sqrt{c^2 - z_1^2} \qquad \text{and} \qquad \frac{b}{c}\sqrt{c^2 - z_1^2}.$$

With this information, it is a simple matter to visualize the surface, which is sketched in Fig. 13–34. When two of the three semiaxes a, b, and c are equal, the surface is an ellipsoid of revolution, and when all three are equal, it is a sphere.

EXAMPLE 2. Consider *the elliptic paraboloid* (Fig. 13–35)

$$\frac{x^2}{a^2} + \frac{y^2}{b^2} = \frac{z}{c}. \tag{4}$$

The surface is symmetrical with respect to the planes $x = 0$ and $y = 0$. The only intercept on the axes is at the origin. Since the left side of the equation is non-negative, the surface is limited to the region $z \geq 0$; that is, it lies above the xy-plane. The section cut out from the surface by the yz-plane is

$$x = 0, \qquad y^2 = \frac{b^2}{c} z,$$

which is a parabola with vertex at the origin and opening upward. Similarly, one finds that when

$$y = 0, \qquad x^2 = \frac{a^2}{c} z,$$

which is also such a parabola. When $z = 0$, the cut reduces to the single point $(0, 0, 0)$. Each plane $z = z_1 > 0$ perpendicular to the z-axis cuts the surface in an ellipse of semiaxes

$$a\sqrt{z_1/c} \quad \text{and} \quad b\sqrt{z_1/c}.$$

These semiaxes increase in magnitude as z_1 increases. The paraboloid extends indefinitely upward. When $a = b$ the paraboloid is a paraboloid of revolution. In this case one may also give its equation very simply in cylindrical coordinates as

$$\frac{r^2}{a^2} = \frac{z}{c}. \tag{5}$$

EXAMPLE 3. *The elliptic cone* (Fig. 13–36)

$$\frac{x^2}{a^2} + \frac{y^2}{b^2} = \frac{z^2}{c^2} \tag{6}$$

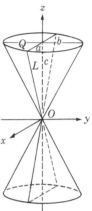

is symmetrical with respect to all three coordinate planes. The plane $z = 0$ cuts the surface in the single point $(0, 0, 0)$. The plane $x = 0$ cuts it in the two intersecting straight lines

$$x = 0, \quad \frac{y}{b} = \pm \frac{z}{c} \tag{7}$$

and when

$$y = 0, \quad \frac{x}{a} = \pm \frac{z}{c}. \tag{8}$$

FIGURE 13–36

The section cut out by a plane $z = z_1 > 0$ is an ellipse with center on the z-axis and vertices lying on the straight lines (7) and (8). In fact, the whole surface is generated by a straight line L passing through the origin and a point Q on the ellipse

$$z = c, \quad \frac{x^2}{a^2} + \frac{y^2}{b^2} = 1.$$

As the point Q traces out the ellipse, the infinite line L generates the surface, which is a cone with elliptic cross sections. To see that this is indeed the case, suppose that $Q(x_1, y_1, z_1)$ is a point on the surface and t is any scalar. Then the vector from O to the point $P(tx_1, ty_1, tz_1)$ is simply t times $\overrightarrow{OQ}$, so that as t varies from $-\infty$ to $+\infty$ the point P traces out the infinite line L. But since Q is assumed to be on the surface, the equation

$$\frac{x_1^2}{a^2} + \frac{y_1^2}{b^2} = \frac{z_1^2}{c^2}$$

is satisfied. Multiplying both sides of this equation by t^2, we see that the point $P(tx_1, ty_1, tz_1)$ is also on the surface. This establishes the validity of the remark that the surface is a cone generated by the line L through O and the point Q on the ellipse.

In case $a = b$, the cone is a right circular cone and its equation in cylindrical coordinates is simply

$$\frac{r}{a} = \frac{z}{c}.$$ (9)

EXAMPLE 4. We now consider the *hyperboloid of one sheet* (Fig. 13–37),

$$\frac{x^2}{a^2} + \frac{y^2}{b^2} - \frac{z^2}{c^2} = 1.$$ (10)

This surface is symmetric with respect to each of the three coordinate planes. The sections cut out by the coordinate planes are:

$$x = 0: \text{ the hyperbola } \frac{y^2}{b^2} - \frac{z^2}{c^2} = 1,$$

$$y = 0: \text{ the hyperbola } \frac{x^2}{a^2} - \frac{z^2}{c^2} = 1,$$ (11)

$$z = 0: \text{ the ellipse } \quad \frac{x^2}{a^2} + \frac{y^2}{b^2} = 1.$$

The plane $z = z_1$ cuts the surface in an ellipse with center on the z-axis and vertices on the hyperbolas in (11). The surface is connected, meaning that it is possible to travel from any point on it to any other point on it without leaving the surface. For this reason, it is said to have *one* sheet, in contrast to the next example, which consists of *two* sheets. In the special case where $a = b$, the surface is a hyperboloid of revolution with equation given in cylindrical coordinates by

$$\frac{r^2}{a^2} - \frac{z^2}{c^2} = 1.$$ (12)

EXAMPLE 5. Next we consider the *hyperboloid of two sheets* (Fig. 13–38),

$$\frac{z^2}{c^2} - \frac{x^2}{a^2} - \frac{y^2}{b^2} = 1.$$ (13)

The surface is symmetric with respect to the three coordinate planes. The plane $z = 0$ does not intersect the surface; in fact, one must have

$$|z| \geq c$$

for real values of x and y in Eq. (13). The hyperbolic sections

$$x = 0: \quad \frac{z^2}{c^2} - \frac{y^2}{b^2} = 1,$$

$$y = 0: \quad \frac{z^2}{c^2} - \frac{x^2}{a^2} = 1$$

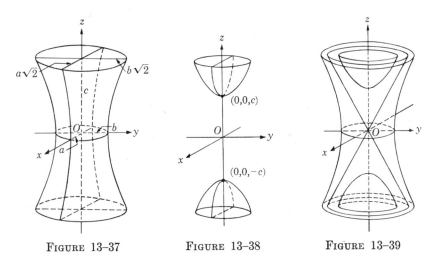

FIGURE 13–37   FIGURE 13–38   FIGURE 13–39

have their vertices and foci on the z-axis. The surface is separated into two portions, one above the plane $z = c$ and the other below the plane $z = -c$. This accounts for its name.

It is worth noting that Eqs. (10) and (13) differ in the number of negative terms that each contains on the left side when the right side is $+1$. The number of negative signs is the same as the number of sheets of the hyperboloid. If we compare with Eq. (6), we see that replacing the unity on the right side of either Eq. (10) or (13) by zero gives the equation of a cone. This cone (Fig. 13–39) is, in fact, asymptotic to both of the hyperboloids (10) and (13) in the same way that the lines

$$\frac{x^2}{a^2} - \frac{y^2}{b^2} = 0$$

are asymptotic to the two hyperbolas

$$\frac{x^2}{a^2} - \frac{y^2}{b^2} = \pm 1$$

in the xy-plane.

EXAMPLE 6. *The hyperbolic paraboloid* (Fig. 13–40)

$$\frac{y^2}{b^2} - \frac{x^2}{a^2} = \frac{z}{c} \tag{14}$$

has symmetry with respect to the planes $x = 0$ and $y = 0$. The sections in these planes are

$$x = 0: \quad y^2 = b^2 \frac{z}{c}, \tag{15a}$$

$$y = 0: \quad x^2 = -a^2 \frac{z}{c}, \tag{15b}$$

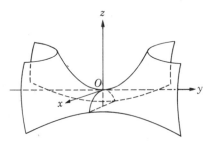

FIGURE 13–40

which are parabolas. In the plane $x = 0$, the parabola opens upward and has vertex at the origin. The parabola in the plane $y = 0$ has the same vertex, but it opens downward. If we cut the surface by a plane $z = z_1 > 0$, the section is a hyperbola,

$$\frac{y^2}{b^2} - \frac{x^2}{a^2} = \frac{z_1}{c}, \tag{16}$$

whose focal axis is parallel to the y-axis and which has its vertices on the parabola in (15a). If, on the other hand, z_1 is negative in Eq. (16), then the focal axis of the hyperbola is parallel to the x-axis, and its vertices lie on the parabola in (15b). Near the origin the surface is shaped very much like a saddle. To a person traveling along the surface in the yz-plane, the origin looks like a minimum. To a person traveling in the xz-plane, on the other hand, the origin looks like a maximum. Such a point is called a *minimax* or *saddle point* of a surface (Fig. 13–40). We shall discuss maximum and minimum points on surfaces in the next chapter.

If $a = b$ in Eq. (14) the surface is not a surface of revolution, but it is possible to express the equation in the alternative form

$$\frac{2x'y'}{a^2} = \frac{z}{c} \tag{17}$$

if we refer it to $x'y'$-axes obtained by rotating the xy-axes through 45°.

PROBLEMS

Describe and sketch each of the following surfaces [(r, θ, z) are cylindrical coordinates]:

1. $x^2 + y^2 + 4x - 6y = z$
2. $x^2 + y^2 + z^2 + 4x - 6y = 3$
3. $x^2 + 4y^2 + z^2 - 8y = 0$
4. $x^2 + 4y^2 + 4z^2 - 8y = 0$
5. $4x^2 + 4y^2 + 4z^2 - 8y = 0$
6. $x^2 - y^2 + z^2 + 4x - 6y = 9$
7. $x^2 - y^2 - z^2 + 4x - 6y = 9$
8. $z^2 = 4x$
9. $z^2 = 4xy$
10. $z = 4xy$

11. $z = r^2$
12. $z = r$
13. $z^2 = r$
14. $z^2 = x^2 + 4y^2$
15. $z^2 = x^2 - 4y^2$
16. $z^2 = 4y^2 - x^2$
17. $z^2 = x^2 + 4y^2 - 2x + 8y + 4z$
18. $z^2 = x^2 + 4y^2 - 2x + 8y + 4z + 1$
19. $x^2 + 4z^2 = 4$
20. $x = y^2 + 4z^2 + 1$
21. $z = r \cos \theta$
22. $z = r \sin \theta$
23. $z = \sin \theta \ (0 \le \theta \le \pi/2)$
24. $z = \cosh \theta \ (0 \le \theta \le \pi/2)$
25. (a) Express the area, $A(z_1)$, of the cross section cut from the ellipsoid

$$\frac{x^2}{a^2} + \frac{y^2}{b^2} + \frac{z^2}{c^2} = 1$$

by the plane $z = z_1$ as a function of z_1. (The area of an ellipse of semiaxes A and B is πAB.) (b) By integration, find the volume of the ellipsoid of part (a). Consider slices made by planes perpendicular to the z-axis. Does your answer give the correct volume of a sphere in case $a = b = c$?

26. By integration, prove that the volume of the segment of the elliptic paraboloid

$$\frac{x^2}{a^2} + \frac{y^2}{b^2} = \frac{z}{c}$$

cut off by the plane $z = h$ is equal to one-half the area of its base times its altitude.

27. (a) By integration, find the volume between the plane $z = 0$ and the plane $z = h$, enclosed by the hyperboloid of one sheet, Eq. (10). (b) Express your answer to part (a) in terms of the altitude h and the areas A_0 and A_h of the plane ends of the segment of the hyperboloid. (c) Verify that the volume of part (a) is also given exactly by the prismoid formula

$$V = h(A_0 + 4A_m + A_h)/6,$$

where A_0 and A_h are the areas of the plane ends of the segment of the hyperboloid and A_m is the area of its mid-section cut out by the plane $z = h/2$.

28. If the hyperbolic paraboloid

$$\frac{y^2}{b^2} - \frac{x^2}{a^2} = \frac{z}{c}$$

is cut by the plane $y = y_1$, the resulting curve is a parabola. Find its vertex and focus.

29. What is the nature, in general, of a surface whose equation in spherical coordinates has the form $\rho = F(\phi)$? Give reasons for your answer.

Describe and sketch the following surfaces, which are special cases of Problem 29.

30. $\rho = a \cos \phi$
31. $\rho = a(1 + \cos \phi)$

REVIEW QUESTIONS AND EXERCISES FOR CHAPTER 13

1. In a single diagram, show the Cartesian, cylindrical, and spherical coordinates of an arbitrary point P, and write the expressions for each set of coordinates in terms of the other two kinds.

2. What is the locus, in space, described by: (a) $x =$ constant, (b) $r =$ constant, (c) $\theta =$ constant, (d) $\rho =$ constant, (e) $\phi =$ constant, (f) $ax + by + cz = d$, (g) $ax^2 + by^2 + cz^2 = d$?

3. What is the length of the vector $a\mathbf{i} + b\mathbf{j} + c\mathbf{k}$? On what theorem of plane geometry does this result depend?

4. Define *scalar product* of two vectors. Which algebraic laws (commutative, associative, distributive) are satisfied by the operations of addition and scalar multiplication of vectors? Which of these laws is (are) not satisfied? Explain. When is the scalar product equal to zero?

5. Suppose that $\mathbf{i}, \mathbf{j}, \mathbf{k}$ is one set of mutually orthogonal unit vectors and $\mathbf{i}', \mathbf{j}', \mathbf{k}'$ is another set of such vectors. Suppose that all the scalar products of a unit vector from one set with a unit vector from the other set are known. Let $\mathbf{A} = a\mathbf{i} + b\mathbf{j} + c\mathbf{k} = a'\mathbf{i}' + b'\mathbf{j}' + c'\mathbf{k}'$ and express a, b, c in terms of a', b', c', and conversely.

6. List four applications of the scalar product.

7. Define *vector product* of two vectors. Which algebraic laws (commutative, associative, distributive) are satisfied by the vector product operation (combined with addition), and which are not? Explain. When is the vector product equal to zero?

8. Derive the formula for expressing the vector product of two vectors as a determinant. What is the effect of interchanging the order of the two vectors and the corresponding rows of the determinant?

9. How may vector and scalar products be used to find the equation of a plane through three given points?

10. With the book closed, develop equations for a line (a) through two given points, (b) through one point and parallel to a given line.

11. With the book closed, develop the equation of a plane (a) through a given point and normal to a given vector, (b) through one point and parallel to a given plane, (c) through a point and perpendicular to each of two given planes.

12. What is the geometrical interpretation of $\mathbf{A} \cdot (\mathbf{B} \times \mathbf{C})$? When is this triple scalar product equal to zero?

13. What is the meaning of (a) $\mathbf{A} \times (\mathbf{B} \times \mathbf{C})$, (b) $\mathbf{A} \times (\mathbf{B} \cdot \mathbf{C})$, (c) $\mathbf{A} \cdot (\mathbf{B} \cdot \mathbf{C})$?

14. Given a parallelogram $PQRS$ in space, how could you find a vector normal to its plane and with length equal to its area?

15. If a vector $\mathbf{V}$ is a differentiable function of t and $|\mathbf{V}| =$ constant, what do you know about $d\mathbf{V}/dt$?

16. Define arc length and curvature of a space curve.

17. For a space curve, explain how to find the unit tangent vector, unit principal normal, and unit binormal.

18. What is the space locus of an equation of the form

(a) $f(x, y) = 0$,   (b) $f(z, r) = 0$,   (c) $z = f(\theta)$, $0 \leq \theta < 2\pi$?

19. Define *quadric surface*. Name and sketch six different quadric surfaces and indicate their equations.

MISCELLANEOUS PROBLEMS FOR CHAPTER 13

1. Find the vector projection of **B** onto **A** if

$$\mathbf{A} = 3\mathbf{i} - \mathbf{j} + \mathbf{k} \quad \text{and} \quad \mathbf{B} = 2\mathbf{i} + \mathbf{j} - 2\mathbf{k}.$$

2. Find the cosine of the angle between the line $(1 - x)/4 = y/3 = -z/5$ and the vector $\mathbf{i} + \mathbf{j}$.

3. Given two noncollinear vectors **A** and **B**. Given also that **A** can be expressed in the form $\mathbf{A} = \mathbf{C} + \mathbf{D}$, where **C** is a vector parallel to **B**, and **D** is a vector perpendicular to **B**. Express **C** and **D** in terms of **A** and **B**.

4. The curve whose vector equation is

$$\mathbf{r} = (t^4 + 2t^2 + 1)\mathbf{i} + (1 - 4t - t^4)\mathbf{j}$$

intersects the line $x + y = 0$, $z = 0$. Find the cosine of the angle which the acceleration vector makes with the radius vector at the point of intersection.

5. *Using vectors*, prove that for any four numbers a, b, c, d we have the inequality $(a^2 + b^2)(c^2 + d^2) \geq (ac + bd)^2$. [*Hint:* Consider $\mathbf{A} = a\mathbf{i} + b\mathbf{j}$ and $\mathbf{B} = c\mathbf{i} + d\mathbf{j}$.]

6. Find a vector parallel to the plane $2x - y - z = 4$ and perpendicular to the vector $\mathbf{i} + \mathbf{j} + \mathbf{k}$.

7. Find a vector which is normal to the plane determined by the points

$$A(1, 0, -1), \quad B(2, -1, 1), \quad \text{and} \quad C(-1, 1, 2).$$

8. Given vectors $\mathbf{A} = 2\mathbf{i} - \mathbf{j} + \mathbf{k}$, $\mathbf{B} = \mathbf{i} + 2\mathbf{j} - \mathbf{k}$, $\mathbf{C} = \mathbf{i} + \mathbf{j} - 2\mathbf{k}$, find a *unit* vector in the plane of **B** and **C** that is $\perp$**A**.

9. By forming the cross product of two appropriate vectors, derive the trigonometric identity $\sin(\alpha - \beta) = \sin \alpha \cos \beta - \cos \alpha \sin \beta$.

10. The line through OA, A being the point $(1, 1, 1)$, is the axis of rotation of a rigid body that is rotating with a constant angular speed of 6 rad/sec. The rotation appears clockwise when we look towards the origin from A. Find the velocity vector of the point of the body that is at the position $(1, 3, 2)$ [see Example 4, Article 4–5].

11. If a particle moves in the xy-plane with velocity **v** and acceleration **a**, show that we have

$$|\mathbf{v} \times \mathbf{a}| = |\mathbf{v}|^3 |\kappa|,$$

where κ is the curvature of the path traced out.

12. Find a vector *of length two* parallel to the line

$$x + 2y + z - 1 = 0, \quad x - y + 2z + 7 = 0.$$

13. Given a tetrahedron with vertices O, A, B, C. A vector is constructed normal to each face, pointing outwards, and having a length equal to the area of the face. Using cross products, prove that the sum of these four outward normals is the zero vector.

14. What angle does the line of intersection of the two planes

$$2x + y - z = 0 \quad \text{and} \quad x + y + 2z = 0$$

make with the x-axis?

15. Let **A** and **C** be given vectors in space, with $\mathbf{A} \neq 0$ and $\mathbf{A} \cdot \mathbf{C} = 0$, and let d be a given scalar. Find a vector **B** that satisfies both equations $\mathbf{A} \times \mathbf{B} = \mathbf{C}$ and $\mathbf{A} \cdot \mathbf{B} = d$ simultaneously. The answer should be given as a formula involving **A**, **C**, and d.

16. Given any two vectors $\mathbf{A} = a_1\mathbf{i} + a_2\mathbf{j}$ and $\mathbf{B} = b_1\mathbf{i} + b_2\mathbf{j}$ in the plane, define a new vector, $\mathbf{A} \otimes \mathbf{B}$, called their "circle product," as follows:

$$\mathbf{A} \otimes \mathbf{B} = (a_1b_1 - a_2b_2)\mathbf{i} + (a_1b_2 + a_2b_1)\mathbf{j}.$$

This product satisfies the following algebraic laws:

(a) $\mathbf{A} \otimes \mathbf{B} = \mathbf{B} \otimes \mathbf{A}$,   (b) $\mathbf{A} \otimes (\mathbf{B} \otimes \mathbf{C}) = (\mathbf{A} \otimes \mathbf{B}) \otimes \mathbf{C}$,
(c) $\mathbf{A} \otimes (\mathbf{B} + \mathbf{C}) = (\mathbf{A} \otimes \mathbf{B}) + (\mathbf{A} \otimes \mathbf{C})$,   (d) $|\mathbf{A} \otimes \mathbf{B}| = |\mathbf{A}|\,|\mathbf{B}|$.

Prove (a) and (d).

17. Find the equations of the straight line that passes through the point $(1, 2, 3)$ and makes an angle of $30°$ with the x-axis and an angle of $60°$ with the y-axis.

18. The line L, whose equations are $x - 2z - 3 = 0$ and $y - 2z = 0$, intersects the plane $x + 3y - z + 4 = 0$. Find the point of intersection P and find the equation of that line in this plane that passes through P and is perpendicular to L.

19. Find the distance of the point $(2, 2, 3)$ from the plane $2x + 3y + 5z = 0$.

20. Given the two parallel planes $Ax + By + Cz + D_1 = 0$ and $Ax + By + Cz + D_2 = 0$, show that the distance between them is given by the formula

$$\frac{|D_1 - D_2|}{|A\mathbf{i} + B\mathbf{j} + C\mathbf{k}|}.$$

21. Consider the straight line through the point $(3, 2, 1)$ and perpendicular to the plane $2x - y + 2z + 2 = 0$. Compute the coordinates of the point of intersection of that line and that plane.

22. Consider the space curve whose parametric equations are $x = t$, $y = t$, $z = \frac{2}{3}t^{3/2}$. Compute the equation of the plane that passes through the point $(1, 1, \frac{2}{3})$ of this curve, and is perpendicular to the tangent of this curve at the same point.

23. Find the equation of the plane parallel to the plane $2x - y + 2z + 4 = 0$ if the point $(3, 2, -1)$ is equidistant from both planes.

24. Given the four points $A = (-2, 0, -3)$, $B = (1, -2, 1)$, $C = (-2, -\frac{13}{5}, \frac{26}{5})$, and $D = (\frac{16}{5}, -\frac{13}{5}, 0)$. (a) Find the equation of the plane through AB that is parallel to CD. (b) Compute the shortest distance between the lines AB and CD.

25. Find the equation of the plane passing through the end points of the three vectors $\mathbf{A} = 3\mathbf{i} - \mathbf{j} + \mathbf{k}$, $\mathbf{B} = \mathbf{i} + 2\mathbf{j} - \mathbf{k}$, and $\mathbf{C} = \mathbf{i} + \mathbf{j} + \mathbf{k}$, supposed to be drawn from the origin.

26. Show that the plane through the three points (x_1, y_1, z_1), (x_2, y_2, z_2), and (x_3, y_3, z_3) is given by

$$\begin{vmatrix} x_1 - x & y_1 - y & z_1 - z \\ x_2 - x & y_2 - y & z_2 - z \\ x_3 - x & y_3 - y & z_3 - z \end{vmatrix} = 0.$$

27. Show that the necessary and sufficient condition that the two straight lines

$$x = a_1 t + b_1, \quad y = a_2 t + b_2, \quad z = a_3 t + b_3,$$

and

$$x = c_1 \tau + d_1, \quad y = c_2 \tau + d_2, \quad z = c_3 \tau + d_3$$

either intersect or be parallel (t and τ are parameters) is

$$\begin{vmatrix} a_1 & c_1 & b_1 - d_1 \\ a_2 & c_2 & b_2 - d_2 \\ a_3 & c_3 & b_3 - d_3 \end{vmatrix} = 0.$$

28. Given the vectors $\mathbf{A} = \mathbf{i} + \mathbf{j} - \mathbf{k}$, $\mathbf{B} = 2\mathbf{i} + \mathbf{j} + \mathbf{k}$, $\mathbf{C} = -\mathbf{i} - 2\mathbf{j} + 3\mathbf{k}$, evaluate (a) $\mathbf{A} \cdot (\mathbf{B} \times \mathbf{C})$, (b) $\mathbf{A} \times (\mathbf{B} \times \mathbf{C})$.

29. Given four points $A = (1, 1, 1)$, $B = (0, 0, 2)$, $C = (0, 3, 0)$, $D = (4, 0, 0)$, find the volume of the tetrahedron with vertices at A, B, C, D, and find the angle between the edges AB and AC.

30. Prove or disprove the formula

$$\mathbf{A} \times [\mathbf{A} \times (\mathbf{A} \times \mathbf{B})] \cdot \mathbf{C} = -|\mathbf{A}|^2 \mathbf{A} \cdot \mathbf{B} \times \mathbf{C}.$$

31. If the four vectors $\mathbf{A}, \mathbf{B}, \mathbf{C}, \mathbf{D}$ are coplanar, show that

$$(\mathbf{A} \times \mathbf{B}) \times (\mathbf{C} \times \mathbf{D}) = 0.$$

32. Prove the following identities in which $\mathbf{i}, \mathbf{j}, \mathbf{k}$ are three mutually perpendicular unit vectors, and $\mathbf{A}, \mathbf{B}, \mathbf{C}$ are any vectors.

(a) $\mathbf{A} \times (\mathbf{B} \times \mathbf{C}) + \mathbf{B} \times (\mathbf{C} \times \mathbf{A}) + \mathbf{C} \times (\mathbf{A} \times \mathbf{B}) = 0.$

(b) $\mathbf{A} \times \mathbf{B} = [\mathbf{A} \cdot (\mathbf{B} \times \mathbf{i})]\mathbf{i} + [\mathbf{A} \cdot (\mathbf{B} \times \mathbf{j})]\mathbf{j} + [\mathbf{A} \cdot (\mathbf{B} \times \mathbf{k})]\mathbf{k}.$

33. Show that

$$(\mathbf{a} \times \mathbf{b}) \cdot (\mathbf{c} \times \mathbf{d}) = \begin{vmatrix} \mathbf{a} \cdot \mathbf{c} & \mathbf{b} \cdot \mathbf{c} \\ \mathbf{a} \cdot \mathbf{d} & \mathbf{b} \cdot \mathbf{d} \end{vmatrix}.$$

34. A curve is given by the parametric equations $x = e^t \sin 2t$, $y = e^t \cos 2t$, $z = 2e^t$. Let P_0 be the point where $t = 0$. Determine (a) the direction cosines of the tangent, principal normal, and binormal at P_0; (b) the curvature at P_0.

35. The *normal plane* to a space curve at any point P of the curve is defined as the plane through P that is perpendicular to the tangent vector. The *osculating plane* at P is the plane containing the tangent and the principal normal.

Given the space curve whose vector equation is $\mathbf{r}(t) = t\mathbf{i} + t^2\mathbf{j} + t^3\mathbf{k}$, find: (a) the equation of the normal plane at $(1, 1, 1)$; (b) the equation of the osculating plane at $(1, 1, 1)$.

36. Given the curve whose vector is $\mathbf{r}(t) = (3t - t^3)\mathbf{i} + 3t^2\mathbf{j} + (3t + t^3)\mathbf{k}$, compute the curvature.

37. Show that the length of the arc described by the end point of

$$\mathbf{R} = 3\cos t\mathbf{i} + 3\sin t\mathbf{j} + t^2\mathbf{k},$$

as t varies from 0 to 2, is $5 + \frac{9}{4}\ln 3$.

38. Sketch the surfaces (a) $(x - 1)^2 + 4(y^2 + z^2) = 16$, (b) $z = r^2$ (cylindrical coordinates), (c) $\rho = a\sin\phi$ (spherical coordinates).

39. Find the equation of the locus of those points in space whose distance from the point $(2, -1, 3)$ is twice their distance from the xy-plane. Name the surface and find its center of symmetry.

40. The curve whose vector equation is

$$\mathbf{r}(t) = 2\sqrt{t}\cos t\mathbf{i} + 3\sqrt{t}\sin t\mathbf{j} + \sqrt{1 - t}\,\mathbf{k}, \qquad (0 \le t \le 1)$$

lies on a quadric surface. Find the equation of this surface and describe it.

41. Find the equation of the sphere that has the two planes $x + y + z - 3 = 0$ and $x + y + z - 9 = 0$ as tangent planes, if the two planes $2x - y = 0$ and $3x - z = 0$ pass through the center of the sphere.

42. The two cylinders $z^3 - x = 0$ and $x^2 - y = 0$ intersect in a curve C. Find the equation of a cylinder parallel to the x-axis which passes through C. This cylinder traces out a curve C' in the yz-plane. Rotate C' about the y-axis and obtain the equation of the surface so generated.

CHAPTER 14

PARTIAL DIFFERENTIATION

14–1 Functions of two or more variables. There are many instances in science, engineering, and everyday life where a quantity w is determined by a number of other quantities. For example, the volume of a right circular cone of radius r and altitude h is

$$V = \tfrac{1}{3}\pi r^2 h. \tag{1}$$

When both r and h are prescribed, the volume is uniquely determined. We say that V is a function of r and h.

DEFINITION. *If w is uniquely determined when the values of x and y are given, we say that w is a single-valued function of x and y and indicate this fact by some notation such as*

$$w = f(x, y). \tag{2}$$

The notation

$$w = f(x, y, z, u, v) \tag{3}$$

means, similarly, that when values are assigned to the five variables x, y, z, u, and v the value of w is uniquely determined. We may also wish to broaden our definition somewhat to include multiple-valued functions w, in which case we would say that to the number pair (x, y) in Eq. (2) there is to correspond one or more values of w. We shall, however, be concerned primarily with single-valued functions. For example, if

$$\rho^2 = x^2 + y^2 + z^2, \tag{4}$$

as in the relationship between $\rho = |\overrightarrow{OP}|$ and the Cartesian coordinates of $P(x, y, z)$, the further condition

$$\rho \geq 0 \tag{5}$$

singles out a unique value of ρ when values are assigned to x, y, and z, namely,

$$\rho = +\sqrt{x^2 + y^2 + z^2}.$$

Continuity. A function $w = f(x, y)$ is said to be *continuous* at (x_0, y_0) provided $w \to w_0 = f(x_0, y_0)$ as $(x, y) \to (x_0, y_0)$, or, in other words, provided $|w - w_0|$ can be made arbitrarily small by making both $|x - x_0|$

and $|y - y_0|$ small. For instance, $\underline{w = xy}$ is continuous at any (x_0, y_0) since

$$|w - w_0| = |xy - x_0 y_0|$$
$$= |xy - xy_0 + xy_0 - x_0 y_0|$$
$$= |x(y - y_0) + y_0(x - x_0)|$$

can be made arbitrarily small by making both $|x - x_0|$ and $|y - y_0|$ small.

On the other hand, the function defined by

$$w = \begin{cases} \dfrac{xy}{x^2 + y^2} & \text{when} \quad (x, y) \neq (0, 0), \\ 0 & \text{when} \quad (x, y) = (0, 0) \end{cases}$$

is not continuous at $(0, 0)$. For, if we take

$$x = r \cos \theta, \qquad y = r \sin \theta, \qquad (r \neq 0),$$

we have

$$w = \sin \theta \cos \theta = \tfrac{1}{2} \sin 2\theta,$$

so that w takes all values between $-\tfrac{1}{2}$ and $+\tfrac{1}{2}$ as the point (x, y), or (r, θ), moves around the origin, no matter how small r may be. That is, we cannot make the w values stay close to zero by simply keeping the (x, y) values close to $(0, 0)$.

In most cases, the so-called elementary functions, which include algebraic expressions as well as trigonometric functions, logarithms, and exponentials, are continuous except possibly where a denominator may vanish or where the logarithm of zero is indicated.

PROBLEMS

1. How close to the point $(0, 0)$ should one take the point (x, y) in order to make $|f(x, y) - f(0, 0)| < \epsilon$ if:

(a) $f(x, y) = x^2 + y^2$ and $\epsilon = 0.01$?

(b) $f(x, y) = \dfrac{y}{x^2 + 1}$ and $\epsilon = 0.001$?

2. (a) How close to the point $(0, 0, 0)$ should one take the point (x, y, z) in order to make $|f(x, y, z) - f(0, 0, 0)| < \epsilon$ if $f(x, y, z) = x^2 + y^2 + z^2$ and $\epsilon = 0.01$? If $f(x, y, z) = xyz$ and $\epsilon = 0.008$? (b) Is the function $f(x, y, z) = x^2 + y^2 + z^2$ continuous at $(0, 0, 0)$? Give reasons for your answer.

3. Let $f(x, y) = (x + y)/(x^2 + y)$ when $x^2 + y \neq 0$. (a) Is it possible to define $f(1, -1)$ in such a way that $f(x, y) \to f(1, -1)$ as $(x, y) \to (1, -1)$ along the line $x = 1$? Along the line $y = -1$? (b) Is it possible to define $f(1, -1)$ in such a way that f is continuous at $(1, -1)$? Give a reason for your answer.

14-2 The directional derivative: special cases. For simplicity, consider a function of the two independent variables x and y and denote the dependent variable by w. The equation

$$w = f(x, y) \tag{1}$$

may be interpreted as representing a surface in xyw-space (Fig. 14-1).

We may also interpret (1) as representing elevation of points on a hill above the plane $w = 0$. We may then draw "level curves," which are the projections of "contour lines" into the xy-plane. In this interpretation, we imagine a base region G in the xy-plane and at every point in G we imagine a marker bearing the w value associated, by (1), with that point. If we connect the points in G which have the same w values, $w = $ constant, then we have a contour curve $f(x, y) = $ constant in the xy-plane.

These two interpretations are illustrated in Fig. 14-3 for the example

$$w = 100 - x^2 - y^2, \qquad w \geq 0. \tag{2}$$

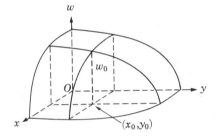

FIGURE 14-1   FIGURE 14-2

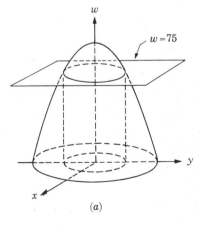 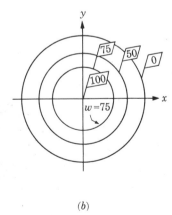

(a)   (b)

FIGURE 14-3

In part (a), we illustrate the surface, which is a paraboloid of revolution, and indicate a cutting plane $w = 75$. The corresponding level curve is the circle

$$x^2 + y^2 = 25$$

in the xy-plane. This is the circle which, in (b), carries the marker $w = 75$. The second interpretation is particularly useful in certain engineering applications. For instance, (2) might represent the temperature w, in degrees centigrade, at each point (x, y) of a flat circular plate at some fixed instant of time. And if we were dealing with temperatures w in a sphere, we might easily extend the second point of view and imagine a marker with the appropriate w value attached to each point in the sphere. The points having the same w value would then constitute an isothermal surface in space.

Suppose, now, that w is a function of x and y, defined for values of (x, y) in some region G of the xy-plane. Let $P_0(x_0, y_0)$ be any point of G and $P_1(x_1, y_1)$ a second point of G. Then the increment in w in going from w_0 at P_0 to w_1 at P_1 is

$$\Delta w = w_1 - w_0 = f(x_1, y_1) - f(x_0, y_0) \tag{3}$$

corresponding to

$$\Delta x = x_1 - x_0, \qquad \Delta y = y_1 - y_0.$$

Keeping P_0 fixed, suppose we require P_1 to approach it along some specific smooth curve in the xy-plane. This curve would in general not be one of the level curves referred to above, but would instead cut across these level curves. To be definite, suppose P_1 approaches P_0 along a straight line L, making an angle ϕ with the x-axis (Fig. 14–4). Then, if the limit

$$\frac{dw}{ds} = \lim_{\Delta s \to 0} \frac{\Delta w}{\Delta s} = \lim_{P_1 \to P_0} \frac{f(x_1, y_1) - f(x_0, y_0)}{\sqrt{\Delta x^2 + \Delta y^2}} \tag{4}$$

exists, its value is called the *directional derivative* of $w = f(x, y)$ at $(x_0 \ y_0)$ in the direction of L. The adjective "directional" is used because the

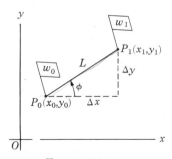

FIGURE 14–4

answer, (4), depends not only upon the function and the point P_0 but also upon the *direction* from which P_1 approaches P_0. We shall investigate the general case of the directional derivative in more detail in a later section. But now we shall investigate two special cases, namely, first the case where P_1 approaches P_0 along the line $y = y_0$ parallel to the x-axis and then the case where the approach is made along the line $x = x_0$ parallel to the y-axis. These two cases are of interest in themselves and also because when we know the values of these directional derivatives, we may calculate the derivative for *any* other direction.

In the case where P_1 approaches P_0 along the line $y = y_0$, we write

$$f_x(x_0, y_0) = \lim_{\Delta x \to 0} \frac{f(x_0 + \Delta x, y_0) - f(x_0, y_0)}{\Delta x} \tag{5}$$

and call the resulting limit the *partial derivative of $w = f(x, y)$ with respect to x at $P_0(x_0, y_0)$*. From the definition (5), this is just the usual derivative with respect to x of the function $F(x) = f(x, y_0)$ obtained from $f(x, y)$ by holding the value of y constant. It measures the instantaneous rate of change, at P_0, of the function $w = f(x, y)$ per unit change in x. The notation $\partial w/\partial x$ is also used to denote the partial derivative of w with respect to x. If we delete the subscript 0 everywhere in (5), the result is the partial derivative at (x, y):

$$\frac{\partial w}{\partial x} = f_x(x, y) = \lim_{\Delta x \to 0} \frac{f(x + \Delta x, y) - f(x, y)}{\Delta x}. \tag{6}$$

To calculate such a partial derivative from the equation for w, we simply apply the rules for ordinary differentiation, treating y as a constant.

In passing to the limit in Eq. (5) or (6), it is understood that Δx may be either positive or negative. If, on the other hand, we calculate the directional derivative in the direction of the *positive* x-axis, then Δx is restricted to positive values only and Eq. (5) is identical with Eq. (4) provided we take $y_1 = y_0$, $x_1 = x_0 + \Delta x$, $\Delta x > 0$, $\Delta y = 0$. The directional derivative and the partial derivative f_x differ in that in the directional derivative the point P_1 approaches P_0 always from the same side, while in f_x, P_1 may approach P_0 either from the left or from the right. In certain "pathological" cases, a function may have a directional derivative from the right but not from the left or may have both directional derivatives but the two may fail to have the same magnitude. In either of these cases, the partial derivative f_x would not exist. If, however, f_x does exist, then it gives the directional derivative to the right, while $-f_x$ gives the directional derivative to the left (the change in sign is due to the fact that $\sqrt{\Delta x^2} = -\Delta x$ if Δx is negative). That is, if f_x exists at a point, then both the right and left directional derivatives exist at that point and have the same magnitude but opposite signs.

For example, if we interpret Eq. (2),

$$w = 100 - x^2 - y^2,$$

as temperature in degrees centigrde at (x, y), where x and y are in centimeters, then we have

$$\frac{\partial w}{\partial x} = -2x$$

and at (3, 4), for example, the temperature is 75°C and

$$\frac{\partial w}{\partial x} = -6 \text{ (°C/cm)}.$$

That is, a small positive change in x would decrease the temperature at the rate of 6°C per cm change in x, while a negative change in x would increase w at the same rate.

The geometric interpretation of Eq. (5), (Fig. 14–5), is that

$$f_x(x_0, y_0) = \left(\frac{\partial w}{\partial x}\right)_{(x_0, y_0)}$$

gives the slope at (x_0, y_0, w_0) of the curve $w = f(x, y_0)$ in which the plane $y = y_0$ cuts the surface $w = f(x, y)$.

Thus, in Fig. 14–5, if x, y, and w are measured in the same units,

$$\boxed{\tan \alpha = \left(\frac{\partial w}{\partial x}\right)_{(x_0, y_0)} = f_x(x_0, y_0),}$$

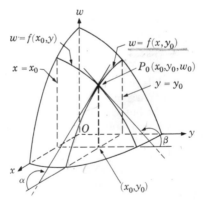

FIGURE 14–5

while, similarly,

$$\tan \beta = \left(\frac{\partial w}{\partial y}\right)_{(x_0, y_0)} = f_y(x_0, y_0).$$

Here the partial derivative of $w = f(x, y)$ with respect to y is denoted either by $\partial w/\partial y$ or by $f_y(x, y)$ and we have the definitions

$$f_y(x_0, y_0) = \lim_{\Delta y \to 0} \frac{f(x_0, y_0 + \Delta y) - f(x_0, y_0)}{\Delta y},$$

$$\frac{\partial w}{\partial y} = f_y(x, y) = \lim_{\Delta y \to 0} \frac{f(x, y + \Delta y) - f(x, y)}{\Delta y}.$$

(7)

There are similar definitions for $\partial w/\partial x$, $\partial w/\partial y$, $\partial w/\partial z$, $\partial w/\partial u$, and $\partial w/\partial v$ in case $w = f(x, y, z, u, v)$; namely, we hold all but one of the variables constant while differentiating with respect to that one. The alternative subscript notation has the advantage of permitting us to exhibit the values of the variables where the derivative is to be evaluated; for example, $f_u(x_0, y_0, z_0, u_0, v_0)$ is the partial derivative of $w = f(x, y, z, u, v)$ with respect to u at $(x_0, y_0, z_0, u_0, v_0)$. This might also be denoted by $(\partial w/\partial u)_{(x_0, y_0, z_0, u_0, v_0)}$ or, more simply, by $(\partial w/\partial u)_0$.

EXAMPLE 1. Three resistors of resistances R_1, R_2, and R_3 connected in parallel produce a resistance R given by

$$\frac{1}{R} = \frac{1}{R_1} + \frac{1}{R_2} + \frac{1}{R_3}.$$

Find $\partial R/\partial R_2$.

Solution. Treat R_1 and R_3 as constants and differentiate both sides of the equation implicitly with respect to R_2. Then

$$-\frac{1}{R^2}\frac{\partial R}{\partial R_2} = -\frac{1}{R_2^2} \quad \text{or} \quad \frac{\partial R}{\partial R_2} = \left(\frac{R}{R_2}\right)^2.$$

EXAMPLE 2. If $w = (xy)^z$, find $\partial w/\partial z$.

Solution. Here, we treat x and y, and hence xy, as constant and apply the law

$$\frac{d(a^u)}{dz} = a^u \ln a \frac{du}{dz}.$$

Hence

$$\frac{\partial w}{\partial z} = (xy)^z \ln (xy).$$

PROBLEMS

In Problems 1–5, show two ways to represent the function $w = f(x, y)$, (a) by sketching a surface in xyw-space, and (b) by drawing a family of level curves, $f(x, y) = $ constant.

1. $f(x, y) = x$ 2. $f(x, y) = y$

3. $f(x, y) = x^2 + y^2$ 4. $f(x, y) = x^2 - y^2$

5. $f(x, y) = ye^x$

In each of the following problems (6–10), find $\partial w/\partial x$ and $\partial w/\partial y$:

6. $w = e^x \cos y$ 7. $w = e^x \sin y$

8. $w = \tan^{-1} \dfrac{y}{x}$ 9. $w = \ln \sqrt{x^2 + y^2}$

10. $w = \cosh{(y/x)}$

In Problems 11–16, find the partial derivatives of the given function with respect to each variable.

11. $f(x, y, z, w) = x^2 e^{2y+3z} \cos{(4w)}$ 12. $f(x, y, z) = z \sin^{-1}{(y/x)}$

13. $f(u, v, w) = \dfrac{u^2 - v^2}{v^2 + w^2}$ 14. $f(r, \theta, z) = \dfrac{r(2 - \cos 2\theta)}{r^2 + z^2}$

15. $f(x, y, u, v) = \dfrac{x^2 + y^2}{u^2 + v^2}$

16. $f(x, y, r, s) = \sin 2x \cosh 3r + \sinh 3y \cos 4s$

In Problems 17 and 18, A, B, C are the angles of a triangle and a, b, c are the respective opposite sides.

17. Express A (explicitly or implicitly) as a function of a, b, c and calculate $\partial A/\partial a$ and $\partial A/\partial b$.

18. Express a (explicitly or implicitly) as a function of A, b, B and calculate $\partial a/\partial A$ and $\partial a/\partial B$.

In Problems 19–24, express the spherical coordinates ρ, ϕ, θ as functions of the Cartesian coordinates x, y, z and calculate:

19. $\partial \rho/\partial x$ 20. $\partial \phi/\partial z$

21. $\partial \theta/\partial y$ 22. $\partial \theta/\partial z$

23. $\partial \phi/\partial x$ 24. $\partial \theta/\partial x$

In Problems 25–27, let $\mathbf{R} = \mathbf{i}x + \mathbf{j}y + \mathbf{k}z$ be the vector from the origin to (x, y, z). Express x, y, z as functions of the spherical coordinates ρ, ϕ, θ, and calculate:

25. $\partial \mathbf{R}/\partial \rho$ 26. $\partial \mathbf{R}/\partial \phi$ 27. $\partial \mathbf{R}/\partial \theta$

28. Express the answers to Problems 25–27 in terms of the unit vectors $\mathbf{u}_\rho$, $\mathbf{u}_\phi$, $\mathbf{u}_\theta$ discussed in Problem 17 of Article 13–8.

29. In Fig. 14–5, let

$$\mathbf{R} = \mathbf{i}x + \mathbf{j}y + \mathbf{k}f(x, y)$$

be the vector from the origin to (x, y, w). What can you say about the direction of the vector (a) $\partial R/\partial x$, (b) $\partial R/\partial y$? (c) Calculate the vector product

$$\mathbf{v} = \left(\frac{\partial \mathbf{R}}{\partial x}\right) \times \left(\frac{\partial \mathbf{R}}{\partial y}\right).$$

What can you say about the direction of this vector $\mathbf{v}$ with respect to the surface $w = f(x, y)$?

14–3 Tangent plane and normal line. In Article 14–2 we saw that the partial derivatives

$$f_x(x_0, y_0) = \left(\frac{\partial w}{\partial x}\right)_{(x_0, y_0)} \tag{1a}$$

and

$$f_y(x_0, y_0) = \left(\frac{\partial w}{\partial y}\right)_{(x_0, y_0)} \tag{1b}$$

give the slopes of the lines L_1 and L_2 which are tangent to the curves C_1 and C_2 in which the planes $y = y_0$ and $x = x_0$, respectively, intersect the surface $w = f(x, y)$. The lines L_1 and L_2 determine a plane. If the surface is sufficiently smooth near $P_0(x_0, y_0, w_0)$, this plane will be tangent to the surface at P_0.

DEFINITION. TANGENT PLANE. *Let* $w = f(x, y)$ *be the equation of a surface* S. *Let* $P_0(x_0, y_0, w_0)$ *be a point on the surface. Let* T *be a plane through* P_0. *Let* $P(x, y, w)$ *be any other point on* S. *If the angle between* T *and the line* P_0P *approaches zero as* P *approaches* P_0, *we say that* T *is tangent to* S *at* P_0.

The line through P_0 which is normal to this plane is called the *normal line* to the surface at P_0.

Remark 1. If a surface has a tangent plane at $P_0(x_0, y_0, w_0)$, the lines L_1 and L_2 tangent to the curves $C_1: w = f(x_0, y)$, $x = x_0$ and $C_2: w = f(x, y_0)$, $y = y_0$ must lie in this tangent plane. Since two intersecting lines determine a plane, the plane determined by L_1 and L_2 is the tangent plane, if there is one.

Remark 2. The curves C_1 and C_2, where the surface is cut by the planes $x = x_0$ and $y = y_0$, may be smooth enough to possess tangent lines L_1 and L_2 and the surface still not have a tangent plane at P_0. In other words, the plane determined by L_1 and L_2 may not, in fact, be tangent to the surface. This would happen, for example, if the curves cut from the surface by other planes, such as the planes $y - y_0 = \pm(x - x_0)$, either fail to have tangent lines, or have tangent lines L', L'' which don't lie in the plane determined by L_1 and L_2. In the next article, we shall show that this does not happen if the partial derivatives $f_x(x, y)$, $f_y(x, y)$ exist in some rectangle centered at (x_0, y_0) and are continuous at (x_0, y_0).

We shall now assume that the surface does have a tangent plane and a normal line and see how we may find their equations. They may easily be written down once we have found a vector $\mathbf{N}$ perpendicular to the plane of L_1 and L_2. For such a vector $\mathbf{N}$, we may use the cross product of vectors $\mathbf{v}_1$ and $\mathbf{v}_2$ along the lines L_1 and L_2. So we now consider how to find $\mathbf{v}_1$ and $\mathbf{v}_2$.

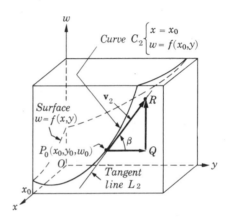

FIGURE 14-6

In Fig. 14–6 we indicate a portion of the curve C_2 cut from the surface by the plane $x = x_0$. Triangle P_0QR is a right triangle with hypotenuse P_0R lying along the tangent line L_2. The slope of L_2 is

$$\tan \beta = \frac{QR}{P_0Q} = f_y(x_0, y_0).$$

Therefore, if we take $P_0Q = 1$ y-unit, QR will be equal to $f_y(x_0, y_0)$ w-units. In terms of vectors, we may take

$$\overrightarrow{P_0Q} = 1\mathbf{j}, \qquad \overrightarrow{QR} = f_y(x_0, y_0)\mathbf{k}$$

and

$$\mathbf{v}_2 = \overrightarrow{P_0Q} + \overrightarrow{QR} = \mathbf{j} + f_y(x_0, y_0)\mathbf{k}, \tag{2a}$$

where $\mathbf{i}$, $\mathbf{j}$, and $\mathbf{k}$ will be used to denote unit vectors along the x-, y-, and w-axes respectively.

Similarly, by considering the curve C_1 out from the surface by the plane $y = y_0$, we see that the vector

$$\mathbf{v}_1 = \mathbf{i} + f_x(x_0, y_0)\mathbf{k} \tag{2b}$$

is parallel to the line L_1.

For the normal vector $\mathbf{N}$ we may therefore take

$$\mathbf{N} = \mathbf{v}_2 \times \mathbf{v}_1 = \begin{vmatrix} \mathbf{i} & \mathbf{j} & \mathbf{k} \\ 0 & 1 & f_y(x_0, y_0) \\ 1 & 0 & f_x(x_0, y_0) \end{vmatrix} = \mathbf{i} f_x(x_0, y_0) + \mathbf{j} f_y(x_0, y_0) - \mathbf{k}. \quad (3)$$

The equations of the tangent plane and normal line at $P_0(x_0, y_0, w_0)$ may now be written down at once as

$$\text{tangent plane:} \quad A(x - x_0) + B(y - y_0) + C(w - w_0) = 0, \quad (4a)$$

$$\text{normal line:} \quad \frac{x - x_0}{A} = \frac{y - y_0}{B} = \frac{w - w_0}{C}, \quad (4b)$$

with coefficients A, B, and C determined from the **normal vector** (3), given by

$$A = f_x(x_0, y_0), \quad B = f_y(x_0, y_0), \quad C = -1. \quad (4c)$$

PROBLEMS

In Problems 1–5, find the plane that is tangent to the given surface $z = f(x, y)$ at the given point P_0. Also find the line normal to the surface at P_0.

1. $z = x^2 + y^2$; (3, 4, 25)   2. $z = \sqrt{9 - x^2 - y^2}$; (1, −2, 2)

3. $z = x^2 - xy - y^2$; (1, 1, −1)   4. $z = \tan^{-1} \frac{y}{x}$; (1, 1, $\pi/4$)

5. $z = x/\sqrt{x^2 + y^2}$; (3, −4, $\frac{3}{5}$)

6. (a) If the equation of a surface is given in the form $x = f(y, z)$, what takes the place of Eq. (3) for a vector $\mathbf{N}$ normal to the surface at a point $P_0(x_0, y_0, z_0)$? (b) Find the tangent plane and normal line to the surface $x = e^{2y-z}$ at the point (1, 1, 2).

7. Show that there is a line on the cone $z^2 = 2x^2 + 4y^2$ where the tangent plane is parallel to the plane $12x + 14y + 11z = 25$. Find the line and the tangent plane.

8. At each point of the curve of intersection of the paraboloid $z = x^2 + y^2$ and the plane $z = z_0$ (>0), a line is drawn normal to the paraboloid. Show that these lines generate a cone and find its vertex. Sketch the paraboloid and the associated cone.

9. The intersection of the surface $z = f(x, y)$ and the surface $z = g(x, y)$ is a curve C. Find a vector tangent to C at a point $P_0(x_0, y_0, z_0)$ on it. Express the result in terms of partial derivatives of f and g at P_0.

10. Apply the result of Problem 9 to find a vector of length $\sqrt{3}$ tangent to the curve of intersection of the cone $z^2 = 4x^2 + 9y^2$ and the plane $6x + 3y + 2z = 5$ at the point $P_0(2, 1, -5)$.

14–4 Approximate value of Δw. We saw in the previous article, Eqs. (4a, c), that if the surface $w = f(x, y)$ has a tangent plane at $P_0(x_0, y_0, w_0)$, then the equation of the tangent plane is

$$w - w_0 = f_x(x_0, y_0)(x - x_0) + f_y(x_0, y_0)(y - y_0). \qquad (1)$$

In this equation, (x_0, y_0, w_0) are coordinates of a point on the surface, while (x, y, w) are coordinates of a point on the *tangent plane*. If we take

$$x = x_0 + \Delta x, \qquad y = y_0 + \Delta y$$

in Eq. (1), and denote the change, $w - w_0$, by Δw_{tan}, we have

$$\Delta w_{\text{tan}} = f_x(x_0, y_0)\, \Delta x + f_y(x_0, y_0)\, \Delta y. \qquad (2)$$

This equation tells us how much change is produced in w, corresponding to the changes Δx and Δy, when we move along the *tangent plane*. In this article we shall see that under suitable restrictions on the function f (a) the surface does have a tangent plane, and (b) the change in w *on the surface* $w = f(x, y)$ differs from Δw_{tan} by an amount $\epsilon_1\, \Delta x + \epsilon_2\, \Delta y$, where both ϵ_1 and ϵ_2 are small when Δx and Δy are small. We shall discuss the suitable restrictions on f and then prove the theorem below.

THEOREM. *Let the function $w = f(x, y)$ be continuous and possess partial derivatives f_x, f_y throughout a region*

$$R: |x - x_0| < h, \qquad |y - y_0| < k$$

of the xy-plane. Let f_x and f_y be continuous at (x_0, y_0). Let

$$\Delta w = f(x_0 + \Delta x, y_0 + \Delta y) - f(x_0, y_0). \qquad (3)$$

Then

$$\Delta w = f_x(x_0, y_0)\, \Delta x + f_y(x_0, y_0)\, \Delta y + \epsilon_1\, \Delta x + \epsilon_2\, \Delta y, \qquad (4)$$

where

$$\epsilon_1 \text{ and } \epsilon_2 \to 0 \qquad \text{when} \qquad \Delta x \text{ and } \Delta y \to 0. \qquad (5)$$

Remark 1. The region R is a rectangle, center at (x_0, y_0) and sides $2h$ by $2k$. We shall restrict Δx and Δy to be so small that the points

$$(x_0, y_0), \quad (x_0 + \Delta x, y_0 + \Delta y), \quad (x_0 + \Delta x, y_0), \quad (x_0, y_0 + \Delta y)$$

all lie inside this rectangle R. The function f is assumed to be continuous and to have partial derivatives f_x and f_y throughout the rectangle R. In particular, these functions are well behaved at each of the points listed

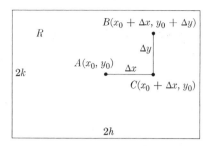

FIGURE 14–7

above and along the segment joining any pair of them. This is sufficient to make valid the applications of the Mean Value Theorem in the proof below.

Proof. The key to the proof is a double application of the Mean Value Theorem. The increment Δw is the change in f from $A(x_0, y_0)$ to $B(x_0 + \Delta x, y_0 + \Delta y)$ in R. We resolve this into two parts

$$\Delta w_1 = f(x_0 + \Delta x, y_0) - f(x_0, y_0) \tag{6}$$

and

$$\Delta w_2 = f(x_0 + \Delta x, y_0 + \Delta y) - f(x_0 + \Delta x, y_0). \tag{7}$$

The first is the change in w from A to C; the second, from C to B, Fig. 14–7. Algebraically, we have

$$\Delta w_2 + \Delta w_1 = f(x_0 + \Delta x, y_0 + \Delta y) - f(x_0 + \Delta x, y_0)$$
$$+ f(x_0 + \Delta x, y_0) - f(x_0, y_0)$$
$$= f(x_0 + \Delta x, y_0 + \Delta y) - f(x_0, y_0)$$
$$= \Delta w. \tag{8}$$

In Δw_1, we hold $y = y_0$ fixed and have an increment of a function of x that is continuous and differentiable. The Mean Value Theorem is therefore applicable and yields

$$\Delta w_1 = f(x_0 + \Delta x, y_0) - f(x_0, y_0) = f_x(x_1, y_0) \Delta x \tag{9}$$

for some x_1 between x_0 and $x_0 + \Delta x$.

Similarly, in Δw_2 we hold $x = x_0 + \Delta x$ and have an increment of a function of y that is continuous and differentiable. By the Mean Value Theorem,

$$\Delta w_2 = f(x_0 + \Delta x, y_0 + \Delta y) - f(x_0 + \Delta x, y_0) = f_y(x_0 + \Delta x, y_1) \Delta y \tag{10}$$

for some y_1 between y_0 and $y_0 + \Delta y$. Hence

$$\Delta w = f_x(x_1, y_0)\, \Delta x + f_y(x_0 + \Delta x, y_1)\, \Delta y \tag{11}$$

for some x_1 between x_0 and $x_0 + \Delta x$, and y_1 between y_0 and $y_0 + \Delta y$.

We now use the hypothesis that f_x and f_y are continuous at $P_0(x_0, y_0)$. This means that

$$f_x(x_1, y_0) \to f_x(x_0, y_0) \tag{12a}$$

and

$$f_y(x_0 + \Delta x, y_1) \to f_y(x_0, y_0) \tag{12b}$$

as Δx and Δy approach zero. Therefore we may write

$$f_x(x_1, y_0) = f_x(x_0, y_0) + \epsilon_1, \tag{13a}$$

$$f_y(x_0 + \Delta x, y_1) = f_y(x_0, y_0) + \epsilon_2, \tag{13b}$$

and ϵ_1, ϵ_2 both approach zero as Δx and Δy approach zero. Substituting (13a, b) into (11) gives the desired result

$$\Delta w = [f_x(x_0, y_0) + \epsilon_1]\, \Delta x + [f_y(x_0, y_0) + \epsilon_2]\, \Delta y,$$

while (12a, b) guarantee that ϵ_1 and $\epsilon_2 \to 0$ when Δx and $\Delta y \to 0$. Q.E.D.

COROLLARY. *Let* $w = f(x, y)$ *be continuous in a region* $R \colon |x - x_0| < h$, $|y - y_0| < k$. *Let* f_x *and* f_y *exist in* R *and be continuous at* (x_0, y_0). *Then the surface* $w = f(x, y)$ *has a tangent plane at* $P_0(x_0, y_0, w_0)$, *where* $w_0 = f(x_0, y_0)$.

Proof. Let $P(x, y, w)$ be any point, different from P_0, on the surface $w = f(x, y)$. Let $\mathbf{N}$ be the vector

$$\mathbf{N} = \mathbf{i}f_x(x_0, y_0) + \mathbf{j}f_y(x_0, y_0) - \mathbf{k}. \tag{14}$$

The cosine of the angle θ between $\overrightarrow{P_0P}$ and $\mathbf{N}$ is

$$\cos \theta = \frac{\overrightarrow{P_0P} \cdot \mathbf{N}}{|\overrightarrow{P_0P}||\mathbf{N}|}. \tag{15}$$

Now

$$\overrightarrow{P_0P} = \mathbf{i}(x - x_0) + \mathbf{j}(y - y_0) + \mathbf{k}(w - w_0)$$

$$= \mathbf{i}\, \Delta x + \mathbf{j}\, \Delta y + \mathbf{k}\, \Delta w. \tag{16}$$

Therefore

$$\cos \theta = \frac{f_x(x_0, y_0)\, \Delta x + f_y(x_0, y_0)\, \Delta y - \Delta w}{|\overrightarrow{P_0 P}||\mathbf{N}|}$$

$$= \frac{-\epsilon_1\, \Delta x - \epsilon_2\, \Delta y}{|\overrightarrow{P_0 P}||\mathbf{N}|}. \tag{17}$$

From (14) we see that $|\mathbf{N}| \geq 1$ and from (16)

$$\frac{|\Delta x|}{|\overrightarrow{P_0 P}|} \leq 1, \qquad \frac{|\Delta y|}{|\overrightarrow{P_0 P}|} \leq 1.$$

Hence, from (17) and the previous theorem,

$$|\cos \theta| \leq |\epsilon_1| + |\epsilon_2| \to 0$$

as $P \to P_0$. Therefore, for any point $P \neq P_0$ on the surface, the angle between the vector $\overrightarrow{P_0 P}$ and the vector $\mathbf{N}$, Eq. (14), approaches 90°. This means that the plane through P_0, perpendicular to $\mathbf{N}$, is tangent to the surface at P_0.

Remark 2. The significance of the theorem lies in Eqs. (4) and (5). It says that

$$\Delta w = \Delta w_{\tan} + \epsilon_1\, \Delta x + \epsilon_2\, \Delta y$$

consists of the part $\Delta w_{\tan}$ which is *linear* in Δx and Δy plus the error terms which are *products* of small terms, $\epsilon_1\, \Delta x$ and $\epsilon_2\, \Delta y$, when Δx and Δy are small.

For example, if

$$w = x^2 + y^2 = f(x, y),$$

then

$$\Delta w = (x + \Delta x)^2 + (y + \Delta y)^2 - (x^2 + y^2)$$

$$= \underbrace{2x\, \Delta x + 2y\, \Delta y}_{\Delta w_{\tan}} + \underbrace{(\Delta x)^2 + (\Delta y)^2}_{\epsilon_1\, \Delta x + \epsilon_2\, \Delta y}.$$

Since $f_x = 2x$, $f_y = 2y$, the part $2x\, \Delta x + 2y\, \Delta y$ is the same as $\Delta w_{\tan}$. Then $\Delta w - \Delta w_{\tan}$, in the particular example, is simply $(\Delta x)^2 + (\Delta y)^2$. This agrees with Eq. (4) with $\epsilon_1 = \Delta x$ and $\epsilon_2 = \Delta y$, which approach zero when Δx and Δy do.

Remark 3. Figure 14–8 represents a portion of the surface $w = f(x, y)$ near $P_0(x_0, y_0, w_0)$, together with a portion of the plane that is tangent to the surface at P_0. Points P_0, P', and P'' have the same elevation

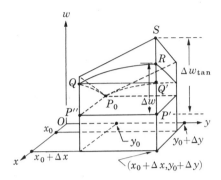

FIGURE 14–8

$w_0 = f(x_0, y_0)$ above the xy-plane. The change in w *on the surface* corresponds to $\Delta w = P'R$ and the change in w *on the tangent plane* corresponds to $\Delta w_{\text{tan}} = P'S$. The change

$$\Delta w_1 = f(x_0 + \Delta x, y_0) - f(x_0, y_0),$$

which corresponds to $P''Q = P'Q'$ in the figure, is caused by changing x from x_0 to $x_0 + \Delta x$ while holding y constant, $y = y_0$. Then we hold x constant, $x = x_0 + \Delta x$, and

$$\Delta w_2 = f(x_0 + \Delta x, y_0 + \Delta y) - f(x_0 + \Delta x, y_0)$$

is the change in w caused by changing y from y_0 to $y_0 + \Delta y$. This is represented by $Q'R$ in the figure. The total change in w is just the sum of these two.

Functions of more variables. An analogous result holds for a function of any finite number of independent variables. For a function of three variables,

$$w = f(x, y, z),$$

that is continuous and has partial derivatives f_x, f_y, f_z at and in some neighborhood of the point (x_0, y_0, z_0), and whose derivatives are continuous at the point, we have

$$\Delta w = f(x_0 + \Delta x, y_0 + \Delta y, z_0 + \Delta z) - f(x_0, y_0, z_0)$$
$$= f_x \, \Delta x + f_y \, \Delta y + f_z \, \Delta z + \epsilon_1 \, \Delta x + \epsilon_2 \, \Delta y + \epsilon_3 \, \Delta z, \qquad (18)$$

where

$$\epsilon_1, \epsilon_2, \epsilon_3 \to 0 \qquad \text{when} \qquad \Delta x, \Delta y, \text{ and } \Delta z \to 0.$$

In this formula, the partial derivatives f_x, f_y, f_z are to be evaluated at the point (x_0, y_0, z_0). This formula will be used in certain theoretical discussions that follow. It is also useful in making *approximations,* for we may approximate Δw by using only the part of Eq. (18) which is linear in Δx, Δy, and Δz. We shall, as in the previous case, denote this linear approximation to Δw by $\Delta w_{\tan}$:

$$\Delta w_{\tan} = f_x(x_0, y_0, z_0)\,\Delta x + f_y(x_0, y_0, z_0)\,\Delta y + f_z(x_0, y_0, z_0)\,\Delta z$$

$$= \left(\frac{\partial w}{\partial x}\right)_0 \Delta x + \left(\frac{\partial w}{\partial y}\right)_0 \Delta y + \left(\frac{\partial w}{\partial z}\right)_0 \Delta z. \tag{19}$$

The reader may prove the result (11) by treating Δw as the sum of the three increments

$$\Delta w_1 = f(x_0 + \Delta x, y_0, z_0) - f(x_0, y_0, z_0), \tag{20a}$$

$$\Delta w_2 = f(x_0 + \Delta x, y_0 + \Delta y, z_0) - f(x_0 + \Delta x, y_0, z_0), \tag{20b}$$

$$\Delta w_3 = f(x_0 + \Delta x, y_0 + \Delta y, z_0 + \Delta z) - f(x_0 + \Delta x, y_0 + \Delta y, z_0) \tag{20c}$$

and applying the Mean Value Theorem to each of these separately. Note that two coordinates remain constant and only one varies in each of these partial increments $\Delta w_1, \Delta w_2, \Delta w_3$. For example, in (20b), only y varies, since x is held equal to $x_0 + \Delta x$ and z is held equal to z_0. The function $f(x_0 + \Delta x, y, z_0)$, being a continuous function of y with a derivative f_y, is subject to the Mean Value Theorem, and we have

$$\Delta w_2 = f_y(x_0 + \Delta x, y_1, z_0)\,\Delta y$$

for some y_1 between y_0 and $y_0 + \Delta y$.

The fact that $\Delta w_{\tan}$ is a good approximation to Δw when the increments in the independent variables are small may be used to advantage in calculating, approximately, small changes in a function of two or more variables in a way which is precisely analogous to the use of the tangent line approximation to the increment for a function $f(x)$ of a single variable.

EXAMPLE 1. Calculate Δw and $\Delta w_{\tan}$ for the function

$$w = x^2 + xy.$$

Solution. Here

$$f(x, y) = x^2 + xy, \qquad f_x = 2x + y, \qquad f_y = x,$$

so that

$$\Delta w_{\tan} = f_x\,\Delta x + f_y\,\Delta y = (2x + y)\,\Delta x + x\,\Delta y.$$

To find Δw, we calculate

$$w + \Delta w = f(x + \Delta x, y + \Delta y) = (x + \Delta x)^2 + (x + \Delta x)(y + \Delta y)$$

$$= x^2 + 2x\,\Delta x + (\Delta x)^2 + xy + x\,\Delta y + y\,\Delta x + (\Delta x)(\Delta y)$$

and then subtract

$$w = x^2 + xy$$

to obtain

$$\Delta w = (2x + y)\, \Delta x + x\, \Delta y + (\Delta x)^2 + (\Delta x)\,(\Delta y).$$

The difference,

$$\Delta w - \Delta w_{\text{tan}} = (\Delta x)^2 + (\Delta x)\,(\Delta y),$$

is thus seen to consist of terms of higher degree than Δx and Δy as they approach zero.

EXAMPLE 2. Use the linear approximation

$$\Delta w \approx \frac{\partial w}{\partial x}\, \Delta x + \frac{\partial w}{\partial y}\, \Delta y + \frac{\partial w}{\partial z}\, \Delta z$$

to calculate

$$\sqrt{(0.98)^2 + (2.01)^2 + (1.94)^2}.$$

Solution. Let

$$w = \sqrt{x^2 + y^2 + z^2} = f(x,\, y,\, z),$$

$$x_0 = 1.00, \qquad y_0 = 2.00, \qquad z_0 = 2.00,$$

$$\Delta x = -0.02, \qquad \Delta y = +0.01, \qquad \Delta z = -0.06.$$

Then the square root we wish to calculate is $w_0 + \Delta w = f(x_0 + \Delta x,\, y_0 + \Delta y,\, z_0 + \Delta z)$, where

$$w_0 = \sqrt{1 + 4 + 4} = 3$$

and

$$\Delta w \approx \frac{\partial w}{\partial x}\, \Delta x + \frac{\partial w}{\partial y}\, \Delta y + \frac{\partial w}{\partial z}\, \Delta z$$

$$= \frac{x\, \Delta x + y\, \Delta y + z\, \Delta z}{\sqrt{x^2 + y^2 + z^2}}$$

$$= \frac{-0.02 + 0.02 - 0.12}{3} = -0.04.$$

Therefore

$$w_0 + \Delta w \approx 3 - 0.04 = 2.96.$$

PROBLEMS

1. Find Δw_{tan} and Δw if $w = x^2 - xy + y^2$, $(x_0, y_0) = (1, -2)$, $\Delta x = 0.01$, $\Delta y = -0.02$.

2. Use Δw_{tan} to calculate how much an error of 2% in each of the factors a, b, c may affect the product abc.

3. Find a reasonable approximation (two decimal places) to the value of

$$\sqrt{(3.01)^2 + (3.97)^2}.$$

4. Carry through the details of deriving Eq. (11).

5. The dimensions of a rectangular box are measured as 3, 4, and 12 in. If the measurements may be in error by ±0.01, ±0.01, and ±0.03 in., respectively, calculate the length of the diagonal and estimate the possible error in this length.

6. A function $w = f(x, y)$ is said to be *differentiable* at $P(a, b)$ if there are constants M and N (possibly depending on f and P) such that

$$\Delta w = M\,\Delta x + N\,\Delta y + \alpha[|\Delta x| + |\Delta y|]$$

and $\alpha \to 0$ as $|\Delta x| + |\Delta y| \to 0$.   Here $\Delta w = f(a + \Delta x, b + \Delta y) - f(a, b)$. Prove that if f is differentiable at (a, b), then $M = f_x(a, b)$ and $N = f_y(a, b)$.

7. If the function $w = f(x, y)$ is differentiable at $P(a, b)$ (see Problem 6), prove it is continuous there.

14–5 The directional derivative: general case.   Let us return once more to the problem of determining the instantaneous rate of change at $P_0(x_0, y_0)$ of a function $w = f(x, y)$ measured in units of change of w per unit of distance along a ray L with vertex at P_0 and making an angle ϕ with the positive x-axis. Hold $P_0(x_0, y_0)$ fixed, and let $P_1(x_1, y_1)$ be a point on L and lying near P_0. Let

$$\Delta x = x_1 - x_0, \qquad \Delta y = y_1 - y_0$$

both tend to zero in such a way that P_1 approaches P_0 along L. Then, for each position of P_1 on L, calculate the ratio

$$\frac{\Delta w}{\Delta s} = \frac{w_1 - w_0}{\sqrt{\Delta x^2 + \Delta y^2}}$$

$$= \frac{f(x_1, y_1) - f(x_0, y_0)}{\sqrt{(x_1 - x_0)^2 + (y_1 - y_0)^2}},$$

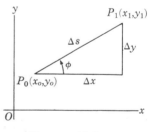

FIGURE 14–9

which measures the average rate of change of w along L from P_0 to P_1. If this average rate of change has a limit as $P_1 \to P_0$, we denote the limit by dw/ds and call it the *directional derivative* of w at P_0. We shall now prove:

THEOREM. *Let $w = f(x, y)$ be continuous and possess partial derivatives f_x, f_y throughout some neighborhood of the point $P_0(x_0, y_0)$. Let f_x and f_y be continuous at P_0. Then the directional derivative at P_0 exists for any direction angle ϕ and is given by*

$$\frac{dw}{ds} = f_x(x_0, y_0) \cos \phi + f_y(x_0, y_0) \sin \phi. \tag{1}$$

Before we prove this result, it is worth noting that the special cases $\phi = 0, \pi/2, \pi, 3\pi/2$ respectively lead to $dw/ds = \partial f/\partial x, \partial f/\partial y, -\partial f/\partial x, -\partial f/\partial y$, in harmony with our earlier discussion.

Proof. To establish Eq. (1), we recall that Eq. (4) of the previous article is valid under the hypotheses we have made for the continuity of $f(x, y)$, $\partial f/\partial x$, and $\partial f/\partial y$.

Hence,

$$\frac{\Delta w}{\Delta s} = f_x(x_0, y_0) \frac{\Delta x}{\Delta s} + f_y(x_0, y_0) \frac{\Delta y}{\Delta s} + \epsilon_1 \frac{\Delta x}{\Delta s} + \epsilon_2 \frac{\Delta y}{\Delta s},$$

where

$$\epsilon_1 \text{ and } \epsilon_2 \to 0 \qquad \text{as} \qquad \Delta x \text{ and } \Delta y \to 0.$$

Now, if $P_1 \to P_0$ along L, or even along a smooth curve which is tangent to L at P_0, we have

$$\lim \frac{\Delta x}{\Delta s} = \frac{dx}{ds} = \cos \phi, \qquad \lim \frac{\Delta y}{\Delta s} = \frac{dy}{ds} = \sin \phi$$

and hence

$$\frac{dw}{ds} = \lim \frac{\Delta w}{\Delta s} = f_x(x_0, y_0) \cos \phi + f_y(x_0, y_0) \sin \phi. \qquad \text{Q.E.D.}$$

EXAMPLE. Let $w = 100 - x^2 - y^2$.

If one starts from the point $P_0(3, 4)$, in which direction should one go in order to make w increase most rapidly?

Solution. We have $f(x, y) = 100 - x^2 - y^2, f_x(3, 4) = -6, f_y(3, 4) = -8$, and $(dw/ds)_{(3,4)} = -6 \cos \phi - 8 \sin \phi$.

In order to make w increase most rapidly, we seek the angle ϕ for which the function

$$F(\phi) = -6 \cos \phi - 8 \sin \phi$$

has a maximum. Since

$$F'(\phi) = 6 \sin \phi - 8 \cos \phi$$

is zero when

$$\tan \phi = \tfrac{4}{3}, \qquad \sin \phi = \pm \tfrac{4}{5}, \qquad \cos \phi = \pm \tfrac{3}{5},$$

while

$$F''(\phi) = 6 \cos \phi + 8 \sin \phi$$

is negative in case both $\sin \phi$ and $\cos \phi$ are negative, we observe that the maximum value of $F(\phi)$ is attained when

$$\cos \phi = -\tfrac{3}{5}, \qquad \sin \phi = -\tfrac{4}{5}.$$

It is readily seen that the geometrical meaning of this result is that w increases most rapidly if the ray L points from $P_0(3, 4)$ toward the origin. The derivative of w with respect to distance in this direction is found to be $+10$; that is, w

increases at the instantaneous rate of 10 w-units per unit of length along this particular ray.

The notion of the directional derivative can easily be extended from the case of functions of two independent variables to the case of functions of three independent variables. To this end, consider the values of a function

$$w = f(x, y, z)$$

at $P_0(x_0, y_0, z_0)$ and at a nearby point $P_1(x_1, y_1, z_1)$ lying on a directed ray L through P_0. It will be convenient to specify the direction of L by means of a unit vector

$$\mathbf{u} = \mathbf{i} \cos \alpha + \mathbf{j} \cos \beta + \mathbf{k} \cos \gamma$$

pointing in the same direction. If we let

$$x_1 - x_0 = \Delta x, \qquad y_1 - y_0 = \Delta y, \qquad z_1 - z_0 = \Delta z,$$

then

$$\overrightarrow{P_0 P_1} = \mathbf{i}\, \Delta x + \mathbf{j}\, \Delta y + \mathbf{k}\, \Delta z.$$

The distance from P_0 to P_1 is

$$\Delta s = \sqrt{(\Delta x)^2 + (\Delta y)^2 + (\Delta z)^2}.$$

Since $\overrightarrow{P_0 P_1}$ has the same direction as $\mathbf{u}$ and has length equal to Δs, it is clear that

$$\frac{\overrightarrow{P_0 P_1}}{\Delta s} = \mathbf{u}.$$

That is,

$$\mathbf{i}\, \frac{\Delta x}{\Delta s} + \mathbf{j}\, \frac{\Delta y}{\Delta s} + \mathbf{k}\, \frac{\Delta z}{\Delta s} = \mathbf{i} \cos \alpha + \mathbf{j} \cos \beta + \mathbf{k} \cos \gamma,$$

or

$$\frac{\Delta x}{\Delta s} = \cos \alpha, \qquad \frac{\Delta y}{\Delta s} = \cos \beta, \qquad \frac{\Delta z}{\Delta s} = \cos \gamma.$$

These direction cosines of $\overrightarrow{P_0 P_1}$ remain constant as P_1 approaches P_0 along L. Hence, in the limit as $\Delta s \to 0$, we also have

$$\frac{dx}{ds} = \cos \alpha, \qquad \frac{dy}{ds} = \cos \beta, \qquad \frac{dz}{ds} = \cos \gamma.$$

With these geometrical considerations out of the way, we now define the directional derivative of w at P_0 in the direction of $\mathbf{u}$ to be the limit, as P_1 approaches P_0 along L, of the average rate of change of w with respect to distance:

$$\frac{dw}{ds} = \lim_{\Delta s \to 0} \frac{\Delta w}{\Delta s} = \lim_{P_1 \to P_0} \frac{f(x_1, y_1, z_1) - f(x_0, y_0, z_0)}{\sqrt{(x_1 - x_0)^2 + (y_1 - y_0)^2 + (z_1 - z_0)^2}}.$$

If f, f_x, f_y, and f_z are all continuous functions of x, y, z in some neighborhood of the point $P_0(x_0, y_0, z_0)$, then Eq. (18) of Article 14–4 applies, and we find that the directional derivative of $w = f(x, y, z)$ at P_0 in the direction of $\mathbf{u} = \mathbf{i} \cos \alpha + \mathbf{j} \cos \beta + \mathbf{k} \cos \gamma$ is

$$\frac{dw}{ds} = f_x(x_0, y_0, z_0) \cos \alpha + f_y(x_0, y_0, z_0) \cos \beta + f_z(x_0, y_0, z_0) \cos \gamma.$$

(2)

This can be expressed as the dot product of the vector $\mathbf{u}$ above and the vector

$$\mathbf{v} = \mathbf{i} f_x(x_0, y_0, z_0) + \mathbf{j} f_y(x_0, y_0, z_0) + \mathbf{k} f_z(x_0, y_0, z_0);$$ (3)

that is,

$$\frac{dw}{ds} = \mathbf{u} \cdot \mathbf{v}.$$

(4)

This factorization separates the directional derivative into a part $\mathbf{u}$ which depends only upon the *direction* and a part $\mathbf{v}$ which depends only upon the *function and the point P*. The vector $\mathbf{v}$ is called the *gradient* of f at P_0. It will be considered in detail in the next article. Equation (4) applies also in two dimensions as well as in three and includes Eq. (1) as a special case, with $\gamma = 90°$, $\cos \gamma = 0$.

Problems

In Problems 1–4, find the directional derivative of the given function, $f = f(x, y, z)$, at the given point, and in the direction of the given vector $\mathbf{A}$.

1. $f = e^x \cos (yz)$, $P_0(0, 0, 0)$, $\mathbf{A} = 2\mathbf{i} + \mathbf{j} - 2\mathbf{k}$.
2. $f = \ln \sqrt{x^2 + y^2 + z^2}$, $P_0(3, 4, 12)$, $\mathbf{A} = 3\mathbf{i} + 6\mathbf{j} - 2\mathbf{k}$.
3. $f = x^2 + 2y^2 + 3z^2$, $P_0(1, 1, 1)$, $\mathbf{A} = \mathbf{i} + \mathbf{j} + \mathbf{k}$.
4. $f = xy + yz + zx$, $P_0(1, -1, 2)$, $\mathbf{A} = 10\mathbf{i} + 11\mathbf{j} - 2\mathbf{k}$.

5. In which direction should one travel, starting from $P_0(1, 1, 0)$, in order to obtain the most rapid rate of decrease of the function $f = (x + y - 2)^2 + (3x - y - 6)^2$?

6. The directional derivative of a given function $w = f(x, y)$ at $P_0(1, 2)$ in the direction toward $P_1(2, 3)$ is $+2\sqrt{2}$, and in the direction toward $P_2(1, 0)$ it is -3. What is the value of dw/ds at P_0 in the direction toward the origin?

7. Investigate the following graphical method of representing the directional derivative. Let $w = f(x, y)$ be a given function and let $P_0(x_0, y_0)$ be a given point. Through P_0 draw any ray making an angle θ with the positive x-direction, $0 \leq \theta \leq 2\pi$. On this directed line (or on its backward extension through P_0, if r is negative) mark the point Q such that the polar coordinates of Q relative to P_0 are (r, θ) with $r = (dw/ds)_0$. Show that the locus of Q is a circle of diameter

$$\sqrt{\left(\frac{\partial w}{\partial x}\right)_0^2 + \left(\frac{\partial w}{\partial y}\right)_0^2}.$$

Show that P_0 and

$$P_1\left[x_0 + \left(\frac{\partial w}{\partial x}\right)_0, \ y_0 + \left(\frac{\partial w}{\partial y}\right)_0\right].$$

are opposite ends of one diameter of the circle. (This gives an easy method for constructing the circle. It is only necessary to locate P_0 and P_1 and then draw the circle. It is analogous to the Mohr circle in mechanics.)

8. Find the directional derivative of $f(x, y) = x \tan^{-1} y/x$ at $(1, 1)$ in the direction of $\mathbf{A} = 2\mathbf{i} - \mathbf{j}$.

9. In which direction is the directional derivative of $f(x, y) = (x^2 - y^2)/(x^2 + y^2)$ at $(1, 1)$ equal to zero?

14–6 The gradient. In the previous article we found that the directional derivative of a function $w = f(x, y, z)$ could be expressed as the dot product of a unit vector $\mathbf{u}$ specifying the direction and the vector $\mathbf{v}$ of Eq. (3). This latter vector depends only upon the values of the partial derivatives of w at P_0 and is called the *gradient of w*. Two symbols are commonly used to denote the gradient, namely, grad w and ∇w, where ∇ is an inverted capital delta and is generally called *del*. The gradient is defined by the equation

$$\text{grad } w = \nabla w = \mathbf{i}\,\frac{\partial w}{\partial x} + \mathbf{j}\,\frac{\partial w}{\partial y} + \mathbf{k}\,\frac{\partial w}{\partial z}. \tag{1}$$

The del operator

$$\nabla = \mathbf{i}\,\frac{\partial}{\partial x} + \mathbf{j}\,\frac{\partial}{\partial y} + \mathbf{k}\,\frac{\partial}{\partial z} \tag{2}$$

is akin to, but somewhat more complex than, the familiar differentiation operator d/dx. When del operates on a differentiable function $w = f(x, y, z)$, it produces a vector, namely the vector grad w or grad f given by Eq. (1).

In courses in advanced calculus and vector analysis, a detailed study is made of the operator ∇, including not only the operation of forming the gradient of a scalar function w but also the additional operations of forming the dot and cross products of the vector operator del with other vectors.*

It is our purpose in this article to develop some of the geometric properties of the gradient. The first property is the connection between the gradient and the directional derivative as developed in the previous article. Using ∇w to represent the gradient, we may write Eq. (2) of Article 14–5 as

$$\left(\frac{dw}{ds}\right)_0 = (\nabla w)_0 \cdot \mathbf{u}, \tag{3}$$

where the subscript 0 is used to indicate the fact that both ∇w and dw/ds are to be evaluated at the point $P_0(x_0, y_0, z_0)$.

From Eq. (3) and the geometric significance of the dot product of two vectors, we can say that

$$\left(\frac{dw}{ds}\right)_0 = |(\nabla w)_0||\mathbf{u}| \cos \theta$$
$$= |(\nabla w)_0| \cos \theta, \tag{4}$$

where θ is the angle between the vector $(\nabla w)_0$ and the unit vector $\mathbf{u}$. That is, $(dw/ds)_0$ is just the scalar projection of grad w at P_0, onto the direction $\mathbf{u}$ (Fig. 14–10a). Since this projection attains its maximum value when $\cos \theta = 1$ in Eq. (4), that is, when $\mathbf{u}$ and ∇w have the same direction, we can say that *the function $w = f(x, y, z)$ changes most rapidly in the direction given by the vector grad w itself*. Moreover, the directional derivative in this direction is equal to the magnitude of the gradient.

We may therefore characterize the gradient of the function $w = f(x, y, z)$ at the point $P_0(x_0, y_0, z_0)$ as a vector

(a) whose *direction* is that in which $(dw/ds)_0$ has its maximum value, and
(b) whose *magnitude* is equal to that maximum value of $(dw/ds)_0$.

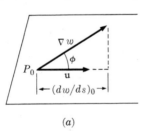

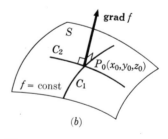

(a)   (b)

FIGURE 14–10

* See, for example, Kaplan, *Advanced Calculus*, Chapters 3 and 5. (Addison-Wesley, 1952)

get   Book

A second interpretation of the gradient vector may be gained from the following considerations. The points at which the function $w = f(x, y, z)$ has the same value w_0 that it has at $P_0(x_0, y_0, z_0)$ will, in general, constitute a surface in space. The equation of this surface is

$$f(x, y, z) = w_0, \tag{5a}$$

$$f(x, y, z) - w_0 = 0, \tag{5b}$$

where w_0 is a constant. If w represents temperature, the surface given by Eq. (5) is an isothermal surface. If w represents electrical potential, then the surface is an equipotential surface. The fact which we now wish to establish is that *the gradient vector is normal to this isothermal or equipotential surface*, as shown in Fig. 14–10(b). To see that this is so, suppose we consider any curve C on the surface S of Eq. (5) and passing through P_0. Let us now calculate the directional derivative $(dw/ds)_0$ in the direction of the tangent to the curve C at P_0. This derivative is zero because w remains constant on C and hence $(\Delta w)_C = 0$, so that

$$\left(\frac{dw}{ds}\right)_0 = \lim \frac{\Delta w}{\Delta s} = 0.$$

If we compare this result with Eq. (4), we see that at any point P_0 where $(\nabla w)_0$ is not zero, $\cos \theta$ vanishes; that is,

$$(\nabla w)_0 \text{ is perpendicular to } \mathbf{u},$$

where $\mathbf{u}$ is a unit vector tangent to C at P_0. Now since C could be any curve on S through P_0, we have the result that $(\nabla w)_0$ *is normal to the surface S at P_0*. In the exceptional case where $(\nabla w)_0$ is the zero vector, then it has no definite direction, but if we adopt the convention that the zero vector is orthogonal to every direction then we may say without exception that the gradient of a function $f(x, y, z)$ at a point $P_0(x_0, y_0, z_0)$ is orthogonal to the surface $f(x, y, z) = $ constant passing through that point.

EXAMPLE. Find the plane which is tangent to the surface $z = x^2 + y^2$ at the point $P_0(1, -2, 5)$.

Solution. Let $w = f(x, y, z) = x^2 + y^2 - z$, so that the equation of the surface has the form

$$f(x, y, z) = \text{constant},$$

where the constant in this case is zero. Then the vector

$$(\text{grad } f)_0 = \left(\mathbf{i}\frac{\partial f}{\partial x} + \mathbf{j}\frac{\partial f}{\partial y} + \mathbf{k}\frac{\partial f}{\partial z} \right)_0$$

$$= (\mathbf{i}2x + \mathbf{j}2y - \mathbf{k})_{(1,-2,5)} = 2\mathbf{i} - 4\mathbf{j} - \mathbf{k}$$

is *normal* to the surface at P_0. But we recall that the equation of the plane through $P_0(x_0, y_0, z_0)$ normal to the vector

$$\mathbf{N} = A\mathbf{i} + B\mathbf{j} + C\mathbf{k}$$

is

$$A(x - x_0) + B(y - y_0) + C(z - z_0) = 0.$$

For the particular case at hand, we therefore have

$$2(x - 1) - 4(y + 2) - (z - 5) = 0,$$

or

$$2x - 4y - z = 5,$$

as the equation of the tangent plane.

Note that the equation of the surface should be put into the form

$$f(x, y, z) = \text{constant}$$

in order to find the normal vector, grad f.

PROBLEMS

In Problems 1–7, find the electric intensity vector $\mathbf{E} = -\text{grad } V$ from the given potential function V, at the given point:

1. $V = x^2 + y^2 - 2z^2$ $(1, 1, 1)$
2. $V = 2z^3 - 3(x^2 + y^2)z$ $(1, 1, 1)$
3. $V = e^{-2y} \cos 2x$ $(\pi/4, 0, 0)$
4. $V = \ln \sqrt{x^2 + y^2}$ $(3, 4, 0)$
5. $V = (x^2 + y^2 + z^2)^{-(1/2)}$ $(1, 2, -2)$
6. $V = e^{3x+4y} \cos 5z$ $(0, 0, \pi/6)$
7. $V = \cos 3x \cos 4y \sinh 5z$ $(0, \pi/4, 0)$

8. Find equations of the line normal to the surface $z^2 = x^2 + y^2$ at $(3, 4, -5)$.

9. Lines are drawn through the origin and normal to the surface $xy + z = 2$. (a) Find equations of all such lines. (b) Find all points of intersection of these lines with the surface.

10. Find the locus of points on the surface

$$(y + z)^2 + (z - x)^2 = 16,$$

where the normal is parallel to the yz-plane.

11. Find the tangent plane and normal to the hyperboloid $x^2 + y^2 - z^2 = 18$ at $(3, 5, -4)$.

12. In which direction should one travel, starting from the point $P_0(2, -1, 2)$, in order to obtain the most rapid rate of increase of the function $f = (x + y)^2 + (y + z)^2 + (z + x)^2$? What is the instantaneous rate of change of f per unit of distance in this direction?

13. Suppose cylindrical coordinates r, θ, z are introduced into a function $w = f(x, y, z)$ to yield $w = F(r, \theta, z)$. Show that the gradient may be expressed in terms of cylindrical coordinates and the unit vectors $\mathbf{u}_r$, $\mathbf{u}_\theta$, $\mathbf{k}$ as follows:

$$\nabla w = \mathbf{u}_r \frac{\partial w}{\partial r} + \frac{1}{r} \mathbf{u}_\theta \frac{\partial w}{\partial \theta} + \mathbf{k} \frac{\partial w}{\partial z}.$$

[*Hint:* The component of ∇w in the direction of $\mathbf{u}_r$ is equal to the directional derivative dw/ds in that direction. But this is precisely $\partial w/\partial r$. Reason similarly for the components of ∇w in the directions of $\mathbf{u}_\theta$ and $\mathbf{k}$.]

14. Express the gradient in terms of spherical coordinates and the appropriate unit vectors $\mathbf{u}_\rho$, $\mathbf{u}_\phi$, $\mathbf{u}_\theta$. Use a geometrical argument to determine the component of ∇w in each of these directions. (See hint for Problem 13.)

15. (a) In the case of a function $w = f(x, y)$ of two independent variables, what is the expression for grad f? (b) Find the direction in which the function $w = x^2 + xy + y^2$ increases most rapidly, at the point $(-1, 1)$. What is the magnitude of dw/ds in this direction?

In Problems 16–23, verify that the function V satisfies Laplace's equation

$$\frac{\partial^2 V}{\partial x^2} + \frac{\partial^2 V}{\partial y^2} + \frac{\partial^2 V}{\partial z^2} = 0,$$

where V is as given:

16. In Problem 1   17. In Problem 2   18. In Problem 3   19. In Problem 4
20. In Problem 5   21. In Problem 6   22. In Problem 7   23. In Problem 8

24. *Method of steepest descent.* Suppose it is desired to find a solution of the equation $f(x, y, z) = 0$. Let $P_0(x_0, y_0, z_0)$ be a first guess, and suppose $f(x_0, y_0, z_0) = f_0$ is not zero. Let $(\nabla f)_0$ be the gradient vector normal to the surface $f(x, y, z) = f_0$ at P_0. If f_0 is positive, we want to decrease the value of f. The gradient points in the direction of most rapid increase, its negative in the direction of "steepest descent." We therefore take as next approximation $x_1 = x_0 - hf_x(x_0, y_0, z_0)$, $y_1 = y_0 - hf_y(x_0, y_0, z_0)$, $z_1 = z_0 - hf_z(x_0, y_0, z_0)$. What value of h corresponds to making $\Delta f_{\text{tan}} = -f_0$? What change is suggested if f_0 is negative? [The method could be applied to the problem of solving the simultaneous equations

$$2x + 3y + 4z = 5 \qquad x^2 + y^2 + z^2 = 7 \qquad xyz = 4$$

by writing

$$f(x, y, z) = (2x + 3y + 4z - 5)^2 + (x^2 + y^2 + z^2 - 7)^2 + (xyz - 4)^2.]$$

14–7 The chain rule for partial derivatives. We recall that the formula

$$\frac{dy}{dt} = \frac{dy}{dx} \frac{dx}{dt}, \tag{1}$$

developed in an early chapter, is useful in connection with problems in related rates and with curves whose equations are given in parametric form. Equation (1) expresses the so-called "chain rule" for differentiating a function

$$y = f(x) \tag{2}$$

with respect to t, when x is a function of t,

$$x = g(t). \tag{3}$$

The result of substituting from Eq. (3) into Eq. (2) gives y as a function $F(t)$:

$$y = f[g(t)] = F(t). \tag{4}$$

Equation (1) tells us that the derivative of this function, namely $F'(t)$, can be found by calculating the terms on the right side of the equation

$$F'(t) = f'(x)g'(t) \tag{5a}$$

or

$$F_t = f_x g_t, \tag{5b}$$

$$y_t = y_x x_t, \tag{5c}$$

where in (5a) we use primes to denote derivatives and in (5b, c) we use subscripts for the same purpose.

In this article we shall extend this "chain rule" to the case of functions of several variables, where partial derivatives will be involved. Suppose then that we have a function, say

$$w = f(x, y, z), \tag{6}$$

which has continuous partial derivatives

$$\frac{\partial w}{\partial x} = f_x, \qquad \frac{\partial w}{\partial y} = f_y, \qquad \frac{\partial w}{\partial z} = f_z \tag{7}$$

throughout some region R of xyz-space. Suppose we want to study the behavior of the function f along some curve C lying in R. Let the equation of C in terms of the parameter t be

$$x = x(t), \qquad y = y(t), \qquad z = z(t). \tag{8}$$

Such a situation arises, for example, in studying the pressure or density in a moving fluid. Then the equation which takes the place of Eq. (1) or (5) is

$$\frac{dw}{dt} = \frac{\partial w}{\partial x}\frac{dx}{dt} + \frac{\partial w}{\partial y}\frac{dy}{dt} + \frac{\partial w}{\partial z}\frac{dz}{dt}, \tag{9}$$

as we shall now show. Let t_0 be a value of t which corresponds to a point P_0 in R and let Δt be an increment in t such that the point P which corresponds to $t_0 + \Delta t$ also lies in R. Let Δx, Δy, Δz, Δw denote the increments in x, y, z, w. Then, by Eq. (18) of Article 14–4, we may write

$$\frac{\Delta w}{\Delta t} = \left(\frac{\partial w}{\partial x}\right)_0 \frac{\Delta x}{\Delta t} + \left(\frac{\partial w}{\partial y}\right)_0 \frac{\Delta y}{\Delta t} + \left(\frac{\partial w}{\partial z}\right)_0 \frac{\Delta z}{\Delta t} + \epsilon_1 \frac{\Delta x}{\Delta t} + \epsilon_2 \frac{\Delta y}{\Delta t} + \epsilon_3 \frac{\Delta z}{\Delta t},$$
(10)

where the subscript zero on the partial derivatives indicates that they are to be evaluated at P_0, and where

$$\epsilon_1, \epsilon_2, \epsilon_3 \to 0 \qquad \text{as} \qquad \Delta x, \Delta y, \Delta z \to 0.$$

Suppose we now let $\Delta t \to 0$ in Eq. (10) and assume that the curve C given by Eqs. (8) is such that the derivatives dx/dt, dy/dt, dz/dt all exist at t_0. Then

$$\Delta x, \Delta y, \Delta z \to 0 \qquad \text{as} \qquad \Delta t \to 0$$

and the three terms in Eq. (10) which involve the epsilons go to zero, while the other terms give

$$\left(\frac{dw}{dt}\right)_0 = \left(\frac{\partial w}{\partial x}\right)_0 \left(\frac{dx}{dt}\right)_0 + \left(\frac{\partial w}{\partial y}\right)_0 \left(\frac{dy}{dt}\right)_0 + \left(\frac{\partial w}{\partial z}\right)_0 \left(\frac{dz}{dt}\right)_0,$$

which is Eq. (9) with all derivatives evaluated for $t = t_0$, $x = x_0$, $y = y_0$, and $z = z_0$.

There is no essential complication introduced by considering the behavior of the function w in Eq. (6) on a *surface* S lying in R. It takes, in general, *two* parameters to give the equations of a surface (for example, *latitude* and *longitude* on the surface of a sphere). Hence, consider the case where x, y, and z are functions of two parameters, say r and s,

$$x = x(r, s), \qquad y = y(r, s), \qquad z = z(r, s), \qquad (11)$$

and calculate

$$\frac{\partial w}{\partial r} = \lim_{\Delta r \to 0} \frac{\Delta w}{\Delta r} \qquad (12)$$

with s held constant. In this case Eq. (10) is to be replaced by a similar equation with Δr in place of Δt throughout. When $\Delta r \to 0$ (s held constant), we have

$$\lim_{\Delta r \to 0} \frac{\Delta x}{\Delta r} = \frac{\partial x}{\partial r}$$

and two similar expressions with y and z in place of x. Thus when $\Delta r \to 0$ the result is

$$\frac{\partial w}{\partial r} = \frac{\partial w}{\partial x}\frac{\partial x}{\partial r} + \frac{\partial w}{\partial y}\frac{\partial y}{\partial r} + \frac{\partial w}{\partial z}\frac{\partial z}{\partial r}. \qquad (13)$$

A similar expression with s in place of r could also be derived for $\partial w/\partial s$. More generally, we may consider a function

$$w = f(x, y, z, u, \ldots, v)$$

of any number of variables $x, y, z, u, \ldots, v$ and study the behavior of this function when these variables are related to any number of other variables $p, q, r, s, \ldots, t$ by equations

$$x = x(p, q, r, s, \ldots, t),$$
$$y = y(p, q, r, s, \ldots, t),$$
$$\vdots$$
$$v = v(p, q, r, s, \ldots, t).$$

Then, suppose it is required to find $\partial w/\partial p$, $\partial w/\partial q$, $\partial w/\partial r$, $\ldots$, $\partial w/\partial t$. By the methods used above, we find

$$\boxed{\frac{\partial w}{\partial p} = \frac{\partial w}{\partial x}\frac{\partial x}{\partial p} + \frac{\partial w}{\partial y}\frac{\partial y}{\partial p} + \frac{\partial w}{\partial z}\frac{\partial z}{\partial p} + \cdots + \frac{\partial w}{\partial v}\frac{\partial v}{\partial p}} \qquad (14)$$

or, in terms of the subscript notation for partial derivatives,

$$w_p = w_x x_p + w_y y_p + w_z z_p + \cdots + w_v v_p.$$

There are analogous equations for $\partial w/\partial q$, $\ldots$, $\partial w/\partial t$ obtained by replacing p by $q, \ldots, t$ respectively. This "chain rule" may be summarized as follows:

Let w be a differentiable function of the variables $x, y, \ldots, v$ and let these in turn be differentiable functions of a second set of variables p, $q, \ldots, t$:

First set of variables: $x, y, z, \ldots, v$,

Second set of variables: $p, q, r, \ldots, t$.

Then the derivative of w with respect to any one of the variables in the second set, say p, may be obtained by the following procedure:

1. Differentiate w with respect to each one of the variables in the first set; that is, calculate

$$\partial w/\partial x, \partial w/\partial y, \ldots, \partial w/\partial v.$$

2. Differentiate each variable of the first set with respect to the one variable, in this case p, of the second set; that is, calculate

$$\partial x/\partial p, \partial y/\partial p, \ldots, \partial v/\partial p.$$

3. Form the products of the corresponding derivatives in 1 and 2, such as $(\partial w/\partial x)(\partial x/\partial p)$, $(\partial w/\partial y)(\partial y/\partial p)$, etc., and add these products together. Their sum gives $\partial w/\partial p$ [Eq. (14)].

Application. We can solve the partial differential equation

$$\frac{\partial w}{\partial x} - a\frac{\partial w}{\partial y} = 0$$

for $w = f(x, y)$, given that a is a constant different from zero. To do so, we introduce new independent variables r, s such that

$$y - ax = r, \qquad y + ax = s.$$

Now we think of w as a function of r, s,

$$w = F(r, s),$$

and apply the chain rule in the form

$$\frac{\partial w}{\partial x} = \frac{\partial w}{\partial r}\frac{\partial r}{\partial x} + \frac{\partial w}{\partial s}\frac{\partial s}{\partial x} = -a\frac{\partial w}{\partial r} + a\frac{\partial w}{\partial s},$$

$$\frac{\partial w}{\partial y} = \frac{\partial w}{\partial r}\frac{\partial r}{\partial y} + \frac{\partial w}{\partial s}\frac{\partial s}{\partial y} = \frac{\partial w}{\partial r} + \frac{\partial w}{\partial s}.$$

When we substitute these expressions for $\partial w/\partial x$ and $\partial w/\partial y$ into the partial differential equation

$$\frac{\partial w}{\partial x} - a\frac{\partial w}{\partial y} = 0,$$

we obtain

$$-2a\frac{\partial w}{\partial r} = 0 \qquad \text{or} \qquad \frac{\partial w}{\partial r} = 0.$$

But this equation is *easy* to solve! It simply requires that $w = F(r, s)$ be a constant when s is constant and r is allowed to vary. That is, w must be a function of s alone:

$$w = \phi(s) = \phi(y + ax).$$

Here $\phi(s)$ is *any* differentiable function of s whatever; for example,

$$\phi(s) = e^{2s} + \tan^{-1}(s^2) + \sqrt{s^2 + 4}$$

would be a suitable function. For this special case, we have

$$w = \phi(y + ax) = e^{2y+2ax} + \tan^{-1}(y + ax)^2 + \sqrt{(y + ax)^2 + 4}$$

as a function which satisfies the original partial differential equation.

Problems

In each of the following problems (1–3), find dw/dt (a) by expressing w explicitly as a function of t and then differentiating, and (b) by using the chain rule.

1. $w = x^2 + y^2 + z^2$, $\quad x = e^t \cos t$, $\quad y = e^t \sin t$, $\quad z = e^t$

2. $w = \dfrac{xy}{x^2 + y^2}$, $\quad x = \cosh t$, $\quad y = \sinh t$

3. $w = e^{2x+3y} \cos 4z$, $\quad x = \ln t$, $\quad y = \ln (t^2 + 1)$, $\quad z = t$

4. If $w = \sqrt{x^2 + y^2 + z^2}$, $x = e^r \cos s$, $y = e^r \sin s$, $z = e^s$, find $\partial w/\partial r$ and $\partial w/\partial s$ by the chain rule and check your answer by using a different method.

5. If $w = \ln (x^2 + y^2 + 2z)$, $x = r + s$, $y = r - s$, $z = 2rs$, find $\partial w/\partial r$ and $\partial w/\partial s$ by the chain rule and check your answer by using a different method.

6. If a and b are constants and $w = (ax + by)^3 + \tanh (ax + by) + \cos (ax + by)$, show that

$$a \frac{\partial w}{\partial y} = b \frac{\partial w}{\partial x}.$$

7. If a and b are constants and $w = f(ax + by)$ is a differentiable function of $u = ax + by$, show that

$$a \frac{\partial w}{\partial y} = b \frac{\partial w}{\partial x}.$$

[*Hint:* Apply the chain rule with u as the only independent variable in the first set of variables.]

8. If $w = f[xy/(x^2 + y^2)]$ is a differentiable function of $u = xy/(x^2 + y^2)$, show that $x(\partial w/\partial x) + y(\partial w/\partial y) = 0$. (See the hint for Problem 7.)

9. If $w = f(x + y, x - y)$ has continuous partial derivatives with respect to $u = x + y$, $v = x - y$, show that

$$\frac{\partial w}{\partial x} \frac{\partial w}{\partial y} = \left(\frac{\partial f}{\partial u}\right)^2 - \left(\frac{\partial f}{\partial v}\right)^2.$$

10. Verify the result given in Problem 13, Article 14–6, by transforming the given expression on the right side of the equation into $\mathbf{i}$, $\mathbf{j}$, $\mathbf{k}$ components and replacing the cylindrical coordinates r, θ by Cartesian coordinates x, y and making use of the chain rule for partial derivatives.

11. Verify the answer obtained in Problem 14, Article 14–6, by transforming the expression you obtained in spherical coordinates back into Cartesian coordinates. Make use of the chain rule for partial derivatives.

12. If we substitute polar coordinates $x = r \cos \theta$ and $y = r \sin \theta$ in a function $w = f(x, y)$, show that

$$\frac{\partial w}{\partial r} = f_x \cos \theta + f_y \sin \theta,$$

$$\frac{1}{r} \frac{\partial w}{\partial \theta} = -f_x \sin \theta + f_y \cos \theta.$$

13. Using determinants, solve the equations given in Problem 12 for f_x and f_y in terms of $(\partial w/\partial r)$ and $(\partial w/\partial \theta)$.

14. In connection with Problem 12, show that

$$\left(\frac{\partial w}{\partial r}\right)^2 + \frac{1}{r^2}\left(\frac{\partial w}{\partial \theta}\right)^2 = f_x^2 + f_y^2.$$

14–8 The total differential. The differential of a function

$$w = f(x, y, z) \tag{1}$$

is defined to be

$$dw = \frac{\partial w}{\partial x}\,dx + \frac{\partial w}{\partial y}\,dy + \frac{\partial w}{\partial z}\,dz. \tag{2}$$

The chain rule [Eq. (9), Article 14–7] tells us that we may formally divide both sides of Eq. (2) by dt to calculate dw/dt in case x, y, z are differentiable functions of t. Or, if x, y, z are functions of the independent variables r, s and we want to calculate $\partial w/\partial r$, we hold s constant in calculating dx, dy, dz and divide both sides of Eq. (2) by dr, but write $\partial w/\partial r$, etc., in place of dw/dr, etc., to show that s has been held constant.

The separate terms

$$\frac{\partial w}{\partial x}\,dx, \qquad \frac{\partial w}{\partial y}\,dy, \qquad \frac{\partial w}{\partial z}\,dz$$

are sometimes called "partial differentials" of w with respect to x, y, z respectively. Then the sum of these partial differentials, Eq. (2), is called the *total differential dw*.

In general, the total differential of a function

$$w = F(x, y, z, u, \ldots, v)$$

is defined to be the sum of all its partial differentials

$$dw = F_x\,dx + F_y\,dy + F_z\,dz + F_u\,du + \cdots + F_v\,dv.$$

If x, y, and z are independent variables in Eq. (1), then dx, dy, and dz are three *new independent* variables in Eq. (2). But in any problem involving increments we shall agree to take

$$dx = \Delta x, \qquad dy = \Delta y, \qquad dz = \Delta z \tag{3}$$

in order to be able to use the differential dw as a good approximation to

Δw [see Eq. (19), Article 14–4]. When x, y, and z are *not* the independent variables but are themselves given by equations such as

$$x = x(t), \qquad x = x(r, s),$$

$$y = y(t), \quad \text{or} \quad y = y(r, s),$$

$$z = z(t), \qquad z = z(r, s),$$

then in the first case we have

$$dx = x'(t)\, dt, \qquad dy = y'(t)\, dt, \qquad dz = z'(t)\, dt,$$

and in the second case,

$$dx = \frac{\partial x}{\partial r}\, dr + \frac{\partial x}{\partial s}\, ds,$$

$$dy = \frac{\partial y}{\partial r}\, dr + \frac{\partial y}{\partial s}\, ds, \tag{4}$$

$$dz = \frac{\partial z}{\partial r}\, dr + \frac{\partial z}{\partial s}\, ds,$$

if we are to be consistent.

Suppose we consider the second case in more detail. If we consider

$$w = f[x(r, s), y(r, s), z(r, s)] = F(r, s)$$

as a function of r and s, then instead of Eq. (2) we should have

$$dw = \frac{\partial w}{\partial r}\, dr + \frac{\partial w}{\partial s}\, ds, \tag{5}$$

where

$$\frac{\partial w}{\partial r} = F_r(r, s), \qquad \frac{\partial w}{\partial s} = F_s(r, s).$$

The question now arises as to whether or not the dw given by Eq. (2) is the same as the dw given by Eq. (5). The answer, which is "yes, they are the same," is a consequence of the chain rule for derivatives. For, if we start with the dw given by Eq. (2) and into it substitute dx, dy, dz given by Eq. (4), we obtain

$$dw = \frac{\partial w}{\partial x}\left(\frac{\partial x}{\partial r}\, dr + \frac{\partial x}{\partial s}\, ds\right) + \frac{\partial w}{\partial y}\left(\frac{\partial y}{\partial r}\, dr + \frac{\partial y}{\partial s}\, ds\right) + \frac{\partial w}{\partial z}\left(\frac{\partial z}{\partial r}\, dr + \frac{\partial z}{\partial s}\, ds\right)$$

$$= \left(\frac{\partial w}{\partial x}\frac{\partial x}{\partial r} + \frac{\partial w}{\partial y}\frac{\partial y}{\partial r} + \frac{\partial w}{\partial z}\frac{\partial z}{\partial r}\right) dr + \left(\frac{\partial w}{\partial x}\frac{\partial x}{\partial s} + \frac{\partial w}{\partial y}\frac{\partial y}{\partial s} + \frac{\partial w}{\partial z}\frac{\partial z}{\partial s}\right) ds,$$

and the expressions in parentheses which here multiply dr and ds are the same as $\partial w/\partial r$ and $\partial w/\partial s$, respectively, by virtue of the chain rule for derivatives. Thus, starting with the expression for dw given by Eq. (2), we have transformed it into the expression for dw given by Eq. (5), thereby establishing the equivalence of the two.

It should be pointed out that in the case just discussed, where r and s are the *independent* variables, we are to treat dr and ds also as independent variables, but *not* dx, dy, and dz, which indeed are given by Eqs. (4). Thus, in a problem involving increments, we could for convenience take

$$dr = \Delta r \quad \text{and} \quad ds = \Delta s,$$

but we should *not* take $dx = \Delta x$, $dy = \Delta y$, and $dz = \Delta z$ since we are bound by Eqs. (4). The differentials dx, dy, and dz will, however (Article 14–4), usually be reasonably good *approximations* to the increments Δx, Δy, and Δz when Δr and Δs are small.

EXAMPLE 1. Consider the function

$$w = x^2 + y^2 + z^2$$

with

$$x = r \cos s, \quad y = r \sin s, \quad z = r.$$

If we use Eq. (2), we have

$$dw = 2(x\,dx + y\,dy + z\,dz)$$

with

$$dx = \cos s\,dr - r \sin s\,ds, \quad dy = \sin s\,dr + r \cos s\,ds, \quad dz = dr,$$

and hence

$$\begin{aligned}
dw &= 2(x \cos s + y \sin s + z)\,dr + 2(-xr \sin s + yr \cos s)\,ds \\
&= 2(r \cos^2 s + r \sin^2 s + r)\,dr + 2(-r^2 \cos s \sin s + r^2 \sin s \cos s)\,ds \\
&= 4r\,dr.
\end{aligned}$$

On the other hand, if we first express w directly in terms of r and s, we obtain

$$w = r^2 \cos^2 s + r^2 \sin^2 s + r^2 = 2r^2,$$

from which we also obtain

$$dw = 4r\,dr.$$

EXAMPLE 2. Show that the slope at the point (x, y) of the plane curve whose equation is given implicitly by

$$F(x, y) = 0$$

is

$$\frac{dy}{dx} = \frac{-F_x(x, y)}{F_y(x, y)} \quad \text{if} \quad F_y(x, y) \neq 0.$$

Solution. Let $w = F(x, y)$ and consider the directional derivative of w at the point (x, y) in the direction of the tangent to the curve. If s denotes arc length along the curve, the directional derivative is

$$\frac{dF}{ds} = F_x \frac{dx}{ds} + F_y \frac{dy}{ds}.$$

But along the given curve F is constant, so that

$$\frac{dF}{ds} = \lim_{\Delta s \to 0} \frac{\Delta F}{\Delta s} = 0.$$

Therefore

$$F_x \frac{dx}{ds} + F_y \frac{dy}{ds} = 0,$$

and hence

$$\frac{dy}{dx} = \frac{dy/ds}{dx/ds} = \frac{-F_x}{F_y}.$$

EXAMPLE 3. Let $w = F(x, y, z)$ be *constant* along a curve C passing through $P_0(x_0, y_0, z_0)$. Let dx, dy, dz be such that the vector

$$d\mathbf{R} = \mathbf{i}\,dx + \mathbf{j}\,dy + \mathbf{k}\,dz$$

is tangent to C at P_0. Show that

$$dw = \text{grad } F \cdot d\mathbf{R} = 0.$$

Solution. By definition,

$$\begin{aligned}
dw &= F_x\,dx + F_y\,dy + F_z\,dz \\
&= (\mathbf{i}F_x + \mathbf{j}F_y + \mathbf{k}F_z) \cdot (\mathbf{i}\,dx + \mathbf{j}\,dy + \mathbf{k}\,dz) \\
&= \text{grad } F \cdot d\mathbf{R}.
\end{aligned}$$

Also, the directional derivative of w, at P_0, in the direction of $d\mathbf{R}$ is

$$\frac{dw}{ds} = \text{grad } F \cdot \mathbf{u},$$

where

$$\mathbf{u} = \frac{d\mathbf{R}}{|d\mathbf{R}|}$$

is a unit vector in the direction of $d\mathbf{R}$. Along C, w remains constant and $dw/ds = 0$. Therefore

$$dw = \text{grad } F \cdot d\mathbf{R} = \text{grad } F \cdot \mathbf{u}\,|d\mathbf{R}| = \frac{dw}{ds}\,|d\mathbf{R}| = 0.$$

PROBLEMS

1. Show that the formulas

　(a) $d(u + v) = du + dv$,　　　　　　(b) $d(uv) = v\,du + u\,dv$,

　(c) $d\left(\dfrac{u}{v}\right) = \dfrac{v\,du - u\,dv}{v^2}$

are valid for total differentials, in case u and v are independent variables or if they are functions of any number of independent variables, such as $u = u(x, y, \ldots, p)$, $v = v(x, y, \ldots, p)$.

2. Using differentials to approximate to increments, find the amount of material in a hollow rectangular box whose inside measurements are 5 ft long, 3 ft wide, 2 ft deep, if the box is made of lumber which is $\frac{1}{2}$ in. thick and the box has no top.

3. The area of a triangle is $A = \frac{1}{2} ab \sin C$, where a and b are two sides of the triangle and C is the included angle. In surveying a particular triangular plot of land, a and b are measured to be 150 ft and 200 ft respectively and C is read to be 60°. By how much (approximately) is the computed area in error if a and b are in error by $\frac{1}{2}$ ft each and C is in error by 2°?

4. (a) Given $x = r \cos \theta$, $y = r \sin \theta$, express dx and dy in terms of dr and $d\theta$. (b) Solve the equations of part (a) for dr and $d\theta$ in terms of dx and dy. (c) In the answer to part (b), suppose A and B are the coefficients of dx and dy in the expression for dr, that is,

$$dr = A\,dx + B\,dy.$$

Verify by direct computation that $A = \partial r/\partial x$ and $B = \partial r/\partial y$, where $r^2 = x^2 + y^2$.

5. Given $x = f(u, v)$, $y = g(u, v)$. If these equations are considered as implicitly defining u and v as functions of x and y:

　(a) Express dx and dy in terms of du and dv.
　(b) Use determinants to solve the equations of part (a) for du and dv in terms of dx and dy.
　(c) Show that

$$\frac{\partial u}{\partial x} = \frac{g_v}{f_u g_v - f_v g_u}$$

　provided

$$f_u g_v - f_v g_u \neq 0.$$

6. (a) Given $x = \rho \sin \phi \cos \theta$, $y = \rho \sin \phi \sin \theta$, $z = \rho \cos \phi$, express dx, dy, dz in terms of $d\rho, d\phi, d\theta$.

(b) Solve the equations of part (a) for $d\rho$ in terms of dx, dy, dz by the use of determinants.

(c) From your answers to part (b), read off $\partial\rho/\partial x$, considering ρ, ϕ, θ as functions of x, y, z that are given implicitly by the equations of part (a).

7. *Newton's method.* It is desired to find values of x and y that satisfy the pair of equations $f(x, y) = 0$ and $g(x, y) = 0$ simultaneously. Suppose that, by

trial and error or otherwise, it is found that $u_0 = f(x_0, y_0)$ and $v_0 = g(x_0, y_0)$ are both small in absolute value. It is now desired to find "corrections" dx and dy such that $f(x_0 + dx, y_0 + dy) = g(x_0 + dx, y_0 + dy) = 0$. Using $u_0 + df$ and $v_0 + dg$ to approximate to $f(x_0 + dx, y_0 + dy)$ and $g(x_0 + dx, y_0 + dy)$ respectively, determine approximate values of dx and dy. The procedure may be repeated with (x_0, y_0) replaced by $(x_1, y_1) = (x_0 + dx, y_0 + dy)$.

8. Generalize the method of Problem 7 to the case of three equations in three unknowns: $f(x, y, z) = 0$, $g(x, y, z) = 0$, $h(x, y, z) = 0$, assuming that $u_0 = f(x_0, y_0, z_0)$, $v_0 = g(x_0, y_0, z_0)$, $w_0 = h(x_0, y_0, z)$ are small in absolute value.

9. Suppose $P_0(x_0, y_0, z_0)$ is a point on the surface $S: F(x, y, z) = 0$. Let dx and dy be arbitrary except that at least one of them should be different from zero. Show that a dz can be found, provided $F_z(x_0, y_0, z_0) \neq 0$, such that the vector $d\mathbf{R} = \mathbf{i}\,dx + \mathbf{j}\,dy + \mathbf{k}\,dz$ is tangent to the surface S at P_0. Find an expression for such a dz. Also show that for such a vector $d\mathbf{R}$, dF is zero at P_0.

10. In Problem 9, consider the equation $F(x, y, z) = 0$ as determining z implicitly as a function of x and y, say $z = \phi(x, y)$. Show that

$$\phi_x = -F_x/F_z, \qquad \phi_y = -F_y/F_z,$$

at any point where $F_z \neq 0$.

11. *Ruled surfaces.* [See "Rulings," by C. S. Ogilvy, *The American Mathematical Monthly*, **59** (1952), pp. 547–549.] The surface $z = f(x, y)$ is said to have *rulings* if through the point $P_0(x_0, y_0, z_0)$ there is a straight line segment all of whose points are on the surface. This happens if through the point $(x_0, y_0, 0)$ in the xy-plane there is a line of points $(x_0 + h, y_0 + k, 0)$ such that along this line dz and Δz are equal. This happens if and only if

$$f(x_0 + h, y_0 + k) - f(x_0, y_0) = \left(\frac{\partial f}{\partial x}\right)_0 h + \left(\frac{\partial f}{\partial y}\right)_0 k$$

when $h = \Delta x = dx$ and $k = \Delta y = dy$. Show that (a) the surface $z = \sqrt{1 + xy}$ has rulings through the point $P_0(2, 4, 3)$, given by the conditions $h = k$ or $4h = k$, (b) the surface $z = x^2 - y^2$ has rulings through any point $P_0(x_0, y_0, z_0)$, given by $h = \pm k$.

14–9 Maxima and minima of functions of two independent variables.
In an early chapter we learned how to use the differential calculus to solve max-min problems for functions $y = f(x)$ of a single independent variable. In this article we shall extend the method to handle problems involving more than one independent variable.

As an illustration of the technique, we shall first discuss a geometrical application. Suppose it is required to find the high and low points on a smooth surface represented by the equation

$$z = f(x, y), \tag{1}$$

where the function f is defined, continuous, and has continuous partial derivatives with respect to x and y in some region R in the xy-plane. If there is a point (a, b) in R such that

$$f(x, y) \geq f(a, b) \tag{2}$$

for all points (x, y) sufficiently near to the point (a, b), then the function f is said to have a *local*, or *relative, minimum* at (a, b). If the inequality (2) holds for all points (x, y) in R, then f has an absolute minimum over R at (a, b). If the inequality in (2) is reversed, f then has a maximum (relative or absolute) at (a, b).

Suppose that the maximum (or minimum) value of f, over the region R, occurs at a point (a, b) that is not on the boundary of R; and that both $\partial f/\partial x$ and $\partial f/\partial y$ exist at (a, b). Then the first *necessary condition* that must be satisfied is that

$$\frac{\partial f}{\partial x} = 0 \quad \text{and} \quad \frac{\partial f}{\partial y} = 0 \quad \text{at} \quad (a, b),$$

as we shall now show. For, the section of the surface (1) lying in the plane $y = b$ is simply the curve whose equation is

$$z = f(x, b), \qquad y = b,$$

and this curve has a high or low turning point at $x = a$ (Fig. 14-11). Hence

$$\left(\frac{\partial z}{\partial x}\right)_{x=a, y=b} = 0.$$

Similarly, the curve

$$z = f(a, y), \qquad x = a,$$

in which the plane $x = a$ intersects the surface, also has a high or low turning point when $y = b$, so that

$$\left(\frac{\partial z}{\partial y}\right)_{x=a, y=b} = 0.$$

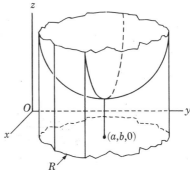

FIGURE 14-11

We shall not at this time enter into a detailed discussion of second derivative tests for distinguishing between maxima and minima. The fundamental principle used in deriving such a test is that the difference

$$D = f(x, y) - f(a, b)$$

should be nonnegative (that is, positive or zero) for all points (x, y) close to the point (a, b) in case of a minimum at (a, b), or nonpositive in the case of a maximum. One way to test for a maximum or a minimum is to take

$$x = a + h, \qquad y = b + k$$

and to examine the difference D for small values of h and k as in the example that follows.

EXAMPLE. Find the high and low points on the surface

$$z = x^2 - xy + y^2 + 2x + 2y - 4 = f(x, y).$$

Solution. We apply the first necessary condition for a maximum or minimum of z, namely,

$$\frac{\partial z}{\partial x} = 0 \qquad \text{and} \qquad \frac{\partial z}{\partial y} = 0.$$

This leads to the simultaneous equations

$$2x - y = -2, \qquad -x + 2y = -2,$$

with solution

$$x = y = -2.$$

Thus, the point which we have been calling (a, b) is here the point $(-2, -2)$. The corresponding value of z is

$$f(-2, -2) = -8.$$

To examine the behavior of the difference $D = f(x, y) - f(-2, -2)$, we let

$$x = -2 + h, \qquad y = -2 + k$$

and obtain

$$D = f(-2 + h, -2 + k) - f(-2, -2) = h^2 - hk + k^2$$

$$= (h - k/2)^2 + 3k^2/4.$$

This is readily seen to be positive for all values of h, k except $h = k = 0$. That is,

$$f(x, y) \geq f(-2, -2)$$

for all (x, y) different from $(-2, -2)$. Thus the surface has a *low* point at $(-2, -2, -8)$. The given function has an absolute minimum -8.

Remark. As with functions of a single independent variable, it is often possible to see that the function $z = f(x, y)$ has exactly one maximum (or minimum), that it occurs at an interior point of the domain of f, and that f everywhere possesses partial derivatives which must be zero at the critical point. No further test is then required. This is true, for instance, in the example above.

PROBLEMS

Examine the following surfaces for high and low points:

1. $z = x^2 + xy + y^2 + 3x - 3y + 4$
2. $z = x^2 + 3xy + 3y^2 - 6x + 3y - 6$
3. $z = 5xy - 7x^2 - y^2 + 3x - 6y + 2$
4. $z = 2xy - 5x^2 - 2y^2 + 4x + 4y - 4$
5. $z = x^2 + xy + 3x + 2y + 5$
6. $z = y^2 + xy - 2x - 2y + 2$
7. Sketch the surface $z = \sqrt{x^2 + y^2}$ over the region R: $|x| \leq 1$, $|y| \leq 1$. Find the high and low points of the surface over R. Discuss the existence, and the values, of $\partial z/\partial x$ and $\partial z/\partial y$ at these points.

14–10 The method of least squares. We next take up an important application of minimizing a function of two variables. It is the so-called "method of least squares" as applied to the problem of fitting a straight line

$$y = mx + b \tag{1}$$

to a set of experimentally observed points (x_1, y_1), (x_2, y_2), $\ldots$, (x_n, y_n). Corresponding to each of the observed values of x there are two values of y, namely, the observed value y_{obs} and the value predicted by the straight line $mx_{\text{obs}} + b$. We shall call the difference,

$$y_{\text{obs}} - (mx_{\text{obs}} + b), \tag{2}$$

a *deviation*. Each deviation measures the amount by which the predicted value of y falls short of the observed value. The set of all deviations

$$d_1 = y_1 - (mx_1 + b), \ldots, d_n = y_n - (mx_n + b) \tag{3}$$

gives a picture of the closeness of fit of the line, Eq. (1), to the observed data. The line is a perfect fit if and only if all of these deviations are zero. But in general no straight line will give a perfect fit. Then we are confronted with the problem of finding a line which fits *best* in some sense or other. Here is where the method of least squares comes in.

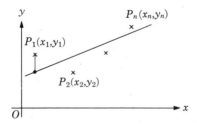

FIGURE 14–12

The method may be motivated as follows. For a straight line which comes *close* to fitting all of the observed points, some of the deviations will probably be positive and some will be negative. But their squares will all be positive, and the expression

$$f(m, b) = (y_1 - mx_1 - b)^2 + (y_2 - mx_2 - b)^2 + \cdots + (y_n - mx_n - b)^2$$

counts a positive deviation d and a negative deviation $-d$ equally. This sum of squares of the deviations depends upon the choice of m and b. It is never negative and it can be zero only if m and b have values which produce a straight line that is a perfect fit.

Whether such a perfectly fitting line can be found or not, the method of least squares says, *"take as the line $y = mx + b$ of best fit that one for which the sum of squares of the deviations*

$$f(m, b) = d_1^2 + d_2^2 + \cdots + d_n^2$$

is a minimum." Thus we try to find the values of m and b where the surface

$$w = f(m, b)$$

in mbw-space has a low point (Fig. 14–13). To do this, we solve the equations

$$\frac{\partial f}{\partial m} = 0 \quad \text{and} \quad \frac{\partial f}{\partial b} = 0$$

simultaneously.

EXAMPLE. Find the straight line that best fits the points $(0, 1)$, $(1, 3)$, $(2, 2)$, $(3, 4)$, $(4, 5)$ according to the method of least squares.

Solution. The sum of squares of the deviations is $f(m, b) = \sum (y_{\text{obs}} - mx_{\text{obs}} - b)^2$, where y_{obs} and x_{obs} are the observed (or given) coordinates of the points to be fitted by the line $y = mx + b$.

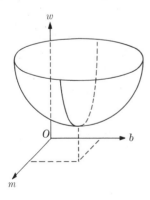

FIGURE 14–13

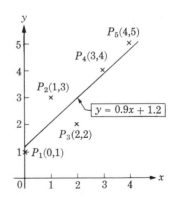

FIGURE 14–14

We list these, together with the deviations and their squares, in the following table.

x_{obs}	y_{obs}	dev = $y_{obs} - mx_{obs} - b$	$(\text{dev})^2$
0	1	$1 - b$	$1 - 2b + b^2$
1	3	$3 - m - b$	$9 - 6b + b^2 - 6m + 2mb + m^2$
2	2	$2 - 2m - b$	$4 - 4b + b^2 - 8m + 4mb + 4m^2$
3	4	$4 - 3m - b$	$16 - 8b + b^2 - 24m + 6mb + 9m^2$
4	5	$5 - 4m - b$	$25 - 10b + b^2 - 40m + 8mb + 16m^2$

$$\sum(\text{dev})^2 = 55 - 30b + 5b^2 - 78m + 20mb + 30m^2 = f(m, b)$$

$$\frac{\partial f}{\partial m} = -78 + 20b + 60m,$$

$$\frac{\partial f}{\partial b} = -30 + 10b + 20m.$$

The values of m and b for which f has a minimum must satisfy the simultaneous equations

$$\frac{\partial f}{\partial m} = 0, \qquad 20b + 60m = 78,$$

$$\frac{\partial f}{\partial b} = 0, \qquad 10b + 20m = 30.$$

The only solution is $m = 0.9$, $b = 1.2$. The "best-fitting" line (in the sense of least sum of squares of deviations) is therefore

$$y = 0.9x + 1.2.$$

To verify that these values of m and b do in fact correspond to a minimum, we let

$$m = 0.9 + h, \qquad b = 1.2 + k$$

and calculate

$$\Delta = f(0.9 + h, 1.2 + k) - f(0.9, 1.2).$$

Doing this algebraically, we find

$$\Delta f = f(m + h, b + k) - f(m, b)$$

$$= (-30 + 10b + 20m)k + (-78 + 20b + 60m)h + 5k^2 + 20kh + 30h^2.$$

The expressions in parentheses are $\partial f/\partial b$ and $\partial f/\partial m$ respectively, and these are zero if $m = 0.9$ and $b = 1.2$. Hence

$$f(0.9 + h, 1.2 + k) - f(0.9, 1.2)$$
$$= 5k^2 + 20kh + 30h^2$$
$$= 5(k + 2h)^2 + 10h^2.$$

This is greater than zero for all values of h and k other than $h = k = 0$. That is,

$$f(0.9 + h, 1.2 + k) \geq f(0.9, 1.2),$$

and we have found the values of m and b for which the function $f(m, b)$ is an absolute minimum.

It is customary to omit the details of testing the answer obtained in solving a problem in least squares. Indeed, it can be shown that for the case of fitting a straight line, the answer *always* corresponds to a minimum.

The method of least squares may also be applied to more complicated equations than the equation of a straight line, and the method has been widely extended. It is even the basis of departure for the modern theory of cybernetics developed by Professor Norbert Wiener of M. I. T.

PROBLEMS

1. The observed points (x_i, y_i), $i = 1, 2, \ldots, n$, are to be fitted by a straight line $y = mx + b$ by the method of least squares. The sum of squares of the deviations is

$$f(m, b) = \sum_{i=1}^{n} (mx_i + b - y_i)^2.$$

(a) Show that the equations $\partial f/\partial b = 0$ and $\partial f/\partial m = 0$ are equivalent to

$$m(\sum x_i) + nb = \sum y_i,$$
$$m(\sum x_i^2) + b(\sum x_i) = \sum x_i y_i,$$

where all sums run from $i = 1$ to $i = n$. (b) Express the solutions b, m of the equations of part (a) in terms of determinants.

In Problems 2–4, apply the method of least squares to obtain the line $y = mx + b$ which best fits the three given points. [The computations can be systematized by making use of the results of Problem 1(b).]

2. $(-1, 2)$, $(0, 1)$, $(3, -1)$
3. $(-2, 0)$, $(0, 2)$, $(2, 3)$
4. $(0, 0)$, $(1, 2)$, $(2, 3)$

5. If $y = mx + b$ is the best-fitting straight line, in the sense of least squares, show that the sum of deviations

$$\sum_{i=1}^{n} (y_i - mx_i - b)$$

is zero. (This means that positive and negative deviations cancel.)

6. Show that the point

$$(\bar{x}, \bar{y}) = \left[\frac{1}{n}\left(\sum_{i=1}^{n} x_i\right), \frac{1}{n}\left(\sum_{i=1}^{n} y_i\right)\right]$$

lies on the straight line $y = mx + b$ that is determined by the method of least squares. (This means that the "best-fitting" line passes through the center of gravity of the n points.)

14–11 Maxima and minima of functions of several independent variables. In certain applications, particularly in statistics, it becomes necessary to find maximum or minimum values of a function

$$w = f(x, y, z, u, \ldots, v)$$

of several independent variables. If the given function has an extreme value at an interior point of the domain, say at

$$x = a, y = b, z = c, \ldots, v = e,$$

then by setting $y = b, z = c, \ldots, v = e$ we obtain a function of x alone,

$$F(x) = f(x, b, c, d, \ldots, e),$$

which has an extreme value at $x = a$. Hence, if f has a partial derivative with respect to x at $x = a, y = b, \ldots, v = e$, that partial derivative must be zero by virtue of the theory for max-min for functions $F(x)$ of a single independent variable. That is,

$$\frac{\partial f}{\partial x} = 0 \quad \text{at} \quad (a, b, c, \ldots, e).$$

By similar reasoning, we arrive at the first necessary condition for extreme values of a function of several independent variables, namely,

$$\frac{\partial f}{\partial x} = 0, \quad \frac{\partial f}{\partial y} = 0, \quad \ldots, \quad \frac{\partial f}{\partial v} = 0 \quad \text{at} \quad (a, b, \ldots, e).$$

The number of simultaneous equations $\partial f/\partial x = 0$, etc., which are thus obtained is precisely equal to the number of *independent variables* $x, y, \ldots, v$. Of course the solutions of this system of equations may correspond to maximum values of f, or to minimum values, or neither, in much the same way as occurs for solutions of the equation $dy/dx = 0$.

Occasionally, the problem arises of finding the extreme value of one function, say

$$w = f(x, y, z, u, \ldots, v),$$

subject to certain auxiliary restrictions that may be represented by such equations as

$$g(x, y, z, u, \ldots, v) = 0,$$

$$h(x, y, z, u, \ldots, v) = 0,$$

and so forth. The theory behind such problems is discussed in most books on advanced calculus. (See Kaplan, *Advanced Calculus*, p. 128). We shall here do no more than point out that the equations representing the side restrictions may be used to express some of the variables x, y, $z, \ldots, v$ in terms of the remaining ones before we take partial derivatives. This is done so that the variables which remain may be *independent*. The following example indicates the method to be used.

EXAMPLE 1. Find the minimum distance from the origin to the plane

$$2x + y - z = 5.$$

Solution. If $P(x, y, z)$ is any point on the plane, then the distance from the origin to P is

$$|\overrightarrow{OP}| = \sqrt{x^2 + y^2 + z^2},$$

and clearly this has a minimum wherever the function

$$f(x, y, z) = |\overrightarrow{OP}|^2 = x^2 + y^2 + z^2$$

has. (The latter is simpler to work with since it does not involve radicals.) But the three variables x, y, z are not all independent, since P is to lie on the plane

$$2x + y - z = 5.$$

If we solve this equation for z, we find

$$z = 2x + y - 5$$

and we may treat x and y as independent variables and minimize the function $g(x, y) = x^2 + y^2 + (2x + y - 5)^2$. The necessary conditions

$$\frac{\partial g}{\partial x} = 0 \quad \text{and} \quad \frac{\partial g}{\partial y} = 0$$

lead to the equations

$$10x + 4y - 20 = 0, \quad 4x + 4y - 10 = 0$$

with solution $x = \frac{5}{3}$, $y = \frac{5}{6}$. The z-coordinate of the corresponding point P is $z = -\frac{5}{6}$ and we thus have found the point $(\frac{5}{3}, \frac{5}{6}, -\frac{5}{6})$ as the *only* point on the plane that satisfies the *necessary* conditions. That is, if the given problem has an answer, this is it. From our knowledge of solid geometry we know that the problem does possess an answer, hence we have found it. Of course, we may solve this same problem by strictly geometrical methods, but our purpose is not so much to solve this specific problem as it is to illustrate the *method* of solving such problems by use of partial differentiation. We may check our answer by noting that the vector from the origin to $P(\frac{5}{3}, \frac{5}{6}, -\frac{5}{6})$ is

$$\overrightarrow{OP} = \tfrac{5}{6}(2\mathbf{i} + \mathbf{j} - \mathbf{k}),$$

which is normal to the plane, as it should be.

Remark. The mechanics of setting $f_x = 0$, $f_y = 0$, etc., may lead to a point not in the region where the function f is defined. Sometimes it is desirable to choose a different set of independent variables when this happens.

EXAMPLE 2.   Find the minimum distance from the origin to the surface $x^2 - z^2 = 1$.

Solution. We seek to minimize

$$w = x^2 + y^2 + z^2,$$

where $x^2 = 1 + z^2$ or $z^2 = x^2 - 1$. If we eliminate z^2, we have

$$w = 2x^2 + y^2 - 1,$$

whose partial derivatives,

$$\frac{\partial w}{\partial x} = 4x, \qquad \frac{\partial w}{\partial y} = 2y,$$

are zero only at $x = 0, y = 0$. But then we run into trouble, for $z^2 = x^2 - 1 = -1$ means that z is imaginary when $x = 0$. In fact, the point $P(x, y, z)$ is on the surface $z^2 = x^2 - 1$ only when $|x| \geq 1$.

If we eliminate x^2, however, and express w as a function of y and z,

$$w = 1 + y^2 + 2z^2$$

has partial derivatives

$$\frac{\partial w}{\partial y} = 2y, \qquad \frac{\partial w}{\partial z} = 4z,$$

which are both zero when $y = z = 0$. This leads to

$$x^2 = 1 + z^2 = 1, x = \pm 1.$$

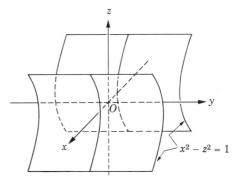

FIGURE 14-15

It is obvious from the expression $w = 1 + y^2 + 2z^2$ that $w \geq 1$ for all real values of y and z, since $y^2 + 2z^2 \geq 0$. Therefore the two points $(\pm 1, 0, 0)$ are nearer the origin than are any other points on the surface. By expressing w in terms of y and z as independent variables, we obtained variables which can take all real values $-\infty < y < \infty$, $-\infty < z < \infty$. The surface is a two-sheeted hyperbolic cylinder with elements parallel to the y-axis (Fig. 14-15).

PROBLEMS

1. Find the point on the surface $z = xy + 1$ that is nearest the origin.

2. A rectangular box, open at the top, is to hold 256 in^3. Find the dimensions of the box for which the surface area is a minimum.

3. The base of a rectangular box costs three times as much per square foot as do the sides and top. Find the relative dimensions for the most economical box of given volume.

4. Find the equation of the plane through the point $(2, 1, 1)$ that cuts off the least volume from the first octant. (Consider only those planes whose intercepts with the coördinate axes are positive.)

5. A pentagon is composed of a rectangle surmounted by an isosceles triangle. If the area is fixed, what are the dimensions for which the perimeter is a minimum?

6. A plane of the form

$$z = Ax + By + C$$

is to be "fitted" to the following points (x_i, y_i, z_i): $(0, 0, 0)$, $(0, 1, 1)$, $(1, 1, 1)$, $(1, 0, -1)$. Find the plane that minimizes the sum of squares of the deviations

$$\sum_{i=1}^{4} (Ax_i + By_i + C - z_i)^2.$$

14–12 Higher order derivatives. Partial derivatives of the second order are denoted by such symbols as

$$\frac{\partial^2 f}{\partial x^2}, \quad \frac{\partial^2 f}{\partial y^2}, \quad \frac{\partial^2 f}{\partial x \, \partial y}, \quad \frac{\partial^2 f}{\partial y \, \partial x}$$

or by

$$f_{xx}, \quad f_{yy}, \quad f_{yx}, \quad f_{xy},$$

where these are defined by the equations

$$\frac{\partial^2 f}{\partial x^2} = \frac{\partial}{\partial x}\left(\frac{\partial f}{\partial x}\right), \qquad \frac{\partial^2 f}{\partial x \, \partial y} = \frac{\partial}{\partial x}\left(\frac{\partial f}{\partial y}\right),$$

and so forth.

For example, if

$$f(x, y) = x \cos y + ye^x,$$

then

$$\frac{\partial f}{\partial x} = \cos y + ye^x,$$

$$\frac{\partial}{\partial y}\left(\frac{\partial f}{\partial x}\right) = -\sin y + e^x = \frac{\partial^2 f}{\partial y \, \partial x},$$

$$\frac{\partial}{\partial x}\left(\frac{\partial f}{\partial x}\right) = ye^x = \frac{\partial^2 f}{\partial x^2},$$

$$\frac{\partial}{\partial x}\left(\frac{\partial^2 f}{\partial x^2}\right) = ye^x = \frac{\partial^3 f}{\partial x^3},$$

$$\frac{\partial}{\partial y}\left(\frac{\partial^2 f}{\partial x^2}\right) = e^x = \frac{\partial^3 f}{\partial y\,\partial x^2},$$

and so on; while

$$\frac{\partial f}{\partial y} = -x\sin y + e^x,$$

$$\frac{\partial}{\partial x}\left(\frac{\partial f}{\partial y}\right) = -\sin y + e^x = \frac{\partial^2 f}{\partial x\,\partial y},$$

$$\frac{\partial}{\partial y}\left(\frac{\partial f}{\partial y}\right) = -x\cos y = \frac{\partial^2 f}{\partial y^2},$$

$$\frac{\partial}{\partial x}\left(\frac{\partial^2 f}{\partial x\,\partial y}\right) = e^x = \frac{\partial^3 f}{\partial x^2\,\partial y},$$

and so on.

The example shows how the order of differentiation is indicated by the notation. Thus, in calculating $\partial^2 f/\partial y\partial x$, we differentiate first with respect to x and then with respect to y. This might also be indicated by $(f_x)_y$ or f_{xy}. Now it is a remarkable fact that the so-called "mixed" second order partial derivatives

$$\frac{\partial^2 f}{\partial y\,\partial x} \quad \text{and} \quad \frac{\partial^2 f}{\partial x\,\partial y}$$

are generally equal, just as they are seen to be equal in the example above. That is, we arrive at the same result whether we differentiate first with respect to x and then with respect to y or do the differentiation in the reverse order. The following theorem supports this assertion under suitable hypotheses.

THEOREM. *If the function $w = f(x, y)$ together with the partial derivatives f_x, f_y, f_{xy}, and f_{yx} are continuous, then*

$$\frac{\partial}{\partial x}\left(\frac{\partial f}{\partial y}\right) = \frac{\partial}{\partial y}\left(\frac{\partial f}{\partial x}\right).$$

Proof. Let (a, b) be a point in the interior of a rectangle R in the xy-plane such that f, f_x, f_y, f_{xy}, and f_{yx} are continuous functions throughout R. Then the fact that

$$f_{xy}(a, b) = f_{yx}(a, b) \tag{1}$$

may be proved by repeated application of the Mean Value Theorem. We let h and k be numbers such that the point $(a + h, b + k)$ also lies in the rectangle R and consider the difference

$$\Delta = F(a + h) - F(a), \tag{2}$$

where we define $F(x)$ in terms of $f(x, y)$ by the equation

$$F(x) = f(x, b + k) - f(x, b). \tag{3}$$

We apply the Mean Value Theorem to the function $F(x)$, and Eq. (2) becomes

$$\Delta = hF'(c_1), \tag{4}$$

where c_1 lies between a and $a + h$. From Eq. (3),

$$F'(x) = f_x(x, b + k) - f_x(x, b),$$

so Eq. (4) becomes

$$\Delta = h[f_x(c_1, b + k) - f_x(c_1, b)]. \tag{5}$$

Now we apply the Mean Value Theorem to the function $g(y) = f_x(c_1, y)$ and have

$$g(b + k) - g(b) = kg'(d_1) \tag{6a}$$

or

$$f_x(c_1, b + k) - f_x(c_1, b) = kf_{xy}(c_1, d_1), \tag{6b}$$

for some d_1 between b and $b + k$. By substituting this into Eq. (5), we get

$$\Delta = hkf_{xy}(c_1, d_1), \tag{7}$$

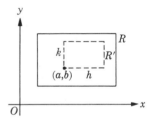

Figure 14–16

for some point (c_1, d_1) in the rectangle R' whose vertices are the four points (a, b), $(a + h, b)$, $(a + h, b + k)$, and $(a, b + k)$. (See Fig. 14–16.)

On the other hand, by substituting from Eq. (3) into Eq. (2), we may also write

$$\begin{aligned}\Delta &= f(a + h, b + k) - f(a + h, b) - f(a, b + k) + f(a, b) \\ &= [f(a + h, b + k) - f(a, b + k)] - [f(a + h, b) - f(a, b)] \\ &= \phi(b + k) - \phi(b),\end{aligned} \tag{8}$$

where

$$\phi(y) = f(a + h, y) - f(a, y). \tag{9}$$

The Mean Value Theorem applied to Eq. (8) now gives

$$\Delta = k\phi'(d_2), \tag{10}$$

for some d_2 between b and $b + k$. By Eq. (9),

$$\phi'(y) = f_y(a + h, y) - f_y(a, y). \tag{11}$$

Substituting from Eq. (11) into Eq. (10), we have

$$\Delta = k[f_y(a + h, d_2) - f_y(a, d_2)]. \tag{12}$$

Finally, we apply the Mean Value Theorem to the expression in parentheses and get

$$\Delta = khf_{yx}(c_2, d_2), \tag{13}$$

for some c_2 between a and $a + h$.

A comparison of Eqs. (7) and (13) shows that

$$f_{xy}(c_1, d_1) = f_{yx}(c_2, d_2), \tag{14}$$

where (c_1, d_1) and (c_2, d_2) both lie in the rectangle R' (Fig. 14–16). Equation (14) is not quite the result we want, since it says only that the mixed derivative f_{xy} has the same value at (c_1, d_1) that the derivative f_{yx} has at (c_2, d_2). But the numbers h and k in our discussion may be made as small as we wish. The hypothesis that f_{xy} and f_{yx} are both continuous throughout R then means that

$$f_{xy}(c_1, d_1) = f_{xy}(a, b) + \epsilon_1$$

and

$$f_{yx}(c_2, d_2) = f_{yx}(a, b) + \epsilon_2,$$

where

$$\epsilon_1, \epsilon_2 \to 0$$

as

$$h, k \to 0.$$

Hence, if we let h and $k \to 0$, we have

$$f_{xy}(a, b) = f_{yx}(a, b). \qquad \text{Q.E.D.}$$

The proof just completed hinges upon the consideration of the so-called "second difference" Δ given by Eq. (8). The reason for calling this a *second* difference is to be found from a closer examination of Eqs. (2) and (3). Note that both

$$F(a) = f(a, b + k) - f(a, b)$$

and

$$F(a + h) = f(a + h, b + k) - f(a + h, b)$$

are themselves differences ("first" differences), while

$$\Delta = F(a + h) - F(a)$$

is the difference between these first differences.

The introduction of such a *second* difference might occur to a mathematician who wishes to prove a theorem involving *second* derivatives, but the student should not feel he is expected to be able to reconstruct the proof from scratch.

An interesting by-product of the proof of the theorem is the fact that this second difference may, under the hypotheses of the theorem, be approximated by

$$\Delta \approx hk f_{xy}(a, b),$$

where the accuracy of the approximation depends upon the size of h and k.

If we refer once more to the example at the beginning of this article, we note not only that

$$\frac{\partial^2 f}{\partial x\, \partial y} = \frac{\partial^2 f}{\partial y\, \partial x},$$

but also that

$$\frac{\partial^3 f}{\partial x^2\, \partial y} = \frac{\partial^3 f}{\partial y\, \partial x^2}.$$

This equality may be derived from the theorem above as follows:

$$\frac{\partial^3 f}{\partial x^2\, \partial y} = \frac{\partial}{\partial x}\left(\frac{\partial^2 f}{\partial x\, \partial y}\right) = \frac{\partial}{\partial x}\left(\frac{\partial^2 f}{\partial y\, \partial x}\right)$$

$$= \frac{\partial}{\partial x}\left(\frac{\partial}{\partial y}\, f_x\right) = \frac{\partial}{\partial y}\left(\frac{\partial}{\partial x}\, f_x\right)$$

$$= \frac{\partial}{\partial y}\left(\frac{\partial^2 f}{\partial x^2}\right) = \frac{\partial^3 f}{\partial y\, \partial x^2}.$$

In fact, if all the partial derivatives that appear are continuous, the notation

$$\frac{\partial^{m+n} f}{\partial x^m\, \partial y^n}$$

may be used to denote the result of differentiating the function $f(x, y)$ m times with respect to x and n times with respect to y, the order in which these differentiations are performed being entirely arbitrary. For example, $\partial^5 f/(\partial x^2 \partial y^3)$ is the result of five successive differentiations, two with respect to x and three with respect to y, such as f_{xyyxy}, where the latter notation means differentiation first with respect to x, then twice with respect to y, then again with respect to x, and finally with respect to y. (The subscripts are read from left to right.)

Problems

1. If $w = \cos(x + y) + \sin(x - y)$, show that $(\partial^2 w/\partial x^2) = (\partial^2 w/\partial y^2)$.

2. If $w = \ln(2x + 2y) + \tan(2x - 2y)$, show that $(\partial^2 w/\partial x^2) = (\partial^2 w/\partial y^2)$.

3. If $w = f(x + y) + g(x - y)$ where $f(u)$ and $g(v)$ are twice-differentiable functions of $u = x + y$ and $v = x - y$ respectively, show that

$$\frac{\partial^2 w}{\partial x^2} = \frac{\partial^2 w}{\partial y^2} = f''(u) + g''(v).$$

(Note that Problems 1 and 2 are special examples of this result.)

4. If c is a constant and $w = \sin(x + ct) + \cos(2x + 2ct)$, show that $(\partial^2 w/\partial t^2) = c^2(\partial^2 w/\partial x^2)$.

5. If c is a constant and $w = 5\cos(3x + 3ct) - 7\sinh(4x - 4ct)$, show that $(\partial^2 w/\partial t^2) = c^2(\partial^2 w/\partial x^2)$.

6. If c is a constant and $w = f(x + ct) + g(x - ct)$, where $f(u)$ and $g(v)$ are twice-differentiable functions of $u = x + ct$ and $v = x - ct$ respectively, show that

$$\frac{\partial^2 w}{\partial t^2} = c^2\frac{\partial^2 w}{\partial x^2} = c^2(f''(u) + g''(v)).$$

(Note that Problems 4 and 5 are special cases. The equation $(\partial^2 w/\partial t^2) = c^2(\partial^2 w/\partial x^2)$ describes the motion of a wave that travels with velocity c. See Sears, *Mechanics, Heat, and Sound*, Chapter 26.)

In each of the following problems (7–13), verify that V satisfies Laplace's equation

$$\frac{\partial^2 V}{\partial x^2} + \frac{\partial^2 V}{\partial y^2} + \frac{\partial^2 V}{\partial z^2} = 0.$$

7. $V = x^2 + y^2 - 2z^2$ 8. $V = 2z^3 - 3(x^2 + y^2)z$

9. $V = e^{-2y}\cos 2x$ 10. $V = \ln\sqrt{x^2 + y^2}$

11. $V = (x^2 + y^2 + z^2)^{-1/2}$ 12. $V = e^{3x+4y}\cos 5z$

13. $V = \cos 3x \cos 4y \sinh 5z$

In each of the following problems (14–17), verify that $w_{xy} = w_{yx}$.

14. $w = e^x \sinh y + \cos(2x - 3y)$ 15. $w = \ln(2x + 3y)$

16. $w = \tan^{-1} y/x$ 17. $w = xy^2 + x^2y^3 + x^3y^4$

18. Let $f(x, y) = x^3y^2$. Following the notation in Eqs. (2) through (7) find: (a) $F(x)$, (b) c_1, (c) $g(y)$, and thus verify Eq. (7) for this particular case. Also show that $f_{xy}(c_1, d_1) \to f_{xy}(a, b)$ as $(h, k) \to (0, 0)$.

19. Use the function $f = x^3y^2$ and carry out the steps of Eqs. (8) to (13). In particular, find (c_2, d_2) and show that $f_{yx}(c_2, d_2) \to f_{xy}(a, b)$ as $(h, k) \to (0, 0)$.

14–13 Exact differentials. We have seen that on numerous occasions the result of translating a physical problem into mathematical terms is a differential equation to be integrated. In the simplest cases, we may be able to separate the variables and write the differential equation in a form such as

$$f(x)\, dx = g(y)\, dy,$$

which can be solved provided we are able to evaluate $\int f(x)\, dx$ and $\int g(y)\, dy$. Sometimes, however, we are not able to separate the variables, as, for example, in the equation

$$(x^2 + y^2)\, dx + 2xy\, dy = 0, \tag{1a}$$

and again in the equation

$$(x^2 + y^2)\, dx - 2xy\, dy = 0. \tag{1b}$$

More generally, we may be led to a differential equation of the form

$$M(x, y)\, dx + N(x, y)\, dy = 0, \tag{2}$$

where $M(x, y)$ and $N(x, y)$ are functions of x and y. (In most cases, they will be continuous and have continuous partial derivatives with respect to x and y.) The differential equation (2) can be solved quite easily provided it is possible to find a function

$$w = f(x, y) \tag{3}$$

such that the left side of Eq. (2) is the total differential of w. For if such is the case, then Eq. (2) becomes

$$dw = 0$$

and the solution of this equation is simply

$$w = C,$$

and the solution of Eq. (2) is

$$f(x, y) = C,$$

where C is an arbitrary constant.

Now expressions of the form given in Eq. (2) aren't always differentials of functions. In fact, of the two expressions in Eq. (1a, b), we shall see that the first is such a differential while the second one is not.

The following terminology is commonly used: an expression

$$M(x, y)\, dx + N(x, y)\, dy \tag{4}$$

is called an *exact differential* provided a function $w = f(x, y)$ exists such that

$$df(x, y) = M(x, y)\, dx + N(x, y)\, dy. \tag{5}$$

If no such function exists, the expression is not an exact differential.

Three questions naturally present themselves:

(a) How can we tell whether a given expression is or is not an exact differential?

(b) In case the expression is exact, how do we find the function $f(x, y)$ of which it is the differential?

(c) In case the expression is not exact, how can we solve the differential equation, Eq. (2)?

In the proof of the theorem below, we shall give answers to the first two of these questions. Differential equations are discussed in more detail in Chapter 18.

THEOREM. *Let the functions $M(x, y)$ and $N(x, y)$ be continuous and possess continuous partial derivatives M_x, M_y, N_x, N_y for all real values of x and y. Then a necessary and sufficient condition for*

$$M(x, y) \, dx + N(x, y) \, dy$$

to be an exact differential is that

$$\frac{\partial M}{\partial y} = \frac{\partial N}{\partial x}.$$

Proof. We shall first prove that the condition is necessary. To this end, suppose the expression is an exact differential; that is, suppose a function $f(x, y)$ exists such that Eq. (5) is satisfied. We also know that

$$df = \frac{\partial f}{\partial x} \, dx + \frac{\partial f}{\partial y} \, dy. \tag{6}$$

In Eqs. (5) and (6), dx and dy are independent variables and we may set either dx or dy equal to zero and keep the other one different from zero. Then the only way that both equations can hold is to have

$$\frac{\partial f}{\partial x} = M(x, y), \qquad \frac{\partial f}{\partial y} = N(x, y). \tag{7}$$

Now, by the theorem of Article 14–12, we know that if M and N are continuous and have continuous partial derivatives, then

$$\frac{\partial}{\partial y} \left(\frac{\partial f}{\partial x} \right) = \frac{\partial}{\partial x} \left(\frac{\partial f}{\partial y} \right),$$

so that the condition

$$\frac{\partial M}{\partial y} = \frac{\partial N}{\partial x} \tag{8}$$

is a necessary condition if Eq. (7) is to be satisfied.

EXAMPLE. The criterion given by Eq. (8) is satisfied by the expression in Eq. (1a), where we have

$$M = x^2 + y^2, \qquad N = 2xy.$$

Here

$$\frac{\partial M}{\partial y} = 2y = \frac{\partial N}{\partial x}.$$

We have not yet proved that this condition is sufficient, however, so we cannot at this point say that the expression is exact.

For Eq. (1b), we have

$$M = x^2 + y^2, \qquad N = -2xy$$

and

$$\frac{\partial M}{\partial y} = 2y, \qquad \frac{\partial N}{\partial x} = -2y,$$

so that

$$\frac{\partial M}{\partial y} \neq \frac{\partial N}{\partial x}.$$

Since Eq. (8) is a necessary condition, we can say that the expression in (1b) is not an exact differential.

It is very easy to apply the criterion of Eq. (8), but we have not yet shown that it is a sufficient condition as well as a necessary one. But we shall now show that if

$$\frac{\partial M}{\partial y} = \frac{\partial N}{\partial x},$$

then there is a function $w = f(x, y)$ such that

$$df = M\, dx + N\, dy.$$

We shall establish this result by showing how to find the function $f(x, y)$ and this will also answer the second question previously raised.

From Eq. (6) we see that our sought-for function must have the property expressed by Eqs. (7), namely,

$$\frac{\partial f}{\partial x} = M(x, y), \qquad \frac{\partial f}{\partial y} = N(x, y).$$

Integrating the first of these with respect to x, we find

$$f(x, y) = \int_x M(x, y)\, dx + g(y), \tag{9}$$

where $g(y)$ represents an unknown function of y which plays the role of an arbitrary constant of integration. The integral, $\int_x M(x, y)\, dx$, is an ordinary indefinite integral with respect to x with y held constant during the integration. The function $f(x, y)$ produced by Eq. (9) satisfies the condition $\partial f/\partial x = M(x, y)$ for any choice of the function $g(y)$, because $g(y)$ acts as a constant under partial differentiation with respect to x. To see how we may satisfy the second condition, $\partial f/\partial y = N(x, y)$, we differentiate both sides of Eq. (9) with respect to y, holding x fixed, and obtain

$$N(x,y) = \frac{\partial f}{\partial y} = \frac{\partial}{\partial y} \int_x M(x, y) \, dx + \frac{\partial g(y)}{\partial y}. \tag{10}$$

Actually, since $g(y)$ is a function of y alone, we may write dg/dy instead of $\partial g/\partial y$. We then set $\partial f/\partial y$ from Eq. (10) equal to $N(x, y)$ and have

$$N(x, y) = \frac{\partial}{\partial y} \int_x M(x, y) \, dx + \frac{dg(y)}{dy}$$

or

$$\boxed{\frac{dg(y)}{dy} = N(x, y) - \frac{\partial}{\partial y} \int_x M(x, y) \, dx.} \tag{11}$$

We use this differential equation to determine $g(y)$ by simply integrating its right member with respect to y and then substituting the result back into Eq. (9) to obtain our final answer, namely $f(x, y)$. Success of the method hinges on the fact that the expression on the right side of Eq. (11) *is a function of y alone, provided that the condition*

$$\frac{\partial M(x, y)}{\partial y} = \frac{\partial N(x, y)}{\partial x}$$

is satisfied. [If the right side of Eq. (11) depended upon x as well as upon y, it could not be equal to dg/dy, which involves only y.]

But how, in general, can we prove that the expression in question is independent of x? By showing that its partial derivative with respect to x is identically zero. That is, we must calculate

$$\frac{\partial}{\partial x}\left(N(x, y) - \frac{\partial}{\partial y} \int_x M(x, y) \, dx \right) = \frac{\partial N}{\partial x} - \frac{\partial^2}{\partial x \, \partial y} \int_x M(x, y) \, dx$$

$$= \frac{\partial N}{\partial x} - \frac{\partial^2}{\partial y \, \partial x} \int_x M(x, y) \, dx$$

$$= \frac{\partial N}{\partial x} - \frac{\partial}{\partial y}\left(\frac{\partial}{\partial x} \int_x M(x, y) \, dx \right)$$

$$= \frac{\partial N}{\partial x} - \frac{\partial}{\partial y}(M),$$

which vanishes if, as we have assumed,

$$\frac{\partial N}{\partial x} = \frac{\partial M}{\partial y}.$$

EXAMPLE. We shall illustrate the method of finding the function $f(x, y)$ such that

$$df = (x^2 + y^2)\, dx + 2xy\, dy.$$

Solution. We set

$$M = x^2 + y^2, \qquad N = 2xy$$

and note that the condition

$$\frac{\partial M}{\partial y} = \frac{\partial N}{\partial x}$$

is satisfied. We seek $f(x, y)$ such that

$$\frac{\partial f}{\partial x} = x^2 + y^2, \qquad \frac{\partial f}{\partial y} = 2xy.$$

Integrating the first of these with respect to x while holding y constant and adding $g(y)$ as our "constant of integration," we have

$$\int df = \int (x^2 + y^2)\, dy$$
$$f = \tfrac{1}{3}x^3 + y^2 x + g(y)$$

$$f(x, y) = \frac{x^3}{3} + y^2 x + g(y).$$

Differentiating this with respect to y with x held constant and setting the result equal to $2xy$, we have

$$\frac{df}{dy} = (2xy) = 0 + 2y x + \frac{g(y)}{dx}$$

$$2xy = 2yx + \frac{dg}{dy} \qquad \text{or} \qquad \frac{dg}{dy} = 0,$$

so that $\dfrac{dg}{dy} = 0$

$$g(y) = C \quad \forall\, y \in \mathbb{R}$$

must be a pure constant. Hence

$$f(x, y) = \frac{x^3}{3} + y^2 x + C.$$

Note that the method is very easy to apply! *yep*

PROBLEMS

In each of the following problems (1–7), determine whether the given expression is or is not an exact differential. If the expression is the differential of a function $f(x, y)$, find f.

1. $2x(x^3 + y^3)\, dx + 3y^2(x^2 + y^2)\, dy$
2. $e^y\, dx + x(e^y + 1)\, dy$
3. $(2x + y)\, dx + (x + 2y)\, dy$
4. $(\cosh y + y \cosh x)\, dx + (\sinh x + x \sinh y)\, dy$
5. $(\sin y + y \sin x)\, dx + (\cos x + x \cos y)\, dy$
6. $(1 + e^x)\, dy + e^x(y - x)\, dx$
7. $(e^{x+y} + e^{x-y})\, (dx + dy)$

14–14 Line integrals. If the point of application of a force

$$\mathbf{F} = \mathbf{i}M(x, y, z) + \mathbf{j}N(x, y, z) + \mathbf{k}P(x, y, z) \tag{1}$$

moves along a curve C from a point $A_1(a_1, b_1, c_1)$ to a point $A_2(a_2, b_2, c_2)$, then the work done by the force is

$$W = \int_C \mathbf{F} \cdot d\mathbf{R}, \tag{2}$$

where

$$\mathbf{R} = \mathbf{i}x + \mathbf{j}y + \mathbf{k}z \tag{3}$$

is the vector from the origin to the point (x, y, z) and

$$d\mathbf{R} = \mathbf{i}\, dx + \mathbf{j}\, dy + \mathbf{k}\, dz. \tag{4}$$

If we calculate the dot product of the vectors $\mathbf{F}$ and $d\mathbf{R}$ from Eqs. (1) and (4), we may write Eq. (2) in the alternative form

$$W = \int_C M\, dx + N\, dy + P\, dz, \tag{5}$$

where M, N, and P are functions of x, y, and z and the subscript C on the integral refers to the curve C along which the integral is taken. Such an integral as Eq. (5) is called a line integral, although *curve integral* would perhaps be a more descriptive name.

In order to evaluate such an integral, we usually express the equation of the curve C in terms of a parameter t,

$$x = x(t), \quad y = y(t), \quad z = z(t), \tag{6}$$

such that the curve is described from A_1 to A_2 as t varies from some value t_1 to a value t_2. Then *all* quantities in the integral may be expressed in terms of one variable t and the result evaluated in the usual manner as a definite integral with respect to t from t_1 to t_2. The value of the integral depends, in general, upon the path C as well as upon its end points A_1 and A_2.

EXAMPLE. Suppose the force is given by

$$\mathbf{F} = \mathbf{i}(x^2 - y) + \mathbf{j}(y^2 - z) + \mathbf{k}(z^2 - x)$$

and that its point of application moves from the origin O to the point A $(1, 1, 1)$ (a) along the straight line OA, and (b) along the curve

$$x = t, \quad y = t^2, \quad z = t^3 \quad (0 \le t \le 1).$$

Find the work done in the two cases.

Solution. (a) Equations for the line OA are

$$x = y = z.$$

The integral to be evaluated is

$$W = \int_C (x^2 - y) \, dx + (y^2 - z) \, dy + (z^2 - x) \, dz,$$

which, for the path (a), becomes

$$W = \int_0^1 3(x^2 - x) \, dx = -\tfrac{1}{2}.$$

(b) Along the curve, we get

$$W = \int_0^1 2(t^4 - t^3)t \, dt + 3(t^6 - t)t^2 \, dt = -\tfrac{29}{60}.$$

Now under certain conditions the line integral between two points A_1 and A_2 is independent of the path C joining them. That is, in circumstances soon to be described, the integral in Eq. (5) has the same value for any two paths C_1 and C_2 joining A_1 and A_2. That happens when there is a function $f(x, y, z)$ whose differential is the integrand of Eq. (5), that is: If there is a function $f(x, y, z)$ such that

$$df = M \, dx + N \, dy + P \, dz, \tag{7}$$

then

$$\int_C M \, dx + N \, dy + P \, dz = \int_{A_1}^{A_2} df = f(x, y, z) \Big]_{(a_1, b_1, c_1)}^{(a_2, b_2, c_2)}$$
$$= f(a_2, b_2, c_2) - f(a_1, b_1, c_1)$$

is independent of the curve C joining the points $A_1(a_1, b_1, c_1)$ and $A_2(a_2, b_2, c_2)$. In this case we say that the expression

$$M(x, y, z) \, dx + N(x, y, z) \, dy + P(x, y, z) \, dz$$

is an *exact differential.*

THEOREM. *Let $M(x, y, z)$, $N(x, y, z)$, and $P(x, y, z)$ be continuous, together with their first order partial derivatives, for all real values of x, y, and z. Then a necessary and sufficient condition for the expression*

$$M \, dx + N \, dy + P \, dz$$

to be an exact differential is for the following equations all to be satisfied:

$$\frac{\partial M}{\partial y} = \frac{\partial N}{\partial x}, \qquad \frac{\partial M}{\partial z} = \frac{\partial P}{\partial x}, \qquad \frac{\partial N}{\partial z} = \frac{\partial P}{\partial y}. \tag{8}$$

The proof of this theorem will be omitted. It is similar to the proof of the theorem in the previous article. The present theorem represents an extension of that theorem from two dimensions to three.

It is worth observing that the equations

$$M = \frac{\partial f}{\partial x}, \qquad N = \frac{\partial f}{\partial y}, \qquad P = \frac{\partial f}{\partial z},$$

which are satisfied if and only if

$$df = M\,dx + N\,dy + P\,dz,$$

mean that the force $\mathbf{F}$ given by Eq. (1) is also given by

$$\mathbf{F} = \mathbf{i}\frac{\partial f}{\partial x} + \mathbf{j}\frac{\partial f}{\partial y} + \mathbf{k}\frac{\partial f}{\partial z}$$

or

$$\mathbf{F} = \operatorname{grad} f. \tag{9}$$

A more thorough analysis can be made to show that the following three statements are, for any given $\mathbf{F}$, all true, or all false, provided $\mathbf{F}$ and its partial derivatives are everywhere continuous:*

(a) $\mathbf{F}\cdot d\mathbf{R}$ is an exact differential,

(b) $\int_C \mathbf{F}\cdot d\mathbf{R}$ has the same value along any two curves joining the points A_1 and A_2, and

(c) $\mathbf{F}$ is the gradient of some function $f(x, y, z)$.

EXAMPLE. Suppose

$$\mathbf{F} = \mathbf{i}(e^x \cos y + yz) + \mathbf{j}(xz - e^x \sin y) + \mathbf{k}(xy + z).$$

Then, to apply the test of Eqs. (8) to the expression

$$\mathbf{F}\cdot d\mathbf{R} = (e^x \cos y + yz)\,dx + (xz - e^x \sin y)\,dy + (xy + z)\,dz,$$

we let

$$M = e^x \cos y + yz, \qquad N = xz - e^x \sin y, \qquad P = xy + z$$

and calculate

$$\frac{\partial M}{\partial z} = y = \frac{\partial P}{\partial x}, \qquad \frac{\partial N}{\partial z} = x = \frac{\partial P}{\partial y},$$

$$\frac{\partial M}{\partial y} = -e^x \sin y + z = \frac{\partial N}{\partial x}.$$

---

* For less stringent requirements, see Kaplan's *Advanced Calculus*, p. 279.

The theorem tells us that there is a function $f(x, y, z)$ such that

$$\mathbf{F} \cdot d\mathbf{R} = df.$$

We find f by integrating the system of equations

$$\frac{\partial f}{\partial x} = e^x \cos y + yz,$$

$$\frac{\partial f}{\partial y} = xz - e^x \sin y, \qquad (10)$$

$$\frac{\partial f}{\partial z} = xy + z.$$

We integrate Eq. (10$_1$) with respect to x, holding y and z constant, and add an arbitrary function $g(y, z)$ as the "constant of integration" to obtain

$$\int \partial f = \int e^x \cos y + yz \, dx$$

$$f(x, y, z) = e^x \cos y + xyz + g(y, z). \qquad (11)$$

Next we differentiate this with respect to y and set it equal to $\partial f/\partial y$ from (10$_2$),

$$\frac{d f(x,y,z)}{\partial y} = \frac{d}{dy}\left(= xz - e^x \sin y = -e^x \sin y + xz + \frac{\partial g(y,z)}{\partial y}\right)$$

or

$$\frac{\partial g(y, z)}{\partial y} = 0. \qquad (12)$$

Integrating Eq. (12) with respect to y, holding z constant, and adding an arbitrary function $h(z)$ as constant of integration, we obtain

$$g(y, z) = h(z). \qquad (13)$$

We substitute this into Eq. (11) and then calculate $\partial f/\partial z$, which we compare with (10$_3$). We have

$$xy + z = xy + \frac{dh(z)}{dz}$$

or

$$\frac{dh(z)}{dz} = z,$$

so that

$$h(z) = (z^2/2) + C.$$

Hence we may write Eq. (11) as

$$f(x, y, z) = e^x \cos y + xyz + (z^2/2) + C.$$

Then

$$\mathbf{F} = \operatorname{grad} f,$$

or

$$\mathbf{F} \cdot d\mathbf{R} = df.$$

A function $f(x, y, z)$ which has the property that its gradient gives the force vector $\mathbf{F}$ is called a "potential" function. (Sometimes a minus sign is introduced. For example, the electric intensity of a field is the negative of the potential gradient in the field. See Sears, *Electricity and Magnetism*, page 63.)

PROBLEMS

In each of the following problems (1–5), find the work done by the given force $\mathbf{F}$ as the point of application moves from $(0, 0, 0)$ to $(1, 1, 1)$, (a) along the straight line $x = y = z$, (b) along the curve $x = t$, $y = t^2$, $z = t^4$, and (c) along the x-axis to $(1, 0, 0)$, then in a straight line to $(1, 1, 0)$, and from there in a straight line to $(1, 1, 1)$.

1. $\mathbf{F} = 2x\mathbf{i} + 3y\mathbf{j} + 4z\mathbf{k}$
2. $\mathbf{F} = \mathbf{i}x \sin y + \mathbf{j} \cos y + \mathbf{k}(x + y)$
3. $\mathbf{F} = \mathbf{i}(y + z) + \mathbf{j}(z + x) + \mathbf{k}(x + y)$
4. $\mathbf{F} = e^{y+2z}(\mathbf{i} + \mathbf{j}x + 2\mathbf{k}x)$
5. $\mathbf{F} = \mathbf{i}y \sin z + \mathbf{j}x \sin z + \mathbf{k}xy \cos z$

In each of the following problems (6–9), find a function $f(x, y, z)$ such that $\mathbf{F} = \operatorname{grad} f$.

6. For $\mathbf{F}$ as in Problem 1
7. For $\mathbf{F}$ as in Problem 3
8. For $\mathbf{F}$ as in Problem 4
9. For $\mathbf{F}$ as in Problem 5

10. The "curl" of a vector $\mathbf{F} = \mathbf{i}f(x, y, z) + \mathbf{j}g(x, y, z) + \mathbf{k}h(x, y, z)$ is defined to be del cross $\mathbf{F}$, that is

$$\operatorname{curl} \mathbf{F} \equiv \nabla \times \mathbf{F} \equiv \begin{vmatrix} \mathbf{i} & \mathbf{j} & \mathbf{k} \\ \dfrac{\partial}{\partial x} & \dfrac{\partial}{\partial y} & \dfrac{\partial}{\partial z} \\ f & g & h \end{vmatrix}$$

or

$$\operatorname{curl} \mathbf{F} \equiv \mathbf{i}\left(\frac{\partial h}{\partial y} - \frac{\partial g}{\partial z}\right) + \mathbf{j}\left(\frac{\partial f}{\partial z} - \frac{\partial n}{\partial x}\right) + \mathbf{k}\left(\frac{\partial g}{\partial x} - \frac{\partial f}{\partial y}\right),$$

and the "divergence" of a vector $\mathbf{V} = \mathbf{i}u(x, y, z) + \mathbf{j}v(x, y, z) + \mathbf{k}w(x, y, z)$ is defined to be del dot $\mathbf{V}$, that is,

$$\operatorname{div} \mathbf{V} \equiv \nabla \cdot \mathbf{V} \equiv \frac{\partial u}{\partial x} + \frac{\partial v}{\partial y} + \frac{\partial w}{\partial z}.$$

If the components f, g, h of $\mathbf{F}$ are functions which possess continuous mixed partial derivatives

$$\frac{\partial^2 h}{\partial x \, \partial y}, \text{ etc.,}$$

show that

$$\operatorname{div}(\operatorname{curl} \mathbf{F}) = 0.$$

14–15 Derivatives of integrals. From the Fundamental Theorem of integral calculus we know that if f is a continuous function on $a \leq t \leq b$, then

$$\frac{d}{dx}\left[\int_a^x f(t)\, dt\right] = f(x).$$ (1)

For example,

$$\frac{d}{dx}\left[\int_0^x e^{-t^2}\, dt\right] = e^{-x^2},$$

and

$$\frac{d}{dx}\left[\int_1^x \frac{1}{t}\, dt\right] = \frac{1}{x}, \qquad (x > 0).$$

Similarly, since

$$\int_x^b f(t)\, dt = -\int_b^x f(t)\, dt$$

we have

$$\frac{d}{dx}\left[\int_x^b f(t)\, dt\right] = -f(x).$$ (2)

Equations (1) and (2) may be combined to give the following result.

THEOREM. *Let f be continuous on $a \leq t \leq b$. Let u and v be differentiable functions of x such that $u(x)$ and $v(x)$ lie between a and b. Then*

$$\frac{d}{dx}\left[\int_{u(x)}^{v(x)} f(t)\, dt\right] = f(v(x))\frac{dv}{dx} - f(u(x))\frac{du}{dx}.$$ (3)

Proof. Let $F(u, v) = \int_u^v f(t)\, dt$. Then, by Eq. (1),

$$\frac{\partial F}{\partial v} = f(v),$$ (4a)

and, by Eq. (2),

$$\frac{\partial F}{\partial u} = -f(u),$$ (4b)

provided u and v lie between a and b. If u and v are differentiable functions of x, and $u(x)$, $v(x)$ are between a and b, we may apply the chain rule:

$$\frac{dF}{dx} = \frac{\partial F}{\partial u}\frac{du}{dx} + \frac{\partial F}{\partial v}\frac{dv}{dx}.$$ (5)

The result of substituting from Eqs. (4a, b) into Eq. (5) is

$$\frac{dF}{dx} = f(v)\frac{dv}{dx} - f(u)\frac{du}{dx}.$$

This establishes Eq. (3).   Q.E.D.

EXAMPLE. Verify Eq. (3) for

$$\frac{d}{dx} \int_x^{2x} \frac{1}{t}\, dt, \qquad (x > 0).$$

Solution. Let $F(u, v) = \int_u^v 1/t\, dt = \ln v - \ln u$.   Then $\partial F/\partial u = -1/u$ and $\partial F/\partial v = 1/v$. If $u = x$ and $v = 2x$, then

$$\frac{du}{dx} = 1, \qquad \frac{dv}{dx} = 2,$$

and

$$\frac{dF}{dx} = \frac{\partial F}{\partial u} \cdot \frac{du}{dx} + \frac{\partial F}{\partial v} \cdot \frac{dv}{dx}$$

$$= -\frac{1}{u} + \frac{2}{v}$$

$$= -\frac{1}{x} + \frac{2}{2x} = 0.$$

Alternatively,

$$F(x, 2x) = \int_x^{2x} \frac{1}{t}\, dt = \ln t \Big|_x^{2x} = \ln 2x - \ln x$$

$$= \ln \frac{2x}{x} = \ln 2, \qquad (0 < x)$$

and

$$\frac{d}{dx} F(x, 2x) = \frac{d}{dx}(\ln 2) = 0.$$

PROBLEMS

Find the derivative, with respect to x, of each of the following (assuming $x > 0$):

1. $\displaystyle\int_x^{x^2} \frac{1}{t}\, dt$ 2. $\displaystyle\int_x^{2x} \frac{1}{t^2}\, dt$ 3. $\displaystyle\int_{2x}^{x^2} \frac{1}{t^2}\, dt$

4. $\displaystyle\int_0^{\sin^{-1} x} \frac{\sin t}{t}\, dt$ 5. $\displaystyle\int_x^{x^2} \ln t\, dt$

6. If u and v are differentiable functions of x and $u(x) > 0$, show (by two different methods) that

$$\frac{d}{dx}\left[(u(x))^{v(x)}\right] = u^v\left[\frac{v}{u} \cdot \frac{du}{dx} + \frac{dv}{dx} \cdot \ln u\right].$$

Find dy/dx if:

7. $y = (e^x)^x$ 8. $y = (\cosh x)^{x^2}$

9. $y = (x^2 + 1)^{1/x}$ 10. $y = (4x^2 + 4x + 3)^{\int_x^{x^2} \ln t\, dt}$

REVIEW QUESTIONS AND EXERCISES FOR CHAPTER 14

1. Let $w = f(x, y)$ define a function of two independent variables, for values of (x, y) in some region G of the xy-plane (the domain of f). Describe two geometrical ways of representing the function.

2. When is a function of two variables continuous at a point of its domain? Give an example, different from those in the text, of a function that is discontinuous at some point(s) of its domain.

3. Let $w = f(x, y)$. Define $\partial w/\partial x$ and $\partial w/\partial y$ at a point (x_0, y_0) in the domain of f.

4. When is a function of three variables continuous at a point of its domain? Give an example of a function of three independent variables that is continuous at some points of its domain and discontinuous at least one place in its domain. Give an example that is discontinuous at all points of a surface $F(x, y, z) = 0$. At all points of a line.

5. Define the directional derivative, at a point in its domain, of a function of three independent variables. Write a formula for the directional derivative in vector form. What is the analogous formula for a function of two variables?

6. Define tangent plane, and normal line, to a surface S at a point P_0 on S. Derive equations of the tangent plane and normal line in terms of the equations of the surface.

7. Write an expression for the tangent plane approximation to the increment of a function of two independent variables. What is the corresponding expression approximating the increment of a function of three variables?

8. Define *gradient* of a scalar function. Give two properties of the gradient that you consider to be important.

9. State the chain rule for partial derivatives of functions of several variables.

10. Define the *total differential* of a function of several variables.

11. Outline a method for finding local maxima or minima of a function of two or three independent variables.

12. Outline the "method of least squares" as applied to fitting a straight line to a set of observations.

13. State an important relationship between the concept of *exact differential* and *line integral*.

MISCELLANEOUS PROBLEMS FOR CHAPTER 14

1. Let $f(x, y) = (x^2 - y^2)/(x^2 + y^2)$ for $x^2 + y^2 \neq 0$. Is it possible to define the value of f at $x = 0$, $y = 0$ in such a way that the function would be continuous at $x = 0$, $y = 0$? Why?

2. Let the function $f(x, y)$ be defined by the relations

$$f(x, y) = [\sin^2 (x - y)]/(|x| + |y|) \quad \text{for} \quad |x| + |y| \neq 0, \quad f(0, 0) = 0.$$

Is f continuous at $x = 0$, $y = 0$?

3. Prove that if $f(x, y)$ is defined for all x, y by

$$f(x, y) = 2xy/(x^2 + y^2) \quad \text{if} \quad (x, y) \neq (0, 0),$$
$$= 0 \quad \text{if} \quad x = y = 0,$$

then (a) for any fixed x, $f(x, y)$ is a continuous function of y; (b) for any fixed y, $f(x, y)$ is a continuous function of x; (c) $f(x, y)$ is not continuous at $(0, 0)$; (d) $\partial f/\partial x$ and $\partial f/\partial y$ exist at $(0, 0)$ but are not continuous there. (This example shows that a function may possess partial derivatives at all points of a region, yet not be continuous in the region.) Contrast the case of a function of one variable, where the existence of a derivative implies continuity.

4. Let $f(x, y)$ be defined and continuous for all x, y (differentiability not assumed). Show that it is always possible to find arbitrarily many points (x_1, y_1), $(x_2, y_2), \ldots, (x_n, y_n)$ such that the function has the same value at each of them.

5. Find the first partial derivatives of the following functions: $(\sin xy)^2$, $\sin [(xy)^2]$.

6. Let α, β, γ be the direction angles of a line and consider γ as a function of α and β. Find the value of $\partial \gamma/\partial \alpha$ when $\alpha = \pi/4$, $\beta = \pi/3$, $\gamma = \pi/3$.

7. Let (r, θ) and (x, y) be polar coordinates and Cartesian coordinates in the plane. Show geometrically why $\partial r/\partial x$ is not equal to $(\partial x/\partial r)^{-1}$ by appealing to the definitions of these derivatives.

8. Consider the surface whose equation is $x^3z + y^2x^2 + \sin (yz) + 54 = 0$. Give an equation of the tangent plane to the surface at the point $P(3, 0, -2)$, and give equations of the straight line through P normal to the surface. Determine direction cosines of the line.

9. (a) Sketch and name the surface $x^2 - y^2 + z^2 = 4$. (b) Find a vector that is normal to this surface at $(2, -3, 3)$. (c) Find equations of the surface's tangent plane and normal line at $(2, -3, 3)$.

10. (a) Find an equation of the plane tangent to the surface

$$x^3 + xy^2 + y^3 + z^3 + 1 = 0$$

at the point $(-2, 1, 2)$. (b) Find equations of the straight line perpendicular to the above plane at the point $(-2, 1, 2)$.

11. The directional derivative of a given function $w = f(x, y)$ at the point $P_0(1, 2)$ in the direction toward $P_1(2, 3)$ is $2\sqrt{2}$, and in the direction toward $P_2(1, 0)$ it is -3. Compute $\partial f/\partial x$ and $\partial f/\partial y$ at $P_0(1, 2)$, and compute the directional derivative dw/ds at $P_0(1, 2)$ in the direction toward $P_3(4, 6)$.

12. Let $z = f(x, y)$ have continuous first partial derivatives. Let C be any curve lying on the surface and passing through (x_0, y_0, z_0). Prove that the tangent line to C at (x_0, y_0, z_0) must lie wholly in the plane determined by the tangent lines to the curves C_x and C_y, where C_x is the curve of intersection of $y = y_0$ and $z = f(x, y)$, and C_y is the curve of intersection of $x = x_0$ and the surface.

13. Let $u = xyz$. Show that if x and y are the independent variables (so u and z are functions of x and y), then $\partial u/\partial x = xy\,(\partial z/\partial x) + yz$; but that if x, y, and z are the independent variables, $\partial u/\partial x = yz$.

14. Let $\mathbf{u} = u_1\mathbf{i} + u_2\mathbf{j} + u_3\mathbf{k}$ and $\mathbf{v} = v_1\mathbf{i} + v_2\mathbf{j} + v_3\mathbf{k}$ be given constant unit vectors and let $f(x, y, z)$ be a given scalar function. Compute (a) the directional derivative $D_u f$, and (b) the directional derivative $D_v(D_u f)$, in terms of derivatives of f and the components of $\mathbf{u}$ and $\mathbf{v}$. (Here $D_u f$ denotes df/ds in the direction of $\mathbf{u}$.)

15. Consider the function $w = xyz$. (a) Compute the directional derivative of w at the point $(1, 1, 1)$ in the direction of the vector $\mathbf{i} + \mathbf{j} + \mathbf{k}$. (b) Compute the largest value of the directional derivative of w at the point $(1, 1, 1)$.

16. The function $w = f(x, y)$ has, at the point $(1, 2)$, directional derivatives which are equal to $+2$ in the direction toward $(2, 2)$, and -2 in the direction toward $(1, 1)$. What is its directional derivative at $(1, 2)$ in the direction toward $(4, 6)$?

17. Given the function $f(x, y, z) = x^2 + y^2 - 3z$, what is the maximum value of the directional derivative df/ds at the point $(1, 3, 5)$?

18. Given the function $(x - 1)^2 + 2(y + 1)^2 + 3(z - 2)^2 - 6$. Find the directional derivative of the function at the point $(2, 0, 1)$ in the direction of the vector $\mathbf{i} - \mathbf{j} + 2\mathbf{k}$.

19. Find the derivative of the function $f(x, y, z) = x^2 - 2y^2 + z^2$ at the point $(3, 3, 1)$ in the direction of the vector $2\mathbf{i} + \mathbf{j} - \mathbf{k}$.

20. The two equations $e^u \cos v - x = 0$ and $e^u \sin v - y = 0$ define u and v as functions of x and y, say $u = u(x, y)$ and $v = v(x, y)$. Show that the angle between the two vectors $(\partial u/\partial x)\mathbf{i} + (\partial u/\partial y)\mathbf{j}$ and $(\partial v/\partial x)\mathbf{i} + (\partial v/\partial y)\mathbf{j}$ is constant.

21. (a) Find a vector $\mathbf{N}(x, y, z)$ normal to the surface $z = \sqrt{x^2 + y^2} + (x^2 + y^2)^{3/2}$ at the point (x, y, z) of the surface. (b) Find the cosine of the angle γ between $\mathbf{N}(x, y, z)$ and the z-axis. Find the limit of $\cos \gamma$ as $(x, y, z) \to (0, 0, 0)$.

22. Find the locus of all points (a, b, c) in space for which the spheres

$$(x - a)^2 + (y - b)^2 + (z - c)^2 = 1 \quad \text{and} \quad x^2 + y^2 + z^2 = 1$$

will intersect orthogonally. (Their tangents are to be perpendicular at each point of intersection.)

23. (a) Find the gradient, at $P_0(1, -1, 3)$, of the function $x^2 + 2xy - y^2 + z^2$. (b) Find the plane that is tangent to the surface $x^2 + 2xy - y^2 + z^2 = 7$ at $P_0(1, -1, 3)$.

24. Find a unit vector normal to the surface $x^2 + y^2 = 3z$ at the point $(1, 3, \frac{10}{3})$.

25. In a flowing fluid, the density $\rho(x, y, z, t)$ depends on position and time.

If $\mathbf{V} = \mathbf{V}(x, y, z, t)$ is the velocity of the fluid particle at the point (x, y, z) at time t, then

$$\frac{d\rho}{dt} = \mathbf{V} \cdot \nabla\rho + \frac{\partial\rho}{\partial t} = V_1\frac{\partial\rho}{\partial x} + V_2\frac{\partial\rho}{\partial y} + V_3\frac{\partial\rho}{\partial z} + \frac{\partial\rho}{\partial t},$$

where $\mathbf{V} = V_1\mathbf{i} + V_2\mathbf{j} + V_3\mathbf{k}$. Explain the physical and geometrical meaning of this relation.

26. Find a constant a such that at any point of intersection of the two spheres $(x - a)^2 + y^2 + z^2 = 3$ and $x^2 + (y - 1)^2 + z^2 = 1$ their tangent planes will be perpendicular to each other.

27. If the gradient of a function $f(x, y, z)$ is always parallel to the vector $x\mathbf{i} + y\mathbf{j} + z\mathbf{k}$, show that the function must assume the same value at the points $(0, 0, a)$, $(0, 0, -a)$.

28. Let $f(P)$ denote a function defined for points P in the plane; i.e., to each point P there is attached a real number $f(P)$. Explain how one could introduce the notions of continuity and differentiability of the function and define the vector ∇f *without* introducing a coordinate system. If one introduces a polar coordinate system r, θ, $\mathbf{U}_r$, $\mathbf{U}_\theta$, what form does the vector $\nabla f(r, \theta)$ take?

29. Show that the directional derivative of $r = \sqrt{x^2 + y^2 + z^2}$ equals unity in any direction at the origin, but that r does not have a gradient vector at the origin.

30. Let $\mathbf{R} = x\mathbf{i} + y\mathbf{j} + z\mathbf{k}$ and $r = |\mathbf{R}|$. (a) From its geometrical interpretation, show that $\nabla r = \mathbf{R}/r$. (b) Show that $\nabla(r^n) = nr^{n-2}\mathbf{R}$. (c) Find a function with gradient equal to $\mathbf{R}$. (d) Show $\mathbf{R} \cdot d\mathbf{R} = r\,dr$. (e) If $\mathbf{A}$ is a constant vector, show that $\nabla(\mathbf{A} \cdot \mathbf{R}) = \mathbf{A}$.

31. If θ is the polar coordinate in the xy-plane, find the direction and magnitude of $\nabla\theta$.

32. If r_1, r_2 are the distances from the point $P(x, y)$ on an ellipse to its foci, show that the equation $r_1 + r_2 = $ const., satisfied by these distances, requires $\mathbf{U} \cdot \nabla(r_1 + r_2) = 0$, where $\mathbf{U}$ is a unit tangent to the curve. By geometrical interpretation, show that the tangent makes equal angles with the lines to the foci.

33. If A, B are fixed points and θ is the angle at $P(x, y, z)$ subtended by the line segment AB, show that $\nabla\theta$ is normal to the circle through A, B, P.

34. Find the general solution of the partial differential equations:

(a) $af_x + bf_y = 0$, a, b constants,   (b) $yf_x - xf_y = 0$.

[*Hint:* Consider the geometrical meaning of the equations.]

35. When y is eliminated from the two equations $z = f(x, y)$ and $g(x, y) = 0$, the result is expressible in the form $z = h(x)$. Express the derivative $h'(x)$ in terms of $\partial f/\partial x$, $\partial f/\partial y$, $\partial g/\partial x$, $\partial g/\partial y$. Check your formula by computing $h(x)$ and $h'(x)$ explicitly in the example where $f(x, y) = x^2 + y^2$ and $g(x, y) = x^3 + y^2 - x$.

36. Suppose the equation $F(x, y, z) = 0$ defines z as a function of x and y, say $z = f(x, y)$, with derivatives $\partial f/\partial x$ and $\partial f/\partial y$. Suppose also that the same equation $F(x, y, z) = 0$ defines x as a function of y and z, say $x = g(y, z)$, with derivatives $\partial g/\partial y$ and $\partial g/\partial z$. Prove that

$$\frac{\partial g}{\partial y} = -\frac{\partial f/\partial y}{\partial f/\partial x}.$$

and also express $\partial g/\partial z$ in terms of $\partial f/\partial x$ and $\partial f/\partial y$.

37. Given $z = x \sin x - y^2$, $\cos y = y \sin z$, find dx/dz.

38. If
$$z = f\left(\frac{x - y}{y}\right),$$
show that $x(\partial z/\partial x) + y(\partial z/\partial y) = 0$.

39. If the substitution $u = (x - y)/2$, $v = (x + y)/2$ changes $f(u, v)$ into $F(x, y)$, express $\partial F/\partial x$ and $\partial F/\partial y$ in terms of the derivatives of $f(u, v)$ with respect to u and v.

40. Given $w = f(x, y)$ with $x = u + v$, $y = u - v$, show that
$$\frac{\partial^2 w}{\partial u\, \partial v} = \frac{\partial^2 w}{\partial x^2} - \frac{\partial^2 w}{\partial y^2}.$$

41. Suppose $f(x, y, z)$ is a function with continuous partial derivatives and satisfies $f(tx, ty, tz) = t^n f(x, y, z)$ for every quadruple of numbers x, y, z, t (where n is a fixed integer). Show the identity: $(\partial f/\partial x)x + (\partial f/\partial y)y + (\partial f/\partial z)z = nf$. [*Hint:* Differentiate with respect to t, then set $t = 1$.]

42. The substitution $u = x + y$, $v = xy^2$ changes the function $f(u, v)$ into $F(x, y)$. Express the partial derivative $\partial^2 F/\partial x \partial y$ in terms of x, y and the partial derivatives of $f(u, v)$ with respect to u, v.

43. Given $z = u(x, y) \cdot e^{ax + by}$, where $u(x, y)$ is a function of x and y such that $\partial^2 u/\partial x \partial y = 0$, $(a, b$ constants). Find values of a and b that will make the expression $\partial^2 z/\partial x \partial y - \partial z/\partial x - \partial z/\partial y + z$ identically zero.

44. Introducing polar coordinates, $x = r \cos\theta$, $y = r \sin\theta$, changes $f(x, y)$ into $g(r, \theta)$. Compute the value of the second derivative $\partial^2 g/\partial\theta^2$ at the point where $r = 2$ and $\theta = \pi/2$, given that $\partial f/\partial x = \partial f/\partial y = \partial^2 f/\partial x^2 = \partial^2 f/\partial y^2 = 1$ at that point.

45. Let $w = f(u, v)$ be a function of u, v with continuous partial derivatives, where u, v in turn are functions of independent variables, x, y, z, with continuous partial derivatives. Show that if w is regarded as a function of x, y, z, its gradient at any point (x_0, y_0, z_0) lies in a common plane with the gradients of $u = u(x, y, z)$ and $v = v(x, y, z)$.

46. Show that if a function u has first derivatives that satisfy a relation of the form $F(u_x, u_y) = 0$, then u also satisfies $u_{xx}u_{yy} - u_{xy}^2 = 0$. [*Hint:* Differentiate $F = 0$ with respect to x and y.]

47. If $f(x, y) = 0$, find d^2y/dx^2.

48. If $F(x, y, z) = 0$, show that $(\partial x/\partial y)_z(\partial y/\partial z)_x(\partial z/\partial x)_y = -1$. [Here $(\partial x/\partial y)_z$ denotes that z is held constant while we compute the partial derivative of x with respect to y, etc.]

49. If $f(x, y, z) = 0$ and $z = x + y$, find dz/dx.

50. The function $v(x, t)$ is defined for $0 \leq x \leq 1$, $0 \leq t$ and satisfies the partial differential equation $v_t = v_x(v - x) + av_{xx}$ ($a = $ constant > 0) and the boundary conditions $v(0, t) = 0$, $v(1, t) = 1$. Suppose that for each fixed t, $v(x, t)$ is a strictly increasing function of x; that is, $v_x(x, t) > 0$. Show that v and t may be introduced as independent variables and x as dependent variable and find the partial differential equation satisfied by the function $x(v, t)$. Find also the region of definition of $x(v, t)$ and boundary values that it satisfies. By

considering level curves, show geometrically why the assumption $v_x(x, t) > 0$ is necessary for the success of this transformation.

51. Let $f(x, y, z)$ be a function depending only on $r = \sqrt{x^2 + y^2 + z^2}$; that is, $f(x, y, z) = g(r)$. Prove that if $f_{xx} + f_{yy} + f_{zz} = 0$, it follows that $f = (a/r) + b$, where a and b are constants.

52. A function $f(x, y)$, defined and differentiable for all x, y, is said to be homogeneous of degree n (a nonnegative integer) if $f(tx, ty) = t^n f(x, y)$ for all $t, x,$ and y. For such a function prove (a) $x(\partial f/\partial x) + y(\partial f/\partial y) = nf(x, y)$ and express this in vector form, (b) $x^2(\partial^2 f/\partial x^2) + 2xy(\partial^2 f/\partial x \partial y) + y^2(\partial^2 f/\partial y^2) = n(n - 1)f$, if f has continuous second partial derivatives, (c) a homogeneous function of degree zero is a constant.

53. Prove the Mean Value Theorem for functions of two variables

$$f(x + h, y + k) - f(x, y) = f_x(x + \theta h, y + \theta k)h + f_y(x + \theta h, y + \theta k)k, \quad 0 < \theta < 1,$$

with suitable assumptions about f. What assumptions? [*Hint:* Apply Mean Value Theorem for functions of one variable to $F(t) = f(x + ht, y + kt)$.]

54. Prove the theorem: If $f(x, y)$ is defined in a region R, and f_x, f_y exist and are bounded in R, then $f(x, y)$ is continuous in R. (The assumption of boundedness is essential.)

55. Using differentials, find a reasonable approximation to the value of

$$w = xy\sqrt{x^2 + y^2}$$

at $x = 2.98, y = 4.04$.

56. A flat circular plate has the shape of the region $x^2 + y^2 \leq 1$. The plate (including the boundary, where $x^2 + y^2 = 1$) is heated so that the temperature T at any point (x, y) is $T = x^2 + 2y^2 - x$. Locate the hottest and coldest point of the plate and find the temperature at each of these points.

57. The temperature T at any point (x, y, z) in space is $T = 400xyz^2$. Find the highest temperature on the surface of the unit sphere $x^2 + y^2 + z^2 = 1$.

58. For each of the following three surfaces, find all the values of x and y for which z is a maximum or minimum (if there are any). Give complete reasonings.

(a) $x^2 + y^2 + z^2 = 3$,   (b) $x^2 + y^2 = 2z$,   (c) $x^2 - y^2 = 2z$.

59. Find the point(s) on the surface $xyz = 1$ whose distance from the origin is a minimum.

60. A closed rectangular box is to be made to hold a given volume, V in^3. The cost of the material used in the box is a cents/in^2 for top and bottom, b cents/in^2 for front and back, c cents/in^2 for the remaining two sides. What dimensions make the total cost of materials a minimum?

61. Find the maximum value of the function $xye^{-(2x+3y)}$ in the first quadrant.

62. A surface is defined by $z = x^3 + y^3 - 9xy + 27$. Prove that the only possible maxima and minima of z occur at $(0, 0)$ or $(3, 3)$. Prove that $(0, 0)$ is neither a maximum nor a minimum. Determine whether $(3, 3)$ is a maximum or a minimum.

63. Given n positive numbers $a_1, a_2, \ldots, a_n$. Find the maximum value of the expression $a_1 x_1 + a_2 x_2 + \cdots + a_n x_n$ if the variables $x_1, x_2, \ldots, x_n$ are restricted so that the sum of their squares is 1.

64. Find the minimum volume bounded by the planes $x = 0$, $y = 0$, $z = 0$ and a plane that is tangent to the ellipsoid $x^2/a^2 + y^2/b^2 + z^2/c^2 = 1$ at a point in the octant $x > 0$, $y > 0$, $z > 0$.

65. Among the points $P(x, y)$ on the level curve $\phi(x, y) = 0$ it is desired to find one where the function $f(x, y)$ has a (relative) maximum. Assuming that such a point, p_0, exists, show that at p_0 the vectors ∇f and $\nabla \phi$ are parallel so that there is a number λ_0 such that $(\nabla f)_0 = \lambda_0 (\nabla \phi)_0$. Explain geometrically by considering the level curves of f and ϕ. (This is the basis of the method of "Lagrange multipliers" in extremal problems — see Kaplan's *Advanced Calculus*, p. 128.)

66. Let z be defined implicitly as a function of x and y by the equation $\sin(x + y) + \sin(y + z) = 1$. Compute $\partial^2 z/\partial x \partial y$ in terms of x, y, and z.

67. Given $z = xy^2 - y \sin x$, calculate the value of $y(\partial^2 z/\partial y \partial x) - \partial z/\partial x$.

68. Let $w = z \tan^{-1}(x/y)$. Compute $\partial^2 w/\partial x^2 + \partial^2 w/\partial y^2 + \partial^2 w/\partial z^2$.

69. Show that the function satisfies the equation:

(a) $\log \sqrt{x^2 + y^2}$, $f_{xx} + f_{yy} = 0$,

(b) $\sqrt{(x^2 + y^2 + z^2)^{-1}}$, $f_{xx} + f_{yy} + f_{zz} = 0$,

(c) $\int_0^{x/2\sqrt{kt}} e^{-\sigma^2}\, d\sigma$, $kf_{xx} + f_t = 0$ (k const.),

(d) $\phi(x + at) + \psi(x - at)$, $f_{tt} = a^2 f_{xx}$.

70. Consider the function defined by

$$f(x, y) = xy\frac{x^2 - y^2}{x^2 + y^2}, \qquad (x, y) \neq (0, 0),$$

$$= 0, \qquad\qquad (x, y) = (0, 0).$$

Then find $f_{yx}(0, 0)$ and $f_{xy}(0, 0)$.

71. Is $2x(x^3 + y^3)\, dx + 3y^2(x^2 + y^2)\, dy$ the total differential df of a function $f(x, y)$? If so, find the function.

72. Find a function $f(x, y)$ whose differential is

$$df = (y/x + e^y)\, dx + (\ln x + 2y + x\, e^y)\, dy,$$

or else show that no such function exists.

73. (a) Find the value of $\int (y\, dx + x\, dy)$ along the path $x = 2t$, $y = 8t^2$, between the points where $t = 0$ and $t = 1$. (b) Without actually integrating, determine the value of the same integral along the path $x = t$, $y = t^3$, from $t = 0$ to $t = 2$. State your reasons.

74. Find a function $w = f(x, y)$ such that $\partial w/\partial x = 1 + e^x \cos y$ and $\partial w/\partial y = 2y - e^x \sin y$, or else explain why no such function exists.

75. In thermodynamics the five quantities S, T, u, p, v are such that any two of them may be considered independent variables, the others then being determined. They are connected by the differential relation $T\, dS = du + p\, dv$. Show that

$$\left(\frac{\partial S}{\partial v}\right)_T = \left(\frac{\partial p}{\partial T}\right)_v \qquad \text{and} \qquad \left(\frac{\partial v}{\partial S}\right)_p = \left(\frac{\partial T}{\partial p}\right)_S.$$

[*Hint:* Use condition for exact differential.] (Here a letter outside the parentheses indicates a quantity held constant during a particular partial differentiation.)

76. Prove that the line integral $\int (z^2\,dx + 2y\,dy + 2x\,z\,dz)$ is independent of the path of integration.

77. If $\mathbf{F} = y\mathbf{i} + x\mathbf{j}$, evaluate the line integral $\int_A^B \mathbf{F} \cdot d\mathbf{R}$ along the straight line from $A(1, 1, 1)$ to $B(3, 3, 3)$.

78. If $\mathbf{F} = \mathbf{i}x^2 + \mathbf{j}yz + \mathbf{k}y^2$, compute $\int_A^B \mathbf{F} \cdot d\mathbf{r}$, where $A = (0, 0, 0)$, $B = (0, 3, 4)$, along the straight line connecting these points.

79. Let C denote the plane curve whose vector equation is

$$\mathbf{r}(t) = e^t \cos t\mathbf{i} + e^t \sin t\mathbf{j}.$$

Evaluate the line integral

$$\int \frac{x\,dx + y\,dy}{(x^2 + y^2)^{3/2}}$$

along that arc of C from the point $(1, 0)$ to the point $(e^{2\pi}, 0)$.

80. If the density $\rho(x, y, z)$ of a fluid is a function of the pressure $p(x, y, z)$, and $\phi(x, y, z) = \int_{p_0}^p (dp/\rho)$ where p_0 is a constant, show that $\nabla\phi = \nabla p/\rho$.

81. If $\mathbf{F} = y\mathbf{i}$, show that the line integral $\int_A^B \mathbf{F} \cdot d\mathbf{r}$ along an arc AB in the xy-plane is equal to an area bounded by the x-axis, the arc, and the ordinates at A and B. (*Remark:* Despite similarity of appearance and identity of value, the integral of this problem and the integral of earlier calculus are conceptually distinct. The latter is a line integral for which the path lies along the x-axis.)

82. In the notation of Problem 10, Article 14–14, (a) prove that if ϕ is a scalar function of x, y, z, curl (grad ϕ) $= \nabla \times (\nabla\phi) = 0$;

(b) state how you would express the condition that $\mathbf{F} \cdot d\mathbf{r}$ be an exact differential in terms of the vector field $\nabla \times \mathbf{F}$;

(c) prove that div $(\phi\mathbf{F}) \equiv \nabla \cdot (\phi\mathbf{F}) = \phi\nabla \cdot \mathbf{F} + \mathbf{F} \cdot \nabla\phi$;

(d) prove that $\nabla \times (\phi\mathbf{F}) = \phi\nabla \times \mathbf{F} + (\nabla\phi) \times \mathbf{F}$;

(e) prove that $\nabla \cdot (\mathbf{F}_1 \times \mathbf{F}_2) = \mathbf{F}_2 \cdot \nabla \times \mathbf{F}_1 - \mathbf{F}_1 \cdot \nabla \times \mathbf{F}_2$;

(f) if $\mathbf{r} = x\mathbf{i} + y\mathbf{j} + z\mathbf{k}$, prove: $\nabla \cdot \mathbf{r} = 3$ and $\nabla \times \mathbf{r} = 0$.

CHAPTER 15

MULTIPLE INTEGRALS

15-1 Double integrals. We shall show how to use the method of double integration to calculate the area or center of gravity of the region A (Fig. 15-1) which is bounded above by the curve $y = f_2(x)$, below by $y = f_1(x)$, on the left by the line $x = a$, and on the right by $x = b$. Before taking up the specific applications referred to, we shall first define what we mean by the double integral of a function $F(x, y)$ of two variables x and y. Then the specific applications follow at once by specializing the function $F(x, y)$ to be

(a) $F(x, y) = 1$, or (b) $F(x, y) = y$

for the calculation of

(a) the area, or
(b) the moment of the area about the x-axis.

The notation

$$\int_A \int F(x, y) \, dA, \qquad (1)$$

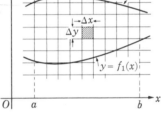

FIGURE 15-1

is used to denote the double integral, over the region A, of the function $F(x, y)$. We imagine the region A as covered by a grid of lines parallel to the x- and y-axes. These lines divide the plane into small pieces of area

$$\Delta A = \Delta x \, \Delta y = \Delta y \, \Delta x, \qquad (2)$$

some of which lie entirely within the given region, some entirely outside of the region, and some of which are intersected by the boundary of the region. We disregard all those which lie outside the region and may or may not take into account those which lie only partly inside, but in particular we take into consideration all the ΔA pieces which lie completely inside. Suppose, to be specific, we focus our attention upon the elements ΔA lying inside the region and number them in some order as

$$\Delta A_1, \Delta A_2, \ldots, \Delta A_n. \qquad (3)$$

Let (x_k, y_k) be any point lying in ΔA_k and form the sum

$$S_n = \sum_{k=1}^{n} F(x_k, y_k) \, \Delta A_k. \qquad (4)$$

730

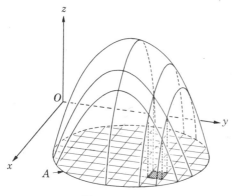

FIGURE 15–2

If the function $F(x, y)$ is continuous throughout A and if the curves which form the boundary of A are continuous and have a finite total length, then as we refine the mesh width in such a way that Δx and Δy tend to zero (we may, for example, take $\Delta y = 2\Delta x$ and then make $\Delta x \to 0$), the limit

$$I = \lim_{\Delta A \to 0} \sum_{k=1}^{n} F(x_k, y_k)\, \Delta A_k \tag{5}$$

exists, and it is this limit that is indicated by the notation in Eq. (1).

The double integral (1) can also be interpreted as a volume, at least in the case where $F(x, y)$ is positive. Suppose, for example, that the region A is the base of a solid (Fig. 15–2) whose altitude above the point (x, y) is given by

$$z = F(x, y).$$

Then the term

$$F(x_k, y_k)\, \Delta A_k$$

represents a reasonable approximation to the volume of that portion of the solid that rests upon the base ΔA_k. The sum S_n in Eq. (4) then gives an approximation to the total volume of the solid, and the limit in Eq. (5) gives the exact volume.

The usefulness of the concept of the double integral should be apparent. Its usefulness as a working tool would be limited, however, if it were necessary to resort to the limit of sums, as in Eq. (5), to find numerical answers to specific problems. Fortunately, there is an alternative method for evaluating double integrals by means of evaluating successive single integrals. That is, in practice, the double integral in (1) is evaluated by calculating one or another of the iterated integrals

$$\int_A \int F(x, y)\, dx\, dy \quad \text{or} \quad \int_A \int F(x, y)\, dy\, dx, \tag{6}$$

which we shall explain below. Before doing so, however, we remark that it is a theorem of analysis, which we shall not prove here, which asserts that the *iterated* integrals (6) are equal to each other and to the double integral (1) provided the function $F(x, y)$ is continuous over A and the boundary of A is not too complicated. The necessary conditions are fulfilled in the examples and problems in this book. For more details see Franklin, *A Treatise on Advanced Calculus*, Chapter XI.

Now we shall explain what we mean by the iterated integral

$$\int_A \int F(x, y)\, dy\, dx.$$

It is the result of:

  (a) integrating $\int F(x, y)\, dy$ with respect to y (with x held fixed) and evaluating the resulting integral between the limits $y = f_1(x)$ and $y = f_2(x)$, then

  (b) integrating the result of (a) with respect to x between the limits $x = a$ and $x = b$.

That is, we start with the innermost integral and perform successive integrations as follows:

$$\int_A \int F(x, y)\, dy\, dx = \int_a^b \left(\int_{f_1(x)}^{f_2(x)} F(x, y)\, dy \right) dx, \qquad (7)$$

treating x as a constant while we perform the y integration.

We can gain some insight into the geometrical significance of Eq. (7) as follows. We may again think of a solid with base covering the region A of the xy-plane and having altitude $z = F(x, y)$ at the point (x, y) of A. (Assume, for sake of simplicity, that F is positive.) Then imagine a slice cut from the solid by planes perpendicular to the x-axis at x and at $x + dx$. We may think of this as approximated by the differential of volume given by

$$dV = A(x)\, dx,$$

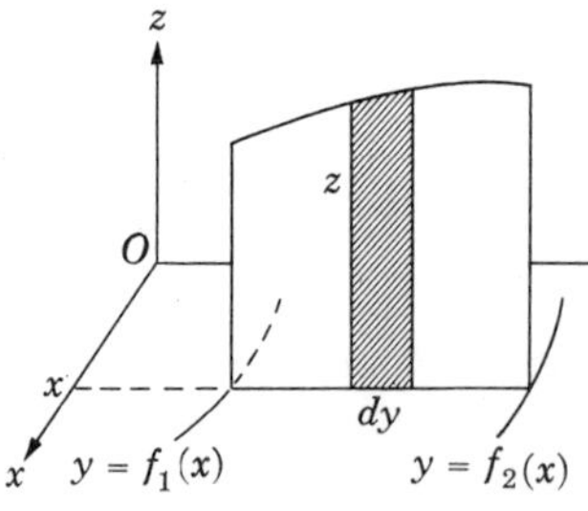

FIGURE 15–3

where $A(x)$ is the cross-sectional area cut from the solid by the plane at x. Now this cross-sectional area (Fig. 15–3) is given by the integral

$$A(x) = \int_{f_1(x)}^{f_2(x)} z\, dy = \int_{f_1(x)}^{f_2(x)} F(x, y)\, dy,$$

where x is held fixed and the limits of integration depend upon where the cutting plane is taken. That is, the y-limits are functions of x, the func-

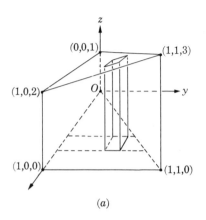
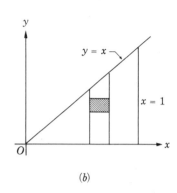

(a)   (b)

FIG. 15–4. (a) Prism, (b) base of prism.

tions that represent the boundary curves. Then, finally, we see that the
iterated integral in Eq. (7) is the same as

$$V = \int_a^b A(x)\,dx = \int_a^b \left(\int_{f_1(x)}^{f_2(x)} F(x, y)\,dy \right) dx.$$

EXAMPLE. Find the volume of the solid whose base is in the xy-plane and is
the triangle bounded by the x-axis, the line $y = x$, and the line $x = 1$, while
the top of the solid is in the plane

$$z = x + y + 1.$$

Solution. The volume dV of a representative prism of altitude z and base $dy\,dx$
is

$$dV = (x + y + 1)\,dy\,dx.$$

For any x between 0 and 1, y may vary from $y = 0$ to $y = x$ (Fig. 15–4b); hence

$$V = \int_0^1 \int_0^x (x + y + 1)\,dy\,dx = \int_0^1 \left[xy + \frac{y^2}{2} + y \right]_{y=0}^x dx$$

$$= \int_0^1 \left(\frac{3x^2}{2} + x \right) dx = 1.$$

PROBLEMS

Evaluate each of the double integrals in Problems 1–4. Also sketch the
region A over which the integration extends.

1. $\int_0^\pi \int_0^x x \sin y\,dy\,dx$ 2. $\int_1^{\ln 8} \int_0^{\ln y} e^{x+y}\,dx\,dy$

3. $\int_0^\pi \int_0^{\sin x} y\,dy\,dx$ 4. $\int_1^2 \int_y^{y^2} dx\,dy$

Write an equivalent double integral with the order of integration reversed for each of Problems 5–8. Check your answer by evaluating *both* double integrals.

5. $\int_0^2 \int_1^{e^x} dy\, dx$

6. $\int_0^1 \int_{\sqrt{y}}^1 dx\, dy$

7. $\int_0^{\sqrt{2}} \int_{-\sqrt{4-2y^2}}^{\sqrt{4-2y^2}} y\, dx\, dy$

8. $\int_{-2}^1 \int_{x^2+4x}^{3x+2} dy\, dx$

9. Find the volume of the solid whose base is the region in the xy-plane that is bounded by the parabola $y = 4 - x^2$ and the line $y = 3x$, while the top of the solid is bounded by the plane $z = x + 4$.

10. The base of a solid is the region in the xy-plane that is bounded by the circle $x^2 + y^2 = a^2$, while the top of the solid is bounded by the paraboloid $az = x^2 + y^2$. Find the volume.

15–2 Area by double integration. The simplest application of double integration is that of finding the area of a region of the xy-plane. The area is given by either of the integrals

$$A = \iint dx\, dy = \iint dy\, dx, \qquad (1)$$

with proper limits of integration to be supplied. We have already illustrated how this is done for the area shown in Fig. 15–1 when the integrations are carried out in the order of first y and then x, namely,

$$A = \int_a^b \int_{f_1(x)}^{f_2(x)} dy\, dx. \qquad (2)$$

If, however, the area is bounded on the left by the curve $x = g_1(y)$, on the right by $x = g_2(y)$, below by the line $y = c$, and above by the line $y = d$ (Fig. 15–5), then it is better to integrate first with respect to x [which may vary from $g_1(y)$ to $g_2(y)$] and then with respect to y. That is,

$$A = \int_c^d \int_{g_1(y)}^{g_2(y)} dx\, dy. \qquad (3)$$

The first integration, with respect to x, may be visualized as adding together all the representative elements

$$dA = dx\, dy$$

that lie in a horizontal strip that extends from the curve $x = g_1(y)$ on the left to the curve $x = g_2(y)$ on the right. The evaluation of this integral gives

$$A = \int_c^d \int_{g_1(y)}^{g_2(y)} dx\, dy = \int_c^d \Big[x\Big]_{g_1(y)}^{g_2(y)} dy = \int_c^d [g_2(y) - g_1(y)]\, dy.$$

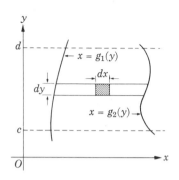

FIGURE 15–5

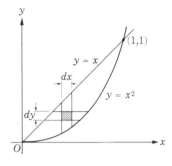

FIGURE 15–6

This latter integral could have been written down at once, since it merely expresses the area as the limit of the sum of horizontal strips of area.

EXAMPLE 1. The integral

$$\int_0^1 \int_{x^2}^{x} dy \, dx$$

represents the area of a region of the xy-plane. Sketch the region and express the same area as a double integral with the order of integration reversed.

Solution. In the inner integral, y varies from the curve $y = x^2$ to the line $y = x$. This gives the area of a vertical strip between x and $x + dx$, for values of x from $x = 0$ to $x = 1$. The region of integration is shown in Fig. 15–6. If we integrate in the other order, taking the x integration first, then x varies from the line $x = y$ to the parabola $x = \sqrt{y}$ to fill out a horizontal strip between y and $y + dy$. These strips must then be added together for values of y from 0 to 1. Hence

$$A = \int_0^1 \int_y^{\sqrt{y}} dx \, dy.$$

As a check, we evaluate the area by both integrals, and find

$$A = \int_0^1 \int_{x^2}^{x} dy \, dx = \int_0^1 (x - x^2) \, dx = \tfrac{1}{6}$$

and

$$A = \int_0^1 \int_y^{\sqrt{y}} dx \, dy = \int_0^1 (\sqrt{y} - y) \, dy = \tfrac{1}{6}.$$

EXAMPLE 2. Find the area bounded by the parabola $y = x^2$ and the line $y = x + 2$.

Solution. The area to be found is shown in Fig. 15–7. We imagine a representative element of area

$$dA = dx \, dy = dy \, dx$$

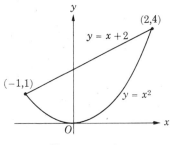

FIGURE 15-7

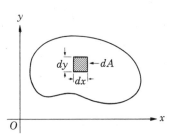

FIGURE 15-8

lying in the region and ask ourselves what order of integration we should choose. We see that *horizontal* strips sometimes go from the line to the right branch of the parabola (if $1 \leq y \leq 4$) but sometimes go from the left branch of the parabola to its right side (if $0 \leq y \leq 1$). Thus integration in the order of first x and then y requires that the area be taken in two separate pieces, with the result given by

$$A = \int_0^1 \int_{-\sqrt{y}}^{\sqrt{y}} dx\, dy + \int_1^4 \int_{y-2}^{\sqrt{y}} dx\, dy.$$

On the other hand, *vertical* strips always go from the parabola as lower boundary up to the line, and the area is given by

$$A = \int_{-1}^2 \int_{x^2}^{x+2} dy\, dx.$$

Clearly, this result is simpler and is the only one we would bother to write down in practice. Evaluation of this integral leads to the result

$$A = \int_{-1}^2 y\Big]_{x^2}^{x+2} dx = \int_{-1}^2 (x + 2 - x^2)\, dx = \tfrac{9}{2}.$$

PROBLEMS

In each of these problems, find the area of the region bounded by the given curves and lines by means of double integration.

1. The coordinate axes and the line $x + y = a$.
2. The x-axis, the curve $y = e^x$, and the lines $x = 0$, $x = 1$.
3. The y-axis, the line $y = 2x$, and the line $y = 4$.
4. The curve $y^2 + x = 0$, and the line $y = x + 2$.
5. The curves $x = y^2$, $x = 2y - y^2$.
6. The semicircle $y = \sqrt{a^2 - x^2}$, the lines $x = \pm a$, and the line $y = -a$.
7. The parabola $x = y - y^2$ and the line $x + y = 0$.

15–3 Physical applications. If the representative element of mass dm in a mass that is continuously distributed over some region A of the xy-plane is taken to be

$$dm = \delta(x, y)\, dy\, dx = \delta(x, y)\, dA, \tag{1}$$

where $\delta = \delta(x, y)$ is the density at the point (x, y) of A (Fig. 15–8), then double integration may be used to calculate:

(a) the mass, $\displaystyle M = \iint \delta(x, y)\, dA, \tag{2}$

(b) the first moment of the mass with respect to the x-axis,

$$M_x = \iint y\, \delta(x, y)\, dA, \tag{3a}$$

(c) its first moment with respect to the y-axis,

$$M_y = \iint x\, \delta(x, y)\, dA. \tag{3b}$$

From (2) and (3) we get the coordinates of the center of mass,

$$\bar{x} = \frac{M_y}{M}, \quad \bar{y} = \frac{M_x}{M}.$$

Other moments of importance in physical application are the *moments of inertia* of the mass. These are the *second* moments that we get by using the squares instead of the first powers of the "lever arm" distances x and y. Thus the moment of inertia about the x-axis, denoted by I_x, is defined by

$$I_x = \iint y^2\, \delta(x, y)\, dA. \tag{4}$$

The moment of inertia about the y-axis is

$$I_y = \iint x^2\, \delta(x, y)\, dA. \tag{5}$$

Also of interest is the *polar moment of inertia* about the origin, I_0, given by

$$I_0 = \iint r^2\, \delta(x, y)\, dA. \tag{6}$$

Here $r^2 = x^2 + y^2$ is the square of the distance from the origin to the representative point (x, y) in the element of mass dm.

In all of these integrals, the same limits of integration are to be supplied as would be called for if one were calculating only the area of A.

Remark 1. When a particle of mass m is rotating about an axis in a circle of radius r with angular velocity ω and linear velocity $v = \omega r$, its kinetic energy is

$$\tfrac{1}{2}mv^2 = \tfrac{1}{2}mr^2\omega^2.$$

If a system of particles of masses $m_1, m_2, \ldots, m_n$ all rotate about the same axis with the same angular velocity ω but their respective distances from the axis of rotation are $r_1, r_2, \ldots, r_n$, then the kinetic energy of the system of particles is

$$\text{K.E.} = \tfrac{1}{2}(m_1 v_1^2 + \cdots + m_n v_n^2) = \tfrac{1}{2}\omega^2 \sum_{k=1}^{n} m_k r_k^2 = \tfrac{1}{2}\omega^2 I, \qquad (7)$$

where

$$I = \sum_{k=1}^{n} m_k r_k^2 \qquad (8)$$

is the *moment of inertia* of the system about the axis in question. It depends only upon the magnitudes m_k of the masses and their distances r_k from the axis. When a mass m is moving in a straight line with velocity v, its kinetic energy is $\tfrac{1}{2}mv^2$, and an amount of work equal to this must be expended to stop the object and bring it to rest. Similarly, when a system of mass is moving in a *rotational* motion (like a turning shaft), the kinetic energy it possesses is

$$\text{K.E.} = \tfrac{1}{2}I\omega^2, \qquad (9)$$

and this amount of work is required to stop the rotating system. It is seen that I here plays the role which m plays in the case of motion in a straight line. In a sense, the *moment of inertia* of a large shaft is what makes it hard to start or to stop the rotation of the shaft in the same way that the *mass* of an automobile is what makes it hard to start or to stop its motion.

If, instead of a system of discrete mass particles as in (7) and (8), we have a continuous distribution of mass in a fine wire, or spread out in a thin film or plate over an area, or distributed throughout a solid, then we may divide the total mass into small elements of mass Δm such that if r represents the distance of some *one* point of the element Δm from an axis, then *all* points of that element will be within a distance $r \pm \epsilon$ of the axis, where $\epsilon \to 0$ as the largest dimension of the elements $\Delta m \to 0$. Then we define the moment of inertia of the total mass about the axis in question to be

$$I = \lim_{\Delta m \to 0} \Sigma r^2 \, \Delta m = \int r^2 \, dm. \qquad (10)$$

Thus, for example, the polar moment of inertia, given by Eq. (6), is the moment of inertia with respect to a z-axis through O perpendicular to the xy-plane.

In addition to its importance in connection with the kinetic energy of rotating bodies, the moment of inertia plays an important part in the theory of the deflection of beams under transverse loading, where the "stiffness factor" is given by EI, where E is Young's modulus, and I is the moment of inertia of a cross section of the beam with respect to a horizontal axis through its center of gravity. The greater the value of I, the stiffer the beam and the less it will deflect. This fact is exploited in so-called I-beams, where the flanges at the top and bottom of the beam are at relatively large distances from the center and hence correspond to large values of r^2 in Eq. (10), thereby contributing a larger amount to the moment of inertia than would be the case if the same mass were all distributed uniformly, say in a beam with a square cross section.

Remark 2. Moments are also of importance in statistics. The *first moment* is used in computing the mean (i.e., average) value of a given set of data. The *second moment* (which corresponds to the moment of inertia) is used in computing the variance (σ^2) or standard deviation (σ). Third and fourth moments are also used for computing statistical quantities known as skewness and kurtosis. The tth moment is defined as

$$M_t = \sum_{k=1}^{n} m_k r_k^t.$$

Here r_k ranges over the values of the statistic under consideration (e.g., r_k might represent height in quarter inches, or weight in ounces, or quiz grades in calculus in percentage points, etc.), while m_k is the number of individuals in the entire group whose "measurements" equal r_k. (For example, if 5 students get a grade of 75 on a quiz, then corresponding to $r_k = 75$ we would have $m_k = 5$.) A table of values of m_k versus r_k is called a "frequency distribution," and one refers to M_t as the tth moment of this frequency distribution. The mean value $\bar{r}$ is defined by

$$\bar{r} = \frac{\sum m_k r_k}{\sum m_k} = \frac{M_1}{m}, \tag{11}$$

where M_1 is the first moment and $m = \sum m_k$ is the total number of individuals in the "population" under consideration. The *variance* σ^2 involves the second moment about the mean. It is defined by

$$\sigma^2 = \frac{\sum (r_k - \bar{r})^2 m_k}{\sum m_k}, \tag{12a}$$

where σ is the so-called *standard deviation*. Both the variance and standard deviation are measures of the way in which the r values tend to bunch up close to $\bar{r}$ (small values of σ) or to be spread out (large values of σ). Algebraic manipulations with (12a) permit one also to write the variance in the alternative form

$$\sigma^2 = \frac{M_2}{m} - \bar{r}^2. \tag{12b}$$

There is a significant difference between the meaning attached to y in the case of the formula

$$A = \int_a^b y \, dx, \tag{13}$$

meaning the area (Fig. 15–9) under a curve $y = f(x)$ from $x = a$ to $x = b$, and the meaning attached to y in these double integrals, Eqs. (2)–(6). In Eq. (13), one must replace y by $f(x)$ from the equation of the curve *before* integrating, because y means the ordinate of the point (x, y) *on* the curve $y = f(x)$. But in the case of the double integrals (2)–(6), one must *not* replace y by a function of x before integrating because the point (x, y) is in general a point of the element $dA = dy \, dx$ and both x and y are *independent* variables. The equations of the boundary curves of the region A enter only as the *limits of integration*. Thus:

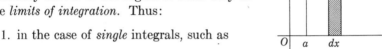

FIGURE 15–9

1. in the case of *single* integrals, such as

$$A = \int_a^b y \, dx, \tag{14}$$

we do not integrate with respect to y and hence we must substitute for it.

2. In the case of *double* integrals, such as

$$I_x = \iint y^2 \, \delta \, dy \, dx, \tag{15}$$

we *do* integrate with respect to y and hence we do not substitute for it before performing the y integration. The equations $y = f_1(x)$ and $y = f_2(x)$ of the boundary curves are used as limits of integration and are only to be substituted after the y integration is performed.

EXAMPLE. A thin plate of uniform thickness and density covers the region of the xy-plane shown in Fig. 15–7. Find its moment of inertia I_y about the y-axis.

Solution. Integrating in the order of first y and then x, we have

$$I_y = \int_{-1}^{2} \int_{x^2}^{x+2} x^2 \, \delta \, dy \, dx$$

$$= \delta \int_{-1}^{2} x^2 y \Big]_{y=x^2}^{y=x+2} dx$$

$$= \delta \int_{-1}^{2} (x^3 + 2x^2 - x^4) \, dx = \frac{63}{20} \, \delta.$$

The equation

$$I_y = MR_y^2$$

defines a number

$$R_y = \sqrt{I_y/M},$$

called the *radius of gyration* with respect to the y-axis. It tells how far from the y-axis the entire mass M might be concentrated and still give the same I_y. In this example, the mass is

$$M = \int_{-1}^{2} \int_{x^2}^{x+2} \delta \, dy \, dx = \tfrac{9}{2} \delta.$$

Hence

$$R_y = \sqrt{I_y/M} = \sqrt{\tfrac{7}{10}}.$$

Note that the density δ in this problem is a constant and hence we were able to move it outside the integral signs. If the density had been given instead as some variable function of x and y, then we would have taken this into account, in both I_y and M, by simply substituting this function for δ before integrating.

Problems

1. Find the center of gravity of the area of Problem 1, Article 15–2.

2. Find the moment of inertia, about the x-axis, of the area of Problem 2, Article 15–2. [For an area, we take $\delta = 1$.]

3. Find the polar moment of inertia, about an axis through O perpendicular to the xy-plane, for the area of Problem 3, Article 15–2.

4. Find the center of gravity of the area of Problem 4, Article 15–2.

5. Find the moment of inertia about the x-axis of the area in Problem 5, Article 15–2, if the density at (x, y) is $\delta = y + 1$.

6. Find the center of gravity of the area of Problem 6, Article 15–2, if the density at (x, y) is $\delta = y + a$.

7. Find the moment of inertia, about the x-axis, of the area of Problem 7, Article 15–2, if the density at (x, y) is $\delta = x + y$.

8. For any area in the xy-plane, show that its polar moment of inertia I_0 about an axis through O perpendicular to the xy-plane is equal to $I_x + I_y$.

15–4 Polar coordinates. Let A be a region of the plane bounded by rays $\theta = \alpha$, $\theta = \beta$, and curves $r = f_1(\theta)$, $r = f_2(\theta)$, as in Fig. 15–10. Suppose that A is completely contained in the wedge R

$$R: \quad 0 \leq r \leq a, \quad \alpha \leq \theta \leq \beta.$$

Let m and n be positive integers and take

$$\Delta r = \frac{a}{m}, \qquad \Delta \theta = \frac{\beta - \alpha}{n}.$$

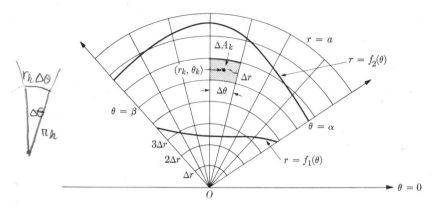

FIG. 15–10. Subdivision of region in polar coordinates: $\Delta A_k = r_k \,\Delta\theta\, \Delta r$.

Now cover R by a grid of circular arcs with centers at O and radii Δr, $2\,\Delta r, \ldots, m\,\Delta r$, and rays through O along $\theta = \alpha$, $\alpha + \Delta\theta$, $\alpha + 2\,\Delta\theta, \ldots$, $\alpha + n\,\Delta\theta = \beta$. This grid partitions R into subregions of three kinds: (a) those exterior to A, (b) those interior to A, and (c) those that intersect the boundary of A. We henceforth ignore those of the first type, but we want to include all those of the second kind, and may include some, none, or all of those of the third kind. Those that are to be included may now be numbered in some order $1, 2, 3, \ldots, N$. In the kth subregion so included, let (r_k, θ_k) be the coordinates of its center.* We multiply the value of F at each of these centers by the area of the corresponding subregion and add the products. That is, we consider the sum

$$S = \sum_{k=1}^{N} F(r_k, \theta_k) \cdot \Delta A_k$$

$$= \sum_{k=1}^{N} F(r_k, \theta_k) \cdot (r_k \,\Delta\theta\, \Delta r), \tag{1}$$

since

$$\Delta A_k = r_k \,\Delta\theta\, \Delta r, \tag{2}$$

as we shall now see. The radius of the inner arc bounding ΔA_k is $r_k - \frac{1}{2}\,\Delta r$; of the outer arc, $r_k + \frac{1}{2}\,\Delta r$. Hence

$$\Delta A_k = \tfrac{1}{2}(r_k + \tfrac{1}{2}\,\Delta r)^2\,\Delta\theta - \tfrac{1}{2}(r_k - \tfrac{1}{2}\,\Delta r)^2\,\Delta\theta,$$

and simple algebra reduces this to Eq. (2).

We now imagine this process repeated over and over again with finer and finer grids, and consider the limit of the sums (1) as the diagonals of all subregions approach zero. If the function F is continuous, and the

* We mean the point halfway between the circular arcs, and on the ray that bisects them.

region A is bounded by continuous, rectifiable, curves, the sums approach as limit the double integral of F over A:

$$\lim_{N\to\infty} \sum_{k=1}^{N} F(r_k, \theta_k) r_k \, \Delta\theta \, \Delta r = \int_A \int F(r, \theta) \, dA. \tag{3}$$

This limit may also be computed from the iterated integral on the right below:

$$\int_A \int F(r, \theta) \, dA = \int_{\theta=\alpha}^{\beta} \int_{r=f_1(\theta)}^{f_2(\theta)} F(r, \theta) \, r \, dr \, d\theta. \tag{4}$$

The question naturally arises whether one might first set up the double integral in Cartesian coordinates and then change to polar coordinates.

A rigorous treatment of the problem of changing the variables in a double integral may be found in Franklin, *A Treatise on Advanced Calculus*, p. 368. We shall here be content with citing the result and showing how it leads to Eq. (4) in the case of polar coordinates. In general, equations of the form

$$x = f(u, v), \quad y = g(u, v) \tag{5}$$

may be interpreted as mapping a region A of the xy-plane into a region G of the uv-plane. Then, under suitable restrictions on the functions f and g, the following equation gives the formula for changing from xy-coordinates to uv-coordinates in a double integral, namely,

$$\int_A \int \phi(x, y) \, dx \, dy = \int_G \int \phi[f(u, v), g(u, v)] \frac{\partial(x, y)}{\partial(u, v)} \, du \, dv, \tag{6}$$

where the symbol $\partial(x, y)/\partial(u, v)$ denotes the so-called "Jacobian" of the transformation (5) and is defined by the determinant

$$\frac{\partial(x, y)}{\partial(u, v)} = \begin{vmatrix} \dfrac{\partial x}{\partial u} & \dfrac{\partial x}{\partial v} \\ \dfrac{\partial y}{\partial u} & \dfrac{\partial y}{\partial v} \end{vmatrix}. \tag{7}$$

In the case of polar coordinates, we have r and θ in place of u and v,

$$x = r \cos \theta, \quad y = r \sin \theta,$$

and

$$\frac{\partial(x, y)}{\partial(r, \theta)} = \begin{vmatrix} \cos \theta & -r \sin \theta \\ \sin \theta & r \cos \theta \end{vmatrix} = r (\cos^2 \theta + \sin^2 \theta) = r.$$

Hence, Eq. (6) becomes

$$\int\int \phi(x, y) \, dx \, dy = \int\int \phi(r \cos \theta, r \sin \theta) r \, dr \, d\theta, \tag{8}$$

which corresponds to Eq. (4).

The total area of a region is given by either one of the double integrals

$$A = \iint dx\, dy = \iint r\, dr\, d\theta \tag{9}$$

with appropriate limits. This means, essentially, that the given region can be divided into pieces of area

$$dA_{xy} = dx\, dy$$

by lines parallel to the x- and y-axes, or that it can be divided into pieces of area

$$dA_{r\theta} = r\, dr\, d\theta$$

by radial lines and circular arcs, and that the total area can be found by adding together all of the elements of area of either type. But it is not to be expected that the *individual pieces* dA_{xy} and $dA_{r\theta}$ will be equal. In fact, an elementary calculation shows that

$$dA_{xy} = dx\, dy = d(r \cos \theta)\, d(r \sin \theta) \neq r\, dr\, d\theta = dA_{r\theta}.$$

It is very much like saying that the two *sums* $1 + 4 = 5$ and $2 + 3 = 5$ are the same even though the individual terms of the two sums are not equal.

EXAMPLE. Find the moment of inertia, about the y-axis, of the area enclosed by the cardioid

$$r = a(1 - \cos \theta).$$

Solution. It is customary to take the density as unity when working with a geometrical area. Thus we have

$$I_y = \int_A \int x^2\, dA,$$

with

$$x = r \cos \theta, \qquad dA = r\, dr\, d\theta.$$

If we integrate first with respect to r, then for any θ between 0 and 2π, r may vary from 0 to $a(1 - \cos \theta)$. This permits the integration to extend over those elements of area lying in the wedge between the radius lines θ and $\theta + d\theta$. Next we integrate with respect to θ from 0 to 2π to allow these wedges to cover the entire area. Hence

$$I_y = \int_0^{2\pi} \int_0^{a(1-\cos\theta)} r^3 \cos^2 \theta\, dr\, d\theta$$

$$= \int_0^{2\pi} \frac{a^4}{4} \cos^2 \theta (1 - \cos \theta)^4\, d\theta.$$

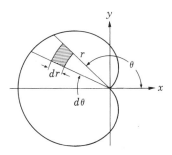

FIGURE 15–11

The evaluation of the integrals

$$\int_0^{2\pi} \cos^n \theta \, d\theta \quad (n = 2, 3, 4, 5, 6)$$

is made easier by use of the reduction formula

$$\int_0^{2\pi} \cos^n \theta \, d\theta = \frac{\cos^{n-1} \theta \sin \theta}{n} \Big]_0^{2\pi} + \frac{n-1}{n} \int_0^{2\pi} \cos^{n-2} \theta \, d\theta$$

or, since $\sin \theta$ vanishes at both limits,

$$\int_0^{2\pi} \cos^n \theta \, d\theta = \frac{n-1}{n} \int_0^{2\pi} \cos^{n-2} \theta \, d\theta.$$

Thus

$$\int_0^{2\pi} \cos^2 \theta \, d\theta = \frac{1}{2} \int_0^{2\pi} d\theta = \pi,$$

$$\int_0^{2\pi} \cos^3 \theta \, d\theta = \frac{2}{3} \int_0^{2\pi} \cos \theta \, d\theta = \frac{2}{3} \sin \theta \Big]_0^{2\pi} = 0,$$

$$\int_0^{2\pi} \cos^4 \theta \, d\theta = \frac{3}{4} \int_0^{2\pi} \cos^2 \theta \, d\theta = \frac{3\pi}{4},$$

$$\int_0^{2\pi} \cos^5 \theta \, d\theta = \frac{4}{5} \int_0^{2\pi} \cos^3 \theta \, d\theta = 0,$$

$$\int_0^{2\pi} \cos^6 \theta \, d\theta = \frac{5}{6} \int_0^{2\pi} \cos^4 \theta \, d\theta = \frac{5\pi}{8}.$$

Therefore

$$I_y = \frac{a^4}{4} \int_0^{2\pi} (\cos^2 \theta - 4 \cos^3 \theta + 6 \cos^4 \theta - 4 \cos^5 \theta + \cos^6 \theta) \, d\theta$$

$$= \frac{a^4}{4} \left[1 + \frac{18}{4} + \frac{5}{8} \right] \pi = \frac{49\pi a^4}{32}.$$

PROBLEMS

Change each of the double integrals of Problems 1–6 to an equivalent double integral in terms of polar coordinates; then evaluate the integrals thus obtained.

1. $\displaystyle\int_{-a}^{a}\int_{-\sqrt{a^2-x^2}}^{\sqrt{a^2-x^2}} dy\, dx$

2. $\displaystyle\int_{0}^{a}\int_{0}^{\sqrt{a^2-y^2}} (x^2 + y^2)\, dx\, dy$

3. $\displaystyle\int_{0}^{a/\sqrt{2}}\int_{y}^{\sqrt{a^2-y^2}} x\, dx\, dy$

4. $\displaystyle\int_{0}^{\infty}\int_{0}^{\infty} e^{-(x^2+y^2)}\, dx\, dy$

5. $\displaystyle\int_{0}^{2}\int_{0}^{x} y\, dy\, dx$

6. $\displaystyle\int_{0}^{2a}\int_{0}^{\sqrt{2ax-x^2}} x^2\, dy\, dx$

7. By double integration, find the area that lies inside the cardioid $r = a(1 + \cos\theta)$ and outside the circle $r = a$.

8. Find the center of gravity of the area of Problem 7.

9. Find the polar moment of inertia I_0 with respect to an axis through O perpendicular to the xy-plane, for the area of Problem 7.

10. The base of a solid is the area of Problem 7 and the top of the solid is bounded by the plane $z = x$. Find the volume.

11. Using double integration, find the total area enclosed by the lemniscate $r^2 = 2a^2 \cos 2\theta$.

12. The base of a solid is the area of Problem 11, while its top is bounded by the sphere $z = \sqrt{2a^2 - r^2}$. Find the volume.

15–5 Triple integrals. Volume. Consider a region V, in xyz-space, completely contained within the box B bounded by the planes $x = a$, $x = b$, $y = c$, $y = d$, $z = e$, and $z = f$, with $a < b$, $c < d$, and $e < f$. Let $F(x, y, z)$ be a function whose domain includes V. Let m, n, p be positive integers, and let

$$\Delta x = \frac{b-a}{m}, \qquad \Delta y = \frac{d-c}{n}, \qquad \Delta z = \frac{f-e}{p}.$$

Divide B into mnp subregions each with dimensions Δx by Δy by Δz, by planes

$$x = a, \quad a + \Delta x, \quad a + 2\,\Delta x, \quad \ldots, \quad a + m\,\Delta x;$$

$$y = c, \quad c + \Delta y, \quad c + 2\,\Delta y, \quad \ldots, \quad c + n\,\Delta y;$$

$$z = e, \quad e + \Delta z, \quad e + 2\,\Delta z, \quad \ldots, \quad e + p\,\Delta z.$$

These subregions are of three kinds: (a) those interior to V, (b) those exterior to V, and (c) those intersecting the boundary of V. We include all those of type (a), exclude all those of type (b), and include some, none, or all those of type (c). Then we number the included subregions

$1, 2, 3, \ldots, N$. Let (x_k, y_k, z_k) be a point in the kth subregion, multiply the value of F at that point by the volume ΔV_k of the subregion, and form the sum

$$S = \sum_{k=1}^{N} F(x_k, y_k, z_k)\, \Delta V_k$$

$$= \sum_{k=1}^{N} F(x_k, y_k, z_k)\, \Delta x\, \Delta y\, \Delta z. \tag{1}$$

Finally, suppose that the function F is continuous throughout V and on its boundary. Then, if the boundary of V is sufficiently "tame," the sums (1) have a limit as $\sqrt{(\Delta x)^2 + (\Delta y)^2 + (\Delta z)^2}$ approaches zero, and this limit is called the (Riemann) triple integral of F over V:

$$\iiint_V F\, dV = \lim \sum_{k=1}^{N} F(x_k, y_k, z_k)\, \Delta x\, \Delta y\, \Delta z. \tag{2}$$

Remark 1. There are many possible interpretations of (2). If $F(x, y, z) = 1$ for all points in V, the integral is just the volume of V. If $F(x, y, z) = x$, the integral is the first moment of the volume V with respect to the yz-plane. If $F(x, y, z)$ is the density at (x, y, z), then the integral is the mass in V. If $F(x, y, z)$ is the product of the density at (x, y, z) and the square of the distance from (x, y, z) to an axis L, then the integral is the moment of inertia of the mass with respect to L.

Remark 2. The triple integral is seldom evaluated directly from its definition as a limit. Instead, it is usually evaluated as an iterated integral. For example, suppose V is bounded below by a surface

$$z = f_1(x, y),$$

above by the surface

$$z = f_2(x, y),$$

and laterally by a cylinder C with elements parallel to the z-axis (Fig. 15–12). Let A denote the region of the xy-plane enclosed by the cylinder C. (That is, A is the region covered by the orthogonal projection of the solid into the xy-plane.) Then the *volume* of the region V (which we shall also denote by V) can be found by evaluating the triply iterated integral

$$V = \int_A \iint_{f_1(x,y)}^{f_2(x,y)} dz\, dy\, dx. \tag{3}$$

The z limits of integration indicate that for every (x, y) in the region A, z may extend from the lower surface $z = f_1(x, y)$ to the upper surface

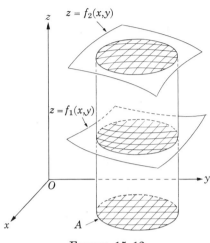

$$z = f_2(x,y)$$
$$z = f_1(x,y)$$

FIGURE 15–12

$z = f_2(x, y)$. The y and x limits of integration have not been given explicitly in Eq. (3), but are indicated as extending over the region A. The problem of supplying these limits is precisely the problem we have previously considered in connection with *double* integrals. It is usually desirable to draw the xy-projection of the solid in order to see more easily what these limits are.

In case the lateral surface of the cylinder reduces to zero (as in the example which follows), one may find the equation of the boundary of the region A by eliminating z between the two equations $z = f_1(x, y)$ and $z = f_2(x, y)$, thus obtaining an equation

$$f_1(x, y) = f_2(x, y), \tag{4}$$

which contains no z. Such an equation, interpreted as the equation of a surface in xyz-space, represents a cylinder with elements parallel to the z-axis. If we interpret it as an equation in the xy-plane, Eq. (4) represents the boundary of the region A.

EXAMPLE. Find the volume enclosed between the two surfaces

$$z = 8 - x^2 - y^2$$

and

$$z = x^2 + 3y^2.$$

Solution. The two surfaces (Fig. 15–13a) intersect on the elliptic cylinder

$$x^2 + 2y^2 = 4.$$

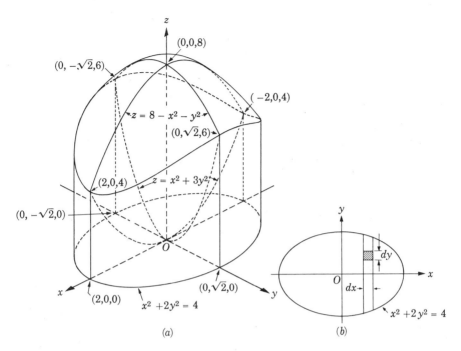

FIGURE 15–13

The volume projects into the region A in the xy-plane enclosed by the ellipse (Fig. 15–13b) having this same equation. In the double integral with respect to y and x over this region A, if we integrate first with respect to y, holding x and dx fixed, we see that y varies from $-\sqrt{(4-x^2)/2}$ to $+\sqrt{(4-x^2)/2}$. Then x varies from -2 to $+2$. Thus we have

$$V = \int_{-2}^{2} \int_{-\sqrt{(4-x^2)/2}}^{\sqrt{(4-x^2)/2}} \int_{x^2+3y^2}^{8-x^2-y^2} dz\, dy\, dx$$

$$= \int_{-2}^{2} \int_{-\sqrt{(4-x^2)/2}}^{\sqrt{(4-x^2)/2}} (8 - 2x^2 - 4y^2)\, dy\, dx$$

$$= \int_{-2}^{2} \left[2(8 - 2x^2)\sqrt{\frac{4-x^2}{2}} - \frac{8}{3}\left(\frac{4-x^2}{2}\right)^{3/2} \right] dx$$

$$= \frac{4\sqrt{2}}{3} \int_{-2}^{2} (4 - x^2)^{3/2}\, dx = 8\pi\sqrt{2}.$$

PROBLEMS

By triple integration, find the volume in each of the following problems.

1. The volume of the tetrahedron bounded by the plane $x/a + y/b + z/c = 1$ and the coordinate planes.

2. The volume in the first octant bounded by the cylinder $x = 4 - y^2$ and the planes $z = y$, $x = 0$, $z = 0$.

3. The volume bounded by the elliptic paraboloids $z = x^2 + 9y^2$ and $z = 18 - x^2 - 9y^2$.

4. The volume common to the two cylinders $x^2 + y^2 = a^2$, $x^2 + z^2 = a^2$.

5. The volume of an ellipsoid of semiaxes a, b, c.

6. The volume bounded below by the plane $z = 0$, laterally by the elliptic cylinder $x^2 + 4y^2 = 4$, and above by the plane $z = x + 2$.

15–6 Cylindrical coordinates. Instead of using an element of volume

$$dV_{xyz} = dz \, dy \, dx, \tag{1}$$

as we have done, we may use an element

$$dV_{r\theta z} = dz \, r \, dr \, d\theta. \tag{2}$$

Equation (2) may be visualized as giving the volume of an element having cross-sectional area $r \, dr \, d\theta$, such as that used with polar coordinates in Article 15–4, and altitude dz. Cylindrical coordinates, r, θ, z, are particularly useful in problems where there is an axis of symmetry of the solid. By proper choice of axes, this axis of symmetry may be taken to be the z-axis.

EXAMPLE. Find the center of gravity of a homogeneous solid hemisphere of radius a.

Solution. We may choose the origin at the center of the sphere and consider the hemisphere that lies above the xy-plane. (See Fig. 15–14.) The equation of the hemispherical surface is

$$z = \sqrt{a^2 - x^2 - y^2}$$

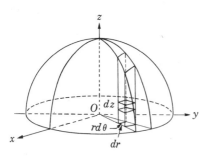

FIGURE 15–14

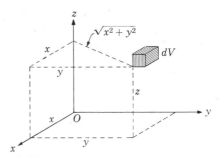

FIGURE 15–15

or, in terms of cylindrical coordinates,

$$z = \sqrt{a^2 - r^2}.$$

By symmetry we have

$$\bar{x} = \bar{y} = 0.$$

We calculate $\bar{z}$:

$$\bar{z} = \frac{\iiint z \, dV}{\iiint dV} = \frac{\int_0^{2\pi} \int_0^a \int_0^{\sqrt{a^2-r^2}} z \, dz \, r \, dr \, d\theta}{\frac{2}{3}\pi a^3} = \frac{3a}{8}.$$

PROBLEMS

By triple integration, find the volume in each of the following problems.

1. The volume cut from the sphere $x^2 + y^2 + z^2 = 4a^2$ by the cylinder $x^2 + y^2 = a^2$.

2. The volume bounded below by the paraboloid $z = x^2 + y^2$ and above by the plane $z = 2y$.

3. The volume bounded above by the sphere $x^2 + y^2 + z^2 = 2a^2$ and below by the paraboloid $az = x^2 + y^2$.

4. The volume in the first octant bounded by the cylinder $x^2 + y^2 = a^2$ and the planes $x = a$, $y = a$, $z = 0$, $z = x + y$.

15–7 Physical applications of triple integration. The mass, center of gravity, and moments of inertia of a mass M distributed over a region V of xyz-space and having density $\delta = \delta(x, y, z)$ at the point (x, y, z) of V (See Fig. 15–15) are given by integrals of the type

$$M = \iiint \delta \, dV, \tag{1}$$

$$\bar{x} = \frac{\iiint x \, \delta \, dV}{\iiint \delta \, dV}, \tag{2}$$

$$I_z = \iiint (x^2 + y^2) \, \delta \, dV, \tag{3}$$

with similar integrals for $\bar{y}$, $\bar{z}$, I_x, and I_y. The integrals in Eqs. (1)–(3) may be evaluated as triple integrals with

$$dV = dz \, dy \, dx$$

or, if it is more convenient to use cylindrical coordinates,

$$dV = dz \, r \, dr \, d\theta.$$

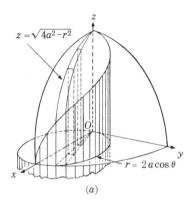

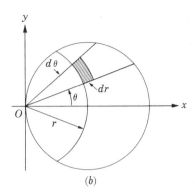

(a)   (b)

FIGURE 15–16

Limits of integration are to be supplied so that the element of volume ranges over the volume V as discussed above.

EXAMPLE. A solid is bounded below by the xy-plane, above by the sphere $x^2 + y^2 + z^2 = 4a^2$, and laterally by the cylinder $r = 2a \cos \theta$. Find its moment of inertia I_z.

Solution. One half of the solid is shown in Fig. 15–16(a), namely, that portion that lies in front of the xz-plane. There is a similar piece also lying in back of the xz-plane. The whole solid projects orthogonally into the interior of the circle $r = 2a \cos \theta$ in the xy-plane. Taking an element of volume $dV = dz\, r\, dr\, d\theta$ enclosing a point r, θ, z, we may take

$$dI_z = r^2\, dV = dz\, r^3\, dr\, d\theta.$$

When we integrate with respect to z, the lower limit is $z = 0$ from the plane and the upper limit is $z = \sqrt{4a^2 - r^2}$ from the sphere. This integral gives the moment of inertia of the elements dV in a prism extending from the xy-plane to the sphere and having its base inside the circle $r = 2a \cos \theta$. In order to add the moments of all of the prisms, we examine this region by itself to see what are the appropriate r and θ limits. If we were finding only the *area* of this region (Fig. 15–16b), we would have

$$A = \int_{-\pi/2}^{\pi/2} \int_0^{2a \cos \theta} r\, dr\, d\theta.$$

In the present problem, we are finding the moment of inertia I_z of a solid standing on this area as a base, but *the same limits of integration* apply to the r and θ integrations. Therefore

$$I_z = \int_{-\pi/2}^{\pi/2} \int_0^{2a \cos \theta} \int_0^{\sqrt{4a^2 - r^2}} dz\, r^3\, dr\, d\theta = \frac{64a^5}{15} \left[\pi - \tfrac{26}{15} \right].$$

Problems

1. Find the moment of inertia about the x-axis for the volume of Problem 1, Article 15–6.

2. Find the moment of inertia about the z-axis for the volume of Problem 2, Article 15–6.

3. Find the x-coordinate of the center of gravity of the volume of Problem 6, Article 15–5.

4. Find the center of gravity of the volume of Problem 3, Article 15–6.

5. Use cylindrical coordinates to find the moment of inertia of a sphere of radius a and mass M about a diameter.

6. Find the volume generated by rotating the cardioid $r = a(1 - \cos \theta)$ about the x-axis. [*Hint:* Use *double* integration. Rotate an area element dA around the x-axis to generate a volume element dV.]

7. Find the moment of inertia, about the x-axis, of the volume of Problem 6.

8. Find the moment of inertia of a right circular cone of base radius a, altitude h, and mass M about an axis through the vertex and parallel to the base.

9. Find the moment of inertia of a sphere of radius a and mass M with respect to a tangent line.

10. Find the center of gravity of that portion of the volume of the sphere $r^2 + z^2 = a^2$ that lies between the planes $\theta = -(\pi/4)$, $\theta = \pi/4$.

11. A torus of mass M is generated by rotating a circle of radius a about an axis in its plane at distance b from the center (b greater than a). Find its moment of inertia about the axis of revolution.

15–8 Spherical coordinates. In a problem where there is symmetry with respect to a point, it may be convenient to choose that point as origin and to use spherical coordinates (Fig. 15–17). These are related to the Cartesian system by the equations

$$x = \rho \sin \phi \cos \theta, \quad y = \rho \sin \phi \sin \theta, \quad z = \rho \cos \phi. \tag{1}$$

If we give ρ, ϕ, and θ increments $d\rho$, $d\phi$, and $d\theta$, we are led to consider the volume element (Fig. 15–18)

$$dV_{\rho\phi\theta} = d\rho \cdot \rho \, d\phi \cdot \rho \sin \phi \, d\theta = \rho^2 \sin \phi \, d\rho \, d\phi \, d\theta \tag{2}$$

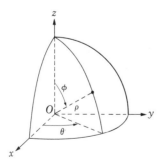

Figure 15–17

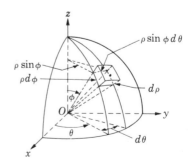

Figure 15–18

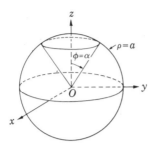

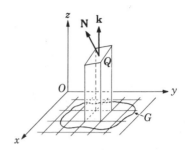

FIGURE 15–19   FIGURE 15–20

and triple integrals of the form

$$\iiint F(\rho, \phi, \theta)\rho^2 \sin \phi \, d\rho \, d\phi \, d\theta. \tag{3}$$

EXAMPLE. Find the volume cut from the sphere $\rho = a$ by the cone $\phi = \alpha$. (See Fig. 15–19.)

Solution. The volume is given by

$$V = \int_0^{2\pi} \int_0^{\alpha} \int_0^{a} \rho^2 \sin \phi \, d\rho \, d\phi \, d\theta = \frac{2\pi a^3}{3} (1 - \cos \alpha).$$

As a check, we note that the special cases $\alpha = \pi/2$ and $\alpha = \pi$ correspond to the cases of a hemisphere and a sphere of volumes $2\pi a^3/3$ and $4\pi a^3/3$, respectively.

PROBLEMS

1. Find the center of gravity of the volume (which resembles a filled ice cream cone) that is bounded above by the sphere $\rho = a$ and below by the cone $\phi = \pi/6$.

2. Find the volume enclosed by the surface $\rho = a(1 - \cos \phi)$. Compare with Problem 6, Article 15–7.

3. Find the radius of gyration, with respect to a diameter, of a spherical shell of mass M bounded by the spheres $\rho = a$ and $\rho = 2a$ if the density is $\delta = \rho^2$.

15–9 Surface area. Let G be a region of the xy-plane and let the function

$$z = f(x, y) \tag{1}$$

together with its first partial derivatives be continuous in G. For simplicity, suppose that the surface represented by Eq. (1) has a normal **N** which is nowhere parallel to the xy-plane. The area of the surface, (1), may then be computed in the following way.

Divide the region G into small rectangles, of dimensions Δx by Δy, by means of a grid of lines parallel to the x- and y-axes. Project a typical rectangle of area

$$\Delta A = \Delta y \, \Delta x \tag{2}$$

vertically upward onto the surface and call the corresponding area on the surface ΔS. Along with ΔS, we also consider the area ΔP of a section of a plane tangent to the surface at some point of ΔS. (See Fig. 15–20.) More precisely, choose any point Q lying on ΔS and consider the plane tangent to the surface at Q. Then project the area ΔA, Eq. (2), vertically upward onto this tangent plane and denote the corresponding area in the tangent plane by ΔP. We shall use ΔP as an approximation to ΔS. If this procedure is carried out for all of the pieces of area ΔA lying in G and we add all the pieces of area ΔP obtained in this way, the result will approximate the total surface area S. That is,

$$S \approx \sum \Delta P. \tag{3}$$

The approximation becomes better as Δx and Δy approach zero. We take the limit of the sum in (3) as the *definition of the surface area* S, that is,

$$S = \lim_{\Delta x, \Delta y \to 0} \sum_{G} \Delta P. \tag{4}$$

Our problem now reduces to that of finding an analytic expression for ΔP as a function of x, y, Δx, and Δy. Then we may anticipate that the limit in Eq. (4) can be expressed as a double integral over G.

Let $(x, y, 0)$, $(x + \Delta x, y, 0)$, $(x, y + \Delta y, 0)$, and $(x + \Delta x, y + \Delta y, 0)$ be the corners of the rectangle in G whose area ΔA projects onto the area ΔP in the tangent plane (Fig. 15–21). For simplicity, let Q be the

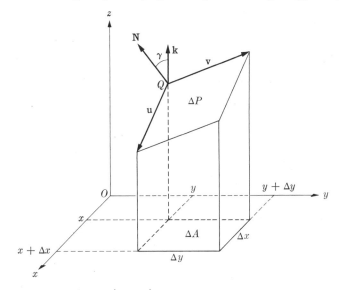

Fig. 15–21. Area $\Delta P = |\mathbf{u} \times \mathbf{v}|$ is projection of ΔA on tangent plane at Q; $\Delta P = \Delta A / \cos \gamma$.

point $(x, y, f(x, y))$ on the surface (1). Let $\mathbf{u}$, $\mathbf{v}$ be vectors from Q forming two adjacent sides of the parallelogram whose area is ΔP. Then

$$\mathbf{u} = \mathbf{i}\,\Delta x + \mathbf{k}f_x(x, y)\,\Delta x,$$

$$\mathbf{v} = \mathbf{j}\,\Delta y + \mathbf{k}f_y(x, y)\,\Delta y.$$

A vector normal to the surface at Q, with magnitude equal to the area ΔP, is

$$\mathbf{N} = \mathbf{u} \times \mathbf{v} = \begin{vmatrix} \mathbf{i} & \mathbf{j} & \mathbf{k} \\ \Delta x & 0 & f_x(x, y)\,\Delta x \\ 0 & \Delta y & f_y(x, y)\,\Delta y \end{vmatrix}$$

$$= \Delta x\,\Delta y(-\mathbf{i}f_x(x, y) - \mathbf{j}f_y(x, y) + \mathbf{k}). \tag{5}$$

Therefore,

$$\Delta P = |\mathbf{u} \times \mathbf{v}| = \Delta x\,\Delta y\sqrt{f_x^2(x, y) + f_y^2(x, y) + 1}. \tag{6}$$

Equations (4) and (6) together yield, for the area S,

$$\boxed{S = \int_G \int \sqrt{\left(\frac{\partial f}{\partial x}\right)^2 + \left(\frac{\partial f}{\partial y}\right)^2 + 1}\; dx\, dy.} \tag{7}$$

Other expressions for the area are easily found. If we apply Eq. (12a), Article 13–6, we have

$$(\mathbf{u} \times \mathbf{v}) \cdot \mathbf{k} = \text{area of projection of } \Delta P \text{ in } xy\text{-plane.}$$

This also agrees with Eq. (5), above, which gives

$$(\mathbf{u} \times \mathbf{v}) \cdot \mathbf{k} = \Delta x\,\Delta y = \Delta A. \tag{8a}$$

From the definition of the dot product, we also know that

$$(\mathbf{u} \times \mathbf{v}) \cdot \mathbf{k} = |\mathbf{u} \times \mathbf{v}|\,|\mathbf{k}|\cos\gamma$$

$$= \Delta P \cos\gamma, \tag{8b}$$

where γ is the angle between $\mathbf{N} = \mathbf{u} \times \mathbf{v}$ and $\mathbf{k}$. Equations (8a) and (8b) give the result

$$\Delta P = \frac{\Delta A}{\cos\gamma}, \tag{9}$$

and from Eqs. (4) and (9) we have

$$\boxed{S = \int_G \int \frac{dA}{\cos\gamma}.} \tag{10}$$

If the equation of the surface is given in the form

$$F(x, y, z) = 0,$$

we may take as normal vector

$$\mathbf{N} = \operatorname{grad} F = \mathbf{i}F_x + \mathbf{j}F_y + \mathbf{k}F_z, \tag{11}$$

and compute $\cos \gamma$ in Eq. (10) from

$$\cos \gamma = \frac{\mathbf{N} \cdot \mathbf{k}}{|\mathbf{N}| \cdot |\mathbf{k}|}.$$

EXAMPLE. Find the area of the paraboloid $z = x^2 + y^2$ below the plane $z = 1$.

Solution. The surface area S in question, Fig. 15–22, projects into the interior of the circle

$$x^2 + y^2 = 1,$$

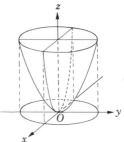

in the xy-plane. This is the region denoted above by G. Here

$$z = f(x, y) = x^2 + y^2,$$

so that

$$\frac{\partial f}{\partial x} = 2x, \qquad \frac{\partial f}{\partial y} = 2y$$

and

$$S = \iint\limits_{x^2+y^2 \le 1} \sqrt{4x^2 + 4y^2 + 1}\, dy\, dx. \tag{12}$$

FIGURE 15–22

Now the double integral (12) is easier to evaluate in polar coordinates, since the combination $x^2 + y^2$ may be replaced by r^2. Taking the element of area to be

$$dA = r\, dr\, d\theta$$

in place of $dy\, dx$, we thus have

$$S = \iint\limits_{r \le 1} \sqrt{4r^2 + 1}\, r\, dr\, d\theta$$

$$= \int_0^{2\pi} \int_0^1 \sqrt{4r^2 + 1}\, r\, dr\, d\theta = \frac{\pi}{6}(5\sqrt{5} - 1).$$

PROBLEMS

1. Derive a formula to replace Eq. (7) for the area of a surface S whose equation is $F(x, y, z) = 0$ and where

(a) the surface S is projected onto a region A in the xy-plane,
(b) the surface S is projected onto a region B in the yz-plane,
(c) the surface S is projected onto a region C in the zx-plane.

2. Find, by integration, the area of the triangle cut from the plane $x/a + y/b + z/c = 1$ by the coordinate planes. Check your answer by vector methods.

3. Find, by integration, the area of that portion of the surface of the sphere $x^2 + y^2 + z^2 = a^2$ that lies in the first octant.

4. Find the area of the surface of that portion of the sphere $x^2 + y^2 + z^2 = a^2$ that lies inside the cylinder $x^2 + y^2 = ax$.

5. In the preceding problem, find the area of that portion of the cylinder that lies inside the sphere. [*Hint:* Project the area into the xz-plane. Or use single integration, $\int z \, ds$, where z is the altitude of the cylinder and ds is the element of arc length in the xy-plane.]

6. Find the area of that portion of the sphere $x^2 + y^2 + z^2 = 2a^2$ that is cut out by the upper nappe of the cone $x^2 + y^2 = z^2$.

7. Find the area cut from the plane $z = cx$ by the cylinder $x^2 + y^2 = a^2$.

8. Find the area of that portion of the cylinder $x^2 + z^2 = a^2$ that lies between the planes $y = \pm a/2$, $x = \pm a/2$.

9. Find the area cut from the surface $az = y^2 - x^2$ by the cylinder $x^2 + y^2 = a^2$.

REVIEW QUESTIONS AND EXERCISES FOR CHAPTER 15

1. Define the double integral of a function of two variables. What geometric interpretation may be given to the integral?

2. List four applications of multiple integration.

3. Define *moment of inertia* and *radius of gyration*.

4. How does a double integral in polar coordinates differ from a double integral in Cartesian coordinates? In what way are they alike?

5. What are the fundamental volume elements for triple integrals (a) in Cartesian coordinates, (b) in cylindrical coordinates, (c) in spherical coordinates?

6. How is surface area defined? Which formula of Article 15-9 is the most general one for computing surface area, in the sense that it includes many others as special cases?

7. How would you define $\iint_S F \, dS$, when S is a surface in space and F is a function defined at points on the surface? Illustrate when S is the hemisphere $z = \sqrt{1 - x^2 - y^2}$, $x^2 + y^2 \leq 1$, and $F(x, y, z) = z$. What is the geometrical interpretation of $\iint z \, dS$?

MISCELLANEOUS PROBLEMS FOR CHAPTER 15

1. Reverse the order of integration and evaluate $\int_0^4 \int_{-\sqrt{4-y}}^{(y-4)/2} dx\, dy$.

2. Sketch the region over which the integral $\int_0^1 \int_{\sqrt{y}}^{2-\sqrt{y}} xy\, dx\, dy$ is to be evaluated and find its value.

3. The integral $\int_{-1}^1 \int_{x^2}^1 dy\, dx$ represents the area of a region of the xy-plane. Sketch the region and express the same area as a double integral with the order of integration reversed.

4. The base of a pile of sand covers the region in the xy-plane that is bounded by the parabola $x^2 + y = 6$ and the line $y = x$. The depth of the sand above the point (x, y) is x^2. Sketch the base of the sand pile and a representative element of volume dV, and find the volume of sand in the pile by double integration.

5. In setting up a double integral for the volume V under the paraboloid $z = x^2 + y^2$ and above a certain region R of the xy-plane, the following sum of iterated integrals was obtained:

$$V = \int_0^1 \left(\int_0^y (x^2 + y^2)\, dx \right) dy + \int_1^2 \left(\int_0^{2-y} (x^2 + y^2)\, dx \right) dy.$$

Sketch the region R in the xy-plane and express V as an iterated integral in which the order of integration is reversed.

6. By change of order of integration, show that the following double integral can be reduced to a single integral

$$\int_0^x du \int_0^u e^{m(x-t)} f(t)\, dt = \int_0^x (x - t) e^{m(x-t)} f(t)\, dt.$$

Similarly, it can be shown that

$$\int_0^x dv \int_0^v du \int_0^u e^{m(x-t)} f(t)\, dt = \int_0^x \frac{(x - t)^2}{2!} e^{m(x-t)} f(t)\, dt.$$

Evaluate integrals for the case $f(t) = \cos at$. (This example illustrates that such reductions usually make calculation easier.)

7. By changing the order of integration, show that

$$\int_0^1 f(x)\, dx \int_0^x \log (x - y) f(y)\, dy = \int_0^1 f(y)\, dy \int_y^1 \log (x - y) f(x)\, dx$$

$$= \frac{1}{2} \int_0^1 \int_0^1 \log |x - y| f(x) f(y)\, dx\, dy.$$

(This example illustrates that sometimes a multiple integral with variable limits may be changed into one with constant limits.)

8. Evaluate the integral

$$\int_0^\infty \frac{e^{-ax} - e^{-bx}}{x}\, dx.$$

[*Hint:* Use the relation

$$\frac{e^{-ax} - e^{-bx}}{x} = \int_a^b e^{-xy}\, dy$$

to form a double integral, and evaluate it by change of the order of integration.]

9. By double integration, find the center of gravity of that part of the area of the circle $x^2 + y^2 = a^2$ contained in the first quadrant.

10. Determine the centroid of the plane area that is given in polar coordinates by $0 \leq r \leq a$, $-\alpha \leq \theta \leq \alpha$.

11. Find the centroid of the area bounded by the lines $\theta = 0°$ and $\theta = 45°$, and by the circles $r = 1$ and $r = 2$.

12. By double integration, find the center of gravity of the area between the parabola $x + y^2 - 2y = 0$ and the line $x + 2y = 0$.

13. For a solid body of constant density, having its center of gravity at the origin, show that the moment of inertia about an axis parallel to Oz through (x_0, y_0) is equal to the moment of inertia about Oz plus $M(x_0^2 + y_0^2)$, where M is the mass of the body.

14. Find the moment of inertia of the angle section shown in the accompanying figure, (a) with respect to the horizontal base, (b) with respect to a horizontal line through its centroid.

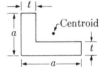

15. Show that for a uniform elliptic lamina of semi-axes a, b, the moment of inertia about an axis in its plane through the center of the ellipse making an angle α with the axis of length $2a$ is $\frac{1}{4}M(a^2 \sin^2 \alpha + b^2 \cos^2 \alpha)$, where M is the mass of the lamina.

16. A counterweight of a flywheel has the form of the smaller segment cut from a circle of radius a by a chord at a distance b from the center ($b < a$). Find the area of this counterweight and its polar moment of inertia about the center of the circle.

17. The radius of gyration of a body with volume V is defined by $K = \sqrt{I/V}$, where K and its moment of inertia I are referred to the same axis. Consider an ellipse $(x^2/a^2) + (y^2/b^2) = 1$ revolving about the x-axis to generate an ellipsoid. Find the radius of gyration of the ellipsoid with respect to the x-axis.

18. Find the radii of gyration about $\theta = 0$ and $\theta = \pi/2$ for the area of a loop of the curve $r^2 = a^2 \cos 2\theta$, ($a > 0$).

19. The hydrostatic pressure at a depth y in a fluid is wy. Taking the x-axis in the surface of the fluid and the y-axis vertically downward, consider a semi-circular lamina, radius a, completely immersed with its bounding diameter horizontal, uppermost, and at a depth c. Show that the depth of the center of pressure is

$$\frac{3\pi a^2 + 32ac + 12\pi c^2}{4(4a + 3\pi c)}.$$

The center of pressure is defined as the point where the entire hydrostatic force could be concentrated so as to produce the same first moment of force.

20. Show that

$$\iint \frac{\partial^2 F(x, y)}{\partial x \, \partial y} \, dx \, dy$$

over the rectangle $x_0 \leq x \leq x_1$, $y_0 \leq y \leq y_1$ is $F(x_1, y_1) - F(x_0, y_1) - F(x_1, y_0) + F(x_0, y_0)$.

21. Change the following double integral to an equivalent double integral in polar coordinates, and sketch the region of integration.

$$\int_{-a}^{a} \int_{0}^{\sqrt{a^2-y^2}} x \, dx \, dy.$$

22. A customary method of evaluating the improper integral $I = \int_0^\infty e^{-x^2} \, dx$ is by considering its squared value

$$I^2 = \left(\int_0^\infty e^{-x^2} \, dx \right) \left(\int_0^\infty e^{-y^2} \, dy \right) = \int_0^\infty \int_0^\infty e^{-(x^2+y^2)} \, dx \, dy.$$

Introduce polar coordinates in the last expression and show that

$$I = \int_0^\infty e^{-x^2} \, dx = \frac{\sqrt{\pi}}{2}.$$

23. By transformation of variables $u = x - y$, $v = y$, show that

$$\int_0^\infty e^{-sx} \, dx \int_0^x f(x - y, y) \, dy = \int_0^\infty \int_0^\infty e^{-s(u+v)} f(u, v) \, du \, dv.$$

24. How must a, b, c be chosen in order that $\int_{-\infty}^{\infty} \int_{-\infty}^{\infty} e^{-(ax^2+2bxy+cy^2)} \, dx \, dy = 1$? [*Hint:* Introduce the transformation

$$\xi = \alpha x + \beta y, \quad \eta = \gamma x + \delta y \quad \text{where} \quad (\alpha\delta - \beta\gamma)^2 = ac - b^2;$$

then

$$ax^2 + 2bxy + cy^2 = \xi^2 + \eta^2.]$$

25. Find the area enclosed by the lemniscate $r^2 = 2a^2 \cos 2\theta$. Also find the moment of inertia of this area about the y-axis.

26. Evaluate the integral

$$\iint \frac{dx \, dy}{(1 + x^2 + y^2)^2}$$

taken (a) over one loop of the lemniscate $(x^2 + y^2)^2 - (x^2 - y^2) = 0$, (b) over the triangle with vertices $(0, 0)$, $(2, 0)$, $(1, \sqrt{3})$. [*Hint:* Transform to polar coordinates.]

27. Show, by transforming to polar coordinates, that

$$K(a) = \int_0^{a \sin \beta} dy \int_{y \cot \beta}^{\sqrt{a^2-y^2}} \ln (x^2 + y^2) \, dx = a^2\beta(\ln a - \tfrac{1}{2}), \quad \left(0 < \beta < \frac{\pi}{2} \right).$$

Changing the order of integration, what expression do you obtain?

28. Find the volume bounded by the cylinder $y = \cos x$ and the planes

$$z = y, \quad x = 0, \quad x = \pi/2, \quad \text{and} \quad z = 0.$$

29. Find the center of mass of the homogeneous pyramid whose base is the square enclosed by the lines $x = 1$, $x = -1$, $y = 1$, $y = -1$ in the plane $z = 0$ and whose vertex is at the point $(0, 0, 1)$.

30. Find the volume bounded above by the sphere $x^2 + y^2 + z^2 = 2a^2$ and below by the paraboloid $az = x^2 + y^2$.

31. Find the volume bounded by the surfaces $z = x^2 + y^2$ and $z = \frac{1}{2}(x^2 + y^2 + 1)$.

32. Determine by triple integration the volume enclosed by the two surfaces $x = y^2 + z^2$ and $x = 1 - y^2$.

33. Find the moment of inertia, with respect to the z-axis, of a solid that is bounded below by the paraboloid $3az = x^2 + y^2$ and above by the sphere $x^2 + y^2 + z^2 = 4a^2$, if its density is constant.

34. Find by integration the volume of the ellipsoid $x^2/a^2 + y^2/b^2 + z^2c^2 = 1$.

35. Evaluate the integral $\iiint |xyz|\, dx\, dy\, dz$ taken throughout the ellipsoid $x^2/a^2 + y^2/b^2 + z^2/c^2 \leq 1$. [*Hint:* Introduce new coordinates:

$$x = a\xi, \quad y = b\eta, \quad z = c\zeta.]$$

36. Two cylinders of radius a have their axes along the x- and y-axes respectively. Find the volume that they have in common.

37. The volume of a certain solid is given by the triple integral

$$\int_0^2 \left[\int_0^{\sqrt{2x-x^2}} \left(\int_{-\sqrt{4-x^2-y^2}}^{\sqrt{4-x^2-y^2}} dz \right) dy \right] dx.$$

(a) Describe the solid by giving the equations of all the surfaces that form its boundary. (b) Express the volume as a triple integral in cylindrical coordinates. Give the limits of integration explicitly, but do not evaluate the integral.

38. A square hole of side $2b$ is cut symmetrically through a sphere of radius a $(a > b\sqrt{2})$. Find the volume removed.

39. A hole is bored through a sphere, the axis of the hole being a diameter of the sphere. The volume of the solid remaining is given by the integral

$$V = 2 \int_0^{2\pi} \int_0^{\sqrt{3}} \int_1^{\sqrt{4-z^2}} r\, dr\, dz\, d\theta.$$

(a) By inspecting the given integral, determine the radius of the hole and the radius of the sphere. (b) Calculate the numerical value of the integral.

40. Set up equivalent triple integrals in rectangular coordinates. (Arrange the order so the first integration is with respect to z, the second with respect to y, and the last with respect to x.)

$$\int_0^{\pi/2} \int_1^{\sqrt{3}} \int_1^{\sqrt{4-r^2}} r^3 \sin\theta \cos\theta\, z^2\, dz\, dr\, d\theta.$$

41. Find the volume bounded by the plane $z = 0$, the cylinder $x^2 + y^2 = a^2$, and the cylinder $az = a^2 - x^2$.

42. Find the volume of that portion of the sphere $r^2 + z^2 = a^2$ that is inside the cylinder $r = a \sin \theta$. (Here r, θ, z are cylindrical coordinates.)

43. Find the moment of inertia, about the z-axis, of the volume that is bounded above by the sphere $\rho = a$ and below by the cone $\phi = \pi/3$. (ρ, ϕ, θ are spherical coordinates.)

44. Find the volume enclosed by the surface $\rho = a \sin \phi$, in spherical coordinates.

45. Find the moment of inertia of the solid of constant density δ bounded by two concentric spheres of radii a and b ($a < b$), about a diameter.

46. Let S be a solid homogeneous sphere of radius a, constant density δ, mass $M = \frac{4}{3}\pi a^3 \delta$. Let P be a particle of mass m situated at distance b ($b > a$) from the center of S. According to Newton, the force of gravitational attraction of the sphere for P is given by the equation

$$ \mathbf{F} = \gamma m \iiint \frac{\mathbf{u}\, \delta\, dV}{r^2}, $$

where γ is the gravitational constant, $\mathbf{u}$ is a unit vector in the direction from P toward the volume element dV in S, r^2 is the square of the distance from P to dV, and the integration is extended throughout S. Take the origin at the center of the sphere and P at $(0, 0, b)$ on the z-axis, and show that $\mathbf{F} = -(\gamma M m/b^2)\mathbf{k}$. [*Remark.* This result shows that the force is the same as though all the mass of the sphere were concentrated at its center.]

47. The density at P, a point of a solid sphere of radius a and center O, is given to be
$$ \rho_0\{1 + \epsilon \cos \theta + \tfrac{1}{2}\epsilon^2(3 \cos \theta - 1)\}, $$

where θ is the angle OP makes with a fixed radius OQ, and ρ_0 and ϵ are constants. Find the average density of the sphere.

48. Find the area of the surface $y^2 + z^2 = 2x$ cut off by the plane $x = 1$.

49. Find the area cut from the plane $x + y + z = 1$ by the cylinder $x^2 + y^2 = 1$.

50. Find the area above the xy-plane cut from the cone $x^2 + y^2 = z^2$ by the cylinder $x^2 + y^2 = 2ax$.

51. Find the surface area of that portion of the sphere $r^2 + z^2 = a^2$ that is inside the cylinder $r = a \sin \theta$. (r, θ, z are cylindrical coordinates.)

52. The cylinder $x^2 + y^2 = 2x$ cuts out a portion of a surface S from the upper nappe of the cone $x^2 + y^2 = z^2$. Compute the value of the surface integral

$$ \iint_S (x^4 - y^4 + y^2 z^2 - z^2 x^2 + 1)\, dS. $$

53. The sphere $x^2 + y^2 + z^2 = 25$ is cut by the plane $z = 3$, the smaller portion cut off forming a solid V which is bounded by a closed surface S_0 made up of two parts, the spherical part S_1 and the planar part S_2. If $\cos \alpha \mathbf{i} + \cos \beta \mathbf{j} + \cos \gamma \mathbf{k}$ is the unit outer normal of S_0, find the value of the surface integral

$$\iint_S (xz \cos \alpha + yz \cos \beta + \cos \gamma) \, dS$$

(a) if S is the spherical cap S_1, (b) if S is the planar base S_2, (c) if S is the complete boundary S_0.

54. Obtain the double integral expressing the surface area cut from the cylinder $z = a^2 - y^2$ by the cylinder $x^2 + y^2 = a^2$, and reduce this double integral to a definite single integral with respect to the variable y.

55. A square hole of side $2\sqrt{2}$ is cut symmetrically through a sphere of radius 2. Show that the area of the surface removed is $16\pi(\sqrt{2} - 1)$.

56. A torus-surface is generated by moving a sphere of unit radius whose center travels on a closed plane circle of radius 2. Calculate the area of this surface.

57. Calculate the area of the surface $(x^2 + y^2 + z^2)^2 = x^2 - y^2$. [Hint: Use polar coordinates.]

58. Calculate the area of the spherical part of the boundary of the region

$$x^2 + y^2 + z^2 = r^2, \quad x^2 + y^2 - rx \geq 0, \quad x^2 + y^2 + rx \geq 0.$$

[Hint: Integrate first with respect to x and y.]

59. Prove that the potential of a circular disk of mass m per unit area, and of radius a, at a point distant h from the center and on the normal to the disk through the center is $2\pi m(\sqrt{(a^2 + h^2)} - h)$. (The potential at a point P due to a mass Δm at Q is $\Delta m/r$, where r is the distance from P to Q.)

60. Find the attraction, at the vertex, of a solid right circular cone of mass M, height h, and radius of base a. (The attraction at P due to a mass Δm at Q is $(\Delta m/r^2)\mathbf{u}$, where r is the distance from P to Q, and $\mathbf{u}$ is a unit vector in the direction of PQ.)

61. The solid angle sustained by a surface Σ bounded by a closed curve is defined with respect to the origin as

$$\Omega = \left| \iint_\Sigma \frac{\cos \theta}{r^2} \, dS \right|,$$

where the area element dS is located at the end of the position vector $\mathbf{R}$, θ is the angle between $\mathbf{R}$ and the normal to dS, and $r = |\mathbf{R}|$. Show that in Cartesian coordinates

$$\Omega = \left| \iint_\Sigma \frac{x \, dy \, dz + y \, dz \, dx + z \, dx \, dy}{(x^2 + y^2 + z^2)^{3/2}} \right|.$$

62. Prove by direct integration that

$$\int_{-\infty}^{\infty} \int_{-\infty}^{\infty} \frac{dx \, dy}{(x^2 + y^2 + 1)^{3/2}} = 2\pi.$$

Interpret this integral as a solid angle sustained by a surface. What surface is this?

63. Show that the average distance of the points of the surface of a sphere of radius a from a point on the surface is $4a/3$.

CHAPTER 16

INFINITE SERIES

16-1 Introduction and definitions. In Article 9–3 we became acquainted with Newton's method for finding a root of an equation $f(x) = 0$. The procedure was:

(a) guess a first approximation x_1, and
(b) from any current approximation x_n get a new approximation x_{n+1} from the formula

$$x_{n+1} = x_n - \frac{f(x_n)}{f'(x_n)}. \tag{1}$$

In theory, this procedure might be continued indefinitely, producing an infinite succession of approximations $x_1, x_2, x_3, \ldots$ Indeed, to each positive integer n there corresponds an nth approximation x_n. The set of all ordered pairs of the form (n, x_n), $n = 1, 2, \ldots$ is an example of a *sequence*.

There are many other ways of producing sequences. Consider, for example, a geometric progression like $1, \frac{1}{2}, \frac{1}{4}, \frac{1}{8}, \ldots$, where each term is one-half of its predecessor. Suppose we number the terms in $1, 2, 3, \ldots$ order as in the following table.

Number of term (index)	1	2	3	4	$\ldots$	n	$\ldots$
Value of term	1	$\frac{1}{2}$	$\frac{1}{4}$	$\frac{1}{8}$	$\ldots$	$(\frac{1}{2})^{n-1}$	$\ldots$

We now consider the set of all pairs of the form $(n, (\frac{1}{2})^{n-1})$, where the first element in each pair is the index that shows the ordinal number of that pair, and the second element is the value of the corresponding term of the geometric progression. This set is another example of a sequence, in agreement with the following general definition.

DEFINITION. *A sequence is a function whose domain is the set of positive integers.*

We may denote the function by f. Then its value at n is $f(n)$. The sequence f is the set $\{(n, f(n)) \mid n = 1, 2, 3, \ldots\}$, that is, the set of all pairs $(n, f(n))$, with n a positive integer.

For example, $\{(n, 1/n) \mid n = 1, 2, 3, \ldots\}$ is a sequence whose value at n is $1/n$ (Fig. 16–1).

Since the domain of a sequence is always the same (the set of positive

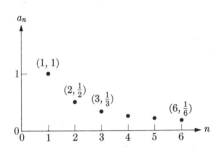

FIG. 16–1. Part of the graph of the sequence $\{(n, 1/n)\,|\,n = 1, 2, \ldots\}$.

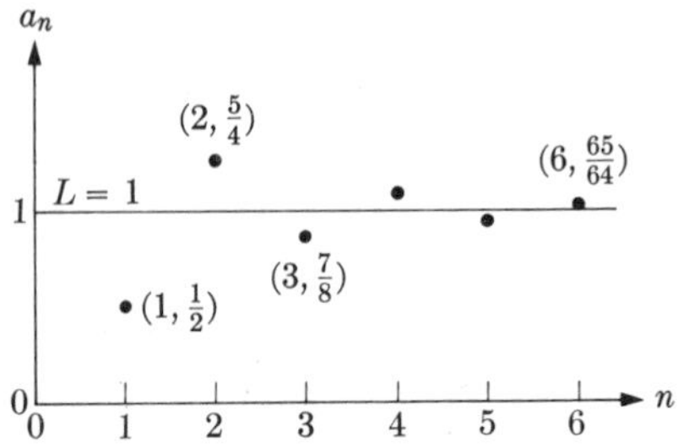

FIG. 16–2. Part of the graph of $\{(n, 1 + (-1)^n/2^n)\}$ and the limit $L = 1$.

integers), it is customary to shorten the notation and just write $\{f(n)\}$ instead of $\{(n, f(n))\}$. Thus the sequence $\{(n, 1/n)\,|\,n = 1, 2, 3, \ldots\}$ would be abbreviated simply $\{1/n\}$. Similarly $\{1/2^{n-1}\}$ would denote the sequence

$$\left\{\left(n, \frac{1}{2^{n-1}}\right)\middle| n = 1, 2, 3, \ldots\right\}.$$

We also write $\{a_n\}$ to denote the sequence whose ordinate is $y = a_n$ at the abscissa $x = n$.

Limit of a sequence. A sequence $\{(n, a_n)\}$ may have a different value a_n for each different value of n. But it may also happen that as n increases, the different a_n's tend to cluster around some fixed number L. If there is such a number L, with the property that $|L - a_n|$ is arbitrarily small for all sufficiently large values of the index n, we say that a_n *converges* to L as limit, and write

$$\lim_{n\to\infty} a_n = L.$$

By the phrase "$|L - a_n|$ is arbitrarily small for all sufficiently large values of n" we mean that to any positive number ϵ there corresponds an index N such that

$$|L - a_n| < \epsilon \qquad \text{for all} \qquad n > N. \tag{2}$$

That is, all terms after the Nth lie within ϵ distance of L. If no such limit exists, we say that the given sequence diverges.

Remark 1. The sequence $\{(n, a_n)\}$ has the limit L just in case its graph has the line $y = L$ as horizontal asymptote. For example, the x-axis ($y = 0$) is an asymptote of the graph of $\{(n, 1/n)\}$, and also of $\{(n, (\frac{1}{2})^{n-1})\}$. Both sequences *converge* to zero as $n \to \infty$. And the sequence

$$\left\{\left(n, 1 + \frac{(-1)^n}{2^n}\right)\right\}$$

converges to 1 as $n \to \infty$ (Fig. 16–2).

Remark 2. As recalled above, Newton's method for finding a solution of an equation $f(x) = 0$ is to guess a first approximation x_1 and then to use the formula

$$x_{n+1} = x_n - \frac{f(x_n)}{f'(x_n)}$$

to generate, by iteration, a sequence $\{x_n\}$. In favorable circumstances, the sequence converges to a number L which satisfies the equation $f(L) = 0$.

Remark 3. Iteration is used as a method for solving many different types of problems, particularly by high-speed computing machines. The technique is to start with a first approximation, use that to compute a second approximation, the second to get a third, then a fourth, and so on. The process generates a sequence which we hope will converge to a solution of the problem. [For a discussion of some specific examples see the article "Feed it back," by Francis Scheid, in the *Mathematics Teacher*, Vol. LII, No. 4, April 1959, pp. 226–229.]

Infinite series. One very important way of creating a sequence $\{s_n\}$ is by addition. Suppose the numbers to be added are $u_1, u_2, u_3, \ldots, u_n, \ldots$ We let

$$s_1 = u_1,$$
$$s_2 = u_1 + u_2,$$
$$s_3 = u_1 + u_2 + u_3,$$
$$\vdots$$
$$s_n = u_1 + u_2 + \cdots + u_n = \sum_{k=1}^{n} u_k. \tag{3}$$

As n increases without bound, we are led to consider the symbol, or "set of marks,"

$$u_1 + u_2 + u_3 + \cdots + u_n + \cdots, \tag{4a}$$

which we shall also denote by

$$\sum_{k=1}^{\infty} u_k. \tag{4b}$$

Such an expression is called an *infinite series.* One object in the present chapter is to see what meaning, if any, can be attached to an expression such as (4).

The sequence $\{s_n\}$, Eq. (3), is called the *sequence of partial sums* of the series (4a, b). The nth partial sum of the series is s_n. If s_n converges to a limit S as $n \to \infty$,

$$\lim_{n \to \infty} s_n = S, \tag{5}$$

we say that the series *converges* and that its *sum* is S. We indicate this by writing

$$\sum_{k=1}^{\infty} u_k = \lim_{n \to \infty} \left(\sum_{k=1}^{n} u_k \right) = S. \tag{6}$$

On the other hand, if the sequence of partial sums diverges, we then say that the series *diverges*. In other words, the behavior of the series (convergence or divergence) is the behavior of its sequence of partial sums. Later in this chapter we shall study several methods for testing a given series in order to determine whether it converges or diverges. For the present, we shall want to use the following theorem.

THEOREM 1. *A necessary condition for the convergence of an infinite series*

$$u_1 + u_2 + \cdots + u_n + \cdots$$

is that

$$\lim_{n \to \infty} u_n = 0. \tag{7}$$

Remark. The statement that the condition (7) is a "necessary condition for convergence" means that the condition must be satisfied if the series converges. Therefore it follows that when (7) is *not* satisfied, then the series *diverges*. This is frequently a useful test for divergence; namely, if the nth term of the series does not have a limit, or if it has a limit different from zero, as $n \to \infty$, then the series diverges. For example, the series

$$\frac{1}{2} + \frac{2}{3} + \frac{3}{4} + \frac{4}{5} + \cdots + \frac{n}{n+1} + \cdots$$

diverges, since $u_n = n/(n+1)$ approaches 1 instead of 0 as $n \to \infty$. *Caution:* The theorem does *not* give a *sufficient* condition for convergence. That is, it does not follow that a series converges just because its nth term approaches zero as $n \to \infty$. The reader may ponder this statement in connection with the series

$$\tfrac{1}{2} + \underbrace{\tfrac{1}{4} + \tfrac{1}{4}}_{2 \text{ terms}} + \underbrace{\tfrac{1}{8} + \tfrac{1}{8} + \tfrac{1}{8} + \tfrac{1}{8}}_{4 \text{ terms}} + \underbrace{\tfrac{1}{16} + \tfrac{1}{16} + \cdots + \tfrac{1}{16}}_{8 \text{ terms}} + \cdots$$

$$+ \underbrace{\frac{1}{2^k} + \frac{1}{2^k} + \cdots + \frac{1}{2^k}}_{2^{k-1} \text{ terms}} + \cdots \tag{8}$$

Proof of the theorem. Let

$$s_n = u_1 + u_2 + \cdots + u_n$$

denote the nth partial sum of the series. Suppose the series converges to S, that is,

$$\lim_{n \to \infty} s_n = S.$$

Then, corresponding to any preassigned positive number ϵ, there is an index N such that all terms of the sequence $\{s_n\}$ after the Nth one lie between $S - \epsilon/2$ and $S + \epsilon/2$. Hence no two of them may differ by as much as ϵ. That is, if m and n are both greater than N, then

$$|s_n - s_m| < \epsilon.$$

In particular, this inequality holds if $m = n - 1$ and $n > N + 1$. But

$$s_n - s_{n-1} = (u_1 + u_2 + \cdots + u_n) - (u_1 + u_2 + \cdots + u_{n-1}) = u_n.$$

Therefore

$$|u_n| < \epsilon \quad \text{when} \quad n > N + 1.$$

Since ϵ was any positive number whatever, this means that

$$\lim_{n \to \infty} u_n = 0. \qquad \text{Q.E.D.}$$

Remark. It is worth noting that the sum

$$u_1 + u_2 + \cdots + u_n$$

is always defined (if n is a positive integer and $u_1, u_2, \ldots, u_n$ are finite numbers). When the series

$$u_1 + u_2 + \cdots + u_n + \cdots$$

has a "sum," in the sense that its sequence of partial sums has a *limit*, the symbol "$+$" has acquired new meaning, as has the word "sum." We can now "add" infinitely many numbers, in certain cases, not by actual addition, but rather by the process of finding a *limit*. This is a typical example of the way in which mathematics generalizes familiar concepts to increase their usefulness.

We shall illustrate the method of finding the "sum" of an infinite series for the case of the repeating decimal

$$0.3333\cdots = \frac{3}{10} + \frac{3}{100} + \frac{3}{1000} + \frac{3}{10,000} + \cdots$$

Here

$$s_1 = \frac{3}{10},$$

$$s_2 = \frac{3}{10} + \frac{3}{10^2},$$

$$\vdots$$

$$s_n = \frac{3}{10} + \frac{3}{10^2} + \cdots + \frac{3}{10^n}.$$

We can obtain a simple expression for s_n in closed form as follows. We multiply both sides of the equation for s_n by $\frac{1}{10}$ and obtain

$$\frac{1}{10} s_n = \frac{3}{10^2} + \frac{3}{10^3} + \cdots + \frac{3}{10^n} + \frac{3}{10^{n+1}} .$$

When we subtract this from s_n, we have

$$s_n - \frac{1}{10} s_n = \frac{3}{10} - \frac{3}{10^{n+1}} = \frac{3}{10} \left(1 - \frac{1}{10^n} \right) .$$

Therefore

$$\frac{9}{10} s_n = \frac{3}{10} \left(1 - \frac{1}{10^n} \right)$$

or

$$s_n = \frac{3}{9} \left(1 - \frac{1}{10^n} \right) .$$

Clearly, as $n \to \infty$, $\left(\frac{1}{10} \right)^n \to 0$ and

$$\lim_{n \to \infty} s_n = \tfrac{3}{9} = \tfrac{1}{3} .$$

We therefore say that the sum of the infinite series

$$\frac{3}{10} + \frac{3}{10^2} + \frac{3}{10^3} + \cdots + \frac{3}{10^n} + \cdots$$

is $\tfrac{1}{3}$.

The repeating decimal illustration is a special case of a *geometric series*.

DEFINITION. *A series of the form*

$$a + ar + ar^2 + ar^3 + \cdots + ar^{n-1} + \cdots \tag{9}$$

is called a geometric *series. The ratio of any term to the one before it is* r.

The sum of the first n terms of (9) is

$$s_n = a + ar + ar^2 + \cdots + ar^{n-1} . \tag{10}$$

Multiplying both sides of (10) by r gives

$$rs_n = ar + ar^2 + \cdots + ar^{n-1} + ar^n . \tag{11}$$

When we subtract (11) from (10), many terms cancel on the right side, leaving

$$(1 - r)s_n = a(1 - r^n) . \tag{12}$$

If $r \neq 1$, we may divide (12) by $(1 - r)$:

$$s_n = \frac{a(1 - r^n)}{1 - r} , \qquad r \neq 1 . \tag{13a}$$

On the other hand, if $r = 1$ in (10), we get

$$s_n = na, \qquad r = 1. \tag{13b}$$

We are interested in the limit as $n \to \infty$ in Eqs. (13a) and (13b).

Clearly, (13b) has no finite limit if $a \neq 0$. If $a = 0$, the series (9) is just

$$0 + 0 + 0 + \cdots$$

and it converges to the sum zero.

If $r \neq 1$, we use (13a). In the right side of (13a), n appears only in the expression r^n. This approaches zero as $n \to \infty$ if $|r| < 1$. Therefore,

$$\lim_{n \to \infty} s_n = \lim_{n \to \infty} \frac{a(1 - r^n)}{1 - r}$$

$$= \frac{a}{1 - r}, \qquad \text{if} \qquad |r| < 1. \tag{14}$$

If $|r| > 1$, then $|r^n| \to \infty$, and (9) diverges.

The remaining case is where $r = -1$. Then $s_1 = a$, $s_2 = a - a = 0$, $s_3 = a$, $s_4 = 0$, and so on. If $a \neq 0$, this sequence of partial sums has no limit as $n \to \infty$, and the series (9) diverges.

We have thus proved the following theorem.

THEOREM 2. *If $|r| < 1$, the geometric series*

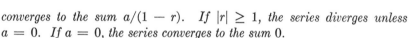

$$a + ar + ar^2 + \cdots + ar^{n-1} + \cdots$$

converges to the sum $a/(1 - r)$. If $|r| \geq 1$, the series diverges unless $a = 0$. If $a = 0$, the series converges to the sum 0.

EXAMPLE. A ball is dropped from a feet above a flat surface. Each time the ball hits the ground after falling a distance h it rebounds a distance rh, where r is a positive fraction less than one. Find the total distance the ball travels.

Solution. (See Fig. 16–3.) The distance is given by the series

$$s = a + 2ar + 2ar^2 + 2ar^3 + \cdots$$

The terms following the first form a geometric series of sum $2ar/(1 - r)$. Hence the distance is

$$s = a + \frac{2ar}{1 - r} = a \frac{1 + r}{1 - r}.$$

For instance, if $a = 6$ (ft) and $r = \frac{2}{3}$, the distance is

$$s = 6 \frac{1 + \frac{2}{3}}{1 - \frac{2}{3}} = 30 \text{ (ft)}.$$

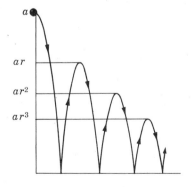

FIGURE 16–3

Problems

Determine which of the following sequences $\{a_n\}$ converge and which of them diverge. Find the limit of each sequence that converges.

1. $a_n = \dfrac{2n + 1}{1 - 3n}$

2. $a_n = \dfrac{n^2 - n}{2n^2 + n}$

3. $a_n = 1 + \dfrac{(-1)^n}{n}$

4. $a_n = \dfrac{1 + (-1)^n}{n}$

5. $a_n = 1 + (-1)^n$

6. $a_n = \sin n$

7. $a_n = \tanh n$

8. $a_n = \dfrac{\ln n}{n}$

9. $a_n = e^n$

10. $a_n = e^{-n}$

11. Prove that a given sequence $\{a_n\}$ cannot converge to two different limits L and L'. [*Hint:* Take $\epsilon = \frac{1}{2}|L - L'|$ in (2).]

12. Suppose the sequence $\{a_n\}$ converges to the limit L and the sequence $\{b_n\}$ converges to L'. Show that

(a) $\{a_n + b_n\}$ converges to $L + L'$,

(b) $\{ca_n\}$ converges to cL,

(c) $\{a_n \cdot b_n\}$ converges to $L \cdot L'$,

(d) $\left\{\dfrac{a_n}{b_n}\right\}$ converges to $\dfrac{L}{L'}$, if $L' \neq 0$.

13. (a) If each term of a given sequence $\{a_n\}$ is less than or equal to a constant M, that is,

$$a_n \leq M \qquad \text{for all} \qquad n = 1, 2, 3, \ldots,$$

and if $\{a_n\}$ converges to L, show that L is also less than or equal to M. (b) Give an example of a sequence $\{a_n\}$ such that $a_n \leq 1$ for all $n = 1, 2, 3, \ldots$, but such that the sequence has no limit.

Find a closed form expression for the sum s_n of the first n terms of each of the following series. Then compute the sum of the series, if the series converges.

14. $(1 - \frac{1}{2}) + (\frac{1}{2} - \frac{1}{3}) + (\frac{1}{3} - \frac{1}{4}) + \cdots + \left(\dfrac{1}{n} - \dfrac{1}{n + 1}\right) + \cdots$

15. $\dfrac{1}{1 \cdot 2} + \dfrac{1}{2 \cdot 3} + \dfrac{1}{3 \cdot 4} + \cdots + \dfrac{1}{n(n + 1)} + \cdots$ [*Hint:* Compare with Problem 14.]

16. $\ln \frac{1}{2} + \ln \frac{2}{3} + \ln \frac{3}{4} + \cdots + \ln \dfrac{n}{n + 1} + \cdots$

17. $1 + \frac{1}{2} + \frac{1}{4} + \cdots + \dfrac{1}{2^{n-1}} + \cdots$ [*Hint:* Multiply s_n by $\frac{1}{2}$ and subtract the result from s_n.]

18. $2 + \frac{2}{3} + \frac{2}{9} + \frac{2}{27} + \cdots + \frac{2}{3^{n-1}} + \cdots$ [*Hint:* Compute $s_n - \frac{1}{3}s_n$.]

19. $5 - \frac{5}{2} + \frac{5}{4} - \frac{5}{8} + \cdots + \frac{(-1)^{n-1}5}{2^{n-1}} + \cdots$ [*Hint:* Compute $s_n + \frac{1}{2}s_n$.]

20. $\frac{9}{100} + \frac{9}{(100)^2} + \frac{9}{(100)^3} + \cdots + \frac{9}{(100)^n} + \cdots$

21. A ball is dropped from a height of 4 ft. Each time it strikes the ground after falling from a height of h feet, it rebounds a distance $\frac{3}{4}h$ ft. Find the total distance traveled by the ball.

22. (a) Express the repeating decimal

$$0.234\ 234\ 234\ldots$$

as a ratio p/q of integers p and q. (b) Is it true that *every* repeating decimal is a rational number p/q? Give a reason for your answer.

23. Express the decimal number

$$1.24\ 123\ 123\ 123\ldots$$

(which is a repeating decimal after the first three figures) as a rational number p/q.

24. (a) Show by long division that

$$\frac{1}{1+t} = 1 - t + t^2 - t^3 + \cdots + (-1)^n t^n + \frac{(-1)^{n+1}t^{n+1}}{1+t}.$$

(b) By integrating the equation of part (a), with respect to t, from 0 to x, show that

$$\ln(1+x) = x - \frac{x^2}{2} + \frac{x^3}{3} - \frac{x^4}{4} + \cdots + (-1)^n \frac{x^{n+1}}{n+1} + R,$$

where

$$R = (-1)^{n+1} \int_0^x \frac{t^{n+1}}{1+t}\, dt.$$

(c) If $x > 0$, show that

$$|R| \le \int_0^x t^{n+1}\, dt = \frac{x^{n+2}}{n+2}.$$

[*Hint:* As t varies from 0 to x, $1 + t \ge 1$.] (d) If $x = \frac{1}{2}$, how large should n be, in part (c) above, in order to be able to guarantee that $|R| < 0.001$? (e) If $x = 1$, how large should n be, in part (c) above, in order to be able to guarantee that $|R| < 0.001$?

16–2 Tests for convergence of a series of constants. It is sometimes hard to apply the definition of convergence in Article 16–1. This is true when we can't find any simple expression for the sum of the first n terms of a series as a function of n. In the present article we shall learn several tests for determining whether or not a given series converges, tests which depend on the individual terms of the series rather than on their sums.

Consider a series of numbers

$$\sum_{k=1}^{\infty} u_k = u_1 + u_2 + u_3 + \cdots + u_n + \cdots \qquad (1)$$

As in Article 16–1, we say that the series (1) converges if the sequence s_n of partial sums

$$
\begin{aligned}
s_1 &= u_1, \\
s_2 &= u_1 + u_2, \\
&\vdots \\
s_n &= u_1 + u_2 + \cdots + u_n
\end{aligned}
\qquad (2)
$$

tends to a definite finite limit as n increases without bound. If the partial sums s_n do not have such a limit, then the series is said to diverge. Most of the series to be considered in this book belong to one or the other of the following two types:

1. *Positive series,* or those in which all terms of the series are positive numbers.

2. *Alternating series,* or those in which the terms are alternately positive and negative, as

$$a_1 - a_2 + a_3 - a_4 + \cdots, \qquad (3)$$

where each of the a's is positive.

Positive series. Suppose all of the numbers u_k in (1) are positive. Then when we calculate the partial sums s_1, s_2, s_3, and so on, we see that each one is greater than its predecessor, since $s_{n+1} = s_n + u_{n+1}$. That is,

$$s_1 \le s_2 \le s_3 \le \cdots \le s_n \le s_{n+1}. \qquad (4)$$

A sequence $\{s_n\}$ that has the property (4) is called an *increasing* sequence. The cardinal principle governing increasing sequences is contained in the following theorem.

THEOREM 1. *Let $s_1, s_2, s_3, \ldots$ be an increasing sequence of real numbers. Then one or the other of the following alternatives must hold:*

A. *There is a finite constant M such that all terms of the sequence are less than or equal to M. In this case the sequence possesses a definite finite limit L which is also less than or equal to M.*

B. *The sequence diverges to plus infinity; that is, the numbers in the sequence $\{s_n\}$ ultimately exceed any preassigned number, no matter how large.*

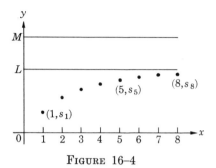

FIGURE 16–4

We shall not attempt to give a rigorous proof of this theorem, but we may gain an intuitive appreciation of the result by adopting the following graphical approach. Suppose we plot the points $(1, s_1)$, $(2, s_2)$, . . . , (n, s_n) in the xy-plane (Fig. 16–4). Then if there is a line $y = M$ such that *none* of the points (n, s_n) lies above this line, it is intuitively clear that there is a *lowest* such line. That is, there is a line

$$y = L$$

such that none of the points lies above it but such that there are points (n, s_n) that lie above any *lower* line

$$y = L - \epsilon,$$

where ϵ is any positive number. Analytically, this means that the number L has the properties (a) $s_n \leq L$ for *all* values of n, (b) given any $\epsilon > 0$, there exists at least one integer N such that

$$s_N > L - \epsilon.$$

Then the fact that $\{s_n\}$ is an increasing sequence tells us further that

$$s_n \geq s_N > L - \epsilon \qquad \text{for all} \qquad n \geq N.$$

This means that *all* the numbers s_n, beyond the Nth one in the sequence, lie within ϵ distance of L. This is precisely the condition for L to be the limit of the sequence s_n,

$$L = \lim_{n \to \infty} s_n.$$

Alternative B of the theorem is what happens when there are points (n, s_n) above any given line $y = M$, no matter how large M may be.

The theorem does not tell us how to find the limit L when it exists; it simply tells us whether or not there is such a limit. Briefly, it says that a *positive series either converges or else it becomes infinite.* Divergence by oscillation is ruled out.

EXAMPLE 1. The series

$$\sum_{k=0}^{\infty} \frac{1}{k!} = 1 + \frac{1}{1!} + \frac{1}{2!} + \frac{1}{3!} + \cdots$$

converges because its terms are all less than or equal to the corresponding terms in the series

$$1 + \sum_{k=0}^{\infty} \frac{1}{2^k} = 1 + 1 + \frac{1}{2} + \frac{1}{2^2} + \cdots$$

The latter series is, after its first term, a simple geometric series of ratio $1/2$. The sum of terms after the first is $1/(1 - \frac{1}{2}) = 2$, so the sum of the series is three. The partial sums of the first series are all less than three. Hence the first series converges by virtue of our theorem about positive series, and its sum is less than or equal to three. In fact, it is the series for e.

EXAMPLE 2. The terms of the "harmonic" series

$$\sum_{k=1}^{\infty} \frac{1}{k} = 1 + \frac{1}{2} + \frac{1}{3} + \cdots$$

may be interpreted as representing the areas of rectangles each of base unity and having altitudes, respectively, equal to $1, \frac{1}{2}, \frac{1}{3}, \ldots$ If we consider the sum of the first n terms of the series

$$s_n = 1 + \frac{1}{2} + \frac{1}{3} + \cdots + \frac{1}{n},$$

we see (Fig. 16-5) that this represents the sum of the areas of n rectangles each of which is somewhat greater than the area under the corresponding portion of the curve $y = 1/x$. Therefore s_n is greater than the area under this curve between $x = 1$ and $x = n + 1$:

$$s_n > \int_1^{n+1} \frac{dx}{x} = \ln (n + 1).$$

By taking n sufficiently large, we can make $\ln (n + 1)$ as large as we please,

$$\lim_{n \to \infty} \ln (n + 1) = +\infty.$$

Since $s_n > \ln (n + 1)$, this also means

$$\lim_{n \to \infty} s_n = +\infty.$$

Therefore the series

$$1 + \frac{1}{2} + \frac{1}{3} + \cdots + \frac{1}{n} + \cdots$$

diverges to plus infinity.

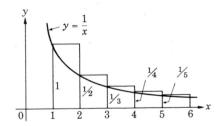

FIGURE 16-5

In the two examples just discussed, we made a *comparison*, between the given series and another series (Example 1), or between the given series and an integral (Example 2).   We now state a theorem which embodies the so-called *comparison test* for positive series.

THEOREM 2.   *If each term of the positive series*

$$\sum_{k=1}^{\infty} u_k = u_1 + u_2 + u_3 + \cdots$$

is less *than the corresponding term of a known* convergent *series*

$$\sum_{k=1}^{\infty} c_k = c_1 + c_2 + c_3 + \cdots,$$

then $\sum u_k$ *converges.   But if each term of the series* $\sum u_k$ *is* greater *than the corresponding term of a known* divergent *positive series*

$$\sum_{k=1}^{\infty} d_k = d_1 + d_2 + d_3 + \cdots,$$

then $\sum u_k$ *diverges.*

This theorem is an immediate consequence of Theorem 1.

When we compare a positive series with an integral, as we did above in Example 2, we are led to the *integral test*, which we now state as a theorem.

THEOREM 3.   *Let the function* $y = f(x)$ *obtained by introducing the continuous variable* x *in place of the discrete variable* n *in the* nth *term of the positive series*

$$u_1 + u_2 + \cdots + u_n + \cdots$$

be a decreasing function of x *for* $x \geq 1$.   *Then the series*

$$\sum_{n=1}^{\infty} u_n$$

and the integral

$$\int_1^{\infty} f(x)\, dx$$

both converge or both diverge.

Proof.   In Fig. 16–6(a), the rectangles of areas $u_1, u_2, \ldots, u_n$ enclose more area than that under the curve from $x = 1$ to $x = n + 1$; that is,

$$u_1 + u_2 + \cdots + u_n > \int_1^{n+1} f(x)\, dx.$$

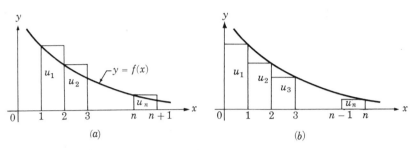

Figure 16-6

In Fig. 16–6(b) the rectangles have been faced to the left instead of to the right. If we momentarily disregard the first rectangle, of area u_1, we see that

$$u_2 + u_3 + \cdots + u_n < \int_1^n f(x) \, dx.$$

If we include u_1, we have

$$u_1 + u_2 + \cdots + u_n < u_1 + \int_1^n f(x) \, dx.$$

Combining these results, we have

$$\int_1^{n+1} f(x) \, dx < u_1 + u_2 + \cdots + u_n < u_1 + \int_1^n f(x) \, dx.$$

If the integral $\int_1^\infty f(x) \, dx$ is finite, the right-hand inequality shows that the infinite series

$$\sum_{n=1}^\infty u_n$$

is also finite. But if $\int_1^\infty f(x) \, dx$ is infinite, then the left-hand inequality shows that the series is also infinite. Hence the series and the integral are both finite or both infinite.

EXAMPLE 3. The p-series

$$\frac{1}{1^p} + \frac{1}{2^p} + \frac{1}{3^p} + \cdots + \frac{1}{n^p} + \cdots$$

converges if $p > 1$ and diverges if $p \leq 1$. To prove this, let

$$f(x) = \frac{1}{x^p}.$$

Then, if $p > 1$, we have

$$\int_1^\infty x^{-p} \, dx = \lim_{b \to \infty} \frac{x^{-p+1}}{-p+1} \Big|_1^b = \frac{1}{p-1},$$

which is finite. Hence the p-series converges if p is greater than one.

If $p = 1$, we have the *harmonic series*

$$1 + \frac{1}{2} + \frac{1}{3} + \cdots + \frac{1}{n} + \cdots,$$

which we already know diverges. Or, by the integral test,

$$\int_1^\infty x^{-1}\, dx = \lim_{b \to \infty} \ln x \Big|_1^b = +\infty,$$

and since the integral diverges the series does likewise.

Finally, if $p < 1$, then the terms of the p-series are greater than the corresponding terms of the divergent harmonic series. Hence the p-series diverges when $p < 1$ by the comparison test.

Remark. An integral may also be used to advantage to estimate the remainder R_n after n terms of a convergent series.

Suppose, for example, that we are interested in learning the numerical value of the series

$$\sum_{k=1}^\infty \frac{1}{k^2} = \frac{1}{1^2} + \frac{1}{2^2} + \frac{1}{3^2} + \cdots$$

This is a p-series with $p = 2$, hence is known to converge. This means that the sequence of partial sums s_n, where

$$s_n = \frac{1}{1^2} + \frac{1}{2^2} + \cdots + \frac{1}{n^2},$$

possesses a limit L. When n is "large enough," s_n is "close to" L. If we want to know L to a couple of decimal places, we might try to find an integer n such that the corresponding *finite* sum s_n differs from L by less, say, than 0.005. Then we would use this s_n in place of L, to two decimals. If we write

$$L = \sum_{k=1}^\infty \frac{1}{k^2} = \frac{1}{1^2} + \frac{1}{2^2} + \cdots + \frac{1}{n^2} + \frac{1}{(n+1)^2} + \cdots$$

and

$$s_n = \sum_{k=1}^n \frac{1}{k^2} = \frac{1}{1^2} + \frac{1}{2^2} + \cdots + \frac{1}{n^2},$$

we see that the error R_n is

$$R_n = L - s_n = \frac{1}{(n+1)^2} + \cdots$$

We may estimate this error by thinking of the area under the curve

$$y = \frac{1}{x^2}$$

from $x = n$ to ∞.

From Fig. 16–7, we see that

$$R_n < \int_n^\infty \frac{1}{x^2}\, dx = \frac{1}{n},$$

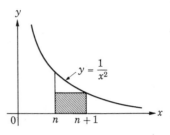

FIGURE 16–7

which tells us that by taking 200 terms of the series we can be sure that the difference between the sum L of the entire series and the sum s_{200} of these 200 terms will be less than 0.005.

A somewhat closer estimate of R_n results from using the trapezoidal rule to approximate the area under the curve in Fig. 16–7. Let us write u_k for $1/k^2$ and consider the trapezoidal approximation

$$T_n = \sum_{k=n}^{\infty} \tfrac{1}{2}(u_k + u_{k+1}) = \tfrac{1}{2}(u_n + u_{n+1}) + \tfrac{1}{2}(u_{n+1} + u_{n+2}) + \cdots$$

$$= \tfrac{1}{2}u_n + u_{n+1} + u_{n+2} + \cdots = \tfrac{1}{2}u_n + R_n.$$

Now since the curve $y = 1/x^2$ is concave upward, it is clear that

$$T_n > \int_n^\infty \frac{1}{x^2}\, dx = \frac{1}{n},$$

and we have

$$R_n = T_n - \tfrac{1}{2}u_n > \frac{1}{n} - \frac{1}{2n^2}.$$

We now know that

$$\frac{1}{n} > R_n > \frac{1}{n} - \frac{1}{2n^2}$$

and $L = s_n + R_n$ may be estimated as follows:

$$s_n + \frac{1}{n} > L > s_n + \frac{1}{n} - \frac{1}{2n^2}.$$

Thus by using $s_n + 1/n$ in place of s_n to estimate L we shall be making an error which is numerically less than $1/(2n^2)$. By taking $n \geq 10$, this error is then made less than 0.005. The difference in time required to compute the sum of 10 terms versus 200 terms is sufficiently great to make this sharper analysis of practical importance.

What we have done in the case of this specific example may be done in any case where the graph of the function $y = f(x)$ is concave upward as in Fig. 16–7. We find that

$$u_1 + u_2 + \cdots + u_n + \int_n^\infty f(x)\, dx \tag{5}$$

tends to overestimate the value of the series, but by an amount that is less than $u_n/2$.

Ratio test. The ratios (u_2/u_1), (u_3/u_2), (u_4/u_3), . . . , (u_{n+1}/u_n), . . . measure the rate of growth of the terms of a series. In a geometric series

$$1 + r + r^2 + r^3 + \cdots$$

this rate of growth is a constant, r. If the rate of growth in a positive series tends to a definite limit ρ (Greek letter rho) as n becomes infinite,

$$\rho = \lim_{n \to \infty} \frac{u_{n+1}}{u_n},$$

we shall show that

  (a) the series *converges* if $\rho < 1$,

  (b) the series *diverges* if $\rho > 1$,

  (c) the series may converge or it may diverge if $\rho = 1$.

Remember that we are still speaking about *positive* series.

To establish the validity of the ratio test, suppose we assume first that ρ is less than one. Let r be a number between ρ and one, for example, $r = (1 + \rho)/2$. Then the number ϵ defined by the equation

$$\epsilon = r - \rho$$

is positive. Since

$$\rho = \lim_{n \to \infty} \frac{u_{n+1}}{u_n},$$

we know that u_{n+1}/u_n must lie within ϵ distance of ρ when n is large enough, say for all $n \geq N$. Then, in particular,

$$\frac{u_{n+1}}{u_n} < r = \rho + \epsilon, \quad \text{when} \quad n \geq N.$$

That is,

$$u_{N+1} < ru_N,$$
$$u_{N+2} < ru_{N+1} < r^2 u_N,$$
$$u_{N+3} < ru_{N+2} < r^3 u_N,$$
$$\vdots$$
$$u_{N+m} < ru_{N+m-1} < r^m u_N,$$

and

$$u_1 + u_2 + \cdots + u_N + u_{N+1} + u_{N+2} + \cdots < u_1 + u_2 + \cdots$$
$$+ u_{N-1} + u_N(1 + r + r^2 + \cdots). \quad (6)$$

Since $|r|$ is less than one, the geometric series $1 + r + r^2 + \cdots$ converges and the right side of the inequality (6) is finite. Therefore the series on the left converges by the comparison test.

Next, suppose ρ is greater than one. Then, from some index m on, we have

$$\frac{u_{n+1}}{u_n} \geq 1 \quad (n \geq m)$$

or

$$u_{m+1} \geq u_m, \; u_{m+2} \geq u_{m+1} \geq u_m, \; \ldots$$

Since u_m is positive, the sum of the terms

$$u_m + u_{m+1} + u_{m+2} + \cdots + u_{m+q} \geq u_m(1 + 1 + \cdots + 1) = (q+1)u_m$$

tends to infinity as q does. Hence in this case the series diverges.

Finally, the two series

$$\sum_{n=1}^{\infty} \frac{1}{n} \quad \text{and} \quad \sum_{n=1}^{\infty} \frac{1}{n^2}$$

both have rate-of-growth ratios that approach one as limit. Since one of these series converges while the other diverges, we have specific examples which show that the ratio test cannot be used to distinguish between convergence and divergence in case $\rho = 1$.

Remark. The ratio test is also useful in estimating the truncation error which results from using

$$s_N = u_1 + u_2 + \cdots + u_N$$

as an approximation to the sum of a convergent series

$$S = u_1 + u_2 + \cdots + u_N + (u_{N+1} + \cdots).$$

For if we know that the rate-of-growth ratio lies between two constants r_1 and r_2, both of which are positive and less than one, when $n \geq N$,

$$r_1 \leq \frac{u_{n+1}}{u_n} \leq r_2 \quad \text{for} \quad n \geq N,$$

then the inequalities

$$r_1 u_n \leq u_{n+1} \leq r_2 u_n; \qquad n = N, N+1, N+2, \ldots$$

enable us to deduce that

$$u_N(r_1 + r_1^2 + r_1^3 + \cdots) \leq u_{N+1} + u_{N+2} + u_{N+3} + \cdots$$
$$\leq u_N(r_2 + r_2^2 + r_2^3 + \cdots).$$

The two geometric series have sums

$$r_1 + r_1^2 + r_1^3 + \cdots = \frac{r_1}{1 - r_1},$$
$$r_2 + r_2^2 + r_2^3 + \cdots = \frac{r_2}{1 - r_2}.$$

Hence the error

$$R_N = u_{N+1} + u_{N+2} + u_{N+3} + \cdots$$

lies between

$$\frac{r_1 u_N}{1 - r_1} \quad \text{and} \quad \frac{r_2 u_N}{1 - r_2}.$$

That is,

$$\frac{r_1 u_N}{1 - r_1} \leq \sum_{k=1}^{\infty} u_k - \sum_{k=1}^{N} u_k \leq \frac{r_2 u_N}{1 - r_2} \tag{7a}$$

if

$$0 \leq r_1 \leq \frac{u_{n+1}}{u_n} \leq r_2 < 1, \quad \text{for} \quad n \geq N. \tag{7b}$$

EXAMPLE 4. For what values of x does the series

$$x + \frac{x^3}{3} + \frac{x^5}{5} + \frac{x^7}{7} + \cdots \tag{8}$$

converge?

Solution. The nth term of the series (assuming the law of formation as indicated) is

$$u_n = \frac{x^{2n-1}}{2n - 1}.$$

We consider first the case where x is positive. Then the series is a positive series and the rate-of-growth ratio is

$$\frac{u_{n+1}}{u_n} = \frac{(2n - 1)x^2}{(2n + 1)}$$

with limit

$$\rho = \lim_{n \to \infty} \frac{2n - 1}{2n + 1} x^2 = x^2.$$

The ratio test therefore tells us that the series converges if x is positive and less than one and diverges if x is greater than one.

Since only odd powers of x occur in the series, we see that the series simply changes sign when x is replaced by $-x$. Therefore the series also converges for $-1 < x \leq 0$ and diverges for $x < -1$. The series converges to zero when $x = 0$.

We know, thus far, that the series

converges for $|x| < 1$,

diverges for $|x| > 1$,

but we don't know what happens when $|x| = 1$. To test at $x = 1$, we apply the integral test to the series

$$1 + \tfrac{1}{3} + \tfrac{1}{5} + \tfrac{1}{7} + \cdots + \frac{1}{2n - 1} + \cdots,$$

which we get by taking $x = 1$ in the series (8). The companion integral is

$$\int_1^\infty \frac{dx}{2x-1} = \tfrac{1}{2}\ln(2x-1)\Big|_1^\infty = \infty.$$

Hence the series diverges to $+\infty$ when $x = 1$. It diverges to $-\infty$ when $x = -1$. We may therefore say that the only values of x for which the given series converges are $-1 < x < 1$.

PROBLEMS

1. Prove that if $\sum u_k$ is a positive series and c is a positive constant, then $\sum u_k$ and $\sum(cu_k)$ both converge or both diverge.

2. What are the two alternatives, analogous to A and B of Theorem 1, for the case of a sequence $\{s_n\}$ that is monotonically decreasing as n increases, that is, for which $s_1 \geq s_2 \geq s_3 \geq \cdots \geq s_n \geq s_{n+1} \geq \cdots$? Draw a graph to illustrate what happens when all terms of the sequence are greater than or equal to some constant m.

3. (a) Show that the sequence of numbers $s_n = (1 + 1/n)^n$ is an increasing sequence and that each s_n is less than 3. [*Hint:* Expand $(1 + 1/n)^n$ by the binomial theorem and show that

$$\left(1+\frac{1}{n}\right)^n = 1 + 1 + \frac{\left(1-\frac{1}{n}\right)}{2!} + \frac{\left(1-\frac{1}{n}\right)\left(1-\frac{2}{n}\right)}{3!} + \cdots$$

$$+ \frac{\left(1-\frac{1}{n}\right)\left(1-\frac{2}{n}\right)\cdots\left(1-\frac{n-1}{n}\right)}{n!}.\big]$$

(b) What conclusion can we draw from these two statements as regards the existence of the limit of s_n as n becomes infinite?

4. Consider the sequence of numbers $1, 0, 1, 0, 1, 0, \ldots (s_{2m-1} = 1, s_{2m} = 0)$. Does this sequence have a limit as n becomes infinite? Give a reason for your answer.

In each of the following problems, determine whether the given series converges or diverges. In each case, give a reason for your answer.

5. $\displaystyle\sum_{n=1}^\infty \frac{1}{10n}$ 6. $\displaystyle\sum_{n=1}^\infty \frac{n}{n+2}$ 7. $\displaystyle\sum_{n=1}^\infty \frac{\sin^2 n}{2^n}$

8. $\displaystyle\sum_{n=1}^\infty \frac{n}{n^2+1}$ 9. $\displaystyle\sum_{n=1}^\infty \frac{1}{1+\ln n}$ 10. $\displaystyle\sum_{n=3}^\infty \frac{1}{n\ln n}$

11. $\displaystyle\sum_{n=0}^\infty \frac{1}{(2n+1)!}$ 12. $\displaystyle\sum_{n=1}^\infty \frac{1}{n^2+1}$ 13. $\displaystyle\sum_{n=1}^\infty \frac{\sqrt{n}}{n^2+1}$

14. $\displaystyle\sum_{n=1}^{\infty} \frac{n!}{n^n}$ 15. $\displaystyle\sum_{n=1}^{\infty} \frac{(n+1)(n+2)}{n!}$ 16. $\displaystyle\sum_{n=1}^{\infty} \frac{n^2}{2^n}$

17. $\displaystyle\sum_{n=0}^{\infty} \frac{(n+3)!}{3!n!3^n}$ 18. $\displaystyle\sum_{n=1}^{\infty} \frac{2^n}{n^3+1}$ 19. $\displaystyle\sum_{n=1}^{\infty} \frac{10^n}{n!}$

16–3 Power series expansions of functions. The rational operations of arithmetic are addition, subtraction, multiplication, and division. Using only these simple operations, we can evaluate any rational function of x. But other functions, such as $\ln x$, e^x, $\sin x$, and so on, cannot be evaluated so simply. Of course, these functions are so important that their values have been computed and the results printed in mathematical tables. But one may wonder how the tables were computed. (The answer is: from power series.)

DEFINITION. *A* power series *is an expression of the form*

$$\sum_{k=0}^{\infty} a_k x^k = a_0 + a_1 x + a_2 x^2 + \cdots$$

In this article we shall show how to use power series to represent a wide variety of functions.

We shall concern ourselves with the problem of approximating to a given function

$$y = f(x) \tag{1}$$

by means of a sequence of polynomials $f_n(x)$ of the form

$$f_n(x) = a_0 + a_1 x + a_2 x^2 + \cdots + a_n x^n. \tag{2}$$

In particular, since we anticipate taking larger and larger values for n, we shall be interested in making the approximation good for small values of x, since we want the terms that come far out in the series to be small. Hence we focus our attention on a portion of the curve $y = f(x)$ in the neighborhood of the point $A[0, f(0)]$ in Fig. 16–8. We then ask the following questions:

1. What polynomial $y = f_0(x) = a_0$, of degree zero, gives the closest approximation to the given curve in the immediate neighborhood of the point A? *Answer:* We want the

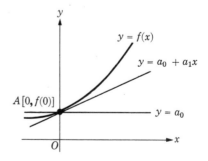

FIGURE 16–8

horizontal line $y = a_0$ to pass through A, hence we take $a_0 = f(0)$, which is the value of the given function at $x = 0$.

2. What polynomial $y = a_0 + a_1x$, of degree one, comes closest to fitting the given curve in the neighborhood of the point A? *Answer:* The tangent line. That is, we want this approximating line to pass through A and to have the same slope there that the given curve has. This means that we should take

$$a_0 = f(0) \quad \text{and} \quad a_1 = f'(0).$$

3. More generally, what polynomial

$$y = a_0 + a_1x + a_2x^2 + \cdots + a_nx^n,$$

of degree n, comes closest to fitting the given curve near A? *Answer:* We take the approximating curve that passes through A and has the highest possible degree of contact with the given curve at A in the sense that its derivatives of orders one, two, three, ..., n match the corresponding derivatives of the given function there. Thus, if we write

$$f_n(x) = a_0 + a_1x + a_2x^2 + a_3x^3 + \cdots + a_nx^n$$

for the approximating polynomial, then its derivatives are

$$f_n'(x) = a_1 + 2a_2x + 3a_3x^2 + \cdots + na_nx^{n-1},$$
$$f_n''(x) = 2a_2 + 3 \cdot 2a_3x + \cdots + n(n-1)a_nx^{n-2},$$
$$\vdots$$
$$f_n^{(n)}(x) = n!a_n.$$

We substitute $x = 0$ on the right side of each of the above equations and set the results, respectively, equal to the values

$$f(0), f'(0), f''(0), \ldots, f^{(n)}(0)$$

of the given function and its first n derivatives at $x = 0$. We then determine the coefficients $a_0, a_1, a_2, \ldots, a_n$ of the approximating polynomial $y = f_n(x)$ that has the highest degree of contact with the given curve at $A[0, f(0)]$ to be

$$a_0 = f(0), \quad a_1 = f'(0), \quad a_2 = \frac{f''(0)}{2!}, \quad \cdots, \quad a_n = \frac{f^{(n)}(0)}{n!}.$$

That is, for our approximating polynomial of degree n, we take

$$f_n(x) = f(0) + f'(0)x + \frac{f''(0)}{2!}x^2 + \frac{f'''(0)}{3!}x^3 + \cdots + \frac{f^{(n)}(0)}{n!}x^n. \tag{3}$$

EXAMPLE. Compute the polynomials $f_n(x)$, given by Eq. (3), that would be used to approximate the exponential function $f(x) = e^x$ near $x = 0$.

Solution. We require $f(0), f'(0), \ldots, f^{(n)}(0)$. For the given function

and
$$f(x) = e^x, \quad f'(x) = e^x, \quad \ldots, \quad f^{(n)}(x) = e^x$$

so that
$$f(0) = e^0 = 1, \quad f'(0) = 1, \quad \ldots, \quad f^{(n)}(0) = 1,$$

$$f_n(x) = 1 + x + \frac{x^2}{2!} + \frac{x^3}{3!} + \cdots + \frac{x^n}{n!}. \tag{4}$$

The question now naturally arises as to whether, for a fixed value of x, our approximating polynomials $f_n(x)$ converge to $f(x)$ as $n \to \infty$. Since $f_n(x)$, Eq. (3), is the nth partial sum of the infinite series

$$f(0) + f'(0) \cdot x + \frac{f''(0)}{2!} x^2 + \cdots + \frac{f^{(n)}(0)}{n!} x^n + \cdots, \tag{5}$$

the question just posed is equivalent to inquiring whether the series (5) converges to $f(x)$ as sum. Of course, *every* one of our approximating polynomials has the correct value $f(0)$ at $x = 0$, but we are interested now in knowing also how far we may go away from $x = 0$ and still have convergence.

The series (5) is known as *Maclaurin's series* for the given function $f(x)$. If, instead of approximating to the function $f(x)$ for values of x near zero, we are concerned with values of x near a, we write our approximating polynomials in powers of $x - a$:

$$f_n(x) = a_0 + a_1(x - a) + a_2(x - a)^2 + \cdots + a_n(x - a)^n.$$

When we now determine the coefficients $a_0, a_1, \ldots, a_n$ so that the polynomial and its first n derivatives agree with the given function and its first n derivatives, at $x = a$, we are led to the series

$$f(a) + f'(a) \cdot (x - a) + \frac{f''(a)}{2!} (x - a)^2 + \frac{f'''(a)}{3!} (x - a)^3 + \cdots$$
$$+ \frac{f^{(n)}(a)}{n!} (x - a)^n + \cdots, \tag{6}$$

where $f^{(n)}(a)$ denotes the value of the nth derivative of the function $f(x)$ at $x = a$. This is known as the *Taylor series* expansion of $f(x)$ about $x = a$. Since this includes the Maclaurin series, (5), as a special case [namely, take $a = 0$ in (6)], we shall henceforth concern ourselves with the Taylor series. It is clear, since Eq. (6) calls for derivatives of *all* orders at $x = a$, that a function cannot possess a Taylor series expansion about $x = a$ unless the function possesses finite derivatives of all orders at $x = a$. For instance, $f(x) = \ln x$ does not possess a Maclaurin series expansion $(a = 0)$, since the function itself (to say nothing of its derivatives) does not have a finite value at $x = 0$. On the other hand, it does possess a Taylor series expansion in powers of $(x - 1)$, since $\ln x$ and all its derivatives are finite at $x = 1$.

EXAMPLE. Let us find the Maclaurin series expansion for the function $f(x) = (1 + x)^m$. We need the derivatives

$$f'(x) = m(1 + x)^{m-1},$$

$$f''(x) = m(m - 1)(1 + x)^{m-2},$$

$$f'''(x) = m(m - 1)(m - 2)(1 + x)^{m-3},$$

$$\vdots$$

$$f^{(k)}(x) = m(m - 1)(m - 2) \cdots (m - k + 1)(1 + x)^{m-k}.$$

If we substitute the values of these at $x = 0$ into the basic Maclaurin series, (5):

$$f(0) + f'(0)x + \frac{f''(0)}{2!} x^2 + \cdots + \frac{f^{(k)}(0)}{k!} x^k + \cdots,$$

we obtain

$$1 + mx + \frac{m(m - 1)}{2!} x^2 + \cdots + \frac{m(m - 1)(m - 2) \cdots (m - k + 1)}{k!} x^k + \cdots$$

For a proof that this series converges to the given function $f(x) = (1 + x)^m$, when $|x| < 1$, see P. Franklin, *Treatise on Advanced Calculus*, p. 148, Problem 29.

PROBLEMS

In each of the following problems (1–6), use Eq. (3) to calculate the polynomial $f_n(x)$ that is associated with the given function $f(x)$.

1. e^{-x} 2. $\sin x$ 3. $\cos x$

4. $\sin (x + \pi/4)$ 5. $\sinh x$ 6. $\cosh x$

In each of the following problems (7–13), use Eq. (6) to find the Taylor series expansion of the given function about the given value of a.

7. $f(x) = \ln x$, $a = 1$ 8. $f(x) = \sqrt{x}$, $a = 4$

9. $f(x) = 1/x$, $a = -1$ 10. $f(x) = \tan x$, $a = \pi/4$
                                                (Find 3 terms of the series.)

11. $f(x) = \ln \cos x$, $a = \pi/3$ 12. $f(x) = \sin x$, $a = \pi/6$
    (Find 3 terms of the series.)

13. $f(x) = \cos x$, $a = -\pi/4$

16–4 Taylor's Theorem with remainder. In the previous article we raised some questions about convergence of the Taylor series. In this section we give a theorem which answers some of these questions. Unfortunately, although several proofs of the theorem are known, none of them is easily motivated. The path we shall follow in arriving at the theorem starts with the simple formula

$$\int_a^b f'(t)\, dt = f(t) \Big]_a^b = f(b) - f(a). \tag{1}$$

We integrate the left side of (1) by parts, with

$$u = f'(t), \quad dv = dt \quad \text{and} \quad du = f''(t)\, dt, \quad v = t - b,$$

where we introduce the constant of integration $-b$ for future convenience. Hence

$$\int_a^b f'(t)\, dt = (t - b) f'(t) \Big]_a^b - \int_a^b (t - b)\, f''(t)\, dt$$

$$= (b - a) f'(a) + \int_a^b (b - t)\, f''(t)\, dt.$$

A further integration by parts, this time with

$$u = f''(t), \quad dv = (b - t)\, dt$$

and

$$du = f'''(t)\, dt, \quad v = -\frac{(b - t)^2}{2},$$

leads to

$$\int_a^b (b - t)\, f''(t)\, dt = -\frac{(b - t)^2}{2} f''(t) \Big]_a^b + \int_a^b \frac{(b - t)^2}{2} f'''(t)\, dt$$

$$= \frac{(b - a)^2}{2!} f''(a) + \int_a^b \frac{(b - t)^2}{2!} f'''(t)\, dt.$$

By continuing in this fashion, we find

$$\int_a^b f'(t)\, dt = (b - a) f'(a) + \frac{(b - a)^2}{2!} f''(a) + \frac{(b - a)^3}{3!} f'''(a) + \cdots$$

$$+ \frac{(b - a)^n}{n!} f^{(n)}(a) + \int_a^b \frac{(b - t)^n}{n!} f^{(n+1)}(t)\, dt.$$

Comparing this with Eq. (1), we have

$$f(b) = f(a) + (b - a)f'(a) + \frac{(b - a)^2}{2!} f''(a) + \cdots$$

$$+ \frac{(b - a)^n}{n!} f^{(n)}(a) + \int_a^b \frac{(b - t)^n}{n!} f^{(n+1)}(t) \, dt.$$

We may now replace b by x, and write

$$f(x) = f(a) + (x - a)f'(a) + \frac{(x - a)^2}{2!} f''(a) + \cdots$$

$$+ \frac{(x - a)^n}{n!} f^{(n)}(a) + R_n(x, a), \qquad (2)$$

where

$$R_n(x, a) = \int_a^x \frac{(x - t)^n}{n!} f^{(n+1)}(t) \, dt. \qquad (3)$$

The term $R_n(x, a)$ is called the *remainder* in the Taylor series expansion for $f(x)$. If the remainder is omitted in Eq. (2), the polynomial on the right side of the equation gives only an approximation to the function on the left. The error in this approximation is what is measured by $R_n(x, a)$. Hence, to investigate convergence of the series, we need to investigate this remainder. The series converges to $f(x)$ provided

$$\lim_{n \to \infty} R_n(x, a) = 0. \qquad (4)$$

When (4) holds, we may also write

$$f(x) = \sum_{k=0}^{\infty} \frac{f^{(k)}(a)}{k!} (x - a)^k,$$

since the series on the right converges, at x, to the value $f(x)$. It is often possible to show that the remainder does approach zero without evaluating the integral in (3) explicitly. (See Problems 1 and 3, and the examples below.)

The application of integration by parts n times in succession requires, of course, that the integral in Eq. (3) exist. This will indeed be the case provided the $(n + 1)$st derivative of the function exists and is continuous in some closed interval that includes the range of integration $a \ldots x$ in (3).

TAYLOR'S THEOREM. *Let f be a function that is continuous together with its first $n + 1$ derivatives on an interval containing a and x. Then the value of the function at x is given by*

$$(x) = f(a) + f'(a) \cdot (x - a) + \frac{f''(a)}{2!} (x - a)^2 + \frac{f'''(a)}{3!} (x - a)^3 + \cdots$$

$$+ \frac{f^{(n)}(a)}{n!} (x - a)^n + R_n(x, a),$$

where

$$R_n(x, a) = \int_a^x \frac{(x - t)^n}{n!} f^{(n+1)}(t) \, dt.$$

EXAMPLE 1. Let $f(x) = e^x$. This function and all its derivatives are every-where continuous, so Taylor's theorem may be applied with any convenient value of a. We take $a = 0$ since the values of f and its derivatives are easy to compute there. Taylor's theorem leads to

$$e^x = 1 + x + \frac{x^2}{2!} + \frac{x^3}{3!} + \cdots + \frac{x^n}{n!} + R_n(x, 0) \tag{5}$$

with

$$R_n(x, 0) = \int_0^x \frac{(x - t)^n}{n!} e^t \, dt. \tag{6}$$

To avoid unnecessary complications, we temporarily assume that x is positive. Then we may *estimate* the remainder (6) by observing that the integrand is positive, for $0 < t < x$, and that $e^t < e^x < 3^x$. Therefore,

$$|R_n(x, 0)| \leq \int_0^x \frac{(x - t)^n}{n!} 3^x \, dt = 3^x \frac{x^{n+1}}{(n + 1)!}; \qquad x > 0.$$

When x is negative we must replace x by $|x|$ on the right side of this inequality. But for all real values of x, $-\infty < x < +\infty$, we have

$$|R_n(x, 0)| \leq 3^{|x|} \frac{|x|^{n+1}}{(n + 1)!}. \tag{7}$$

With this estimate of the remainder term we are ready to discuss the conver-gence of the Maclaurin series (Taylor series with $a = 0$) for e^x. There are two separate cases to be considered according to whether or not $|x| \leq 1$.

(a) If $|x| \leq 1$, then $3^{|x|} \leq 3$, and (7) tells us that

$$|R_n(x, 0)| \leq \frac{3}{(n + 1)!} \qquad \text{if} \qquad |x| \leq 1. \tag{8}$$

Hence $R_n(x, 0)$ certainly approaches zero as n tends to infinity and the follow-ing series converges to e^x for any number x whose absolute value is less than or equal to 1:

$$e^x = 1 + x + \frac{x^2}{2!} + \frac{x^3}{3!} + \cdots + \frac{x^n}{n!} + \cdots, \qquad |x| \leq 1. \tag{9}$$

Using the estimate of the remainder given by (8), we may determine n (and thus the number of terms of the series to use) to guarantee specified accuracy in computing the value of e^x. For example, we may calculate e by taking $x = 1$ in Eq. (9). If we do this, with $n = 3$, say, the error we make will be less than $3/4! = \frac{1}{8} = 0.125$. If we take $n = 7$, then the error is less than $3/8! < 0.75 \times 10^{-4}$ and the approximation

$$e \approx 1 + 1 + \frac{1}{2!} + \frac{1}{3!} + \cdots + \frac{1}{7!}$$

is good to within one unit in the fourth decimal place. Since the remainder goes to zero as n tends to infinity, we also have the infinite series expansion for e,

$$e = 1 + 1 + \frac{1}{2!} + \frac{1}{3!} + \cdots \qquad (10)$$

The first two terms in the series (9) can be written as $1/0!$ and $x/1!$, provided we adopt the definition

$$0! = 1.$$

This definition of $0!$ is commonly accepted, and with it the identity $n! = n(n - 1)!$ is satisfied for all positive integers n, including $n = 1$. The series for e^x, Eq. (9), now takes the compact form

$$e^x = \sum_{k=0}^{\infty} \frac{x^k}{k!}. \qquad (11)$$

So far, we have only established Eq. (11) for $|x| \leq 1$, but we shall see that it is in fact valid for all real x.

Graphs of some of the approximating polynomials

$$f_n(x) = 1 + x + \frac{x^2}{2!} + \cdots + \frac{x^n}{n!} = \sum_{k=0}^{\infty} \frac{x^k}{k!},$$

for $-1 \leq x \leq 1$, are shown in Fig. 16-9 for $n = 1, 2$, and 3. All three approximations are tangent to the curve $y = e^x$ at $P_0(0, 1)$, and therefore lie close to that curve near P_0. But as $|x|$ increases, the parabola B is a better approximation than the straight line A; and the cubic curve C is better than either A or B. This is to be expected since the error (remainder term in the series) decreases as n increases.

(b) We now consider what happens to the remainder term Eq. (6) as n increases, if $|x| > 1$. Then both $|x|^{n+1}$ and $(n + 1)!$ increase indefinitely as n does. But the factorial increases so much faster (for large n) that the ratio approaches zero;

$$\lim_{n \to \infty} \frac{|x|^{n+1}}{(n + 1)!} = 0. \qquad (12)$$

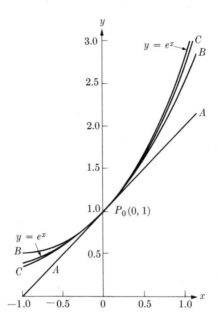

Fig. 16–9. Approximations to $y = e^x$: (A) $y = 1 + x$, (B) $y = 1 + x + x^2/2!$, (C) $y = 1 + x + x^2/2! + x^3/3!$.

(See Problem 3 below.) For example, if $x = 5$, the ratio $5^{n+1}/(n+1)!$ increases with n until we get to $n = 4$. But as n continues to increase, one unit at a time, the numerator is multiplied each time by 5, but the denominator is multiplied by 6, or 7, or 8, and so on, and the ratio ultimately approaches zero. The additional factor $3^{|x|}$ doesn't change as $n \to \infty$, so we have

$$\lim_{n \to \infty} 3^{|x|} \frac{|x|^{n+1}}{(n+1)!} = 0$$

and, from (7),

$$\lim_{n \to \infty} R_n(x, 0) = 0,$$

for any real x, $-\infty < x < +\infty$. Therefore,

$$e^x = \sum_{k=0}^{\infty} \frac{x^k}{k!}, \qquad -\infty < x < +\infty. \tag{13}$$

The following table of values shows e^x, $1 + x$, $1 + x + x^2/2!$, and $1 + x + x^2/2! + x^3/3!$ for values of x from -1 to $+1$ at intervals of one-tenth.

DATA FOR FIG. 16–9

x	e^x	$1 + x$	$1 + x + \dfrac{x^2}{2!}$	$1 + x + \dfrac{x^2}{2!} + \dfrac{x^3}{3!}$
0	1	1	1	1
0.1	1.1052	1.1	1.105	1.10517–
0.2	1.2214	1.2	1.220	1.22133+
0.3	1.3499	1.3	1.345	1.34950
0.4	1.4918	1.4	1.480	1.49067–
0.5	1.6487	1.5	1.625	1.64583+
0.6	1.8221	1.6	1.780	1.81600
0.7	2.0138	1.7	1.945	2.00217–
0.8	2.2255	1.8	2.120	2.20533+
0.9	2.4596	1.9	2.305	2.42650
1.0	2.7183	2.0	2.500	2.66667–
–0.1	0.90484	0.9	0.905	0.904833+
–0.2	0.81873	0.8	0.820	0.818667–
–0.3	0.74082	0.7	0.745	0.740500
–0.4	0.67032	0.6	0.680	0.669333+
–0.5	0.60653	0.5	0.625	0.604167–
–0.6	0.54881	0.4	0.580	0.544000
–0.7	0.49659	0.3	0.545	0.487833+
–0.8	0.44933	0.2	0.520	0.434667–
–0.9	0.40657	0.1	0.505	0.383500
–1.0	0.36788	0.0	0.500	0.333333+

The remainder term (other forms). In the formula

$$f(x) = f(a) + f'(a)(x - a) + \frac{f''(a)}{2!} (x - a)^2 + \cdots$$

$$+ \frac{f^{(n)}(a)}{n!} (x - a)^n + R_n(x, a), \tag{14}$$

we have expressed the remainder as an integral:

$$R_n(x, a) = \int_a^x \frac{(x - t)^n}{n!} f^{(n+1)}(t) \, dt. \tag{15}$$

Other expressions for the remainder may be obtained by applying to this integral the following theorem.

THEOREM. *Let $g(t)$ and $h(t)$ be continuous for $a \leq t \leq b$ and suppose that $h(t)$ does not change sign in this interval. Then there exists a number c*

between a and b such that

$$\int_a^b g(t)\, h(t)\, dt = g(c) \int_a^b h(t)\, dt. \tag{16}$$

Proof. Let m and M be respectively the least and greatest values of $g(t)$ for $a \leq t \leq b$. Then

$$m \leq g(t_i) \leq M \tag{17}$$

for any t_i between a and b inclusive. We form a subdivision

$$a = t_0 < t_1 < t_2 < \cdots < t_n = b$$

of the interval $a \leq t \leq b$ with

$$t_i - t_{i-1} = \Delta t = (b - a)/n; \qquad i = 1, \ldots, n$$

and multiply each term in the inequalities (17) by $h(t_i)\, \Delta t$. Since the sign of $h(t)$ does not change over the interval $a \leq t \leq b$, all the terms $h(t_1)\, \Delta t$ are of the same sign, say positive. [If they are all negative, replace $h(t)$ by $-h(t)$ in the argument that follows.] Then

$$m\, h(t_i)\, \Delta t \leq g(t_i)\, h(t_i)\, \Delta t \leq M\, h(t_i)\, \Delta t,$$

and the order of inequality is preserved when we now sum on i from 1 to n; that is,

$$\sum_{i=1}^n m\, h(t_i)\, \Delta t \leq \sum_{i=1}^n g(t_i)\, h(t_i)\, \Delta t \leq \sum_{i=1}^n M\, h(t_i)\, \Delta t. \tag{18}$$

Finally, we let n increase indefinitely and recall that the sums then become definite integrals. Hence (18) leads to

$$m \int_a^b h(t)\, dt \leq \int_a^b g(t)\, h(t)\, dt \leq M \int_a^b h(t)\, dt,$$

or

$$m \leq \frac{\displaystyle\int_a^b g(t)\, h(t)\, dt}{\displaystyle\int_a^b h(t)\, dt} \leq M. \tag{19}$$

Since

$$Q = \frac{\displaystyle\int_a^b g(t)\, h(t)\, dt}{\displaystyle\int_a^b h(t)\, dt} \tag{20}$$

is a number between the least and greatest values taken on by $g(t)$ for $a \le t \le b$ and $g(t)$ is assumed to be continuous, there is a number c between a and b such that

$$Q = g(c).$$

This leads at once to the result in Eq. (16) and completes the proof of the theorem.

We now apply this theorem to the integral in Eq. (15) with

$$h(t) = \frac{(x - t)^n}{n!}, \quad g(t) = f^{(n+1)}(t).$$

As t varies from a to x, $h(t)$ is continuous and does not change sign. Hence, if $f^{(n+1)}(t)$ is continuous, Eq. (16) applies, and we have

$$R_n(x, a) = f^{(n+1)}(c) \int_a^x \frac{(x - t)^n}{n!} \, dt$$

$$= f^{(n+1)}(c) \frac{(x - a)^{n+1}}{(n + 1)!} .$$

This is known as *Lagrange's* form of the remainder:

$$R_n(x, a) = f^{(n+1)}(c) \frac{(x - a)^{n+1}}{(n + 1)!}, \quad c \text{ between } a \text{ and } x.^* \qquad (21)$$

In applying Eq. (21), we can, in general, only estimate $f^{(n+1)}(c)$, since we do not know c itself exactly. But if we know that

$$m \le f^{(n+1)}(t) \le M \quad \text{for} \quad a \le t \le x, \quad \text{or} \quad x \le t \le a,$$

then we know, from (21), that

$$R_n(x, a) \text{ lies between } m \frac{(x - a)^{n+1}}{(n + 1)!} \quad \text{and} \quad M \frac{(x - a)^{n+1}}{(n + 1)!} .$$

Another form of the remainder, known as *Cauchy's* form:

$$R_n(x, a) = \frac{(x - c')^n (x - a)}{n!} f^{(n+1)}(c'), \quad c' \text{ between } a \text{ and } x, \qquad (22)$$

may be obtained by applying Eq. (16) to Eq. (15) with

$$h(t) = 1, \quad g(t) = \frac{(x - t)^n}{n!} f^{(n+1)}(t).$$

---

* Another proof of Taylor's theorem, leading directly to the Lagrange form of the remainder, is outlined in Problem 74 (Extended Mean Value Theorem), in the miscellaneous problems at the end of Chapter 3.

In general, the Lagrange form, Eq. (21), is easier to apply, and gives satisfactory results. However, the Cauchy form is useful in proving convergence of certain series, such as the Maclaurin series for $\ln(1+x)$ when $-1 < x < 0$.

EXAMPLE 2. Find the Maclaurin series expansion for $\sin x$, and show that the series converges to $\sin x$ for all finite x, $-\infty < x < +\infty$.

Solution. In Eq. (14), we take $f(x) = \sin x$, $a = 0$. Then

$$
\begin{aligned}
f(x) &= \sin x, & f(0) &= 0 \\
f'(x) &= \cos x = \sin\left(x + \frac{\pi}{2}\right), & f'(0) &= 1 \\
f''(x) &= -\sin x = \sin(x + \pi), & f''(0) &= 0 \\
f'''(x) &= -\cos x = \sin\left(x + \frac{3\pi}{2}\right), & f'''(0) &= -1 \\
&\;\vdots & &\;\vdots \\
f^{(k)}(x) &= \sin\left(x + \frac{k\pi}{2}\right), & f^{(k)}(0) &= \sin\frac{k\pi}{2}.
\end{aligned}
$$

The values of the function and its derivatives at $x = 0$ are given by the formula

$$
f^{(k)}(0) = \sin\frac{k\pi}{2}, \qquad k = 0, 1, 2, \ldots, \tag{23}
$$

where the notation $f^{(k)}(0)$ means the value of the kth derivative of $f(x)$ at $x = 0$ and the zeroth derivative of the function means the function itself. When k is an even integer $0, 2, 4, \ldots$, $\sin(k\pi/2)$ is zero. When k is one of the integers $1, 5, 9, 13, \ldots$ of the form $4m + 1$, then $\sin(k\pi/2)$ is plus one, while if k is one of the integers $3, 7, \ldots$ of the form $4m + 3$, then $\sin(k\pi/2)$ is minus one. Thus, when we substitute these values into the Taylor series formula, Eq. (14), with $a = 0$, we obtain

$$
\sin x = x - \frac{x^3}{3!} + \frac{x^5}{5!} - \frac{x^7}{7!} + \cdots + \frac{(-1)^{n-1}x^{2n-1}}{(2n-1)!} + 0 \cdot x^{2n} + R_{2n}(x, 0). \tag{24}
$$

By Eq. (24), the remainder is

$$
R_{2n}(x, 0) = \frac{x^{2n+1}}{(2n+1)!}\sin\left(c + \frac{(2n+1)\pi}{2}\right).
$$

Even though the only thing we know about c is that it lies between 0 and x, we know that the sine never exceeds 1 in absolute value. Hence

$$
|R_{2n}(x, 0)| \le \frac{|x|^{2n+1}}{(2n+1)!}. \tag{25}
$$

Now for any finite x whatever, no matter how large, the $(2n + 1)!$ in the denominator of Eq. (25) goes to infinity more rapidly than the $|x|^{2n+1}$ in the numerator, and

$$\lim_{n \to \infty} \frac{|x|^{2n-1}}{(2n+1)!} = 0. \qquad (26)$$

[See Problem 3 below for a discussion that establishes Eq. (26).] Therefore the sequence of partial sums $f_n(x)$ of the Maclaurin series

$$x - \frac{x^3}{3!} + \frac{x^5}{5!} - \frac{x^7}{7!} + \cdots$$

converges to sin x, for any x, $-\infty < x < +\infty$, and we may write

$$\sin x = \sum_{k=1}^{\infty} \frac{(-1)^{k-1} x^{2k-1}}{(2k-1)!}, \qquad -\infty < x < +\infty. \qquad (27)$$

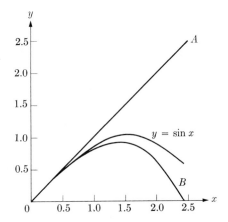

Fig. 16–10. Graph of $y = \sin x$ and two approximating polynomials: (A) $y = x$, (B) $y = x - x^3/6$. The three curves are also symmetric with respect to the origin, but negative portions are not shown.

Figure 16–10 shows graphs of $y = \sin x$ and the first two approximating polynomials

$$A: y = x, \qquad B: y = x - \frac{x^3}{3!}.$$

The cubic approximation is in error by less than $x^5/120$, so it is almost indistinguishable from the sine curve from $x = -1$ to $x = +1$. However, it crosses the x-axis at $\pm\sqrt{6} \approx \pm 2.45$, whereas the sine curve crosses at $\pm\pi \approx \pm 3.14$. The table of data for Fig. 16–10 also shows that the cubic approximation is in error by less than 0.01 from $x = 0$ to $x = 1$. The values of sin x were taken from a four-place table, x in radians.

DATA FOR FIG. 16-10

x	$\sin x$	$x - \dfrac{x^3}{3!}$
0	0	0
0.1	0.0998	0.09983+
0.2	0.1987	0.19867−
0.3	0.2955	0.29550
0.4	0.3894	0.38933+
0.5	0.4794	0.47917−
0.6	0.5646	0.56400
0.7	0.6442	0.64283+
0.8	0.7174	0.71467−
0.9	0.7833	0.77850
1.0	0.8415	0.83333+
1.41	0.9871	0.94280−
1.5	0.9975	0.93750
1.57	1.0000−	0.92502
1.58	1.0000−	0.92261
1.6	0.9996	0.91733
2.45	0.63776	−0.00102

Analogous methods may be used to show that

$$\cos x = \sum_{k=0}^{\infty} \frac{(-1)^k x^{2k}}{(2k)!}, \qquad -\infty < x < \infty. \tag{28}$$

PROBLEMS

1. In connection with Eq. (15), show that the remainder term $R_n(x, a)$ in Taylor's theorem satisfies the inequality

$$|R_n(x, a)| \leq M \frac{|x - a|^{n+1}}{(n + 1)!}$$

if there is a positive constant M such that $|f^{(n+1)}(t)| \leq M$ for all t between a and x inclusive.

2. Using series, calculate e to five decimal places.

3. We encounter series where the nth term involves the fraction $x^n/n!$ and it is important to know how this function of the two variables x and n behaves for fixed values of x as n becomes larger and larger. The following analysis can be used to show that when $n \geq 2$, $n!$ is greater than $e(n/e)^n$, where $e = 2.718...$ is the base of natural logarithms.

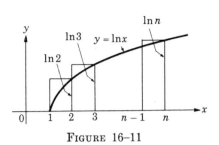

FIGURE 16–11   FIGURE 16–12

(a) $\ln n! = \ln 2 + \ln 3 + \cdots + \ln n$ can be represented as the sum of the areas of $n - 1$ rectangles as indicated in Fig. 16–11, where the first rectangle has its base on the x-axis from 1 to 2 and altitude equal to $\ln 2$, etc. Since each base is of unit length, the area of the rectangle has the same magnitude as its altitude. Show that

$$\ln n! > \int_1^n \ln x \, dx = n \ln n - n + 1$$

provided $n \geq 2$.

(b) From the result of part (a), show that $n! > e(n/e)^n$ when $n \geq 2$.

(c) If x is any finite real number, use the result of (b) to show that $\lim_{n\to\infty}(x^n/n!) = 0$. In particular, show that $|x^n/n!| < 2^{-n}$ when n is greater than 2 and also greater than $2|ex|$.

4. For what range of values of x can one replace $\sin x$ by $x - x^3/6$ with an error not greater than 5×10^{-4}?

5. If $\cos x$ is replaced by $1 - x^2/2$ and $|x| < 0.1$, what estimate can you give of the error?

6. For what range of values of x can one replace $\ln(1 + x)$ by x with an error not greater than one percent of the absolute value of x?

7. The approximation $\sqrt{1 + x} = 1 + x/2$ is used when $|x|$ is small. Give an estimate of the error if $|x| < 0.01$.

8. A log-log slide rule gives readings of e^h for $0.01 \leq h \leq 10$. When $0 \leq h \leq 0.01$, show that e^h may be replaced simply by $1 + h$ with an error not greater than six-tenths of one percent of h.

9. $\sqrt{e} = e^{0.5}$ is to be computed from the series $e^x = 1 + x + x^2/2! + \cdots + x^n/n! + R_n(x, 0)$. How large should one choose n in order to guarantee that $|R_n(x, 0)| < 0.0005$?

16–5 Application to max-min theory for functions of two independent variables. In this article we propose to apply Taylor's theorem to study the behavior of a function

$$w = f(x, y)$$

when the point (x, y) is close to a point (a, b) where the first order partial derivatives vanish,

$$f_x(a, b) = f_y(a, b) = 0. \tag{1}$$

We shall assume that w is continuous, together with its first and second order partial derivatives, throughout some neighborhood G of the point $P(a, b)$, Fig. 16–12. In the discussion that follows, a, b, h, and k are held fixed. In addition, h and k are to be small, so that the point $Q(a + h, b + k)$ together with all points

$$x = a + ht, \quad y = b + kt, \quad 0 \le t \le 1 \tag{2}$$

on the line PQ also lie in G. We consider the values of $w = f(x, y)$ along the line PQ of Eq. (2) as t varies from 0 to 1. Thus, if we let

$$F(t) = f(a + ht, b + kt), \tag{3}$$

we have

$$F(0) = f(a, b) \quad \text{when} \quad t = 0,$$

$$F(1) = f(a + h, b + k) \quad \text{when} \quad t = 1.$$

Now by Taylor's theorem, we have

$$F(t) = F(0) + tF'(0) + \frac{t^2}{2!} F''(t_1),$$

where t_1 is between 0 and t. In particular, taking $t = 1$,

$$F(1) = F(0) + F'(0) + \tfrac{1}{2}F''(t_1), \tag{4}$$

with $0 < t_1 < 1$.

The derivatives in Eq. (4) may be calculated from (3) by using the chain rule for partial derivatives. We have two variables, x and y, in the first set, and only one variable, t, in the second set, and they are related as in (2). Hence

$$F'(t) = \frac{\partial f}{\partial x} \frac{dx}{dt} + \frac{\partial f}{\partial y} \frac{dy}{dt}$$

and, since

$$\frac{dx}{dt} = h, \quad \frac{dy}{dt} = k,$$

this means that

$$F'(t) = h \frac{\partial f}{\partial x} + k \frac{\partial f}{\partial y}. \tag{5}$$

The same chain rule may be applied to calculate

$$F''(t) = h \frac{\partial [\ ]}{\partial x} + k \frac{\partial [\ ]}{\partial y}, \tag{6}$$

where we have used the brackets to indicate the expression on the right side of Eq. (5), that is,

$$[\ ] = h\frac{\partial f}{\partial x} + k\frac{\partial f}{\partial y},$$

$$\frac{\partial[\ ]}{\partial x} = h\frac{\partial^2 f}{\partial x^2} + k\frac{\partial^2 f}{\partial x\,\partial y}, \tag{7}$$

$$\frac{\partial[\ ]}{\partial y} = h\frac{\partial^2 f}{\partial y\,\partial x} + k\frac{\partial^2 f}{\partial y^2}.$$

When we substitute from (7) into (6), we have

$$F''(t) = h^2\frac{\partial^2 f}{\partial x^2} + 2hk\frac{\partial^2 f}{\partial x\,\partial y} + k^2\frac{\partial^2 f}{\partial y^2}. \tag{8}$$

Equations (5) and (8) may be given the following interpretation in terms of operators. The operator d/dt operating on $F(t)$ is the same as the operator $h(\partial/\partial x) + k(\partial/\partial y)$ operating on $f(x, y)$; and the operator d^2/dt^2 operating on $F(t)$ is the same as the operator

$$\left(h\frac{\partial}{\partial x} + k\frac{\partial}{\partial y}\right)^2 = h^2\frac{\partial^2}{\partial x^2} + 2hk\frac{\partial^2}{\partial x\,\partial y} + k^2\frac{\partial^2}{\partial y^2}$$

operating on $f(x, y)$. This may be extended, more generally, to say that

$$\frac{d^n}{dt^n}F(t) = \left(h\frac{\partial}{\partial x} + k\frac{\partial}{\partial y}\right)^n f(x, y),$$

where the term in parentheses on the right should be expanded by the binomial theorem and then made to operate on $f(x, y)$.

If we now take $t = 0$ in Eq. (5) and $t = t_1$ in Eq. (8) and substitute the results into Eq. (4), we obtain

$$\boxed{\begin{aligned} f(a + h, b + k) = f(a, b) &+ (hf_x + kf_y)_{(a,b)} \\ &+ \tfrac{1}{2}(h^2 f_{xx} + 2hkf_{xy} + k^2 f_{yy})_{(a+t_1 h,\, b+t_1 k)}. \end{aligned}} \tag{9}$$

If we extend the Maclaurin series for $F(t)$ to more terms:

$$F(t) = F(0) + F'(0)\cdot t + \frac{F''(0)}{2!}t^2 + \cdots + \frac{F^{(n)}(0)}{n!}t^n + \cdots,$$

and then take $t = 1$:

$$F(1) = F(0) + F'(0) + \frac{F''(0)}{2!} + \cdots + \frac{F^{(n)}(0)}{n!} + \cdots,$$

we obtain the expansion

$$f(a + h, b + k) = f(a, b) + (hf_x + kf_y)_{(a,b)}$$

$$+ \frac{1}{2!}(h^2 f_{xx} + 2hk f_{xy} + k^2 f_{yy})_{(a,b)}$$

$$+ \frac{1}{3!}(h^3 f_{xxx} + 3h^2 k f_{xxy} + 3hk^2 f_{xyy} + k^3 f_{yyy})_{(a,b)} \qquad (10)$$

$$+ \cdots$$

$$+ \frac{1}{n!}\left[\left(h\frac{\partial}{\partial x} + k\frac{\partial}{\partial y}\right)^n f\right]_{(a,b)} + \cdots$$

This expresses the value of the function $f(x, y)$ at $x = a + h$, $y = b + k$ in terms of the values of the function and its partial derivatives at (a, b), and powers of $h = x - a$ and $k = y - b$. This is the Taylor series expansion, about the point (a, b), of the function $f(x, y)$. Analogous formulas hold for functions of more independent variables.

Suppose, now, that we have found a point (a, b) where the first order derivatives f_x and f_y are both zero, and we wish to determine whether the function $w = f(x, y)$ has or has not a maximum or a minimum at (a, b). We may then rewrite Eq. (9) in the form

$$f(a + h, b + k) - f(a, b) = \tfrac{1}{2}(h^2 f_{xx} + 2hk f_{xy} + k^2 f_{yy})_{(a+t_1 h, b+t_1 k)}$$

$$= \phi(t_1).$$

Since a maximum or minimum value of w at (a, b) is reflected in the sign of $\phi(t_1)$, we are led to a consideration of the sign of $\phi(t)$. The second order derivatives which enter this expression are to be evaluated at a point on the line segment PQ (Fig. 16–12). This is not convenient for our purposes, since we do not know precisely where to take this point, that is, we do not know anything more about t_1 than that $0 \le t_1 \le 1$. However, since we are assuming that f_{xx}, f_{xy}, and f_{yy} are *continuous* throughout the region G, and since both h and k are assumed to be *small*, the values of these derivatives at $(a + t_1 h, b + t_1 k)$ are nearly the same as their values at (a, b). In particular, the *sign* of $\phi(t_1)$ is the same, for sufficiently small values of h and k, as the sign of

$$\phi(0) = h^2 f_{xx}(a, b) + 2hk f_{xy}(a, b) + k^2 f_{yy}(a, b). \qquad (11)$$

We therefore have the following criteria:

1. $f(x, y)$ has a relative *minimum* at (a, b) provided $f_x(a, b) = f_y(a, b) = 0$ and $\phi(0)$, Eq. (11), is *positive* for all sufficiently small values of h and k (excluding, of course, the case where $h = k = 0$).

2. $f(x, y)$ has a relative *maximum* at (a, b) provided $f_x(a, b) = f_y(a, b) = 0$

and $\phi(0)$, Eq. (11), is *negative* for all sufficiently small values of h and k (again excluding $h = k = 0$).

3. $f(x, y)$ has a *saddle point* at (a, b) provided $f_x(a, b) = f_y(a, b) = 0$ and $\phi(0)$ is positive for some and negative for other small values of h and k. [For further discussion, see Problems 1 and 3 below.]

EXAMPLE. The function

$$f(x, y) = x^2 + xy + y^2 + x - 4y + 5$$

has partial derivatives

$$f_x = 2x + y + 1,$$
$$f_y = x + 2y - 4,$$

which vanish at $(-2, 3)$. The second partial derivatives are all constant:

$$f_{xx} = 2, \quad f_{xy} = 1, \quad f_{yy} = 2,$$

and the expression whose sign determines whether f has a maximum, a minimum, or a saddle point at $(-2, 3)$ is

$$2h^2 + 2hk + 2k^2.$$

If we multiply this by 2, we have

$$4h^2 + 4hk + 4k^2 = (2h + k)^2 + 3k^2,$$

which is the sum of two nonnegative terms and is zero only when $h = k = 0$. Hence, the function has a relative *minimum* at $(-2, 3)$. In fact, this is its absolute minimum, since

$$f(-2 + h, 3 + k) \geq f(-2, 3)$$

for *all* h and k.

PROBLEMS

1. (a) Let $A = f_{xx}(a, b)$, $B = f_{xy}(a, b)$, $C = f_{yy}(a, b)$ and show that the expression for $\phi(0)$, in Eq. (11), when multiplied by A becomes the same as

$$A\phi(0) = (Ah + Bk)^2 + (AC - B^2)k^2.$$

(b) Suppose $f_x(a, b) = f_y(a, b) = 0$ and $A \neq 0$. Use the result of part (a) above to show that $f(x, y)$ has at (a, b):

(1) a relative minimum if $AC - B^2 > 0$ and $A > 0$,
(2) a relative maximum if $AC - B^2 > 0$ and $A < 0$,
(3) a saddle point if $AC - B^2 < 0$.

2. Test the following surfaces for maxima, minima, and saddle points:

(a) $z = x^2 + y^2 - 2x + 4y + 6$,
(b) $z = x^2 - y^2 - 2x + 4y + 6$,

(c) $z = x^2 - 2xy + 2y^2 - 2x + 2y + 1$,
(d) $z = x^2 + 2xy$,
(e) $z = 3 + 2x + 2y - 2x^2 - 2xy - y^2$,
(f) $z = x^3 - y^3 - 2xy + 6$,
(g) $z = x^3 + y^3 + 3x^2 - 3y^2 - 8$.

3. In Eq. (11), let

$$h = c \cos \alpha, \quad k = c \sin \alpha, \quad c > 0,$$

and show that $\phi(0) = c^2(d^2f/ds^2)$, where d^2f/ds^2 is the second order directional derivative of f at (a, b) in the direction of the unit vector $\mathbf{u} = \mathbf{i} \cos \alpha + \mathbf{j} \sin \alpha$. Express the three criteria for maxima, minima, and saddle points at the end of Article 16–5 in terms of d^2f/ds^2. [Similar criteria also apply in higher dimensional problems.]

4. (a) Taking $a + h = x$, $b + k = y$, and $a = b = 0$ in Eq. (10), obtain the series through the terms of second degree in x and y, for the function $f(x, y) = e^x \cos y$. (b) Obtain the series for part (a) more simply by multiplication of the series for e^x by the series for $\cos y$.

5. Write out explicitly, through the terms of second degree, the Taylor series for a function $f(x, y, z)$, in powers of $(x - a)$, $(y - b)$, $(z - c)$, and the values of f and its partial derivatives at (a, b, c).

16–6 Computations. The Taylor series expansion

$$f(x) = f(a) + f'(a)(x - a) + \frac{f''(a)}{2!}(x - a)^2 + \cdots$$

$$+ \frac{f^{(n)}(a)}{n!}(x - a)^n + R_n(x, a) \tag{1}$$

expresses the value of the function at x in terms of its value and the values of its derivatives at a, plus a remainder term which we hope is so small that it may safely be omitted. In applying series to numerical computations, it is therefore *necessary* that a be chosen so that $f(a), f'(a), f''(a), \ldots$ are known. In dealing with the trigonometric functions, for example, one might take $a = 0, \pm\pi/6, \pm\pi/4, \pm\pi/3, \pm\pi/2$, and so on. It is also clear that it is *desirable* to choose the value of a near to the value of x for which the function is to be computed, in order to make $x - a$ small, so that the terms of the series decrease rapidly as n increases.

EXAMPLE 1. What value of a might one choose in the Taylor series (1) in order to compute (a) $\cos 5°$, and (b) $\sin 35°$?

Solution. (a) In the first case, one would probably choose $a = 0$. The series for $\cos x$, in powers of $x - 0$, as found by substituting $f(x) = \cos x$ and $a = 0$ in Eq. (1) is

$$\cos x = 1 - \frac{x^2}{2!} + \frac{x^4}{4!} - \cdots + (-1)^n \frac{x^{2n}}{(2n)!} + 0 \cdot x^{2n+1} + R_{2n+1}(x, 0). \tag{2}$$

Since the derivatives of $\cos x$ are $\pm \sin x$ or $\pm \cos x$, which never exceed one in absolute value, the remainder, with $|f^{(2n+1)}(c)| \leq 1$, leads to the estimate

$$| R_{2n+1}(x, 0)| \leq \frac{|x|^{2n+2}}{(2n+2)!}$$

and this tends to zero as $n \to \infty$, for all $|x| < \infty$. In particular, to calculate $\cos 5°$, we take

$$x = \frac{5\pi}{180} = 0.08726 \; 65 \quad \text{(radian measure!)}$$

and see that

$$\left| R_5 \left(\frac{5\pi}{180}, 0 \right) \right| \leq \frac{(0.088)^6}{6!} < \frac{(0.1)^6}{6!} < 10^{-8}.$$

Hence we may calculate $\cos 5°$ accurately to seven decimal places by using the approximation

$$\cos x \approx 1 - \frac{x^2}{2} + \frac{x^4}{24}, \qquad \left(x = \frac{5\pi}{180} \right).$$

(b) In calculating $\sin 35°$, we could again choose $a = 0$ and use the series

$$\sin x = x - \frac{x^3}{3!} + \frac{x^5}{5!} - \cdots + (-1)^n \frac{x^{2n+1}}{(2n+1)!} + 0 \cdot x^{2n+2} + R_{2n+2}(x, 0),$$

$$(3)$$

or we could choose $a = \pi/6$ (which corresponds to 30°) and use the series

$$\sin x = \sin \frac{\pi}{6} + \cos \frac{\pi}{6} \left(x - \frac{\pi}{6} \right) - \sin \frac{\pi}{6} \frac{(x - \pi/6)^2}{2!} - \cos \frac{\pi}{6} \frac{(x - \pi/6)^3}{3!} + \cdots$$

$$+ \sin \left(\frac{\pi}{6} + n \frac{\pi}{2} \right) \frac{(x - \pi/6)^n}{n!} + R_n \left(x, \frac{\pi}{6} \right).$$

The remainder in the series (3) satisfies the inequality

$$|R_{2n+2}(x, 0)| \leq \frac{|x|^{2n+3}}{(2n+3)!},$$

$$(4)$$

which tends to zero as n becomes infinite, no matter how large $|x|$ may be. We could therefore calculate $\sin 35°$ by placing

$$x = \frac{35\pi}{180} = 0.61086 \; 53$$

in the approximation

$$\sin x \approx x - \frac{x^3}{6} + \frac{x^5}{120} - \frac{x^7}{5040},$$

with an error no greater than $(0.5)10^{-7}$, since

$$\left| R_8\left(\frac{35\pi}{180}, 0\right)\right| \le \frac{(0.62)^9}{9!} < \frac{0.016}{360,000} < (0.5)10^{-7}.$$

By using the series with $a = \pi/6$, we could obtain equal accuracy with a smaller exponent n, but at the expense of introducing $\cos \pi/6 = \sqrt{3}/2$ as one of the coefficients. In this series, with $a = \pi/6$, we would take

$$x = \frac{35\pi}{180},$$

but the quantity that appears raised to the various powers is

$$x - \frac{\pi}{6} = \frac{5\pi}{180} = 0.08726\ 65,$$

which decreases rapidly when raised to high powers.

As a matter of fact, various trigonometric identities may be used, such as

$$\sin\left(\frac{\pi}{2} - x\right) = \cos x,$$

to enable one to calculate quite easily the sine or cosine of any angle by means of the series in Eqs. (2) and (3). This method of finding the sine or cosine of an angle is used in modern high-speed computers. It is more efficient for these large machines to calculate these trigonometric functions from series than it is for them to "read" tables.

EXAMPLE 2. *Computation of logarithms.* Tables of natural logarithms are computed from series. The starting point is the series for $\ln(1 + x)$ in powers of x:

$$\ln(1 + x) = x - \frac{x^2}{2} + \frac{x^3}{3} - \cdots + (-1)^{n-1}\frac{x^n}{n} + \cdots$$

This series may be found directly from the Taylor series expansion, Eq. (1), with $a = 0$. It may also be obtained by integrating the geometric series for $1/(1 + t)$ from $t = 0$ to $t = x$:

$$\int_0^x \frac{dt}{1+t} = \int_0^x (1 - t + t^2 - t^3 + \cdots)\ dt,$$

$$\ln(1 + t)\Big]_0^x = t - \frac{t^2}{2} + \frac{t^3}{3} - \frac{t^4}{4} + \cdots \Big]_0^x,$$

$$\ln(1 + x) = x - \frac{x^2}{2} + \frac{x^3}{3} - \frac{x^4}{4} + \cdots \qquad (5)$$

The expansion (5) is valid for $|x| < 1$, since then the remainder, $R_n(x, 0)$, approaches zero as $n \to \infty$, as we shall now see. The remainder is given by the integral of the remainder in the geometric series, that is,

$$R_n(x, 0) = \int_0^x \frac{(-1)^n t^n}{1 + t}\, dt. \tag{6}$$

We now suppose that $|x| < 1$. For every t between 0 and x inclusive we have

$$|1 + t| \geq 1 - |x|$$

and

$$|(-1)^n t^n| = |t|^n,$$

so that

$$\left| \frac{(-1)^n t^n}{1 + t} \right| \leq \frac{|t|^n}{1 - |x|}.$$

Therefore,

$$|R_n(x, 0)| \leq \int_0^{|x|} \frac{t^n}{1 - |x|}\, dt = \frac{1}{n + 1} \frac{|x|^{n+1}}{1 - |x|}. \tag{7}$$

When $n \to \infty$, the right side of the inequality (7) approaches zero, and so must the left side. Thus (5) holds for $|x| < 1$.

If we replace x by $-x$, we obtain

$$\ln(1 - x) = -x - \frac{x^2}{2} - \frac{x^3}{3} - \cdots - \frac{x^n}{n} - \cdots, \tag{8}$$

which is also valid for $|x| < 1$. When we subtract (8) from (5), we get

$$\ln \frac{1 + x}{1 - x} = 2\left(x + \frac{x^3}{3} + \frac{x^5}{5} + \cdots + \frac{x^{2k-1}}{2k - 1} + \cdots \right) \tag{9}$$

true for $|x| < 1$. Equation (9) may be used to compute the natural logarithm of any positive number y by taking

$$y = \frac{1 + x}{1 - x} \qquad \text{or} \qquad x = \frac{y - 1}{y + 1}.$$

But the series converges most rapidly for values of x near zero, or when $(1 + x)/(1 - x)$ is near one. For this reason, the logarithms of the numbers

$$\frac{2}{1}, \frac{3}{2}, \frac{4}{3}, \frac{5}{4}, \ldots, \frac{N + 1}{N}$$

are ordinarily computed first in forming a table of natural logarithms of the integers. Then it is a matter of simple arithmetic to compute

$$\ln 3 = \ln \tfrac{2}{1} + \ln \tfrac{3}{2},$$

$$\ln 4 = \ln 3 + \ln \tfrac{4}{3},$$

$$\ln 5 = \ln 4 + \ln \tfrac{5}{4},$$

$$\vdots$$

$$\ln (N + 1) = \ln N + \ln \frac{N+1}{N}.$$

For this purpose, one may solve the equation

$$\frac{1+x}{1-x} = \frac{N+1}{N}$$

for

$$x = \frac{1}{2N + 1}.$$

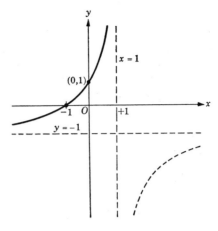

FIGURE 16–13

This may be substituted into Eq. (9), which becomes

$$\ln \frac{N+1}{N} = 2 \left(\frac{1}{2N+1} + \frac{1}{3(2N+1)^3} + \frac{1}{5(2N+1)^5} + \cdots \right). \qquad (10)$$

For example, to calculate $\ln 2$, we take $N = 1$, $x = \tfrac{1}{3}$, and calculate

$$x = 0.33333 \quad 33,$$

$$\frac{x^3}{3} = 0.01234 \quad 57,$$

$$\frac{x^5}{5} = 0.00082 \quad 30,$$

$$\frac{x^7}{7} = 0.00006 \quad 53,$$

$$\frac{x^9}{9} = 0.00000 \quad 56,$$

$$\frac{x^{11}}{11} = 0.00000 \quad 05,$$

$$\overline{\text{Sum} = 0.34657 \quad 34,} \quad \ln 2 \approx 0.693146 \ 68.$$

EXAMPLE 3. *Computation of π.* Archimedes (287–212 B.C.) gave the approximation

$$3\tfrac{1}{7} > \pi > 3\tfrac{10}{71},$$

in the third century B.C. A French mathematician, Vieta (1540–1603), gave the formula

$$\frac{2}{\pi} = \sqrt{\tfrac{1}{2}} \times \sqrt{(\tfrac{1}{2} + \tfrac{1}{2}\sqrt{\tfrac{1}{2}})} \times \sqrt{(\tfrac{1}{2} + \tfrac{1}{2} \sqrt{(\tfrac{1}{2} + \tfrac{1}{2}\sqrt{\tfrac{1}{2}}))}} \times \cdots$$

which Turnbull* calls "the first actual formula for the time-honoured number π."
Other interesting formulas for π include the following:[†]

$$\frac{4}{\pi} = \cfrac{1}{1 + \cfrac{1^2}{2 + \cfrac{3^2}{2 + \cfrac{5^2}{2 + \cdots}}}}$$

credited to Lord Brouncker, an Irish peer;

$$\frac{\pi}{4} = \frac{2 \times 4 \times 4 \times 6 \times 6 \times 8 \times \cdots}{3 \times 3 \times 5 \times 5 \times 7 \times 7 \times \cdots},$$

discovered by the English mathematician Wallis; and

$$\frac{\pi}{4} = 1 - \tfrac{1}{3} + \tfrac{1}{5} - \tfrac{1}{7} + \cdots$$

known as Leibniz's formula. All of these formulas involve limits. For example,
Vieta's formula may be expressed in terms of the sequences $\{x_n\}$ and $\{s_n\}$ defined as follows:

$$x_1 \quad = \sqrt{\tfrac{1}{2}},$$
$$x_2 \quad = \sqrt{\tfrac{1}{2} + \tfrac{1}{2}x_1},$$
$$x_3 \quad = \sqrt{\tfrac{1}{2} + \tfrac{1}{2}x_2},$$
$$\vdots$$
$$x_{n+1} = \sqrt{\tfrac{1}{2} + \tfrac{1}{2}x_n}$$

and

$$s_1 \quad = x_1,$$
$$s_2 \quad = x_1\sqrt{x_2} = x_1 x_2^{1/2},$$
$$s_3 \quad = x_1 \sqrt{x_2\sqrt{x_3}} = x_1 x_2^{1/2} x_3^{1/4},$$
$$s_4 \quad = x_1 \sqrt{x_2 \sqrt{x_3\sqrt{x_4}}} = x_1 x_2^{1/2} x_3^{1/4} x_4^{1/8},$$
$$\vdots$$
$$s_{n+1} = x_1 x_2^{1/2} x_3^{1/4} \ldots x_n^{1/2^n}.$$

Vieta's formula says that

$$\lim_{n \to \infty} s_n = \frac{2}{\pi}.$$

---

* *World of Mathematics*, Vol. 1, p. 121.
† *World of Mathematics*, Vol. 1, p. 138.

Similarly, we could interpret the other formulas as expressing certain limits in terms of π. However, we now turn our attention to the series for $\tan^{-1} x$, since it leads to the Leibniz formula and others from which π has been computed to a great many decimal places.

Since

$$\tan^{-1} x = \int_0^x \frac{dt}{1 + t^2},$$

we integrate the geometric series, with remainder,

$$\frac{1}{1 + t^2} = 1 - t^2 + t^4 - t^6 + \cdots + (-1)^n t^{2n} + \frac{(-1)^{n+1} t^{2n+2}}{1 + t^2}. \quad (11)$$

Thus

$$\tan^{-1} x = x - \frac{x^3}{3} + \frac{x^5}{5} - \frac{x^7}{7} + \cdots + (-1)^n \frac{x^{2n+1}}{2n + 1} + R,$$

where

$$R = \int_0^x \frac{(-1)^{n+1} t^{2n+2}}{1 + t^2} \, dt.$$

The denominator of the integrand is greater than or equal to 1, hence

$$|R| \leq \int_0^{|x|} t^{2n+2} \, dt = \frac{|x|^{2n+3}}{2n + 3}.$$

If $|x| \leq 1$, the right side of this inequality approaches zero as $n \to \infty$. Therefore R also approaches zero and we have

$$\tan^{-1} x = \sum_{n=0}^{\infty} \frac{(-1)^n x^{2n+1}}{2n + 1},$$

or

$$\tan^{-1} x = x - \frac{x^3}{3} + \frac{x^5}{5} - \frac{x^7}{7} + \cdots, \quad |x| \leq 1. \quad (12)$$

This equation has recently been used as the basis for computing π to 2035 decimal places on the Eniac (Electronic Numerical Integrator and Calculator). Various trigonometric identities are useful if one wishes to use Eq. (12) to calculate π. For example, if

$$\alpha = \tan^{-1} \tfrac{1}{2} \quad \text{and} \quad \beta = \tan^{-1} \tfrac{1}{3},$$

then

$$\tan (\alpha + \beta) = \frac{\tan \alpha + \tan \beta}{1 - \tan \alpha \tan \beta} = \frac{\tfrac{1}{2} + \tfrac{1}{3}}{1 - \tfrac{1}{6}} = 1 = \tan \frac{\pi}{4}$$

and

$$\frac{\pi}{4} = \alpha + \beta = \tan^{-1} \tfrac{1}{2} + \tan^{-1} \tfrac{1}{3}. \quad (13)$$

Now Eq. (12) may be used with $x = \frac{1}{2}$ to evaluate $\tan^{-1} \frac{1}{2}$ and with $x = \frac{1}{3}$ to give $\tan^{-1} \frac{1}{3}$. The sum of these results, multiplied by 4, gives π. The identity used in place of Eq. (13) for the calculations made by the Eniac is

$$\frac{\pi}{4} = 4 \tan^{-1} \frac{1}{5} - \tan^{-1} \frac{1}{239}. \tag{14}$$

More details may be found in the article "An Eniac determination of π and e to more than 2000 decimal places," pp. 11–15 of the January 1950 issue of the journal *Mathematical Tables and Other Aids to Computation*.

Perhaps it is not out of place to mention the two types of numerical errors that occur in computing with series. On the one hand there is the so-called *truncation error* which is the remainder $R_n(x, a)$ and consists of the sum of the infinite number of terms in the series that follow the term $(x - a)^n f^{(n)}(a)/n!$. This is the only error we have discussed so far. On the other hand, there is the so-called *round-off error* that enters in calculating the sum of the finite number of terms

$$f(a) + f'(a)(x - a) + \cdots + \frac{f^{(n)}(a)(x - a)^n}{n!}$$

when we approximate each of these terms by a decimal number with only a finite number of decimal places. For example, taking 0.3333 in place of $\frac{1}{3}$ introduces a round-off error equal to $10^{-4}/3$. There is likely to be a round-off error associated with each term in our computations, some of these being positive and some negative. In highly accurate computations, such as the fifteen-place tables of functions published by the Works Progress Administration, it is important to control both the truncation error and the round-off errors. *Truncation* errors can be reduced by taking more terms of the series; *round-off* errors can be reduced by taking more decimal places.

Problems

In each of the following problems (1–8), use a suitable series to calculate the indicated quantity to three decimal places. In each case, show that the remainder term does not exceed 5×10^{-4}.

1. $\cos 31°$ 2. $\tan 46°$ 3. $\sqrt[3]{9}$ 4. $(36)^{-1/5}$

5. $\cosh 0.5$ 6. $\sinh 0.5$ 7. $\ln 1.25$ 8. $\tan^{-1} 1.02$

9. Show that the ordinate of the catenary $y = a \cosh x/a$ deviates from the ordinate of the parabola $x^2 = 2a(y - a)$ by less than $0.003 |a|$ over the range $|x/a| \leq \frac{1}{3}$.

Use series to evaluate the following integrals, Problems 10–11, to three decimals.

10. $\displaystyle\int_0^{0.1} \frac{\sin x}{x} \, dx$ 11. $\displaystyle\int_0^{0.1} e^{-x^2} \, dx$

12. Construct a table of natural logarithms $\ln N$ for $N = 1, 2, 3, \ldots, 10$ by the method discussed in connection with Eq. (10), but taking advantage of the relationships

$$\ln 4 = 2 \ln 2, \quad \ln 6 = \ln 2 + \ln 3, \quad \ln 8 = 3 \ln 2,$$

$$\ln 9 = 2 \ln 3, \quad \ln 10 = \ln 2 + \ln 5$$

to reduce the job to the calculation of relatively few logarithms by series. In fact, you may use $\ln 2$ as given in the text and calculate $\ln \frac{3}{2}$, $\ln \frac{5}{4}$, and $\ln \frac{7}{6}$ by series, and then combine these in suitable ways to get the logarithms of numbers N from 1 to 10.

13. Use Eqs. (12, 14) to calculate π to three decimals.

14. (a) Show that

$$\int_0^x \frac{dt}{1 - t^2} = \int_0^x \left(1 + t^2 + t^4 + \cdots + t^{2n} + \frac{t^{2n+2}}{1 - t^2} \right) dt$$

or, in other words, that

$$\tanh^{-1} x = x + \frac{x^3}{3} + \frac{x^5}{5} + \cdots + \frac{x^{2n+1}}{2n + 1} + R,$$

where

$$R = \int_0^x \frac{t^{2n+2}}{1 - t^2} \, dt.$$

(b) Show that R, in part (a), is not greater than

$$\frac{1}{1 - x^2} \cdot \frac{|x|^{2n+3}}{2n + 3}, \quad \text{if} \quad x^2 < 1.$$

15. (a) Differentiate the identity

$$\frac{1}{1 - x} = 1 + x + x^2 + \cdots + x^n + \frac{x^{n+1}}{1 - x}$$

to obtain the expansion

$$\frac{1}{(1 - x)^2} = 1 + 2x + 3x^2 + \cdots + nx^{n-1} + R.$$

(b) Prove that if $|x| < 1$, then $R \to 0$ as $n \to \infty$.

(c) In one throw of two dice, the probability of getting a score of 7 is $p = \frac{1}{6}$. If the dice are thrown repeatedly, the probability that a 7 will appear for the first time at the nth throw is $q^{n-1} p$, where $q = 1 - p = \frac{5}{6}$. The expected number of throws until a 7 first appears is $\sum_{n=1}^{\infty} nq^{n-1}p$. Evaluate this series numerically.

(d) In applying statistical quality control to an industrial operation, an engineer inspects items taken at random from the assembly line. He classifies each item sampled as "good" or "bad." If the probability of a good item is p and of a bad item is $q = 1 - p$, the probability that the first bad item he finds is the nth inspected is $p^{n-1}q$. The average number inspected up to and including the first bad item found is $\sum_{n=1}^{\infty} np^{n-1}q$. Evaluate this series, assuming $0 < p < 1$.

16. In probability theory, a random variable X may assume the values $1, 2, 3, \ldots$, with probabilities $p_1, p_2, p_3, \ldots$, where p_k is the probability that X is equal to k, $(k = 1, 2, \ldots)$. It is customary to assume $p_k \geq 0$ and $\sum_{k=1}^{\infty} p_k = 1$. The *expected value* of X denoted by $E(X)$ is defined as $\sum_{k=1}^{\infty} kp_k$, provided this series converges. In each of the following cases, show that $\sum p_k = 1$ and find $E(X)$, if it exists. [*Hint:* See Problem 15.]

(a) $p_k = 2^{-k}$,   (b) $p_k = \dfrac{5^{k-1}}{6^k}$,   (c) $p_k = \dfrac{1}{k(k+1)} = \dfrac{1}{k} - \dfrac{1}{k+1}$.

16–7 Indeterminate forms. (1) *The indeterminate form 0/0.* In considering the ratio of two functions $f(x)$ and $g(x)$, we sometimes wish to know the value of

$$\lim_{x \to a} \frac{f(x)}{g(x)} \tag{1}$$

at a point a where both $f(x)$ and $g(x)$ vanish. In such a case we are led to the meaningless expression $0/0$ if we substitute $x = a$ in the numerator and denominator of the fraction.

For example, both x and $\sin x$ are zero at $x = 0$. So we cannot just put $x = 0$ in the numerator and denominator if we want to find the limit

$$\lim_{x \to 0} \frac{\sin x}{x},$$

which we know (from earlier investigations) is one. This is also the derivative of $\sin x$ at $x = 0$. Indeed, the derivative

$$f'(a) = \lim_{x \to a} \frac{f(x) - f(a)}{x - a}$$

was our first example of the indeterminate form $0/0$, since both the numerator and the denominator of the fraction $(f(x) - f(a))/(x - a)$ approach zero when x approaches a.

Suppose the functions f and g both possess Taylor series expansions in powers of $x - a$:

$$f(x) = f(a) + f'(a) \cdot (x - a) + \frac{f''(a)}{2!}(x - a)^2 + \cdots, \tag{2a}$$

$$g(x) = g(a) + g'(a) \cdot (x - a) + \frac{g''(a)}{2!}(x - a)^2 + \cdots, \tag{2b}$$

that converge to $f(x)$ and $g(x)$ respectively in some interval $|x - a| < \delta$, where δ is a positive number. Then the series $(2a, b)$ may be used to calculate the limit (1), provided the limit exists.

EXAMPLE 1.   Evaluate $\lim\limits_{x\to 1} \dfrac{\ln x}{x-1}$.

Solution. Let $f(x) = \ln x$, $g(x) = x - 1$. The Taylor series for $f(x)$, with $a = 1$, is found as follows:

$$f(x) = \ln x, \qquad f(1) = \ln 1 = 0,$$
$$f'(x) = 1/x, \qquad f'(1) = 1,$$
$$f''(x) = -1/x^2, \quad f''(1) = -1,$$

so that
$$\ln x = 0 + (x - 1) - \tfrac{1}{2}(x - 1)^2 + \cdots$$

Hence
$$\frac{\ln x}{x-1} = 1 - \tfrac{1}{2}(x - 1) + \cdots$$

and
$$\lim_{x\to 1} \frac{\ln x}{x-1} = \lim_{x\to 1} [1 - \tfrac{1}{2}(x - 1) + \cdots] = 1.$$

EXAMPLE 2.   Evaluate $\lim\limits_{x\to 0} \dfrac{\sin x - \tan x}{x^3}$.

Solution. The Maclaurin series for $\sin x$ and $\tan x$, to terms in x^5, are

$$\sin x = x - \frac{x^3}{3!} + \frac{x^5}{5!} - \cdots,$$

$$\tan x = x + \frac{x^3}{3} + \frac{2x^5}{15} + \cdots$$

Hence
$$\sin x - \tan x = -\frac{x^3}{2} - \frac{x^5}{8} - \cdots$$

and
$$\lim_{x\to 0} \frac{\sin x - \tan x}{x^3} = \lim_{x\to 0} \left(-\frac{1}{2} - \frac{x^2}{8} - \cdots \right) = -\frac{1}{2}.$$

It is sometimes more convenient to apply the following theorem instead of resorting to the use of series to evaluate the limit (1).

THEOREM (*l'Hôpital's rule*). *If $f(a) = g(a) = 0$ and if the limit of the ratio $f'(t)/g'(t)$ as t approaches a exists, then*

$$\boxed{\lim_{t\to a} \frac{f(t)}{g(t)} = \lim_{t\to a} \frac{f'(t)}{g'(t)}.} \qquad (3)$$

The primes denote derivatives with respect to t and it is tacitly assumed when we write $f'(t)/g'(t)$ that both $f'(t)$ and $g'(t)$ exist and that $g'(t)$ is not zero when t is different from, but sufficiently near to, $t = a$. Notice particularly that $f'(t)/g'(t)$ is the derivative of the numerator divided by the derivative of the denominator, which is not the same as the derivative of the fraction $f(t)/g(t)$.

We shall establish Eq. (3) for the case where $t \to a+$. The method needs only minor modifications, such as reversing certain inequalities, to apply to $t \to a-$. The combination of these two cases then establishes the result.

Suppose then that $f(a) = g(a) = 0$ and that

(a) $f(t)$ and $g(t)$ are continuous functions of t for all t in the closed interval $a \le t \le b$,

(b) $f'(t)$ and $g'(t)$ exist for each t in the open interval $a < t < b$, and

(c) $g'(t) \ne 0$ for all t in the open interval $a < t < b$.

Now consider any t in the open interval $a < t < b$. The fraction $F(t) = f(t)/g(t)$ can be interpreted as the slope of the chord OP (Fig. 16–14) joining the point $O[g(a), f(a)]$ and the point $P[g(t), f(t)]$ on the curve represented by the parametric equations

$$x = g(t), \qquad y = f(t), \qquad a \le t \le b.$$

Our hypotheses are such that we may conclude that there is a point Q on the arc OP where the tangent to the curve is parallel to the chord. But the slope of the tangent at Q is

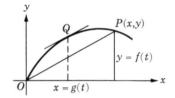

FIGURE 16–14

$$\left(\frac{dy}{dx}\right)_Q = \left(\frac{dy/dt}{dx/dt}\right)_Q = \frac{f'(t_1)}{g'(t_1)},$$

where t_1 is the value of t that corresponds to the point Q on the curve. We therefore have the result that if t is any number in the open interval $a < t < b$, then there is at least one number t_1 between a and t such that

$$\frac{f(t)}{g(t)} = \frac{f'(t_1)}{g'(t_1)}. \tag{4}$$

[Note that the hypothesis $g'(t) \ne 0$ for $a < t < b$ assures us that the denominator on the right does not vanish.]

Now as $t \to a+$, t_1 does likewise, and

$$\lim_{t \to a+} \frac{f(t)}{g(t)} = \lim_{t_1 \to a+} \frac{f'(t_1)}{g'(t_1)} = \lim_{t \to a+} \frac{f'(t)}{g'(t)},$$

provided the last limit above exists. This establishes the theorem for the case where t approaches a from above. The case where t approaches a from below is proved in an analogous manner, and the two cases together give us the result as stated in l'Hôpital's rule.

From the geometric interpretation, Fig. 16–14, it is clear that when the limit

$$\lim_{t \to a} \frac{f(t)}{g(t)} = \lim_{P \to O} (\text{slope of } OP)$$

exists, it is the same as the slope of the tangent to the curve at O. If

$$\frac{dx}{dt} = g'(t) \text{ did not vanish at } t = a,$$

we could simply write this slope as $f'(a)/g'(a)$ and have

$$\lim_{t \to a} \frac{f(t)}{g(t)} = \frac{f'(a)}{g'(a)}.$$

Equation (3) does better than this, however. Since it was established on the assumption that $g'(t)$ is different from zero in an *open* interval $a < t < b$, it is valid whether or not $g'(a)$ is zero. Thus if $f'(a) = g'(a) = 0$, we are led to another indeterminate form 0/0 and may again apply l'Hôpital's rule:

$$\lim_{t \to a} \frac{f'(t)}{g'(t)} = \lim_{t \to a} \frac{f''(t)}{g''(t)},$$

provided the limit on the right exists.

In practice, the functions we deal with in this book are such as to satisfy the hypotheses laid down in deriving l'Hôpital's rule. We apply the method by proceeding to differentiate the numerator and denominator separately so long as we still get the form 0/0 at $t = a$. As soon as one or the other of these derivatives is *different* from zero at $t = a$, we stop differentiating! It may happen that *one* of the derivatives is zero at $t = a$ and the other one not. Then the limit of the fraction is either zero or infinity, according as the zero derivative occurs in the numerator or in the denominator. In case we arrive at a limit that can be evaluated by some special method that we recognize, we may use that method instead of continuing with l'Hôpital's method.

EXAMPLE 3.

$$\lim_{t \to 0} \frac{\sqrt{1+t} - (1+t/2)}{t^2} \qquad [= \tfrac{0}{0}]$$

$$= \lim_{t \to 0} \frac{\tfrac{1}{2}(1+t)^{-1/2} - \tfrac{1}{2}}{2t} \qquad [\text{still} = \tfrac{0}{0}]$$

$$= \lim_{t \to 0} \frac{-\tfrac{1}{4}(1+t)^{-3/2}}{2} = -\frac{1}{8}.$$

Note that one obtains the same result by making use of the binomial series

$$(1+t)^{1/2} = 1 + \tfrac{1}{2}t - \tfrac{1}{8}t^2 + \cdots$$

(2) *The indeterminate forms* ∞/∞ *and* $\infty \cdot 0$. In more advanced textbooks it is proved that if $f(t) \to \infty$ and $g(t) \to \infty$ as $t \to a$, then

$$\lim_{t \to a} \frac{f(t)}{g(t)} = \lim_{t \to a} \frac{f'(t)}{g'(t)},$$

provided the limit on the right exists. (For more details, see P. Franklin, *Treatise on Advanced Calculus*, p. 132.)[*] This simply says that l'Hôpital's rule applies to the indeterminate form ∞/∞ as well as to the form $0/0$. The form $\infty \cdot 0$ must be reduced to one or the other of these two. In the notation $t \to a$, a may either be finite or infinite.

EXAMPLE 4. Find the limit

$$\lim_{t \to \infty} \frac{t^2 + t}{2t^2 + 1}.$$

Solution. This assumes the form ∞/∞ as $t \to \infty$.
(a) We apply l'Hôpital's rule and have

$$\lim_{t \to \infty} \frac{t^2 + t}{2t^2 + 1} = \lim_{t \to \infty} \frac{2t + 1}{4t} \left[\text{still} = \frac{\infty}{\infty} \right] = \lim_{t \to \infty} \frac{2}{4} = \frac{1}{2}.$$

(b) Notice that this could also have been evaluated by writing $t = 1/h$ and letting $h \to 0$:

$$\lim_{t \to \infty} \frac{t^2 + t}{2t^2 + 1} = \lim_{h \to 0} \frac{\dfrac{1}{h^2} + \dfrac{1}{h}}{\dfrac{2}{h^2} + 1} = \lim_{h \to 0} \frac{1 + h}{2 + h^2} = \frac{1}{2}.$$

(c) Another way is to divide both the numerator and denominator by t^2 (the highest power of t that occurs in either numerator or denominator) and observe that $1/t$ and $1/t^2$ approach zero as t increases without bound:

$$\lim_{t \to \infty} \frac{t^2 + t}{2t^2 + 1} = \lim_{t \to \infty} \frac{1 + \dfrac{1}{t}}{2 + \dfrac{1}{t^2}} = \frac{1 + 0}{2 + 0} = \frac{1}{2}.$$

This is actually the same as the method given above in (b).

(3) *The indeterminate form* $\infty - \infty$. The differences $n - n = 0$, $n - n^2 = n(1 - n)$, and $n^2 - n = n(n - 1)$ behave entirely differently as $n \to \infty$. They all become formally $\infty - \infty$ and illustrate why such an expression is called an indeterminate form.

---

[*] There is also a proof of l'Hôpital's rule for both forms $0/0$ and ∞/∞ in the article "L'Hôpital's Rule," by A. E. Taylor, *American Mathematical Monthly*, **59**, 20–24 (1952).

It may be possible, by preliminary algebraic manipulations, to reduce an expression $F(t) - G(t)$ that becomes $\infty - \infty$ as t approaches a to a form $f(t)/g(t)$ that becomes $0/0$ or ∞/∞. Although l'Hôpital's rule is not to be applied to the original form, it may be applied to either of the forms ∞/∞ or $0/0$.

EXAMPLE 5. Find

$$\lim_{x \to 0} \left(\frac{1}{\sin x} - \frac{1}{x} \right).$$

Solution. If $x \to 0+$, then $\sin x \to 0+$ and $1/\sin x \to +\infty$, while $1/x \to +\infty$ and the expression $(1/\sin x) - (1/x)$ formally becomes $+\infty - (+\infty)$, which is indeterminate. On the other hand, if $x \to 0-$, then $1/\sin x \to -\infty$ and $1/x \to -\infty$, so that $(1/\sin x) - (1/x)$ becomes $-\infty + \infty$, which is also indeterminate. But we may also write

$$\frac{1}{\sin x} - \frac{1}{x} = \frac{x - \sin x}{x \sin x} = \frac{x - \left[x - \dfrac{x^3}{3!} + \dfrac{x^5}{5!} - \cdots \right]}{x \cdot \left[x - \dfrac{x^3}{3!} + \dfrac{x^5}{5!} - \cdots \right]}$$

$$= \frac{x^3 \left[\dfrac{1}{3!} - \dfrac{x^2}{5!} + \cdots \right]}{x^2 \left[1 - \dfrac{x^2}{3!} + \cdots \right]} = x \, \frac{\dfrac{1}{3!} - \dfrac{x^2}{5!} + \cdots}{1 - \dfrac{x^2}{3!} + \cdots}.$$

Therefore,

$$\lim_{x \to 0} \left(\frac{1}{\sin x} - \frac{1}{x} \right) = \lim_{x \to 0} \left[x \, \frac{\dfrac{1}{3!} - \dfrac{x^2}{5!} + \cdots}{1 - \dfrac{x^2}{3!} + \cdots} \right] = 0.$$

In fact, from the series expressions above we can see that if $|x|$ is small, then

$$\frac{1}{\sin x} - \frac{1}{x} \approx x \cdot \frac{1}{3!} = \frac{x}{6}$$

or

$$\csc x \approx \frac{1}{x} + \frac{x}{6}.$$

(4) *The indeterminate forms* 0^0, 1^∞, *and* ∞^0. The expressions 0^0, 1^∞, and ∞^0 symbolize the situations which arise in considering the limit, as t approaches a, of a function of the form

$$y = f(t)^{g(t)},$$

where

$$f(a) = g(a) = 0;$$

or $$f(a) = 1 \quad \text{and} \quad \lim_{t \to a} g(t) = \infty;$$

or $$g(a) = 0 \quad \text{and} \quad \lim_{t \to a} f(t) = \infty.$$

In any such case, the natural logarithm of y becomes an indeterminate form of the type $0 \cdot (-\infty)$ or $\infty \cdot 0$. The method of dealing with such cases is illustrated in the following example.

EXAMPLE 6. Evaluate $\lim_{h \to 0} (1 + h)^{1/h}$.

Solution. Let
$$y = (1 + h)^{1/h},$$
so that
$$\ln y = \ln (1 + h)^{1/h} = \frac{1}{h} \ln (1 + h) = \frac{\ln (1 + h)}{h}.$$

This would assume the form
$$\frac{\ln (1 + 0)}{0} = \frac{0}{0}$$

if we were to substitute $h = 0$. By l'Hôpital's rule, we have
$$\lim_{h \to 0} \frac{\ln (1 + h)}{h} = \lim_{h \to 0} \frac{1/(1 + h)}{1} = 1.$$

That is,
$$\ln y \to 1 \quad \text{as} \quad h \to 0$$

and, since $\ln y$ is a continuous function of y, which means that
$$\lim_{h \to 0} \ln y = \ln \left(\lim_{h \to 0} y \right) = 1,$$

we have
$$\lim_{h \to 0} y = e^1 = e.$$

Remark. Many people feel that the expression 1^∞ cannot represent an indeterminate form. They say that one to any finite power is one, hence one to the infinity power is also one. But notice, in the example above, that the base $1 + h$ is a variable which is not exactly equal to 1 except in the *limit* as $h \to 0$. There is a difference, in other words, between

$$1^{1/h} \quad \text{and} \quad (1 + h)^{1/h},$$

even though both expressions formally become 1^∞ as $h \to 0$. If the reader is still skeptical, let him write out a few terms of the binomial expansion of $(1 + 1/n)^n$ for some large value of n, say $n = 10,000$. The result will be a fairly good approximation to $\lim_{h \to 0} (1 + h)^{1/h}$ (since $h = 1/n = 0.0001$ when $n = 10,000$).

PROBLEMS

Evaluate the following limits by using series, or l'Hôpital's rule, or otherwise.

1. $\lim\limits_{t\to 0} \dfrac{1 - \cos t - \frac{1}{2}t^2}{t^4}$

2. $\lim\limits_{h\to 0} \dfrac{\sqrt{4 + h} - 2}{h}$

3. $\lim\limits_{x\to 0} \dfrac{\sqrt[3]{1 + x} - (1 + x/3)}{x^2}$

4. $\lim\limits_{x\to 0} \dfrac{\sinh x - \sin x}{x^3}$

5. $\lim\limits_{x\to 0} \dfrac{e^x - (1 + x)}{x^2}$

6. $\lim\limits_{h\to 0} \dfrac{\dfrac{\sin h}{h} - \cos h}{h^2}$

7. $\lim\limits_{z\to 0} \dfrac{\sin (z^2) - \sin^2 z}{z^4}$

8. $\lim\limits_{n\to\infty} \dfrac{n^3 + 3n^2}{2n^3 - n}$

9. $\lim\limits_{x\to \pi/2} \left(x - \dfrac{\pi}{2}\right) \tan 3x$

10. $\lim\limits_{x\to 0+} x \ln x$

11. $\lim\limits_{x\to +\infty} \dfrac{\ln x}{x}$

12. $\lim\limits_{x\to +\infty} \dfrac{x^{100}}{e^x}$

13. $\lim\limits_{x\to +\infty} x \sin \dfrac{1}{x}$

14. $\lim\limits_{x\to +\infty} (x - \sqrt{x^2 + x})$

15. $\lim\limits_{x\to 1+} \left(\dfrac{1}{x - 1} - \dfrac{1}{\sqrt{x - 1}}\right)$

16. $\lim\limits_{x\to 0} (1 - 2x)^{3/x}$

17. $\lim\limits_{x\to +\infty} \left(1 + \dfrac{2}{x}\right)^x$

18. $\lim\limits_{x\to +\infty} (x + e^x)^{2/x}$

19. $\lim\limits_{x\to 0+} (x + \sin x)^{\tan x}$

20. $\lim\limits_{x\to 0+} x^x$

21. $\lim\limits_{x\to 1-} x^{1/(1 - x^2)}$

22. $\lim\limits_{x\to 0+} (\cos \sqrt{x})^{1/x}$

23. $\lim\limits_{x\to +\infty} x^{1/x}$

24. $\lim\limits_{x\to +\infty} (\cosh x)^{1/x}$

25. (a) Prove that $\left(\displaystyle\int_0^x e^{t^2}\, dt\right) \to +\infty$ as $x \to +\infty$.

   (b) Find $\lim\limits_{x\to\infty} x \displaystyle\int_0^x e^{t^2 - x^2}\, dt$.

26. Find values of r and s such that
$$\lim\limits_{x\to 0} (x^{-3} \sin 3x + rx^{-2} + s) = 0.$$

*16–8 Fourier series. We have seen how the Taylor series is a natural outgrowth of the problem of approximating to a given function $f(x)$ by means of polynomials. This approximation is based on getting a close fit to $f(x)$ near some particular point, $x = a$. The Taylor series usually converges in an interval about a (in fact, in an interval having a as center), but any one of its partial sums is a polynomial which can only be expected to come close to fitting $f(x)$ in a rather restricted neighborhood of a. We might say that the Taylor series does a good job *locally*, or *in the small*. In many important applications, however, it is desirable to approximate to a function $f(x)$ over a fairly wide interval, or *in the large*. For such purposes, the *Fourier series* is often used. Whereas the power series uses powers of x as its fundamental elements, the Fourier series uses sines and cosines as basic components. Suppose, for instance, that a function $f(x)$ is to be approximated on the interval $0 \le x \le 2\pi$ by a trigonometric polynomial

$$\phi_n(x) = a_0 + (a_1 \cos x + b_1 \sin x) + (a_2 \cos 2x + b_2 \sin 2x) + \cdots$$

$$+ (a_n \cos nx + b_n \sin nx)$$

$$= \sum_{k=0}^{n} (a_k \cos kx + b_k \sin kx). \tag{1}$$

What choice of the coefficients $a_0, a_1, \ldots, a_n, b_1 \ldots, b_n$ will make $\phi_n(x)$ the "best possible" approximation to $f(x)$? Of course the words "best possible" need some further interpretation. Suppose we require that $f(x)$ and $\phi_n(x)$ shall give the same answer when integrated with respect to x from 0 to 2π. More than this, we further require that when $f(x)$ and $\phi_n(x)$ are both multiplied by $\cos kx$ or $\sin kx$, $(k = 1, \ldots, n)$, and the results integrated from 0 to 2π, the integrals shall be the same. That is, we shall impose upon $\phi_n(x)$ the $2n + 1$ conditions

$$\int_0^{2\pi} \phi_n(x)\, dx = \int_0^{2\pi} f(x)\, dx,$$

$$\int_0^{2\pi} \phi_n(x) \frac{\cos}{\sin} kx\, dx = \int_0^{2\pi} f(x) \frac{\cos}{\sin} kx\, dx, \quad k = 1, 2, \ldots n. \tag{2}$$

We may ask whether or not these conditions can be met. The right sides of Eqs. (2) are integrals which depend upon the particular function f. But the left sides of the equations involve only the constants $a_0, a_1, \ldots, a_n, b_1, \ldots, b_n$, as we shall now see. From Eq. (1), we have

$$\int_0^{2\pi} \phi_n(x)\, dx = 2\pi a_0,$$

since all of the cosine and sine terms give zero when integrated from 0 to 2π. Next, suppose we multiply both sides of Eq. (1) by $\cos x$ and integrate from 0 to 2π. The only nonzero term we get from the right side of the equation is

$$\int_0^{2\pi} a_1 \cos^2 x\, dx = \pi a_1.$$

This results from the fact that

$$\int_0^{2\pi} \cos px \cos qx \, dx = \int_0^{2\pi} \cos px \sin mx \, dx = \int_0^{2\pi} \sin px \sin qx \, dx = 0,$$

provided p, q, and m are integers and p is not equal to q. Similarly, if we multiply Eq. (1) by $\sin x$ and integrate from 0 to 2π, the only nonzero term remaining on the right is

$$\int_0^{2\pi} b_1 \sin^2 x \, dx = \pi b_1.$$

Proceeding in like fashion with $\cos 2x$, $\sin 2x$, . . . , $\cos nx$, $\sin nx$, we obtain each time only one nonzero term, and that is the one which has the square of a cosine or sine term. These results are all summarized by saying that

$$\int_0^{2\pi} \phi_n(x) \, {\cos \atop \sin} \, kx \, dx = \pi {a_k \brace b_k}, \qquad k = 1, 2, \ldots, n$$

and

$$\int_0^{2\pi} \phi_n(x) \, dx = 2\pi a_0.$$

If we now require that Eqs. (2) be satisfied, we see that the coefficients must be

$$
\boxed{
\begin{aligned}
a_0 &= \frac{1}{2\pi} \int_0^{2\pi} f(x) \, dx, \\
{a_k \brace b_k} &= \frac{1}{\pi} \int_0^{2\pi} f(x) \, {\cos \atop \sin} \, kx \, dx, \qquad k = 1, 2, \ldots, n.
\end{aligned}
}
\qquad (3)
$$

Clearly, these conditions can be met if the required integrals exist. If we let n tend to infinity, we obtain an infinite series in Eq. (1), and if the coefficients are determined as in Eqs. (3), this series is the *Fourier series* for $f(x)$.

Remark 1. The Fourier series also has the property that the coefficients as given by Eqs. (3) are precisely those that one should choose in order to minimize the integral of the square of the error in approximating $f(x)$ by $\phi_n(x)$. That is,

$$\int_0^{2\pi} [f(x) - \phi_n(x)]^2 \, dx$$

is minimized by choosing $a_0, a_1, \ldots, a_n, b_1, \ldots, b_n$ as in Eqs. (3).

Remark 2. If we approximate the function $f(x)$ by one trigonometric polynomial $\phi_n(x)$, using Eqs. (3), and then decide to take instead a second approximation $\phi_N(x)$ using more terms ($N > n$), we may simply add more terms to $\phi_n(x)$ without changing any of the coefficients $a_0, \ldots, b_n$ used in the first approximation.

Remark 3. Fourier series can be used to represent some functions which cannot be expanded in power series. For example, a step function like

$$f(x) = \begin{cases} 1 \text{ for } 0 < x < \pi, \\ 2 \text{ for } \pi < x < 2\pi \end{cases} \tag{4}$$

can be represented by a Fourier series. At $x = \pi$, the Fourier series compromises between the left-hand limit of $f(x)$ and its right-hand limit and gives a value of $\frac{3}{2}$, which is simply the average of the two values on either side of the discontinuity. The reason that a Fourier series may be used to represent some functions which cannot be represented by power series is that the Fourier series depends upon the existence of certain *integrals*, whereas the power series depends upon the existence of *derivatives*. A function must be very "smooth" in order to possess derivatives, but it may be fairly "rough" and still be integrable. (For more details see Franklin, *A Treatise on Advanced Calculus*, Chapter XIV.)

Remark 4. If a function is to be represented by a Fourier series for $0 \le x \le L$ instead of for $0 \le x \le 2\pi$, one may substitute $t = (2\pi x)/L$ and work with the Fourier series in terms of t. If the interval is $a \le x \le b$, one may first take $x' = x - a$ and then $t = (2\pi x')/(b - a)$.

EXAMPLE. As an illustration of the method to be followed in finding the Fourier series for a given function $f(x)$, we shall analyze the step function in Eq. (4).

Solution. We find

$$a_0 = \frac{1}{2\pi} \int_0^{2\pi} f(x)\, dx = \frac{1}{2\pi} \left\{ \int_0^{\pi} 1\, dx + \int_{\pi}^{2\pi} 2\, dx \right\} = \frac{3}{2},$$

$$a_k = \frac{1}{\pi} \int_0^{2\pi} f(x) \cos kx\, dx = \frac{1}{\pi} \left\{ \int_0^{\pi} \cos kx\, dx + \int_{\pi}^{2\pi} 2 \cos kx\, dx \right\}$$

$$= \frac{1}{\pi} \left\{ \frac{\sin kx}{k} \Big|_0^{\pi} + \frac{2 \sin kx}{k} \Big|_{\pi}^{2\pi} \right\} = 0, \qquad k \ge 1,$$

$$b_k = \frac{1}{\pi} \int_0^{2\pi} f(x) \sin kx\, dx = \frac{1}{\pi} \left\{ \int_0^{\pi} \sin kx\, dx + \int_{\pi}^{2\pi} 2 \sin kx\, dx \right\}$$

$$= \frac{1}{\pi} \left\{ -\frac{\cos kx}{k} \Big|_0^{\pi} - \frac{2 \cos kx}{k} \Big|_{\pi}^{2\pi} \right\} = \frac{\cos k\pi - 1}{k\pi} = \frac{(-1)^k - 1}{k\pi}.$$

That is,

$$a_0 = \tfrac{3}{2}, \qquad a_1 = a_2 = \cdots = 0,$$

$$b_1 = \frac{-2}{\pi}, \ b_2 = 0, \ b_3 = \frac{-2}{3\pi}, \ b_4 = 0, \ b_5 = \frac{-2}{5\pi}, \ b_6 = 0, \ldots,$$

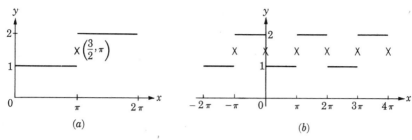

FIGURE 16–15

and the Fourier series is

$$\frac{3}{2} - \frac{2}{\pi}\left(\sin x + \frac{\sin 3x}{3} + \frac{\sin 5x}{5} + \cdots\right).$$

We see that all the sine terms vanish when $x = \pi$, leaving $\frac{3}{2}$ as the value of the series at this point. It is also to be noted that the series gives the value $\frac{3}{2}$ at $x = 0$ and $x = 2\pi$ as well as at $x = \pi$. In fact, all terms in the Fourier series are periodic, of period 2π. Such a series thus has the same value at $x + 2\pi$ or $x - 2\pi$ as it has at x. The present series represents the function shown in Fig. 16–15(a) between 0 and 2π, but the series repeats this same pattern between -2π and 0, between 2π and 4π, and so on to the left and to the right. This extended function will then be seen to have jumps at $x = n\pi$, $n = 0, \pm1, \pm2, \ldots$ and the value $\frac{3}{2}$ is the average of the values of the function immediately on either side of one of these points of discontinuity. The Fourier series converges to the function shown in Fig. 16–15(b).

PROBLEMS

Find the Fourier series associated with each of the following functions. Sketch each function

1. $f(x) = 1,$ $0 < x < \pi$
   $= 0,$ $\pi < x < 2\pi$

2. $f(x) = -1,$ $0 < x < \pi$
   $= 1,$ $\pi < x < 2\pi$

3. $f(x) = x,$ $0 < x < 2\pi$

4. $f(x) = x,$ $0 < x < \pi$
   $= 2\pi - x,$ $\pi < x < 2\pi$

5. $f(x) = x,$ $0 < x < \pi$
   $= x - 2\pi,$ $\pi < x < 2\pi$

16–9 Convergence of power series. Absolute convergence. Example 4 in Article 16–2 showed how the ratio test may be applied to find the region of convergence of a power series. The ratio test applies, however, only to *positive* series. For a negative series we simply factor out a minus sign from every term. This doesn't work, however, for a series like

$$1 + 2x + 3x^2 + 4x^3 + \cdots + nx^{n-1} + \cdots, \tag{1}$$

which becomes an alternating series when x is negative. To handle such series, we introduce the concept of *absolute* convergence.

DEFINITION. *A series*

$$\sum_{k=1}^{\infty} u_k = u_1 + u_2 + \cdots$$

is said to be absolutely *convergent if the corresponding series of absolute values,*

$$\sum_{k=1}^{\infty} |u_k| = |u_1| + |u_2| + \cdots,$$

converges.

One reason that absolute convergence is important is given by the following theorem.

THEOREM 1. *If a series converges absolutely, then it also converges when the absolute value signs are removed.*

Proof. Let the sum of the first n terms of $\sum u_k$ be denoted as usual by s_n and the sum of the first n terms of $\sum |u_k|$ be denoted by p_n. Suppose that

$$\lim_{n \to \infty} p_n = p$$

exists. We want to prove that $\lim s_n$ also exists. The following trick is effective! Consider the sum

$$q_n = (u_1 + |u_1|) + (u_2 + |u_2|) + \cdots + (u_n + |u_n|) = s_n + p_n. \quad (2)$$

Each term of the series $\sum (u_k + |u_k|)$ is greater than or equal to zero, so the sequence of numbers $\{q_n\}$ is a monotone increasing sequence. On the other hand,

$$q_n \leq (|u_1| + |u_1|) + (|u_2| + |u_2|) + \cdots + (|u_n| + |u_n|)$$

or

$$q_n \leq 2p_n. \quad (3)$$

And, since $\{p_n\}$ is a monotone increasing sequence whose limit is p, we have

$$p_n \leq p \text{ for all } n.$$

The inequality (3) therefore tells us that

$$q_n \leq 2p,$$

and alternative A of Theorem 1, Article 16–2, holds with $M = 2p$.

Therefore

$$\lim_{n \to \infty} q_n = q$$

exists. Hence, from Eq. (2), $s_n = q_n - p_n$ also has a limit as n becomes infinite, namely,

$$\lim_{n \to \infty} s_n = \lim_{n \to \infty} q_n - \lim_{n \to \infty} p_n = q - p.$$

We also repeat the following theorem from Article 16–1.

THEOREM 2. *If a series $\sum u_k$ converges, then*

$$\lim_{n \to \infty} u_n = 0. \tag{4}$$

Remark. In determining the interval of convergence of a power series we shall apply the ratio test to the series of *absolute values*. Thus, if

$$\rho = \lim_{n \to \infty} |u_{n+1}/u_n|,$$

the series

(a) converges absolutely if $\rho < 1$,
(b) diverges if $\rho > 1$, and
(c) may either converge or diverge if $\rho = 1$.

The only case that requires further discussion because we have now introduced absolute value signs is case 2, $\rho > 1$. In this case, the terms do not get smaller in magnitude as n increases, since there is then an index N such that

$$|u_{n+1}/u_n| \geq 1 \quad \text{for all } n \geq N.$$

This, in turn, implies

$$|u_N| \leq |u_{N+1}| \leq |u_{N+2}| \leq |u_{N+3}| \leq \cdots,$$

so that the nth term does not approach zero as n becomes infinite. Hence the series diverges (with or without absolute value signs) in case $\rho > 1$.

THEOREM 3. *If a power series*

$$\sum_{k=0}^{\infty} a_k x^k = a_0 + a_1 x + a_2 x^2 + \cdots \tag{5}$$

converges for $x = c(c \neq 0)$, then it converges absolutely for all $|x| < |c|$. If the series diverges for $x = d$, then it diverges for all $|x| > |d|$.

Proof. Suppose the series

$$\sum_{k=0}^{\infty} a_k c^k \tag{6}$$

converges.

Then, by Theorem 2, $\qquad \lim\limits_{n\to\infty} a_n c^n = 0.$

Hence there is an index N such that

$$|a_n c^n| < 1 \quad \text{for all } n \geq N.$$

That is,

$$|a_n| < \frac{1}{|c|^n} \quad \text{for } n \geq N. \tag{7}$$

Now take any x such that $|x| < |c|$ and consider

$$|a_0| + |a_1 x| + \cdots + |a_{N-1} x^{N-1}| + |a_N x^N| + |a_{N+1} x^{N+1}| + \cdots$$

There is only a finite number of terms prior to $|a_N x^N|$ and their sum is finite. Starting with $|a_N x^N|$ and beyond, the terms are less than

$$\left|\frac{x}{c}\right|^N + \left|\frac{x}{c}\right|^{N+1} + \left|\frac{x}{c}\right|^{N+2} + \cdots \tag{8}$$

by virtue of the inequality (7). But the series in (8) is a geometric series with ratio $r = |x/c|$, which is less than one, since $|x| < |c|$. Hence the series (8) converges so that the original series (5) converges absolutely. This proves the first half of the theorem.

The second half of the theorem involves nothing new. For if the series diverges at $x = d$ and converges at a value x_0 with $|x_0| > |d|$, we may take $c = x_0$ in the first half of the theorem and conclude that the series converges absolutely at d. But the series cannot both converge absolutely and diverge at one and the same time. Hence if it diverges at d, it diverges for all $|x| > |d|$.

It is a consequence of Theorem 3 that a power series behaves in one or another of the following ways:

1. It may converge only at $x = 0$.
2. It may converge absolutely for all finite x, $-\infty < x < \infty$.
3. There may be a positive number c such that the series converges absolutely for $|x| < c$ and diverges for $|x| > c$. In this case the series may converge or diverge at either or both of the points $x = c$, $x = -c$, which are the end points of the interval of convergence.

EXAMPLE. Find the interval of convergence for the series

$$\sum_{n=1}^{\infty} n x^{n-1}.$$

Solution. First we test for absolute convergence by calculating

$$\rho = \lim_{n\to\infty} \left| \frac{(n+1)x^n}{nx^{n-1}} \right| = |x|.$$

By the ratio test, the series converges absolutely if $|x| < 1$ and diverges if $|x| > 1$. When x is either $+1$ or -1 the nth term does not approach zero as n becomes infinite. Hence the series diverges at $x = \pm 1$. The interval of convergence is $-1 < x < 1$.

PROBLEMS

In each of the following problems, find the interval in which the given power series converges absolutely.

1. $\displaystyle\sum_{n=0}^{\infty} x^n$

2. $\displaystyle\sum_{n=0}^{\infty} \frac{x^n}{n+1}$

3. $\displaystyle\sum_{n=1}^{\infty} n^2 x^n$

4. $\displaystyle\sum_{n=1}^{\infty} \frac{nx^n}{2^n}$

5. $\displaystyle\sum_{n=0}^{\infty} \frac{x^n}{n!}$

6. $\displaystyle\sum_{n=1}^{\infty} \frac{(-1)^{n-1} x^{2n-1}}{(2n-1)!}$

7. $\displaystyle\sum_{n=1}^{\infty} (-1)^{n-1} \frac{(x-1)^n}{n}$

8. $\displaystyle\sum_{n=1}^{\infty} \frac{n^2}{2^n} (x+2)^n$

9. $\displaystyle\sum_{n=1}^{\infty} \frac{2^n}{n(n+1)} (x-3)^{2n-1}$

10. $\displaystyle\sum_{n=0}^{\infty} \frac{(-1)^n x^{2n}}{2^{2n}(n!)^2}$

16–10 Alternating series. Conditional convergence. When some of the terms of a series $\sum u_k$ are positive and some are negative, the series *converges if* $\sum |u_k|$ *converges.* Thus we may apply any of our tests for convergence of positive series provided we apply them to the series of absolute values. But we do not know, when the series of absolute values *diverges,* whether the *original* series diverges or not. If it converges, but not absolutely, we say that it *converges conditionally.*

We shall discuss one simple case of series with mixed signs, namely, the case of an alternating series of the form

$$a_1 - a_2 + a_3 - a_4 + \cdots + (-1)^{n-1} a_n + \cdots, \qquad (1)$$

where the a's are all positive.

THEOREM. *If the following three conditions are all satisfied, then the series does converge:*

(a) *The series $\sum u_k$ is strictly alternating.*

(b) *The nth term tends to zero as n becomes infinite.*

(c) *Each term is numerically less than, or at most equal to, its predecessor.*

Proof. Suppose these three conditions are satisfied. Then we may write

$$u_k = (-1)^{k-1} a_k$$

and put the series in the form of (1) with $a_{n+1} \leq a_n$. If n is an even integer, say $n = 2m$, then the sum of the first n terms is

$$s_{2m} = (a_1 - a_2) + (a_3 - a_4) + \cdots + (a_{2m-1} - a_{2m})$$

$$= a_1 - (a_2 - a_3) - (a_4 - a_5) - \cdots - (a_{2m-2} - a_{2m-1}) - a_{2m}.$$

The first way of writing s_{2m} exhibits it as the sum of m nonnegative terms, since each expression in parentheses is positive or zero. Hence $s_{2m+2} \geq s_{2m}$ and the sequence $\{s_{2m}\}$ is monotonically increasing. The second way of expressing s_{2m} shows, on the other hand, that

$$s_{2m} \leq a_1.$$

Hence we have a sequence $\{s_{2m}\}$ that is monotone increasing and is bounded above. Such a sequence has a limit, say

$$\lim_{m \to \infty} s_{2m} = L. \tag{2}$$

If we now form the sum of an odd number of terms, say

$$s_{2m+1} = a_1 - a_2 + a_3 - \cdots + a_{2m-1} - a_{2m} + a_{2m+1}$$

$$= s_{2m} + a_{2m+1},$$

the fact that the nth term approaches zero as n becomes infinite means that

$$\lim_{m \to \infty} a_{2m+1} = 0.$$

Hence, as $m \to \infty$,

$$\lim s_{2m+1} = \lim s_{2m} + \lim a_{2m+1} = L. \tag{3}$$

Finally, we may combine Eqs. (2) and (3) and say simply

$$\lim_{n \to \infty} s_n = L,$$

where n may be either even or odd.

We use the following graphical interpretation of the partial sums to gain added insight into the way in which an alternating series converges to its limit L when the three conditions of the theorem are satisfied. Starting from the origin O on a scale of real numbers (Fig. 16–16), we lay off the positive distance

$$s_1 = a_1.$$

To find the point corresponding to

$$s_2 = a_1 - a_2$$

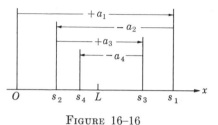

we must back up a distance equal to a_2. Since $a_2 \leq a_1$, we do not back up any farther than O at most. Next we go forward a distance a_3 and mark the point corresponding to

$$s_3 = a_1 - a_2 + a_3.$$

FIGURE 16–16

Since $a_3 \leq a_2$, we go forward by an amount which is no greater than the previous backward step; that is, s_3 is less than or equal to s_1. We continue in this seesaw fashion, backing up or going forward as the signs in the series demand. But each forward or backward step is shorter than (or at most the same size as) the preceding step, because $a_{n+1} \leq a_n$. And since the nth term approaches zero as n increases, the size of step we take forward or backward gets smaller and smaller. We thus oscillate across the limit L, but the amplitude of oscillation continually decreases and approaches zero as its limit. The even-numbered partial sums $s_2, s_4, s_6,$ $\ldots, s_{2m}$ continually increase toward L, while the odd-numbered sums $s_1, s_3, s_5, \ldots, s_{2m+1}$ continually decrease toward L. The limit L is between any two successive sums s_n and s_{n+1} and hence differs from either of them by an amount not greater than a_{n+1}.

EXAMPLE 1. The series

$$1 - \frac{1}{2} + \frac{1}{3} - \frac{1}{4} + \cdots + \frac{(-1)^{n-1}}{n} + \cdots$$

satisfies the three conditions of the theorem:

(a) It is alternating.
(b) The nth term is $(-1)^{n-1}/n$, which tends to zero as n increases.
(c) $\dfrac{1}{n+1} < \dfrac{1}{n}$, so the terms decrease in absolute value.

Hence this series converges. But it converges conditionally and not absolutely, since the series of absolute values is

$$1 + \frac{1}{2} + \frac{1}{3} + \cdots + \frac{1}{n} + \cdots,$$

which we know diverges.

Remark. In computing the numerical value of an alternating series that satisfies the three conditions of the theorem and converges to a limit L, if we stop after computing the sum s_n of the first n terms, then the error, which is represented by the remainder

$$R_n = L - s_n = (-1)^n(a_{n+1} - a_{n+2} + a_{n+3} - \cdots),$$

has the same sign, $(-1)^n$, as the next term, and its absolute value is no greater than the absolute value of that term. That is,

$$L = s_n + R_n,$$

R_n has the same sign as $\pm a_{n+1}$, and $|R_n| \leq a_{n+1}$. This follows at once from the fact that

$$R_n = (-1)^n[a_{n+1} - (a_{n+2} - a_{n+3}) - (a_{n+4} - a_{n+5}) - \cdots]$$
$$= (-1)^n[(a_{n+1} - a_{n+2}) + (a_{n+3} - a_{n+4}) + \cdots]$$

and the expression in brackets is positive (second form) but not greater than a_{n+1} (first form). Thus in the example above, if we stop with

$$s_{10} = 1 - \tfrac{1}{2} + \tfrac{1}{3} - \cdots - \tfrac{1}{10},$$

we know that the exact value of the series is $L = s_{10} + R_{10}$, where R_{10} is positive since the next term is $+\tfrac{1}{11}$, and $|R_{10}| < \tfrac{1}{11}$.

EXAMPLE 2. We can now show that the series

$$\sum_{k=1}^{\infty} \frac{x^k}{k} = x + \frac{x^2}{2} + \frac{x^3}{3} + \frac{x^4}{4} + \cdots \tag{4}$$

converges for $-1 \leq x < 1$. To find this interval of convergence, we let

$$u_n = x^n/n$$

and use the ratio test:

$$\rho = \lim_{n\to\infty} \left| \frac{u_{n+1}}{u_n} \right| = \lim_{n\to\infty} \left| \frac{x^{n+1}}{n+1} \frac{n}{x^n} \right| = |x|.$$

Hence the series converges absolutely if $|x| < 1$ and it diverges if $|x| > 1$. When $x = +1$, the series becomes

$$1 + \tfrac{1}{2} + \tfrac{1}{3} + \tfrac{1}{4} + \cdots,$$

which diverges to $+\infty$. When $x = -1$ the series becomes

$$-(1 - \tfrac{1}{2} + \tfrac{1}{3} - \tfrac{1}{4} + \cdots),$$

which is just the negative of the convergent alternating series considered in Example 1. Hence the series (4) converges for $-1 \leq x < 1$ and diverges for all other values of x.

PROBLEMS

Find the interval of absolute convergence for each of the following series. If the interval is finite, determine whether the series converges or diverges at the end points.

1. $\displaystyle\sum_{n=0}^{\infty} \frac{x^{2n+1}}{2n+1}$

2. $\displaystyle\sum_{n=0}^{\infty} (-1)^n \frac{x^{2n+1}}{2n+1}$

3. $\displaystyle\sum_{n=1}^{\infty} \frac{(x-2)^n}{n^2}$

4. $\displaystyle\sum_{n=1}^{\infty} (-1)^{n-1} \frac{(x+1)^n}{n}$

5. $\displaystyle\sum_{n=1}^{\infty} \frac{(-1)^{n-1}(x-2)^n}{n \cdot 2^n}$

6. $\displaystyle\sum_{n=0}^{\infty} (-2)^n(n+1)(x-1)^n$

7. $\displaystyle\sum_{k=0}^{\infty} \frac{(3x+6)^k}{k!}$

8. $\displaystyle\sum_{n=0}^{\infty} n! x^n$

9. $\displaystyle\sum_{n=1}^{\infty} (-1)^n \frac{(2n-2)!}{2^{2n-2}(n-1)!(n-1)!} \frac{x^{2n-1}}{2n-1}$

10. $\displaystyle\sum_{n=1}^{\infty} \frac{(x+3)^{n-1}}{n}$

REVIEW QUESTIONS AND EXERCISES FOR CHAPTER 16

1. Define "sequence," "series," "sequence of partial sums of a series."
2. Define "convergence" (a) of a sequence, (b) of an infinite series.
3. Which of the following statements are true, and which are false?

(a) If a sequence does not converge, then it diverges.
(b) If a sequence $\{n, f(n)\}$ does not converge, then $f(n)$ tends to infinity as n does.
(c) If a series does not converge, then its nth term does not approach zero as n tends to infinity.
(d) If the nth term of a series does not approach zero as n tends to infinity, then the series diverges.
(e) If a sequence $\{n, f(n)\}$ converges, then there is a number L such that $f(n)$ lies within 1 unit of L (i) for all values of n, (ii) for all but a finite number of values of n.
(f) If all partial sums of a series are less than some constant L, then the series converges.
(g) If a series converges, then its partial sums s_n are bounded (that is. $m \le s_n \le M$ for some constants m and M).

4. List three tests for convergence (or divergence) of an infinite series.
5. Under what circumstances do you know that a bounded sequence converges?

6. Define "absolute convergence" and "conditional convergence." Give examples of series that are (a) absolutely convergent, (b) conditionally convergent.

7. State Taylor's theorem, with remainder, giving two different expressions for the remainder.

8. It can be shown (though not very simply) that the function f defined by

$$f(x) = \begin{cases} 0 & \text{when} \quad x = 0 \\ e^{-1/x^2} & \text{when} \quad x \neq 0 \end{cases}$$

is everywhere continuous, together with its derivatives of all orders. At 0, the derivatives are all equal to 0.

   (a) Write the Taylor series expansion of f in powers of x.
   (b) What is the remainder $R_n(x, 0)$ for this function? Does the Taylor series for f converge to $f(x)$ at some value of x different from zero? Give a reason for your answer.

9. If a Taylor series in powers of $x - a$ is to be used for the numerical evaluation of a function, what is necessary and/or desirable in the choice of a?

10. Write the Taylor series in powers of $x - a$ and $y - b$ for a function f of two variables x and y, about the point (a, b).

11. List two methods that may be useful in finding $\lim_{x \to a} f(x)/g(x)$ if $f(a) = g(a) = 0$. Illustrate both methods with a single example.

12. What test is usually used to find the interval of convergence of a power series? Does this test also work at the end points of the interval? Illustrate with examples.

13. What test is usually used to decide whether or not a given alternating series converges? Give examples of convergent and divergent alternating series.

MISCELLANEOUS PROBLEMS FOR CHAPTER 16

1. Find explicitly the nth partial sum of the series $\sum_{n=2}^{\infty} \ln (1 - 1/n^2)$, and thereby determine whether or not the series converges.

2. Evaluate $\sum_{k=2}^{\infty} 1/(k^2 - 1)$ by finding the nth partial sum and taking the limit as n becomes infinite.

3. Prove that the sequence $\{x_n\}$ and the series $\sum_{k=1}^{\infty} (x_{k+1} - x_k)$ both converge or both diverge.

4. In an attempt to find a root of the equation $x = f(x)$, a first approximation x_1 is estimated from the graphs of $y = x$ and $y = f(x)$. Then $x_2, x_3, \ldots,$ $x_n, \ldots$ are computed successively from the formula $x_n = f(x_{n-1})$. If the points $x_1, x_2, \ldots, x_n, \ldots$ all lie on an interval $a \le x \le b$ on which $f(x)$ has a derivative such that $|f'(x)| < M < 1$, show that the sequence $\{x_n\}$ converges to a root of the given equation.

5. Assuming $|x| > 1$, show that

$$\frac{1}{1 - x} = -\frac{1}{x} - \frac{1}{x^2} - \frac{1}{x^3} - \cdots$$

6. (a) Find the expansion in powers of x of $x^2/(1 + x)$. (b) Does the series expansion of $x^2/(1 + x)$ in powers of x converge when $x = 2$? (Give a brief reason.)

7. Obtain the Maclaurin series expansion for $\sin^{-1} x$ by integrating the series for $(1 - t^2)^{-1/2}$ from 0 to x. Find the intervals of convergence of these series.

8. Obtain the Maclaurin series for $\ln (x + \sqrt{x^2 + 1}) = \sinh^{-1} x$ by integrating the series for $(1 + t^2)^{-1/2}$ from 0 to x. Find the intervals of convergence of these two series.

9. Obtain the first four terms in the Maclaurin series for $e^{\sin x}$ by substituting the series for $y = \sin x$ in the series for e^y.

10. Assuming $|x| > 1$, obtain the expansions

$$\tan^{-1} x = \frac{\pi}{2} - \frac{1}{x} + \frac{1}{3x^3} - \frac{1}{5x^5} + \cdots, \qquad x > 1$$

$$\tan^{-1} x = -\frac{\pi}{2} - \frac{1}{x} + \frac{1}{3x^3} - \frac{1}{5x^5} + \cdots, \qquad x < -1$$

by integrating the series

$$\frac{1}{1 + t^2} = \frac{1}{t^2} \cdot \frac{1}{1 + (1/t^2)} = \frac{1}{t^2} - \frac{1}{t^4} + \frac{1}{t^6} - \frac{1}{t^8} + \cdots$$

from x (> 1) to $+\infty$ or from $-\infty$ to x (< -1).

11. (a) Obtain the Maclaurin series, through the term in x^6, for $\ln (\cos x)$ by substituting the series for $y = 1 - \cos x$ in the series for $\ln (1 - y)$. (b) Use the result of part (a) to estimate $\int_0^{0.1} \ln (\cos x) \, dx$ to five decimal places.

12. Compute $\int_0^1 [(\sin x)/x] \, dx$ to three decimal places.

13. Compute $\int_0^1 e^{-x^2} \, dx$ to three decimal places.

14. Expand the function $f(x) = \sqrt{1 + x^2}$ in powers of $(x - 1)$, obtaining three nonvanishing terms.

15. Expand the function $f(x) = 1/(1 - x)$ in powers of $(x - 2)$, and find the interval of convergence.

16. If $\tan x$ has the Maclaurin expansion $a_0 + a_1 x + a_2 x^2 + a_3 x^3 + \cdots$, find the first three nonvanishing terms.

17. Determine the Taylor series expansion of the function $f(x) = 1/(x + 1)$ in powers of $(x - 3)$.

18. Expand $\cos x$ in powers of $(x - \pi/3)$.

19. Find the first three terms of the Taylor series expansion of the function $1/x$ about the point π.

20. Let f and g be functions satisfying the following conditions: (a) $f(0) = 1$, (b) $f'(x) = g(x)$, $g'(x) = f(x)$, (c) $g(0) = 0$. Find $f(1)$, accurate to three decimal places.

21. Suppose $f(x) = \sum_{n=0}^{\infty} a_n x^n$. Prove that (a) if $f(x)$ is an even function, then $a_1 = a_3 = a_5 = \cdots = 0$; (b) if $f(x)$ is an odd function, then $a_0 = a_2 = a_4 = \cdots = 0$.

22. Show that the function $f(x) = e^{(e^x)}$ can be expanded into a power series in x, and find the first four terms (up to x^3).

23. Using a suitable series, complete the following four-place table of the function $f(x) = \arctan(x)$:

$x = 0.00$	0.01	0.02	0.03	0.04	0.05	0.06	0.10
$f(x) = 0.0000$	0.0100	0.0200	0.0300	0.0400			

24. Give a quantitative estimate of the error involved in using $x - x^2/2$ as an approximation to $\ln (1 + x)$ for values of x between 0 and 0.2 inclusive.

25. If $(1 + x)^{1/3}$ is replaced by $1 + x/3$ and $0 \le x \le \frac{1}{10}$, what estimate can be given for the error?

26. By considering the quotient of the power series for numerator and denominator, find the limit

$$\lim_{x \to 0} \frac{\ln (1 - x) - \sin x}{1 - \cos^2 x}.$$

27. Find the limit of $[(\sin x)/x]^{1/x^2}$ as x approaches zero.

28. (a) Find the Fourier series of period 2π generated by the function

$$f(x) = -\pi, \quad \text{if} \quad -\pi < x < 0,$$
$$= x, \quad \text{if} \quad 0 < x < \pi.$$

(b) Take $x = 0$ in your result in (a) to find the sum of the series

$$\frac{1}{1^2} + \frac{1}{3^2} + \frac{1}{5^2} + \frac{1}{7^2} + \cdots + \frac{1}{(2n - 1)^2} + \cdots$$

(The Fourier series converges to the "average value" $-\pi/2$ at $x = 0$.)

29. Does the series $\sum_{n=1}^{\infty} \operatorname{sech} n$ converge or diverge? Why?

30. Does the series $\sum_{n=1}^{\infty} (-1)^n \tanh n$ converge or diverge? Why?

31. If $a_n > 0$ and $\sum_{n=1}^{\infty} a_n$ converges, prove that $\sum_{n=1}^{\infty} (1/a_n)$ diverges.

32. Establish the convergence or divergence of the series whose nth term is:

(a) $\dfrac{1}{\ln(n+1)}$,

(b) $\dfrac{n}{2(n+1)(n+2)}$,

(c) $\dfrac{\sqrt{n+1}-\sqrt{n}}{\sqrt{n}}$,

(d) $\dfrac{1}{n(\ln n)^2}$, $\qquad n \ge 2$,

(e) $\dfrac{1+(-2)^{n-1}}{2^n}$,

(f) $\dfrac{n}{1000n^2+1}$,

(g) $e^n/n!$,

(h) $\dfrac{1}{n\sqrt{n^2+1}}$,

(i) $\dfrac{1}{n^{1+1/n}}$,

(j) $\dfrac{1\cdot 3\cdot 5\cdots(2n-1)}{2\cdot 4\cdot 6\cdots(2n)}$,

(k) $\dfrac{n^2}{n^3+1}$,

(l) $\dfrac{n+1}{n!}$.

33. Find the sum of the convergent series

$$\sum_{n=1}^{\infty}\frac{1}{(n+1)(n+2)}.$$

34. (a) Suppose $a_1, a_2, a_3, \ldots, a_n$ are positive numbers satisfying the following conditions:

(1) $a_1 \ge a_2 \ge a_3 \ge \cdots$;
(2) the series $a_2 + a_4 + a_8 + a_{16} + \cdots$ diverges.

Show that the series

$$\frac{a_1}{1} + \frac{a_2}{2} + \frac{a_3}{3} + \cdots$$

is divergent. (b) Use the result above to show that the series

$$\sum_{n=2}^{\infty}\frac{1}{n\ln n}$$

is divergent.

35. Given $a_n \ne 1$, $a_n > 0$, $\sum a_n$ converges. (a) Show that $\sum a_n^2$ converges. (b) Does $\sum a_n/(1-a_n)$ converge? (c) Does $\sum \ln(1+a_n)$ converge? Justify your conclusions.

36. Show that the series $\sum_{n=2}^{\infty} 1/[n(\ln n)^k]$ is convergent for $k > 1$.

37. Find the interval of convergence of each of the following series and test for convergence or divergence at the end points if the interval is finite:

(a) $1 + \dfrac{x+2}{3\cdot 1} + \dfrac{(x+2)^2}{3^2\cdot 2} + \cdots + \dfrac{(x+2)^n}{3^n\cdot n} + \cdots$,

(b) $1 + \dfrac{(x-1)^2}{2!} + \dfrac{(x-1)^4}{4!} + \cdots + \dfrac{(x-1)^{2n-2}}{(2n-2)!} + \cdots$,

(c) $\displaystyle\sum_{n=1}^{\infty}\frac{x^n}{n^n}$,

(d) $\displaystyle\sum_{n=1}^{\infty}\frac{n!x^n}{n^n}$,

(e) $\displaystyle\sum_{n=0}^{\infty} \frac{n+1}{2n+1} \frac{(x-3)^n}{2^n}$,

(f) $\displaystyle\sum_{n=0}^{\infty} \frac{n+1}{2n+1} \frac{(x-2)^n}{3^n}$,

(g) $\displaystyle\sum_{n=1}^{\infty} \frac{(-1)^{n-1}(x-1)^n}{n^2}$,

(h) $\displaystyle\sum_{n=1}^{\infty} \frac{x^n}{n}$.

38. Determine *all* the values of x for which each of the following series converges:

(a) $\displaystyle\sum_{n=1}^{\infty} \frac{(x-2)^{3n}}{n!}$,

(b) $\displaystyle\sum_{n=1}^{\infty} \frac{2^n(\sin x)^n}{n^2}$,

(c) $\displaystyle\sum_{n=1}^{\infty} \frac{1}{n}\left(\frac{x-1}{x}\right)^n$.

39. A function is defined by the power series

$$y = 1 + \frac{1}{6}x^3 + \frac{1}{180}x^6 + \cdots + \frac{1 \cdot 4 \cdot 7 \cdots (3n-2)}{(3n)!} x^{3n} + \cdots$$

(a) Find the interval of convergence of the series. (b) Show that there exist two constants a and b such that the function so defined satisfies a differential equation of the form $y'' = x^a y + b$.

40. (a) Show that the series

$$1 - \int_1^2 \frac{dx}{x} + \frac{1}{2} - \int_2^3 \frac{dx}{x} + \frac{1}{3} - \int_3^4 \frac{dx}{x} + \frac{1}{4} - \int_4^5 \frac{dx}{x} + \frac{1}{5} - \cdots$$

is convergent. (b) If S is the sum of the series in (a), deduce that

$$\lim_{n \to \infty} \left(1 + \frac{1}{2} + \frac{1}{3} + \cdots + \frac{1}{n} - \ln n\right) = S.$$

41. (a) Does the series

$$\sum_{n=1}^{\infty} \frac{1}{[1 + (1/n)]^n}$$

converge or diverge? Why? (b) Does the series

$$\sum_{n=1}^{\infty} \frac{1}{[1 + (1/n)]^{n^2}}$$

converge or diverge? Why?

42. If $a_n > 0$ and the series $\sum_{n=1}^{\infty} a_n$ converges, prove that $\sum_{n=1}^{\infty} a_n/(1 + a_n)$ converges.

43. If $1 > a_n > 0$ and $\sum_{n=1}^{\infty} a_n$ converges, prove that $\sum_{n=1}^{\infty} \ln(1 - a_n)$ converges. [*Hint:* First show that $|\ln(1 - a_n)| \leq a_n/(1 - a_n)$, then apply the answer to Problem 35(b).]

44. An infinite product, indicated by $\Pi_{n=1}^{\infty}(1 + a_n)$, is said to converge if the series $\sum_{n=1}^{\infty} \ln(1 + a_n)$ converges. (The series is the natural logarithm of the product.) Prove that the product converges if every $a_n > -1$ and $\sum_{n=1}^{\infty} |a_n|$ converges. [*Hint:* Show that

$$|\ln(1 + a_n)| \leq |a_n|/(1 - |a_n|) < 2|a_n|$$

when $|a_n| < \frac{1}{2}$.]

CHAPTER 17

COMPLEX NUMBERS AND FUNCTIONS

17–1 Invented number systems. In this chapter we shall discuss complex numbers. These are expressions of the form $a + ib$, where a and b are "real" numbers and i is a symbol for $\sqrt{-1}$. Unfortunately, the words "real" and "imaginary" have connotations which somehow place $\sqrt{-1}$ in a less favorable position than $\sqrt{2}$ in our minds. As a matter of fact, a good deal of imagination, in the sense of *inventiveness*, has been required to construct the *real* number system which forms the basis of the calculus we have studied thus far. In this article we shall review the various stages of this invention. The further invention of a complex number system does not then seem to be so strange. It is fitting for us to study such a system, since modern engineering has found therein a convenient language for expressing vibratory motion, harmonic oscillation, damped vibrations, alternating currents, and other wave phenomena.

The earliest stage of development of man's number consciousness was his recognition of the *counting numbers* 1, 2, 3, . . . , which we now refer to as the *positive integers*.* Certain simple arithmetical operations can be performed with these numbers without getting outside the system. That is, the system of positive integers is *closed* with respect to the operations of *addition* and *multiplication*. By this we mean that if m and n are any positive integers, then

$$m + n = p \quad \text{and} \quad mn = q \tag{1}$$

are also positive integers. Given the two positive integers on the *left side* of either equation in (1), we can find the positive integer on the right. More than this, we may sometimes specify the positive integers m and p and find a positive integer n such that $m + n = p$. For instance, $3 + n = 7$ can be *solved* when the only numbers we know are the positive integers. But the equation $7 + n = 3$ cannot be solved unless we enlarge our number system. Man therefore used his *imagination* and invented the number concepts which we denote by zero and the *negative* integers. In a civilization which recognizes all the integers

$$\ldots, -3, -2, -1, 0, 1, 2, 3, \ldots, \tag{2}$$

an educated man may always find the missing integer which solves the equation $m + n = p$ when he is given two of the integers in the equation.

---

* Also called *natural numbers.*

Suppose our educated man also knows how to multiply any two integers of the set in (2). If, in Eq. (1), he is given m and q, he discovers that sometimes he can find n and sometimes he can't. If his *imagination* is still in good working order he may be inspired to invent still more numbers and introduce fractions, which are just ordered pairs m/n of integers m and n. The number zero has special properties that may bother him for awhile, but he ultimately discovers that it is handy to have all ratios of integers m/n, excluding only those having zero in the denominator. This system, called the set of *rational numbers,* is now rich enough for him to perform the so-called *rational operations* of

1. (a) addition,   2. (a) multiplication,
   (b) subtraction   (b) division

FIGURE 17-1

on any two numbers in the system, *except that he cannot divide by zero.*

The geometry of the unit square (Fig. 17–1) and the Pythagorean Theorem showed that man could construct a geometrical line segment which, in terms of some basic unit of length, has length equal to $\sqrt{2}$. Thus man could solve the equation

$$x^2 = 2$$

by means of a geometrical construction. But then he discovered that the line segment representing $\sqrt{2}$ and the line segment representing the unit of length 1 were incommensurable quantities. This means that their ratio $\sqrt{2}/1$ cannot be expressed as the ratio of two *integral* multiples of some other, presumably more fundamental, unit of length. That is, man could not solve the equation $x^2 = 2$ in terms of his rational numbers.

For if there is a rational number whose square is equal to 2, we may find integers p and q such that they have no common factor other than unity, and such that

$$p^2 = 2q^2. \qquad (3)$$

Since p and q are integers, p must then be even, say $p = 2p_1$, where p_1 is an integer. This in turn leads to $2p_1^2 = q^2$, which then says that q must also be even, say $q = 2q_1$, where q_1 is also an integer. But this is contrary to our choice of p and q as integers having no common factor other than unity. Hence there is no rational number whose square is 2.

Our educated man *could,* however, get a *sequence* of rational numbers

$$\frac{1}{1}, \frac{7}{5}, \frac{41}{29}, \frac{239}{169}, \cdots \qquad (4)$$

whose squares form a sequence

$$\frac{1}{1}, \frac{49}{25}, \frac{1681}{841}, \frac{57{,}121}{28{,}561}, \ldots \tag{5}$$

which converges to 2 as its *limit*. This time his *imagination* suggested to him that he needed the concept of a *limit of a sequence* of rational numbers. If we accept the fact that a monotone increasing sequence which is bounded above possesses a limit, and observe that the sequence in (4) has these properties, then we want it to have a limit L. This would also mean, from (5), that $L^2 = 2$, and hence L is *not* one of our rational numbers. If to the *rational* numbers we further add the *limits* of all bounded monotone increasing sequences, we arrive at the system of all "real" numbers. The word *real* is placed in quotes because there is nothing which is either "more real" or "less real" about this system than there is about any other well-defined mathematical system.

Man's *imagination* was called upon at many stages in the development of the real number system from the system of positive integers. In fact, the art of invention was needed at least three times in constructing the systems we have discussed so far:

1. The *first invented* system; the set of *all integers* as constructed from the counting numbers.

2. The *second invented* system; the set of *rational* numbers m/n as constructed from the integers.

3. The *third invented* system; the set of all *"real"* numbers x as constructed from the rational numbers.

These invented systems form a hierarchy in which each system contains the previous system. Each system is also richer than its predecessor in that it permits more operations to be performed without going outside the system. Expressed in algebraic terms, we may say that:

1. In the system of all integers, we can solve all equations of the form

$$x + a = 0, \tag{6}$$

where a may be any integer.

2. In the system of all rational numbers, we can solve all equations of the form

$$ax + b = 0 \tag{7}$$

provided a and b are rational numbers and $a \neq 0$.

3. In the system of all real numbers, we can solve all of the Eqs. (6) and (7) and, in addition, all quadratic equations

$$ax^2 + bx + c = 0 \quad \text{having} \quad a \neq 0 \quad \text{and} \quad b^2 - 4ac \geq 0. \tag{8}$$

Every student of algebra is familiar with the formula that gives the solutions of (8), namely,

$$x = \frac{-b \pm \sqrt{b^2 - 4ac}}{2a}, \tag{9}$$

and with the further fact that when the discriminant, $d = b^2 - 4ac$, is *negative*, the solutions in (9) do *not* belong to any of the systems discussed above. In fact, the very simple quadratic equation

$$x^2 + 1 = 0 \tag{10}$$

is impossible to solve if the only number systems that can be used are the three invented systems so far described.

Thus we come to the *fourth invented* system, the set of all complex numbers $a + ib$. We could, in fact, dispense entirely with the symbol i and use a notation such as (a, b). We would then speak simply of a pair of real numbers a and b. Since, under algebraic operations, the numbers a and b are treated somewhat differently, it is essential to keep the *order* straight. We therefore might say that *the complex number system consists of all ordered pairs of real numbers* (a, b) subject to certain laws to be set forth below. We shall use both the (a, b) notation and the notation $a + ib$. We call a the "real part" and b the "imaginary part" of (a, b). We make the following definitions.

Equality

$a + ib = c + id$ Two complex numbers (a, b) and
if and only if (c, d) are *equal* if and only if $a = c$
$a = c$ and $b = d$.   and $b = d$.

Addition

$(a + ib) + (c + id)$ The sum of the two complex
$= (a + c) + i(b + d)$ numbers (a, b) and (c, d) is the complex number $(a + c, b + d)$.

Multiplication

$(a + ib)(c + id)$ The product of two complex
$= (ac - bd) + i(ad + bc)$ numbers (a, b) and (c, d) is the complex number $(ac - bd, ad + bc)$.

$c(a + ib) = ac + i(bc)$ The product of a real number c and the complex number (a, b) is the complex number (ac, bc).

The set of all complex numbers (a, b) in which the second number is zero has all the properties of the set of ordinary "real" numbers a. For example, addition and multiplication of $(a, 0)$ and $(c, 0)$ give

$$(a, 0) + (c, 0) = (a + c, 0),$$
$$(a, 0) \cdot (c, 0) = (ac, 0),$$

which are numbers of the same type with "imaginary part" equal to zero. Also, if we multiply a "real number" $(a, 0)$ times the "complex number" (c, d), we get

$$(a, 0) \cdot (c, d) = (ac, ad) = a(c, d).$$

In particular, the complex number $(0, 0)$ plays the role of zero in the complex number system and the complex number $(1, 0)$ plays the role of unity.

The number pair $(0, 1)$ which has "real part" equal to zero and "imaginary part" equal to one has the property that its square,

$$(0, 1)(0, 1) = (-1, 0),$$

has "real part" equal to minus one and "imaginary part" equal to zero. Therefore, in the system of complex numbers (a, b), there is a number $x = (0, 1)$ whose square can be added to unity $= (1, 0)$ to produce zero $= (0, 0)$; that is,

$$(0, 1)^2 + (1, 0) = (0, 0).$$

The equation

$$x^2 + 1 = 0$$

therefore has a solution $x = (0, 1)$ in this new number system.

The student is probably more familiar with the $a + ib$ notation than he is with the notation (a, b). And since our laws of algebra for the ordered pairs enable us to write

$$(a, b) = (a, 0) + (0, b) = a(1, 0) + b(0, 1)$$

while $(1, 0)$ behaves like unity and $(0, 1)$ behaves like a square root of minus one, we need not hesitate to write $a + ib$ in place of (a, b). The i associated with b is like a tracer element which tags the "imaginary part" of $a + ib$. We can pass at will from the realm of ordered pairs (a, b) to the realm of expressions $a + ib$, and conversely. But there is nothing less "real" about the symbol $(0, 1)(= i)$ than there is about the symbol $(1, 0)(=1)$, once we have learned the laws of algebra in the complex number system (a, b).

PROBLEMS

1. In the definition of multiplication of complex numbers as ordered pairs of real numbers, the product $(a, b) \cdot (c, d)$ can be found by writing a and b on one line, c and d beneath them, and then:

For the *real* part of the product, multiply the numbers a and c in the first column and from their product subtract the product of the numbers b and d in the second column.

For the *imaginary* part of the product, cross-multiply and add the products ad and bc.

Apply this method to find the following products:

   (a) $(2, 3) \cdot (4, -2)$,   (b) $(2, -1) \cdot (-2, 3)$,   (c) $(-1, -2) \cdot (2, 1)$.

[*Note:* This is the way in which complex numbers are multiplied on modern computing machinery.]

   2. Solve the following equations for the real numbers x and y:

   (a) $(3 + 4i)^2 - 2(x - iy) = x + iy$,

   (b) $\left(\dfrac{1 + i}{1 - i}\right)^2 + \dfrac{1}{x + iy} = 1 + i$,

   (c) $(3 - 2i)(x + iy) = 2(x - 2iy) + 2i - 1$.

17–2 The Argand diagram. In order to reduce any rational combination of complex numbers to a single complex number, we need only apply the laws of elementary algebra and whenever i^2 appears replace it by -1. Of course, we cannot divide by the complex number $(0, 0) = 0 + i0$. But if $a + ib \neq 0$, then we proceed as follows when we have a division:

$$\frac{c + id}{a + ib} = \frac{(c + id)(a - ib)}{(a + ib)(a - ib)} = \frac{(ac + bd) + i(ad - bc)}{a^2 + b^2}.$$

The result is a complex number $x + iy$ with

$$x = \frac{ac + bd}{a^2 + b^2}, \qquad y = \frac{ad - bc}{a^2 + b^2},$$

and $a^2 + b^2 \neq 0$, since $a + ib = (a, b) \neq (0, 0)$. The number $a - ib$ used as multiplier in order to clear the i out of the denominator is called the *complex conjugate* of $a + ib$. It is customary to use $\bar{z}$ (read "z bar") to denote the complex conjugate of z; thus

$$z = a + ib, \qquad \bar{z} = a - ib.$$

Thus, we multiplied the numerator and denominator of the complex fraction $(c + id)/(a + ib)$ by the complex conjugate of the denominator. This will always replace the denommator by a real number.

There are two geometric representations of the complex number $z = x + iy$:

   (a) as the point $P(x, y)$ in the xy-plane, or

   (b) as the vector $\overrightarrow{OP}$ from the origin to P.

In either representation, the x-axis is called the "axis of reals" and the

y-axis is the "imaginary axis." Either representation is called an *Argand diagram*.

In terms of its polar coordinates (r, θ), we have

$$x = r \cos \theta, \qquad y = r \sin \theta,$$

and

$$z = x + iy = r(\cos \theta + i \sin \theta). \tag{1}$$

We define the *absolute value* of a complex number $x + iy$ to be the length r of a vector $\overrightarrow{OP}$ from the origin to $P(x, y)$. We denote the absolute value by vertical bars, thus:

$$|x + iy| = \sqrt{x^2 + y^2}. \tag{2a}$$

Since we can always choose the polar coordinates r and θ so that $r \geq 0$, we have

$$r = |x + iy|. \tag{2b}$$

The polar angle θ is called the *argument* of z and written $\theta = \arg z$. Of course, any integral multiple of 2π may be added to θ to produce another appropriate angle. The *principal value* of the argument will, in this book, be taken to be that value of θ for which $-\pi < \theta \leq +\pi$.

The following equation gives a useful formula connecting a complex number z, its conjugate $\bar{z}$, and its absolute value $|z|$, namely,

$$z \cdot \bar{z} = |z|^2. \tag{2c}$$

We shall show in a later section how $\cos \theta + i \sin \theta$ can be expressed very conveniently as $e^{i\theta}$. But for the present, let us just introduce the abbreviation

$$\operatorname{cis} \theta = \cos \theta + i \sin \theta. \tag{3}$$

Since $\operatorname{cis} \theta$ is what we get from Eq. (1) by taking $r = 1$, we can say that $\operatorname{cis} \theta$ is represented by a *unit* vector that makes an angle θ with the positive x-axis (Fig. 17–3).

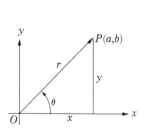

FIGURE 17–2

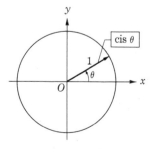

FIGURE 17–3

For example,

$$\text{cis } 0 = \cos 0 + i \sin 0 = 1,$$

$$\text{cis } \frac{\pi}{4} = \cos \frac{\pi}{4} + i \sin \frac{\pi}{4} = \frac{1 + i}{\sqrt{2}},$$

$$\text{cis } \frac{3\pi}{2} = \cos \frac{3\pi}{2} + i \sin \frac{3\pi}{2} = -i.$$

The complex-valued function cis θ has some interesting properties. For example, we shall show that

$$\left.\begin{array}{rl} \text{(a)} & \text{cis } \theta_1 \cdot \text{cis } \theta_2 = \text{cis } (\theta_1 + \theta_2), \\ \text{(b)} & (\text{cis } \theta)^{-1} = \text{cis } (-\theta), \\ \text{(c)} & \dfrac{\text{cis } \theta_1}{\text{cis } \theta_2} = \text{cis } (\theta_1 - \theta_2). \end{array}\right\} \tag{4}$$

To prove the first of these, we simply multiply

$$\text{cis } \theta_1 \cdot \text{cis } \theta_2 = (\cos \theta_1 + i \sin \theta_1)(\cos \theta_2 + i \sin \theta_2)$$
$$= (\cos \theta_1 \cos \theta_2 - \sin \theta_1 \sin \theta_2) + i(\sin \theta_1 \cos \theta_2 + \cos \theta_1 \sin \theta_2).$$

From trigonometry we recognize the expressions in parentheses to be

$$\cos (\theta_1 + \theta_2) = \cos \theta_1 \cos \theta_2 - \sin \theta_1 \sin \theta_2,$$
$$\sin (\theta_1 + \theta_2) = \sin \theta_1 \cos \theta_2 + \cos \theta_1 \sin \theta_2,$$

which gives us

$$\text{cis } \theta_1 \cdot \text{cis } \theta_2 = \cos (\theta_1 + \theta_2) + i \sin (\theta_1 + \theta_2) = \text{cis } (\theta_1 + \theta_2),$$

and establishes (4a). In particular

$$\text{cis } \theta \cdot \text{cis } (-\theta) = \text{cis } (\theta - \theta) = \text{cis } 0 = 1,$$

whence

$$\text{cis } (-\theta) = \frac{1}{\text{cis } \theta},$$

which establishes (4b). Finally, we may combine Eqs. (4a, b) and write

$$\frac{\text{cis } \theta_1}{\text{cis } \theta_2} = (\text{cis } \theta_1)(\text{cis } \theta_2)^{-1} = \text{cis } \theta_1 \cdot \text{cis } (-\theta_2) = \text{cis } (\theta_1 - \theta_2).$$

These properties of cis θ lead to interesting geometrical interpretations of the product and quotient of two complex numbers in terms of the vectors which represent them.

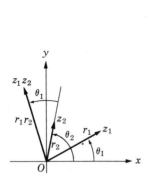

FIGURE 17–4

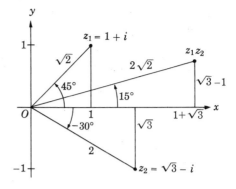

FIGURE 17–5

Product. Let

$$z_1 = r_1 \operatorname{cis} \theta_1, \qquad z_2 = r_2 \operatorname{cis} \theta_2, \tag{5}$$

so that

$$|z_1| = r_1, \ \arg z_1 = \theta_1; \qquad |z_2| = r_2, \ \arg z_2 = \theta_2. \tag{6}$$

Then

$$z_1 z_2 = r_1 \operatorname{cis} \theta_1 \cdot r_2 \operatorname{cis} \theta_2 = r_1 r_2 \operatorname{cis} (\theta_1 + \theta_2)$$

and hence

$$|z_1 z_2| = r_1 r_2 = |z_1| \cdot |z_2|,$$
$$\arg (z_1 z_2) = \theta_1 + \theta_2 = \arg z_1 + \arg z_2. \tag{7}$$

Thus the product of two complex numbers is represented by a vector whose length is the product of the lengths of the two factors and whose argument is the sum of their arguments (Fig. 17–4). In particular, a vector may be rotated in the counterclockwise direction through an angle θ by simply multiplying it by cis θ. Multiplication by i rotates 90°, by -1 rotates 180°, by $-i$ rotates 270°, etc.

EXAMPLE. Let $z_1 = 1 + i, \quad z_2 = \sqrt{3} - i.$

We plot these complex numbers in an Argand diagram (Fig. 17–5) from which we read off the polar representations

$$z_1 = \sqrt{2} \operatorname{cis} \frac{\pi}{4}, \qquad z_2 = 2 \operatorname{cis} \left(-\frac{\pi}{6}\right).$$

Then

$$z_1 z_2 = 2\sqrt{2} \operatorname{cis} \left(\frac{\pi}{4} - \frac{\pi}{6}\right)$$

$$= 2\sqrt{2} \operatorname{cis} \frac{\pi}{12}$$

$$= 2\sqrt{2} \, (\cos 15° + i \sin 15°)$$

$$\approx 2.73 + 0.73 \, i.$$

Quotient. Suppose $r_2 \neq 0$ in Eq. (5). Then

$$\frac{z_1}{z_2} = \frac{r_1 \operatorname{cis} \theta_1}{r_2 \operatorname{cis} \theta_2} = \frac{r_1}{r_2} \operatorname{cis} (\theta_1 - \theta_2).$$

Hence

$$\left| \frac{z_1}{z_2} \right| = \frac{r_1}{r_2} = \frac{|z_1|}{|z_2|},$$

$$\arg (z_1/z_2) = \theta_1 - \theta_2 = \arg z_1 - \arg z_2.$$

That is, we divide lengths and subtract angles. In the example above, if we divide z_1 by z_2, we would thus have

$$\frac{1 + i}{\sqrt{3} - i} = \frac{\sqrt{2} \operatorname{cis} \pi/4}{2 \operatorname{cis} (-\pi/6)} = \frac{\sqrt{2}}{2} \operatorname{cis} (5\pi/12)$$

$$\approx 0.707 \,(\cos 75° + i \sin 75°)$$

$$\approx 0.183 + 0.683 \, i.$$

Powers. If n is a positive integer, we may apply the product formulas, Eq. (7), to find

$$z^n = z \cdot z \cdot z \cdot \,\cdots\, \cdot z \quad (n \text{ factors})$$

when

$$z = r \operatorname{cis} \theta.$$

Doing so, we obtain

$$(r \operatorname{cis} \theta)^n = r^n \operatorname{cis} (\theta + \theta + \cdots + \theta) \quad (n \text{ summands})$$

$$= r^n \operatorname{cis} n\theta. \tag{8}$$

In vector language, we see that the length, $r = |z|$, is raised to the nth power and the angle, $\theta = \arg z$, is multiplied by n.

In particular, if we place $r = 1$ in Eq. (8), we obtain *De Moivre's theorem:*

$$\boxed{(\cos \theta + i \sin \theta)^n = \cos n\theta + i \sin n\theta.} \tag{9}$$

If we expand the left side of this equation by the binomial theorem and reduce it to the standard form $a + ib$, we obtain formulas for $\cos n\theta$ and $\sin n\theta$ as polynomials of degree n in $\cos \theta$ and $\sin \theta$.

EXAMPLE. If we take $n = 3$ in Eq. (9), we have

$$(\cos \theta + i \sin \theta)^3 = \cos 3\theta + i \sin 3\theta.$$

The left side of this equation is

$$\cos^3 \theta + 3 \, i \cos^2 \theta \sin \theta - 3 \cos \theta \sin^2 \theta - i \sin^3 \theta.$$

The real part of this must equal $\cos 3\theta$ and the imaginary part must equal $\sin 3\theta$; hence

$$\cos 3\theta = \cos^3 \theta - 3 \cos \theta \sin^2 \theta,$$

$$\sin 3\theta = 3 \cos^2 \theta \sin \theta - \sin^3 \theta.$$

Roots. If $z = r \operatorname{cis} \theta$ is a complex number different from zero and n is a positive integer, then there are precisely n different complex numbers $w_0, w_1, \ldots, w_{n-1}$, each of which is an nth root of z. For, let $w = \rho \operatorname{cis} \alpha$ be an nth root of $z = r \operatorname{cis} \theta$, so that

$$w^n = z$$

or

$$\rho^n \operatorname{cis} n\alpha = r \operatorname{cis} \theta. \tag{10}$$

Then

$$\rho = \sqrt[n]{r} \tag{11}$$

is the real, positive, nth root of r. As regards the angle, although we cannot say that $n\alpha$ and θ must be equal, we can say that they may differ only by an integral multiple of 2π. That is,

$$n\alpha = \theta + 2k\pi, \qquad k = 0, \pm 1, \pm 2, \ldots \tag{12}$$

Therefore

$$\alpha = \frac{\theta}{n} + k \frac{2\pi}{n}.$$

Hence all nth roots of $z = r \operatorname{cis} \theta$ are given by

$$\sqrt[n]{r \operatorname{cis} \theta} = \sqrt[n]{r} \operatorname{cis} \left(\frac{\theta}{n} + k \frac{2\pi}{n} \right), \qquad k = 0, \pm 1, \pm 2, \ldots \tag{13}$$

Remark. It might appear that there are infinitely many different answers corresponding to the infinitely many possible values of k. But one readily sees that $k = n + m$ gives the same answer as $k = m$ in Eq. (13). Thus we need only take n consecutive values for k to obtain all the different nth roots of z. For convenience, we may take

$$k = 0, 1, 2, \ldots, n - 1.$$

It is worth noting that all the nth roots of $r \operatorname{cis} \theta$ lie on a circle centered at the origin O and having radius equal to the real, positive nth root of r. One of them has argument $\alpha = \theta/n$. The others are uniformly spaced around the circumference of the circle, each being separated from its neighbors by an angle equal to $2\pi/n$. Figure 17–6 illustrates the placement of the three cube roots, w_0, w_1, w_2, of the complex number $z = r \operatorname{cis} \theta$.

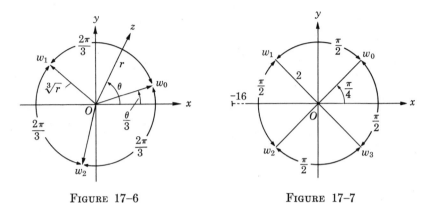

FIGURE 17–6   FIGURE 17–7

EXAMPLE. Find the four fourth roots of -16.

Solution. As our first step, we plot the given number in an Argand diagram (Fig. 17–7) and determine its polar representation r cis θ. Here,

$$z = -16, \qquad r = +16, \qquad \theta = \pi.$$

One of the fourth roots of 16 cis π is 2 cis $(\pi/4)$. We obtain others by successive additions of $2\pi/4 = \pi/2$ to the argument of this first one. Hence

$$\sqrt[4]{16 \text{ cis } \pi} = 2 \text{ cis} \left(\frac{\pi}{4}, \frac{3\pi}{4}, \frac{5\pi}{4}, \frac{7\pi}{4} \right)$$

and the four roots are

$$w_0 = 2\left[\cos \frac{\pi}{4} + i \sin \frac{\pi}{4} \right] = \sqrt{2}(1 + i),$$

$$w_1 = 2\left[\cos \frac{3\pi}{4} + i \sin \frac{3\pi}{4} \right] = \sqrt{2}(-1 + i),$$

$$w_2 = 2\left[\cos \frac{5\pi}{4} + i \sin \frac{5\pi}{4} \right] = \sqrt{2}(-1 - i),$$

$$w_3 = 2\left[\cos \frac{7\pi}{4} + i \sin \frac{7\pi}{4} \right] = \sqrt{2}(1 - i).$$

Remark. The reader may well say that the invention of $\sqrt{-1}$ is all well and good and leads to a number system which is richer than the real number system alone. But where will this process end? Are we also going to invent still more systems so as to obtain $\sqrt[4]{-1}$, $\sqrt[6]{-1}$, and so on? By now it should be clear that this is not necessary. These numbers are already expressible in terms of the complex number system $a + ib$. In fact, the *fundamental theorem of algebra* (which is rather difficult to prove;

we can only state it here) says that: Every polynomial equation of the form

$$a_0 z^n + a_1 z^{n-1} + a_2 z^{n-2} + \cdots + a_{n-1} z + a_n = 0$$

in which the coefficients $a_0, a_1, \ldots, a_n$ are any complex numbers, whose degree n is greater than or equal to one, and whose leading coefficient a_0 is not zero, possesses precisely n roots in the complex number system, provided each multiple root of multiplicity m is counted as m roots.

Problems

1. Show by means of an Argand diagram that the law for addition of complex numbers is the same as the parallelogram law for adding vectors.

2. How may the following complex numbers be obtained from $z = x + iy$ geometrically? Sketch. (a) $\bar{z}$, (b) $(-\bar{z})$, (c) $-z$, (d) $1/z$.

3. Show that the conjugate of the sum (product, or quotient) of two complex numbers z_1 and z_2 is the same as the sum (product, or quotient) of their conjugates.

4. (a) Extend the results of Problem 3 to show that $f(\bar{z}) = \overline{f(z)}$ if $f(z) = a_0 z^n + a_1 z^{n-1} + \cdots + a_{n-1} z + a_n$ is a polynomial with real coefficients $a_0, a_1, \ldots, a_n$. (b) If z is a root of the equation $f(z) = 0$, where $f(z)$ is a polynomial with real coefficients as in part (a) above, show that the conjugate $\bar{z}$ is also a root of the equation. [*Hint:* Let $f(z) = u + iv = 0$, then both u and v are zero. Now make use of the fact that $f(\bar{z}) = \overline{f(z)} = u - iv$.]

5. Show that $|\bar{z}| = |z|$.

6. If z and $\bar{z}$ are equal, what can you say about the location of the point z in the complex plane?

7. Let $R(z)$, $I(z)$ denote respectively the real and imaginary parts of z. Show that:

(a) $z + \bar{z} = 2R(z)$,   (b) $z - \bar{z} = 2iI(z)$,
(c) $|R(z)| \leq |z|$,   (d) $|z_1 + z_2|^2 = |z_1|^2 + |z_2|^2 + 2R(z_1 \bar{z}_2)$,
(e) $|z_1 + z_2| \leq |z_1| + |z_2|$.

8. Show that the distance between the two points z_1 and z_2 in an Argand diagram is equal to $|z_1 - z_2|$.

In Problems 9–13, indicate graphically the locus of points $z = x + iy$ that satisfy the given conditions:

9. (a) $|z| = 2$,   (b) $|z| < 2$,   (c) $|z| > 2$
10. $|z - 1| = 2$ 11. $|z + 1| = 1$
12. $|z + 1| = |z - 1|$ 13. $|z + i| = |z - 1|$

Express the answer to each of the Problems 14–17 in the form $r \operatorname{cis} \theta$, with $r \geq 0$ and $-\pi < \theta \leq \pi$. Sketch.

14. $(1 + \sqrt{-3})^2$ 15. $\dfrac{1 + i}{1 - i}$

16. $\dfrac{1 + i\sqrt{3}}{1 - i\sqrt{3}}$ 17. $(2 + 3i)(1 - 2i)$

18. Use De Moivre's theorem to express $\cos 4\theta$ and $\sin 4\theta$ as polynomials in $\cos \theta$ and $\sin \theta$.

19. Find the three cube roots of unity.

20. Find the two square roots of i.

21. Find the three cube roots of $-8i$.

22. Find the six sixth roots of 64.

23. Find the four roots of the equation $z^4 - 2z^2 + 4 = 0$.

24. Find the six roots of the equation $z^6 + 2z^3 + 2 = 0$.

25. Find all roots of the equation $x^4 + 4x^2 + 16 = 0$.

26. Solve: $x^4 + 1 = 0$.

17–3 The complex variable. A set S of complex numbers $z = x + iy$ may be represented by points in an Argand diagram. For instance, S might be all complex z for which $|z| \leq 1$. The corresponding points in the Argand diagram, or in the z-plane as it is called, then would be all points inside or on the circumference of a circle of radius 1 centered at O. During a discussion, we might wish to consider the symbol z as representing any one of the complex numbers in the set S. We would then think of z as a variable whose domain is S. Or, we may wish to consider a moving point which starts at time $t = 0$ from the point z_0 and moves continuously along some path in the z-plane as t increases to a second value, say $t = 1$. We would again consider the complex number z associated with this moving point (x, y) by the equation $z = x + iy$ to be a variable. This time it is a dependent variable, since its value depends upon the value of t.

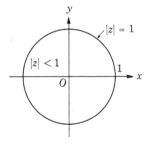

FIGURE 17–8

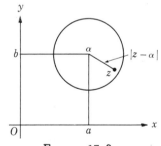

FIGURE 17–9

We say that the complex variable $z = x + iy$ approaches the *limit* $\alpha = a + ib$ if the **distance** between z and α approaches zero. That is,

$$z \rightarrow \alpha \qquad \text{if and only if} \qquad |z - \alpha| \rightarrow 0. \tag{1}$$

If we imagine z to be a function of time, we would say, for example, that

$$\lim_{t \rightarrow 1} z = \alpha \tag{2}$$

provided it is true that

$$\lim_{t \to 1} |z - \alpha| = 0. \tag{3}$$

One way of interpreting Eq. (3) is to say that if it holds, then one may prescribe as small a circle about α as center as one pleases, and the point $z = x + iy$ will be inside that circle for all values of t sufficiently close to 1. That is, $|z - \alpha|$ is small when $|t - 1|$ is small. Since

$$|z - \alpha| = |(x + iy) - (a + ib)|$$
$$= |(x - a) + i(y - b)|$$
$$= \sqrt{(x - a)^2 + (y - b)^2} \le |x - a| + |y - b|,$$

while both

$$|x - a| \quad \text{and} \quad |y - b| \quad \text{are} \quad \le |z - \alpha|,$$

we see that

$$\boxed{z \to \alpha \quad \text{if and only if} \quad x \to a \quad \text{and} \quad y \to b.} \tag{4}$$

For both $|x - a|$ and $|y - b|$ are small when $|z - \alpha|$ is small; and conversely, if both $|x - a|$ and $|y - b|$ are small, then $|z - \alpha|$ is also small.

Function. We say that w is a single-valued function of z on a domain S and write

$$w = f(z), \qquad z \text{ in } S \tag{5}$$

if to each z in the set S there corresponds a complex number $w = u + iv$. For instance, S may be the set of all complex numbers and

$$w = z^2. \tag{6}$$

For each point $z = x + iy$ in the z-plane, Eq. (6) produces a complex number $w = u + iv$:

$$u + iv = (x + iy)^2 = x^2 + 2ixy + i^2y^2 = (x^2 - y^2) + i(2xy). \tag{7}$$

One way of representing such a function graphically is by means of a technique called "mapping." For example, we may use Eq. (7) to map a vertical line, $x = a$, into the w-plane. What does the image point w do as the z point traverses the line $x = a$ from $y = -\infty$ to $y = +\infty$? To find out, we separate the real and imaginary parts of Eq. (7) and obtain

$$u = x^2 - y^2 = a^2 - y^2, \qquad v = 2xy = 2ay. \tag{8a}$$

These equations are parametric equations (in terms of the parameter y) of the parabola

$$v^2 = 4a^2(a^2 - u). \tag{8b}$$

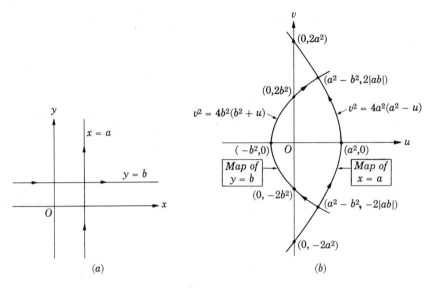

FIGURE 17–10

For the case illustrated in Fig. 17–10, a is positive, hence $v = 2ay$ has the same sign as y. Thus as the z point moves up along the line $x = a$ from $y = -\infty$ to $y = +\infty$, the w point moves upward along the parabola, (8b), in the direction indicated by the arrows in the figure.

Similarly, the map in the w-plane of the line $y = b$ has parametric equations

$$u = x^2 - b^2, \qquad v = 2bx, \qquad -\infty < x < +\infty, \qquad (9a)$$

which represent the parabola

$$v^2 = 4b^2(b^2 + u). \qquad (9b)$$

It is easily seen from (8a, b) that the line $x = -a$ maps into the same parabola (8b) as does the line $x = a$; but this time the parabola is described in the opposite sense as y varies from $-\infty$ to $+\infty$. Similarly, the line $y = -b$ maps into the same parabola as does the line $y = b$. These phenomena are to be expected, since the point z and the point $-z$ both map into the same point $w = z^2 = (-z)^2$ in the w-plane.

Continuity. A function $w = f(z)$ which is defined throughout some neighborhood of the point $z = \alpha$ is said to be *continuous* at α if

$$|f(z) - f(\alpha)| \to 0 \qquad \text{as} \qquad |z - \alpha| \to 0. \qquad (10)$$

Expressed in the language of mapping, the conditions in (10) say simply that the point w which is the image of z is near the point β which is the

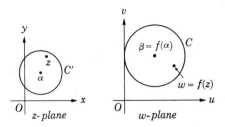

FIGURE 17–11

image of α when z is near α. That is, the image points are close to each other when the original points are. Another way of saying it is that when a small circle C is prescribed in the w-plane with β as its center, then it is possible to describe a circle C' in the z-plane with center at α and radius sufficiently small so that whenever z is inside C' the image point w is guaranteed to be inside C. (See Fig. 17–11).

EXAMPLE. $f(z) = z^2$ is continuous at any point $z = \alpha$. For we have

$$|f(z) - f(\alpha)| = |z^2 - \alpha^2| = |(z - \alpha)(z + \alpha)| = |z - \alpha| \cdot |z + \alpha|.$$

Now as $z \to \alpha$, we have

$$\lim_{z \to \alpha} (z + \alpha) = 2\alpha,$$

so that

$$\lim_{z \to \alpha} |f(z) - f(\alpha)| = \lim_{z \to \alpha} |(z - \alpha)| \cdot |(z + \alpha)|$$

$$= |2\alpha| \lim_{z \to \alpha} |z - \alpha| = 0,$$

so that condition (10) is satisfied.

PROBLEMS

1. In connection with the function $w = z^2$ discussed in the text, sketch the maps in the w-plane of the following figures in the z-plane. [*Hint:* Use polar coordinates.]

(a) $|z| = 1$, $0 \le \arg z \le \pi$;   (b) $|z| = 2$, $\pi/2 \le \arg z \le \pi$;
(c) $\arg z = \pi/4$;   (d) $|z| < 1$, $-\pi < \arg z \le 0$;
(e) the x-axis;   (f) the y-axis.

2. Show that the two parabolas in the w-plane in Fig. 17–10 intersect orthogonally if neither a nor b is zero.

3. Show that the function $w = z^3$ maps the wedge $0 \le \arg z \le \pi/3$ in the z-plane onto the upper half of the w-plane. Use polar coordinates and sketch.

4. Show that $f(z) = z^3$ is continuous at $z = \alpha$ for any α.

5. Show that $f(z) = 1/z$ is continuous at $z = \alpha$ if $\alpha \ne 0$.

17–4 Derivatives. The derivative of a function $w = f(z)$ is defined in the same way as the derivative of a real-valued function of the real variable x. Namely, the derivative at $z = \alpha$ is

$$f'(\alpha) = \lim_{z \to \alpha} \frac{f(z) - f(\alpha)}{z - \alpha}, \tag{1}$$

provided the limit exists. By saying that the limit in (1) exists, we mean, of course, that there is some complex number, which we have called $f'(\alpha)$, such that

$$\left| f'(\alpha) - \frac{f(z) - f(\alpha)}{z - \alpha} \right| \to 0 \quad \text{as} \quad |z - \alpha| \to 0. \tag{2}$$

Since z may approach α from *any direction* (how does this differ from the real variable case?), the existence of such a limit imposes a rather strong restriction on the function $w = f(z)$.

Thus, the rather simple function

$$w = \bar{z} = f(z), \tag{3}$$

where

$$z = x + iy, \qquad \bar{z} = x - iy$$

can be shown to have no derivative at any point. For if we take $\alpha = a + ib$, then

$$\frac{f(z) - f(\alpha)}{z - \alpha} = \frac{\bar{z} - \bar{\alpha}}{z - \alpha} = \frac{(x - a) - i(y - b)}{(x - a) + i(y - b)}. \tag{4}$$

Now from among the many different ways in which z might approach α, we shall single out for special attention the following two:

(a) along the line $y = b$, and   (b) along the line $x = a$. (See Fig. 17–12.)

In the first case, we therefore take $y = b$ and let $x \to a$. Then Eq. (4) becomes

$$y = b: \quad \frac{f(z) - f(\alpha)}{z - \alpha} = \frac{x - a}{x - a} = +1,$$

so that

$$\lim_{\substack{x \to a \\ y = b}} \frac{f(z) - f(\alpha)}{z - \alpha} = +1. \tag{5a}$$

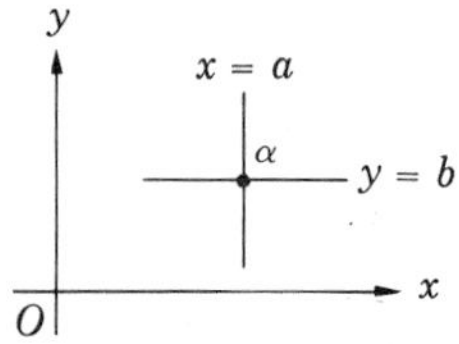

FIGURE 17–12

In the second case, we take $x = a$ and let $y \to b$. This time Eq. (4) becomes

$$x = a: \quad \frac{f(z) - f(\alpha)}{z - \alpha} = \frac{-i(y - b)}{i(y - b)} = -1,$$

and hence

$$\lim_{\substack{x=a \\ y \to b}} \frac{f(z) - f(\alpha)}{z - \alpha} = -1. \tag{5b}$$

Since these two different paths along which z may approach α lead to two different answers, there is no single complex number which we can call $f'(\alpha)$ in Eq. (1) or (2). That is, the function $w = \bar{z}$ does not possess a derivative. *Question:* Is the function $w = \bar{z}$ *continuous* for some, none, or all values of z? Can you justify your answer?

In terms of the Δ-notation, we may call

$$z - \alpha = \Delta z, \qquad f(z) - f(\alpha) = \Delta w$$

and say that $w = f(z)$ has a derivative

$$\frac{dw}{dz} = \lim_{\Delta z \to 0} \frac{\Delta w}{\Delta z} \tag{6}$$

provided the limit exists and is independent of the manner in which $\Delta z \to 0$.

The formulas for differentiating sums, products, quotients, and powers are the same for the complex variable z as for the real variable x. In other words, if c is any complex constant, n is a positive integer, and if $f(z)$ and $g(z)$ are functions which have derivatives at $z = \alpha$, then at $z = \alpha$:

1. $\dfrac{dc}{dz} = 0,$ 2. $\dfrac{dcf(z)}{dz} = c\,\dfrac{df(z)}{dz},$

3. $\dfrac{d[f(z) + g(z)]}{dz} = \dfrac{df(z)}{dz} + \dfrac{dg(z)}{dz},$

4. $\dfrac{d}{dz}[f(z)g(z)] = f(z)\,\dfrac{dg(z)}{dz} + g(z)\,\dfrac{df(z)}{dz},$

5. $\dfrac{d}{dz}\dfrac{f(z)}{g(z)} = \dfrac{g(z)\,\dfrac{df(z)}{dz} - f(z)\,\dfrac{dg(z)}{dz}}{[g(z)]^2},$ $g(z) \neq 0,$

6. (a) $\dfrac{d}{dz}[f(z)]^n = n[f(z)]^{n-1}\,\dfrac{df(z)}{dz},$ (b) $\dfrac{d(z^n)}{dz} = nz^{n-1}.$

These formulas may all be derived rather easily in the Δ-notation, provided one first proves that the limit of a sum, product, or quotient of two complex functions is the sum, product, or quotient of their limits (always, of course, excluding division by zero) provided the individual limits exist. We shall omit these proofs and content ourselves here with a simple example.

EXAMPLE. Show that

$$\frac{d(z^3)}{dz} = 3z^2.$$

Solution. Let $w = z^3$. Then

$$w + \Delta w = z^3 + 3z^2 \Delta z + 3z (\Delta z)^2 + (\Delta z)^3,$$

$$\frac{\Delta w}{\Delta z} = 3z^2 + 3z (\Delta z) + (\Delta z)^2,$$

and

$$\left| \frac{\Delta w}{\Delta z} - 3z^2 \right| = |3z + \Delta z| \cdot |\Delta z| \to 0 \quad \text{as} \quad \Delta z \to 0. \tag{7}$$

Therefore,

$$\lim_{\Delta z \to 0} \frac{\Delta w}{\Delta z} = 3z^2;$$

that is,

$$\frac{d(z^3)}{dz} = 3z^2.$$

Note that it makes no difference *how* Δz approaches zero in (7) above. When $|\Delta z|$ is small, the whole right side of the equation is small.

PROBLEMS

In Problems 1–3, find the derivative with respect to z of the given function at the given point z_0.

1. $\dfrac{z + 1}{z - 1}$, $z_0 = 1 + i$

2. $z^3 + 3z^2 + 3z + 2$, $z_0 = -1 + 2i$

3. $\sqrt{z^2 + 1}$, $z_0 = (1 + i)/\sqrt{2}$. (Here we get *two* answers, depending upon our choice of the square root.)

4. Use the definition in Eq. (1) to find $f'(\alpha)$ if $f(z) = 1/z$ and $\alpha \neq 0$.

17–5 Cauchy-Riemann differential equations. If the complex function $w = u + iv = f(z)$ is differentiable (i.e., has a derivative) at the point $\alpha = a + ib$, then by making $z \to \alpha$, once along the line $y = b$ (i.e., take $\Delta y = 0$ and make $\Delta x \to 0$) and then along the line $x = a$ (i.e., take $\Delta x = 0$ and make $\Delta y \to 0$), we quickly learn that the equations

$$\boxed{\frac{\partial u}{\partial x} = \frac{\partial v}{\partial y} \quad \text{and} \quad \frac{\partial v}{\partial x} = -\frac{\partial u}{\partial y}} \tag{1}$$

must be satisfied at the point (a, b).

For, assuming that dw/dz does exist at $z = \alpha$, we have

$$f'(\alpha) = \lim_{\substack{\Delta y = 0 \\ \Delta x \to 0}} \frac{\Delta u + i\,\Delta v}{\Delta x + i\,\Delta y} = \lim_{\Delta x \to 0} \left(\frac{\Delta u}{\Delta x} + i\,\frac{\Delta v}{\Delta x} \right)$$

$$= \left(\frac{\partial u}{\partial x} + i\,\frac{\partial v}{\partial x} \right)_{z=\alpha} \tag{2a}$$

and also

$$f'(\alpha) = \lim_{\substack{\Delta x = 0 \\ \Delta y \to 0}} \frac{\Delta u + i\,\Delta v}{\Delta x + i\,\Delta y} = \lim_{\Delta y \to 0} \left(\frac{\Delta u}{i\,\Delta y} + \frac{\Delta v}{\Delta y} \right)$$

$$= \left(\frac{1}{i}\frac{\partial u}{\partial y} + \frac{\partial v}{\partial y} \right)_{z=\alpha}$$

$$= \left(-i\frac{\partial u}{\partial y} + \frac{\partial v}{\partial y} \right)_{z=\alpha}. \tag{2b}$$

We have now only to equate the real and imaginary parts of these two expressions for $f'(\alpha)$, Eq. (2a, b), in order to obtain the results in Eq. (1).

These relationships which connect the four partial derivatives of u and v with respect to x and y are known as the *Cauchy-Riemann* differential equations. We have just shown that they must be satisfied at any point where $w = f(z)$ has a derivative. Thus we cannot, in general, specify the functions $u = u(x, y)$ and $v = v(x, y)$ independently and then hope that the resulting function $w = u + iv$ is differentiable with respect to $z = x + iy$. However, if we take functions which do satisfy the Cauchy-Riemann equations and which, in addition, have *continuous* partial derivatives, u_x, u_y, v_x, v_y, then it is true (but we shall not prove it here) that the resulting function $w = u + iv$ is differentiable with respect to z. In a sense, this says that if the derivatives as calculated along the *two* directions $x = a$ and $y = b$ are equal, and if the partial derivatives u_x, etc., are *continuous*, then one will also get the same answer for $f'(\alpha)$ along *all* directions.

If a function $w = f(z)$ has a derivative at every point of some region G in the z-plane, then the function is said to be *analytic* in G. If a function fails to have a derivative at one point α but does have a derivative everywhere else in a region G, we still say that it is analytic in G *except* at α and say that α is a *singular* point of the function. Thus, for example, a rational function $f(z)/g(z)$, where $f(z)$ and $g(z)$ are polynomials, is analytic everywhere except at those points where the denominator is zero. For all points where $g(z) \neq 0$, the function has a derivative

$$\frac{g(z)f'(z) - f(z)g'(z)}{[g(z)]^2}.$$

EXAMPLE. Show that the real and imaginary parts of the function $w = 1/z$ satisfy the Cauchy-Riemann equations at all points where $z \neq 0$.

Solution. Let

$$w = u + iv = \frac{1}{x + iy} = \frac{x - iy}{x^2 + y^2},$$

so that

$$u = \frac{x}{x^2 + y^2}, \qquad v = \frac{-y}{x^2 + y^2}; \qquad x^2 + y^2 \neq 0.$$

Then we find, by calculating the partial derivatives, that

$$\frac{\partial u}{\partial x} = \frac{y^2 - x^2}{(x^2 + y^2)^2} = \frac{\partial v}{\partial y},$$

$$\frac{\partial v}{\partial x} = \frac{2xy}{(x^2 + y^2)^2} = -\frac{\partial u}{\partial y},$$

so that the Cauchy-Riemann equations are satisfied at all points where

$$x^2 + y^2 \neq 0, \qquad \text{that is,} \qquad z \neq 0.$$

PROBLEMS

Find the real and imaginary parts of the functions $w = f(z)$, $w = u + iv$, $z = x + iy$, and show that they satisfy the Cauchy-Riemann equations

1. z^2 2. z^3 3. z^4 4. $1/z^2$, $z \neq 0$

5. If the partial derivatives of first and second order of the real and imaginary parts $u = u(x, y)$, $v = v(x, y)$ of an analytic function $w = f(z)$ are continuous, show that

$$\frac{\partial^2 u}{\partial x^2} + \frac{\partial^2 u}{\partial y^2} = 0$$

and

$$\frac{\partial^2 v}{\partial x^2} + \frac{\partial^2 v}{\partial y^2} = 0.$$

6. Verify that the equations in Problem 5 are satisfied by the real and imaginary parts of the functions (a) z, (b) z^2, (c) z^3.

17–6 Complex series. The simplest functions of the complex variable $z = x + iy$ are polynomials and rational functions (ratios of polynomials) in z. These have been briefly discussed above. We might now ask whether or not it is possible to make useful definitions of some other elementary functions, such as $\sin z$, $\cos z$, e^z, $\cosh z$, and so on. It is hard for us to imagine $\sin (2 + 3i)$, for example, if we try to think of $2 + 3i$ as meaning an angle. In fact, we may have had trouble thinking of the meaning of the simpler expression $\sin 2$. Of course, in the latter case, we ask ourselves

"2 what?" and then answer "2 radians," and then we can translate this into degrees and look it up in a table. But how was the table itself constructed? Why, by means of the series

$$\sin x = x - \frac{x^3}{3!} + \frac{x^5}{5!} - \frac{x^7}{7!} + \cdots \tag{1}$$

To use the series to calculate sin 2, for example, we don't need to think of radians at all, but just take $x = 2$ as a pure number. To be sure, certain basic trigonometric identities for sin $(x + y)$, cos $(x + y)$, and so on are also used in constructing tables, but the series in Eq. (1) is the basic thing.

Now, we may ask ourselves, why can't we go ahead and define sin $z = \sin(x + iy)$ by a series like (1) but having z in place of x? The answer is, of course, we can do this if we want to and if the series converges. We are therefore led to investigate power series in z, such as

$$\sin z = z - \frac{z^3}{3!} + \frac{z^5}{5!} - \frac{z^7}{7!} + \cdots \tag{2}$$

When y is zero, then $z = x + iy = x$ and the series in (2) is the same as the series in (1). Thus it would not be inconsistent for us to extend the domain of definition of sin z from the real axis into the complex plane by means of the series.

Convergence. We say that a power series

$$\sum_{n=0}^{\infty} a_n z^n = a_0 + a_1 z + a_2 z^2 + \cdots \tag{3}$$

converges at a point z if the sequence of partial sums

$$s_0 = a_0,$$
$$s_1 = a_0 + a_1 z,$$
$$\vdots$$
$$s_n = a_0 + a_1 z + \cdots + a_n z^n \tag{4}$$

tends to a limit as n becomes infinite. If we separate s_n into its real and imaginary parts,

$$s_n = u_n(x, y) + iv_n(x, y), \tag{5}$$

then

$$s_n \to u + iv \quad \text{if and only if} \quad u_n \to u \quad \text{and} \quad v_n \to v. \tag{6}$$

This follows from the fact that

$$|s_n - (u + iv)| = |(u_n - u) + i(v_n - v)|$$
$$= \sqrt{(u_n - u)^2 + (v_n - v)^2}$$

approaches zero if and only if $u_n - u \to 0$ and $v_n - v \to 0$.

We say that the series (3) *converges absolutely* if and only if the corresponding series of absolute values

$$\sum_{n=0}^{\infty} |a_n z^n| = |a_0| + |a_1 z| + |a_2 z^2| + \cdots \tag{7}$$

converges. Since this is a series of nonnegative real numbers, we are already familiar with certain tests (the comparison test, integral test, ratio test) for determining whether or not it converges. Then, if (7) does converge, the following theorem tells us that (3) also converges.

THEOREM. *If a series $\sum_{n=0}^{\infty} a_n z^n$ converges absolutely, then it converges.*

Proof. Separate each term of the series into its real and imaginary parts, say

$$a_k z^k = c_k + i\, d_k, \qquad k = 0, 1, 2, \ldots, \tag{8}$$

where c_k and d_k are real. Then if the series (7) converges, we use the fact that

$$|c_k| \le \sqrt{c_k^2 + d_k^2} = |a_k z^k|, \qquad |d_k| \le \sqrt{c_k^2 + d_k^2} = |a_k z^k|,$$

and the comparison test for nonnegative real series, to tell us that

$$\sum |c_k| \qquad \text{and} \qquad \sum |d_k|$$

both converge. But from this we may also conclude that the series without absolute value signs:

$$\sum c_k \qquad \text{and} \qquad \sum d_k,$$

both converge. Hence

$$\sum (c_k + i\, d_k) = \sum c_k + i \sum d_k$$

also converges. Q.E.D.

EXAMPLE. The series for $\sin z$ in Eq. (2) converges for all complex numbers z, $|z| < \infty$.

Proof. We test (2) for *absolute* convergence and examine

$$\sum_{k=1}^{\infty} \left| \frac{(-1)^{k-1} z^{2k-1}}{(2k-1)!} \right|. \tag{9}$$

As usual when we have a power series, we apply the ratio test. We take

$$U_n = \left| \frac{(-1)^{n-1} z^{2n-1}}{(2n-1)!} \right|$$

and calculate

$$\frac{U_{n+1}}{U_n} = \frac{|z^2|}{2n(2n+1)}.$$

For *any* fixed z such that $|z| < \infty$, we then find

$$\lim_{n\to\infty} \frac{U_{n+1}}{U_n} = \lim_{n\to\infty} \frac{|z^2|}{2n(2n+1)} = 0.$$

Since this limit is less than unity, series (9) converges. That is, series (2) converges *absolutely*. Hence, by our theorem, it also converges without the absolute value signs.

PROBLEMS

Find the region in which each of the following series, Problems 1–5, converges absolutely. Sketch the region of absolute convergence.

1. $1 + z + z^2 + z^3 + \cdots$

2. $1 - 2z + 3z^2 - 4z^3 + \cdots$

3. $(z - 1) - \dfrac{(z - 1)^2}{2} + \dfrac{(z - 1)^3}{3} - \dfrac{(z - 1)^4}{4} + \cdots$

4. $(z + i) + \dfrac{(z + i)^2}{2} + \dfrac{(z + i)^3}{3} + \dfrac{(z + i)^4}{4} + \cdots$

5. $1 - \dfrac{(z + 1)}{2} + \dfrac{(z + 1)^2}{4} - \dfrac{(z + 1)^3}{8} + \dfrac{(z + 1)^4}{16} - \cdots$

6. Show that the series $\sum z^k/k!$ converges absolutely for all $|z| < \infty$.
7. Show that the series $\sum (-1)^k z^{2k}/(2k)!$ converges absolutely for all $|z| < \infty$.
8. Show that the series $\sum (-1)^{k-1} z^k/k$ converges absolutely for $|z| < 1$.
9. Use the series (2) to compute sin 2 to three decimals.

17–7 Certain elementary functions. In addition to defining $\sin z$, we may also define other functions by means of series. Thus, extending formulas which we developed in the case of real valued functions of x, we define the following functions by the series we get when we substitute z for x:

$$e^z = 1 + z + \frac{z^2}{2!} + \frac{z^3}{3!} + \cdots = \sum_{k=0}^{\infty} \frac{z^k}{k!}, \tag{1}$$

$$\sin z = z - \frac{z^3}{3!} + \frac{z^5}{5!} - \frac{z^7}{7!} + \cdots = \sum_{k=1}^{\infty} \frac{(-1)^{k-1} z^{2k-1}}{(2k-1)!}, \tag{2}$$

$$\cos z = 1 - \frac{z^2}{2!} + \frac{z^4}{4!} - \frac{z^6}{6!} + \cdots = \sum_{k=0}^{\infty} \frac{(-1)^k z^{2k}}{(2k)!}, \tag{3}$$

$$\tan^{-1} z = z - \frac{z^3}{3} + \frac{z^5}{5} - \frac{z^7}{7} + \cdots = \sum_{k=1}^{\infty} \frac{(-1)^{k-1} z^{2k-1}}{2k-1}, \quad (4)$$

$$\ln (1 + z) = z - \frac{z^2}{2} + \frac{z^3}{3} - \frac{z^4}{4} + \cdots = \sum_{k=1}^{\infty} (-1)^{k-1} \frac{z^k}{k}. \quad (5)$$

It is easy to show, by the ratio test, that the first three of these series converge absolutely for $|z| < \infty$. The last two converge absolutely if z is inside the unit circle $|z| < 1$, and diverge if $|z| > 1$. We realize that the inverse tangent function is multiple-valued, and the series in (4) gives the so-called *principal value* of $\tan^{-1} z$. We shall show that the logarithm of a complex number is also multiple-valued, and the series in (5) gives the principal value of $\ln (1 + z)$ when $|z| < 1$.

It is a basic theorem in the theory of functions of a complex variable that a power series $\sum a_k z^k$ either

(a) converges only at $z = 0$, or
(b) converges inside a circle $|z| < R$, or
(c) converges for all z, $|z| < \infty$.

The second case occurs when the function represented by the power series is analytic everywhere inside the circle $|z| < R$, but has a singularity on the circle $|z| = R$. In this case, the theorem tells us that the *largest* circle throughout which the series will converge has radius R equal to the distance from $z = 0$ to the nearest singular point of the function. Thus, for example,

$$\frac{1}{1 + z^2} = 1 - z^2 + z^4 - z^6 + \cdots \quad (6)$$

converges in a circle of radius $R = 1$, since the singularities of the function occur at $z = \pm i$, which are at distance $R = 1$ from the origin. We call the circle $|z| = 1$ the "circle of convergence," by which we mean that the series converges for all z *inside* this circle and diverges for any z *outside* it. Behavior *on* the circle of convergence constitutes a difficult problem which we are not prepared to discuss.

Certain basic properties of the elementary functions can be shown to extend from the domain of real variables x to complex variables z by algebraic manipulation with series. For example, we can show that

$$\boxed{e^{z_1} \cdot e^{z_2} = e^{z_1 + z_2}} \quad (7)$$

by substituting the series definitions of the various terms.

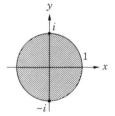

FIGURE 17–13

To prove Eq. (7), we multiply the series for e^{z_1} by the series for e^{z_2} and collect terms of like degree. By the *degree* of a term

$$z_1^p z_2^q,$$

we mean simply the sum of the exponents $p + q$. We shall focus our attention on all those terms in the product that are of a certain degree, say n. Then we may safely ignore all powers

$$z_1^{n+1}, \quad z_1^{n+2}, \dots \quad \text{and} \quad z_2^{n+1}, \quad z_2^{n+2}, \dots,$$

since these would only enter in terms of degree greater than n. Now we want all terms of the form $z_1^k z_2^{n-k}$, with $k = 0, 1, 2, \dots, n$. When we multiply

$$e^{z_1} = 1 + z_1 + \frac{z_1^2}{2!} + \frac{z_1^3}{3!} + \cdots + \frac{z_1^n}{n!} + \cdots$$

by

$$e^{z_2} = 1 + z_2 + \frac{z_2^2}{2!} + \frac{z_2^3}{3!} + \cdots + \frac{z_2^n}{n!} + \cdots,$$

the following terms are of degree n:

$$\frac{z_1^n}{n!} \cdot 1 + \frac{z_1^{n-1}}{(n-1)!} \cdot z_2 + \frac{z_1^{n-2}}{(n-2)!} \cdot \frac{z_2^2}{2!} + \cdots + \frac{z_1^{n-k}}{(n-k)!} \cdot \frac{z_2^k}{k!} + \cdots$$

$$+ 1 \cdot \frac{z_2^n}{n!} = \sum_{k=0}^{n} \frac{z_1^{n-k} z_2^k}{(n-k)!k!}. \tag{8}$$

On the other hand, the terms of degree n in the series for

$$e^{z_1+z_2} = 1 + (z_1 + z_2) + \frac{(z_1 + z_2)^2}{2!} + \cdots + \frac{(z_1 + z_2)^n}{n!} + \cdots$$

are in the one binomial expression

$$\frac{(z_1 + z_2)^n}{n!} = \frac{1}{n!}\left[z_1^n + n z_1^{n-1} z_2 + \frac{n(n-1)}{2!} z_1^{n-2} z_2^2 + \cdots \right.$$

$$\left. + \frac{n(n-1)\cdots(n-k+1)}{k!} z_1^{n-k} z_2^k + \cdots + z_2^n \right].$$

By noticing that

$$\frac{n(n-1)\cdots(n-k+1)}{k!} \cdot \frac{(n-k)!}{(n-k)!} = \frac{n!}{k!(n-k)!},$$

we may also write this in summation form as

$$\frac{(z_1 + z_2)^n}{n!} = \frac{1}{n!} \sum_{k=0}^{n} \frac{n!}{k!(n-k)!} z_1^{n-k} z_2^k = \sum_{k=0}^{n} \frac{z_1^{n-k} z_2^k}{(n-k)!k!}. \tag{9}$$

A comparison of Eqs. (8) and (9) shows us that we have precisely the same terms of degree n in the product of the two series for e^{z_1} and e^{z_2} that we have in the series for $e^{z_1+z_2}$. The above argument is valid for any positive integer n. For $n = 0$, the terms of degree zero are

$$z_1^0 \cdot z_2^0 = 1 \qquad \text{and} \qquad (z_1 + z_2)^0 = 1$$

respectively, and these again are equal. Thus the terms of degree $n(n = 0, 1, 2, 3, \ldots)$ are the same in the product of the series for e^{z_1} and e^{z_2} as they are in the series for $e^{z_1+z_2}$; that is,

$$(\text{the series for } e^{z_1}) \cdot (\text{the series for } e^{z_2}) = (\text{the series for } e^{z_1+z_2}).$$

Remark. It is not always true that one may multiply two series together and then arrange the terms in groups which are then to be added in the most convenient way. For instance, in multiplying the series for e^{z_1} and e^{z_2} we might have wanted to write the answer as

$$1 \cdot \left(1 + z_2 + \frac{z_2^2}{2!} + \cdots\right) + z_1 \left(1 + z_2 + \frac{z_2^2}{2!} + \cdots\right) + \cdots$$

$$+ \frac{z_1^n}{n!}\left(1 + z_2 + \frac{z_2^2}{2!} + \cdots\right) + \cdots,$$

where we agree to add all terms not containing z_1, then all terms containing only the first power of z_1, then all terms containing only the second power of z_1, and so on. This certainly isn't convenient to do if we are trying to show that the result is the same as

$$1 + (z_1 + z_2) + \frac{(z_1 + z_2)^2}{2!} + \frac{(z_1 + z_2)^3}{3!} + \cdots$$

And conceivably it might lead to a different answer. However, it is shown in more advanced courses in analysis that when both of the series in a product are *absolutely convergent*, then it is permissible to arrange the terms in any way one may wish, provided one ultimately takes all terms into account. The series for e^z does converge absolutely for all values of z. Hence the series for e^{z_1} and e^{z_2} satisfy the requirements of this theorem, and it is permissible to arrange the terms according to ascending degree, as we have done above.

By similar operations with power series, one can show that

$$\sin (z_1 + z_2) = \sin z_1 \cos z_2 + \cos z_1 \sin z_2,$$

$$\cos (z_1 + z_2) = \cos z_1 \cos z_2 - \sin z_1 \sin z_2,$$

$$\sin^2 z + \cos^2 z = 1.$$

One of the most famous results involving the elementary complex functions is the formula

$$e^{iz} = \cos z + i \sin z,$$ (10)

which is known as *Euler's formula*. To establish Eq. (10) we simply substitute iz in place of z in the series (1). The various powers of i that enter can all be reduced to one of the four numbers

$$i, -1, -i, +1$$

by observing that

$$i^2 = -1, \quad i^3 = i^2 \cdot i = -i, \quad i^4 = (i^2)^2 = (-1)^2 = +1, \quad i^5 = i^4 \cdot i = i,$$

and so on. In fact, if n is any integer, then

$$i^{4n} = +1, \quad i^{4n+1} = i, \quad i^{4n+2} = -1, \quad i^{4n+3} = -i.$$

Thus we have

$$e^{iz} = 1 + iz + \frac{(iz)^2}{2!} + \frac{(iz)^3}{3!} + \frac{(iz)^4}{4!} + \frac{(iz)^5}{5!} + \cdots$$

$$= \left(1 - \frac{z^2}{2!} + \frac{z^4}{4!} - \frac{z^6}{6!} + \cdots\right) + i\left(z - \frac{z^3}{3!} + \frac{z^5}{5!} - \frac{z^7}{7!} + \cdots\right)$$

$$= \cos z + i \sin z,$$

where we have recognized the series for $\sin z$ and $\cos z$, Eqs. (2) and (3).

If we make use of Euler's formula (10) and the companion equation

$$e^{-iz} = \cos z - i \sin z,$$ (11)

which results from replacing z by $-z$ in (10), we may express the trigonometric functions of z in terms of exponentials. For example, if we add Eqs. (10) and (11) and then divide by two, we obtain

$$\cos z = \tfrac{1}{2}(e^{iz} + e^{-iz}).$$ (12a)

On the other hand, if we subtract (11) from (10) we may express $\sin z$ in the form

$$\sin z = \frac{1}{2i}(e^{iz} - e^{-iz}).$$ (12b)

The other trigonometric functions of z are defined in the usual way in terms of $\sin z$ and $\cos z$.

Thus, for example,

$$\tan z = \frac{\sin z}{\cos z} = \frac{1}{i} \frac{e^{iz} - e^{-iz}}{e^{iz} + e^{-iz}}.$$

The usual trigonometric identities can be established by expressing the trigonometric functions as exponentials and then making use of the basic identity (7).

For example, suppose we wish to show that

$$\cos^2 z + \sin^2 z = 1.$$

We simply square both sides of Eqs. (12a, b) and add:

$$\cos^2 z + \sin^2 z = \tfrac{1}{4}(e^{2iz} + 2e^0 + e^{-2iz}) - \tfrac{1}{4}(e^{2iz} - 2e^0 + e^{-2iz})$$

$$= \tfrac{1}{4}(4e^0) = 1.$$

Equations (12a, b) show the very intimate relationship between the circular functions and the hyperbolic functions. For if we define, as in the real case,

$$\cosh z = \tfrac{1}{2}(e^z + e^{-z}) = 1 + \frac{z^2}{2!} + \frac{z^4}{4!} + \frac{z^6}{6!} + \cdots,$$

$$\sinh z = \tfrac{1}{2}(e^z - e^{-z}) = z + \frac{z^3}{3!} + \frac{z^5}{5!} + \frac{z^7}{7!} + \cdots,$$

then Eqs. (12a, b) say that

$$\cos z = \cosh iz, \qquad (13a)$$

$$i \sin z = \sinh iz. \qquad (13b)$$

These relationships explain the similarity in form between the identities of circular trigonometry, such as

$$\cos^2 z + \sin^2 z = 1, \qquad (14a)$$

and the corresponding identities of hyperbolic trigonometry, such as

$$\cosh^2 u - \sinh^2 u = 1. \qquad (14b)$$

In fact, any identity in circular functions produces a corresponding identity in hyperbolic functions, provided $\sin^2$ is replaced by $-\sinh^2$. The minus is a consequence of the i in Eq. (13b).

Problems

1. Take $z = (1 + i)/\sqrt{2}$ in Eq. (1), and calculate an approximation to $e^{(1+i)/\sqrt{2}}$ by using the first four terms of the series.

2. Express the sines and cosines in the following identity in terms of exponentials and thereby show that

$$\sin (A + B) = \sin A \cos B + \cos A \sin B$$

is a consequence of the exponential law $e^{z_1} \cdot e^{z_2} = e^{z_1 + z_2}$.

3. By differentiating the appropriate series, Eqs. (1)–(5), term by term, show that

(a) $\dfrac{de^z}{dz} = e^z$,

(b) $\dfrac{d \sin z}{dz} = \cos z$,

(c) $\dfrac{d \cos z}{dz} = -\sin z$,

(d) $\dfrac{d \tan^{-1} z}{dz} = \dfrac{1}{1 + z^2}$,

(e) $\dfrac{d \ln (1 + z)}{dz} = \dfrac{1}{1 + z}$.

4. (a) Show that $y = e^{i\omega x}$ and $y = e^{-i\omega x}$ are solutions of the differential equation

$$\frac{d^2 y}{dx^2} + \omega^2 y = 0.$$

(b) Show that $y = e^{(a+ib)x}$ and $y = e^{(a-ib)x}$ are solutions of the differential equation

$$\frac{d^2 y}{dx^2} - 2a \frac{dy}{dx} + (a^2 + b^2)y = 0.$$

(c) Assuming that a and b are real in part 4(b) above, show that both

$$e^{ax} \cos bx = R(e^{(a+ib)x}) \quad \text{and} \quad e^{ax} \sin bx = I(e^{(a+ib)x})$$

are solutions of the given differential equation.

5. Find values of m such that $y = e^{mx}$ is a solution of the differential equation:

(a) $\dfrac{d^2 y}{dx^2} + 2 \dfrac{dy}{dx} + 5y = 0$,

(b) $\dfrac{d^4 y}{dx^4} + 4y = 0$,

(c) $\dfrac{d^3 y}{dx^3} - 8y = 0$.

6. Show that the point (x, y) describes a unit circle with angular velocity ω if $z = x + iy = e^{i\omega t}$ and ω is a real constant.

7. If x and y are real, show that $|e^{x+iy}| = e^x$.

8. Show that the real and imaginary parts of $w = e^z$ satisfy the Cauchy-Riemann equations.

9. Show by reference to the appropriate series that (a) $\sin (iz) = i \sinh z$, (b) $\cos (iz) = \cosh z$.

10. Show, by reference to the results of Problems 2 and 9, that $\sin (x + iy) = \sin x \cosh y + i \cos x \sinh y$, and find a value of z such that $\sin z = 2$.

11. Show that the real and imaginary parts of $w = \sin z$, Problem 10, satisfy the Cauchy-Riemann equations.

12. Show that $|\sin (x + iy)| = \sqrt{\sin^2 x + \sinh^2 y}$ if x and y are real.

13. Let $z = x + iy$, $w = u + iv$, $w = \sin z$. Show that the line segment $y = $ constant, $-\pi < x \leq +\pi$, in the z-plane maps into the ellipse

$$\frac{u^2}{\cosh^2 y} + \frac{v^2}{\sinh^2 y} = 1$$

in the w-plane.

14. Show that the only complex roots $z = x + iy$ (x and y real) of the equation $\sin z = 0$ are at points on the real axis ($y = 0$) at which $\sin x = 0$.

15. Show that $\cosh (x + iy) = \cosh x \cos y + i \sinh x \sin y$.

16. Show that $|\cosh (x + iy)| = \sqrt{\cos^2 y + \sinh^2 x}$ if x and y are real.

17. If x and y are real and $\cosh (x + iy) = 0$, show that $x = 0$ and $\cos y = 0$.

18. What is the image in the w-plane of a line $x = $ const in the z-plane if (a) $w = e^z$, (b) $w = \sin z$? Sketch.

19. Integrate: $\int e^{(a+ib)x} \, dx$ and, by equating real and imaginary parts, obtain formulas for $\int e^{ax} \cos bx \, dx$ and $\int e^{ax} \sin bx \, dx$.

17–8 Logarithms. In the previous article, we mentioned that the logarithm (as an inverse of the exponential) is a multiple-valued function of z. The multiple-valuedness is introduced by the polar angle θ. We see this when we write

$$z = r \operatorname{cis} \theta$$

or, as we may do in view of Euler's formula,

$$z = re^{i\theta}, \tag{1}$$

and ask that

$$\boxed{\begin{aligned} \log_e z &= \log_e r + \log_e e^{i\theta} \\ &= \ln r + i\theta. \end{aligned}} \tag{2}$$

Then the angle θ may be given its principal value θ_0, $-\pi < \theta_0 \leq \pi$, which leads to the *principal value* of $\log z$,

$$\ln z = \ln r + i\theta_0, \qquad -\pi < \theta_0 \leq \pi. \tag{3}$$

But many other values of θ will still give the same z in Eq. (1), namely,

$$\theta = \theta_0 + 2n\pi, \qquad n = 0, \pm 1, \pm 2, \ldots, \tag{4}$$

and each of these values of θ gives rise, in turn, to a value of $\log z$ (we shall omit writing the base e henceforth), namely,

$$\log z = \ln r + i(\theta_0 + 2n\pi). \tag{5a}$$

In terms of the principal value, we have

$$\boxed{\log z = \ln z + 2n\pi i,} \tag{5b}$$

so that all of the infinitely many different values of $\log z$ differ from the principal value by an integral multiple of $2\pi i$.

EXAMPLE. Find all values of $\log (1 + i)$.

Solution. The complex number $1 + i$ is seen to have polar coordinates $r = \sqrt{2}$, $\theta_0 = \pi/4$ (Fig. 17–14). Hence

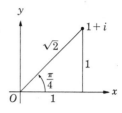

$$1 + i = \sqrt{2}\, e^{i(\pi/4 + 2n\pi)}$$

and

$$\log (1 + i) = \ln \sqrt{2} + i\left(\frac{\pi}{4} + 2n\pi\right),$$

$$n = 0, \pm 1, \pm 2, \ldots$$

FIGURE 17–14

PROBLEMS

1. Find the principal value of $\log z$ for each of the following complex numbers z:

(a) $2 - 2i$, (b) $\sqrt{3} + i$, (c) -4,

(d) $+4$, (e) $2i$, (f) $\dfrac{1 + i}{1 - i}$.

2. Find *all* values of $\log z$ for each of the following complex numbers z:

(a) 2, (b) -2, (c) $2i$,
(d) $-2i$, (e) $i - \sqrt{3}$.

3. Express $w = \tan z$ in terms of exponentials; then solve for z in terms of w and thereby show that

$$\tan^{-1} w = \frac{1}{2i} \log \frac{1 + iw}{1 - iw}.$$

4. (a) Show that

$$\sin^{-1} z = -i \log (iz + \sqrt{1 - z^2}).$$

(b) Find $\sin^{-1} 3$.

5. Sketch the maps in the w-plane of the following loci in the z-plane, under the mapping function $w = \ln z$:

(a) $|z| = $ constant, $-\pi < \arg z \leq +\pi$,
(b) $\arg z = $ constant, $0 < |z| < +\infty$.

REVIEW QUESTIONS FOR CHAPTER 17

1. Define the system of complex numbers.

2. Define, for complex numbers, the concepts of equality, addition, multiplication, and division.

3. Is the system of complex numbers closed under the operations of addition, subtraction, multiplication, division (by numbers $\neq 0$), and raising to powers (including complex exponents; see Article 6–9, Eq. (3))? [A system is said to be *closed* under an operation $\otimes$ if $a \otimes b$ is in the system whenever a and b are.]

4. How may the complex number $a + ib$ be represented graphically in an Argand diagram?

5. Illustrate, on an Argand diagram, how the absolute values and arguments of the product and quotient of two complex numbers z_1 and z_2 are related to the absolute values and the arguments of z_1 and z_2.

6. State De Moivre's theorem, and explain how it may be used to find expressions for $\cos n\theta$ and $\sin n\theta$ as polynomials in $\cos \theta$ and $\sin \theta$.

7. Prove that if n is an even positive integer, then $\cos n\theta$ may be expressed as a polynomial, with integral coefficients, in $\cos^2 \theta$. [Example: $\cos 2\theta = 2 \cos^2 \theta - 1$.]

8. Using an Argand diagram, explain how to find the n complex nth roots of any complex number $a + ib$.

9. On an Argand diagram, illustrate how the conjugate and the reciprocal of a complex number $a + ib$ are related to that number.

10. If the conjugate of a complex number is equal to the number, what else can you conclude about the number?

11. If z is a complex number such that $z = -\bar{z}$, what more can you conclude about z?

12. What is the locus of the complex variable z if:

$$\text{(a)} \ |z - \alpha| = k, \qquad \text{(b)} \ |z - \alpha| < k, \qquad \text{(c)} \ |z - \alpha| > k,$$

when $\alpha = a + ib$ is a given complex number and k is a positive real constant?

13. Define the concept of continuity of a function of a complex variable, $w = f(z)$. Define the derivative of f at $\alpha = a + ib$.

14. What are the Cauchy-Riemann equations, and when are they known to be satisfied?

15. Define convergence of a series of complex numbers.

16. How do we define e^z, $\sin z$, $\cos z$, $\log z$, and $\tan z$ for complex $z = x + iy$?

17. How would you define z^α for complex z and α? Illustrate for $z = 1 + i$, $\alpha = 2i$.

MISCELLANEOUS PROBLEMS FOR CHAPTER 17

1. Let $z = 2 - 2i$, $i = \sqrt{-1}$. (a) Plot the points z, $\bar{z}$, and z^2. (b) Plot the three complex cube roots of z^2 (that is, $z^{2/3}$).

2. Express each of the following complex numbers in the form $re^{i\theta}$ with $r \geq 0$ and $-\pi < \theta \leq \pi$. Sketch.

(a) $(1 + i)(1 - i\sqrt{3})^2$,   (b) $\sqrt[3]{2 - 2i}$ (three answers).

3. Express the following complex numbers in the form $a + bi$.

(a) The four 4th roots of $-16i$,   (b) $\sin^{-1}(5)$.

4. (a) Solve the equation $z^4 + 16 = 0$, obtaining four distinct roots. (b) Express the five roots of the equation $z^5 + 32 = 0$ in polar form.

5. (a) Find all complex numbers z such that $z^4 + 1 + i\sqrt{3} = 0$. (b) Express the number $e^{2+\pi i/4}$ in the form $a + bi$.

6. Plot the complex number $2 - 2\sqrt{3}i$ in an Argand diagram and find (a) its two square roots, (b) the principal value of its logarithm.

7. Find values of r and θ such that $3 + 4i = re^{i\theta}$.

8. If $z = 3 - 3i$, find all values of $\log z$.

9. Find a complex number $a + ib$ that will satisfy the equation

$$e^{a+ib} = 1 - i\sqrt{3}.$$

10. Express the following in the form $a + bi$:

(a) $(-1 - i)^{1/3}$ (write down all the roots),
(b) $\ln(3 + i\sqrt{3})$,
(c) $e^{2+\pi i}$.

11. Let $f(z) = \bar{z} = $ the conjugate of z. (a) Study the behavior of the quotient

$$\frac{f(z) - f(z_1)}{z - z_1}$$

when $z \to z_1$ along straight lines of slope m. (b) From the results of (a) what can you conclude about the derivative of $f(z)$?

12. If $f(z) = \sum_{n=0}^{\infty} a_n z^n$ and $f(\bar{z}) = \overline{f(z)}$, for $|z| < R$, show that the a_n are real.

13. If $f(z) = \sum_{n=0}^{\infty} a_n z^n$ and $f(\bar{z}) = f(z)$, for $|z| < R$, show that $f(z)$ is a constant.

14. Show that $(d^n/d\theta^n)(\cos\theta + i\sin\theta) = i^n(\cos\theta + i\sin\theta)$.

15. In each of the following, indicate graphically the locus of points $z = x + iy$ that satisfy the given condition:

(a) $R(z) > 0$,   (b) $I(z - i) \leq 0$,   (c) $\left|\dfrac{z - i}{z + i}\right| < 1$,

(d) $|e^z| \geq 1$,   (e) $|\sin z| \leq 1$.

16. If $u(x, y)$, $v(x, y)$ are the real and imaginary parts of an analytic function of $z = x + iy$, show that the family of curves $u = constant$ is orthogonal to the family $v = constant$ at every point of intersection where $f'(z) \neq 0$.

17. Let $u(x, y) + iv(x, y) = (x + iy)^2$.   Sketch the curves $u(x, y) = a$, $v(x, y) = b$, for the cases $a = 1, 0, -1$, and $b = 1, 0, -1$. Show that the locus $u = 0$ is not orthogonal to the locus $v = 0$.

18. Verify that the real and imaginary parts of the following functions satisfy Laplace's equation $\phi_{xx} + \phi_{yy} = 0$:

(a) $\sin z$,   (b) $\ln z\ (z \neq 0)$,   (c) e^z,   (d) $\cosh z$.

19. Find all solutions of the following equations:

(a) $z^5 = 32$,   (b) $e^z = -2$,   (c) $\cos z = 10$,
(d) $\tanh z = 2$,   (e) $z = i^i$,   (f) $z^3 + 3z^2 + 3z + 9 = 0$.

CHAPTER 18

DIFFERENTIAL EQUATIONS

18–1 Introduction. A differential equation is an equation that involves one or more derivatives, or differentials. Differential equations are classified as to:

(a) type (namely, *ordinary* or *partial*),

(b) order (that of the highest order derivative which occurs in the equation), and

(c) degree (the exponent of the highest power of the highest order derivative, after the equation has been cleared of fractions and radicals in the dependent variable and its derivatives).

For example,

$$\left(\frac{d^3y}{dx^3}\right)^2 + \left(\frac{d^2y}{dx^2}\right)^5 + \frac{y}{x^2+1} = e^x \tag{1}$$

is an ordinary differential equation, of order three and degree two.

Only "ordinary" derivatives occur when the dependent variable y is a function of a single independent variable x. On the other hand, if the dependent variable y is a function of two or more independent variables, say

$$y = f(x, t),$$

where x and t are independent variables, then partial derivatives of y may occur. For example,

$$\frac{\partial^2 y}{\partial t^2} = a^2 \frac{\partial^2 y}{\partial x^2} \tag{2}$$

is a partial differential equation, of order two and degree one. (It is the one-dimensional "wave equation." A systematic treatment of partial differential equations lies beyond the scope of this book. For a discussion of partial differential equations, including the wave equation, and solutions of associated physical problems, see Kaplan, *Advanced Calculus*, Chapter 10.)

Many physical problems, when formulated in mathematical terms, lead to differential equations. In Article 6–11, for example, we discussed two differential equations from the field of electrical engineering, namely,

$$\frac{dQ}{dt} = -kQ \tag{3}$$

875

and

$$L \frac{di}{dt} + Ri = E. \tag{4}$$

Again, in Article 12–1, we solved the system of differential equations

$$m \frac{d^2x}{dt^2} = 0, \qquad m \frac{d^2y}{dt^2} = -mg \tag{5}$$

which arose from the formulation of the laws of motion of a projectile (neglecting air resistance). Indeed, one of the chief sources of differential equations in mechanics is Newton's second law:

$$\mathbf{F} = \frac{d}{dt} (m\mathbf{v}), \tag{6}$$

where $\mathbf{F}$ is the resultant of the forces acting on a body of mass m and $\mathbf{v}$ is its velocity.

In the field of radiochemistry, the following situation is typical of what may happen. Suppose that, at time t, there are x, y, and z grams respectively of three radioactive substances A, B, and C which have the following properties. A, through radioactive decomposition, transforms into B at a rate proportional to the amount of A present. B, in turn, transforms into C at a rate which is proportional to the amount of B present. Finally, C transforms back into A at a rate which is proportional to the amount of C present. If we call the proportionality factors k_1, k_2, and k_3, respectively, we have the following system of differential equations:

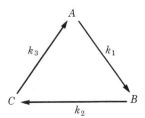

FIGURE 18–1

$$\frac{dx}{dt} = -k_1 x + k_3 z, \qquad \frac{dy}{dt} = k_1 x - k_2 y, \qquad \frac{dz}{dt} = k_2 y - k_3 z. \tag{7}$$

The first of these simply says that the amount of A present at time t, namely x, is decreasing at a rate $k_1 x$ through transformation into substance B, but is gaining at a rate $k_3 z$ from substance C. The other two equations have similar meanings. It is an immediate consequence of Eqs. (7) that

$$\frac{dx}{dt} + \frac{dy}{dt} + \frac{dz}{dt} = 0. \tag{8}$$

From Eq. (8), in turn, we readily deduce that

$$x + y + z = \text{constant.}$$

In other words, in the hypothetical case under consideration, the total amount of substances A, B, and C remains constant.

18–2 Solutions. A function

$$y = f(x)$$

is said to be a *solution* of a differential equation if the latter is identically satisfied when y and its derivatives are replaced throughout by $f(x)$ and its corresponding derivatives. For example, if c_1 and c_2 are any constants, then

$$y = c_1 \cos x + c_2 \sin x \tag{1a}$$

is a solution of the differential equation

$$\frac{d^2y}{dx^2} + y = 0. \tag{1b}$$

A physical problem which translates into a differential equation usually involves additional conditions not expressed by the differential equation itself. In mechanics, for example, the initial position and velocity of the moving body are usually prescribed, as well as the forces. The differential equation, or equations, of motion will usually have solutions in which certain arbitrary constants occur. [As in (1a) above.] However, it will be necessary to assign specific values to these arbitrary constants in order to meet the prescribed initial conditions. (See the examples worked out in Articles 6–11 and 12–1.)

A differential equation of order n will, in general, possess a solution involving n arbitrary constants. (There is a more precise mathematical theorem, which we shall neither state nor prove.) This solution is called the *general* solution. Once this general solution is known, it is only a matter of algebra to determine specific values of the constants if initial conditions are also prescribed. Hence we shall devote our attention to the problem of finding the general solutions of certain types of differential equations.

The subject of differential equations is a complex one. The interested reader may consult textbooks on differential equations,* or on advanced calculus,† for more exhaustive treatments than we shall present here. The field is also the subject of current research by several eminent mathematicians, and nobody "knows all the answers."

In the remainder of this chapter, the following topics will be treated. Throughout, only *ordinary* differential equations will be considered.

---

* See, for example, Martin and Reissner, *Elementary Differential Equations.* Addison-Wesley, 1956.

† See, for example, Kaplan, *Advanced Calculus.* Addison-Wesley, 1952.

1. First order.
   (a) Variables separable.   (c) Linear.
   (b) Homogeneous.   (d) Exact differentials.
2. Special types of second order.
3. Linear equations with constant coefficients.
   (a) Homogeneous.
   (b) Nonhomogeneous.

Several new terms occur in this list, and they will be defined in the appropriate places.

18–3 First order: variables separable. A first order differential equation can be solved by integration if it is possible to collect all y terms with dy and all x terms with dx. That is, if it is possible to write the equation in the form

$$f(y)\, dy + g(x)\, dx = 0,$$

then the general solution is

$$\int f(y)\, dy + \int g(x)\, dx = C,$$

where C is an arbitrary constant.

EXAMPLE. Solve the equation

$$(x + 1)\frac{dy}{dx} = x(y^2 + 1).$$

Solution. We change to differential form, separate the variables, and integrate:

$$(x + 1)\, dy = x(y^2 + 1)\, dx,$$

$$\frac{dy}{y^2 + 1} = \frac{x\, dx}{x + 1},$$

$$\tan^{-1} y = x - \ln|x + 1| + C.$$

PROBLEMS

Separate the variables and solve the following differential equations.

1. $x(2y - 3)\, dx + (x^2 + 1)\, dy = 0$ 2. $x^2(y^2 + 1)\, dx + y\sqrt{x^3 + 1}\, dy = 0$

3. $\dfrac{dy}{dx} = e^{x-y}$ 4. $\sqrt{2xy}\,\dfrac{dy}{dx} = 1$

5. $\sin x \dfrac{dx}{dy} + \cosh 2y = 0$ 6. $\ln x \dfrac{dx}{dy} = \dfrac{x}{y}$

7. $xe^y\, dy + \dfrac{x^2 + 1}{y}\, dx = 0$ 8. $y\sqrt{2x^2 + 3}\, dy + x\sqrt{4 - y^2}\, dx = 0$

9. $\sqrt{1 + x^2}\, dy + \sqrt{y^2 - 1}\, dx = 0$ 10. $x^2 y \dfrac{dy}{dx} = (1 + x)\csc y.$

18–4 First order: homogeneous. A differential equation that can be put into the form

$$\frac{dy}{dx} = F\left(\frac{y}{x}\right) \tag{1}$$

is said to be *homogeneous.* Such an equation can be solved by introducing a new dependent variable,

$$v = \frac{y}{x}. \tag{2}$$

Then

$$y = vx, \qquad \frac{dy}{dx} = v + x\,\frac{dv}{dx},$$

and (1) becomes

$$v + x\,\frac{dv}{dx} = F(v). \tag{3}$$

Equation (3) can be solved by separation of variables:

$$\frac{dx}{x} + \frac{dv}{v - F(v)} = 0. \tag{4}$$

After (4) is solved, the solution of the original equation is obtained when we replace v by y/x.

EXAMPLE. Show that the equation

$$(x^2 + y^2)\,dx + 2xy\,dy = 0$$

is homogeneous, and solve it.

Solution. From the given equation, we have

$$\frac{dy}{dx} = -\frac{x^2 + y^2}{2xy} = -\frac{1 + (y/x)^2}{2(y/x)}.$$

This has the form of Eq. (1), with

$$F(v) = -\frac{1 + v^2}{2v}, \qquad \text{where} \qquad v = \frac{y}{x}.$$

Then Eq. (4) becomes

$$\frac{dx}{x} + \frac{dv}{v + \dfrac{1 + v^2}{2v}} = 0,$$

or

$$\frac{dx}{x} + \frac{2v\,dv}{1 + 3v^2} = 0.$$

The solution of this is

$$\ln|x| + \tfrac{1}{3}\ln(1 + 3v^2) = \tfrac{1}{3}\ln C,$$

or $$x^3(1 + 3v^2) = \pm C.$$

In terms of y and x, the solution is

$$x(x^2 + 3y^2) = C.$$

PROBLEMS

Show that the following equations are homogeneous, and solve.

1. $(x + y) \, dy + (x - y) \, dx = 0$ 2. $x^2 \, dy + (y^2 - xy) \, dx = 0$

3. $(xe^{y/x} + y) \, dx - x \, dy = 0$ 4. $(x^2 + y^2) \, dy - y^2 \, dx = 0$

5. $\dfrac{dy}{dx} = \dfrac{-x + \sqrt{x^2 + y^2}}{y}$

6. If every member of a family of curves is a solution of the differential equation

$$M(x, y) \, dx + N(x, y) \, dy = 0,$$

while every member of a second family of curves is a solution of the related equation

$$N(x, y) \, dx - M(x, y) \, dy = 0,$$

then each curve of the one family is orthogonal to every curve of the other family. Each family is said to be a family of *orthogonal trajectories* of the other. Find the family of solutions of the differential equation

$$\frac{dy}{dx} = \frac{y^2 - x^2}{2xy}$$

and their orthogonal trajectories. Sketch both families of curves.

18–5 First order: linear. The complexity of a differential equation depends primarily upon the way in which the *dependent* variable and its derivatives occur. Of particular importance are those equations that are linear. In a linear differential equation, each term of the equation is of degree one or zero, where, in computing the degree of a term, we add the exponents of the dependent variable and/or any of its derivatives which occur. Thus, for example, (d^2y/dx^2) is of the first degree, while $y(dy/dx)$ is of the second degree because we must add 1 for the exponent of y, and 1 for the exponent of dy/dx.

A differential equation of first order, which is also linear, can always be put into the standard form

$$\boxed{\frac{dy}{dx} + Py = Q,} \tag{1}$$

where P and Q are functions of x.

One method for solving Eq. (1) is to find a function $\rho = \rho(x)$ such that if the equation is multiplied by ρ, the left side becomes the derivative of the product ρy. That is, we multiply (1) by ρ,

$$\rho \frac{dy}{dx} + \rho P y = \rho Q, \tag{1'}$$

and then try to impose upon ρ the condition that

$$\rho \frac{dy}{dx} + \rho P y = \frac{d}{dx}(\rho y). \tag{2}$$

When we expand the right side of (2) and cancel terms, we obtain, as the condition to be satisfied by ρ,

$$\frac{d\rho}{dx} = \rho P. \tag{3}$$

In Eq. (3), $P = P(x)$ is a known function, so we can separate the variables and solve for ρ:

$$\frac{d\rho}{\rho} = P\,dx, \qquad \ln|\rho| = \int P\,dx + \ln C,$$

$$\rho = \pm C e^{\int P\,dx}. \tag{4}$$

Since we do not require the most general function ρ, we may take $\pm C = 1$ in (4) and use

$$\boxed{\rho = e^{\int P\,dx}.} \tag{5}$$

This function is called an *integrating factor* for Eq. (1). With its help, (1') becomes

$$\frac{d}{dx}(\rho y) = \rho Q,$$

whose solution is

$$\boxed{\rho y = \int \rho Q\,dx + C.} \tag{6}$$

Since ρ is given by (5), while P and Q are known from the given differential equation (1), we have in Eqs. (5) and (6) a summary of all that is required to solve (1).

EXAMPLE 1. $\qquad\qquad \dfrac{dy}{dx} + y = e^x.$

Solution. $\qquad\qquad P = 1, \qquad Q = e^x,$

$$\rho = e^{\int dx} = e^x,$$

$$e^x y = \int e^{2x}\,dx + C = \tfrac{1}{2}e^{2x} + C,$$

$$y = \tfrac{1}{2}e^x + Ce^{-x}.$$

EXAMPLE 2.
$$x \frac{dy}{dx} - 3y = x^2.$$

Solution. We put the equation in standard form,

$$\frac{dy}{dx} - \frac{3}{x} y = x,$$

and then read off

$$P = -\frac{3}{x}, \qquad Q = x.$$

Hence

$$\rho = e^{\int -(3/x) \, dx} = e^{-3 \ln x} = \frac{1}{e^{3 \ln x}} = \frac{1}{x^3},$$

and

$$\frac{1}{x^3} y = \int \frac{x}{x^3} \, dx + C = -\frac{1}{x} + C,$$

$$y = -x^2 + Cx^3.$$

Remarks. Note that whenever $\int P \, dx$ involves logarithms, as in the last example, it is profitable to simplify the expression for $e^{\int P \, dx}$ before substituting into Eq. (6). We make use of the properties of the logarithmic and exponential functions:

$$e^{\ln A} = A, \qquad e^{m \ln A} = A^m, \qquad e^{n+m \ln A} = A^m e^n.$$

A differential equation which is linear in y and dy/dx may also be separable, or homogeneous. In such cases, we have a choice of methods of solution. Observe also that an equation which is linear in x and dx/dy can be solved by the technique of this article; one need only interchange the roles of x and y in Eqs. (1), (5), and (6).

PROBLEMS

Solve:

1. $\dfrac{dy}{dx} + 2y = e^{-x}$

2. $2\dfrac{dy}{dx} - y = e^{x/2}$

3. $x\dfrac{dy}{dx} + 3y = \dfrac{\sin x}{x^2}$

4. $x \, dy + y \, dx = \sin x \, dx$

5. $x \, dy + y \, dx = y \, dy$

6. $(x - 1)^3 \dfrac{dy}{dx} + 4(x - 1)^2 y = x + 1$

7. $\cosh x \, dy + (y \sinh x + e^x) \, dx = 0$

8. $e^{2y} \, dx + 2(xe^{2y} - y) \, dy = 0$

9. $(x - 2y) \, dy + y \, dx = 0$

10. $(y^2 + 1) \, dx + (2xy + 1) \, dy = 0$

· **18–6 First order: exact.** An equation that can be written in the form

$$M(x, y)\ dx + N(x, y)\ dy = 0, \qquad (1)$$

and having the property that

$$\frac{\partial M}{\partial y} = \frac{\partial N}{\partial x}, \qquad (2)$$

is said to be *exact*, because its left side is an exact differential. The technique of solving an exact equation consists in finding a function $f(x, y)$ such that

$$df = M\ dx + N\ dy. \qquad (3)$$

Then (1) becomes

$$df = 0$$

and the solution is

$$f(x, y) = C,$$

where C is an arbitrary constant. The method of finding $f(x, y)$ to satisfy (3) is discussed and illustrated in Article 14–13.

We remark, in conclusion, that mathematicians have proved that every first order differential equation

$$P(x, y)\ dx + Q(x, y)\ dy = 0$$

can be made exact by multiplication by a suitable *integrating factor* $\rho(x, y)$. Such an integrating factor has the property that

$$\frac{\partial}{\partial y}\ [\rho(x, y)P(x, y)] = \frac{\partial}{\partial x}\ [\rho(x, y)Q(x, y)].$$

It is not easy to determine ρ from this equation. However, one can often recognize certain combinations of differentials which can be made exact by the use of "ingenious devices."

EXAMPLE. $\qquad x\ dy - y\ dx = xy^2\ dx.$

Solution. The combination $x\ dy - y\ dx$ may "ring a bell" in our memories and cause us to recall the formula

$$d\left(\frac{u}{v}\right) = \frac{v\ du - u\ dv}{v^2} = -\left[\frac{u\ dv - v\ du}{v^2}\right].$$

Therefore we might divide the given equation by x^2, or change signs and divide by y^2. Clearly, the latter approach will be more profitable, so we proceed as follows:

$$x\,dy - y\,dx = xy^2\,dx, \qquad \frac{y\,dx - x\,dy}{y^2} = -x\,dx,$$

$$d\left(\frac{x}{y}\right) + x\,dx = 0, \qquad \frac{x}{y} + \frac{x^2}{2} = C.$$

The same result would be obtained if we wrote our equation in the form

$$(xy^2 + y)\,dx - x\,dy = 0$$

and multiplied by the integrating factor $1/y^2$. This would give

$$(x + 1/y)\,dx - x/y^2\,dy = 0,$$

which is exact, since

$$\frac{\partial}{\partial y}\left(x + \frac{1}{y}\right) = \frac{\partial}{\partial x}\left(-\frac{x}{y^2}\right).$$

Problems

Solve:

1. $(x + y)\,dx + (x + y^2)\,dy = 0$
2. $(2xe^y + e^x)\,dx + (x^2 + 1)e^y\,dy = 0$
3. $(2xy + y^2)\,dx + (x^2 + 2xy - y)\,dy = 0$
4. $(x + \sqrt{y^2 + 1})\,dx - \left(y - \dfrac{xy}{\sqrt{y^2 + 1}}\right)dy = 0$
5. $x\,dy - y\,dx + x^3\,dx = 0$ 6. $x\,dy - y\,dx = (x^2 + y^2)\,dx$
7. $(x^2 + x - y)\,dx + x\,dy = 0$
8. $\left(e^x + \ln y + \dfrac{y}{x}\right)dx + \left(\dfrac{x}{y} + \ln x + \sin y\right)dy = 0$
9. $\left(\dfrac{y^2}{1 + x^2} - 2y\right)dx + (2y\tan^{-1}x - 2x + \sinh y)\,dy = 0$
10. $dy + \dfrac{y - \sin x}{x}\,dx = 0.$

18–7 Special types of second order equations. Certain types of second order differential equations, of which the general form is

$$F\left(x, y, \frac{dy}{dx}, \frac{d^2y}{dx^2}\right) = 0, \tag{1}$$

can be reduced to first order equations by a suitable change of variables.

Type 1. Equations with dependent variable missing. In case Eq. (1) has the special form

$$F\left(x, \frac{dy}{dx}, \frac{d^2y}{dx^2}\right) = 0, \tag{2}$$

we can reduce it to a first order equation by substituting

$$p = \frac{dy}{dx}, \quad \frac{d^2y}{dx^2} = \frac{dp}{dx}.$$

Then Eq. (2) takes the form

$$F\left(x, p, \frac{dp}{dx}\right) = 0,$$

which is of the first order in p. If this can be solved for p as a function of x, say

$$p = \phi(x, C_1),$$

then we can find y by an additional integration:

$$y = \int (dy/dx)\, dx = \int p\, dx = \int \phi(x, C_1)\, dx + C_2.$$

For an example, see Article 10–6, where the differential equation

$$\frac{d^2y}{dx^2} = \frac{w}{H}\sqrt{1 + \left(\frac{dy}{dx}\right)^2}$$

is solved.

Type 2. *Equations with independent variable missing.* In case Eq. (1) does not contain x explicitly but has the form

$$F\left(y, \frac{dy}{dx}, \frac{d^2y}{dx^2}\right) = 0, \tag{3}$$

the substitutions to use are

$$p = \frac{dy}{dx}, \quad \frac{d^2y}{dx^2} = p\frac{dp}{dy}.$$

Then Eq. (3) takes the form

$$F\left(y, p, p\frac{dp}{dy}\right) = 0,$$

which is of the first order in p. Its solution gives p in terms of y, and then a further integration gives the solution of Eq. (3).

EXAMPLE.

$$\frac{d^2y}{dx^2} + y = 0.$$

Solution. Let

$$\frac{dy}{dx} = p, \qquad \frac{d^2y}{dx^2} = \frac{dp}{dx} = \frac{dp}{dy}\frac{dy}{dx} = \frac{dp}{dy}\,p.$$

Then we proceed as follows:

$$p\,\frac{dp}{dy} + y = 0, \qquad p\,dp + y\,dy = 0,$$

$$\frac{p^2}{2} + \frac{y^2}{2} = \frac{C_1^2}{2}, \qquad p = \frac{dy}{dx} = \pm\sqrt{C_1^2 - y^2},$$

$$\frac{dy}{\sqrt{C_1^2 - y^2}} = \pm\,dx, \qquad \sin^{-1}\frac{y}{C_1} = \pm(x + C_2),$$

$$y = C_1 \sin\left[\pm(x + C_2)\right] = \pm C_1 \sin\,(x + C_2).$$

Since C_1 is arbitrary, there is no need for the $\pm$ sign, and we have

$$y = C_1 \sin\,(x + C_2)$$

as the general solution.

PROBLEMS

Solve:

1. $\dfrac{d^2y}{dx^2} + \dfrac{dy}{dx} = 0$ 2. $\dfrac{d^2y}{dx^2} + y\dfrac{dy}{dx} = 0$ 3. $\dfrac{d^2y}{dx^2} + x\dfrac{dy}{dx} = 0$

4. $x\dfrac{d^2y}{dx^2} + \dfrac{dy}{dx} = 0$ 5. $\dfrac{d^2y}{dx^2} - y = 0$ 6. $\dfrac{d^2y}{dx^2} + \omega^2 y = 0$

$(\omega = \text{constant} \neq 0)$

7. A body of mass m is suspended from one end of a spring whose other end is attached to a rigid support. The body is allowed to come to rest, and is then pulled down an additional slight amount A and released. Find its motion. [*Hint:* Assume Newton's second law of motion and Hooke's law (which says that the tension in the spring is proportional to the amount it is stretched). Let x denote the displacement of the body at time t, measured from the equilibrium position. Then $m(d^2x/dt^2) = -kx$, where k, the "spring constant," is the proportionality factor in Hooke's law.]

8. A man suspended from a parachute falls through space under the pull of gravity. If air resistance produces a retarding force proportional to the man's velocity and he starts from rest at time $t = 0$, find the distance he falls in time t.

18–8 Linear equations with constant coefficients. An equation of the form

$$\frac{d^ny}{dx^n} + a_1\frac{d^{n-1}y}{dx^{n-1}} + a_2\frac{d^{n-2}y}{dx^{n-2}} + \cdots + a_{n-1}\frac{dy}{dx} + a_ny = F(x), \quad (1)$$

which is linear in y and its derivatives, is called a *linear* equation of order n. If $F(x)$ is identically zero, the equation is said to be *homogeneous*, otherwise it is called nonhomogeneous. The equation is linear even though the coefficients $a_1, a_2, \ldots, a_n$ are functions of x. However, we shall consider only the case where these coefficients are *constants*.

It is convenient to introduce the symbol D to represent the operation of differentiation with respect to x. That is, we write $Df(x)$ to mean the same thing as $(d/dx) f(x)$. Furthermore, we define powers of D to mean taking successive derivatives:

$$D^2 f(x) = D\{Df(x)\} = \frac{d^2 f(x)}{dx^2},$$

$$D^3 f(x) = D\{D^2 f(x)\} = \frac{d^3 f(x)}{dx^3},$$

and so on. A polynomial in D is to be interpreted as an operator which, when applied to $f(x)$, produces a linear combination of f and its successive derivatives. For example,

$$(D^2 + D - 2)f(x) = D^2 f(x) + Df(x) - 2f(x)$$

$$= \frac{d^2 f(x)}{dx^2} + \frac{df(x)}{dx} - 2f(x).$$

Such a polynomial in D is called a "linear differential operator" and may be denoted by the single letter L. If L_1 and L_2 are two such linear operators, their sum and product are defined by the equations

$$(L_1 + L_2)f(x) = L_1 f(x) + L_2 f(x),$$

$$L_1 L_2 f(x) = L_1\{L_2 f(x)\}.$$

Linear differential operators that are polynomials in D with constant coefficients satisfy basic algebraic laws which make it possible to treat them like ordinary polynomials so far as addition, multiplication, and factoring are concerned. Thus,

$$(D^2 + D - 2)f(x) = (D + 2)(D - 1)f(x)$$

$$= (D - 1)(D + 2)f(x).$$

Since this is true for any twice-differentiable function f, we also write the equality between operators:

$$D^2 + D - 2 = (D + 2)(D - 1) = (D - 1)(D + 2).$$

18–9 Linear, second order, homogeneous equations with constant coefficients. Suppose, now, we wish to solve a differential equation of order two, say

$$\frac{d^2y}{dx^2} + 2a\frac{dy}{dx} + by = 0, \tag{1}$$

where a and b are constants. In operator notation, this becomes

$$(D^2 + 2aD + b)y = 0. \tag{1'}$$

Associated with this differential equation, we consider the algebraic equation

$$r^2 + 2ar + b = 0, \tag{1''}$$

which we get by replacing D by r and suppressing y. This is called the *characteristic equation* of the differential equation. Suppose the roots of (1'') are r_1 and r_2. Then

$$r^2 + 2ar + b = (r - r_1)(r - r_2)$$

and

$$D^2 + 2aD + b = (D - r_1)(D - r_2).$$

Hence Eq. (1') is equivalent to

$$(D - r_1)(D - r_2)y = 0. \tag{2}$$

If we now let

$$(D - r_2)y = u \tag{3a}$$

and

$$(D - r_1)u = 0, \tag{3b}$$

we can solve Eq. (1') in two steps. From Eq. (3b), which is separable, we find

$$u = C_1 e^{r_1 x}.$$

We substitute this into (3a), which becomes

$$(D - r_2)y = C_1 e^{r_1 x}$$

or

$$\frac{dy}{dx} - r_2 y = C_1 e^{r_1 x}.$$

This equation is linear. Its integrating factor is

$$\rho = e^{-r_2 x}.$$

Its solution is (see Article 18–5)

$$e^{-r_2 x} y = C_1 \int e^{(r_1 - r_2)x}\, dx + C_2. \tag{4}$$

At this point, two cases must be considered, depending upon whether or not r_1 and r_2 are equal.

Case 1. If $r_1 \neq r_2$, the evaluation of the integral in Eq. (4) leads to

$$e^{-r_2 x} y = \frac{C_1}{r_1 - r_2} e^{(r_1 - r_2)x} + C_2$$

or

$$y = \frac{C_1}{r_1 - r_2} e^{r_1 x} + C_2 e^{r_2 x}.$$

Since C_1 is an arbitrary constant, so is $C_1/(r_1 - r_2)$, and the solution of Eq. (2) can be written simply as

$$\boxed{y = C_1 e^{r_1 x} + C_2 e^{r_2 x}, \qquad \text{if} \qquad r_1 \neq r_2,} \qquad (5)$$

Case 2. If $r_1 = r_2$, then $e^{(r_1 - r_2)x} = e^0 = 1$, and Eq. (4) reduces to

$$e^{-r_2 x} y = C_1 x + C_2$$

or

$$\boxed{y = (C_1 x + C_2) e^{r_2 x}, \qquad \text{if} \qquad r_1 = r_2.} \qquad (6)$$

EXAMPLE 1.
$$\frac{d^2 y}{dx^2} + \frac{dy}{dx} - 2y = 0.$$

Solution. $r^2 + r - 2 = 0$ has roots $r_1 = 1$, $r_2 = -2$. Hence, by Eq. (5), the solution of the differential equation is

$$y = C_1 e^x + C_2 e^{-2x}.$$

EXAMPLE 2.
$$\frac{d^2 y}{dx^2} + 4 \frac{dy}{dx} + 4y = 0.$$

Solution.
$$r^2 + 4r + 4 = (r + 2)^2,$$
$$r_1 = r_2 = -2,$$
$$y = (C_1 x + C_2) e^{-2x}.$$

Imaginary roots. If the coefficients a and b in Eq. (1) are real, the roots of the characteristic Eq. (1″) will either be real, or will be a pair of complex conjugate numbers:

$$\boxed{r_1 = \alpha + i\beta, \qquad r_2 = \alpha - i\beta.} \qquad (7)$$

If $\beta \neq 0$, Eq. (5) applies, with the result

$$y = c_1 e^{(\alpha+i\beta)x} + c_2 e^{(\alpha-i\beta)x}$$

$$= e^{\alpha x}[c_1 e^{i\beta x} + c_2 e^{-i\beta x}]. \tag{8}$$

By Euler's formula, Eq. (10) of Article 17–7,

$$e^{i\beta x} = \cos \beta x + i \sin \beta x,$$

$$e^{-i\beta x} = \cos \beta x - i \sin \beta x.$$

Hence, Eq. (8) may be replaced by

$$y = e^{\alpha x}[(c_1 + c_2) \cos \beta x + i(c_1 - c_2) \sin \beta x]. \tag{9}$$

Finally, if we introduce new arbitrary constants

$$C_1 = c_1 + c_2, \qquad C_2 = i(c_1 - c_2),$$

Eq. (9) takes the form

$$\boxed{y = e^{\alpha x}[C_1 \cos \beta x + C_2 \sin \beta x].} \tag{9'}$$

The arbitrary constants C_1 and C_2 in (9′) will be real provided the constants c_1 and c_2 in (9) are complex conjugates:

$$c_1 = \tfrac{1}{2}(C_1 - iC_2), \qquad c_2 = \tfrac{1}{2}(C_1 + iC_2).$$

To solve a problem where the roots of the characteristic equation are complex conjugates, we simply write down the answer by Eq. (9′).

EXAMPLE 3. $\dfrac{d^2 y}{dx^2} + 2 \dfrac{dy}{dx} + 2y = 0.$

Solution. $r^2 + 2r + 2 = 0$ has roots $r_1 = -1 + i$, $r_2 = -1 - i$. Hence, in Eq. (9′), we take

$$\alpha = -1, \qquad \beta = 1,$$

and obtain

$$y = e^{-x}[C_1 \cos x + C_2 \sin x].$$

EXAMPLE 4. $\dfrac{d^2 y}{dx^2} + \omega^2 y = 0, \qquad \omega \neq 0,$

Solution. $r^2 + \omega^2 = 0$ has roots $r_1 = i\omega$, $r_2 = -i\omega$. Hence we take $\alpha = 0$, $\beta = \omega$ in Eq. (9′), and

$$y = C_1 \cos \omega x + C_2 \sin \omega x.$$

PROBLEMS

Solve:

1. $\dfrac{d^2y}{dx^2} + 2\dfrac{dy}{dx} = 0$

2. $\dfrac{d^2y}{dx^2} + 5\dfrac{dy}{dx} + 6y = 0$

3. $\dfrac{d^2y}{dx^2} + 6\dfrac{dy}{dx} + 5y = 0$

4. $\dfrac{d^2y}{dx^2} - 2\dfrac{dy}{dx} - 3y = 0$

5. $\dfrac{d^2y}{dx^2} + \dfrac{dy}{dx} + y = 0$

6. $\dfrac{d^2y}{dx^2} - 4\dfrac{dy}{dx} + 4y = 0$

7. $\dfrac{d^2y}{dx^2} + 6\dfrac{dy}{dx} + 9y = 0$

8. $\dfrac{d^2y}{dx^2} - 6\dfrac{dy}{dx} + 10y = 0$

9. $\dfrac{d^2y}{dx^2} - 2\dfrac{dy}{dx} + 4y = 0$

10. $\dfrac{d^2y}{dx^2} - 10\dfrac{dy}{dx} + 16y = 0$

18–10 Linear, second order, nonhomogeneous equations with constant coefficients. In Article 18–9, we learned how to solve the homogeneous equation

$$\frac{d^2y}{dx^2} + 2a\frac{dy}{dx} + by = 0. \tag{1}$$

We are now in a position to describe a method for solving the nonhomogeneous equation

$$\frac{d^2y}{dx^2} + 2a\frac{dy}{dx} + by = F(x). \tag{2}$$

To solve Eq. (2), we first obtain the general solution of the related homogeneous Eq. (1) obtained by replacing $F(x)$ by zero. Denote this solution by

$$\boxed{y_h = C_1u_1(x) + C_2u_2(x),} \tag{3}$$

where C_1 and C_2 are arbitrary constants and $u_1(x)$, $u_2(x)$ are functions of one or more of the following forms:

$$e^{rx}, \quad xe^{rx}, \quad e^{\alpha x}\cos\beta x, \quad e^{\alpha x}\sin\beta x.$$

Now we might, by inspection or by inspired guesswork, be able to discover *one* particular function $y = y_p(x)$ which satisfies Eq. (2). In this case, we would be able to solve Eq. (2) completely, as

$$\boxed{y = y_h(x) + y_p(x).}$$

EXAMPLE. $\dfrac{d^2y}{dx^2} + 2\dfrac{dy}{dx} - 3y = 6.$

Solution. y_h satisfies

$$\frac{d^2 y_h}{dx^2} + 2 \frac{dy_h}{dx} - 3y_h = 0.$$

The characteristic equation is

$$r^2 + 2r - 3 = 0,$$

and its roots are

$$r_1 = -3, \qquad r_2 = 1.$$

Hence

$$y_h = C_1 e^{-3x} + C_2 e^x.$$

Now, to find a particular integral of the original equation, observe that $y = $ constant would do, provided $-3y = 6$. Hence,

$$y_p = -2$$

is one particular solution. The complete solution is

$$y = y_p + y_h = -2 + C_1 e^{-3x} + C_2 e^x.$$

Variation of parameters. Fortunately, there is a general method for finding the solution of the nonhomogeneous Eq. (2) once the general solution of the corresponding homogeneous equation is known. The method is known as the method of *variation of parameters*. It consists in replacing the constants C_1 and C_2 in Eq. (3) by functions $v_1 = v_1(x)$ and $v_2 = v_2(x)$, and requiring (in a way to be explained) that the resulting expression satisfy Eq. (2). There are two functions to be determined, and requiring that Eq. (2) be satisfied is only one condition. As a second condition, we also require that

$$\boxed{v_1' u_1 + v_2' u_2 = 0.} \tag{4}$$

Then we have

$$y = v_1 u_1 + v_2 u_2,$$

$$\frac{dy}{dx} = v_1 u_1' + v_2 u_2',$$

$$\frac{d^2 y}{dx^2} = v_1 u_1'' + v_2 u_2'' + v_1' u_1' + v_2' u_2'.$$

If we substitute these expressions into the left side of Eq. (2), we obtain

$$v_1 \left[\frac{d^2 u_1}{dx^2} + 2a \frac{du_1}{dx} + b u_1 \right] + v_2 \left[\frac{d^2 u_2}{dx^2} + 2a \frac{du_2}{dx} + b u_2 \right]$$
$$+ v_1' u_1' + v_2' u_2' = F(x).$$

The two bracketed terms are zero, since u_1 and u_2 are solutions of the homogeneous Eq. (1). Hence Eq. (2) is satisfied if, in addition to Eq. (4), we require that

$$v_1'u_1' + v_2'u_2' = F(x). \tag{5}$$

Equations (4) and (5) together may be solved for the unknown functions v_1' and v_2'. Then v_1 and v_2 can be found by integration. In applying the method, we can work directly from Eqs. (4) and (5); it is not necessary to rederive them.

EXAMPLE.   (As above) $\dfrac{d^2y}{dx^2} + 2\dfrac{dy}{dx} - 3y = 6.$

Solution. $u_1(x) = e^{-3x}, \qquad u_2(x) = e^x.$

$$v_1'e^{-3x} + v_2'e^x = 0,$$

$$v_1'(-3e^{-3x}) + v_2'e^x = 6.$$

By Cramer's rule:

$$v_1' = \frac{\begin{vmatrix} 0 & e^x \\ 6 & e^x \end{vmatrix}}{\begin{vmatrix} e^{-3x} & e^x \\ -3e^{-3x} & e^x \end{vmatrix}} = -\tfrac{3}{2}e^{3x}, \qquad v_2' = \frac{\begin{vmatrix} e^{-3x} & 0 \\ -3e^{-3x} & 6 \end{vmatrix}}{\begin{vmatrix} e^{-3x} & e^x \\ -3e^{-3x} & e^x \end{vmatrix}} = \tfrac{3}{2}e^{-x}.$$

Hence

$$v_1 = \int -\tfrac{3}{2}e^{3x}\, dx = -\tfrac{1}{2}e^{3x} + c_1,$$

$$v_2 = \int \tfrac{3}{2}e^{-x}\, dx = -\tfrac{3}{2}e^{-x} + c_2,$$

and

$$y = v_1u_1 + v_2u_2$$

$$= (-\tfrac{1}{2}e^{3x} + c_1)e^{-3x} + (-\tfrac{3}{2}e^{-x} + c_2)e^x$$

$$= -2 + c_1e^{-3x} + c_2e^x.$$

PROBLEMS

Solve:

1. $\dfrac{d^2y}{dx^2} + \dfrac{dy}{dx} = x$

2. $\dfrac{d^2y}{dx^2} + y = \tan x$

3. $\dfrac{d^2y}{dx^2} + y = \sin x$

4. $\dfrac{d^2y}{dx^2} + 2\dfrac{dy}{dx} + y = e^x$

5. $\dfrac{d^2y}{dx^2} + 2\dfrac{dy}{dx} + y = e^{-x}$ 6. $\dfrac{d^2y}{dx^2} - y = x$

7. $\dfrac{d^2y}{dx^2} - y = e^x$ 8. $\dfrac{d^2y}{dx^2} - y = \sin x$

9. $\dfrac{d^2y}{dx^2} + 4\dfrac{dy}{dx} + 5y = 10$ 10. $\dfrac{d^2y}{dx^2} + 4\dfrac{dy}{dx} + 5y = x + 2$

18–11 Higher order linear equations with constant coefficients. The methods of Articles 18–9 and 18–10 can be extended to equations of higher order. The characteristic algebraic equation associated with the differential equation

$$(D^n + a_1 D^{n-1} + \cdots + a_{n-1}D + a_n)y = F(x) \tag{1}$$

is

$$r^n + a_1 r^{n-1} + \cdots + a_{n-1}r + a_n = 0. \tag{2}$$

If its roots $r_1, r_2, \ldots, r_n$ are all distinct, the solution of the homogeneous equation obtained by replacing $F(x)$ by 0 in Eq. (1) is

$$y_h = c_1 e^{r_1 x} + c_2 e^{r_2 x} + \cdots + c_n e^{r_n x}.$$

Pairs of complex conjugate roots $\alpha \pm i\beta$ can be grouped together, and the corresponding part of y_h can be written in terms of the functions

$$e^{\alpha x} \cos \beta x \quad \text{and} \quad e^{\alpha x} \sin \beta x.$$

In case the roots of Eq. (2) are not all distinct, the portion of y_h which corresponds to a root r of multiplicity m is to be replaced by

$$(C_1 x^{m-1} + C_2 x^{m-2} + \cdots + C_m)e^{rx}.$$

Note that the polynomial in parentheses contains m arbitrary constants.

EXAMPLE. $\dfrac{d^4y}{dx^4} - 3\dfrac{d^3y}{dx^3} + 3\dfrac{d^2y}{dx^2} - \dfrac{dy}{dx} = 0.$

Solution. $r^4 - 3r^3 + 3r^2 - r = r(r - 1)^3$. The roots of the characteristic equation are

$$r_1 = 0, \qquad r_2 = r_3 = r_4 = 1.$$

The solution is

$$y = C_1 + (C_2 x^2 + C_3 x + C_4)e^x.$$

Variation of parameters. If the general solution of the homogeneous equation is

$$y_h = C_1 u_1 + C_2 u_2 + \cdots + C_n u_n,$$

then

$$y = v_1 u_1 + v_2 u_2 + \cdots + v_n u_n$$

will be a solution of the nonhomogeneous Eq. (1), provided

$$v_1' u_1 + v_2' u_2 \quad + \quad \cdots + v_n' u_n = 0,$$
$$v_1' u_1' + v_2' u_2' \quad + \quad \cdots + v_n' u_n' = 0,$$
$$\vdots$$
$$v_1' u_1^{(n-2)} + v_2' u_2^{(n-2)} + \cdots + v_n' u_n^{(n-2)} = 0,$$
$$v_1' u_1^{(n-1)} + v_2' u_2^{(n-1)} + \cdots + v_n' u_n^{(n-1)} = F(x).$$

These equations may be solved for $v_1', v_2', \ldots, v_n'$ by Cramer's rule, and the results integrated to give $v_1, v_2, \ldots, v_n$.

PROBLEMS

Solve:

1. $\dfrac{d^3 y}{dx^3} - 3 \dfrac{d^2 y}{dx^2} + 2 \dfrac{dy}{dx} = 0$

2. $\dfrac{d^3 y}{dx^3} - y = 0$

3. $\dfrac{d^4 y}{dx^4} - 4 \dfrac{d^2 y}{dx^2} + 4y = 0$

4. $\dfrac{d^4 y}{dx^4} - 16y = 0$

5. $\dfrac{d^4 y}{dx^4} + 16y = 0$

6. $\dfrac{d^3 y}{dx^3} - 3 \dfrac{dy}{dx} + 2y = e^x$

7. $\dfrac{d^4 y}{dx^4} - 4 \dfrac{d^3 y}{dx^3} + 6 \dfrac{d^2 y}{dx^2} - 4 \dfrac{dy}{dx} + y = 7$

8. $\dfrac{d^4 y}{dx^4} + y = x + 1$

18–12 Vibrations.　A spring of natural length L has its upper end fastened to a rigid support at A (Fig. 18–2). A weight W, of mass m, is suspended from the spring. The weight stretches the spring to a length $L + s$ when the system is allowed to come to rest in a new equilibrium position. By Hooke's law, the tension in the spring is ks, where k is the so-called spring constant. The force of gravity pulling down on the weight is $W = mg$. Equilibrium requires

$$ks = mg. \tag{1}$$

Suppose now that the weight is pulled down an additional amount a beyond the equilibrium position, and released. We shall discuss its motion.

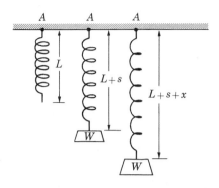

FIGURE 18–2

Let x, positive direction downward, denote the displacement of the weight away from equilibrium at any time t after the motion has started. Then the forces acting upon the weight are

$+mg$, due to gravity,

$-k(s + x)$, due to the spring tension.

The resultant of these forces is, by Newton's second law, also equal to

$$m \frac{d^2x}{dt^2}.$$

Therefore

$$m \frac{d^2x}{dt^2} = mg - ks - kx. \tag{2}$$

By Eq. (1), $mg - ks = 0$, so that (2) becomes

$$m \frac{d^2x}{dt^2} + kx = 0. \tag{3}$$

In addition to the differential equation (3), the motion satisfies the initial conditions:

$$\text{at} \quad t = 0: x = a \quad \text{and} \quad \frac{dx}{dt} = 0. \tag{4}$$

Let $\omega = \sqrt{k/m}$. Then Eq. (3) becomes

$$\frac{d^2x}{dt^2} + \omega^2 x = 0$$

or

$$(D^2 + \omega^2)x = 0,$$

where

$$D = \frac{d}{dt}.$$

The roots of the characteristic equation

$$r^2 + \omega^2 = 0$$

are complex conjugates

$$r = \pm \omega i.$$

Hence

$$x = c_1 \cos \omega t + c_2 \sin \omega t \qquad (5)$$

is the general solution of the differential equation. In order to fit the initial conditions, we also compute

$$\frac{dx}{dt} = -c_1 \omega \sin \omega t + c_2 \omega \cos \omega t,$$

and then substitute from (4). This yields

$$a = c_1, \qquad 0 = c_2 \omega.$$

Therefore

$$c_1 = a, \qquad c_2 = 0,$$

and

$$x = a \cos \omega t \qquad (6)$$

describes the motion of the weight. Equation (6) represents simple harmonic motion of amplitude a and period $T = 2\pi/\omega$.

The two terms on the right side of Eq. (5) can be combined into a single term by making use of the trigonometric identity

$$\sin (\omega t + \phi) = \cos \omega t \sin \phi + \sin \omega t \cos \phi.$$

This can be applied to Eq. (5), provided we take

$$c_1 = C \sin \phi, \qquad c_2 = C \cos \phi, \qquad (7a)$$

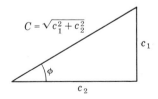

FIGURE 18–3

where (see Fig. 18–3)

$$C = \sqrt{c_1^2 + c_2^2}, \qquad \phi = \tan^{-1}\frac{c_1}{c_2}. \tag{7b}$$

Then Eq. (5) can be written in the alternative form

$$x = C \sin(\omega t + \phi). \tag{8}$$

Here C and ϕ may be taken as two new arbitrary constants, replacing the two constants c_1 and c_2 of Eq. (5). Equation (8) represents simple harmonic motion of amplitude C and period $T = 2\pi/\omega$. The angle $\omega t + \phi$ is called the *phase angle*, and ϕ may be interpreted as the initial value of the phase angle. A graph of Eq. (8) is given in Fig. 18–4.

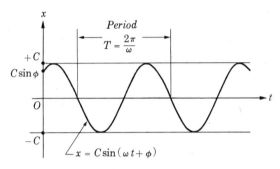

FIGURE 18–4

Equation (3) assumes that there is no friction in the system. Next, consider the case where the motion of the weight is retarded by a friction force $c\,(dx/dt)$ proportional to the velocity, where c is a positive constant. Then the differential equation is

$$m\frac{d^2x}{dt^2} = -kx - c\frac{dx}{dt},$$

or

$$\frac{d^2x}{dt^2} + 2b\frac{dx}{dt} + \omega^2 x = 0, \tag{9}$$

where

$$2b = \frac{c}{m} \qquad \text{and} \qquad \omega = \sqrt{\frac{k}{m}}.$$

If we introduce the operator $D = d/dt$, Eq. (9) becomes

$$(D^2 + 2bD + \omega^2)x = 0.$$

The characteristic equation is

$$r^2 + 2br + \omega^2 = 0$$

with roots

$$r = -b \pm \sqrt{b^2 - \omega^2}. \tag{10}$$

Three cases now present themselves, depending upon the relative sizes of b and ω.

Case 1. If $b = \omega$, the two roots in Eq. (10) are equal, and the solution of (9) is

$$x = (c_1 + c_2 t)e^{-\omega t}. \tag{11}$$

As time goes on, x approaches zero. The motion is not oscillatory.

Case 2. If $b > \omega$, then the roots (10) are both real but unequal, and

$$x = c_1 e^{r_1 t} + c_2 e^{r_2 t}, \tag{12}$$

where

$$r_1 = -b + \sqrt{b^2 - \omega^2} \quad \text{and} \quad r_2 = -b - \sqrt{b^2 - \omega^2}.$$

Here again the motion is not oscillatory. Both r_1 and r_2 are negative, and x approaches zero as time goes on.

Case 3. If $b < \omega$, let

$$\omega^2 - b^2 = \alpha^2.$$

Then

$$r_1 = -b + \alpha i, \quad r_2 = -b - \alpha i$$

and

$$x = e^{-bt}[c_1 \cos \alpha t + c_2 \sin \alpha t]. \tag{13a}$$

If we introduce the substitutions (7), we may also write Eq. (13a) in the equivalent form

$$x = Ce^{-bt} \sin (\alpha t + \phi). \tag{13b}$$

This equation represents damped vibratory motion. It is analogous to simple harmonic motion, of period $T = 2\pi/\alpha$, except that the amplitude is not constant but is given by Ce^{-bt}. Since this tends to zero as t increases, the vibrations tend to die out as time goes on. Observe, however, that Eq. (13b) reduces to Eq. (8) in the absence of friction. The effect of friction is twofold:

1. $b = c/(2m)$ appears as a coefficient in the exponential *damping factor* e^{-bt}. The larger b is, the more quickly do the vibrations tend to become unnoticeable.

2. The period $T = 2\pi/\alpha$ is greater than the period $T_0 = 2\pi/\omega$ in the friction-free system.

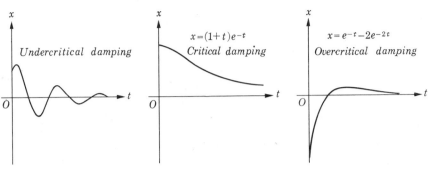

Undercritical damping

$x = (1+t)e^{-t}$
Critical damping

$x = e^{-t} - 2e^{-2t}$
Overcritical damping

FIGURE 18–5

Curves representing solutions of Eq. (9) in typical cases are depicted in Figs. 18–4 and 18–5. The size of b, relative to ω, determines the kind of solution, and b also determines the rate of damping. It is therefore customary to say that there is

(a) critical damping if $b = \omega$,   (b) overcritical damping if $b > \omega$,

(c) undercritical damping if $0 < b < \omega$,   (d) no damping if $b = 0$.

PROBLEMS

1. Suppose the motion of the weight in Fig. 18–2 is governed by the differential equation (3). Find the motion if $x = x_0$ and $dx/dt = v_0$ at $t = 0$. Express the answer in two equivalent forms [Eqs. (5) and (8)].

2. A 5-lb weight is suspended from the lower end of a spring whose upper end is attached to a rigid support. The weight extends the spring by 2 in. If, after the weight has come to rest in its new equilibrium position, it is struck a sharp blow which starts it downward with a velocity of 4 ft/sec, find its subsequent motion, assuming there is no friction.

3. A simple electrical circuit contains a capacitor of capacity C farads, a coil of inductance L henrys, a resistance of R ohms, and a generator which produces an electromotive force E volts, in series. If the current intensity at time t at some point of the circuit is I amperes, the differential equation governing the current I is

$$L \frac{d^2 I}{dt^2} + R \frac{dI}{dt} + \frac{1}{C} I = \frac{dE}{dt}.$$

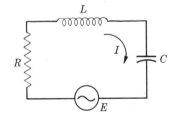

FIGURE 18–6

Find I as a function of t if

(a) $R = 0$, $1/(LC) = \omega^2$, $E = $ constant,

(b) $R = 0$, $1/(LC) = \omega^2$, $E = A \sin \alpha t$; $\alpha = $ constant $\neq \omega$,

(c) $R = 0$, $1/(LC) = \omega^2$, $E = A \sin \omega t$,

(d) $R = 50$, $L = 5$, $C = 9 \times 10^{-6}$, $E = $ constant.

4. A simple pendulum of length l makes an angle θ with the vertical. As it swings back and forth, its motion, neglecting friction, is governed by the differential equation

$$\frac{d^2\theta}{dt^2} = -\frac{g}{l} \sin \theta,$$

where g (the acceleration due to gravity, $g \approx 32 \text{ ft/sec}^2$) is a constant. Solve the differential equation of motion, under the assumption that θ is sufficiently small that $\sin \theta$ may be replaced by θ without appreciable error. Assume that $\theta = \theta_0$ and $d\theta/dt = 0$ when $t = 0$.

5. A circular disk of mass m and radius r is suspended by a thin wire attached to the center of one of its flat faces. If the disk is twisted through an angle θ, torsion in the wire tends to turn the disk back in the opposite direction. The differential equation that governs the motion is

$$\frac{1}{2} mr^2 \frac{d^2\theta}{dt^2} = -k\theta,$$

where k is the coefficient of torsion of the wire. Find the motion if $\theta = \theta_0$ and $d\theta/dt = v_0$ at $t = 0$.

6. A cylindrical spar buoy, diameter 1 foot, weight 100 lb, floats, partially submerged, in an upright position. When it is depressed slightly from its equilibrium position and released, it bobs up and down, its motion being governed by the differential equation

$$\frac{100}{g} \frac{d^2x}{dt^2} = -16\pi x - c \frac{dx}{dt}.$$

Here $c \, (dx/dt)$ is the frictional resistance of the water. Find c if the period of oscillation is observed to be 1.6 sec. (Take $g = 32 \text{ ft/sec}^2$.)

7. Suppose the upper end of the spring in Fig. 18–2 is attached, not to a rigid support at A, but to a member which itself undergoes up and down motion given by a function of the time t, say $y = f(t)$. If the positive direction of y is downward, the differential equation of motion is

$$m \frac{d^2x}{dt^2} + kx = kf(t).$$

Let $x = x_0$ and $dx/dt = 0$ when $t = 0$, and solve for x:

(a) if $f(t) = A \sin \alpha t$ and $\alpha \neq \sqrt{k/m}$,

(b) if $f(t) = A \sin \alpha t$ and $\alpha = \sqrt{k/m}$.

18–13 Poisson probability distribution. In the study of emission of particles from a radioactive substance, it is found that the number X of particles emitted during a fixed time interval is not precisely predictable. In fact X is a variable that can assume only the values $0, 1, 2, \ldots$ Some of these values are more likely to be observed than others. It is useful to introduce the symbol $P_n(t)$ to denote the *probability* that n particles will be emitted in a t-second interval. It is possible to arrive at a formula for $P_n(t)$ if we make the following assumptions:

1. The number of particles emitted in any time interval is independent of the number emitted in any other nonoverlapping time interval.

2. The probability that a single particle is emitted in an interval $(t, t + h)$ is $\lambda \cdot h + o(h)$, where λ is a constant (for a particular substance) and $o(h)$, read "small oh of h," denotes any function having the property

$$\lim_{h \to 0} \frac{o(h)}{h} = 0. \tag{1}$$

3. The probability that more than one particle will be emitted in $(t, t + h)$ is $o(h)$.

A variable that satisfies these three postulates will be called a *Poisson* random variable. The significance of the postulates is as follows:

1. Independence of numbers of particles emitted in nonoverlapping time intervals means that the probability of r particles in one interval and s in another is the product of the respective probabilities:

(Probability of r particles in 1st time interval)

times

(Probability of s particles in 2nd time interval).

2. (Probability of particle in interval $t, t + h$) $= \lambda \cdot h + o(h)$ means that the probability is approximately proportional to the length h of the time interval. The approximation λh is better the smaller h is, the error $o(h)$ being composed of terms (like h^2 or $h \sin h$, for instance) which are themselves small compared to h, since $(o(h)/h) \to 0$ as $h \to 0$.

3. The probability that more than one particle is emitted in a very short time interval $(t, t + h)$ is $o(h)$, and is small compared to h.

From postulates 2 and 3 it follows that the probability of one *or more* particles in the interval $[t, t + h]$ is also $\lambda h + o(h)$, because

$$P(1 \text{ or more particles})^* = P(1 \text{ particle}) + P(\text{more than 1 particle})$$

and

$$P(1 \text{ particle}) = \lambda h + o_1(h), \qquad P(\text{more than 1 particle}) = o_2(h).$$

---

* The notation $P(1$ or more particles) is an abbreviation for "probability that 1 or more particles are emitted."

Hence

$$P(1 \text{ or more particles}) = \lambda h + o_1(h) + o_2(h)$$
$$= \lambda h + o(h), \tag{2}$$

since the sum of two functions $o_1(h)$ and $o_2(h)$ having the property that

$$\lim_{h \to 0} \frac{o_1(h)}{h} = 0, \qquad \lim_{h \to 0} \frac{o_2(h)}{h} = 0$$

is a function having the same property:

$$\lim_{h \to 0} \frac{o_1(h) + o_2(h)}{h} = \lim_{h \to 0} \frac{o_1(h)}{h} + \lim_{h \to 0} \frac{o_2(h)}{h} = 0.$$

From the postulates for a Poisson random variable we may deduce the following system of differential equations:

$$\frac{dP_0(t)}{dt} = -\lambda P_0(t), \tag{3a}$$

$$\frac{dP_n(t)}{dt} = -\lambda P_n(t) + \lambda P_{n-1}(t), \qquad n = 1, 2, 3, \ldots \tag{3b}$$

Demonstration. We first establish (3a). Consider

$$P_0(t + h) = P(0 \text{ emissions in time } t + h)$$
$$= P(0 \text{ in time } t) \times P(0 \text{ in time } [t, t + h])$$
$$= P_0(t) \cdot \{1 - P(1 \text{ or more in } [t, t + h])\}$$
$$= P_0(t) \cdot [1 - \lambda h - o(h)].$$

Therefore

$$P_0(t + h) - P_0(t) = -P_0(t) \cdot [\lambda h + o(h)],$$
$$\frac{P_0(t + h) - P_0(t)}{h} = -P_0(t) \cdot \left[\lambda + \frac{o(h)}{h}\right],$$
$$\frac{dP_0(t)}{dt} = \lim_{h \to 0} \frac{P_0(t + h) - P_0(t)}{h} = -P_0(t) \cdot [\lambda + 0] = -\lambda P_0(t).$$

Thus (3a) holds.

To establish (3b), consider the probability of n emissions in time $(0, t + h)$, where n is a positive integer. Consider the nonoverlapping intervals of time $(0, t)$ and $(t, t + h)$. The only possibilities for n particles in $(0, t + h)$ are:

(a) n particles in $(0, t)$ and 0 in $(t, t + h)$,
(b) $(n - 1)$ particles in $(0, t)$ and 1 in $(t, t + h)$,
(c) $(n - 2)$ particles in $(0, t)$ and 2 in $(t, t + h)$,
(d) $(n - 3)$ particles in $(0, t)$ and 3 in $(t, t + h)$, and so on.

Since these are mutually exclusive events, their probabilities add, and

$$P_n(t + h) = P_n(t) \cdot P_0(h) + P_{n-1}(t) \cdot P_1(h) + P_{n-2}(t) \cdot P_2(h) + \cdots$$
$$+ P_0(t) \cdot P_n(h). \qquad (4)$$

Now for any $t \geq 0$,

$$P_0(t) + P_1(t) + P_2(t) + \cdots = 1, \qquad (5)$$

since it is certain (that is, the probability $= 1$) that the number of particles emitted in time t is one of the integers 0, or 1, or 2, or 3, ..., and these possibilities are mutually exclusive so their probabilities add. Hence, in particular, if $t = h$ is small, we may replace t by h in (5) and use the fact, Eq. (2), that

$$P(1 \text{ or more particles}) = P_1(h) + P_2(h) + \cdots$$
$$= \lambda h + o(h)$$

to obtain

$$P_0(h) = 1 - \lambda h - o(h). \qquad (6)$$

Hence Eq. (4) becomes

$$P_n(t + h) = P_n(t) \cdot [1 - \lambda h - o(h)] + P_{n-1}(t) \cdot [\lambda h + o_1(h)] + o_2(h) \qquad (7)$$

since

$$P_{n-2}(t) \cdot P_2(h) + P_{n-3}(t) \cdot P_3(h) + \cdots + P_0(t) \cdot P_n(h)$$
$$\leq 1 \cdot P_2(h) + 1 \cdot P_3(h) + \cdots + 1 \cdot P_n(h) = o(h).$$

Therefore, from Eq. (7),

$$P_n(t + h) - P_n(t) = -P_n(t) \cdot [\lambda h + o(h)]$$
$$+ P_{n-1}(t) \cdot [\lambda h + o_1(h)] + o_2(h)$$

and

$$\frac{dP_n}{dt} = \lim_{h \to 0} \frac{P_n(t + h) - P_n(t)}{h}$$
$$= \lim_{h \to 0} \left[-P_n(t) \cdot \left(\lambda + \frac{o(h)}{h} \right) + P_{n-1}(t) \cdot \left(\lambda + \frac{o_1(h)}{h} \right) + \frac{o_2(h)}{h} \right]$$
$$= -\lambda P_n(t) + \lambda P_{n-1}(t). \qquad \text{Q.E.D.}$$

The probabilities $P_0(t), P_1(t), \ldots$ satisfy the system of differential equations (3a, b) and the initial conditions:

$$P_0(0) = 1, \quad P_1(0) = P_2(0) = \cdots P_n(0) = 0, \qquad n > 1. \qquad (8)$$

That is, the number of particles emitted in 0 time is 0, with probability 1.

The solution of Eq. (3a), with $P_0(0) = 1$, is

$$P_0(t) = e^{-\lambda t}.$$

If we substitute this into Eq. (3b), with $n = 1$, we have

$$\frac{dP_1(t)}{dt} = -\lambda P_1(t) + e^{-\lambda t},$$

or

$$\frac{dP_1(t)}{dt} + \lambda P_1(t) = e^{-\lambda t}.$$

This equation is linear in $P_1(t)$, with integrating factor $e^{\lambda t}$. It is equivalent to

$$\frac{d}{dt}[e^{\lambda t}P_1(t)] = \lambda.$$

Hence

$$e^{\lambda t}P_1(t) = \lambda t + C_1.$$

But when $t = 0$, $P_1(0) = 0$, so

$$C_1 = 0.$$

Therefore

$$P_1(t) = \lambda t e^{-\lambda t}.$$

We can now substitute this into (3b) with $n = 2$ and have

$$\frac{dP_2(t)}{dt} + \lambda P_2(t) = \lambda(\lambda t\ ^{-\lambda t}.$$

Again the equation is linear, with integrating factor $e^{\lambda t}$, and

$$\frac{d}{dt}[e^{\lambda t}P_2(t)] = e^{\lambda t} \cdot \lambda(\lambda t)e^{-\lambda t}$$
$$= \lambda^2 t.$$

Hence

$$e^{\lambda t}P_2(t) = \frac{\lambda^2 t^2}{2} + C_2,$$

but $P_2(0) = 0$, so

$$C_2 = 0.$$

Therefore

$$P_2(t) = \frac{(\lambda t)^2}{2!} e^{-\lambda t}.$$

Proceeding in this fashion, one discovers that

$$P_3(t) = \frac{(\lambda t)^3}{3!} e^{-\lambda t},$$

$$P_4(t) = \frac{(\lambda t)^4}{4!} e^{-\lambda t},$$

and so on. The general term is

$$P_n(t) = e^{-\lambda t} \frac{(\lambda t)^n}{n!}, \qquad n = 0, 1, 2, \ldots \tag{9}$$

The set of numbers $0, 1, 2, 3, \ldots$ with corresponding probabilities given by Eq. (9) is called a *Poisson probability distribution*. Figure 18–7 shows the graph of a Poisson distribution with $\lambda t = 2$. The viewpoint to adopt when considering a Poisson distribution is, in most instances, to imagine λt as fixed, and then Eq. (9) gives the probability of observing n occurrences of the event in question, for all possible different values of n.

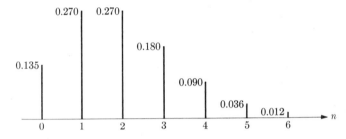

Fig. 18–7. Poisson distribution with $\lambda t = 2$.

The probability of 0 emissions is $P_0(t) = e^{-\lambda t}$. Observe that this probability tends to 0 as t increases: it becomes very improbable that *no* emissions occur over a very long interval of time.

Do the probabilities found in Eq. (9) add up to 1, as Eq. (4) requires? Let's try it and see:

$$P_0(t) + P_1(t) + \cdots = e^{-\lambda t}\left[1 + \frac{\lambda t}{1!} + \frac{(\lambda t)^2}{2!} + \cdots\right]$$

$$= e^{-\lambda t} \sum_{n=0}^{\infty} \frac{(\lambda t)^n}{n!}$$

$$= e^{-\lambda t} \cdot e^{\lambda t}$$

$$= e^0 = 1. \qquad \text{Q.E.D.}$$

Interpretation of λ. The *mean* value of a random variable X is obtained by taking the weighted average of the possible values X may assume, each weighted according to its probability of occurring. Equations (8) give these probabilities for a Poisson random variable:

Possible values of X	Probabilities of these possibilities	(Possible values) $\times$ (probability)
0	$e^{-\lambda t}$	$0 \cdot e^{-\lambda t}$
1	$e^{-\lambda t} \cdot (\lambda t)$	$1 \cdot e^{-\lambda t} \cdot (\lambda t)$
2	$e^{-\lambda t} \cdot (\lambda t)^2/2!$	$2 \cdot e^{-\lambda t} \cdot (\lambda t)^2/2!$
3	$e^{-\lambda t} \cdot (\lambda t)^3/3!$	$3 \cdot e^{-\lambda t} \cdot (\lambda t)^3/3!$
$\vdots$	$\vdots$	$\vdots$
n	$e^{-\lambda t}(\lambda t)^n/n!$	$n \cdot e^{-\lambda t}(\lambda t)^n/n!$
$\vdots$	$\vdots$	$\vdots$

Thus, the mean value of the Poisson random variable is

$$e^{-\lambda t}[0 + 1 \cdot (\lambda t) + 2 \cdot (\lambda t)^2/2! + 3 \cdot (\lambda t)^3/3! + \cdots + n \cdot (\lambda t)^n/n! + \cdots]$$
$$= e^{-\lambda t} \cdot (\lambda t) \cdot [1 + (\lambda t) + (\lambda t)^2/2! + \cdots + (\lambda t)^{n-1}/(n-1)! + \cdots]$$
$$= e^{-\lambda t} \cdot (\lambda t) \cdot e^{\lambda t} = \lambda t.$$

Therefore λt is the *mean* number of particles emitted in time $(0, t)$. In particular, the mean number emitted in unit time, $t = 1$, is λ. In 2 units of time, it is 2λ, and so on. The mean number in t units of time is proportional to t, and λ is the proportionality factor.

Remarks. Many phenomena have been found that satisfy the postulates for a Poisson random variable, or nearly do.[*] Among these are: the number of telephone calls coming into a central office during a particular hour of the day, the number of splices in a certain manufactured tape (per linear foot), the number of surface flaws (per square foot) in plating sheets of metal, the number of failures of electron tubes (per hour) in a given airborne instrumentation device, the number of flying bomb hits in the south of London during World War II (on regions of area = $\frac{1}{4}$ square kilometer). In some of these cases, the "t" in Eqs. (8) should be interpreted as so many units of length, or of area, rather than of time; but the formulas are correct with such interpretations and with λ equal to the mean number of occurrences of the event in question per unit of t.

EXAMPLE 1. Suppose there are 500 misprints in a book of 750 pages. Assuming that the number of misprints per page is (approximately) a Poisson random variable, find:

(a) the probability that a page selected at random has no misprints,
(b) the probability of more than one misprint on a given page.

---

[*] *References:* W. Feller, *An Introduction to Probability Theory and Its Applications*, 2nd ed. Wiley, 1957. Pp. 142–154, 400–402. B. W. Lindgren and G. W. McElrath, *Introduction to Probability and Statistics.* Macmillan, 1959. Pp. 54–59.

Solution. Let one page be the unit, $t = 1$. The mean number of misprints, per page, is $500/750 = \frac{2}{3}$. So we apply (9) with $\lambda = \frac{2}{3}$:

$$P_n(t) = \text{probability of } n \text{ misprints on } t \text{ pages}$$

$$= e^{(2/3)t} \frac{(\frac{2}{3}t)^n}{n!}, \qquad n = 0, 1, 2, \ldots$$

(a) The probability of no misprints on a single page is $P_n(t)$ with $n = 0$, $t = 1$, or

$$P_0(1) = e^{-2/3} \approx 0.514.$$

(b) The probability of more than one misprint on a single page is $\sum_{n=2}^{\infty} P_n(t)$ with $t = 1$. This is also equal to $1 - P_0(t) - P_1(t)$, or

$$1 - e^{-2/3}[1 + \tfrac{2}{3}] \approx 0.143.$$

PROBLEMS

1. Substitute $n = 3$ and $P_2(t) = e^{-\lambda t}(\lambda t)^2/2!$ into Eq. (3b) and solve for $P_3(t)$, subject to the appropriate initial condition.

2. Assuming that Eq. (9) is correct for some integer $n - 1$, so that $P_{n-1}(t) = e^{-\lambda t}(\lambda t)^{n-1}/(n - 1)!$, solve Eq. (3b) for $P_n(t)$, subject to the appropriate initial condition. [In other words, show that Eq. (9) is valid for all integers $n \geq 0$ by the method of mathematical induction.]

3. Sketch the graph of $y = P_n(t)$ as a function of t, $t \geq 0$, for $n = 2$ and $\lambda = 2, 1$, and $\frac{1}{2}$. Find the maximum, minimum, and inflection points.

4. Prove directly that $e^{-\lambda t}(\lambda t)^n/n!$ is never greater than 1 if $\lambda > 0$, $t \geq 0$, and n is an integer ≥ 0. This result must be true, of course, since $P_n(t)$ is a probability and hence is never greater than 1.

5. In the example of the book of 750 pages and 500 misprints, what is the probability:

(a) that a chapter of 15 pages has no misprints?
(b) that a section of 6 pages has 1 or more misprints?

6. Assume that a certain manufacturer of automobile radiators has found that the number of minor defects in his radiators is (approximately) a Poisson random variable with mean equal to 0.02. If 20 radiators are selected at random from his production line, what is the probability that there will be:

(a) no minor defects in the entire group of 20 radiators?
(b) one or more minor defects in the group of 20 radiators?
(c) no minor defects in the first radiator of the 20?

7. A baker finds that the number of raisins, per loaf, in his raisin bread is (approximately) a Poisson random variable with mean equal to 200 raisins per loaf. Suppose that each loaf is sliced into 20 slices of uniform size.

(a) What is the mean number of raisins per slice?
(b) What is the probability of getting 5 or fewer raisins in a slice?

8. The first term of a certain Poisson probability distribution is $P_0(t) = 0.135$. Find (a) $P_1(t)$, (b) $P_3(t)$, (c) $P_0(t/2)$, (d) $P_1(2t)$.

9. Assume that the number of α-particles registered by a Geiger counter in a certain experiment is a Poisson random variable. Suppose that the mean number registered per ten-second interval of time is eight. What is the probability that there will be exactly four registered in a given interval of five seconds?

10. Let $Q_n(t, t + h)$ be the probability that the nth particle is emitted between times t and $t + h$. Then, explain why it is true that if $t + h > t > 0$,

$$Q_n(t, t + h) = P_{n-1}(t) \cdot P_1(h) + P_{n-2}(t) \cdot P_2(h) + \cdots + P_0(t) \cdot P_n(h);$$

and from this show that

$$Q_n(t, t + h) = he^{-\lambda t}\lambda^n t^{n-1}/(n - 1)! + o(h).$$

11. Using the result in Problem 10, show that

$$Q_n(a, b) = \int_a^b \frac{e^{-\lambda t}\lambda^n t^{n-1}}{(n - 1)!}\, dt, \qquad b > a > 0.$$

[*Hint*: Let p be a positive integer, $\Delta t = h = (b - a)/p$, and

$$Q_n(a, b) = Q_n(a, a + h) + Q_n(a + h, a + 2h) + \cdots + Q_n(b - h, b)$$

$$= \sum_{i=1}^{p} f(t_i)\, \Delta t + \frac{b - a}{h}\, o(h),$$

with $f(t) = e^{-\lambda t}\lambda^n t^{n-1}/(n - 1)!$ and $t_i = a + (i - 1)h$. Then let $p \to \infty$.]

12. Let $F(n) = \int_0^\infty e^{-\lambda t}\lambda^n t^{n-1}\, dt = \int_0^\infty e^{-u}\, u^{n-1}\, du$.

(a) Integrate by parts and show that $F(n) = (n - 1)F(n - 1)$.

(b) Show directly that $F(1) = 1$.

(c) From (a) and (b), show that $F(2) = 1$, $F(3) = 2F(2) = 2!$, and in general $F(n) = (n - 1)!$.

(d) Using the result of part (c) above, and of Problem 11, show that $Q_n(0, \infty) = 1$, for any integer $n \geq 1$. What does this mean in terms of probability?

REVIEW QUESTIONS AND EXERCISES FOR CHAPTER 18

1. List some differential equations (having physical interpretations) that you have come across in your courses in chemistry, physics, or engineering; or look for some in the articles on differential equations, dynamics, electromagnetic waves, hydromechanics, quantum mechanics, or thermodynamics, in the *Encyclopædia Britannica*.

2. How are differential equations classified?

3. What is meant by a "solution" of a differential equation?

4. Review methods for solving ordinary, first order, and first degree differential equations:

(a) when the variables are separable,
(b) when the equation is homogeneous,
(c) when the equation is linear in one variable,
(d) when the equation is exact.
Illustrate each with an example.

5. Review methods of solving second order equations:

(a) with dependent variable missing,
(b) with independent variable missing.
Illustrate each with an example.

6. Review methods for solving linear differential equations with constant coefficients:

(a) in the homogeneous case,
(b) in the nonhomogeneous case.
Illustrate each with an example.

7. If an external force F acts upon a system whose mass varies with time, Newton's law of motion is

$$\frac{d(mv)}{dt} = F + (v + u)\,\frac{dm}{dt}.$$

(See H. B. Phillips, *Differential Equations*, 3rd ed. Wiley, p. 84.) In this equation, m is the mass of the system at time t, v its velocity, and $v + u$ is the velocity of the mass that is entering (or leaving) the system at the rate dm/dt. Suppose that a rocket of initial mass m_0 starts from rest, but is driven upward by firing some of its mass directly backward at the constant rate of $dm/dt = -b$ units per second and at constant speed relative to the rocket $u = -c$. The only external force acting on the rocket is $F = -mg$ due to gravity. Under these assumptions, show that the height of the rocket above the ground at the end of t seconds (t small compared to m_0/b) is

$$y = c\left[t + \frac{m_0 - bt}{b}\ln\frac{m_0 - bt}{m_0}\right] - \frac{1}{2}\,gt^2.$$

MISCELLANEOUS PROBLEMS FOR CHAPTER 18

Solve the following differential equations:

1. $y \ln y \, dx + (1 + x^2) \, dy = 0$

2. $\dfrac{dy}{dx} = \dfrac{y^2 - y - 2}{x^2 + x}$

3. $e^{x+2y} \, dy - e^{y-2x} \, dx = 0$

4. $\sqrt{1 + \left(\dfrac{dy}{dx}\right)^2} = ky$

5. $y \, dy = \sqrt{1 + y^4} \, dx$

6. $(2x + y) \, dx + (x - 2y) \, dy = 0$

7. $\dfrac{dy}{dx} = \dfrac{x^2 + y^2}{2xy}$

8. $x \dfrac{dy}{dx} = y + \sqrt{x^2 + y^2}$

9. $x \, dy = \left(y + x \cos^2 \dfrac{y}{x}\right) dx$

10. $x(\ln y - \ln x) \, dy = y(1 + \ln y - \ln x) \, dx$

11. $x \, dy + (2y - x^2 - 1) \, dx = 0$

12. $\cos y \, dx + (x \sin y - \cos^2 y) \, dy = 0$

13. $\cosh x \, dy - (y + \cosh x) \sinh x \, dx = 0$

14. $(x + 1) \, dy + (2y - x) \, dx = 0$

15. $(1 + y^2) \, dx + (2xy + y^2 + 1) \, dy = 0$

16. $(x^2 + y) \, dx + (e^y + x) \, dy = 0$

17. $(x^2 + y^2) \, dx + (2xy + \cosh y) \, dy = 0$

18. $(e^x + \ln y) \, dx + \dfrac{x + y}{y} \, dy = 0$

19. $x(1 + e^y) \, dx + \tfrac{1}{2}(x^2 + y^2)e^y \, dy = 0$

20. $\left(\sin x + \tan^{-1} \dfrac{y}{x}\right) dx - (y - \ln \sqrt{x^2 + y^2}) \, dy = 0$

21. $\dfrac{d^2 y}{dx^2} - 2y \dfrac{dy}{dx} = 0$

22. $\dfrac{d^2 x}{dy^2} + 4x = 0$

23. $\dfrac{d^2 y}{dx^2} = 1 + \left(\dfrac{dy}{dx}\right)^2$

24. $\dfrac{d^2 x}{dy^2} = 1 - \left(\dfrac{dx}{dy}\right)^2$

25. $x^2 \dfrac{d^2 y}{dx^2} + x \dfrac{dy}{dx} = 1$

26. $\dfrac{d^2 y}{dx^2} - 4 \dfrac{dy}{dx} + 3y = 0$

27. $\dfrac{d^3 y}{dx^3} - 2 \dfrac{d^2 y}{dx^2} + \dfrac{dy}{dx} = 0$

28. $\dfrac{d^2 y}{dx^2} + 4y = \sec 2x$

29. $\dfrac{d^2 y}{dx^2} - \dfrac{dy}{dx} - 2y = e^{2x}$

30. $\dfrac{d^2 y}{dx^2} - 2 \dfrac{dy}{dx} + 5y = e^{-x}$

31. Find the *general solution* of the differential equation $4x^2 y'' + 4xy' - y = 0$, given that there is a particular solution of the form $y = x^c$ for some constant c.

32. Show that the only curves having constant curvature are circles and straight lines.

33. Find the orthogonal trajectories of the family of curves $x^2 = Cy^3$. [*Caution:* the differential equation should not contain the arbitrary constant C.]

34. Find the orthogonal trajectories of the family of circles $(x - C)^2 + y^2 = C^2$.

35. Find the orthogonal trajectories of the family of parabolas $y^2 = 4C(C - x)$.

36. The equation $d^2y/dt^2 + 100y = 0$ represents a simple harmonic motion. Find the general solution of the equation and determine the constants of integration if $y = 10$, $dy/dt = 50$, when $t = 0$. Find the period and the amplitude of the motion.

ANSWERS TO PROBLEMS

CHAPTER 1

15. If P is the point (x, y), the other points are $Q(x, -y)$, $R(-x, y)$, $S(-x, -y)$, $T(y, x)$.

16. $45°$ 　　　　　17. 2 　　　　　19. -1

20. No, because the line joining the given points crosses the y-axis at $(0, \frac{1}{2})$.

1. $(3, 1)$; 　　2; 　　3; 　$\sqrt{13}$ 　　2. $(1, 4)$; 　　-2; 　-3; 　$\sqrt{13}$

3. $(2, 2)$; 　　3; 　-3; 　$\sqrt{18}$ 　　4. $(-1, -1)$; 　-3; 　　3; 　$\sqrt{18}$

5. $(1, -1)$; 　　2; 　　3; 　$\sqrt{13}$ 　　6. $(-1, 2)$; 　　-2; 　-3; 　$\sqrt{13}$

7. $(-1, 2)$; 　　2; 　-4; 　$\sqrt{20}$ 　　8. $(-3, -2)$; 　-2; 　　4; 　$\sqrt{20}$

9. $(-1, -2)$; 　2; 　　1; 　$\sqrt{5}$ 　　10. $(-3, -1)$; 　-2; 　-1; 　$\sqrt{5}$

11. (a) $x^2 + y^2 = 25$, 　　　　　　(b) $x^2 + y^2 - 10x = 0$,

　　(c) $x^2 + y^2 - 6x - 8y = 0$, 　　(d) $(x - h)^2 + (y - k)^2 = 25$

1. $-3; \frac{1}{3}$ 　　　　　2. $3; -\frac{1}{3}$ 　　　　　3. $-\frac{1}{3}; 3$

4. $-\frac{1}{2}; 2$ 　　　　　5. $-1; 1$ 　　　　　6. $0; \infty$

7. $0; \infty$ 　　　　　8. $-3; \frac{1}{3}$ 　　　　　9. $-1; 1$

10. $\infty; 0$ 　　　　　11. $\frac{2}{3}; -\frac{3}{2}$ 　　　　12. $y/x; -x/y$

13. $0; \infty$ 　　　　　14. $\infty; 0$ 　　　　　15. $-b/a; a/b$

16. Rectangle 　　　　17. Parallelogram 　　　18. Rectangle

19. Parallelogram 　　20. No 　　　　　21. $(1, 2)$

23. Yes, they lie on a line because the slope of BA is equal to the slope of AC.

24. No, because the slope of AC is 1 but the slope of CB is 3.

25. Yes, because $m_{AB} = m_{BC} = m_{CD} = 2$.

26. No 　　　　　27. Yes 　　　　　28. $\left(\dfrac{x_1 + x_2}{2}, \dfrac{y_1 + y_2}{2} \right)$

29. Center $(\frac{3}{2}, \frac{3}{2})$; radius $= \sqrt{8.5}$

1. $2y = 3x$ 　　　　2. $y = 1$ 　　　　　3. $x = \cdot 1$

4. $3x + 4y + 2 = 0$ 　5. $x = -2$ 　　　　6. $x + y = 4$

7. $x/a + y/b = 1$ 　8. $y = 0$ 　　　　　9. $x = 0$

10. $x + y = 1$ 　　11. 3 　　　　　　12. $\frac{3}{2}$

13. -1 14. 2   15. $\frac{1}{2}$

16. $-\frac{3}{4}$ 17. $\frac{4}{3}$ 18. $\frac{1}{2}$

19. $-b/a$ 20. $-x_1/y_1$ 21. $x + 2y = 5$

22. (a) $x - 2y + 6 = 0$ (b) $(\frac{2}{5}, \frac{16}{5})$ (c) $6/\sqrt{5}$

23. $y - 4 = \sqrt{3}(x - 1)$ 24. $180° - \tan^{-1} 2$

26. (a) $F = 1.8C + 32$ (b) $F = C$ at -40 deg

ARTICLE 1–6

1. $x = \pm\sqrt{y}; \quad -\infty < x < \infty, y \geq 0$

2. $x = \dfrac{y + 1}{y - 1}; \quad x \neq 1, y \neq 1$

3. $x = \pm\sqrt{\dfrac{y}{1 - y}}; \quad -\infty < x < \infty, 0 \leq y < 1$

4. $x = \dfrac{y^2}{1 - y^2}; \quad x < -1 \quad \text{or} \quad x \geq 0, y \geq 0, y \neq 1$

5. $x = \dfrac{y \pm \sqrt{y^2 + 4}}{2}; \quad x \neq 0, -\infty < y < \infty$

6. $x = \dfrac{-y \pm \sqrt{12 - 3y^2}}{2}; \quad -2 \leq y \leq 2, -2 \leq x \leq 2$

7. $\frac{9}{2}, 0, \dfrac{1}{x^2} + x, x^2 + 2x\,\Delta x + (\Delta x)^2 + \dfrac{1}{x + \Delta x}$

8. Figure

9. (a) $-2 < x < 2$ (b) $x \leq -2$ or $x \geq 2$

   (c) $-2 \leq x \leq 4$ (d) $0 < x \leq 2$

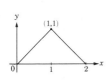

Problem 1–8

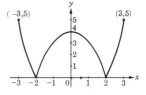

Problem 1–10

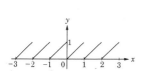

Problem 1–12

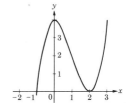

Problem 1–15

10. Figure

11. $|1 - x| = 1 - x$ if $x \leq 1$
$|1 - x| = x - 1$ if $x \geq 1$

12. Figure

ARTICLE 1–7

15. Figure

ARTICLE 1–8

1. $2x$ 2. $3x^2$ 3. 2

4. $2x - 1$ 5. $-1/x^2$ 6. $-2/x^3$

7. $-2/(2x + 1)^2$ 8. $1/(x + 1)^2$ 9. $4x - 1$

10. $3x^2 - 12$ 11. $4x^3$ 12. $2ax + b$

13. $1 + \dfrac{1}{x^2}$ 14. $a - \dfrac{b}{x^2}$ 15. $1/\sqrt{2x}$

16. $1/(2\sqrt{x + 1})$ 17. $1/\sqrt{2x + 3}$ 18. $-1/(2x\sqrt{x})$

19. $-1/(2x + 3)^{3/2}$ 20. $x/\sqrt{x^2 + 1}$

ARTICLE 1–9

2. $4t + 5$ 3. $gt + v_0$ 4. 4

5. $2t - 3$ 6. $-2 - 2t$ 7. $8t + 12$

8. $2t - 4$ 9. $-4t$ 10. $64 - 32t$

12. 8,000 gal/min; 10,000 gal/min

13. (a) $2\pi r + \pi \Delta r$ 14. $4\pi r^2$ 15. πh^2
(b) $2\pi r$

ARTICLE 1–10

1. $\frac{5}{4}$ 2. 2 3. 5

4. -1 5. -2 6. 0

7. $\frac{1}{2}$

8. (c) Take δ less than or equal to the smaller of the two numbers 1 and $\epsilon/8$. In particular, for (a) take $\delta = 1/80$; for (b) take $\delta = 1/800$.

9. $1/x^2$ increases most rapidly, $1/\sqrt{x}$ least rapidly.

CHAPTER 1: MISCELLANEOUS

1. (b) $-\frac{3}{2}, \frac{2}{3}, -\frac{3}{2}, \frac{2}{3}, 0, \infty$

(c) Yes, $ABCD$ (d) Yes, AEB (e) Yes, CD

(f) $2y + 3x = 26$; $2y + 3x = 0$; $3y - 2x + 13 = 0$; $y = 6$; $x = 2$

(g)

L	AB	CD	AD	CE	BD
y-intercept	13	0	$-\frac{13}{3}$	6	none
x-intercept	$\frac{26}{3}$	0	$\frac{13}{2}$	none	2

2. (a) $3y + 2x = -7$ (b) $\sqrt{13}$

3. (a) No   (b) No   (c) Outside   (d) $(-2, -\frac{9}{7})$

4. $4y + 3x = 0; \quad x = 0$ 5. $[(x_1 + x_2)/2, (y_1 + y_2)/2]$

7. (a) $-a/b$ (b) $(0, -c/b)$ (c) $(-c/a, 0)$ (d) $ay - bx = 0$

9. Four; centers: $(0, \sqrt{5} - 2), (0, -\sqrt{5} - 2), (-\sqrt{5} - 1, 1), (\sqrt{5} - 1, 1)$
   Radii (in same order): $(3\sqrt{2} - \sqrt{10})/2, (3\sqrt{2} + \sqrt{10})/2,$
   $$(\sqrt{10} + \sqrt{2})/2, (\sqrt{10} - \sqrt{2})/2$$

10. $|b' - b|/\sqrt{1 + m^2}$

11. Straight line through point of intersection of the two given lines.

12. $(\frac{17}{18}, \frac{23}{6})$ 13. $x + 5y = \pm 5\sqrt{2}$

14. $x = \sqrt{(y + 2)/(y - 1)}; \quad y \leq -2, y > 1$

15. $A = \pi r^2, C = 2\pi r, A = C^2/4\pi$

16. (a) $x < -1, x > -1; y < 0, y > 0$
    (b) All $x; 0 < y \leq 1$
    (c) $x \geq 0; 0 < y \leq 1$

17. $-5 < x < 3$ 18. For $y \leq 4, x = y - 2$
                                     For $y \geq 4, x = (y + 2)/3$

19. $y > 2, x = (y + 2)/2$ 20. $x = \dfrac{y \pm \sqrt{y^2 - 4}}{2}, \quad |y| \geq 2$

21. (a) $f(-2) = -3$ 22. (c) $(\frac{1}{2}, -\frac{3}{4})$
    $f(-1) = -4$
    $f(x_1) = x_1^2 + 2x_1 - 3$
    $f(x_1 + \Delta x) = x_1^2 + 2x_1\Delta x + (\Delta x)^2 + 2x_1 + 2\Delta x - 3$

24. $m(a, b) = (a + b - |a - b|)/2$

26. Take $\phi_k(x) = g_k(x)/g_k(x_k)$ where $g_k(x)$ is the product
    $$(x - x_1)(x - x_2) \cdots (x - x_n)$$
    with the factor $(x - x_k)$ deleted.

27. $f(d) = g(b)$

29. (a) $1/(1 - x)$ (b) $x/(x + 1)$ (c) x (d) $1 - x$

30. (a) $2/(x + 1)^2$ (b) $3\sqrt{x}/2$ (c) $\frac{1}{3}x^{-2/3}$

31. (a) $2x - 3$ (b) $-1/(3x)^2 + 2$ (c) $1/(2\sqrt{t - 4})$

32. (a) 6   (b) $(0, 2)$

33. (a) $f(0) = 0, f(-1) = 1, f(1/x) = 2/(1 - x)$

(b) $\dfrac{-2}{(x-1)(x+\Delta x - 1)}$

(c) $-2/(x-1)^2$

34. $P(\frac{45}{8}, \frac{2025}{4})$

35. $v = 180 - 32t$

$t = \frac{45}{8}$

36. $t = 1$ sec, $s = 16$ ft

37. (a) $-\dfrac{1}{V(V + \Delta V)}$

(b) $-\frac{1}{4}$

38. 28 in^3/sec

39. (a) 0 (b) $-\frac{1}{3}$

(c) $f\left(-\dfrac{1}{x}\right) = \dfrac{-x(x+1)}{5x^2 + 7x + 2}$

$f(0) = -\frac{1}{5}, 1/f(x) = 2x - 5$

40. $\left(\dfrac{c+1}{3c+2}, \ -\dfrac{1}{5(3c+2)}\right)$, $(\frac{2}{5}, \ -\frac{1}{25})$

41. (a) 0 (b) $\frac{1}{2}$

42. δ less than smaller of 1 and $\epsilon^2/3$.   43. $M = 1 + 1/\epsilon$

CHAPTER 2

ARTICLE 2–1

1. $v = 2t - 4, a = 2$

2. $v = 6t^2 - 10t + 4, a = 12t - 10$

3. $v = gt + v_0, a = g$

4. $v = 4 - 2t, a = -2$

5. $v = 8t + 12, a = 8$

6. $y' = 4x^3 - 21x^2 + 4x$

$y'' = 12x^2 - 42x + 4$

7. $y' = 15(x^2 - x^4)$

$y'' = 30(x - 2x^3)$

8. $y' = 8(x - 1), y'' = 8$

9. $y' = x^3 - x^2 + x - 1$

$y'' = 3x^2 - 2x + 1$

10. $y' = 8(x^3 - x)$

$y'' = 8(3x^2 - 1)$

11. $y' = 2x^3 - 3x - 1$

$y'' = 6x^2 - 3$

12. $y' = 21(x^6 - x^2 + 2x)$

$y'' = 42(3x^5 - x + 1)$

13. $y' = 5x^4 - 2x$

$y'' = 20x^3 - 2$

14. $y' = 2x + 1$

$y'' = 2$

15. $y' = 12x + 13$

$y'' = 12$

16. (a) 400 ft   (b) 96 ft/sec

17. $y = 8x - 5$

18. $y = 4x \pm 2$

Least slope is $+1$, at $(0, 0)$.

19. $(-1, 27), (2, 0)$

20. $a = b = 1, c = 0$

21. $a = -3, b = 2, c = 1$

22. $c = \frac{1}{4}$

ARTICLE 2–2

1. $x^2 - x + 1$

2. $(x - 1)^2 (x + 2)^3 (7x + 2)$

3. $10x(x^2 + 1)^4$

4. $12(x^2 - 1)(x^3 - 3x)^3$

5. $-2(2x^2 + 3x - 1)(x + 1)(x^2 + 1)^{-4}$

6. $-2(x^2 + x + 1)/(x^2 - 1)^2$ 7. $-19/(3x - 2)^2$

8. $-4(x + 1)(x - 1)^{-3}$ 9. $(1 - t^2)/(t^2 + 1)^2$

10. $6(2t + 3)^2$ 11. $-2(2t - 1)(t^2 - t)^{-3}$

12. $(t^2 + 2t)(t + 1)^{-2}$ 13. $(2 - 6t^2)/(3t^2 + 1)^2$

14. $2(t - t^{-3})$ 15. $3(2t + 3)(t^2 + 3t)^2$

ARTICLE 2-3

1. $-x/y$ 2. $\dfrac{1}{y(x + 1)^2}$

3. $-(2x + y)/x$ 4. $-(2xy + y^2)/(x^2 + 2xy)$

5. $\dfrac{3x^2}{2y}$ 6. $-(y/x)^{1/3}$ 7. $-(y/x)^{1/2}$

8. $\dfrac{y - 3x^2}{3y^2 - x}$ 9. $\dfrac{y}{x} - (x + y)^2$ 10. $(x^2 + 1)^{-3/2}$

11. $(2x^2 + 1)(x^2 + 1)^{-1/2}$ 12. $\dfrac{x^4 - 1}{x^3 y}$

13. $\dfrac{1 - 2y}{2x + 2y - 1}$ 14. $\tfrac{1}{2}x^{-1/2} + \tfrac{1}{3}x^{-2/3} + \tfrac{1}{4}x^{-3/4}$

15. $\dfrac{2x}{y(x^2 + 1)^2}$ 16. $\dfrac{2x^3 - 3x^2 - 3y^2}{6xy - 2y^3}$

17. $5(3x + 7)^4/(2y^2)$

18. $(10x^2 + 30x - 8)(x + 5)^3 (x^2 - 2)^2$

19. $-y^2/x^2$ 20. $(6x + 15)(x^2 + 5x)^2$

21. $(2x - 1)/(2y)$ 22. $\dfrac{x(y^2 - 1)}{y(1 - x^2)}$

23. $-\dfrac{x^2 + 9}{3x^2(x^2 + 3)^{2/3}}$ 25. (a) $-x/y$ (b) $-1/y^3$

26. (a) $-x^2/y^2$ (b) $-2x/y^5$ 27. (a) $-x^{-1/3}y^{1/3}$ (b) $\tfrac{1}{3}x^{-4/3}y^{-1/3}$

28. (a) $-y(x + 2y)^{-1}$ (b) $2(x + 2y)^{-3}$

30. (a) $7x - 4y = 2$ (b) $4x + 7y = 29$

31. (a) $3x - 4y = 25$ (b) $4x + 3y = 0$

32. (a) $y = 3x + 6$ (b) $x + 3y = 8$

33. (a) $x = 3y$ (b) $3x + y = 10$

34. (a) $3x - 4y = 10$ (b) $4x + 3y = 30$

ARTICLE 2-4

1. (a) $(2x + 2)\,\Delta x + (\Delta x)^2$ 2. (a) $(4x + 4)\,\Delta x + 2\,(\Delta x)^2$
   (b) $(2x + 2)\,\Delta x$ (b) $(4x + 4)\,\Delta x$
   (c) $(\Delta x)^2$ (c) $2\,(\Delta x)^2$

3. (a) $(3x^2 - 1) \, \Delta x + 3x \, (\Delta x)^2 + (\Delta x)^3$
   (b) $(3x^2 - 1) \, \Delta x$
   (c) $3x \, (\Delta x)^2 + (\Delta x)^3$

4. (a) $4x^3 \, \Delta x + 6x^2 \, (\Delta x)^2 + 4x \, (\Delta x)^3 + (\Delta x)^4$
   (b) $4x^3 \, \Delta x$
   (c) $6x^2 \, (\Delta x)^2 + 4x \, (\Delta x)^3 + (\Delta x)^4$

5. (a) $-\dfrac{\Delta x}{x(x + \Delta x)}$ 6. 2.13

   (b) $-\Delta x/x^2$

   (c) $\dfrac{(\Delta x)^2}{x^2(x + \Delta x)}$

7. 1.96   8. 0.48

9. 5.16   10. 0.58

ARTICLE 2–5

1. $9y = (x - 1)^2$ 2. $y^2 = x^3$

3. $y = \left(\dfrac{x}{1 + x}\right)^2$ 4. $y = \dfrac{x^2}{1 - x}$

5. -3 6. $8x + 10$

7. $\dfrac{1}{2(x + 1)^2}$ 8. $\dfrac{4x}{3(x^2 + 1)^{1/3}}$

9. $18x + \dfrac{1}{3x^2}$ 10. $12\,\dfrac{(3x + 2)^4 - 1}{(3x + 2)^3}$

ARTICLE 2–7

1. $(3x^2 - 6x + 5) \, dx$ 2. $\dfrac{9x}{2y} \, (3x^2 + 1)^{1/2} \, dx$

3. $-\dfrac{2xy + y^2}{2xy + x^2} \, dx$ 4. $2(1 - x^2)(1 + x^2)^{-2} \, dx$

5. $\dfrac{1 - 2x^2}{\sqrt{1 - x^2}} \, dx$ 6. $(6 - 2x - x^2)(x^2 - 2x + 4)^{-2} \, dx$

7. $3(1 - x)^2(2x - 1)(2 - 3x)^{-2} \, dx$

8. $(2 - 2x + x^2)(1 - x)^{-2} \, dx$ 9. 12.04

10. 9.2   11. 2.03

12. 0.5013   13. 79.69

14. (c) $5x - 3y = 8$ 15. (c) $15x - y = 20$

16. (c) $11y = x + 16$ 17. (c) $9x + y = 6$

18. (c) $4x + 2y = 9$ 19. $-4t^3(t^2 - 1)^{-3}$

20. $2(t + 1)^3(t - 1)^{-3}$

ARTICLE 2–8

1. (b) Take δ less than or equal to the smaller of the two numbers 1 and $\epsilon/91$. Then $|x^2 + 5x + 25| < 91$ and $|x^3 - 5^3| < \epsilon$ when $|x - 5| < \delta$.

2. (a) $x = -1$ (b) $x = 1$ or 3

3. Continuous

4. Take $\delta \le \epsilon$.

5. Max = 1, min = 0

6. Neither a maximum nor a minimum since $f(x_2) > f(x_1)$ if $0 < x_1 < x_2 < 1$. Hence we can always find x_2 such that $f(x_2) > f(x_1)$, so $f(x_1)$ is *not* the maximum. This is true for any x_1 in the given domain. The same argument shows that no x_2 in the domain can give a minimum.

7. Take $a = 0$, $b = 1$, and $N = 0$ in Theorem 3, part (ii).

8. Continuous but not differentiable.

10. 7.

CHAPTER 2: MISCELLANEOUS

1. $-4(x^2 - 4)^{-3/2}$

2. $(5 - 2x - y)/(x + 2y)$

3. $-y/(x + 2y)$

4. $(3x^2 + 4y)/(9y^2 - 4x)$

5. $-\dfrac{y(2x + y)}{x(2y + x)}$

6. $\dfrac{-2(x + 1)(x^2 + 2x + 2)}{x^3(x + 2)^3}$

7. $(1 - x^2)^{-3/2}$

8. $\dfrac{-(2x + 3y^2)}{3y(2x + y)}$

9. $(x + 1)^{-2}$

10. $(2x + 1)^{-1/2}$

11. $(3x^3 - 2a^2 x)/\sqrt{x^2 - a^2}$

12. $-4(2x - 1)^{-2}$

13. $2x(1 - x^2)^{-2}$

14. $3(x^2 + x + 1)^2(2x + 1)$

15. $-\dfrac{2x + 1}{2}(x^2 + x - 1)^{-3/2}$

16. $2x + 1$

17. $\dfrac{4x + 5}{2}\sqrt{2x^2 + 5x}$

18. $-(9/2)(4x + 5)(2x^2 + 5x)^{-5/2}$

19. $-\dfrac{y}{x}\left(\dfrac{2y\sqrt{xy} + 1}{4y\sqrt{xy} + 1}\right)$

20. $\dfrac{y - 2x}{2y - x}$

21. $-(y/x)^{1/3}$ 22. $-\sqrt{y/x}$ 23. $-y/x$ 24. $-y/x$

25. $-\dfrac{1}{2}\left(\dfrac{x + 2y + y^2}{x + 2y + xy}\right)$

26. $\dfrac{x^2 - 2x - 1}{2(1 - x)^{1/2}(1 + x^2)^{3/2}}$

27. $\dfrac{1}{2y(x + 1)^2}$

28. $\dfrac{12x - 2xy - y^2}{x^2 + 2xy - 12y}$

29. $-\dfrac{y + 2}{x + 3}$

30. 1

31. $\dfrac{4x + 8}{\sqrt{4x^2 + 16x + 15}}$

32. $\dfrac{2t(1 + t^2)^2}{(1 - t^2)}$

33. $2x\left[1 + \dfrac{(1 - x^2)}{(1 + x^2)^3}\right]$

34. $m = 1, y = x$ 35. $y + 2x = 6$ 36. $c = 4$

37. $m = 2, y - 2x = -5$ 38. $(2, 0)$ and $(-1, 27)$

39. (a) $10(x^2 + 2x)^4(x + 1)$ 40. $27y + x = 28$

 (b) $\dfrac{3t - 1}{\sqrt{3t^2 - 2t}}$

 (c) $r[(r^2 + 5)^{-1/2} + (r^2 - 5)^{-1/2}]$

 (d) $\dfrac{4x}{(x^2 + 1)^2}$

41. $y + x = 3$ 42. $(2x + 3)^{-1/2}$

43. $-6(2 - 3x), f(x) = (2 - 3x)^2$ 44. $-\frac{8}{5}$

45. $6\pi(\Delta r)^2$; a shell around the can with thickness Δr.

46. $\pi x(20 - x)$ 47. $x_1 = 40, p = 4(= 20\rlap{/}c)$

49. $(x - 1)(2x - 1)$ 50. $(2x + 1)/9$

51. 56 ft/sec   52. $-\frac{12}{5}$

53. (a) $h + 2k = 5$ 54. $2\sqrt{x^2 + 1}$
 (b) $h = -4, k = \frac{9}{2}, r = 5\sqrt{5}/2$

55. $\dfrac{2}{3(2y + 1)(2x + 1)\sqrt{x^2 + x}}$ 56. $2x\sqrt{3x^4 - 1}$

57. $\dfrac{3}{(x + 1)^2}\sin\left[\left(\dfrac{2x - 1}{x + 1}\right)^2\right]$ 58. $y' = 2x - 3, y'' = 2$

59. $a = -32$ 60. $\dfrac{3(x - 2)}{(2x - 3)^{3/2}}$

61. $-\frac{3}{32}$ 62. $y' = 2, y'' = -2$

64. (a) $3(2x - 1)^{-5/2}$ 66. $\Delta y = 0.92$, principal part $= 0.9$
 (b) $-162(3x + 2)^{-4}$
 (c) $6a$

67. $\sqrt{26} \approx 5.1$
 $\sqrt[3]{26} \approx 2.963, y = x^{1/3}$
 $x = 27, \Delta x = -1$

68. 0.9999   69. $14 \pm .044$ ft

70. (a) $\dfrac{x(x + 2)}{(x + 1)^2}\,dx$ (b) $\dfrac{x}{y}\,dx$ (c) $\dfrac{-y}{x + 2y}\,dx$

72. $\delta = \epsilon/4$; the function is uniformly continuous for $-2 \leq x \leq 2$.

75. $m = \frac{1}{2}, C = \sqrt{2}$

CHAPTER 3

ARTICLE 3–1

1. Falling $x < \frac{1}{2}$, rising $x > \frac{1}{2}$. Low point at $(\frac{1}{2}, \frac{3}{4})$.

2. Rising $x < -1$, falling $-1 < x < 2$, rising $x > 2$. High point at $(-1, \frac{3}{2})$, low at $(2, -3)$.

3. Rising $x < 0$, falling $0 < x < 1$, rising $x > 1$. High at $(0, 3)$, low at $(1, 2)$.

4. Rising $x < -3$, falling $-3 < x < 3$, rising $x > 3$. High at $(-3, 90)$, low at $(3, -18)$.

5. Falling $x < -2$, rising $-2 < x < 0$, falling $0 < x < 2$, rising $x > 2$. Low points $(\pm 2, 0)$, high $(0, 16)$.

ARTICLE 3–2

1. $\dfrac{dA}{dt} = 2\pi r \, \dfrac{dr}{dt}$

2. $\dfrac{dV}{dt} = 4\pi r^2 \, \dfrac{dr}{dt}$

3. $\dfrac{8}{5\pi}$ ft/min

5. $\dfrac{ax + by}{\sqrt{x^2 + y^2}}$ ft/sec

6. $\dfrac{25}{9\pi}$ ft/min

7. $\dfrac{10}{\sqrt{21}} = 2.2$ ft/sec

8. Increasing 33.7 ft/sec.

9. $\dfrac{125}{144\pi}$ ft/min

10. $\dfrac{dy}{dt} = -x$. Clockwise.

11. 8 ft/sec toward the lamppost. Decreasing 3 ft/sec.

12. Increasing 8.75 psi/sec.

13. 1500 ft/sec

14. 20 ft/sec

15. Thickness decreasing at the rate of $\dfrac{5}{72\pi}$ in/min. Area decreasing at the rate of $\frac{10}{3}$ in^2/min.

16. $\dfrac{260}{\sqrt{37}}$ mi/hr

ARTICLE 3–4

1. (a) $x > 2$ (b) $x < 2$ (c) Always (d) Never $m(2, -1)$

2. (a) Always (b) Never (c) $x < -1$ (d) $x > -1$

3. (a) $-1 < x < 1$ (b) $x < -1, x > 1$ (c) $x < 0$ (d) $x > 0$
   $M(1, 6)$; $m(-1, 2)$; $I(0, 4)$

4. (a) $x < -2, x > 3$ (b) $-2 < x < 3$ (c) $x > \frac{1}{2}$ (d) $x < \frac{1}{2}$
   $M(-2, \frac{22}{3})$; $m(3, -\frac{27}{2})$; $I(\frac{1}{2}, -\frac{37}{12})$

5. (a) $x < -2, x > 2$ (b) $-2 < x < 2, x \neq 0$ (c) $x > 0$ (d) $x < 0$
   $M(-2, -4)$; $m(2, 4)$

In Problems 8–12: M = high turning point,
m = low turning point,
I = inflection point.

8. $M(-1, 7)$ 9. $m(1, 1)$

10. $M(-2, 28)$; $m(2, -4)$; $I(0, 12)$

11. $m(2, 0)$ 12. $M(0, 2)$; $m(2, -2)$; $I(1, 0)$

13. $(1, -1)$ 14. $(16, -3)$, $(-16, 1)$

15. $(2, 0)$, $(1, \pm1)$ 16. $(3, 1)$

19. Concave downward because $f''(x) = -\dfrac{1}{x^2}$ is negative.

21. (a) 3 times; near $x = -1.2$, -0.4, $+0.8$. (b) Once; near $x = -1.8$. (c) Once; near $x = 1.2$.

ARTICLE 3–6

2. $(r\sqrt{2}) \times (r/\sqrt{2})$ 3. 32

4. $\frac{5}{3} \times \frac{14}{3} \times \frac{35}{3}$ (inches)   5. Use one-half of the fence parallel to the river.

6. $\sqrt{\dfrac{A}{3}} \times \sqrt{\dfrac{A}{3}} \times \dfrac{1}{2}\sqrt{\dfrac{A}{3}}$ where   7. $4'' \times 4'' \times 2''$

A = given amount of material.

8. 4   9. 9 inches wide and 18 inches high.

10. $V_{\max} = \dfrac{2\pi h^3}{9\sqrt{3}}$, h = given hypotenuse.

11. $(100 + c)/2$ 12. $0.58L$

13. (a) 16 (b) -54 (c) -1 (d) $f'(x) = 0$ when $2x^3 = a$ and then $f''(x) = +6$ or $+2$ according as $a \neq 0$ or $a = 0$.

14. (a) $a = -3, b = -9$ (b) $a = -3, b = -24$

15. (a) $\dfrac{4L}{4 + 3\sqrt{3}}$ for the square, $\dfrac{3\sqrt{3}L}{4 + 3\sqrt{3}}$ for the triangle.

(b) Use it all for the square.

16. $(\frac{1}{2}, -\frac{1}{2})$ and $(-\frac{1}{2}, \frac{1}{2})$ 17. (a) $(c - \frac{1}{2}, \sqrt{c - \frac{1}{2}})$ (b) $(0, 0)$

18. $\frac{32}{81}\pi r^3$ 19. $\frac{4}{9}\pi r^3\sqrt{3}$

21. Width $= \dfrac{2r}{\sqrt{3}}$, depth $= 2r\sqrt{\frac{2}{3}}$. 22. Width of beam = radius of log.

23. $\dfrac{x}{c-x} = \sqrt[3]{\dfrac{a}{b}}$ where x is the distance from the source of strength a.

24. Height of rectangle $= (4+\pi)/8$ times diameter of semicircle.

25. $4/\pi$

26. Diameter $=$ alt. of cylinder $= \sqrt[3]{\dfrac{3V}{\pi}}$, $V =$ total volume.

27. (a) Unity   (b) Infinity

31. Before tax: Production $= 7,500$; price $= \$1.25$, profit $= \$5,425$.
 After tax: Production $= 7,000$; price $= \$1.30$, profit $= \$4,700$.
 To maximize his profit he should absorb 5¢ of the tax and add 5¢ to the price.

ARTICLE 3–8

1. $\frac{1}{2}$ 2. $\sqrt{3}$ 3. $\frac{8}{27}$ 4. 1

5. $\frac{3}{2}$ 7. (a) $3\frac{1}{6}$ (b) 4.012   (c) 0.0101

CHAPTER 3: MISCELLANEOUS

1. (a) $x < \frac{9}{2}$
   (b) $x > \frac{9}{2}$
   (c) no values
   (d) all values

2. (a) $x > 3, x < \frac{1}{3}$
   (b) $\frac{1}{3} < x < 3$
   (c) $x > \frac{5}{3}$
   (d) $x < \frac{5}{3}$

3. (a) $x < 3$
   (b) $x > 3$
   (c) $0 < x < 2$
   (d) $x < 0, x > 2$

4. (a) $|x| > \frac{1}{2}$
   (b) $|x| < \frac{1}{2}$
   (c) $x > 0$
   (d) $x < 0$

5. (a) $x > \sqrt[3]{2}$
   (b) $x < \sqrt[3]{2}$
   (c) $x > 0, x < -\sqrt[3]{4}$
   (d) $-\sqrt[3]{4} < x < 0$

6. (a) $x < 0, x > 2$
   (b) $0 < x < 2$
   (c) $x \neq 0$
   (d) never

7. (a) $x < 0$
   (b) $x > 0$
   (c) $x \neq 0$
   (d) never

8. (a) $x \neq -1$
   (b) never
   (c) $x < -1$
   (d) $x > -1$

9. (a) $x \neq 0$
   (b) never
   (c) $x < 0$
   (d) $x > 0$

10. (a) $-1 < x < 0, x > 1$
    (b) $x < -1, 0 < x < 1$
    (c) $x < -1/\sqrt{3}, x > 1/\sqrt{3}$
    (d) $|x| < 1/\sqrt{3}$

11. (a) $x < -2b/a, x > 0$
    (b) $-2b/a < x < 0$
    (c) $x > -b/a$
    (d) $x < -b/a$

12. (a) $x < 1, x > 2$
    (b) $1 < x < 2$
    (c) $x > \frac{3}{2}$
    (d) $x < \frac{3}{2}$

13. (a) $x < -1, x > \frac{1}{3}$
    (b) $-1 < x < \frac{1}{3}$
    (c) $x > -\frac{1}{3}$
    (d) $x < -\frac{1}{3}$

14. (a) $0 < x < 4$
    (b) $x < 0, x > 4$
    (c) $x < 2$
    (d) $x > 2$

15. (a) At $x = 1$; because y' goes from $+$ to $-$
    (b) At $x = 3$; because y' goes from $-$ to $+$

17. If $v = k/\sqrt{s}$, then $dv/dt = -k^2/2s^2$

18. $k^2/2$ 19. $\frac{1}{4}$ in/min   20. $(3/400\pi)$ ft/min

21. $dr/dt = -(3/400)$ ft/min
    $dA/dt = -\frac{6}{5}\pi$ ft^2/min
    $\Delta r \approx -(3/4000)$ ft; $\Delta A \approx -(3\pi/25)$ ft^2

22. (a) Approx. 606 mi/hr   (b) Approx. 0.83 mi

23. $\frac{1}{2}\sqrt{3}$ 24. $-480\sqrt{2}/7$

25. Yes, it will fill, because $dy/dt > 0.007$ for $y \le 10$.

26. $a = -gR^2/s^2$ 28. $(\sqrt{3}/30)\ r$, increasing

29. ≈ 18 mi/hr   30. $(8/9\pi)$ ft/min

31. $\frac{20}{3}$ and $\frac{40}{3}$ 32. 10

33. 18 and 18. No.   34. $a = 1; b = -3; c = -9; d = 5$

35. $\frac{1}{2}$ 36. $r = 25$ ft

37. $t = 1, s = 16$ 38. $r = 4, h = 4$

39. Diameter = height = 4 in.   40. $4\sqrt{3}$

41. 276 (approx.)   42. (a) $(2, \pm\sqrt{3})$,   (b) and (c) $(1, 0)$

43. (a) $2\frac{1}{12}$ mi from A; (b) $2\frac{1}{12}$ mi from A; (c) at B

44. (a) True   (b) False   (c) True   (d) False

45. Each $= (P - b)/2$

46. Each $= \tan^{-1}(4k/b^2)$ 48. $m = \frac{1}{4}$

50. Sides 110 yd; radius of semicircular ends $110/\pi$ yd

57. 6×18 ft   58. approx. 16.4 in.   59. $(h^{2/3} + w^{2/3})^{3/2}$ ft

60. $v = \sqrt[n]{\dfrac{a}{(n-1)b}}$ 61. $r = \sqrt{A}, \theta = 2$ rad

62. Approx. 1.94 gal   63. (a) A decreasing 0.04π in^2/sec
                               (b) $t = (5b - 3a)/(a^2 - b^2)$

64. $t = (R - cr)/(ca - b)$, where $c = \sqrt{a/b}$

66. (a) True;   (b) not necessarily true; $f = x^3, g = x^5, a = 0$

67. $x = \dfrac{1}{n}\sum_{i=1}^{n} c_i$ 68. $m = \frac{5}{7}$

70. Doesn't apply; derivative doesn't exist at $x = 0$.

72. $c = \pm\left(\dfrac{b^{2/3} + a^{1/3}b^{1/3} + a^{2/3}}{3}\right)^{3/2}$

73. Root -0.67

75. (a) $x = (c - b)/(2e)$ (b) $P = \frac{1}{2}(b + c)$ (c) $-a + (c - b)^2/(4e)$
    (d) $P = \frac{1}{2}(b + t + c)$; that is, he adds $\frac{1}{2}t$ to his previous price

CHAPTER 4

ARTICLE 4–2

1. $y = \dfrac{x^3}{3} + x + C$

2. $y = -\dfrac{1}{x} + \dfrac{x^2}{2} + C$

3. $y^2 = x^2 + C$

4. $3y^{1/2} = x^{3/2} + C$

5. $y^{2/3} = x^{2/3} + C$

6. $-\dfrac{1}{y} = x^2 + C$

7. $y = x^3 - x^2 + 5x + C$

8. $s = t^3 + 2t^2 - 6t + C$

9. $r = (2z + 1)^4/8 + C$

10. $-u^{-1} = 2v^4 - 4v^{-2} + C$

11. $x^{1/2} = 4t + C$

12. $y = 4t^3/3 + 4t - t^{-1} + C$

13. $y = z^3/3 - z^{-1} + C$

14. $x^2 + 3x + C$

15. $\dfrac{x^3}{3} - \dfrac{2x^{3/2}}{3} + C$

16. $\dfrac{(3x - 1)^{235}}{705} + C$

17. $\dfrac{-3(2 - 7t)^{5/3}}{35} + C$

18. $\dfrac{2(2 + 5y)^{3/2}}{15} + C$

19. $\dfrac{-1}{9x + 6} + C$

20. $-3\sqrt{1 - r^2} + C$

21. $\dfrac{(2x^2 + 1)^{3/2}}{6} + C$

22. $\frac{1}{2}(1 + 2t^3)^{1/3} + C$

23. $\frac{1}{2}\sqrt{2y^2 + 1} + C$

24. $\frac{2}{3}x^{3/2} + 2x^{1/2} + C$

25. $\frac{3}{4}(z^2 + 2z + 2)^{2/3} + C$

ARTICLE 4–3

1. $s = t^3 + s_0$

2. $s = t^2 + t + s_0$

3. $s = \frac{1}{3}(t + 1)^3 - \frac{1}{3} + s_0$

4. $s = \frac{1}{5}t^5 + \frac{2}{3}t^3 + t + s_0$

5. $s = -(t + 1)^{-1} + 1 + s_0$

6. $s = s_0 + t\sqrt{2gs_0} + \frac{1}{2}gt^2$

7. $v = gt + v_0$
   $s = \frac{1}{2}gt^2 + v_0t + s_0$

8. $v = \frac{1}{2}t^2 + v_0$
   $s = \frac{1}{6}t^3 + v_0t + s_0$

9. $v = \frac{3}{8}(2t + 1)^{4/3} + v_0 - \frac{3}{8}$
   $s = \frac{9}{112}(2t + 1)^{7/3} + (v_0 - \frac{3}{8})t + s_0 - \frac{9}{112}$

10. $v = -\frac{1}{4}(2t + 1)^{-2} + v_0 + \frac{1}{4}$
    $s = \frac{1}{8}(2t + 1)^{-1} + (v_0 + \frac{1}{4})t + s_0 - \frac{1}{8}$

11. $v = \frac{1}{5}t^5 + \frac{2}{3}t^3 + t + v_0$
    $s = \frac{1}{30}t^6 + \frac{1}{6}t^4 + \frac{1}{2}t^2 + v_0t + s_0$

13. $4\sqrt{y} = x^2 + 4$

14. $-y^{-1} = x^2 - 2$

15. $(3y + 10)^2 = (1 + x^2)^3$

16. $(1 + y^2)^{-1/2} = \dfrac{1}{\sqrt{2}} - 4x$

ARTICLE 4–4

9. $\cos^2 A + \sin^2 A = \cos 0 = 1$ 10. $\sin 0 = 0$

11. $\tan (A - B) = \dfrac{\tan A - \tan B}{1 + \tan A \tan B}$

12. $\tan (A + B) = \dfrac{\tan A + \tan B}{1 - \tan A \tan B}$

14. Cosine and secant are even. Sine, tangent, cotangent, cosecant are odd.

15. $\cos 2A = \cos^2 A - \sin^2 A$, $\sin 2A = 2 \sin A \cos A$.

ARTICLE 4–5

1. 1   2. 1   3. 2   4. $\frac{1}{3}$ 5. $\frac{5}{3}$ 6. $\frac{1}{2}$

7. 0   8. 0   9. $\frac{1}{2}$ 10. $\frac{2}{3}$ 11. $\frac{3}{5}$ 12. 1

13. 2π 14. 2   15. $\frac{1}{2}$ 16. 1   17. 2   18. $\cos a$

19. $-\sin a$ 20. $\pi/4$ 21. $3 \cos (3x + 4)$

22. $x \cos x + \sin x$

23. $(x \cos x - \sin x)/x^2$

24. $-5 \sin 5x$

25. $3x^2 \cos 3x + 2x \sin 3x$

26. $-\sin 2x/(2 + \cos 2x)^{1/2}$

27. 0

28. $6 \sin 3x/\cos^2 3x$

29. $6 \cos 2x + 8 \sin 2x$

30. $-24 \sin 2x \cos 2x$ or $-12 \sin 4x$

31. $2(\cos^2 x - \sin^2 x)$ or $2 \cos 2x$

32. $-\cos x/\sin^2 x$

33. $-3 \sin 6x$

34. $-1/\sin^2 x$

35. $\dfrac{\sin 2y + 2y \sin 2x}{\cos 2x - 2x \cos 2y}$

36. $-\dfrac{\sin 8x}{y}$

40. $-\frac{1}{3} \cos 3x + C$

41. $\frac{1}{2} \sin (2x + 4) + C$

42. $-\frac{1}{4} \cos (2x^2) + C$

43. $2 \sin \sqrt{x} + C$

44. $-\frac{1}{2} \cos 2t + C$

45. $\frac{1}{3} \sin (3\theta - 1) + C$

46. $\frac{4}{3} \sin 3y + C$

47. $\sin^2 z + C$

48. $\frac{1}{3} \sin^3 x + C$

49. $-\frac{1}{6} \cos^3 2y + C$

50. $\frac{1}{3} \sin 3t - \frac{1}{9} \sin^3 3t + C$

51. $1/\cos x + C$

52. $-1/\sin x + C$

53. $\frac{2}{9}(2 + \sin 3t)^{3/2} + C$

54. $\sqrt{2 - \cos 2t} + C$

55 $\dfrac{1}{2} \sin^4 \dfrac{y}{2} + C$

56. $3 \sec \dfrac{z - 1}{3} + C$

57. $-\dfrac{1}{2} \cos^3 \dfrac{2x}{3} + C$

58. $\frac{1}{5}(1 + \sin 2t)^{5/2} + C$

59. $-\frac{3}{2} \cos 2x + \frac{4}{3} \sin 3x + C$

60. $\frac{1}{3}(\sin^3 t - \cos^3 t) + C$

ARTICLE 4–6

1. 1.75, 2.25   2. 0.25, 1.25

3. $\pi/(2\sqrt{2}) \approx 1.12$, $(\pi/2)(1 + 1/\sqrt{2}) \approx 2.68$

4. 0.6345, 0.7595   5. 4.146, 6.146

ARTICLE 4–8

1. 12	2. 4	3. $8\frac{2}{3}$
4. 2	5. $\frac{1}{15}$	6. $57\frac{1}{3}$
7. 10	8. $4\frac{1}{3}$	9. 1
10. $\frac{2}{9}$	11. $\frac{1}{2}$	12. $10\frac{2}{3}$
13. 2	14. $\frac{2}{3}$	15. $\frac{4}{3}$
16. $\frac{2}{3}$	17. $\pi/6$	18. (b) $\pi a^2/4$

ARTICLE 4–9

1. (a) $c_k = \frac{1}{2}(x_k + x_{k-1})$

(b) $c_k = \pm \sqrt{\dfrac{x_{k-1}^2 + x_{k-1}x_k + x_k^2}{3}}$,

the sign being determined by the interval x_{k-1}, x_k.

(c) $c_k = \sqrt[3]{\dfrac{x_{k-1}^3 + x_{k-1}^2 x_k + x_{k-1}x_k^2 + x_k^3}{4}}$

(d) $c_k = \left(\dfrac{\sqrt{x_{k-1}} + \sqrt{x_k}}{2}\right)^2$

4. $S_n = \dfrac{b^4}{4}$ 5. $S_n = 2(\sqrt{b} - 1)$

6. 8	7. $\frac{7}{3}$	8. $\frac{8}{3}$
9. $\frac{13}{3}$	10. 2	11. 0
12. $\sqrt{2} - 1$	13. $\frac{1}{2}$	14. $\pi/2$
15. π/ω	16. $\frac{2}{9}$	

17. (a) $A = \lim\limits_{n \to \infty} \sum\limits_{k=1}^{n} (18 - 2x_k^2)\, \Delta x_k$, $(x_1 = -3, x_{n+1} = 3)$

(b) $A = \displaystyle\int_{-3}^{3} (18 - 2x^2)\, dx = 72$

18. 0.692

ARTICLE 4–10

2. Integral $= 2$, approximation $= 2$.

3. Integral $= \frac{8}{3}$, approximation $= 2.75$.

4. Integral $= 4\sqrt{2}/3$, approximation ≈ 1.82

5. Integral $= \frac{1}{2}$, approximation ≈ 0.53

ARTICLE 4–12

1. $\int_a^b f(t)\, dt = -\int_b^a f(t)\, dt,$

$\int_a^c f(t)\, dt = \int_a^b f(t)\, dt + \int_b^c f(t)\, dt,$

$\dfrac{d}{dx} \int_a^x f(t)\, dt = f(x),$

$\int_a^b f(t)\, dt = f(c) \cdot (b - a),$

$\int_a^b f(t)\, dt = F(b) - F(a).$

2. (a) $\int_0^1 x\, dx + \int_1^2 \sin(\pi x)\, dx = \dfrac{1}{2} + \dfrac{2}{\pi},$

(b) $\int_0^1 (1 - x)^{1/2}\, dx + \int_1^2 (7x - 6)^{-1/3}\, dx = \dfrac{55}{42}.$

3. (a) $F'(\frac{1}{2}) = \frac{1}{2}, \quad F'(\frac{3}{2}) = -1,$

(b) $F'(\frac{1}{2}) = \sqrt{\frac{1}{2}}, \quad F'(\frac{3}{2}) = (\frac{9}{2})^{-1/3}$

(c) $F'(\frac{1}{2}) = \frac{2}{3}, \quad F'(\frac{3}{2}) = -\frac{2}{5}.$

CHAPTER 4: MISCELLANEOUS

1. $x^2 y + 2 = cy$

2. $3\sqrt{y + 1} = (1 + x)^{3/2} + c$

3. $y^3 + 3y = x^3 - 3x + c$

4. $3(x^2 - y^2) + 4(x^{3/2} + y^{3/2}) = c$

5. $(2 + x)^{-1} = -(3 - y)^{-1} + c$

6. (a) $y = \frac{1}{3}(x^2 - 4)^{3/2} + 3$

(b) $y^2(1 - x^2) = 1$

7. Yes; $y = x$ is such a curve.

8. $y = x^3 + 2x - 4$

9. $(2\sqrt{2}/3)b^{3/4}$

10. (a) $v = \frac{2}{3}t^{3/2} - 2\sqrt{t} + 2$

(b) $s = \frac{4}{15}t^{5/2} - \frac{4}{3}t^{3/2} + 2t + 5$

11. $v = t^2 + 3t + 4, \ \Delta s = 61\frac{1}{3}$

12. -8 ft/sec $\quad$ [*Note:* $d^2x/dt^2 = v\,(dv/dx)$, where $v = dx/dt$.]

13. $h(10) = h(0) = 5$

14. $(1 + y')(1 + y'^2) + y''(y - x) = 0$

15. (a) $k = 38.72$ ft/sec^2;

(b) 25 ft

16. $3y = (1 + x^2)^{3/2} - 7$

17. $h = 96t - 16t^2$; 144 ft

19. (a) $\approx 1.76 \quad$ (b) ≈ 1.73

20. (a) 4 ft/sec; $\quad$ (b) $\frac{64}{3}$ ft

21. $(x^2/2) - x^{-1} + c$

22. $\frac{1}{3}(y^2 + 1)^{3/2} + c$

23. $-\frac{1}{8}(1 + t^{4/3})^{-6} + c$

24. $\frac{4}{3}(1 + \sqrt{u})^{3/2} + c$

25. $-\frac{3}{5}(7 - 5r)^{1/3} + c$

26. $\frac{1}{4}\sin 4x + c$

27. $\frac{1}{9}\sin^3 3x + c$

28. $2\sqrt{\sin x} + c$

29. $\frac{1}{2}\sin(2x - 1) + c$

30. $-\frac{1}{4}\sqrt{25 - 4y^2} + c$

31. $-\sqrt{2/t} + c$

32. $\frac{1}{3}(x^3 - 2x^{3/2}) + c$

33. $\frac{1}{3}(2 - 3x)^{-1} + c$

34. $2 \sin(1 - 2x)$

35. $-\csc^2 x$

36. $10 \sec^2 5x \tan 5x$

37. $20 \sin^3 5x \cos 5x$

38. $\dfrac{\sin x \cos x (\sin x - \cos x)}{(\sin^3 x + \cos^3 x)^{2/3}}$

39. 0

42. $r\sqrt{2}/2$ ft

44. $|a|$

45. Yes; no; applies to identities, but not to equations.

46. 480π mi/hr

47. $|3a\omega \sin \theta \cos \theta|$

48. $f(x) = x/\sqrt{x^2 - a^2}$

49. (a) $\frac{10}{3}$ (b) $\frac{5}{3}$ (c) $\frac{1}{2}$

50. $dy/dx = -2x,\ d^2y/dx^2 = -2$

51. $\displaystyle\int_0^1 f(x)\, dx$

52. (a) $\frac{1}{16}$ (b) $\frac{2}{3}$ (c) $2/\pi$ (d) $\sqrt{1 + x^2} - x$ (e) $x_1 f(x_1)$

53. $d^2y/dx^2 = 4y$

CHAPTER 5

ARTICLE 5–2

1. (a) $\displaystyle\lim_{\Delta y \to 0} \sum_a^b (f(y) - g(y))\, \Delta y$ (b) $\displaystyle\int_a^b (f(y) - g(y))\, dy$

2. $\frac{4}{3}$

3. $\frac{1}{12}$

4. $\frac{32}{3}$

5. $\frac{32}{3}$

6. $\frac{1}{6}$

7. $\frac{4}{3}$

8. $\frac{128}{15}$

9. $\sqrt{2} - 1$

10. $\sqrt[3]{16} \approx 2.52$

11. $\frac{1}{6}$

ARTICLE 5–3

1. 6 ft

2. $5\frac{1}{6}$ ft

3. $3\frac{2}{3}$ ft

4. 1 ft

5. 6 ft

6. 8 ft

7. $2\sqrt{2}$ ft

8. $2\frac{2}{3}$ ft

9. $6 - \sin 2 \approx 5.09$ (ft)

10. $1 + \cos 2 \approx 0.58$ (ft)

11. $2g$

12. $4\frac{29}{30}$ ft

13. $3\frac{1}{6}$ ft

15. 6.45 ft; 3.22 ft/sec

ARTICLE 5–4

1. $\dfrac{8\pi}{3}$

2. $\dfrac{\pi^2}{2}$

3. $\dfrac{\pi}{30}$

4. $\dfrac{56\pi}{15}$

5. $\dfrac{8\pi}{3}$

6. $\dfrac{2\pi}{3}$

7. $\dfrac{256\pi}{5}$

8. $\dfrac{48\pi}{5}$

9. (a) $\dfrac{\pi r^2 h}{3}$ (b) $\frac{2}{3}\pi h^2 r$

10. (a) $\pi/6$ (b) $2\pi/15$

11. (a) 8π (b) $\dfrac{512\pi}{15}$ (c) $\dfrac{256\pi}{5}$ (d) $\dfrac{1088\pi}{15}$ (e) $\dfrac{128\pi}{3}$

12. (a) $\pi h^2 \left(a - \dfrac{h}{3}\right)$ (b) $0.1/12\pi$ (ft/sec) $= 6/\pi$ (in/min)

13. $\frac{4}{3}\pi ab^2$ 14. $\frac{512\pi}{15}$ 15. $\frac{16a^3}{3}$ 16. $\frac{8a^3}{3}$

17. $\frac{8a^3}{3}$ 18. $\frac{\pi\sqrt{3}}{16}$ 19. $15{,}990$ ft^3 20. $2\pi^2 a^2 b$

ARTICLE 5–5

1. $(b^3 - a^3)/3$

ARTICLE 5–6

1. 12 2. $\frac{8}{27}(10\sqrt{10} - 1)$ 3. $\frac{14}{3}$

4. $\frac{53}{6}$ 5. $\frac{123}{32}$ 6. $\frac{4}{27}(10\sqrt{10} - 1)$

7. $\frac{a\pi^2}{8}$ 8. 12 9. $\frac{21}{2}$

ARTICLE 5–7

1. $\frac{12\pi a^2}{5}$ 2. $\frac{99\pi}{2}$ 3. $\frac{\pi}{27}(10\sqrt{10} - 1)$

4. $\frac{\pi}{6}(17\sqrt{17} - 1)$ 5. $\frac{1823\pi}{18}$ 6. $\frac{253\pi}{20}$

7. $\frac{2\pi}{3}(26\sqrt{26} - 2\sqrt{2})$

8. $56\pi\sqrt{3}/5$

ARTICLE 5–8

1. (a) $2/\pi$ 2. (a) $\frac{1}{2}$
  (b) 0   (b) $\frac{1}{2}$

3. $\frac{49}{12}$ 4. $\frac{1}{2}$

5. $\alpha\,\frac{a + b}{2} + \beta$ 6. $\pi a/2$

7. $4a/\pi$ 8. $8a^2/3$

9. $2a^2$

ARTICLE 5–9

1. $\left(\frac{4a}{3\pi}, \frac{4a}{3\pi}\right)$ 2. $(0, \frac{2}{5}h^2)$

3. $\left(\frac{2a}{3(4 - \pi)}, \frac{2a}{3(4 - \pi)}\right)$ 4. $\left(\frac{\pi}{2}, \frac{\pi}{8}\right)$

5. $(\frac{2}{5}, 1)$ 6. $\frac{3}{7}h$

7. $\frac{3}{5}h$ 8. On the axis, $\frac{3}{4}h$ from vertex

9. On the axis, $\frac{3}{5}h$ from vertex 10. On the axis, $\frac{1}{2}h$ from vertex

11. $\left(0, \frac{\pi}{4}r\right)$

ARTICLE 5–10

1. $(0, \frac{2}{5}c^2)$

2. $(\frac{16}{105}, \frac{8}{15})$

3. $(0, \frac{12}{5})$

4. $(1, -\frac{3}{5})$

5. $(\frac{3}{5}, 1)$

6. On the axis, $\frac{3}{4}h$ from the vertex

7. $(0, \frac{8}{3})$

8. $(\frac{4}{5}, 0)$

9. On the axis, $\frac{2}{3}h$ from the vertex

10. $\left(-r, \ \dfrac{3}{\pi + 2}\, r\right)$

11. $\dfrac{17\sqrt{17} - 1}{12}$

12. $\left(\dfrac{2r}{\pi}, \dfrac{2r}{\pi}\right)$

ARTICLE 5–11

2. $\left(0, \dfrac{2r}{\pi}\right)$

3. $2\pi(\pi - 2)r^2$

4. $\dfrac{3\pi + 4}{3}\pi r^3$

5. $\dfrac{3\pi + 4}{3}\dfrac{\pi r^3}{\sqrt{2}}$

6. $\pi\sqrt{2}(\pi + 2)r^2$

7. $2r^3/3$

8. $(4 + 3\pi)r^3/6$

9. $(4 + 3\pi)r^3/(6\sqrt{2})$

ARTICLE 5–12

1. 375 lb

2. $111\frac{1}{9}$ lb

3. $1666\frac{2}{3}$ lb

4. $116\frac{2}{3}$ lb

5. $41\frac{2}{3}$ lb

6. 975 tons

7. 8450 ton-ft

ARTICLE 5–13

1. $c = 5$ lb/in; 80 inch-lb

2. $c = \dfrac{10}{\sin 10°}$ lb; 78.5 inch-lb

3. $\frac{1}{2}k$, where k is the proportionality factor

4. $\frac{1}{3}k$, k as in Problem 3

5. $\frac{1}{2}mgR$

6. 1944 ft-lb

8. (Work done *on* the gas) $= -$(Work done *by* the gas) $= 3164\frac{1}{16}$ ft-lb

9. $\dfrac{200\pi}{3}$ ft-tons

10. 27.2 ft-tons

CHAPTER 5: MISCELLANEOUS

1. $\frac{9}{2}$

2. $6\frac{3}{4}$

3. 1

4. $(7 - 4\sqrt{2})/2$

5. $\frac{9}{2}$

6. $\frac{32}{3}$

7. 18

8. $3^5/2^3$

9. $a^2/6$

10. 14.95 correct value

11. 8

12. $\pi/4$

13. $\frac{13}{3}$

14. $\frac{9}{8}$

15. $\frac{64}{3}$

16. (a) $0 \le x < 2$ (b) $2 < x < 3$ (c) $\frac{29}{2}$ ft

17. (a) $\frac{3}{7}$ (b) $\frac{3}{8}$ (c) $y = \frac{3}{2}(1 + 3x)^{-1/2}$ (d) $\frac{3}{7}$

18. $f(x) = \sqrt{(2x - a)/\pi}$

19. (a) $3^5\pi/5$ (b) $189\pi/2$ (c) $81\pi/2$ (d) $2^9\pi/15$ (e) $2^7\pi/3$

20. $f(x) = \sqrt{(2x + 1)/\pi}$ 21. $32\pi/3$

22. (a) $2\pi a^3$ (b) $(\frac{16}{15})\pi a^3$ (c) $(\frac{8}{5})\pi a^3$

23. $V = 2\pi \int_0^2 x^2/\sqrt{x^3 + 8}\, dx = (8\pi/3)(2 - \sqrt{2})$

24. $(\pi/15)(88\sqrt{2} - 107)$ 25. $112\pi a^3/15$

26. $V = hs^2$ 27. $(\frac{8}{3})r^3$

28. $\pi^2/4$ 29. $28\pi/3$

30. $72\pi/35$ 31. $2\sqrt{3}a^3$

32. $\frac{19}{3}$ 33. $424\pi/15$

34. $\frac{27}{20}$ 35. $153\pi/40$

36. $(a/3)(3\sqrt{3} - 1)$ 37. (a) $(\frac{2}{3})b^2$ (b) $(\frac{2}{3})b$

38. (a) $f(x) = a \pm x\sqrt{A^2 - 1}, |A| \ge 1$ (b) No

39. (a) $\bar{v} = 72$ (b) $82\frac{2}{3}$ 40. Vol. 401π; average area 40.1π

41. $(\frac{9}{10}, \frac{9}{5})$ 42. $(\frac{3}{2}, \frac{12}{5})$ 43. $(1, \frac{12}{5})$ 44. $(\frac{3}{4}, \frac{3}{10})$

46. (a) $(5a/7, 0)$ (b) $(2a/3, 0)$

47. (a) $\bar{x} = \bar{y} = \dfrac{4(a^2 + ab + b^2)}{3\pi(a + b)}$ 48. (a) $(2a/5, 2a/5)$

   (b) $(2a/\pi, 2a/\pi)$ (b) $(0, 15\pi a/256)$

49. 5 in., $7\frac{1}{9}$ in., $4\frac{8}{9}$ in.

50. $7000/3$ lb   51. $5 \times 10^6/3$ lb

52. (a) $2h/3$ below surface (b) $a + h(4a + 3h)/(6a + 4h)$ below surface

53. $504d_1 + 72d_2$ 54. $Mah + (h^2/a)$ 55. $k(b - a)/ab$

56. $wr[1 - r/2R]$ ft-lb, $R = $ radius of earth in feet

57. $(320w/3)(15\pi + 8)$ ft-lb

CHAPTER 6

ARTICLE 6–1

13. $6x \sec^2 (3x^2)$ 14. $-2 \sin x \tan (\cos x) \sec^2 (\cos x)$

15. $-3 \csc^2 (3x + 5)$ 16. $-\frac{1}{2} (\cot x)^{-1/2} \csc^2 x$

17. 0   18. $\sec^3 x \tan x$

19. $3(1 + \sec^2 3x)$ 20. $6 \sec^2 2x$

21. $-\tan^2 x$ 22. $4 \sec^2 x \tan x$

23. $-2 \csc x (\csc x + \cot x)^2$ 24. $12 \sin 3x \cos 3x$, or $6 \sin 6x$

25. $\frac{1}{2}(1 - \cos 2x)$, or $\sin^2 x$ 26. $\frac{1}{2}(1 + \cos 2x)$, or $\cos^2 x$

27. $-\cos^3 (x/3)$

28. $-3 \cos \dfrac{x}{2} \sin \dfrac{x}{2}$, or $-\dfrac{3}{2} \sin x$

29. $\dfrac{x}{2} \sin \dfrac{x}{2}$

30. $\dfrac{2x}{\cos y + 2 \cos 2y}$

31. $3(\sin^2 x \cos x - \cos 3x)$

32. $-5 \cos^3 5x$

33. $-\dfrac{\cos^2 (xy) + y}{x}$

34. 10 when $x = -\sin^{-1} \frac{4}{5}$

35. max $y = 3/2$ when $x = \pi/6$,
min $y = 1$ when $x = 0$ or $\pi/2$

38. 1.6π mi/sec

39. $120°$

40. $-\frac{1}{3} \cos 3t + C$

41. $\frac{1}{2} \tan 2\theta + C$

42. $\frac{1}{4} \tan^4 x + C$

43. $\frac{1}{3} \sec^3 x + C$

44. $2 \sec (x/2) + C$

45. $\frac{1}{2}y + \frac{1}{4} \sin 2y + C$

46. $\tan \theta + C$

47. $-3 \cot (\theta/3) + C$

48. $\frac{3}{2}$

49. $(\pi/4)(4 - \pi)$

ARTICLE 6–2

1. $\dfrac{\sqrt{3}}{2}, \dfrac{\sqrt{3}}{3}, \dfrac{2\sqrt{3}}{3}, 2$

2. $\dfrac{\sqrt{3}}{2}, -\sqrt{3}, -2, \dfrac{2\sqrt{3}}{3}$

3. π 4. $\pi/2$ 5. $-\pi/3$

8. (a) 0.735, (b) 0.6, (c) 0.96, (d) $\pi/3$, (e) $2\pi/3$, (f) $\pi/6$

ARTICLE 6–3

5. $\dfrac{1}{\sqrt{4 - x^2}}$

6. $\dfrac{1}{9 + x^2}$

7. $\dfrac{1}{|x|\sqrt{25x^2 - 1}}$

8. $\dfrac{-2}{\sqrt{1 - 4x^2}}$

9. $\dfrac{4}{4 + x^2}$

10. $\dfrac{1}{(x + 1)\sqrt{x}}$

11. $\dfrac{1}{x^2 + 1}$

12. $\sin^{-1} x$

13. $(\sin^{-1} x)^2$

14. $\cos^{-1} 2x$

15. $\sqrt{b(a + b)}$ ft

16. $\pi/6$

17. $\pi/2$

18. $\pi/12$

19. $-\pi/12$

20. $\frac{1}{2} \sin^{-1} 2x + C$

21. $\pi/6$

ARTICLE 6–4

1. 0.1826

2. 0.3369

3. 0.6938

4. −0.6956

5. (a) Circumscribed   (b) Inscribed

6. (a) 0.0392   (b) −0.0408

7. $\ln 2 \approx \frac{2}{3}$ 8. $0.18226 < \ln 1.2 < 0.18267$

ARTICLE 6–5

1. $\dfrac{2x + 2}{x^2 + 2x}$

2. $\dfrac{3}{x} (\ln x)^2$

3. $-\tan x$

4. $\sec x$

5. $\dfrac{1}{x} + \dfrac{x}{x^2 + 1}$

6. $\dfrac{1}{x} + \dfrac{1}{2(x + 2)}$

7. $\ln x$

8. $3x^2 \ln (2x) + x^2$

9. $\dfrac{1}{1 - x^2}$

10. $\dfrac{1}{x(1 + x^3)}$

11. $\dfrac{2}{x(2 + 3x)}$

12. $-\tan^{-1} \dfrac{x}{2}$

13. $\dfrac{\tan^{-1} x}{x^2}$

14. $3 (\ln x)^2 + (\ln x)^3$

15. $2 \cos (\ln x)$

16. $\sec^{-1} x$

17. $\ln (a^2 + x^2)$

18. $\dfrac{1}{x \ln x}$

19. $\frac{1}{2} \ln |2x + 3| + C$

20. $-\frac{1}{3} \ln |2 - 3x| + C$

21. $\frac{1}{8} \ln (4x^2 + 1) + C$

22. $\ln (2 - \cos x) + C$

23. $\ln |\sin x| + C$

24. $2x - 5 \ln |x| + C$

25. $x - \ln |x + 1| + C$

26. $-\frac{1}{3} \ln |4 - x^3| + C$

27. $-\frac{1}{2} \ln |1 - x^2| + C$

28. $2 \ln (1 + \sqrt{x}) + C$

29. $\frac{1}{3} (\ln x)^3 + C$

30. $\dfrac{-1}{4x + 6} + C$

ARTICLE 6–6

1. $4a$

2. $2b/3$

3. $3a/2$

4. $-2a$

5. $2a - 2b$

6. $2a + b$

7. $2b - 3a$

8. $2a + 2b$

9. $2b - a$

10. $(3b - a)/2$

ARTICLE 6–7

2. No inflection point since $y'' = 1/x$ is positive since x is positive.

3. Slope at $(x, y) = y$. Concave up because $y'' = y' = y$ is positive.

7. $\log_{10} N = \dfrac{\ln N}{\ln 10}$

ARTICLE 6–8

1. (a) x (b) x (c) x^{-2}
   (d) $-x^2$ (e) $1/x$ (f) $-x$
   (g) $1/x$ (h) x (i) $2x$
   (j) x^2 (k) $x - x^2$ (l) $-2x + 2\ln x$
   (m) xe^x (n) x/y^2

2. $(x^2 + 2x)e^x$

3. $13e^{2x}\cos 3x$

4. $\dfrac{1}{1 + e^x}$

5. $\frac{1}{2}(e^x + e^{-x})$

6. $\frac{1}{2}(e^x - e^{-x})$

7. $\dfrac{4}{(e^x + e^{-x})^2}$

8. $\dfrac{e^{\sin^{-1}x}}{\sqrt{1 - x^2}}$

9. $-4xe^{-2x}$

10. $27x^2 e^{3x}$

11. xe^{ax}

12. $-2xe^{-x^2}$

13. $2e^{-x^2}(x - x^3)$

14. $e^x\left(\ln x + \dfrac{1}{x}\right)$

15. $\dfrac{e^x}{1 + e^{2x}}$

16. $\dfrac{2}{\sqrt{e^{4x} - 1}}$

17. $\frac{2}{3}e^{2x}\sec(x + 3y) - \frac{1}{3}$

18. $-e^{1/x}/x^2$

19. $(\cos^2 y)\left(e^x + \dfrac{1}{x}\right)$

20. (b) $y = 3e^{-2t}$

22. $\frac{1}{2}e^{2x} + C$

23. $\frac{1}{2}e^{x^2} + C$

24. $e^{\sin x} + C$

25. $3e^{x/3} + C$

26. $\dfrac{-4}{3}e^{-3x} + C$

27. $\frac{1}{2}\ln|1 + 2e^x| + C$

28. $\ln 2$

29. $\ln|e^x + e^{-x}| + C$

ARTICLE 6–9

1. $\dfrac{y(2x + 1)}{2x(x + 1)}$

2. $\dfrac{-2y}{3(x^2 - 1)}$

3. $\dfrac{y(4x^3 + 6x^2 + x + 3)}{3x(x + 1)(x^2 + 1)}$

4. $\dfrac{y}{3}\left[\dfrac{1}{x} + \dfrac{1}{x + 1} + \dfrac{1}{x - 2} - \dfrac{2x}{x^2 + 1} - \dfrac{2}{2x + 3}\right]$

5. $y\left[\dfrac{\sin x}{x} + \cos x \cdot \ln x\right]$

6. $y[1 + \sec^2 x \cdot \ln(\sin x)]$

7. $y(\sec x \tan x)\ln 2$

8. $\dfrac{2y \ln x}{x}$

11. $\frac{3}{8}$

12. $(3^{1.2} - 1)/\ln 3 \approx 2.49$

13. $(4 \ln 4)^{-1} \approx 0.180$ 14. $24/(50 \ln 5) \approx 0.298$

15. $(2 \ln 4)^{-1} \approx 0.360$

ARTICLE 6–10

1. (a) 2   (b) $\frac{5}{3}$ 2. (a) 2   (b) $\frac{1}{2}$
   (c) -2 (d) -2 (c) $\frac{4}{3}$ (d) $\frac{2}{5}$

3. $\log_{1.5} 2 = \dfrac{\ln 2}{\ln 1.5}$ 4. 12

6. (a) 1.30103,   2.30103,
       $9.30103 - 10$, $8.30103 - 10$
   (b) 2.99574,   5.29833,
       $8.39056 - 10$, $6.08797 - 10$

7. (a) 1.46   8. (a)   2.02
   (b) 0.68   (b) -1.36
   (c) 2.47

9. (a) $3^{\tan x} \sec^2 x \ln 3$

   (b) $y \left[\dfrac{1}{x} \ln (x^2 + 1) + \dfrac{2x}{x^2 + 1} \ln x \right]$

   (c) $-2t (\ln 2) 2^{-t^2}$

   (d) $e^{-2\theta}(1 - 2\theta)$

ARTICLE 6–11

1. $\dfrac{mv_0}{k} [1 - e^{-kt/m}]$ where k is a constant of proportionality.

2. $Q_0 e^{-kt}$ 3. $N_0 e^{kt}$

4. 1, 3   5. $-1, 2$

6. $-5, -1$ 7. $\pm 3, \pm 2$

CHAPTER 6: MISCELLANEOUS

1. $2 \cos 2x$ 2. $-8 \sin (2x + \pi/4)$

3. $2 \cos x + 2 \cos 2x$ 4. $(1 + \cos x)^{-1}$

5. $-\csc y$ 6. $\cos^2 y$

7. $-2 \cos (x/2)$ 8. $-\cos x$

9. $1 - \cos x$

10. $\dfrac{x \cos x - \sin x}{x^2} \begin{cases} y \to 1 \text{ as } x \to 0 \\ y \to 0 \text{ as } x \to \infty \end{cases}$

11. $\dfrac{x \cos x - 2 \sin x}{x^3} \begin{cases} y \to \infty \text{ as } x \to 0 \\ y \to 0 \text{ as } x \to \infty \end{cases}$

12. $\sin \dfrac{1}{x} - \dfrac{1}{x} \cos \dfrac{1}{x} \begin{cases} y \to 0 \text{ as } x \to 0 \\ y \to 1 \text{ as } x \to \infty \end{cases}$

13. $2x \sin \dfrac{1}{x} - \cos \dfrac{1}{x}$ $\begin{cases} y \to 0 \text{ as } x \to 0 \\ y \to \infty \text{ as } x \to \infty \end{cases}$

14. $(2/\pi) \cos^2 (\pi y/2)$

15. (a) $\frac{1}{2}(e^x - e^{-x})$ (b) $\frac{1}{2}(e^x + e^{-x})$ (c) $4(e^x + e^{-x})^{-2}$

16. $e^{-x}(1 - x)$

17. (a) $1 + \ln x$ (b) $\frac{1}{2}x^{-1/2}(2 + \ln x)$

18. (a) $x^{-2}(1 - \ln x)$ (b) $\frac{1}{2}x^{-3/2}(2 - \ln x)$ (c) $x^{-3}(1 - 2 \ln x)$

19. $e^{-x}(2 \cos 2x - \sin 2x)$

20. (a) $2 - e^{2x}$ (b) $(2 - e^{2x})e^{(2x - \frac{1}{2}e^{2x})}$

21. (a) $1 - e^x$ (b) $(1 - e^x)e^{(x - e^x)}$

22. $(1 + x^2)^{-1/2}$ 23. $(1 - x^2)^{-1}$

24. $\dfrac{2x}{x^2 + 4}$ 25. $\tan^{-1}(x/2) + 2x/(x^2 + 4)$

26. $8(e^{2x} + e^{-2x})^{-2}$ 27. $2 \sec x$

28. $xe^{2x}(3x \cos 3x + 2x \sin 3x + 2 \sin 3x)$

29. $2x(1 - x^4)^{-1/2} - (2x^2 + 1)e^{x^2}$ 30. $\dfrac{4 + x^3}{x(1 + x^3)} + \dfrac{2}{3} x^{-1/3} 7^{x^{2/3}} \ln 7$

31. $2x(2 - x)(x^2 + 2)^{1-x} - (x^2 + 2)^{2-x} \ln (x^2 + 2)$

32. $x^{-1}e^{-x}(1 - x \ln x)$ 33. $1/x(x^2 + 1)$

34. $3/(3x - 4)$ 35. $(6x + 4)/(3x^2 + 4x)$

36. $(\ln x)^2 (\ln x + 3)$ 37. $3(1 + \ln x)$ 38. $x^2(1 + 3 \ln x)$

39. 1 40. $(x^2 + 2x)e^x$ 41. e^x 42. $1/x \ln x$

43. (a) $(1 - x^2)/(1 + x^2)^2$
     (b) $\frac{2}{3}(x^2 + x - 1)x^{-2/3}(x - 2)^{-2/3}(x^2 + 1)^{-4/3}$

44. $f(0) = 1$ 45. (a) $a^{x^2 - x}(2x - 1) \ln a$
     $f'(0) = 5$ (b) $(1 + e^x)^{-1}$
     $f(0.01) \approx 1.05$ (c) $x^x(1 + \ln x)$
                                (d) $x^{(1 - 2x)/x}(1 - \ln x)$

48. $x = 1 + \sqrt{2}$ 49. $\dfrac{d^2 y}{dx^2} = 4(e^x + e^{-x})^{-2}$

                                 $y = \ln (e^x + e^{-x}) + c$

50. $y = \ln |2x - 9|$ 52. 0.88

53. $E = E_0 e^{-t/40}$, $t = 92.1$ sec   54. (b) $L = \dfrac{e^{x_1} - e^{-x_1}}{2}$

55. $\pi^2/2$ 56. $\dfrac{y}{y_1} = \left(\dfrac{x}{x_1}\right)^2$

57. $y = 1 - \frac{1}{2}(e^x + e^{-x})$

58. $t(1/4) = 1/\pi$; it will not reach $x = 1/2$, because $t = (1/\pi) \tan (\pi x)$.

59. $1 + 4 \ln \frac{3}{2} \approx 2.62$ 60. $2\sqrt{2}$

61. $y = 2e^x/(2 - e^x)$ 62. $N = N_0 e^{0.02t}$, $t = 34.7$ yr

64. $(\pm a/\sqrt{2}, e^{-1/2})$ 65. $3\pi/8$ 66. $\pi\sqrt{3}$

67. (a) $\sec x$ 68. $(64a^2 + b^2 \ln 3)/8a$
    (b) $\ln(1 + \sqrt{2})$

69. $\pi(e^4 - 1)/2 \approx 84.2$ 70. $(e - e^{-1})a^2 \approx 2.35a^2$

71. $y^2 = 4x$ 72. (a) $\ln 0.5 = -0.693$,
                                                     (b) $\ln 3 = 1.099$ (from tables)

73. (a) $y' = \ln x$ 74. (a) $-\frac{1}{3}\ln|4 - 3x| + c$
    (b) 1.3   (b) $5\ln|x - 3| + c$

75. (a) $\frac{1}{2}\ln 3 = 0.550$;   (b) $\frac{1}{6}$

76. (a) $x + \ln x + C$,   (b) $-\frac{1}{4}\ln|2x + 1| + x/2 + C$

77. $\ln 0.1 = -2.3026$ 78. $\pi \ln 4 \approx 4.35$ 79. $28\pi/3 \approx 29.4$
    $\ln 0.25 = -1.3864$
    $\ln 10 = 2.3026$
    $\ln 20 = 2.9958$

80. (a) $\frac{1}{3}\ln 2 \approx 0.23$ (b) $\frac{1}{2}(e^8 - e^{-1}) \approx 1490$ (c) $\ln 3 \approx 1.10$
    (d) $\frac{1}{2}\ln 26 \approx 1.63$ (e) e

81. 585 lb   82. $2000\pi(\frac{9}{10})^t$ ft^3

84. (a) No, x could $= 4$.
    (b) Yes; consider the graph of $y = (\ln x)/x$ for $x > 0$.

90. $e - 1$

CHAPTER 7

ARTICLE 7–1

1. $\frac{1}{3}(2x + 3)^{3/2} + C$

2. $\frac{1}{3}\ln|3x + 5| + C$

3. $\dfrac{-1}{4x - 14} + C$

4. $\frac{1}{2}\ln|x^2 + 2x + 3| + C$

5. $-\ln|2 + \cos x| + C$

6. $\frac{1}{8}\tan^4 2x + C$

7. $-\frac{1}{4}\sqrt{1 - 4x^2} + C$

8. $\frac{1}{2}(x^{4/3} - 1)^{3/2} + C$

9. $\dfrac{-1}{12(3x^2 + 4)^2} + C$

10. $\frac{2}{9}(x^3 + 5)^{3/2} + C$

11. $\frac{2}{3}(x^3 + 5)^{1/2} + C$

12. $\frac{1}{8}\ln(4x^2 + 1) + C$

13. $\frac{1}{2}e^{2x} + C$

14. $-e^{\cos x} + C$

15. $-\frac{1}{3}e^{-3x} + C$

16. $2e^{\sqrt{x+1}} + C$

17. $-\frac{1}{3}\cos^3 x + C$

18. $-\frac{1}{2}\csc^2 x + C$

19. $-\frac{1}{4}\cot^4 x + C$

20. $\frac{1}{6}\tan^2 3x + C$

21. $\frac{1}{2}\ln|e^{2x} - e^{-2x}| + C$

22. $-\frac{1}{6}\cos^3 2x + C$

23. $-\frac{1}{4}(1 + \cos\theta)^4 + C$

24. $-\frac{1}{2}e^{-t^2} + C$

25. $\ln|\sin x| + C$

26. $\ln|1 + \sin x| + C$

27. $\frac{1}{3}\sec^3 x + C$

28. $-2\sqrt{1 + \cos\theta} + C$

29. $\frac{1}{3}e^{\tan 3x} + C$

30. $-\frac{1}{3}(4 - \sin 2t)^{3/2} + C$

31. $-\frac{1}{2}(\csc 2x + \cot 2x) + C$

32. $x - \frac{1}{2}\sin 2x + C$

33. $-\sqrt{1 + \cot 2t} + C$

34. $\frac{1}{3}e^{3x} + C$

35. $\frac{1}{2}e^{\tan^{-1} 2t} + C$

36. $-\frac{1}{2}e^{-x^2} + C$

37. $\dfrac{3^x}{\ln 3} + C$

38. $\dfrac{10^{2x}}{2\ln 10} + C$

39. (a) -1; $\frac{1}{2}(\ln x)^2 + C$ (b) 2; $\frac{1}{3}e^{x^3} + C$ (c) $-\frac{1}{2}$; $-2\cos\sqrt{x} + C$

ARTICLE 7-2

1. $-\frac{2}{3}(1 + \cos t)^{3/2} + C$

2. $\ln|2 - \cos\theta| + C$

3. $\frac{1}{2}\ln|1 + \tan 2x| + C$

4. $-\frac{1}{3}\ln|\cos 3x| + C$

5. $\sin x - \frac{1}{3}\sin^3 x + C$

6. $\frac{1}{4}\tan 4\theta - \theta + C$

7. (a) $\frac{1}{5}\cos^5 x - \frac{1}{3}\cos^3 x + C$ (b) $\cos x + \sec x + C$

8. $\dfrac{\sec^n x}{n} + C$ if $n \neq 0$

$\ln|\sec x| + C$ if $n = 0$

9. $\dfrac{\tan^{n+1} x}{n + 1} + C$ if $n \neq -1$

$\ln|\tan x| + C$ if $n = -1$

10. $\dfrac{\sin^{n+1} x}{n + 1} + C$ if $n \neq -1$

$\ln|\sin x| + C$ if $n = -1$

11. $\dfrac{-\cos^{n+1} x}{n + 1} + C$ if $n \neq -1$

$-\ln|\cos x| + C$ if $n = -1$

12. $\frac{1}{9}\sin^3 3x + C$

13. $-\frac{1}{8}\cos^4 2x + C$

14. $\frac{1}{12}\sec^4 3x + C$

15. $\frac{1}{9}\tan^3 3x + \frac{1}{3}\tan 3x + C$

16. $\frac{1}{2}\sin 2x - \frac{1}{6}\sin^3 2x + C$

17. $\frac{1}{4}\tan^2 2x + \frac{1}{2}\ln|\cos 2x| + C$

18. $\frac{1}{3}\sec^3 x - \sec x + C$

19. $\frac{1}{3}\cos^3 x - \cos x + C$

20. $\dfrac{-1}{1 + \sin x} + C$

21. $\ln|2 + \tan x| + C$

22. $-\sin t - \csc t + C$

23. $\ln|1 + e^x| + C$

24. $\dfrac{(\ln ax)^{n+1}}{n + 1} + C$ if $n \neq -1$

$\ln|\ln ax| + C$ if $n = -1$

25. $\ln|\ln 3x| + C$

26. $-\ln|\sin x| - \frac{1}{2}\cot^2 x + C$

27. $-\frac{1}{6}\csc^3 2t + C$

28. $-\cot x - \frac{1}{3}\cot^3 x + C$

29. $-\dfrac{\cot^{n-1} ax}{(n - 1)a} - \displaystyle\int \cot^{n-2} ax\,dx,$

$-\dfrac{\cot^3 3x}{9} + \dfrac{\cot 3x}{3} + x + C$

ARTICLE 7-3

1. $\frac{1}{3}\sin^3 x - \frac{1}{5}\sin^5 x + C$

2. $\cos x + \sec x + C$

3. $\frac{1}{2}t - \frac{1}{8}\sin 4t + C$

4. $\frac{1}{2}\theta + \frac{1}{12}\sin 6\theta + C$

5. $\dfrac{3}{8}x - \dfrac{1}{4a}\sin 2ax + \dfrac{1}{32a}\sin 4ax + C$

6. $\frac{1}{8}y - \frac{1}{32}\sin 4y + C$

7. $\tan x + C$

8. $-\frac{1}{3}\cot^3 x - \cot x + C$ 9. $-\frac{1}{6}\csc^3 2t + C$

10. $\frac{5}{16}x - \frac{1}{4}\sin 2x + \frac{3}{64}\sin 4x + \frac{1}{48}\sin^3 2x + C$

ARTICLE 7–4

1. a

2. $\frac{1}{2}\sin^{-1} 2x + C$

3. $\dfrac{\pi a^2}{4}$

4. $\sin^{-1}\dfrac{x-1}{2} + C$

5. $\frac{1}{2}\ln|\sec 2t + \tan 2t| + C$

6. $\ln(1+\sqrt{2}) \approx 0.88$

7. $\pi/6$

8. $\sqrt{4+x^2} + C$

9. $\frac{1}{2}\ln 2$

10. $\pi/8$

11. $\frac{1}{4}\ln 3 = 0.2747$

12. $-\ln|\csc u + \cot u| + C$

13. $\dfrac{1}{a}\ln\left|\dfrac{x}{a+\sqrt{a^2+x^2}}\right| + C$

14. $-\sqrt{4-x^2} + \sin^{-1}\dfrac{x}{2} + C$

15. $\dfrac{1}{\sqrt{5}}\sin^{-1}(x\sqrt{5}/2) + C$

16. $\cos^{-1}\left(\dfrac{\cos\theta}{\sqrt{2}}\right) + C$

17. $\dfrac{1}{|a|}\sec^{-1}\left|\dfrac{x}{a}\right| + C$

18. $\dfrac{1}{a}\ln\left|\dfrac{x}{a+\sqrt{a^2-x^2}}\right| + C$

19. $\dfrac{1}{a^2}\left(\dfrac{x}{\sqrt{a^2-x^2}}\right) + C$

20. $\dfrac{1}{2a^3}\left(\tan^{-1}\dfrac{x}{a} + \dfrac{ax}{a^2+x^2}\right) + C$

ARTICLE 7–5

1. $\pi/8$

2. $\sqrt{x^2-2x+5} + \ln|x-1+\sqrt{x^2-2x+5}| + C$

3. $2\sin^{-1}(x-1) - \sqrt{2x-x^2} + C$

4. $\sqrt{x^2-4x+3} + \ln|x-2+\sqrt{x^2-4x+3}| + C$

5. $2\sin^{-1}\dfrac{x-2}{3} - \sqrt{5+4x-x^2} + C$

6. $\ln|x-1+\sqrt{x^2-2x-8}| + C$

7. $\sqrt{8+2x-x^2} + C$

8. $\sqrt{x^2+4x+5} - 2\ln|x+2+\sqrt{x^2+4x+5}| + C$

9. $\frac{1}{2}\ln(x^2+4x+5) - 2\tan^{-1}(x+2) + C$

10. $\frac{1}{4}\ln(4x^2+4x+5) + \frac{1}{2}\tan^{-1}(x+\frac{1}{2}) + C$

ARTICLE 7–6

1. $\frac{1}{6}\ln|(x+5)^5(x-1)| + C$

2. $\frac{3}{4}\ln|x-3| + \frac{1}{4}\ln|x+1| + C$

3. $\frac{2}{3}\ln|x+5| + \frac{1}{3}\ln|x-1| + C$

4. $x - 2\ln|x+1| - \dfrac{1}{x+1} + C$

5. $\ln\left|\dfrac{x}{x+1}\right| + \dfrac{1}{x+1} + C$

6. $\dfrac{1}{4}\ln\dfrac{(x+1)^2}{x^2+1} + \dfrac{1}{2}\tan^{-1}x + C$

7. $\dfrac{1}{2}\ln\dfrac{x^2}{x^2+x+1} - \dfrac{1}{\sqrt{3}}\tan^{-1}\dfrac{2x+1}{\sqrt{3}} + C$

8. $\dfrac{1}{3}\ln\dfrac{2+\cos\theta}{1-\cos\theta}+C$

9. $\ln\dfrac{1+e^t}{2+e^t}+C$

10. $\dfrac{1}{2}\left(\tan^{-1}x+\dfrac{x}{1+x^2}\right)+C$

11. $x-\dfrac{3}{2}\tan^{-1}x+\dfrac{1}{2}\dfrac{x}{1+x^2}+C$

ARTICLE 7-7

1. $\dfrac{x^2}{2}\ln x-\dfrac{x^2}{4}+C$

2. $\dfrac{x^{n+1}}{n+1}\ln ax-\dfrac{x^{n+1}}{(n+1)^2}+C$

3. $\dfrac{x^2+1}{2}\tan^{-1}x-\dfrac{1}{2}x+C$

4. $x\sin^{-1}ax+\dfrac{1}{a}\sqrt{1-a^2x^2}+C$

5. $\dfrac{1}{a^2}\sin ax-\dfrac{1}{a}x\cos ax+C$

6. $\dfrac{2x}{a^2}\cos ax-\dfrac{2}{a^3}\sin ax+\dfrac{x^2}{a}\sin ax+C$

7. $\dfrac{x}{a}\tan ax-\dfrac{1}{a^2}\ln|\sec ax|+C$

8. $\dfrac{e^{ax}}{a^2+b^2}(a\sin bx-b\cos bx)+C$

9. $\dfrac{x}{2}[\sin(\ln x)-\cos(\ln x)]+C$

10. $\dfrac{x}{2}[\sin(\ln x)+\cos(\ln x)]+C$

11. $x\ln(a^2+x^2)-2x+2a\tan^{-1}\dfrac{x}{a}+C$

12. $\dfrac{x}{2}\sin(2x+1)+\dfrac{1}{4}\cos(2x+1)+C$

13. $\left(\dfrac{x^2}{2}-\dfrac{1}{4}\right)\sin^{-1}x+\dfrac{x}{4}\sqrt{1-x^2}+C$

14. $\dfrac{4\pi+3\sqrt{3}}{6}$

15. $\dfrac{4\pi-3\sqrt{3}}{3}$

16. $\dfrac{x^3}{3}\tan^{-1}x-\dfrac{x^2}{6}+\dfrac{1}{6}\ln(x^2+1)+C$

17. (b) $\dfrac{x^4}{32}[8(\ln x)^2-4\ln x+1]+C$

18. (b) $\pi/16$

19. (b) $(x^3-3x^2+6x-6)e^x+C$

20. (b) $\frac{1}{2}(\sec x\tan x+\ln|\sec x+\tan x|)+C$

(c) $\frac{1}{2}(x\sqrt{x^2+a^2}+a^2\ln|x+\sqrt{x^2+a^2}|)+C$

21. $P(x)=1-3x^2$

ARTICLE 7-8

1. 2

2. 1

3. $\tan x+\sec x+C$

4. $\dfrac{\pi}{3\sqrt{3}}$

5. $\dfrac{4}{\sqrt{3}}\tan^{-1}\left(\sqrt{3}\tan\dfrac{x}{2}\right)-x+C$

6. $-\frac{2}{5}$

7. 0

8. π

ARTICLE 7–9

1. $-x + 4\sqrt{x} - 4 \ln |1 + \sqrt{x}| + C$

2. $\dfrac{2\sqrt{x}}{b} - \dfrac{2a}{b^2} \ln |a + b\sqrt{x}| + C$

3. $\dfrac{2(x + a)^{3/2}}{105} (15x^2 - 12ax + 8a^2) + C$

4. $2\sqrt{x + a} - 2\sqrt{b - a} \tan^{-1} \sqrt{\dfrac{x + a}{b - a}} + C$

5. $\dfrac{b - a}{2} \ln \left| \dfrac{u - 1}{u + 1} \right| - \dfrac{2u}{u^2 - 1} + C$, where $u = \sqrt{\dfrac{a + x}{b + x}}$

6. $\dfrac{1}{2} \ln |x + \sqrt{x^2 + a^2}| + \dfrac{x\sqrt{a^2 + x^2} - x^2}{2a^2} + C$

7. $(3\sqrt{2} - 4)/2$

8. $\dfrac{1}{nc} \ln \left| \dfrac{x^n}{ax^n + c} \right| + C$

9. $2 + 2 \ln (\tfrac{3}{2})$

10. $3 \ln |\sqrt[3]{x} - 1| + C$

11. $-1 + 4 \ln (\tfrac{3}{2})$

12. $4 \ln \left| \dfrac{\sqrt[4]{x}}{1 - \sqrt[4]{x}} \right| + C$

13. $\tfrac{3}{2} y^{2/3} + \ln |1 + y^{1/3}| - \tfrac{1}{2} \ln |y^{2/3} - y^{1/3} + 1| - \sqrt{3} \tan^{-1} \dfrac{2y^{1/3} - 1}{\sqrt{3}} + C$

14. $\tfrac{2}{9}(z^3 - 2)\sqrt{z^3 + 1} + C$

15. $\tfrac{2}{3}(\sqrt{t^3 - 1} - \tan^{-1}\sqrt{t^3 - 1}) + C$

16. $\ln (\tfrac{4}{3})$

17. $2 + 4 \ln (\tfrac{2}{3})$

18. $-\tfrac{1}{2} \ln |\sin x + \cos^2 x| - \dfrac{1}{2\sqrt{5}} \ln \left| \dfrac{2\sin x - 1 - \sqrt{5}}{2\sin x - 1 + \sqrt{5}} \right| + C$

19. $\tfrac{1}{3} \ln |x + 1| - \tfrac{1}{6} \ln |x^2 - x + 1| + \dfrac{1}{\sqrt{3}} \tan^{-1} \dfrac{2x - 1}{\sqrt{3}} + C$

20. $-2y^{1/2} - 3y^{1/3} - 6y^{1/6} - 6 \ln |y^{1/6} - 1| + C$

ARTICLE 7–10

1. $\pi/2$	2. 2	3. 6
4. 1000	5. 4	6. $\pi/2$
7. $\tfrac{1}{2}$	8. 1000	9. Diverges
10. Converges	11. Converges	12. Diverges
13. Converges	14. Converges	15. Diverges
16. Diverges	17. Converges	18. Diverges
19. Converges		

ARTICLE 7–11

1. $\tfrac{8}{3}, \tfrac{8}{3}, \tfrac{8}{3}$

2. $2\pi/3$, $(1 + 2\sqrt{2})\pi/6$, 2

3. $2\pi/3$, 2.28

4. $5\pi/9$, 1.8, $\pi/\sqrt{3}$

5. 1.86, 1.85

6. 0.78, 0.785

CHAPTER 7: MISCELLANEOUS

1. $2\sqrt{1 + \sin x} + C$

2. $(\sin^{-1} x)^2/2 + C$

3. $(\tan^2 x)/2 + C$

4. $\tan x + \sec x + C$

5. $(2x^{3/2})/3 + C$

6. $2 \sin \sqrt{x} + C$

7. $\ln |x + 1 + \sqrt{x^2 + 2x + 2}| + C$

8. $\ln |(x - 2)(x - 3)/(x - 1)^2| + C$

9. $(x^2 - 2x + 2)e^x + C$

10. $\frac{1}{2} (\ln |x + \sqrt{x^2 + 1}| + x\sqrt{1 + x^2}) + C$

11. $\tan^{-1} (e^t) + C$

12. $\tan^{-1} (e^x) + C$

13. $2\sqrt{x} - 2 \ln (1 + \sqrt{x}) + C$

14. $\frac{4}{3}(\sqrt{x} - 2)\sqrt{1 + \sqrt{x}} + C$

15. $\frac{9}{25}(t^{5/3} + 1)^{5/3} + C$

16. $\ln |\ln \sin x| + C$

17. $\ln \dfrac{\sqrt{1 + e^t} - 1}{\sqrt{1 + e^t} + 1} + C$

18. $t + 2 \ln (1 + \sqrt{1 - e^{-t}}) + C$

19. $e^{\sec x} + C$

20. $\tan^{-1} (\sin x) + C$

21. $\sin^{-1} (x - 1) + C$

22. $\cot^{-1} (\cos x) + C$

23. $\frac{1}{2} \ln |1 + \sin 2t| + C$

24. $\ln |\tan x| + C$

25. $(-2 \cos x)/\sqrt{1 + \sin x} + C$

26. $(2 \cos x)/\sqrt{1 - \sin x} + C$

27. $x/(a^2\sqrt{a^2 - x^2}) + C$

28. $x/(a^2\sqrt{a^2 + x^2}) + C$

29. $\dfrac{1}{3} \ln \dfrac{1 - \cos x}{4 - \cos x} + C$

30. $\frac{3}{10}(2e^x - 3)(1 + e^x)^{2/3} + C$

31. $\displaystyle\sum_{k=0}^{m} \dfrac{(-1)^k}{k!(m - k)!} \ln |x + k| + C$

32. $\dfrac{1}{12} \ln \dfrac{(x - 1)^2(x^2 - x + 1)}{(x + 1)^2(x^2 + x + 1)} - \dfrac{\sqrt{3}}{6} \tan^{-1} \left(\dfrac{x\sqrt{3}}{1 - x^2}\right) + C$

33. $\frac{1}{3}[(2y^3 + 1)^{-1} + \ln |2y^3/(2y^3 + 1)|] + C$

34. $\frac{2}{3}x^{3/2} - x + 2x^{1/2} - 2 \ln (1 + x^{1/2}) + C$

35. $\frac{1}{2}[\ln x^2 - \ln (1 + x^2) - x^2(1 + x^2)^{-1}] + C$

36. $(x - 1) \ln \sqrt{x - 1} - (x/2) + C$

37. $\ln |e^x - 1| - x + C$

38. $\dfrac{1}{4} \ln \left|\dfrac{1 + \tan \theta}{1 - \tan \theta}\right| + \dfrac{1}{2} \theta + C$

39. $x^{-1} + 2 \ln |1 - x^{-1}| + C$

40. $\frac{1}{2} \ln |(x + 3)^3(x + 1)^{-1}| + C$

41. $-\dfrac{1}{4} \dfrac{e^u + e^{-u}}{e^u - e^{-u}} + C$

42. $\ln |x/\sqrt{x^2 + 4}| + C$

43. $\frac{1}{3} \tan^{-1} [(5x + 4)/3] + C$

44. $\sqrt{x^2 - a^2} - a \tan^{-1} (\sqrt{x^2 - a^2}/a) + C$

45. $e^x(\cos 2x + 2 \sin 2x)/5 + C$

46. $\ln x - 2 \ln (1 + 3\sqrt{x}) + C$

47. $\ln |x| - 3 \ln |1 + \sqrt[3]{x}| + C$ 48. $\ln |\sin \theta| - \frac{1}{2} \ln (1 + \sin^2 \theta) + C$

49. $\frac{1}{15}(8 - 4z^2 + 3z^4)(1 + z^2)^{1/2} + C$

50. $\frac{3}{8}(e^{2t} - 3)(1 + e^{2t})^{1/3} + C$ 51. $\frac{5}{2}(1 + x^{4/5})^{1/2} + C$

52. $x \tan x + \ln |\cos x| + C$

53. $\frac{1}{4}[(2x^2 - 1) \sin^{-1} x + x\sqrt{1 - x^2}] + C$

54. $\dfrac{x^2}{2} + \dfrac{4}{3} \ln |x + 2| + \dfrac{2}{3} \ln |x - 1| + C$

55. $x + \ln |(x - 1)/x| + C$ 56. $\ln |x - 1| - (x - 1)^{-1} + C$

57. $\dfrac{2}{3} (3e^{2x} - 6e^x - 1)^{1/2} + \dfrac{1}{\sqrt{3}} \ln |e^x - 1 + \sqrt{e^{2x} - 2e^x - \frac{1}{3}}| + C$

58. $\frac{3}{2}(x^2 + 2x - 3)^{1/3} + C$ 59. $\tan^{-1} (2\sqrt{y^2 + y}) + C$

60. $-\sqrt{a^2 - x^2}/a^2 x + C$

61. $\frac{3}{8} \sin^{-1} x + \frac{1}{8}(5x - 2x^3)\sqrt{1 - x^2} + C$

62. $x \ln (x + \sqrt{1 + x^2}) - \sqrt{1 + x^2} + C$

63. $x \tan x - (x^2/2) + \ln |\cos x| + C$

64. $-(\tan^{-1} x)/x + \ln |x| - \ln \sqrt{1 + x^2} + C$

65. $\dfrac{x^2}{4} + \dfrac{x \sin 2x}{4} + \dfrac{\cos 2x}{8} + C$ 66. $-x^2 \cos x + 2x \sin x + 2 \cos x + C$

67. $\dfrac{x^2}{4} - \dfrac{x \sin 2x}{4} - \dfrac{\cos 2x}{8} + C$ 68. $\dfrac{1}{2} \tan^{-1} t - \dfrac{1}{2\sqrt{3}} \tan^{-1} \left(\dfrac{t}{\sqrt{3}}\right) + C$

69. $\frac{1}{12}[4u - 3 \ln (1 + e^{2u}) + \ln (3 + e^{2u})] + C$

70. $\frac{1}{4}(x^2 - 4) \ln (x + 2) - x^2/8 + x/2 + C$

71. $(x^2 + 1)e^x + C$ 72. $x \sec^{-1} x - \ln (|x| + \sqrt{x^2 - 1}) + C$

73. $-2x^{-2} + 2x^{-1} + \ln |x/(x + 2)| + C$

74. $\frac{1}{16} \ln |(x^2 - 4)/(x^2 + 4)| + C$ 75. $2 - \sqrt{2} \ln (1 + \sqrt{2})$

76. $\ln |\cot x| + C$ 77. $\dfrac{1}{4} \dfrac{e^u - e^{-u}}{e^u + e^{-u}} + C$

78. $x - 2\sqrt{x} + \dfrac{4}{\sqrt{3}} \tan^{-1} \left(\dfrac{1 + 2\sqrt{x}}{\sqrt{3}}\right) + C$

79. $\ln |\tan t - 2| - \ln |\tan t - 1| + C$

80. $-t + \sqrt{2} \tan^{-1} (\sqrt{2} \tan t) + C$ 81. $\dfrac{1}{\sqrt{2}} \tan^{-1} \left(\dfrac{\tan x}{\sqrt{2}}\right) + C$

82. $e^t \sin (e^t) + \cos (e^t) + C$ 83. $x \ln \sqrt{x^2 + 1} - x + \tan^{-1} x + C$

84. $\frac{1}{2}x^2 \ln (x^3 + x) - \frac{3}{4}x^2 + \frac{1}{2} \ln (x^2 + 1) + C$

85. $\frac{1}{2}(x^2 - 1)e^{x^2} + C$

86. $\ln |\sin x + \sqrt{3 + \sin^2} x| + C$ 87. $\sin^{-1} (3^{-1/2} \tan x) + C$

88. $(x^2 - 2) \cos (1 - x) + 2x \sin (1 - x) + C$

89. $\tan x - \sec x + C$

90. $3^{-1/2} \left[\ln |1 + 2 \sin x| - \ln |2 + \sin x + \sqrt{3} \cos x| \right] + C$

91. $-\dfrac{1}{2} \cot x \csc x + \dfrac{1}{4} \ln \dfrac{1 - \cos x}{1 + \cos x} + C$

92. $\frac{1}{2} \tan^2 x + \ln |\cos x| + C$

93. $x \left(\sin^{-1} x \right)^2 - 2x + 2\sqrt{1 - x^2} \sin^{-1} x + C$

94. $\frac{1}{54}(9x^2 - 1) \ln |3x + 1| - x^2/12 + x/18 + C$

95. $\frac{1}{2} \ln (x^2 + 1) + \frac{1}{2}(x^2 + 1)^{-1} + C$

96. $-\frac{2}{3}(x + 2)\sqrt{1 - x} + C$ \qquad 97. $\frac{1}{15}(3x - 1)(2x + 1)^{3/2} + C$

98. $x \ln (x + \sqrt{x^2 - 1}) - \sqrt{x^2 - 1} + C$

99. $x \ln (x - \sqrt{x^2 - 1}) + \sqrt{x^2 - 1} + C$

100. $\frac{1}{2} \ln |t - \sqrt{1 - t^2}| - \frac{1}{2} \tan^{-1} (t/\sqrt{1 - t^2}) + C$

101. $x - e^{-x} \tan^{-1} (e^x) - \frac{1}{2} \ln (1 + e^{2x}) + C$

102. $\frac{1}{2}(x - x^2)^{1/2} - \frac{1}{2}(1 - 2x) \sin^{-1} \sqrt{x} + C$

103. $x \ln (x + \sqrt{x}) - 2x + 2\sqrt{x} - 2 \ln (1 + \sqrt{x}) + C$

104. $(x + 1) \tan^{-1} \sqrt{x} - \sqrt{x} + C$

105. $x \ln (x^2 + x) + \ln (x + 1) - 2x + C$

106. $(x + \frac{1}{2}) \ln (\sqrt{x} + \sqrt{1 + x}) - \frac{1}{2}\sqrt{x^2 + x} + C$

107. $2\sqrt{x} \sin \sqrt{x} + 2 \cos \sqrt{x} + C$ \qquad 108. $-2\sqrt{x} \cos \sqrt{x} + 2 \sin \sqrt{x} + C$

109. $(x + 2) \tan^{-1} \sqrt{x + 1} - \sqrt{x + 1} + C$

110. $\frac{1}{4}(\sin^{-1} x)^2 + \frac{1}{2}x\sqrt{1 - x^2} \sin^{-1} x - x^2/4 + C$

111. $\frac{1}{4}x^2 - \frac{1}{8}x \sin 4x - \frac{1}{32} \cos 4x + C$

112. $\sec x - \tan x + x + C$ \qquad 113. $\ln (\sqrt{e^{2t} + 1} - 1) - t + C$

114. $\ln \left[(1 - \sin x)^{1/2}(1 + \sin x)^{-1/18}(2 - \sin x)^{-4/9} \right] + 1/(6 - 3 \sin x) + C$

115. $\dfrac{1}{ac} \ln \left| \dfrac{e^{ct}}{a + be^{ct}} \right| + C$ \qquad 116. $-2 \sin^{-1} \left[\dfrac{\cos (x/2)}{\cos (\alpha/2)} \right] + C$

117. $\dfrac{1}{\sqrt{2}} \ln \left| \csc \left(x - \dfrac{\pi}{4} \right) - \cot \left(x - \dfrac{\pi}{4} \right) \right| + C$

118. $x \ln \sqrt{1 + x^2} - x + \tan^{-1} x + C$

119. $x \ln (2x^2 + 4) + 2\sqrt{2} \tan^{-1} (x/\sqrt{2}) - 2x + C$

120. $-\frac{1}{3}(1 - x^2)^{1/2}(2 + x^2) + C$ \qquad 121. $\ln |2 + \ln x| + C$

122. $x - \tan x + C$

123. $\dfrac{1}{3} \ln |x + 1| - \dfrac{1}{6} \ln (x^2 - x + 1) + \dfrac{1}{\sqrt{3}} \tan^{-1} \dfrac{2x - 1}{\sqrt{3}} + C$

124. $\frac{4}{21}(e^x + 1)^{3/4}(3e^x - 4) + C$ \qquad 125. $\tan^{-1} (e^x) + C$

126. $2e^{\sqrt{t}}(\sqrt{t} - 1) + C$

127. $-2\sqrt{x+1}\cos\sqrt{x+1} + 2\sin\sqrt{x+1} + C$

128. $-2\sqrt{1-x}\sin\sqrt{1-x} - 2\cos\sqrt{1-x} + C$

129. $\ln 2$ 130. $2\sqrt{2} - 2$ 131. $2/\pi$

132. $e - 1$ 133. $\pi/4$ 134. $2\ln 2 - 1$

135. $\pi/2$ 136. $1/2$ 137. -1

139. e^{-4} 140. $4p^2(2\sqrt{2} - 1)/3$

141. Area $(\pi - 2)r^2/4$; centroid $2r\sqrt{2}/(3\pi - 6)$ from center.

142. $[1/(2e - 4), (e^2 - 3)/(4e - 8)] \approx (0.7, 1.5)$

143. $2\pi^2 kr^2$ 144. $w(3e^8 - 20e^4 + 9)/4 \approx 123{,}000$ lb

145. Only V is finite; integrals for A and for S diverge.

146. $A = e^{-1}$, $V = \pi/(2e^2)$, $S = \pi[e^{-1}\sqrt{1 + e^{-2}} + \ln(e^{-1} + \sqrt{e^{-2} + 1})]$

147. $(0.58, 0.93)$ 148. $(1.53, 0.696)$ 149. About 2

150. About 23   151. About 6.8   152. About 175

153. $2\pi[\sqrt{2} + \ln(1 + \sqrt{2})] \approx 14.4$

154. About 3.82

155. $(0, 0.6)$ for arch $|x| \leq \pi/2$ 156. 2π

157. $6a$ 158. $\ln(2 + \sqrt{3}) \approx 1.32$

159. $12\pi a^2/5$

160. $(2a/5, 2a/5)$ for first-quadrant arch.

161. Converges, compare with $\displaystyle\int_1^\infty x^{-3/2}\,dx$.

162. (c) $1 - e^{-e^b}$ 164. Converges   165. $x = \cos kt$

     (d) 1

166. $\frac{1}{2}$

CHAPTER 8

ARTICLE 8–1

1. 7   2. 3   3. -32

4. 0   5. $x = 1$, $y = 1$ 6. $x = 3$, $y = 2$

10. $x' = x\cos\alpha + y\sin\alpha$

     $y' = -x\sin\alpha + y\cos\alpha$

ARTICLE 8–2

1. 4   3. -9 5. -4

6. -33 7. 6

ARTICLE 8–3

1. Index of 4 3 2 1 is $3 + 2 + 1 = 6$

     Sign of $a_{14}\,a_{23}\,a_{32}\,a_{41}$ is $+$

ARTICLE 8–4

  1. $q = 4$, $r = 3$, $s = 0$

     $q' = 4$, $r' = 4$, $s' = 0$

  4. 118   5. 0

ARTICLE 8–5

  1. Differentiate the elements of any one row of the determinant and leave the remaining unaltered. The sum of the n determinants which can be obtained in this manner is the derivative of the original nth order determinant.

  2. $-2(3) - 3(-2) + 2(0) = 0$

ARTICLE 8–6

  1. $x = \frac{6}{7}$, $y = \frac{10}{7}$, $z = -\frac{2}{7}$ 2. $x = 3$, $y = -1$, $z = 3$

  3. Multiply the equations respectively by -14, -7, $+9$ and -3 and add to obtain $-50z = -50$.

  4. -2.

ARTICLE 8–7

  1. 16.5   2. $x = y = a$, $z = 2a$ (a arbitrary).

  4. $x = k$, $y = -3k$, $z = -5k$, k arbitrary

  5. $r = 0$, $A = -B$; $r = 3$, $A = 2B$

  6. $r = 2$, $A = -B$

  7. $r = 0$, $A = -B$; $r = 2$, $A = B$

  8. $r = 1$, $A = -3B$; $r = -1$, $A = -B$

  9. $r = 1$, $A = B$; $r = -3$, $A = -B$

  10. $r = -1$, $A = B$; $r = -3$, $A = -B$

  11. $r = 2$, $A = 0$, B arbitrary; $r = -2$, $A = -B$

  12. $r = 2$, $A = -4B$; $r = -1$, $A = -B$

CHAPTER 8: MISCELLANEOUS

  1. $x = y = 1$ 2. $x = \frac{5}{7}$, $y = \frac{6}{7}$, $z = 1$

  3. $\frac{14}{33}$, $-\frac{2}{33}$, $\frac{25}{33}$ 4. 3, -1, -1

  5. $x = y = z = 0$ 6. $-\frac{1}{6}$, $\frac{2}{6}$, $\frac{7}{6}$

  7. 1, -1, 0 8. 2, 1, 1

  9. No solution   10. 0, 0, 0, -1

  12. (d) 4   16. -16

  17. $x = a$, $y = b$, $z = c$ 20. (b) No

  21. The converse is false.

CHAPTER 9

[*Note:* sketches for Problems 1–10 on the following page.]

1. (a) About the x-axis
   (b) No curve for $0 < x < 2$
   (c) $(0, 0)$, $(2, 0)$
   (e) ∞

2. (a) About the x-axis
   (b) No curve for $0 < x \leq 2$
   (c) $(0, 0)$
   (d) $y = \pm 1$; $x = 2$
   (e) ∞

3. (a) About both axes, the origin and the line $y = x$
   (b) Curve is inside the square $|x| \leq 1$, $|y| \leq 1$
   (c) $(0, \pm 1)$, $(\pm 1, 0)$
   (e) Slope is 0 at $(0, \pm 1)$, ∞ at $(\pm 1, 0)$

4. (a) About both axes, and the origin.
   (b) No curve for $|y| \geq 1$. No curve for $|x| < 1$
   (c) $(\pm 1, 0)$
   (d) $y = \pm 1$
   (e) ∞

5. (a) About both axes and the origin
   (b) No curve for $|y| \leq 1$. No curve for $|x| \leq 1$
   (c) No intercepts
   (d) $x = \pm 1$; $y = \pm 1$

6. (a) About the origin
   (b) No curve for $|y| < 2$
   (c) No intercepts
   (d) $x = 0$; $y = x$ is also an asymptote
   (e) Low point at $(1, 2)$; high point at $(-1, -2)$

7. (a) About the y-axis
   (b) Curve is confined to $y \geq 1$
   (c) $(0, 1)$
   (e) 0

8. (a) About the y-axis
   (b) $0 < y \leq 1$
   (c) $(0, 1)$
   (d) $y = 0$
   (e) 0

9. (a) About the y-axis
   (b) $y \geq -1$
   (c) $(0, -1)$; $(\pm 1, 0)$
   (e) 0; ± 2

10. (a) About the y-axis
    (b) No curve for $-1 < y \leq 0$
    (c) $(0, -1)$
    (d) $x = \pm 1$; $y = 0$
    (e) 0

1. $x + y + 1 = 0$

2. $x + 2y = 7$

3. $6x - y = 14$; $y - 6x = 18$

4. $2x + y = \pm 3$

7. Yes; $(-2, -8)$

8. $(-1, -1)$. No, because $2x_1^3 - 3x_1^2 + 5 = 0$ and this equation has only one real root.

9. $2x + 3y = \pm 12$

10. $x + y = 1$; $4x + y = -2$

11. $(-\frac{13}{4}, \frac{17}{16})$

15. ± 16

16. $\pm 1/\sqrt{3}$

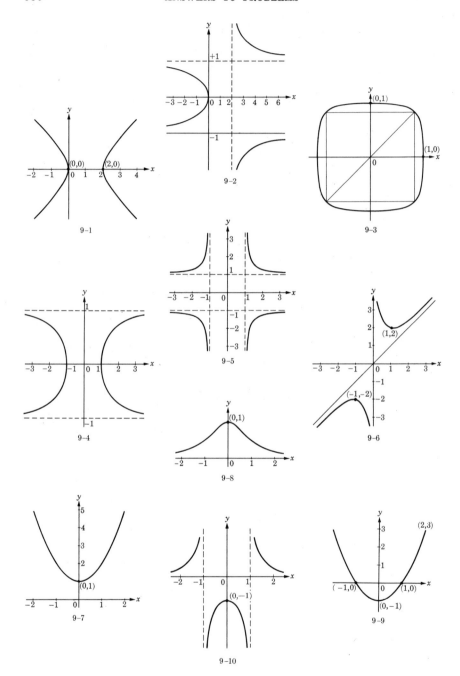

9–1

9–2

9–3

9–4

9–5

9–6

9–7

9–8

9–9

9–10

17. $A = \tan^{-1} \frac{5}{3}$, $B = \tan^{-1} 5$, $C = \tan^{-1} \frac{10}{11}$

21. (a) $45°$ (b) $\tan^{-1} 3$ (c) $\tan^{-1} (5/\sqrt{3})$ (d) $\tan^{-1} (\frac{14}{3})$

ARTICLE 9–3

1. 0.618   2. 0.682   3. 1.165   4. 1.189

5. −1.189   6. 3

7. $x_1 = x_2 = x_3$, etc.   9. $m_1 = (q - 1)/q$, $m_2 = 1/q$

12. Yes, they may get worse.

ARTICLE 9–4

1. $x - y = 1$ 2. $x^2 + y^2 - 6x + 5 = 0$

3. $(x^2 + y^2)^2 + 8(y^2 - x^2) = 0$ 4. $3x^2 + 3y^2 + 2xy - 4x - 4y = 0$

5. $3x^2 + 4y^2 - 20x + 12 = 0$ 6. $5x^2 - 4y^2 = 20$ (right half only)

7. $x^2 = 10 - 2y + 6|y - 1|$ 8. $x^2 + y^2 - 4x - 6y + 4 = 0$

or $\begin{cases} x^2 = 4y + 4 & \text{when } y \geq 1 \\ x^2 = 16 - 8y & \text{when } y < 1 \end{cases}$

9. $(2, 2); \sqrt{5}$ 10. $\dfrac{|Ax_1 + By_1 + C|}{\sqrt{A^2 + B^2}}$

ARTICLE 9–5

1. $x^2 + y^2 - 4y = 0$ 2. $x^2 + y^2 + 4x = 5$

3. $x^2 + y^2 - 6x + 8y = 0$ 4. $x^2 + y^2 - 2x - 2y = 0$

5. $x^2 + y^2 + 4x + 2y = 1$ 6. $x^2 + y^2 + 8x - 4y + 4 = 0$

7. $(0, 1); 2$ 8. $(-1, 0); 3$

9. $(-1, 0); 2/\sqrt{3}$ 10. $(-\frac{1}{4}, -\frac{1}{4}); 1/(2\sqrt{2})$

11. $(-1, 2); 0$ 12. No real locus, radius becomes imaginary.

13. $x^2 + y^2 - 4x - 4y = 5$ 14. $5x^2 + 5y^2 + 10x - 10y + 1 = 0$

15. $(x - 0.7)^2 + (y - 1.3)^2 = 12.58$

17. $x^2 + y^2 + 2x + 2y - 23 = 0$ 18. Circle, center $(-2, 3)$, radius 4.

19. Center of circle is $(1, 2)$; radius $\sqrt{2}$.
Distance of $(0.1, 3.1)$ from center is $\sqrt{2.02}$.
Point is outside the circle.

20. Center $(-2, 4)$, radius $2\sqrt{5}$ 21. Center $(-1, 1)$, radius 5

24. (a) $C_1 = -2h$, $C_2 = -2k$, $C_3 = h^2 + k^2 - r^2$

(b) $h = -\dfrac{C_1}{2}$, $k = -\dfrac{C_2}{2}$, $r = \sqrt{\dfrac{C_1^2 + C_2^2 - 4C_3}{4}}$

ARTICLE 9–6

1. $x^2 = 8y; y = -2$ 2. $y^2 = -8x; x = 2$

3. $(x + 2)^2 = 4(y - 3); y = 2$ 4. $(y - 3)^2 = -4x; x = 1$

5. $(y - 1)^2 = 12(x + 3); x = -6$ 6. $(x - 1)^2 = 12(y + 3); y = -6$

7. $y^2 = 8(x - 2); F(4, 0)$ 8. $(x - 1)^2 = -8(y + 2); F(1, -4)$

9. $(y - 1)^2 = -16(x + 3); F(-7, 1)$

10. $(x + 2)^2 = 4(y + 2); F(-2, -1)$

11. $(y - 1)^2 = 4x; F(1, 1)$ 12. $x^2 = -4(y - 1); F(0, 0)$

13. $V(1, 1); x = 1; F(1, -1); y = 3$

14. $V(-4, -3); x = -4; F(-4, -\frac{5}{2}); y = -\frac{7}{2}$

15. $V(2, 0); y = 0; F(1, 0); x = 3$

16. $V(0, -\frac{1}{2}); x = 0; F(0, \frac{3}{2}); y = -\frac{5}{2}$

17. $V(-1, -1); x = -1; F(-1, 0); y = -2$

18. $V(\frac{1}{4}, -\frac{1}{2}); y = -\frac{1}{2}; F(0, -\frac{1}{2}); x = \frac{1}{2}$

19. $V(2, 1); y = 1; F(\frac{29}{16}, 1); x = \frac{35}{16}$

20. $V(2, -3); y = -3; F(\frac{3}{2}, -3); x = \frac{5}{2}$

21. $V(2, -2); x = 2; F(2, -\frac{4}{3}); y = -\frac{8}{3}$

22. $V(-3, -1); y = -1; F(-\frac{21}{8}, -1); x = -\frac{27}{8}$

23. Points above parabola $x^2 = 8y$

26. $(x - y)^2 - 8(x + y) + 16 = 0$

27. $b^2y = 4hx(b - x)$

28. (a) $7y^2 - 3y + 6x - 16 = 0$

 (b) $7x^2 - 9x - 6y - 4 = 0$

30. The product is zero if and only if at least one factor is zero. Locus is the line $2x + y - 3 = 0$, the circle $x^2 + y^2 - 4 = 0$, and the parabola $x^2 - 8y = 0$.

ARTICLE 9–7

1. $x^2/12 + y^2/16 = 1; e = \frac{1}{2}$ 2. $x^2/25 + y^2/16 = 1; e = \frac{3}{5}$

3. $9x^2 + 5(y - 2)^2 = 45; e = \frac{2}{3}$ 4. $(x + 3)^2/12 + y^2/16 = 1; e = \frac{1}{2}$

5. $(x - 2)^2 + 10(y - 2)^2 = 10; e = 3/\sqrt{10}$

6. $9(x - 1)^2 + 4(y - 4)^2 = 36; F(1, 4 \pm \sqrt{5})$

7. $(2, -3); (2, 2), (2, -8); (2, 1), (2, -7)$

9. $x^2 + 2y^2 - 4y = 0$ 10. $e = \frac{3}{4}; y = \pm\frac{16}{3}$

11. $\frac{4}{3}\pi ab^2$ 12. (a) $\int_0^a \sqrt{a^2 - x^2}\, dx (= \frac{1}{4}\pi a^2$ for $\frac{1}{4}$

  of a circle)

  (b) $\frac{b}{a} \int_0^a \sqrt{a^2 - x^2}\, dx$

  Area of ellipse $= \pi ab$.

14. $2b^2/a$ 15. $5x^2 + 9y^2 = 180$

16. $A = C = 0$, $B = -4$

18. Interior of ellipse $9x^2 + 16y^2 = 144$

19. Graph consists of parabola $x^2 + 4y = 0$, straight line $2x - y - 3 = 0$, circle $x^2 + y^2 - 25 = 0$, ellipse $x^2 + 4y^2 - 4 = 0$.

20. One factor must be positive, the other negative. Graph consists of region between circle $x^2 + y^2 = 1$ and ellipse $9x^2 + 4y^2 = 36$.

ARTICLE 9–8

2. $C(2, -3)$; $V(2 \pm 2, -3)$; $F(2 \pm \sqrt{13}, -3)$
   $A: 3(x - 2) = \pm 2(y + 3)$

3. $C(2, -3)$; $V(2 \pm 3, -3)$; $F(2 \pm \sqrt{13}, -3)$
   $A: 2(x - 2) = \pm 3(y + 3)$

4. $C(2, -3)$; $V(2, -3 \pm \frac{1}{2})$; $F(2, -3 \pm \sqrt{13}/6)$
   $A: 2(y + 3) = \pm 3(x - 2)$

5. $C(-2, 1)$; $V(-2 \pm 2, 1)$; $F(-2 \pm 3, 1)$
   $A: \sqrt{5}(x + 2) = \pm 2(y - 1)$

6. $C(0, 2)$; $V(\pm 1, 2)$; $F(\pm \sqrt{5}, 2)$
   $A: 2x = \pm (y - 2)$

7. $C(2, 0)$; $V(2 \pm 2, 0)$, $F(2 \pm \sqrt{5}, 0)$
   $A: x - 2 = \pm 2y$

8. $C(2, 1)$; $V(2, 1 \pm 2)$, $F(2, 1 \pm 3)$
   $A: 2(x - 2) = \pm \sqrt{5}(y - 1)$

10. $\frac{4}{3}\pi \dfrac{b^4}{a}$

12. $x^2 - 3y^2 + 12y = 9$ 13. $4x^2 - 5y^2 - 8x + 60y + 4 = 0$

ARTICLE 9–9

2. $15x^2 + 13y^2 - 2\sqrt{3}xy - 14\sqrt{3}y + 18x = 33$, $\alpha = 60°$

7. $2y'^2 = 1$ 8. $4x'^2 + 2y'^2 = 19$

9. $5y'^2 - x'^2 = 10$ 10. $5x'^2 - 3y'^2 = 7$

ARTICLE 9–10

1. Ellipse	2. Hyperbola	3. Parabola
4. Circle	5. Hyperbola	6. Parabola
7. Hyperbola	8. Ellipse	9. Ellipse

10. After rotation of axes to a form with $B' = 0$, we have $A' = \dfrac{1}{a^2}$, $C' = \dfrac{1}{b^2}$. Then $B'^2 - 4A'C' = -4/(a^2 b^2)$, hence

$$\pi ab = 2\pi/\sqrt{4A'C' - B'^2} = 2\pi/\sqrt{4AC - B^2}.$$

12. If $C = -A$, then $A + C = A' + C' = 0$ and $C' = -A'$. Hence $A' = C' = 0$ if $\tan 2\alpha = -2A/B$ by Eqs. (6), Article 9–9.

3. Line L and the point D do not exist.

4. $(1 - e^2)x^2 + y^2 - 2pe^2x - p^2e^2 = 0$

1.
$$\begin{vmatrix} y & x^n & x^{n-1} & \cdots & x & 1 \\ y_1 & x_1^n & x_1^{n-1} & \cdots & x_1 & 1 \\ y_2 & x_2^n & x_2^{n-1} & \cdots & x_2 & 1 \\ \vdots & \vdots & \vdots & & \vdots & \vdots \\ y_{n+1} & x_{n+1}^n & x_{n+1}^{n-1} & \cdots & x_{n+1} & 1 \end{vmatrix} = 0$$

2.
$$\begin{vmatrix} x & y^2 & y & 1 \\ -1 & 0 & 0 & 1 \\ 2 & 1 & 1 & 1 \\ 1 & 1 & -1 & 1 \end{vmatrix} = 0, \quad \text{or} \quad 2x - 5y^2 - y + 2 = 0.$$

3.
$$\begin{vmatrix} x^2 & xy & y^2 & 1 \\ 9 & 0 & 0 & 1 \\ 1 & 2 & 4 & 1 \\ 1 & 1 & 1 & 1 \end{vmatrix} = 0, \quad \text{or} \quad x^2 + 12xy - 4y^2 = 9.$$

CHAPTER 9: MISCELLANEOUS

1. (a) A. Symmetric about the x-axis
   B. $0 \le x \le 4$, $-2 \le y \le 2$
   C. $(0, 0)$, $(4, 0)$
   D. None
   E. ∞ at both intercepts

(b) A. Symmetric about the x-axis
   B. $x \le 0$, $x \ge 4$, all y
   C. $(0, 0)$, $(4, 0)$
   D. Asymptotic to $y = \pm(x - 2)$
   E. ∞ at both intercepts

(c) A. Symmetric about the x-axis
   B. $0 \le x < 4$, all y
   C. $(0, 0)$
   D. Asymptotic to $x = 4$
   E. ∞ at $(0, 0)$

2. (a) A. None
   B. All y, $|x| > 0$
   C. $(-1, 0)$
   D. $y = x$, $x = 0$
   E. 3

(b) A. Symmetric about the x-axis
   B. All y; $-1 \le x < 0$, $x > 0$
   C. $(-1, 0)$
   D. $x = 0$
   E. ∞

(c) A. None
   B. All y, $|x| > 0$
   C. $(-1, 0)$
   D. $x = 0$
   E. -3

3. (a) A. None
   B. All y, all x
   C. $(0, 0)$, $(-1, 0)$, $(2, 0)$
   D. None
   E. -2 at $(0, 0)$
   3 at $(-1, 0)$
   6 at $(2, 0)$
   (b) A. Symmetric about the x-axis
   B. All y, $-1 \leq x \leq 0$, $x \geq 2$
   C. $(0, 0)$, $(-1, 0)$, $(2, 0)$
   D. None
   E. ∞ at all intercepts

4. (a) A. Symmetric about the y-axis
   B. All x, $0 < y \leq 2$
   C. $(0, 2)$
   D. $y = 0$
   E. 0
   (b) A. Symmetric about the y-axis
   B. $y < 0$, $y \geq 2$; $x^2 \neq 4$
   C. $(0, 2)$
   D. $y = 0$, $x = \pm 2$
   E. 0
   (c) A. Symmetric about the origin
   B. $|y| \leq 2$, all x
   C. $(0, 0)$
   D. $y = 0$
   E. 2

5. (a) A. Symmetric about the origin
   B. $|y| \geq 2$, $|x| > 0$
   C. None
   D. $y = x$, $x = 0$
   E. ———
   (b) A. About $(1, 2)$
   B. $y \leq 0$, $y \geq 4$; $x \neq 1$
   C. $(0, 0)$
   D. $x = 1$, $y = x + 1$
   E. 0
   Remark: Translate axes to new origin at $(1, 2)$; becomes same as 5(a).

6. (a) A. Symmetric about both axes and the origin
   B. All y, $|x| \geq 1$ and $x = 0$
   C. $(0, 0)$, $(-1, 0)$, $(1, 0)$
   D. None
   E. ∞ at $(\pm 1, 0)$; no derivative exists at the isolated point $(0, 0)$
   (b) A. Symmetric about the x-axis
   B. $x \leq 1$, $x > 2$; $y^2 \neq 1$
   C. $(0, \pm\sqrt{2}/2)$, $(1, 0)$
   D. $y = \pm 1$, $x = 2$
   E. $\mp\sqrt{2}/8$ at $(0, \pm\sqrt{2}/2)$, ∞ at $(1, 0)$

7. A. None
   B. $y \leq 4 - 2\sqrt{3}$, $y \geq 4 + 2\sqrt{3}$; $x^2 \neq 1$
   C. $(0, 8)$, $(2, 0)$
   D. $x = \pm 1$, $y = 0$
   E. -4 at $(0, 8)$
   $\frac{4}{3}$ at $(2, 0)$

8. A. Symmetric about the y-axis
   B. $y \leq -1$, $y > 1$; $x^2 \neq 1$
   C. $(0, -1)$
   D. $x = \pm 1$, $y = 1$
   E. 0

9. A. Symmetric about the origin
   B. $|x| \leq 2$, $|y| \leq 2$
   C. $(0, \pm\sqrt{3})$, $(\pm\sqrt{3}, 0)$
   D. None
   E. $-\frac{1}{2}$ at $(0, \pm\sqrt{3})$
   -2 at $(\pm\sqrt{3}, 0)$

10. $x^2 + xy + y^2 = 3k^2$

12. $a = c = d = e = 1$
   $b = f = g = 0$

14. $y + 2x = 6$

16. $y = 6x - 14$
   $y = 6x + 18$

18. (b) 1:1

21. $5x^2 + 5y^2 = 4x + 8y$ 23. $x = 2pm$

24. $Q(4p^3/y_1^2, -4p^2/y_1)$ 25. $(\pm\frac{8}{9}\sqrt{3}, \frac{4}{3})$.

27. $(-2, 1), (2, -1)$ 28. $27x - 3y + 56 = 0$
$$27x - 3y - 104 = 0$$

30. $r = 2.56$, center $(4, 1.61)$; results are approximate and are based on 1.55 as positive root of $x^4 + 4x - 12 = 0$.

31. $(-\frac{16}{5}, \frac{53}{10})$

32. (a) A conic passing through the points of intersection of the three lines, and tangent to the lines $L_1 + hL_3 = 0, L_2 + kL_3 = 0, hL_2 + kL_1 = 0$.
    (b) $3x^2 + 3y^2 - 8x - 16y + 20 = 0$
    (c) $2y = 3x^2 - 4x + 4$

33. 10^7 mi   34. $\pi/2$ 35. $y^2 = 2x - 7$ 36. $(5, 10\sqrt{10}/3)$

38. $3x^2 + 3y^2 - 16y + 16 = 0$, circle

40. Locus consists of circle $x^2 + y^2 = 9$ and hyperbola $y^2 - x^2 = 9$.

41. No; for points inside the circle, $x^2 + (y^2 - 9)$ is negative while $x^2 - (y^2 - 9)$ is positive, so their product cannot equal 1.

43. $5x^2 + 9y^2 - 30x = 0$

44. (a) $F_1P = 5, F_2P = \sqrt{5}$
    (b) Outside, since $OF_1 + OF_2 = 8 > F_1P + F_2P = 5 + \sqrt{5}$

45. $2ab$ 47. $x^2 + 4xy + 5y^2 = 1$

48. $(x + 3)^2/36 + (y - 1)^2/20 = 1$ 50. $x^2 - y^2 = 4$

51. Center at $(\frac{1}{2}\sqrt{2}, 0), e = \sqrt{2}$

52. [Hint: Eliminate λ^2 and obtain the differential equation
$$xy(y')^2 + (x^2 - y^2 - c^2)y' - xy = 0$$
for both families. The product of the roots $y' = m_1$ and $y' = m_2$ is $m_1m_2 = -1$.]

53. Square, area $= 2$

55. (a) Center $(2, -1)$, foci $\left(\dfrac{4 \pm 3\sqrt{3}}{2}, -1\right)$, major axis 6, minor axis 3, $e = \sqrt{3}/2$
    (b) Center $(-2, -\frac{3}{2})$, foci $(-2 \pm \sqrt{13}, -\frac{3}{2})$, major axis $= \sqrt{13}$, conjugate axis $= \sqrt{39}, e = 2$, asymptotes: $2y \pm 2\sqrt{3}x + (3 \pm 4\sqrt{3}) = 0$

57. (b) Bounded; both $9x^2 + 4y^2 - 36$ and $4x^2 + 9y^2 - 36$ exceed one when $4(x^2 + y^2) > 37$

58. Foci: $(\pm\sqrt{p - q}, 0)$ 59. $\sqrt{2}$

60. On a branch of a hyperbola with the rifle and target at its foci

62. Center $(1, -2)$; foci $(1, -2 \pm \sqrt{13})$; asymptotes: $2(y + 2) = \pm3(x - 1)$

63. $9x^2 - y^2 = 9$ or $9y^2 - x^2 = 9$

65. (a) Center $(3, 2)$; $e = \sqrt{\frac{11}{12}}$ (b) $(3, 0)$

66. $x^2 + y^2 - 6x - 15y + 9 = 0$

67. With $A(0, 0)$ and $B(c, 0)$, locus is left branch of hyperbola
$$3x^2 - y^2 - 4cx + c^2 = 0$$

68. $2y'^2 - 2a\sqrt{2}x' + a^2 = 0$

CHAPTER 10

ARTICLE 10-2

6. Values of sinh u, cosh u, tanh u, coth u, sech u, csch u are listed in the order given:

(a) $-\frac{3}{4}, \frac{5}{4}, -\frac{3}{5}, -\frac{5}{3}, \frac{4}{5}, -\frac{4}{3}$

(b) $\pm\frac{8}{15}, \frac{17}{15}, \pm\frac{8}{17}, \pm\frac{17}{8}, \frac{15}{17}, \pm\frac{15}{8}$

(c) $-\frac{7}{24}, \frac{25}{24}, -\frac{7}{25}, -\frac{25}{7}, \frac{24}{25}, -\frac{24}{7}$

(d) $\frac{12}{5}, \frac{13}{5}, \frac{12}{13}, \frac{13}{12}, \frac{5}{13}, \frac{5}{12}$

(e) $\pm\frac{4}{3}, \frac{5}{3}, \pm\frac{4}{5}, \pm\frac{5}{4}, \frac{3}{5}, \pm\frac{3}{4}$

(f) Same as (d).

ARTICLE 10-3

2. $3 \cosh 3x$

3. $10 \cosh 5x \sinh 5x = 5 \sinh 10x$

4. 0

5. $2 \operatorname{sech}^2 2x$

6. $-\sec^2 x \operatorname{csch}^2 (\tan x)$

7. $-3 \operatorname{sech}^3 x \tanh x$

8. $-\operatorname{csch} \dfrac{x}{4} \coth \dfrac{x}{4}$

9. $\sec^2 x \operatorname{sech} y$

10. $\frac{1}{2} \sinh (2x + 1) + C$

11. $\ln \cosh x + C$

12. $-\frac{1}{3} \operatorname{sech}^3 x + C$

13. $\tanh x + C$

14. $\ln \cosh x + C$

15. $x - \tanh x + C$

16. $2 \cosh \sqrt{x} + C$

17. $\frac{1}{2}x + \frac{1}{12} \sinh 6x + C$

18. $2\sqrt{2} \cosh \dfrac{x}{2} + C$

19. $u/2$

21. (a) 115 ft   (b) 16 lb

ARTICLE 10-5

2. $\cosh^{-1} x = \ln (x + \sqrt{x^2 - 1})$

6. $\dfrac{2}{\sqrt{1 + 4x^2}}$

7. $-\csc x$

8. $\sec x$ if $\tan x > 0$,
   $-\sec x$ if $\tan x < 0$

9. $-\csc x$

10. $-2 \csc 2x$ if $\cos 2x > 0$,
    $2 \csc 2x$ if $\cos 2x < 0$

11. $\frac{1}{2} \sinh^{-1} 2x + C$

12. $\sinh^{-1} \dfrac{x}{2} + C$

13. 0.5493

14. -0.5493

15. $-\frac{1}{2} \operatorname{csch}^{-1} \dfrac{|x|}{2} + C = -\frac{1}{2} \sinh^{-1} \dfrac{2}{|x|} + C$

ARTICLE 10–6

1. $a \sinh (x_1/a)$

3. $\dfrac{\pi a}{2}\left(2x_1 + a \sinh \dfrac{2x_1}{a}\right)$

4. $\bar{x} = 0, \bar{y} = \frac{1}{2}y_1 + \dfrac{x_1}{2} \operatorname{csch} \dfrac{x_1}{a}$

5. $\dfrac{\pi a^2}{4}\left(2x_1 + a \sinh \dfrac{2x_1}{a}\right)$

6. (b) $\dfrac{dx}{ds} = \dfrac{a}{\sqrt{s^2 + a^2}}, \dfrac{dy}{ds} = \dfrac{s}{\sqrt{a^2 + s^2}}$

7. (c) $a = 25$ ft, dip ≈ 4.6 ft

   (d) $H = 50$ lb

CHAPTER 10: MISCELLANEOUS

3. $\lim PQ = 0$

4. $\sinh x = \pm\frac{3}{4}, \tanh x = \pm\frac{3}{5}$

5. $\cosh x = \frac{41}{9}, \tanh x = -\frac{40}{41}$

9. $x = -1, y = 1$

12. $3 \sinh 6x$

13. $\sec^2 x/(2 \tanh y \operatorname{sech}^2 y)$

14. $-(\cosh y \coth y)/\sqrt{1 - x^2}$

15. $\tanh y \tan x$

16. $(1 + y^2)/(1 - x^2)$

17. $x^{-1} \operatorname{sech}^2 (\ln x) = 4x(x^2 + 1)^{-2}$

18. $y \operatorname{csch} (\ln y)$

19. $3e^{3x} \cosh (\tan^{-1} e^{3x})/(1 + e^{6x})$

20. $|\sec x|$

21. $-(\cosh y + \sinh 2x)/(2y + x \sinh y)$

22. $-e^{-\theta} + C$

23. $(2\theta - e^{-2\theta})/4$

24. $(\cosh^3 x - 3 \cosh x)/3 + C$

25. $(e^{3x} + 3e^{-x})/6 + C$

26. $\ln (\cosh x) + C$

27. $\frac{1}{2} \tanh^{-1} (\frac{1}{2})$

28. $\frac{1}{2}(\coth^{-1} \frac{5}{2} - \coth^{-1} \frac{3}{2})$

29. $\sinh^{-1} (e^t) + C$

30. $-\tanh^{-1} (\cos x) + C$

31. $\cosh^{-1} (\tan \theta) + C$

36. (a) $\lim v = \sqrt{mg/k}$ where k = resistance proportionality factor; m = mass of body; g = acceleration due to gravity.

    (b) $s = (m/k) \ln \cosh (t\sqrt{gk/m})$

37. $\ln 2$

38. $\ln \dfrac{2}{1 + \sqrt{2}}$

CHAPTER 11

ARTICLE 11–1

1. (a) $\left(3, \dfrac{\pi}{4} + 2n\pi\right), \left(-3, -\dfrac{3\pi}{4} + 2n\pi\right),$

  (b) $\left(-3, \dfrac{\pi}{4} + 2n\pi\right), \left(3, -\dfrac{3\pi}{4} + 2n\pi\right),$

where $n = 0, \pm 1, \pm 2, \ldots$

  (c) $\left(3, -\dfrac{\pi}{4} + 2n\pi\right), \left(-3, \dfrac{3\pi}{4} + 2n\pi\right),$

  (d) $\left(-3, -\dfrac{\pi}{4} + 2n\pi\right), \left(3, \dfrac{3\pi}{4} + 2n\pi\right),$

3. (a) $(3/\sqrt{2}, 3/\sqrt{2})$ (b) $(-3/\sqrt{2}, -3/\sqrt{2})$

   (c) $(3/\sqrt{2}, -3/\sqrt{2})$ (d) $(-3/\sqrt{2}, 3/\sqrt{2})$

5. $(2, \frac{3}{4}\pi)$ is the same as $\left(-2, -\frac{\pi}{4}\right)$ and $2\sin\left(-\frac{\pi}{2}\right) = -2$.

6. $(\frac{1}{2}, \frac{3}{2}\pi) = \left(-\frac{1}{2}, \frac{\pi}{2}\right)$ and $-\sin\frac{\pi}{6} = -\frac{1}{2}$

7. If (r_1, θ_1) satisfies $r_1 = \cos\theta_1 + 1$, then the same point has coordinates $(-r_1, \theta_1 + \pi)$ which satisfy the second equation. Also, if (r_2, θ_2) satisfies the second equation, the coordinates $(-r_2, \theta_2 + \pi)$ of the same point satisfy the first equation.

8. $(\pm a, 15°), (\pm a, 75°)$ 9. The origin and $\left(\dfrac{a}{\sqrt{2}}, 45°\right)$

10. The origin and $\left(a + \dfrac{a}{\sqrt{2}}, -\dfrac{\pi}{4}\right), \left(a - \dfrac{a}{\sqrt{2}}, \dfrac{3\pi}{4}\right)$

11. The origin and $(\frac{8}{5}a, \sin^{-1}\frac{3}{5})$

12. The origin, $\left(a, \pm\dfrac{\pi}{2}\right), \left(\dfrac{a}{2}, \pm\dfrac{2\pi}{3}\right), (0.22a, \pm 141°.3)$

ARTICLE 11–2

1. $r[3\cos\theta + 4\sin\theta] = 5$ 2. $x^2 + y^2 = 2ax$

11. (a) $(\frac{3}{2}a, \pm 60°), (0, 180°)$ 12. $30°$

   (b) $(2a, 0°), (\frac{1}{2}a, \pm 120°)$

ARTICLE 11–3

1. $r = a\sin 2\theta$; rose of 4 leaves   2. $r = 2a\sin\theta\tan\theta$

                                      $x = r\cos\theta = 2a\sin^2\theta \to 2a$ as

                                      $\theta \to \pi/2$

3. $r = 2a\sin\theta$

4. $r = a(1 - \cos\theta), r = -a(1 + \cos\theta)$ (Both equations represent the same curve.)

5. $r\cos(\theta - \alpha) = p$

6. $r(1 - \cos\theta) = 2a, r(1 + \cos\theta) = -2a$ (Both equations represent the same curve.)

7. $r^2 = \cos 2\theta$ 8. $x^2 + y^2 = 4x$

9. $x^2 + y^2 = 6y$ 10. $(x^2 + y^2)^3 = 4x^2y^2$

11. $(x^2 + y^2)^2 = 2a^2(x^2 - y^2)$ 12. $3x^2 - y^2 + 32x + 64 = 0$

13. $x^2 + y^2 - ay = a\sqrt{x^2 + y^2}$

15. (a) $p = \dfrac{|c|}{\sqrt{a^2 + b^2}}, \quad \cos\beta = \dfrac{a}{\sqrt{a^2 + b^2}}, \quad \sin\beta = \dfrac{b}{\sqrt{a^2 + b^2}}$

   (b) $p = 3, \beta = 30°$

16. $r = \dfrac{4}{1 - \sin\left(\theta - \dfrac{\pi}{6}\right)}$

17. $(50, 0°)$, $r = \dfrac{45}{4 + 5\cos\theta}$

18. $r = a(1 + \cos\theta)$

19. (a) max $= \sqrt{a^2 + b^2}$
        min $= \sqrt{|a^2 - b^2|}$

    (b) max $= a\sqrt{5}$, min $= a\sqrt{3}$
        max $= a\sqrt{2}$, min $= 0$
        max $= a\sqrt{5}/2$, min $= a\sqrt{3}/2$

20. ± 1 21. $(\tfrac{2}{3}, 0°)$ 22. $\pm\sqrt{e^2 - 1}$

ARTICLE 11–4

2. When $\tan\psi_2 = -1/\tan\psi_1$.   3. $(2, \pm 60°)$; $90°$

4. $(\tfrac{3}{2}a, \pm 60°)$, $(0, 180°)$ 5. $8a$

6. $(\tfrac{4}{5}a, 0)$ 7. $4\pi a^2(2 - \sqrt{2})$

8. $2a$.   The curve is the cardioid $r = \dfrac{a}{2}(1 - \cos\theta)$.

9. $\dfrac{a}{3}[(4 + \pi^2)^{3/2} - 8]$.   10. $\dfrac{a}{8}(4\pi - 3\sqrt{3})$

11. $4\pi^2 a^2$

ARTICLE 11–5

1. $\tfrac{3}{2}\pi a^2$ 2. πa^2 3. $2a^2$

4. $\dfrac{a^2}{3}(3\sqrt{3} - \pi)$ 5. $\tfrac{9}{2}\pi a^2$ 6. $\dfrac{a^2}{2}(\pi - 2)$

7. πa^2 9. $(\tfrac{5}{6}a, 0)$ 10. $\dfrac{4a}{3\pi}$ from center

REVIEW QUESTIONS AND EXERCISES FOR CHAPTER 11

6. (a) $e = \tfrac{7}{93} \approx 0.0754$ (b) $r = ke/(1 - e\cos\theta) \approx 4623/(1 - 0.0754\cos\theta)$

CHAPTER 11: MISCELLANEOUS

15. $\pi/3$ at $(a, \pi/6)$ and $(a, 5\pi/6)$ 16. $\pi/4$ at $(a, 0)$ and (a, π)

17. 0 at $(a\sqrt{2}, \pi/4)$ 18. $\pi/2$ at $r = 0$

19. $\pi/4$ at $r = 0$; $2\tan^{-1}(\sqrt{3}/6)$ at $(a/2, \theta_i)$ where $\theta_i = \pm\pi/3$, $\pm 2\pi/3$

20. $\pi/3$ at $(\sqrt{2}, \pm\pi/6)$ and $(\sqrt{2}, \pm 5\pi/6)$

21. $r = 2/(1 + \cos\theta)$ 22. $r(b\cos\theta + a\sin\theta) = ab$

23. $r = -2a\cos\theta$ 24. $r[1 + \cos(\theta - \pi/4)] = 2a$

25. $r = 8/(3 - \cos\theta)$ 26. $r = 3/(1 + 2\sin\theta)$

27. $(0.75a, -3.44)$, approx.   29. $\pi/4$

30. $\pi/2$ 31. -1 32. $\pi/2$

33. (b) $xy = 1$ 34. (a) $(1/4)\tan\alpha$
   (c) $\pi/2$ (b) $\sec\alpha$

35. (a) $32\pi a^2/5$

   (b) $\bar{y} = 0; \bar{x} = 5a \int_0^{\pi} \sin^6\frac{\theta}{2} \cos\frac{\theta}{2} \cos\theta \, d\theta$

   (c) $\bar{x} = -50a/63$

38. $P = 3\pi a/2$ 39. $2a^2$ 40. $(3\pi - 8)a^2/2$

41. a^2 42. $9a^2\pi/2$ 43. $3\pi a^2/2$

44. πa^2 45. πa^2 46. $4a^2$

47. $a^2(\pi + 2)$ 48. $5\pi a^2/4$

CHAPTER 12

ARTICLE 12–1

1. $\alpha_1 = \frac{1}{2}\sin^{-1} 0.8 = 26°34'$ 5. $x = e^t, y = -(7 + e^{2t})/2$
   $\alpha_2 = 90° - \alpha_1 = 63°26'$

6. $y = (1 - t)^{-1}, x = -\ln|1 - t|$

7. $x = \sin t, y = 1 + (t - \sin t \cos t)/2$, for $0 \le t \le \pi/2$;
   $x = 1, y = t + 1 - \pi/4$, for $t > \pi/2$

ARTICLE 12–2

1. $x^2 + y^2 = 1$ 2. $x = 1 - 2y^2; |y| \le 1$

3. $x^2 - y^2 = 1; x > 0$ 4. $\dfrac{(x - 2)^2}{16} + \dfrac{(y - 3)^2}{4} = 1$

5. $y = x^2 - 6x$ 6. $4x^2 - y^2 = 4; x \ge 1, y \ge 0$

7. $(x - 2)(y - 2) + 1 = 0; x > 2, y < 2$

8. $y = x^2 - 2x + 5; x \ge 1$ 9. $2(x + y) = (x - y)^2$

10. $\dfrac{(x - 3)^2}{4} + \dfrac{(y - 4)^2}{9} = 1; x > 3$

11. $x = \dfrac{-at}{\sqrt{t^2 + 1}}, y = \dfrac{a}{\sqrt{t^2 + 1}}$ 12. $x = a\tanh\theta, y = a\operatorname{sech}\theta$

13. $x = a\cos\dfrac{s}{a}, y = a\sin\dfrac{s}{a}$ 14. $x = a\sinh^{-1}\dfrac{s}{a}, y = \sqrt{a^2 + s^2}$

15. $x = a\cos\phi + a\phi\sin\phi$
    $y = a\sin\phi - a\phi\cos\phi$

16. $x = (a + b)\cos\theta - b\cos\left(\dfrac{a + b}{b}\theta\right)$

    $y = (a + b)\sin\theta - b\sin\left(\dfrac{a + b}{b}\theta\right)$

17. $x = (a - b) \cos \theta + b \cos \left(\dfrac{a - b}{b} \theta \right)$

$y = (a - b) \sin \theta - b \sin \left(\dfrac{a - b}{b} \theta \right)$

18. $8a$

21. (a) $x = 2a \cot \theta, \; y = 2a \sin^2 \theta$

(b) $y = \dfrac{8a^3}{x^2 + 4a^2}$

ARTICLE 12–3

1. $\mathbf{i} - 4\mathbf{j}$

2. $-\mathbf{i} + \mathbf{j}$

3. $-2\mathbf{i} - 3\mathbf{j}$

4. 0

5. $\frac{1}{2}\sqrt{3}\mathbf{i} + \frac{1}{2}\mathbf{j}$

6. $\frac{1}{2}\sqrt{3}\mathbf{i} - \frac{1}{2}\mathbf{j}$

7. $\frac{3}{5}\mathbf{i} - \frac{4}{5}\mathbf{j}$

8. $\dfrac{\mathbf{i} + 4\mathbf{j}}{\sqrt{17}}$

9. $\dfrac{-4\mathbf{i} + \mathbf{j}}{\sqrt{17}}$

10. $\mathbf{i} \cos \theta + \mathbf{j} \sin \theta$

11. $\sqrt{2}, \; 45°$

12. $\sqrt{13}, \; \tan^{-1}(-1.5) = -56°.3$

13. $2, \; 30°$

14. $\sqrt{13}, \; 130° - \tan^{-1}(1.5) = 123°.7$

15. $13, \; \tan^{-1}\frac{12}{5} = 67.°4$

16. $13, \; 180° + \tan^{-1}\frac{12}{5} = 247°.4$

ARTICLE 12–4

1. $\mathbf{v} = -a\omega \sin \omega t \mathbf{i} + a\omega \cos \omega t \mathbf{j}, \; \mathbf{a} = -a\omega^2 \cos \omega t \mathbf{i} - a\omega^2 \sin \omega t \mathbf{j} = -\omega^2 \mathbf{R};$

when $\omega t = \dfrac{\pi}{3}: \mathbf{v} = a\omega \left(-\dfrac{\sqrt{3}}{2}\mathbf{i} + \dfrac{1}{2}\mathbf{j} \right),$ speed $= a\omega,$

$\mathbf{a} = -a\omega^2 \left(\dfrac{1}{2}\mathbf{i} + \dfrac{\sqrt{3}}{2}\mathbf{j} \right)$

2. $\mathbf{v} = -2 \sin t \mathbf{i} + 3 \cos t \mathbf{j}, \; \mathbf{a} = -2 \cos t \mathbf{i} - 3 \sin t \mathbf{j};$

at $t = \dfrac{\pi}{4}: \mathbf{v} = -\sqrt{2}\mathbf{i} + \frac{3}{2}\sqrt{2}\mathbf{j},$ speed $= \sqrt{6.5}, \; \mathbf{a} = -\sqrt{2}\mathbf{i} - \frac{3}{2}\sqrt{2}\mathbf{j}$

3. $\mathbf{v} = \mathbf{i} + 2t\mathbf{j}$
$\mathbf{a} = 2\mathbf{j}$
$t = 2: \mathbf{v} = \mathbf{i} + 4\mathbf{j}, \; \mathbf{a} = 2\mathbf{j},$
speed $= \sqrt{17}$

4. $\mathbf{v} = -2 \sin 2t \mathbf{i} + 2 \cos t \mathbf{j}$
$\mathbf{a} = -4 \cos 2t \mathbf{i} - 2 \sin t \mathbf{j}$
$t = 0: \mathbf{v} = 2\mathbf{j}, \; \mathbf{a} = -4\mathbf{i},$
speed $= 2$

5. $\mathbf{v} = e^t \mathbf{i} - 2e^{-2t}\mathbf{j}$
$\mathbf{a} = e^t \mathbf{i} + 4e^{-2t}\mathbf{j}$
$t = \ln 3: \mathbf{v} = 3\mathbf{i} - \frac{2}{9}\mathbf{j},$
$\mathbf{a} = 3\mathbf{i} + \frac{4}{9}\mathbf{j},$
speed $= \frac{1}{9}\sqrt{733}$

6. $\mathbf{v} = \sec t \tan t \mathbf{i} + \sec^2 t \mathbf{j}$
$\mathbf{a} = (\sec^3 t + \sec t \tan^2 t)\mathbf{i}$
$\qquad + 2 \sec^2 t \tan t \mathbf{j}$
$t = \dfrac{\pi}{6}: \mathbf{v} = \frac{2}{3}\mathbf{i} + \frac{4}{3}\mathbf{j}, \; \mathbf{a} = \dfrac{10\mathbf{i} + 8\mathbf{j}}{3\sqrt{3}},$
speed $= \frac{1}{3}\sqrt{20}$

7. $\mathbf{v} = 3 \sinh 3t \mathbf{i} + 2 \cosh t \mathbf{j}$
$\mathbf{a} = 9 \cosh 3t \mathbf{i} + 2 \sinh t \mathbf{j}$
$t = 0: \mathbf{v} = 2\mathbf{j}, \; \mathbf{a} = 9\mathbf{i},$ speed $= 2$

8. $\mathbf{v} = \dfrac{\mathbf{i}}{t+1} + 2t\mathbf{j}$

$\mathbf{a} = \dfrac{-\mathbf{i}}{(t+1)^2} + 2\mathbf{j}$

$t = 1: \mathbf{v} = \frac{1}{2}\mathbf{i} + 2\mathbf{j}, \ \mathbf{a} = -\frac{1}{4}\mathbf{i} + 2\mathbf{j}, \ \text{speed} = \frac{1}{2}\sqrt{17}$

9. $\mathbf{R} = -\frac{1}{2}gt^2\mathbf{j} + \mathbf{v}_0t = tv_0\cos\alpha\,\mathbf{i} + (tv_0\sin\alpha - \frac{1}{2}gt^2)\mathbf{j}$

ARTICLE 12–5

1. $-\mathbf{i}\sin t + \mathbf{j}\cos t$

2. $\dfrac{e^t\mathbf{i} + 2t\mathbf{j}}{\sqrt{e^{2t} + 4t^2}}$

3. $-\cos t\mathbf{i} + \sin t\mathbf{j}$

4. $\dfrac{\mathbf{i} + 2x\mathbf{j}}{\sqrt{1 + 4x^2}}$

5. $-\dfrac{2\cos t\mathbf{i} + \mathbf{j}}{\sqrt{1 + 4\cos^2 t}}$

ARTICLE 12–6

1. $\dfrac{1}{a}\operatorname{sech}^2\dfrac{x}{a}$

2. $-\cos x$

3. $\dfrac{4e^{2x}}{(1 + 4e^{4x})^{3/2}}$

4. $\dfrac{-1}{3a\sin t\cos t}$

5. $\dfrac{1}{a\theta}$

6. $-\dfrac{1}{4a}\csc\dfrac{\theta}{2}$

7. $-\cos y$

8. $\dfrac{2}{\sqrt{y^2 + 2(y^2 + 1)^2}}$

9. $\dfrac{48y^5}{(4y^6 + 1)^2}$

10. $(x + 2)^2 + (y - 3)^2 = 8.$

For the circle: $y' = -\dfrac{x + 2}{y - 3}, \ y'' = \dfrac{-8}{(y - 3)^3}.$

Both of these $= +1$ at $(0, 1)$.

ARTICLE 12–7

2. $\mathbf{v} = 2\mathbf{i}\sinh 2t + 2\mathbf{j}\cosh 2t$

$\mathbf{a} = 4\mathbf{i}\cosh 2t + 4\mathbf{j}\sinh 2t$

$\dfrac{ds}{dt} = |\mathbf{v}| = 2\sqrt{\sinh^2 2t + \cosh^2 2t} = 2\sqrt{\cosh 4t}$

$a_T = \dfrac{d^2s}{dt^2} = \dfrac{4\sinh 4t}{\sqrt{\cosh 4t}}$

$a_N = \sqrt{|\mathbf{a}|^2 - a_T^2} = 4\sqrt{\operatorname{sech} 4t}$

3. $a_T = \dfrac{2t}{\sqrt{1 + t^2}}, \ a_N = \dfrac{2}{\sqrt{1 + t^2}}$

4. $a_T = 0, \ a_N = \omega^2 a$

5. $a_T = 0, \ a_N = \dfrac{2}{t^2 + 1}$

6. $a_T = \sqrt{2}e^t, \ a_N = \sqrt{2}e^t$

ARTICLE 12–8

2. $\mathbf{v} = 3a\sin\theta\mathbf{u}_r + 3a(1 - \cos\theta)\mathbf{u}_\theta$

$\mathbf{a} = 9a(2\cos\theta - 1)\mathbf{u}_r + 18a\sin\theta\mathbf{u}_\theta$

3. $\mathbf{v} = 4at \cos 2\theta \mathbf{u}_r + 2at \sin 2\theta \mathbf{u}_\theta$
   $\mathbf{a} = (4a \cos 2\theta - 20at^2 \sin 2\theta)\mathbf{u}_r + (2a \sin 2\theta + 16at^2 \cos 2\theta)\mathbf{u}_\theta$

4. $\mathbf{v} = 2ae^{a\theta}\mathbf{u}_r + 2e^{a\theta}\mathbf{u}_\theta$
   $\mathbf{a} = 4e^{a\theta}(a^2 - 1)\mathbf{u}_r + 8ae^{a\theta}\mathbf{u}_\theta$

5. $\mathbf{v} = a \cos t\mathbf{u}_r + ae^{-t}(1 + \sin t)\mathbf{u}_\theta$
   $\mathbf{a} = -a[\sin t + e^{-2t}(1 + \sin t)]\mathbf{u}_r + ae^{-t}[2 \cos t - 1 - \sin t]\mathbf{u}_\theta$

6. $\mathbf{v} = -8 \sin 4t\mathbf{u}_r + 4 \cos 4t\mathbf{u}_\theta$
   $\mathbf{a} = -40 \cos 4t\mathbf{u}_r - 32 \sin 4t\mathbf{u}_\theta$

CHAPTER 12: MISCELLANEOUS

1. $x = (1 - t)^{-1}, y = 1 - \ln(1 - t), t < 1$

2. $x = \tan^{-1}(t + 1)$
   $y = (t + 1) \tan^{-1}(t + 1) - \pi/4 - \frac{1}{2} \ln(1 + t + \frac{1}{2}t^2)$

3. $x = e^t, y = e^{e^t} - e$

4. $x = 3 - 3 \cos 2t, y = 4 + 2 \sin 2t$

5. $x = t - \sin t, y = 1 - \cos t$

6. $y = e^t, x = 2\sqrt{1 + e^t} - 2\sqrt{2} - 2 \coth^{-1}\sqrt{1 + e^t} + 2 \coth^{-1}\sqrt{2}$

7. $x = \sinh^{-1} t, y = t \sinh^{-1} t - \sqrt{1 + t^2} + 1$

8. $x = 2 + 2 \sinh(t/2), y = 2t - 4 + 4 \cosh(t/2)$

9. $x = 4 \sin t, y = 4 \cos t$ 10. $x = 2 - e^{-t}, y = 2t + e^{-t}$

12. $x = 8t - 2 \sin 2t, y = 4 - 2 \cos 2t$

13. $x = 2a \sin^2 \theta \tan \theta, y = 2a \sin^2 \theta$

14. $x = \cot \theta \pm a \cos \theta, y = \pm a \sin \theta$

15. (a) $3\pi a^2$ (b) $8a$ (c) $-4a \sin(t/2)$ (d) $64\pi a^2/3$
    (e) $(\pi a, 5a/6)$

17. 0

24. (a) $\mathbf{v} = 2^{-3/2}(-\mathbf{i} + \mathbf{j}), \mathbf{a} = 2^{-5/2}(\mathbf{i} - 3\mathbf{j})$ (b) $t = 0$

25. (a) $\mathbf{v} = \pi(\mathbf{i}(1 - \cos \pi t) + \mathbf{j} \sin \pi t), \mathbf{a} = \pi^2(\mathbf{i} \sin \pi t + \mathbf{j} \cos \pi t)$
    (b) Slope of $PC = \cot \pi t$, slope of $PQ = \csc \pi t + \cot \pi t$
    (c) Slope of $\mathbf{v}$ = slope of PQ, slope of $\mathbf{a}$ = slope of PC

26. Speed $= a\sqrt{1 + t^2}, a_t = at/\sqrt{1 + t^2}, a_n = a(t^2 + 2)/\sqrt{1 + t^2}$

28. (b) $\pi/2$

29. $(a^2 + b^2)^{3/2}/|ad - bc|$, provided $ad \neq bc$

30. $x = a\theta + a \sin \theta, y = -a(1 - \cos \theta)$

31. $(-\frac{1}{2} \ln 2, 1/\sqrt{2})$ 32. (b) $\pi ab, \pi a^2$ 33. $\kappa = \pi s$

34. $y = \pm\sqrt{1 - x^2} \pm \ln[(1 - \sqrt{1 - x^2})/x] + C$. Set $C = 0$. Then,
    $x = e^{-s}$ [$s = -\ln x$, measured from $(1, 0)$],
    $y = \pm\sqrt{1 - e^{-2s}} \pm \ln(e^s - \sqrt{e^{2s} - 1})$.

35. $s = s_0 + 2\pi p$, $A = A_0 + s_0 p + \pi p^2$, $R = R_0 + p$, where s_0, A_0, R_0 are the length of arc, area, and radius of curvature of the original curve.

36. (a) $320\sqrt{10}$ (b) $16[\sqrt{2} + \ln(\sqrt{2} + 1)]$

37. $\mathbf{v} = 3\cos t\,\mathbf{i} - 2\sin t\,\mathbf{j}$
$\mathbf{a} = -3\sin t\,\mathbf{i} - 3\cos t\,\mathbf{j}$
Speed $= (4 + 5\cos^2 t)^{1/2}$
$a_t = -5\sin t\cos t\,(4 + 5\cos^2 t)^{-1/2}$
$a_n = 6(4 + 5\cos^2 t)^{-1/2}$

38. (a) $a_t = 0$, $a_n = 4$ (b) 1   (c) $r = 2\cos\theta$

39. $\mathbf{v} = (\cos t - t\sin t)\mathbf{i} + (\sin t + t\cos t)\mathbf{j}$
$\mathbf{a} = -(t\cos t + 2\sin t)\mathbf{i} - (t\sin t - 2\cos t)\mathbf{j}$
$\kappa = (t^2 + 2)/(t^2 + 1)$

40. $\kappa = (f^2 + 2f'^2 - ff'')/(f^2 + f'^2)^{3/2}$

41. (a) $r = e^{2\theta}$ (b) $\sqrt{\frac{5}{2}}(e^{4\pi} - 1)$

42. $\sqrt{2}\mathbf{u}_r$ 43. $2(\omega^2 - 1)\mathbf{i}$

44. (a) $\mathbf{v} = -\mathbf{u}_r + 3\mathbf{u}_\theta$, $\mathbf{a} = 3\mathbf{u}_r - 6\mathbf{u}_\theta$
(b) $\sqrt{37} + \frac{1}{6}\ln(3 + \sqrt{10})$

45. $r = a\cosh\omega t$

46. $\dfrac{1}{r} = \dfrac{\gamma M}{v_0^2 r_0^2} + \left(\dfrac{1}{r_0} - \dfrac{\gamma M}{v_0^2 r_0^2}\right)\cos\theta$

CHAPTER 13

ARTICLE 13–1

1. Straight line parallel to z-axis.

2. Straight line, 5 units above and parallel to the line $y = x$ in the xy-plane.

3. Circle in the plane $z = -2$, center $(0, 0, -2)$, radius 2.

4. Ellipse in the yz-plane, center $(0, 0, 0)$, semi-axes a and b.

5. Circle in the plane $z = 3$, radius 2, center $(0, 0, 3)$.

6. Straight line in the plane $\theta = \pi/6$, making an angle of $45°$ with the plane $z = 0$.

7. A right circular helix (Fig. 13–28) wound on a cylinder of radius 3.

8. A right conical helix wound on a right circular cone.

9. A semicircle of radius 5, center at the origin, lying in the plane $\theta = \pi/4$.

10. The intersection of the sphere $\rho = 5$ and the cone $\phi = \pi/4$ is a circle of radius $\rho\sin\phi = 5/\sqrt{2}$.

11. The plane $\theta = \pi/4$ and the cone $\phi = \pi/4$ intersect in a straight line through the origin.

12. A circle in the yz-plane, center at $(0, 0, 2)$ on the z-axis, radius 2.

13. $\rho = 2$; $r^2 + z^2 = 4$.   14. $\rho = 4\cos\phi$; $r^2 + z^2 = 4z$.

15. $z^2 = x^2 + y^2$; $\phi = \pi/4$, $\phi = 3\pi/4$.

16. $x^2 + y^2 + z^2 = 6z$; $r^2 + z^2 = 6z$.

17. Plane $x = 0$ and half-space where $x > 0$.

18. Spheres $\rho = 3$, $\rho = 5$, and shell between them.

19. On or inside sphere $\rho = 5$ but outside or on cylinder $r = 2$.

20. Wedge with two intersecting plane boundaries $\theta = 0$, $\theta = \pi/4$, and curved boundary part of cone $\phi = \pi/4$.

21. Interior and boundary of elliptic cylinder $4x^2 + 9y^2 = 36$.

ARTICLE 13–2

1. $(-2, 0, 2)$, $\sqrt{8}$

2. $(-\frac{1}{4}, -\frac{1}{4}, -\frac{1}{4})$, $\sqrt{75}/4$

3. $(0, 0, a)$, $|a|$.

4. $(0, -\frac{1}{3}, \frac{1}{3})$, $\sqrt{29}/3$

5. (a) $\sqrt{y^2 + z^2}$, (b) $\sqrt{z^2 + x^2}$, (c) $\sqrt{x^2 + y^2}$, (d) $|z|$

6. (a) $x^2 + y^2 + (z - 4)^2 = 4$

   (b) $4x^2 + 4y^2 + 3(z - \frac{3}{2})^2 = 27$

   (c) $5(z - \frac{3}{2})^2 - 4x^2 - 4y^2 = 5$

7. 3   8. 7   9. 9   10. 11

11. $(4\mathbf{i} + 3\mathbf{j} + 12\mathbf{k})/13$ 12. $(2\mathbf{i} + 2\mathbf{j} + 4\mathbf{k})/3$

ARTICLE 13–3

1. No; we cannot conclude that $\mathbf{B}_1 = \mathbf{B}_2$. All we can say is that $\mathbf{B}_1$ and $\mathbf{B}_2$ have the same projection on $\mathbf{A}$ when all three vectors start from the same initial point.

2. (a) $\dfrac{\mathbf{A} \cdot \mathbf{B}}{\mathbf{A} \cdot \mathbf{A}} \mathbf{A}$ (b) $\frac{7}{45}\mathbf{A}$ 3. $\angle A = \angle C = 71°.1$, $\angle B = 37°.8$

4. $(3, 3, 0)$ 5. $\frac{13}{15}$ 6. $\cos^{-1}(1/\sqrt{3}) = 54°.7$

7. $\cos^{-1}(\sqrt{6}/3) = 35°.3$ 8. $\cos^{-1}(\frac{13}{45}) = 73°.2$

9. Two. $45°$, $135°$ 13. $w(z_1 - z_2)$

16. (a) $\dfrac{dx}{dt} = \cos\theta \dfrac{dr}{dt} - \sin\theta \dfrac{r\,d\theta}{dt}$, $\dfrac{dy}{dt} = \sin\theta \dfrac{dr}{dt} + \cos\theta \dfrac{r\,d\theta}{dt}$

   (b) $\dfrac{dr}{dt} = \cos\theta \dfrac{dx}{dt} + \sin\theta \dfrac{dy}{dt}$, $\dfrac{r\,d\theta}{dt} = -\sin\theta \dfrac{dx}{dt} + \cos\theta \dfrac{dy}{dt}$

ARTICLE 13–4

1. $-\mathbf{i} - 3\mathbf{j} + 4\mathbf{k}$

2. $c(2\mathbf{i} + \mathbf{j} + \mathbf{k})$, $c = $ scalar

3. $2\sqrt{6}$

4. $\sqrt{6}/2$

5. $c(\mathbf{i} - \mathbf{j})$, $c = $ scalar

6. $\pm[4/(3\sqrt{2}), 1/(3\sqrt{2}), 1/(3\sqrt{2})]$

7. $11/\sqrt{107}$

8. (a) $60°.6$

   (b) Yes, because the angle between the two planes is equal to the angle between their normals and this angle is neither $0°$ nor $180°$.

   (c) $\mathbf{j} + \mathbf{k}$

ARTICLE 13–5

1. $(9, -5, 12)$

2. $x = 1 + t, y = 2 + t, z = -1 - t$
$$x - 1 = y - 2 = -(z + 1)$$

4. (a) The complement of the angle between the line and a normal to the plane.

(b) $22°.4$

5. $3x + y + z = 5$

6. $|D_2 - D_1|/7$

8. $7x - 5y - 4z = 6$

9. Plane through the three points.

10. $x - 2y + z = 6$

11. $x - y + z = 0$

12. $x + 6y + z = 16$

13. 3

14. (b) Yes

16. $17x - 26y + 11z = -40$

17. $2x - y + z = 5$

18. $1/\sqrt{75}, 5/\sqrt{75}, 7/\sqrt{75}$.

19. Locus is the set of points in the half-space that lies on the side of the plane toward which $\mathbf{N}$ points.

20. $\cos \alpha (x - x_0) + \cos \beta (y - y_0) + \cos \gamma (z - z_0) = 0$.

ARTICLE 13–6

1. $-2\mathbf{c} = -6\mathbf{i} + 8\mathbf{j} - 24\mathbf{k}; -22\mathbf{A} = -88\mathbf{i} + 176\mathbf{j} - 22\mathbf{k}$

2. 245

3. (a) $\mathbf{A} \times \mathbf{B} = 15\mathbf{i} + 10\mathbf{j} + 20\mathbf{k}$

$(\mathbf{A} \times \mathbf{B}) \times \mathbf{C} = 200\mathbf{i} - 120\mathbf{j} - 90\mathbf{k}$

(b) $(\mathbf{A} \cdot \mathbf{C})\mathbf{B} - (\mathbf{B} \cdot \mathbf{C})\mathbf{A} = 56\mathbf{B} + 22\mathbf{A} = 200\mathbf{i} - 120\mathbf{j} - 90\mathbf{k}$

5. $a = (\mathbf{A} \times \mathbf{B}) \cdot \mathbf{D}, b = -(\mathbf{A} \times \mathbf{B}) \cdot \mathbf{C}$

6. $\frac{2}{3}$

10. $7 - x = \dfrac{3y - 19}{12} = \dfrac{4 - 3z}{30}$

11. (a) $S(0, 9, -3)$

(b) Area $PQRS = |-29\mathbf{i} - \mathbf{j} + 11\mathbf{k}| = \sqrt{963} \approx 31.03$

(c) $11; 29; 1$.

ARTICLE 13–7

1. $\mathbf{v} = e^t[\mathbf{i} + \mathbf{j} (\cos t + \sin t) + \mathbf{k} (\cos t - \sin t)]$

$\mathbf{a} = e^t[\mathbf{i} + 2\mathbf{j} \cos t - 2\mathbf{k} \sin t]$

$\theta = \cos^{-1} (\sqrt{15}/5) = 39°.2$

2. $\mathbf{v} = \mathbf{i} \sec^2 t + 2\mathbf{j} \cosh 2t - 3\mathbf{k} \operatorname{sech} 3t \tanh 3t$

$\mathbf{a} = 2\mathbf{i} \sec^2 t \tan t + 4\mathbf{j} \sinh 2t + 9\mathbf{k} \operatorname{sech} 3t (\tanh^2 3t - \operatorname{sech}^2 3t)$

$\theta = 90°$

3. $\mathbf{v} = \dfrac{2t}{t^2 + 1} \mathbf{i} + \dfrac{1}{t^2 + 1} \mathbf{j} + \dfrac{t}{\sqrt{t^2 + 1}} \mathbf{k}$ (concluded overleaf)

$$\mathbf{a} = \frac{2(1 - t^2)}{(1 + t^2)^2}\,\mathbf{i} - \frac{2t}{(1 + t^2)^2}\,\mathbf{j} + \frac{\mathbf{k}}{(t^2 + 1)^{3/2}}$$

$\theta = 90°$

ARTICLE 13–8

1. $\mathbf{T} = \frac{1}{13}(12 \cos 2t\mathbf{i} - 12 \sin 2t\mathbf{j} + 5\mathbf{k})$

2. $\mathbf{T} = \sqrt{\frac{1}{3}}\,[(\cos t - \sin t)\mathbf{i} + (\cos t + \sin t)\mathbf{j} + \mathbf{k}]$

3. $\mathbf{T} = (\mathbf{i} \tanh 2t + \mathbf{j} + \mathbf{k} \operatorname{sech} 2t)/\sqrt{2}$

4. $\mathbf{T} = (9t^2 + 25)^{-1/2}[3 (\cos t - t \sin t)\mathbf{i} + 3 (\sin t + t \cos t)\mathbf{j} + 4\mathbf{k}]$

5. 13π 6. $\sqrt{3}\,(e^\pi - 1)$ 7. $3\sqrt{2} \sinh 2\pi$

8. $\dfrac{\pi\sqrt{9\pi^2 + 25}}{2} + \dfrac{25}{6} \sinh^{-1} \dfrac{3\pi}{5}$

9. $\mathbf{N} = -\mathbf{i} \sin 2t - \mathbf{j} \cos 2t$

$\kappa = \frac{24}{169}$

$\mathbf{B} = \frac{1}{13}(5 \cos 2t\mathbf{i} - 5 \sin 2t\mathbf{j} - 12\mathbf{k})$

10. $\mathbf{N} = \dfrac{-\mathbf{i}}{\sqrt{2}}\,(\sin t + \cos t) + \dfrac{\mathbf{j}}{\sqrt{2}}\,(\cos t - \sin t)$

$\kappa = \sqrt{2}\,e^{-t}/3$

$\mathbf{B} = [\mathbf{i}(\sin t - \cos t) - \mathbf{j}(\sin t + \cos t) + 2\mathbf{k}]/\sqrt{6}$

11. $\mathbf{N} = \mathbf{i} \operatorname{sech} 2t - \mathbf{k} \tanh 2t$

$\kappa = \frac{1}{6} \operatorname{sech}^2 2t$

$\mathbf{B} = (-\mathbf{i} \tanh 2t + \mathbf{j} - \mathbf{k} \operatorname{sech} 2t)/\sqrt{2}$

12. $d\mathbf{R}/dt = \mathbf{T}\,(ds/dt)$

$d^2\mathbf{R}/dt^2 = \mathbf{T}\,(d^2s/dt^2) + \mathbf{N}\kappa\,(ds/dt)^2$

13. $\mathbf{R} = r\mathbf{u}_r + z\mathbf{k}$

14. $\mathbf{v} = \mathbf{u}_r \dfrac{dr}{dt} + \mathbf{u}_\theta \dfrac{r\,d\theta}{dt} + \mathbf{k} \dfrac{dz}{dt}$

$$\mathbf{a} = \mathbf{u}_r \left[\frac{d^2r}{dt^2} - r\left(\frac{d\theta}{dt}\right)^2\right] + \mathbf{u}_\theta \left[r\frac{d^2\theta}{dt^2} + 2\frac{dr}{dt}\frac{d\theta}{dt}\right] + \mathbf{k}\frac{d^2z}{dt^2}$$

15. (a) $2\sqrt{\dfrac{\pi bg}{a^2 + b^2}}$ (b) $\theta = \dfrac{b}{a^2 + b^2}\,(\frac{1}{2}gt^2),\ z = \dfrac{b^2}{a^2 + b^2}\,(\frac{1}{2}gt^2)$

(c) $\dfrac{d\mathbf{R}}{dt} = gt \dfrac{b}{\sqrt{a^2 + b^2}}\,\mathbf{T},\ \dfrac{d^2\mathbf{R}}{dt^2} = g \dfrac{b}{\sqrt{a^2 + b^2}}\,\mathbf{T} + (gt)^2 \dfrac{ab^2}{(a^2 + b^2)^2}\,\mathbf{N}$

There is never any component of acceleration in the direction of the binormal.

16. (a) $\dfrac{d\theta}{dt} = \sqrt{\dfrac{2gb\theta}{a^2 + b^2 + a^2\theta^2}}$

(b) $\frac{1}{2}\left[\theta\sqrt{a^2 + b^2 + a^2\theta^2} + \dfrac{a^2 + b^2}{a} \sinh^{-1} \dfrac{a\theta}{\sqrt{a^2 + b^2}}\right]$

17. (a) $\mathbf{u}_\rho = \mathbf{i} \sin\phi \cos\theta + \mathbf{j} \sin\phi \sin\theta + \mathbf{k} \cos\phi$

    $\mathbf{u}_\phi = \mathbf{i} \cos\phi \cos\theta + \mathbf{j} \cos\phi \sin\theta - \mathbf{k} \sin\phi$

    $\mathbf{u}_\theta = -\mathbf{i} \sin\theta + \mathbf{j} \cos\theta$

(d) Yes, they form a right-handed system of mutually orthogonal vectors because of (b) and (c).

18. $\mathbf{R} = \rho\mathbf{u}_\rho$, $\dfrac{d\mathbf{R}}{dt} = \mathbf{u}_\rho \dfrac{d\rho}{dt} + \mathbf{u}_\phi\rho \dfrac{d\phi}{dt} + \mathbf{u}_\theta\rho \sin\phi \dfrac{d\theta}{dt}$

19. (a) $ds^2 = dr^2 + r^2\,d\theta^2 + dz^2$ (b) $ds^2 = d\rho^2 + \rho^2\,d\phi^2 + \rho^2 \sin^2\phi\,d\theta^2$

20. (a) $7\sqrt{3}\,a$ (b) $7\sqrt{5}$

21. $x = \dfrac{a\cos\theta}{\sqrt{1+\sin^2\theta}}$, $y = \dfrac{a\sin\theta}{\sqrt{1+\sin^2\theta}}$, $z = \dfrac{-a\sin\theta}{\sqrt{1+\sin^2\theta}}$

ARTICLE 13–9

1. Circular cylinder of radius a, axis along Oz.

2. Hyperbolic cylinder, axis along Oy.

3. Circular cylinder of radius a, one element being the z-axis.

4. Cylinder with elements parallel to Oz. Cross sections are cardioids.

5. Circular cylinder of radius 2, one element being the x-axis.

6. Elliptic cylinder, one element being the y-axis.

ARTICLE 13–10

1. Paraboloid of revolution, vertex $(-2, 3, -13)$ and opening upward.

2. Sphere of radius 4, center $(-2, 3, 0)$.

3. Ellipsoid, center $(0, 1, 0)$, semi-axes $a = 2$, $b = 1$, $c = 2$.

4. Ellipsoid, center $(0, 1, 0)$, $a = 2$, $b = c = 1$.

5. Sphere, center $(0, 1, 0)$, radius 1.

6. One-sheeted hyperboloid of revolution, axis of symmetry parallel to Oy, center $(-2, -3, 0)$.

7. Two-sheeted hyperboloid of revolution, axis parallel to Ox, center $(-2, -3, 0)$.

8. Parabolic cylinder, one element being Oy.

9. Rotate the xy-axes through $45°$ and have $z^2 + 2y'^2 = 2x'^2$; elliptic cone with vertex O, axis along Ox'.

10. Rotate xy-axes $45°$; $z = 2(x'^2 - y'^2)$, hyperbolic paraboloid ("saddle").

11. Paraboloid of revolution obtained by rotating the parabola $z = x^2$ about the z-axis.

12. Rotate the line $z = x$ about the z-axis, right circular cone.

13. Rotate $z^2 = x$ about the z-axis.

14. Elliptic cone, vertex O, axis Oz.

15. Elliptic cone, vertex O, axis Ox.

16. Right circular cone, vertex O, axis Oy.

17. $(x - 1)^2 + 4(y + 1)^2 - (z - 2)^2 = 1$. One-sheeted hyperboloid, center $(1, -1, 2)$, axis $x - 1 = y + 1 = 0$.

18. $(z - 2)^2 = (x - 1)^2 + 4(y + 1)^2$. Elliptic cone, vertex $(1, -1, 2)$, axis $x - 1 = y + 1 = 0$.

19. Elliptic cylinder, axis along Oy.

20. Elliptic paraboloid, vertex $(1, 0, 0)$, axis along Ox.

21. Plane, $z = x$.

22. Plane, $z = y$.

23. Ruled surface generated by rotating about Oz a line parallel to the xy-plane and passing through Oz, whose distance above the xy-plane is $z = \sin \theta$.

24. Ruled surface generated by rotating about Oz a line, parallel to the xy-plane and passing through Oz, whose distance above the xy-plane is $z = \cosh \theta$.

25. (a) $A(z_1) = \pi ab \left(1 - \dfrac{z_1^2}{c^2} \right)$ (b) $V = \tfrac{4}{3} \pi abc$

27. (a) $\pi abh \left(1 + \dfrac{h^2}{3c^2} \right)$

   (b) $A_0 = \pi ab$, $A_h = \pi ab \left(1 + \dfrac{h^2}{c^2} \right)$, $V = \dfrac{h}{3} (2A_0 + A_h)$

28. Vertex $(0, y_1, cy_1^2/b^2)$, focus $\left(0, y_1, \dfrac{cy_1^2}{b^2} - \dfrac{a^2}{4c} \right)$

29. In any plane $\theta = $ constant, the equation $\rho = F(\phi)$ may be considered as the polar equation of a plane curve C having polar coordinates ρ and ϕ. Since the space equation is independent of θ, the surface is generated by rotating the curve C around the z-axis.

30. A sphere, center $\rho = \dfrac{a}{2}$, $\phi = 0$, $\theta = 0$ and radius $\dfrac{a}{2}$.

31. A cardioid of revolution.

CHAPTER 13: MISCELLANEOUS

1. $\tfrac{3}{11}(3\mathbf{i} - \mathbf{j} + \mathbf{k})$

2. $-\tfrac{1}{10}$

3. $\mathbf{C} = \dfrac{\mathbf{A} \cdot \mathbf{B}}{\mathbf{B} \cdot \mathbf{B}} \mathbf{B}$, $\mathbf{D} = \dfrac{(\mathbf{B} \cdot \mathbf{B})\mathbf{A} - (\mathbf{A} \cdot \mathbf{B})\mathbf{B}}{\mathbf{B} \cdot \mathbf{B}}$

4. $7\sqrt{2}/10$

6. $\mathbf{j} - \mathbf{k}$

7. $5\mathbf{i} + 7\mathbf{j} + \mathbf{k}$

8. $(\mathbf{j} + \mathbf{k})/\sqrt{2}$

10. $-2\sqrt{3}(\mathbf{i} + \mathbf{j} - 2\mathbf{k})$

12. $(10\mathbf{i} - 2\mathbf{j} - 6\mathbf{k})/\sqrt{35}$

14. $\cos^{-1} (3/\sqrt{35})$

15. $\mathbf{B} = \dfrac{1}{|\mathbf{A}|^2} (d\mathbf{A} + \mathbf{C} \times \mathbf{A})$

17. $z = 3$, $x - \sqrt{3} y + 2\sqrt{3} - 1 = 0$

18. $(1, -2, -1)$; $(x - 1)/-5 = (y + 2)/3 = (z + 1)/4$

19. $25/\sqrt{38}$

21. $(\tfrac{11}{9}, \tfrac{26}{9}, -\tfrac{7}{9})$

22. $3x + 3y + 3z - 8 = 0$ 23. $2x - y + 2z - 8 = 0$

24. (a) $2x + 7y + 2z + 10 = 0$ (b) $173/5\sqrt{57}$

25. $2x + 2y + z = 5$ 28. (a) 1 (b) $-10\mathbf{i} - 2\mathbf{j} - 12\mathbf{k}$

29. $\frac{1}{3}$, $\cos\theta = -\sqrt{2}/3$

34. (a) $\mathbf{t}(\frac{2}{3}, \frac{1}{3}, \frac{2}{3})$, $\mathbf{n}(1/\sqrt{5}, -2/\sqrt{5}, 0)$, $\mathbf{b}(4/3\sqrt{5}, 2/3\sqrt{5}, -5/3\sqrt{5})$
    (b) $2\sqrt{5}/9$

35. (a) $x + 2y + 3z = 6$ (b) $3x - 3y + z = 1$

36. $\frac{1}{3}(t^2 + 1)^{-2}$

39. Hyperboloid of two sheets; center $(2, -1, -1)$

40. $x^2/4 + y^2/9 + z^2/1 = 1$, ellipsoid

41. $(x - 1)^2 + (y - 2)^2 + (z - 3)^2 = 3$

42. $z^6 - y = 0$; $y = (x^2 + z^2)^3$

CHAPTER 14

ARTICLE 14–1

1. Let $r = \sqrt{x^2 + y^2}$. (a) $r < 0.1$ (b) $r < 0.001$

2. (a) Let $\rho = \sqrt{x^2 + y^2 + z^2}$; $\rho < 0.1$, $\rho < 0.2\sqrt{3}$
    (b) Yes, because $|f(x, y, z) - f(0, 0, 0)| = x^2 + y^2 + z^2 = \rho^2$ is less than any positive ϵ if $\rho < \sqrt{\epsilon}$.

3. (a) Along line $x = 1, f(x, y) = f(1, y) \to 1$.
      Along line $y = -1, f(x, y) = f(x, -1) \to \frac{1}{2}$.
    (b) No, because different limits are approached as $(x, y) \to (1, -1)$ in different ways. [See answer to part (a) above.]

ARTICLE 14–2

6. $\dfrac{\partial w}{\partial x} = e^x \cos y$, $\dfrac{\partial w}{\partial y} = -e^x \sin y$

7. $\dfrac{\partial w}{\partial x} = e^x \sin y$, $\dfrac{\partial w}{\partial y} = e^x \cos y$

8. $\dfrac{\partial w}{\partial x} = \dfrac{-y}{x^2 + y^2}$, $\dfrac{\partial w}{\partial y} = \dfrac{x}{x^2 + y^2}$

9. $\dfrac{\partial w}{\partial x} = \dfrac{x}{x^2 + y^2}$, $\dfrac{\partial w}{\partial y} = \dfrac{y}{x^2 + y^2}$

10. $\dfrac{\partial w}{\partial x} = -\dfrac{y}{x^2} \sinh \dfrac{y}{x}$, $\dfrac{\partial w}{\partial y} = \dfrac{1}{x} \sinh \dfrac{y}{x}$

11. $f_x = 2xe^{2y+3z} \cos(4w)$
    $f_y = 2f$
    $f_z = 3f$
    $f_w = -4x^2 e^{2y+3z} \sin(4w)$

12. $f_x = \dfrac{-yz}{\sqrt{x^4 - x^2y^2}}$

   $f_y = \dfrac{|x|z}{x\sqrt{x^2 - y^2}}$

   $f_z = \sin^{-1}(y/x)$

13. $f_u = \dfrac{2u}{v^2 + w^2}$

$f_v = \dfrac{-2v(u^2 + w^2)}{(v^2 + w^2)^2}$

$f_w = \dfrac{-2w(u^2 - v^2)}{(v^2 + w^2)^2}$

14. $f_r = \dfrac{(z^2 - r^2)(2 - \cos 2\theta)}{(r^2 + z^2)^2}$

$f_\theta = \dfrac{2r \sin 2\theta}{r^2 + z^2}$

$f_z = \dfrac{-2rz(2 - \cos 2\theta)}{(r^2 + z^2)^2}$

15. $f_x = \dfrac{2x}{u^2 + v^2}$

$f_y = \dfrac{2y}{u^2 + v^2}$

$f_u = \dfrac{-2u(x^2 + y^2)}{(u^2 + v^2)^2}$

$f_v = \dfrac{-2v(x^2 + y^2)}{(u^2 + v^2)^2}$

16. $f_x = 2 \cos 2x \cosh 3r$

$f_y = 3 \cosh 3y \cos 4s$

$f_r = 3 \sin 2x \sinh 3r$

$f_s = -4 \sinh 3y \sin 4s$

17. By the law of cosines, $\cos A = (b^2 + c^2 - a^2)/(2bc)$.

$\dfrac{\partial A}{\partial a} = \dfrac{a}{bc \sin A}$, $\quad \dfrac{\partial A}{\partial b} = \dfrac{c^2 - a^2 - b^2}{2b^2c \sin A}$

18. By the law of sines, $a = b \sin A \csc B$.

$\dfrac{\partial a}{\partial A} = b \cos A \csc B$, $\quad \dfrac{\partial a}{\partial B} = -b \sin A \csc B \cot B$

19. $\dfrac{x}{\rho} = \dfrac{x}{\sqrt{x^2 + y^2 + z^2}}$

20. $-\dfrac{x^2 + y^2}{\rho^3 \sin \phi} = -\dfrac{\sqrt{x^2 + y^2}}{x^2 + y^2 + z^2}$

21. $\dfrac{x}{x^2 + y^2}$

22. 0

23. $\dfrac{xz}{\rho^3 \sin \phi} = \dfrac{xz}{(x^2 + y^2 + z^2)\sqrt{x^2 + y^2}}$

24. $\dfrac{-y}{x^2 + y^2}$

25. $\mathbf{i} \sin \phi \cos \theta + \mathbf{j} \sin \phi \sin \theta + \mathbf{k} \cos \phi$

26. $\rho \cos \phi (\mathbf{i} \cos \theta + \mathbf{j} \sin \theta) - \mathbf{k}\rho \sin \phi$

27. $\rho \sin \phi(-\mathbf{i} \sin \theta + \mathbf{j} \cos \theta)$

28. $\dfrac{\partial \mathbf{R}}{\partial \rho} = \mathbf{u}_\rho;$ $\quad \dfrac{\partial \mathbf{R}}{\partial \phi} = \rho \mathbf{u}_\phi;$ $\quad \dfrac{\partial \mathbf{R}}{\partial \theta} = \rho \sin \phi \mathbf{u}_\theta$

29. (a) $\partial \mathbf{R}/\partial x$ is tangent to the curve in which the surface $w = f(x, y)$ and the plane $y = y_0$ intersect.

(b) $\partial \mathbf{R}/\partial y$ is tangent to the curve in which the surface $w = f(x, y)$ and the plane $x = x_0$ intersect.

(c) $\mathbf{v} = -\mathbf{i}f_x(x_0, y_0) - \mathbf{j}f_y(x_0, y_0) + \mathbf{k}$ is normal to the surface at (x_0, y_0, w_0).

ARTICLE 14–3

1. $6x + 8y = z + 25$, $\dfrac{x - 3}{6} = \dfrac{y - 4}{8} = \dfrac{z - 25}{-1}$

2. $x - 2y + 2z = 9$, $2x = -y = z$

3. $x - 3y = z - 1$, $x - 1 = \dfrac{1 - y}{3} = -z - 1$

4. $x - y + 2z = \pi/2$, $x - 1 = 1 - y = \frac{1}{2}\left(z - \dfrac{\pi}{4}\right)$

5. $16x + 12y = 125z - 75$, $\dfrac{x - 3}{16} = \dfrac{y + 4}{12} = \dfrac{3 - 5z}{625}$

6. (a) $\mathbf{N} = c(-\mathbf{i} + \mathbf{j}f_y + \mathbf{k}f_z)$, $c =$ scalar

   (b) $x - 2y + z = 1$, $2x = 3 - y = 2(z - 1)$

7. Line: $z = \dfrac{-11x}{6} = \dfrac{-22y}{7}$

   Plane: $12x + 14y + 11z = 0$

8. Vertex: $(0, 0, z_0 + \frac{1}{2})$

9. $\begin{vmatrix} \mathbf{i} & \mathbf{j} & \mathbf{k} \\ f_x & f_y & -1 \\ g_x & g_y & -1 \end{vmatrix}$

10. $\pm\sqrt{3/1105}\,[3\mathbf{i} + 14\mathbf{j} - 30\mathbf{k}]$

ARTICLE 14–4

1. $\Delta w_{\tan} = 0.14$, $\Delta w = 0.1407$

2. 6%

3. 4.98

5. (13 ± 0.03) in.

ARTICLE 14–5

1. $\frac{2}{3}$

2. $\frac{9}{1183}$

3. $4\sqrt{3}$

4. $\frac{43}{15}$

5. In the direction of $3\mathbf{i} - \mathbf{j}$

6. $-7/\sqrt{5}$

8. $\dfrac{\pi - 3}{2\sqrt{5}} \approx 0.032$

9. $\pm(\mathbf{i} + \mathbf{j})$

ARTICLE 14–6

1. $-2\mathbf{i} - 2\mathbf{j} + 4\mathbf{k}$

2. $6\mathbf{i} + 6\mathbf{j}$

3. $2\mathbf{i}$

4. $(-3\mathbf{i} - 4\mathbf{j})/25$

5. $(\mathbf{i} + 2\mathbf{j} - 2\mathbf{k})/27$

6. $(3\sqrt{3}\mathbf{i} + 4\sqrt{3}\mathbf{j} + 5\mathbf{k})/2$

7. $5\mathbf{k}$

8. $\dfrac{x - 3}{3} = \dfrac{y - 4}{4} = \dfrac{z + 5}{5}$

9. (a) $x = y = z$; $-x = -y = z$; $x = y = 0$

   (b) $(1, 1, 1)$ and $(-2, -2, -2)$; $(2, 2, -2)$ and $(-1, -1, 1)$; $(0, 0, 2)$

10. Two lines: $x = z = -y \pm 4$

11. Tangent plane: $3x + 5y + 4z = 18$

   Normal line: $\dfrac{x - 3}{3} = \dfrac{y - 5}{5} = \dfrac{z + 4}{4}$

12. In the direction of grad $f = 10\mathbf{i} + 4\mathbf{j} + 10\mathbf{k}$

   Max $(df/ds) = |\text{grad } f| = \sqrt{216}$

14. $\operatorname{grad} w = \mathbf{u}_\rho \dfrac{\partial w}{\partial \rho} + \mathbf{u}_\phi \dfrac{1}{\rho} \dfrac{\partial w}{\partial \phi} + \mathbf{u}_\theta \dfrac{1}{\rho \sin \phi} \dfrac{\partial w}{\partial \theta}$

15. (a) $\mathbf{i} \dfrac{\partial f}{\partial x} + \mathbf{j} \dfrac{\partial f}{\partial y}$

   (b) In the direction given by the vector $\operatorname{grad} f = -\mathbf{i} + \mathbf{j}$.

   $\left| \dfrac{dw}{ds} \right| = \sqrt{2}$ in this direction.

24. $h = f_0/(f_x^2 + f_y^2 + f_z^2)_0$

ARTICLE 14–7

1. $2e^t[x(\cos t - \sin t) + y(\sin t + \cos t) + z] = 4e^{2t}$

2. $\dfrac{y(y^2 - x^2) \sinh t + x(x^2 - y^2) \cosh t}{(x^2 + y^2)^2} = \operatorname{sech}^2 2t$

3. $e^{2x+3y} \dfrac{(8t^2 + 2) \cos 4z}{t(t^2 + 1)} - 4 \sin 4z$

$$= 2t(t^2 + 1)^2[(4t^2 + 1) \cos 4t - 2t(t^2 + 1) \sin 4t]$$

4. $\dfrac{\partial w}{\partial r} = e^{2r}/\sqrt{e^{2r} + e^{2s}} \; ; \quad \dfrac{\partial w}{\partial s} = e^{2s}/\sqrt{e^{2r} + e^{2s}}$

5. $\dfrac{\partial w}{\partial r} = \dfrac{\partial w}{\partial s} = \dfrac{2}{r + s}$

13. $f_x = \dfrac{\partial w}{\partial r} \cos \theta - \dfrac{1}{r} \dfrac{\partial w}{\partial \theta} \sin \theta$

$f_y = \dfrac{\partial w}{\partial r} \sin \theta + \dfrac{1}{r} \dfrac{\partial w}{\partial \theta} \cos \theta$

ARTICLE 14–8

2. $\frac{47}{24}$ ft^3 3. Approx. 340 ft^2

4. (a) $dx = \cos \theta \, dr - r \sin \theta \, d\theta, \; dy = \sin \theta \, dr + r \cos \theta \, d\theta$

   (b) $dr = \cos \theta \, dx + \sin \theta \, dy, \; d\theta = -\dfrac{\sin \theta}{r} \, dx + \dfrac{\cos \theta}{r} \, dy$

   (c) $\dfrac{\partial r}{\partial x} = \cos \theta = \dfrac{x}{r}, \dfrac{\partial r}{\partial y} = \sin \theta = \dfrac{y}{r}$

5. (a) $dx = f_u \, du + f_v \, dv, \; dy = g_u \, du + g_v \, dv$

   (b) $du = \dfrac{\begin{vmatrix} dx & f_v \\ dy & g_v \end{vmatrix}}{\begin{vmatrix} f_u & f_v \\ g_u & g_v \end{vmatrix}}, \quad dv = \dfrac{\begin{vmatrix} f_u & dx \\ g_u & dy \end{vmatrix}}{\begin{vmatrix} f_u & f_v \\ g_u & g_v \end{vmatrix}}$

6. (a) $dx = \sin \phi \cos \theta \, d\rho + \rho \cos \phi \cos \theta \, d\phi - \rho \sin \phi \sin \theta \, d\theta$

   $dy = \sin \phi \sin \theta \, d\rho + \rho \cos \phi \sin \theta \, d\phi + \rho \sin \phi \cos \theta \, d\theta$

   $dz = \cos \phi \, d\rho - \rho \sin \phi \, d\phi$

   (b)

$$d\rho = \dfrac{\begin{vmatrix} dx & \rho \cos \phi \cos \theta & -\rho \sin \phi \sin \theta \\ dy & \rho \cos \phi \sin \theta & \rho \sin \phi \cos \theta \\ dz & -\rho \sin \phi & 0 \end{vmatrix}}{\begin{vmatrix} \sin \phi \cos \theta & \rho \cos \phi \cos \theta & -\rho \sin \phi \sin \theta \\ \sin \phi \sin \theta & \rho \cos \phi \sin \theta & \rho \sin \phi \cos \theta \\ \cos \phi & -\rho \sin \phi & 0 \end{vmatrix}}$$

(c) $\dfrac{\partial \rho}{\partial x} = \sin \phi \cos \theta = \dfrac{x}{\rho}$

7. $df = -u_0$ and $dg = -v_0$ provided

$$dx = \left(\frac{vf_y - ug_y}{f_x g_y - g_x f_y}\right)_0 \quad \text{and} \quad dy = \left(\frac{ug_x - vf_x}{f_x g_y - g_x f_y}\right)_0 .$$

8.

$$dx = -\frac{\begin{vmatrix} u_0 & f_y & f_z \\ v_0 & g_y & g_z \\ w_0 & h_y & h_z \end{vmatrix}}{\begin{vmatrix} f_x & f_y & f_z \\ g_x & g_y & g_z \\ h_x & h_y & h_z \end{vmatrix}}, \quad \text{with similar expressions for } dy \text{ and } dz.$$

ARTICLE 14–9

1. Low: $(-3, 3, -5)$
2. Low: $(15, -8, -63)$
3. High: $(-8, -23, 59)$
4. High: $(\tfrac{2}{3}, \tfrac{4}{3}, 0)$
5. $(-2, 1, 3)$ is a saddle point.
6. $(-2, 2, 2)$ is a saddle point.
7. Low: $(0, 0, 0)$; high: $(\pm 1, \pm 1, \sqrt{2})$. The partial derivatives do not exist at $(0, 0)$. They exist but are not zero at $(\pm 1, \pm 1)$.

ARTICLE 14–10

1. (b)

$$m = \frac{\begin{vmatrix} \sum y_i & n \\ \sum x_i y_i & \sum x_i \end{vmatrix}}{D}, \quad b = \frac{\begin{vmatrix} \sum x_i & \sum y_i \\ \sum x_i^2 & \sum x_i y_i \end{vmatrix}}{D},$$

where

$$D = \begin{vmatrix} \sum x_i & n \\ \sum x_i^2 & \sum x_i \end{vmatrix}.$$

2. $26y + 19x = 30$
3. $12y = 9x + 20$
4. $6y = 9x + 1$

ARTICLE 14–11

1. $(0, 0, 1)$

2. Square bottom 8 in. by 8 in., 4 in. deep.

3. Square bottom $\sqrt[3]{V/2}$ by $\sqrt[3]{V/2}$, depth $= \sqrt[3]{4V}$, where V is the given volume.

4. $x + 2y + 2z = 6$

5. $h = $ altitude of triangle $= \sqrt{\dfrac{A}{6 + 3\sqrt{3}}}$

$2x = $ width of rectangle $= 2\sqrt{3}\, h$

$y = $ altitude of rectangle $= (1 + \sqrt{3})h$

6. $z = -\tfrac{1}{2}x + \tfrac{3}{2}y - \tfrac{1}{4}$

ARTICLE 14–12

14. $e^x \cosh y + 6 \cos (2x - 3y)$

15. $\dfrac{-6}{(2x + 3y)^2}$

16. $(y^2 - x^2)(x^2 + y^2)^{-2}$

17. $2y + 6xy^2 + 12x^2 y^3$

18. (a) $F(x) = (2bk + k^2)x^3$

    (b) $c_1 = \pm\sqrt{a^2 + ah + \frac{1}{3}h^2}$

        ($\pm$ sign to be chosen depending upon the signs of a and $a + h$)

    (c) $g(y) = 3c_1^2 y^2 = (3a^2 + 3ah + h^2)y^2$

    (d) $d_1 = b + k/2$

19. $d_2 = b + \dfrac{k}{2}$, $c_2 = \pm\sqrt{a^2 + ah + \frac{1}{3}h^2}$

    (with the $\pm$ sign depending upon the signs of a and $a + h$.)

ARTICLE 14–13

  1. Exact, $f = (2x^5 + 5x^2y^3 + 3y^5)/5 + C$

  2. Not exact

  3. Exact, $f = x^2 + xy + y^2 + C$

  4. Exact, $f = x \cosh y + y \sinh x + C$

  5. Not exact

  6. Exact, $f = e^x(y - x + 1) + y + C$

  7. Not exact

ARTICLE 14–14

  1. (a) $\frac{9}{2}$ (b) $\frac{9}{2}$ (c) $\frac{9}{2}$

  2. (a) 2.143 (b) 2.538 (c) $2 + \sin 1$

  3. (a) 3 (b) 3 (c) 3   4. (a) e^3 (b) e^3 (c) e^3

  5. (a) $\sin 1 = 0.8415$ (b) $\sin 1$ (c) $\sin 1$

  6. $f(x, y, z) = x^2 + \frac{3}{2}y^2 + 2z^2 + C$ 7. $f(x, y, z) = xy + yz + zx + C$

  8. $f(x, y, z) = xe^{y+2z}$ 9. $f(x, y, z) = xy \sin z + C$

CHAPTER 14: MISCELLANEOUS

1. No, $\lim\limits_{x \to 0} f(x, 0) = 1$, $\lim\limits_{x \to 0} f(x, x) = 0$ 2. Yes

4. Let P be a point which is not a local maximum or minimum of f. Consider a circle C_1 of radius r_1 with P as center. Inside C_1 are points Q'_1, Q''_1 such that $f(Q'_1) < f(P) < f(Q''_1)$. Join Q'_1, Q''_1 by an arc not through P. Since f is continuous along this arc, it takes all values between $f(Q'_1)$ and $f(Q''_1)$. Hence there is a P'_1 on it such that $f(P'_1) = f(P)$. Repeat the argument with a new circle C_2 of radius r_2 less than the length of PP'_1. Inside it is a point P'_2 such that $f(P'_2) = f(P)$. Continue.

5. $\dfrac{\partial}{\partial x} (\sin xy)^2 = y \sin 2xy$, $\dfrac{\partial}{\partial y} (\sin xy)^2 = x \sin 2xy$

$\dfrac{\partial}{\partial x} \sin (xy)^2 = 2xy^2 \cos (xy)^2$

$\dfrac{\partial}{\partial y} \sin (xy)^2 = 2x^2y \cos (xy)^2$

6. $-2/\sqrt{3}$

8. $54(x - 3) + 2y - 27(z + 2) = 0$
   $(x - 3)/54 = y/2 = -(z + 2)/27$
   $(54/\sqrt{3649}, 2/\sqrt{3649}, -27/\sqrt{3649})$

9. (a) Hyperboloid of one sheet
   (b) $2\mathbf{i} + 3\mathbf{j} + 3\mathbf{k}$
   (c) $2(x - 2) + 3(y + 3) + 3(z - 3) = 0$
   $(x - 2)/2 = (y + 3)/3 = (z - 3)/3$

10. (a) $13(x + 2) - (y - 1) + 12(z - 2) = 0$
    (b) $(x + 2)/13 = 1 - y = (z - 2)/12$

11. $\partial f/\partial x = 1$, $\partial f/\partial y = 3$, $dw/ds = 3$

14. (a) $D_u f = f_x u_1 + f_y u_2 + f_z u_3$
    (b) $D_v(D_u f) = f_{xx} u_1 v_1 + f_{yy} u_2 v_2 + f_{zz} u_3 v_3 + f_{xy}(u_1 v_2 + u_2 v_1)$
    $+ f_{xz}(u_1 v_3 + u_3 v_1) + f_{yz}(u_2 v_3 + u_3 v_2)$

15. $dw/ds = \sqrt{3}$, maximum $= \sqrt{3}$ 16. $(f_x = f_y = 2)\ df/ds = \frac{14}{5}$

17. 7   18. $-14/\sqrt{6}$ 19. $-\sqrt{\frac{2}{3}}$

21. (a) $\mathbf{N}(x, y, z) = (x^2 + y^2)^{-1/2}[x(1 + 3x^2 + 3y^2)\mathbf{i}$
    $+ y(1 + 3x^2 + 3y^2)\mathbf{j} - \sqrt{x^2 + y^2}\,\mathbf{k}]$
    (b) $[(1 + 3x^2 + 3y^2)^2 + 1]^{-1/2}$, $1\sqrt{2}$

22. $a^2 + b^2 + c^2 = 2$

23. (a) $4\mathbf{j} + 6\mathbf{k}$ (b) $4(y + 1) + 6(z - 3) = 0$

24. $(2\mathbf{i} + 6\mathbf{j} - 3\mathbf{k})/7$ 26. $\pm\sqrt{3}$

28. $\nabla f = \mathbf{u}_r(\partial f/\partial r) + \mathbf{u}_\theta(1/r)(\partial f/\partial \theta)$

30. (c) $(x^2 + y^2 + z^2)/2$ 31. $\theta + (\pi/2)$, $1/r$

34. (a) $f = \phi(bx - ay)$ (b) $f = \phi(x^2 + y^2)$, ϕ arbitrary in each case

35. $h'(x) = f_x(x, y) + f_y(x, y)[-g_x(x, y)/g_y(x, y)]$

36. $\partial g/\partial z = 1/(\partial f/\partial x)$

37. $dx/dz = (\sin y + \sin z - 2y^2 \cos z)(\sin y + \sin z)^{-1} (\sin x + x \cos x)^{-1}$

39. $\partial F/\partial x = \frac{1}{2}(\partial f/\partial u + \partial f/\partial v)$, $\partial F/\partial y = \frac{1}{2}(\partial f/\partial v - \partial f/\partial u)$

42. $\partial^2 f/\partial u^2 + 4xy(\partial^2 f/\partial u \partial v) + 4x^2 y^2(\partial^2 f/\partial v^2) + 2y(\partial f/\partial v)$

43. $a = b = 1$ 44. 2

47. $d^2 y/dx^2 = -(1/f_y^3)(f_{xx} f_y^2 - 2f_{xy} f_x f_y + f_{yy} f_x^2)$

49. $dz/dx = (f_y - f_x)/(f_y + f_z)$

50. $x_t = x - v + ax_{vv}/x_v^2$, $0 \leq v \leq 1$, $t \geq 0$, $x(0, t) = 0$, $x(1, t) = 1$

55. 60.44

56. Minimum $(\frac{1}{2}, 0)$, $T = -\frac{1}{4}$.   Maximum $(-\frac{1}{2}, \pm\sqrt{3}/2)$, $T = 3$.

57. 50

58. (a) Max $z = \sqrt{3}$ at $(0, 0)$, min $z = -\sqrt{3}$ at $(0, 0)$
    (b) Min $z = 0$ at $(0, 0)$
    (c) None

59. $(1, 1, 1)$; $(1, -1, -1)$; $(-1, 1, -1)$; $(-1, -1, 1)$

60. Length $= (c^2V/ab)^{1/3}$, depth $= (b^2V/ca)^{1/3}$, height $= (a^2V/bc)^{1/3}$

61. $e^{-2}/6$ 62. Minimum

63. $\left(\sum_{i=1}^{n} a_i^2\right)^{1/2}$ 64. $(\sqrt{3}/2)abc$

66. $\partial^2 z/\partial x \partial y = \cos^{-3}(y+z)[\cos^2(y+z)\sin(x+y)$
$+ \sin(y+z)\cos^2(x+y) + \sin(y+z)\cos(y+z)\cos(x+y)]$

67. y^2 68. $2xyz(x^2+y^2)^{-2}$

70. $f_{yx}(0,0) = -1$, $f_{xy}(0,0) = 1$

71. $f(x,y) = \frac{1}{5}(2x^5 + 5x^2y^3 + 3y^5) + C$

72. $f(x,y) = y\ln x + xe^y + y^2 + C$

73. (a) and (b) 16; exact differential

74. $w = f(x,y) = x + e^x \cos y + y^2 + C$

77. 8   78. 24

79. $1 - e^{-2\pi}$ 82. (b) $\nabla \times \mathbf{F} = 0$

CHAPTER 15

ARTICLE 15–1

1. $(4 + \pi^2)/2$ 2. $8\ln 8 - 16 + e$

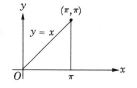   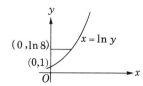

3. $\pi/4$ 4. $\frac{5}{6}$

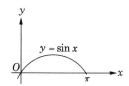   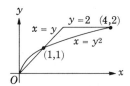

5. $\displaystyle\int_1^{e^2}\int_{\ln y}^{2} dx\, dy = e^2 - 3$ 6. $\displaystyle\int_0^1\int_0^{x^2} dy\, dx = \frac{1}{3}$

7. $\displaystyle\int_{-2}^{2}\int_0^{\sqrt{(4-x^2)/2}} y\, dy\, dx = \frac{8}{3}$ 8. $\displaystyle\int_{-4}^{5}\int_{(y-2)/3}^{-2+\sqrt{y+4}} dx\, dy = \frac{9}{2}$

9. $V = \displaystyle\int_{-4}^{1} \int_{3x}^{4-x^2} (x+4)\,dy\,dx = \frac{625}{12}$

10. $V = 4\displaystyle\int_{0}^{a} \int_{0}^{\sqrt{a^2-x^2}} \frac{x^2+y^2}{a}\,dy\,dx = \frac{\pi a^3}{2}$

ARTICLE 15–2

1. $a^2/2$ 2. $e-1$ 3. 4

4. $\frac{9}{2}$ 5. $\frac{1}{3}$ 6. $a^2(\pi+4)/2$

7. $\frac{4}{3}$

ARTICLE 15–3

1. $\left(\dfrac{a}{3}, \dfrac{a}{3}\right)$ 2. $I_x = (e^3-1)/9$

3. $\frac{104}{3}$ 4. $\left(-\frac{8}{5}, -\frac{1}{2}\right)$

5. $\frac{1}{6}$ 6. $\left(0, a\,\dfrac{8+3\pi}{40+12\pi}\right)$

7. $\frac{64}{105}$

ARTICLE 15–4

1. $\displaystyle\int_{0}^{2\pi} \int_{0}^{a} r\,dr\,d\theta = \pi a^2$ 2. $\displaystyle\int_{0}^{\pi/2} \int_{0}^{a} r^3\,dr\,d\theta = \frac{\pi a^4}{8}$

3. $\displaystyle\int_{0}^{\pi/4} \int_{0}^{a} r^2 \cos\theta\,dr\,d\theta = \frac{a^3\sqrt{2}}{6}$ 4. $\displaystyle\int_{0}^{\pi/2} \int_{0}^{\infty} e^{-r^2} r\,dr\,d\theta = \frac{\pi}{4}$

5. $\displaystyle\int_{0}^{\pi/4} \int_{0}^{2\sec\theta} r^2 \sin\theta\,dr\,d\theta = \frac{4}{3}$ 6. $\displaystyle\int_{0}^{\pi/2} \int_{0}^{2a\cos\theta} r^3 \cos^2\theta\,dr\,d\theta = \frac{5\pi a^4}{8}$

7. $a^2(8+\pi)/4$ 8. $\bar{x} = \dfrac{32+15\pi}{48+6\pi}\,a, \bar{y} = 0$

9. $I_0 = a^4(320+81\pi)/96$ 10. $a^3(15\pi+32)/24$

11. $2a^2$ 12. $(3\pi+20-16\sqrt{2})2\sqrt{2}a^3/9$

ARTICLE 15–5

1. $\frac{1}{6}|abc|$ 2. 4   3. 27π

4. $16a^3/3$ 5. $\frac{4}{3}\pi abc$ 6. 4π

ARTICLE 15–6

1. $4\pi a^3(8-3\sqrt{3})/3$ 2. $\pi/2$

3. $(8\sqrt{2}-7)\pi a^3/6$ 4. $a^3/3$

ARTICLE 15–7

1. $64\pi a^5\left(\dfrac{4}{15} - \dfrac{17\sqrt{3}}{160}\right) = 16.7a^5$ 2. $2\pi/3$

3. $\bar{x} = \frac{1}{2}$ 4. $\bar{x} = \bar{y} = 0, \bar{z} = \dfrac{7a}{2(8\sqrt{2}-7)}$

5. $\frac{2}{5}Ma^2$

6. $\frac{8\pi a^3}{3}$

7. $\frac{64\pi a^5}{35}$

8. $\frac{3}{20}(a^2 + 4h^2)M$

9. $\frac{7}{5}Ma^2$

10. $\bar{y} = \bar{z} = 0, \bar{x} = \frac{3\sqrt{2}}{8} a$

11. $M(3a^2 + 4b^2)/4$

ARTICLE 15–8

1. $\bar{x} = \bar{y} = 0, \bar{z} = \dfrac{3a}{16(2 - \sqrt{3})} = 0.7a$

2. $8\pi a^3/3$

3. $a\sqrt{\frac{1270}{651}} \approx 1.4a$

ARTICLE 15–9

1. (a) $\displaystyle\int_A\!\!\int \frac{\sqrt{F_x^2 + F_y^2 + F_z^2}}{|F_z|} \, dx \, dy$

(b) $\displaystyle\int_B\!\!\int \frac{\sqrt{F_x^2 + F_y^2 + F_z^2}}{|F_x|} \, dy \, dz$

(c) $\displaystyle\int_C\!\!\int \frac{\sqrt{F_x^2 + F_y^2 + F_z^2}}{|F_y|} \, dx \, dz$

2. $\frac{1}{2}\sqrt{b^2c^2 + a^2c^2 + a^2b^2}$

3. $\pi a^2/2$

4. $2a^2(\pi - 2)$

5. $4a^2$

6. $2\pi a^2(2 - \sqrt{2})$

7. $\pi a^2\sqrt{1 + c^2}$

8. $2\pi a^2/3$

9. $(5\sqrt{5} - 1)\pi a^2/6$

CHAPTER 15: MISCELLANEOUS

1. $\displaystyle\int_{-2}^0\!\int_{2x+4}^{4-x^2} dy \, dx = \frac{4}{3}$

2. $\frac{2}{5}$

3. $\displaystyle\int_0^1\!\int_{-\sqrt{y}}^{\sqrt{y}} dx \, dy$

4. 87.95

5. $\displaystyle\int_0^1\!\int_x^{2-x} (x^2 + y^2) \, dy \, dx = \frac{8}{3}$

6. (a) $(a^2 + m^2)^{-2}\{(m^2 - a^2) \cos ax - 2am \sin ax$
$+ [(a^2 - m^2) + mx(a^2 + m^2)]e^{mx}\}$
(b) $(a^2 + m^2)^{-3}\{m(3a^2 - m^2) \cos ax + a(3m^2 - a^2) \sin ax$
$+ [(m/2)(a^2 + m^2)^2x^2 + (a^4 - m^4)x + m(m^2 - 3a^2)]e^{mx}\}$

8. $\ln (b/a)$

9. $(4a/3\pi, 4a/3\pi)$

10. $(2a \sin \alpha/3\alpha, 0)$

11. $(14\sqrt{2}/9\pi, 14\sqrt{2}(\sqrt{2} - 1)/9\pi)$ (Cartesian coordinates)

12. $(-\frac{12}{5}, 2)$ 14. (a) $\frac{1}{3}(a^3t + at^3 - t^4)$ (b) 0

16. $A = a^2 \cos^{-1}(b/a) - b\sqrt{a^2 - b^2}$
$I_0 = (a^4/2) \cos^{-1}(b/a) - b\sqrt{a^2 - b^2}(a^2 + 2b^2)/6$

17. $a\sqrt{2/5}$ 18. (a) $(a/2)\sqrt{\pi/4 - \frac{2}{3}}$
       (b) $(a/2)\sqrt{\pi/4 + \frac{2}{3}}$

21. $\int_{-\pi/2}^{\pi/2} \int_0^a r^2 \cos\theta \, dr \, d\theta$ 25. $A = 2a^2, \quad I_0 = 7\pi a^4/64$

26. (a) $(\pi - 2)/4$ (b) $(\sqrt{3}/4)\tan^{-1}\frac{4}{3}$

27. $K(a) = \int_0^{a \cos \beta} dx \int_0^{x \tan \beta} \ln(x^2 + y^2) \, dy$
$+ \int_{a \cos \beta}^a dx \int_0^{\sqrt{a^2-x^2}} \ln(x^2 + y^2) \, dy$

28. $\pi/8$ 29. $(0, 0, \frac{1}{4})$ 30. $(4\pi a^3/3)(\sqrt{2} - \frac{7}{8})$

31. $\pi/4$ 32. $\pi/\sqrt{2}$ 33. $139\pi a^5/15$

34. $\frac{4}{3}\pi abc$ 35. $a^2 b^2 c^2/6$ 36. $16a^3/3$

37. $x^2 + y^2 + z^2 = 4; x^2 + y^2 = 2x; y = 0; \int_0^{\pi/2} \int_0^{2\cos\theta} \int_{-\sqrt{4-r^2}}^{\sqrt{4-r^2}} dz \, r \, dr \, d\theta$

38. $4\pi a^3/3 + (16/3)[(b/2)(3a^2 - 2b^2) \sin^{-1}(b/\sqrt{a^2 - b^2})$
$+ (b^2/2)\sqrt{a^2 - 2b^2} - a^3 \tan^{-1}(a/\sqrt{a^2 - 2b^2})]$

39. (a) Radius of sphere $= 2$, of hole $= 1$ (b) $4\pi\sqrt{3}$

40. $\int_0^1 \int_{\sqrt{1-x^2}}^{\sqrt{3-x^2}} \int_1^{\sqrt{4-x^2-y^2}} xyz^2 \, dz \, dy \, dx$
$+ \int_1^{\sqrt{3}} \int_0^{\sqrt{3-x^2}} \int_1^{\sqrt{4-x^2-y^2}} xyz^2 \, dz \, dy \, dx$

41. $3\pi a^3/4$ 42. $2a^3(3\pi - 4)/9$ 43. $\pi a^5/12$

44. $\pi^2 a^3/4$ 45. $8\pi\delta(b^5 - a^5)/15$ 47. $\rho_0(1 - \frac{1}{2}\epsilon^2)$

48. $2\pi(\sqrt{3} - 1)$ 49. $\pi\sqrt{3}$ 50. $\pi\sqrt{2}a^2$

51. $2a^2(\pi - 2)$ 52. $\pi\sqrt{2}$ 53. (a) 132π (b) 16π
       (c) 148π

54. $4\int_0^a \sqrt{a^2 - y^2}\sqrt{4y^2 + 1} \, dy$ 55. $16\pi(\sqrt{2} - 1)$

56. $8\pi^2$ 57. $\pi^2/2$ 58. $8r^2$

60. $\dfrac{6M}{a^2}(1 - h/\sqrt{a^2 + h^2})$ 62. $z = 1$

63. $4a/3$

CHAPTER 16

1. Converges to $-\frac{2}{3}$ 2. Converges to $\frac{1}{2}$ 3. Converges to 1

4. Converges to 0 5. Diverges 6. Diverges

7. Converges to 1 8. Converges to 0 9. Diverges

10. Converges to 0 13. (b) $a_n = \sin n$ is an example.
$a_n = -n$ is another example.

14. $s_n = 1 - \dfrac{1}{n+1}$, sum $= 1$

15. Same as Problem 14. Note that $\dfrac{1}{n \cdot (n+1)} = \dfrac{1}{n} - \dfrac{1}{n+1}$.

16. $s_n = \ln \dfrac{1}{n+1}$. Diverges

17. $s_n = 2 - \dfrac{1}{2^{n-1}}$, sum $= 2$

18. $s_n = 3 - \dfrac{1}{3^{n-1}}$, sum $= 3$

19. $s_n = \dfrac{10}{3}\left[1 + \dfrac{(-1)^{n+1}}{2^n}\right]$, sum $= \dfrac{10}{3}$

20. $s_n = \dfrac{1}{11}\left(1 - \dfrac{1}{100^n}\right)$, sum $= \dfrac{1}{11}$

21. 28 ft

22. (a) $\frac{234}{999}$
   (b) Yes, because it is of the form $p \cdot 10^{-k} + p \cdot 10^{-2k} + \cdots$
   $= p/(10^k - 1)$, where p and $10^k - 1 = q$ are integers.

23. $\dfrac{124}{100} + \dfrac{123}{99900} = \dfrac{123,999}{99,900}$ 24. (d) $n = 6$ (e) $n = 999$

2. If the sequence is bounded below, then it has a definite finite limit. Otherwise, it diverges to minus infinity.

3. The limit exists and is less than or equal to three.

4. No. It diverges by oscillation.

5. Diverges by the integral test.

6. The nth term approaches 1. Series diverges to plus infinity by comparison with $\sum 1/n$.

7. Converges; by comparison with $\sum 1/2^n$.

8. Diverges; integral test.   9. Diverges; compare with $\sum 1/n$.

10. Diverges; integral test.   11. Converges; ratio test.

12. Converges; compare with $\sum 1/n^2$.

13. Converges; compare with $\sum 1/n^{3/2}$.

14. Converges; ratio test.   15. Converges; ratio test.

16. Converges; ratio test.   17. Converges; ratio test.

18. Diverges; ratio test.   19. Converges; ratio test.

ARTICLE 16–3

1. $1 - x + \dfrac{x^2}{2!} - \dfrac{x^3}{3!} + \cdots + \dfrac{(-1)^n x^n}{n!}$

2. $x - \dfrac{x^3}{3!} + \dfrac{x^5}{5!} - \dfrac{x^7}{7!} + \cdots + \dfrac{(-1)^m x^{2m+1}}{(2m+1)!}$

3. $1 - \dfrac{x^2}{2!} + \dfrac{x^4}{4!} - \dfrac{x^6}{6!} + \cdots + \dfrac{(-1)^m x^{2m}}{(2m)!}$

4. $\dfrac{\sqrt{2}}{2}\left(1 + x - \dfrac{x^2}{2!} - \dfrac{x^3}{3!} + \dfrac{x^4}{4!} + \dfrac{x^5}{5!} - \dfrac{x^6}{6!} - \cdots \right.$

$\left. + \dfrac{x^{4m}}{(4m)!} + \dfrac{x^{4m+1}}{(4m+1)!} - \dfrac{x^{4m+2}}{(4m+2)!} - \dfrac{x^{4m+3}}{(4m+3)!}\right)$

5. $x + \dfrac{x^3}{3!} + \dfrac{x^5}{5!} + \dfrac{x^7}{7!} + \cdots + \dfrac{x^{2m+1}}{(2m+1)!}$

6. $1 + \dfrac{x^2}{2!} + \dfrac{x^4}{4!} + \cdots + \dfrac{x^{2m}}{(2m)!}$

7. $(x - 1) - \dfrac{(x-1)^2}{2} + \dfrac{(x-1)^3}{3} - \dfrac{(x-1)^4}{4} + \cdots$

8. $2 + \dfrac{1}{2}\dfrac{(x-4)}{2} - \dfrac{1}{2\cdot 4}\dfrac{(x-4)^2}{2^3} + \dfrac{1\cdot 3}{2\cdot 4\cdot 6}\dfrac{(x-4)^3}{2^5}$

$- \dfrac{1\cdot 3\cdot 5}{2\cdot 4\cdot 6\cdot 8}\dfrac{(x-4)^4}{2^7} + \cdots$

9. $-1 - (x + 1) - (x + 1)^2 - (x + 1)^3 - \cdots$

10. $1 + 2\left(x - \dfrac{\pi}{4}\right) + 2\left(x - \dfrac{\pi}{4}\right)^2 + \cdots$

11. $-\ln 2 - \sqrt{3}\left(x - \dfrac{\pi}{3}\right) - 2\left(x - \dfrac{\pi}{3}\right)^2 - \cdots$

12. $\dfrac{1}{2} + \dfrac{\sqrt{3}}{2}\left(x - \dfrac{\pi}{6}\right) - \dfrac{1}{2}\dfrac{(x - \pi/6)^2}{2!} - \dfrac{\sqrt{3}}{2}\dfrac{(x - \pi/6)^3}{3!} + \cdots$

13. $\dfrac{\sqrt{2}}{2}\left[1 + \left(x + \dfrac{\pi}{4}\right) - \dfrac{(x + \pi/4)^2}{2!} - \dfrac{(x + \pi/4)^3}{3!} + \cdots\right]$

ARTICLE 16–4

4. $|x| < \sqrt[5]{0.06} \approx 0.57$ 5. $|R_3(x, 0)| < 10^{-5}/12$

6. $|x| < 0.02$

7. $|R_1(x, 0)| < \dfrac{x^2}{8(0.99)^{2/3}} < 1.3 \times 10^{-5}$

9. $n \geq 4$

ARTICLE 16–5

2. (a) Minimum at $x = 1, y = -2$
   (b) Saddle point at $x = 1, y = 2$
   (c) Minimum at $x = 1, y = 0$
   (d) Saddle point at $x = 0, y = 0$
   (e) Maximum at $x = 0, y = 1$
   (f) Saddle point $(0, 0, 6)$; relative max. $(-\frac{2}{3}, \frac{2}{3}, 6 + \frac{8}{27})$
   (g) Saddle points $(0, 0, -8)$, $(-2, 2, -8)$; relative max. $(-2, 0, -4)$; relative min. $(0, 2, -12)$

3. If $f_x(a, b) = f_y(a, b) = 0$, then $f(x, y)$ has at the point $x = a, y = b$:
   (a) a relative minimum if d^2f/ds^2 is positive in all directions emanating from (a, b);
   (b) a relative maximum if d^2f/ds^2 is negative in all directions emanating from (a, b); and
   (c) a saddle point if d^2f/ds^2 is positive in some directions and negative in other directions emanating from (a, b).

4. $1 + x + \dfrac{x^2 - y^2}{2!} + \cdots$

5. $f(x, y, z) = f(a, b, c) + f_x(a, b, c) \cdot (x - a) + f_y(a, b, c) \cdot (y - b)$
   $$+ f_z(a, b, c) \cdot (z - c) + \frac{1}{2!} [f_{xx}(a, b, c) \cdot (x - a)^2$$
   $$+ f_{yy}(a, b, c) \cdot (y - b)^2 + f_{zz}(a, b, c) \cdot (z - c)^2$$
   $$+ 2f_{xy}(a, b, c) \cdot (x - a)(y - b) + 2f_{xz}(a, b, c) \cdot (x - a)(z - c)$$
   $$+ 2f_{yz}(a, b, c) \cdot (y - b)(z - c)] + \cdots$$

ARTICLE 16–6

1. 0.85717   2. 1.0355
3. 2.08008   4. 0.48836
5. 1.1276   6. 0.5211
7. 0.22314   8. $\pi/4 + 0.01 = 0.795$
10. 0.09994   11. 0.09967
15. (c) 6   (d) $1/q$
16. (a) $E(X) = 2$ (b) $E(X) = 6$ (c) The series for $E(X)$ diverges.

ARTICLE 16–7

1. $-\frac{1}{24}$	2. $\frac{1}{4}$	3. $-\frac{1}{9}$	4. $\frac{1}{3}$
5. $\frac{1}{2}$	6. $\frac{1}{3}$	7. $\frac{1}{3}$	8. $\frac{1}{2}$
9. $-\frac{1}{3}$	10. 0	11. 0	12. 0
13. 1	14. $-\frac{1}{2}$	15. $+\infty$	16. e^{-6}
17. e^2	18. e^2	19. 1	20. 1
21. $e^{-1/2}$	22. $e^{-1/2}$	23. 1	24. e
25. (b) $\frac{1}{2}$		26. $r = -3, s = \frac{9}{2}$	

ARTICLE 16-8

1. $\dfrac{1}{2} + \displaystyle\sum_{n=1}^{\infty} \dfrac{1 - \cos n\pi}{n\pi} \sin nx = \dfrac{1}{2} + \dfrac{2}{\pi}\left(\sin x + \dfrac{\sin 3x}{3} + \dfrac{\sin 5x}{5} + \cdots\right)$

2. $-\dfrac{4}{\pi}\left(\sin x + \dfrac{\sin 3x}{3} + \dfrac{\sin 5x}{5} + \cdots\right)$

3. $\pi - 2\left(\sin x + \dfrac{\sin 2x}{2} + \dfrac{\sin 3x}{3} + \cdots\right)$

4. $\dfrac{\pi}{2} - \dfrac{4}{\pi}\left(\cos x + \dfrac{\cos 3x}{3^2} + \dfrac{\cos 5x}{5^2} + \cdots\right)$

5. $2\left(\sin x - \dfrac{\sin 2x}{2} + \dfrac{\sin 3x}{3} - \dfrac{\sin 4x}{4} + \cdots\right)$

ARTICLE 16-9

1. $-1 < x < 1$ 2. $-1 < x < 1$
3. $-1 < x < 1$ 4. $-2 < x < 2$
5. $-\infty < x < \infty$ 6. $-\infty < x < \infty$
7. $0 < x < 2$ 8. $-4 < x < 0$
9. $|x - 3| < 1/\sqrt{2}$ 10. $-\infty < x < \infty$

ARTICLE 16-10

1. $|x| < 1$; diverges at both $x = \pm 1$.
2. $|x| < 1$; converges at both $x = \pm 1$.
3. $|x - 2| \le 1$
4. $|x + 1| < 1$; converges at $x = 0$, diverges at -2.
5. $|x - 2| < 2$; diverges at $x = 0$, converges at $x = 4$.
6. $|x - 1| < \frac{1}{2}$; diverges at both $x = \frac{1}{2}$, $x = \frac{3}{2}$.
7. $-\infty < x < \infty$
8. Converges only at $x = 0$.
9. $|x| < 1$; converges at both $x = \pm 1$.
10. $|x + 3| < 1$; converges at $x = -4$, diverges at -2.

CHAPTER 16: MISCELLANEOUS

1. $s_n = \ln\left[(n + 1)/(2n)\right]$, series converges to $-\ln 2$.
2. $s_n = \frac{1}{2}\left[\frac{3}{2} - 1/(n + 1)\right]$, limit $= \frac{3}{4}$
6. (a) $\displaystyle\sum_{n=2}^{\infty} (-1)^n x^n$

   (b) No, because it will converge in an interval symmetric about $x = 0$, and it cannot converge when $x = -1$.

7. $(1 - t^2)^{-1/2} = 1 - \displaystyle\sum_{k=0}^{\infty} \frac{(2k)!t^{2k+2}}{2^{2k+1}k!(k+1)!}$, $-1 < t < 1$

$\sin^{-1} x = x - \displaystyle\sum_{k=0}^{\infty} \frac{(2k)!x^{2k+3}}{2^{2k+1}(2k+3)k!(k+1)!}$, $-1 \leq x \leq 1$

8. $(1 + t^2)^{-1/2} = 1 + \displaystyle\sum_{k=0}^{\infty} \frac{(-1)^k(2k)!t^{2k+2}}{2^{2k+1}k!(k+1)!}$, $-1 \leq t \leq 1$

$\sinh^{-1} x = x + \displaystyle\sum_{k=0}^{\infty} \frac{(-1)^k(2k)!x^{2k+3}}{2^{2k+1}(2k+3)k!(k+1)!}$, $-1 \leq x \leq 1$

9. $e^{\sin x} = 1 + x + \dfrac{x^2}{2!} - \dfrac{3x^4}{4!} - \cdots$

11. (a) $\ln \cos x = -(x^2/2) - (x^4/12) - (x^6/45) - \cdots$
    (b) -0.00017

12. 0.946   13. 0.747

14. $\sqrt{2}[1 + (x - 1)/2 + (x - 1)^2/8 + \cdots]$

15. $\displaystyle\sum_{n=0}^{\infty} (-1)^{n+1}(x - 2)^n$, $1 < x < 3$

16. $\tan x = x + x^3/3 + 2x^5/15 + \cdots$

17. $\displaystyle\sum_{n=0}^{\infty} \frac{(-1)^n(x - 3)^n}{4^{n+1}}$

18. $\cos x = \dfrac{1}{2} \displaystyle\sum_{n=0}^{\infty} (-1)^n \left[\frac{1}{(2n)!} \left(x - \frac{\pi}{3} \right)^{2n} + \frac{\sqrt{3}}{(2n+1)!} \left(x - \frac{\pi}{3} \right)^{2n+1} \right]$

19. $\displaystyle\sum_{n=0}^{\infty} \frac{(-1)^n(x - \pi)^n}{\pi^{n+1}}$ 20. 1.543

22. $e^{e^x} = e(1 + x + 2x^2/2! + 5x^3/3! + 15x^4/4! + 52x^5/5! + \cdots)$

23. $\tan^{-1} 0.05 = 0.0500$, $\tan^{-1} 0.06 = 0.0592$, $\tan^{-1} 0.1 = 0.0967$

24. 0.0027   25. -0.0011 26. $-\infty$ 27. $e^{-1/6}$

28. (a) $-\pi/4 - (2/\pi) \displaystyle\sum_{n=0}^{\infty} \frac{\cos (2n + 1)x}{(2n + 1)^2} + \displaystyle\sum_{n=1}^{\infty} \left[\frac{3 \sin (2n - 1)x}{(2n - 1)} - \frac{\sin 2nx}{2n} \right]$

    (b) $\pi^2/8$

29. Converges, by integral test.

30. Diverges, since nth term doesn't approach zero.

32. (a) Converges   (b) Diverges
    (c) Diverges   (d) Converges
    (e) Diverges   (f) Diverges
    (g) Converges   (h) Converges
    (i) Diverges   (j) Diverges
    (k) Diverges   (l) Converges

33. $\frac{1}{2}$ 35. (b) Converges (c) Converges, by comparison test.

37. (a) $-5 \leq x < 1$ (b) $-\infty < x < \infty$
    (c) $-\infty < x < \infty$ (d) $-e < x < e$
    (e) $1 < x < 5$ (f) $-1 < x < 5$
    (g) $0 \leq x \leq 2$ (h) $-1 \leq x < 1$

38. (a) $-\infty < x < \infty$
    (b) $(6n - 1)\pi/6 \leq x \leq (6n + 1)\pi/6$ $(n = 0, \pm 1, \pm 2, \ldots)$
    (c) $x \geq \frac{1}{2}$

39. (a) $-\infty < x < \infty$
    (b) $y'' = xy$ $(a = 1, b = 0)$

41. (a) Diverges because nth term approaches e, not zero, as $n \to \infty$.
    (b) Converges by comparison with $\sum e^{-n}$.

CHAPTER 17

ARTICLE 17–1

1. (a) $(14, 8)$ 2. (a) $(-\frac{7}{3}, -24)$
   (b) $(-1, 8)$ (b) $(\frac{2}{5}, -\frac{1}{5})$
   (c) $(0, -5)$ (c) $(-1, 0)$

ARTICLE 17–2

2. (a) By reflecting z across the real axis.
   (b) By reflecting z across the imaginary axis.
   (c) By reflecting z in the origin.
   (d) By reflecting z in the real axis and then multiplying the length of
       the vector by $1/|z|^2$.

6. On the real axis.

9. (a) Points on the circle $x^2 + y^2 = 4$.
   (b) Points inside the circle $x^2 + y^2 = 4$.
   (c) Points outside the circle $x^2 + y^2 = 4$.

10. Points on a circle of radius 2, center $(1, 0)$.

11. Points on a circle of radius 1, center $(-1, 0)$.

12. Points on the y-axis.   13. Points on the line $y = -x$.

14. $4 \operatorname{cis} (2\pi/3)$ 15. $1 \operatorname{cis} (\pi/2)$

16. $1 \operatorname{cis} (2\pi/3)$

17. $\sqrt{65} \operatorname{cis} (-\tan^{-1} 0.125) = \sqrt{65} \operatorname{cis} (-7°7'.5)$

18. $\cos 4\theta = \cos^4 \theta - 6 \cos^2 \theta \sin^2 \theta + \sin^4 \theta$
    $\sin 4\theta = 4 \sin \theta \cos \theta (\cos^2 \theta - \sin^2 \theta)$

19. $1, \operatorname{cis} (2\pi/3) = (-1 + i\sqrt{3})/2, \operatorname{cis} (-2\pi/3) = (-1 - i\sqrt{3})/2$

20. $\operatorname{cis}(\pi/4, 5\pi/4) = \pm\operatorname{cis} (\pi/4) = \pm(1 + i)/\sqrt{2}$

21. $2i, 2 \operatorname{cis} (-5\pi/6) = -\sqrt{3} - i, 2 \operatorname{cis} (-\pi/6) = \sqrt{3} - i$

22. $2 \operatorname{cis} (0°, 60°, 120°, 180°, 240°, 300°)$; that is, $2, 1 + i\sqrt{3}, -1 + i\sqrt{3}$,
$-2, -1 - i\sqrt{3}, 1 - i\sqrt{3}$.

23. $\pm\sqrt{2}$ cis $(\pm 30°)$; that is $(\sqrt{3} + i)/\sqrt{2}$, $-(\sqrt{3} + i)/\sqrt{2}$, $(\sqrt{3} - i)/\sqrt{2}$, $(-\sqrt{3} + i)/\sqrt{2}$.

24. $\sqrt[6]{2}$ cis $(45°, 165°, 285°, 75°, 195°, 315°)$

25. 2 cis $(60°, 120°, 240°, 300°)$; or, $1 \pm i\sqrt{3}$, $-1 \pm i\sqrt{3}$.

26. cis $(45°, 135°, 225°, 315°)$; or, $(1 \pm i)/\sqrt{2}$, $(-1 \pm i)/\sqrt{2}$.

ARTICLE 17–3

1. (a) $|w| = 1, 0 \le \arg w \le 2\pi$
   (b) $|w| = 4, \pi \le \arg w \le 2\pi$
   (c) $\arg w = \pi/2$
   (d) $|w| < 1, -2\pi < \arg w \le 0$
   (e) The u-axis, $u \ge 0$
   (f) The u-axis, $u \le 0$

ARTICLE 17–4

1. $\dfrac{-2}{(z_0 - 1)^2} = +2$ 2. $3(z_0 + 1)^2 = -12$

3. $\dfrac{z_0}{\sqrt{z_0^2 + 1}} = 2^{-1/4}$ cis $(\pi/8, 9\pi/8)$

ARTICLE 17–5

1. $u = x^2 - y^2, v = 2xy$
2. $u = x^3 - 3xy^2, v = 3x^2y - y^3$
3. $u = x^4 - 6x^2y^2 + y^4, v = 4x^3y - 4xy^3$
4. $u = (x^2 - y^2)/(x^2 + y^2)^2, v = -2xy/(x^2 + y^2)^2$

ARTICLE 17–6

1. $|z| < 1$ 2. $|z| < 1$ 3. $|z - 1| < 1$

4. $|z + i| < 1$ 5. $|z + 1| < 2$ 9. 0.909

ARTICLE 17–7

1. $1.59 + 1.32i$

5. (a) $-1 \pm 2i$ (b) $1 \pm i, -1 \pm i$ (c) $2, -1 \pm i\sqrt{3}$

18. (a) The circle $u^2 + v^2 = e^{2x}$, described once in the counterclockwise direction each time y increases through a 2π interval of values; for instance, $-\pi < y \le \pi$, etc.

(b) The branch of the hyperbola

$$\frac{u^2}{\sin^2 x} - \frac{v^2}{\cos^2 x} = 1$$

(x not a multiple of $\pi/2$) on which u and $\sin x$ have the same sign. The lines $x = n\pi(n = 0, \pm 1, \ldots)$ map into the v-axis. The lines $x = \pi/2 + 2n\pi(n = 0, \pm 1, \ldots)$ map into the u-axis, $u \ge 1$. The lines $x = -\pi/2 + 2n\pi(n = 0, \pm 1, \ldots)$ map into the u-axis, $u \le -1$.

19. $\int e^{ax} \cos bx \, dx = \dfrac{e^{ax}}{a^2 + b^2} \, (a \cos bx + b \sin bx) + C$

$\int e^{ax} \sin bx \, dx = \dfrac{e^{ax}}{a^2 + b^2} \, (a \sin bx - b \cos bx) + C$

ARTICLE 17–8

1. (a) $\ln 2^{3/2} - i(\pi/4)$
   (b) $\ln 2 + i(\pi/6)$
   (c) $\ln 4 + i\pi$
   (d) $\ln 4$
   (e) $\ln 2 + i(\pi/2)$
   (f) $i(\pi/2)$

2. (a) $\ln 2 + 2n\pi i$
   (b) $\ln 2 + (2n + 1)\pi i$
   (c) $\ln 2 + (2n + \frac{1}{2})\pi i$
   (d) $\ln 2 + (2n - \frac{1}{2})\pi i$
   (e) $\ln 2 + (2n + \frac{5}{6})\pi i$
   $(n = 0, \pm 1, \pm 2, \ldots)$

4. (b) $\left(\dfrac{\pi}{2} + 2n\pi\right) - i \ln (3 + 2\sqrt{2})$

5. (a) Locus is a straight line segment joining the points $(\ln |z|, -\pi)$ and $(\ln |z|, +\pi)$.
   (b) Locus is the line $v = \arg z$, parallel to the real axis.

CHAPTER 17: MISCELLANEOUS

2. (a) $r = 4\sqrt{2}, \theta = -\tan^{-1}(2 + \sqrt{3})$
   (b) $r = \sqrt{2}, \theta = -\pi/12, 7\pi/12, 15\pi/12$

3. (a) $\pm(\sqrt{2 + \sqrt{2}} - i\sqrt{2 - \sqrt{2}}), \pm(\sqrt{2 - \sqrt{2}} + i\sqrt{2 + \sqrt{2}})$
   (b) $\sin^{-1} 5 = 2n\pi + \pi/2 - i \ln (5 + \sqrt{24}), (n = 0, \pm 1, \pm 2, \ldots)$

4. (a) $\pm\sqrt{2}(1 + i), \pm\sqrt{2}(1 - i)$
   (b) $2e^{i(2n\pi + \pi)/5} \quad (n = 0, 1, 2, 3, 4)$

5. (a) $2^{1/4}e^{i\pi(2 + 3n)/6} \quad (n = 0, 1, 2, 3)$ (b) $e^2/\sqrt{2} + i(e^2/\sqrt{2})$

6. (a) $\pm(\sqrt{3} - i)$ (b) $\ln 4 - i\pi/3$

7. $r = 5, \theta = \tan^{-1} \frac{4}{3}$

8. $\ln (3\sqrt{2}) + i(2n\pi - \pi/4) \quad (n \text{ any integer})$

9. $\ln 2 - i\pi/3$

10. (a) $2^{1/3}(-1 - i), 2^{5/6}(\sqrt{2 + \sqrt{3}} - i\sqrt{2 - \sqrt{3}}),$
    $2^{-5/6}(-\sqrt{2 - \sqrt{3}} + i\sqrt{2 + \sqrt{3}})$
    (b) $\ln (3\sqrt{2}) + i(2n\pi + \pi/4) \quad (n \text{ any integer})$
    (c) $-e^2$

11. (b) Derivative doesn't exist.

19. (a) $2e^{i2n\pi/5} \quad (n = 0, 1, 2, 3, 4)$
    (b) $\ln 2 + (2n + 1)\pi i \quad (n \text{ any integer})$
    (c) $2n\pi \pm \tan^{-1}(2\sqrt{6}/5) - i \ln 7 \quad (n \text{ any integer})$
    (d) $\ln \sqrt{3} + (2n + 1)\pi i/2 \quad (n \text{ any integer})$
    (e) $e^{-(4n+1)\pi/2} \quad (n \text{ any integer})$
    (f) $-3, \pm i\sqrt{3}$

CHAPTER 18

ARTICLE 18–3

1. $(x^2 + 1)(2y - 3) = C$

2. $\frac{2}{3}\sqrt{x^3 + 1} + \frac{1}{2}\ln(y^2 + 1) = C$

3. $e^y = e^x + C$

4. $y^{3/2} = 3\sqrt{x/2} + C$

5. $\sinh 2y - 2\cos x = C$

6. $\frac{1}{2}(\ln|x|)^2 = \ln|y| + C$

7. $(y - 1)e^y + \frac{x^2}{2} + \ln|x| = C$

8. $\sqrt{2x^2 + 3} - 2\sqrt{4 - y^2} = C$

9. $\cosh^{-1} y + \sinh^{-1} x = C$

10. $-y\cos y + \sin y = -x^{-1} + \ln|x| + C$

ARTICLE 18–4

1. $2\tan^{-1}\frac{y}{x} + \ln(x^2 + y^2) = C$

2. $\frac{x}{y} = \ln|x| + C$; or $y = 0$

3. $\ln|x| + e^{-y/x} = C$

4. $\ln|y| + \frac{2}{\sqrt{3}}\tan^{-1}\frac{2y - x}{x\sqrt{3}} = C$

5. $y^2 = 2cx + c^2$

6. (a) $x^2 + y^2 = Cx$

   (b) $x^2 + y^2 = Cy$

ARTICLE 18–5

1. $y = e^{-x} + Ce^{-2x}$

2. $y = \frac{1}{2}(x + C)e^{x/2}$

3. $x^3 y = C - \cos x$

4. $xy = C - \cos x$

5. $x = \frac{y}{2} + \frac{C}{y}$

6. $(x - 1)^4 y = \frac{x^3}{3} - x + C$

7. $y\cosh x = C - e^x$

8. $xe^{2y} = y^2 + C$

9. $xy = y^2 + C$

10. $x = \frac{C - y}{1 + y^2}$

ARTICLE 18–6

1. $\frac{x^2}{2} + xy + \frac{y^3}{3} = C$

2. $e^x + e^y(x^2 + 1) = C$

3. $x^2 y + xy^2 - \frac{y^2}{2} = C$

4. $x^2 + 2x\sqrt{y^2 + 1} - y^2 = C$

5. $2y + x^3 = Cx$

6. $y = x\tan(x + C)$

7. $y = x(C - x - \ln|x|)$

8. $e^x + x\ln y + y\ln x - \cos y = C$

9. $y^2 \tan^{-1} x - 2xy + \cosh y = C$

10. $xy + \cos x = C$

ARTICLE 18–7

1. $y = C_1 e^{-x} + C_2$

2. $y = C$, or $y = a\tan(ax + C)$, or $y = a\tanh(ax + C)$

3. $y = C_1 \int e^{-x^2/2}\, dx + C_2$. Note that the integral appearing here could be evaluated as an infinite series, giving

$$y = C_1 \left[x - \frac{x^3}{2 \cdot 3} + \frac{x^5}{2 \cdot 4 \cdot 5} - \frac{x^7}{2 \cdot 4 \cdot 6 \cdot 7} + \cdots \right] + C_2.$$

4. $y = C_1 \ln |x| + C_2$

5. $y = C_1 \sinh (x + C_2)$

6. $y = C_1 \sin (\omega x + C_2)$

7. $x = A \sin \left(\sqrt{\dfrac{k}{m}}\, t + \dfrac{\pi}{2} \right) = A \cos \left(\sqrt{\dfrac{k}{m}}\, t \right)$

8. $s = \dfrac{m^2 g}{k^2} \left[\dfrac{kt}{m} + e^{-kt/m} - 1 \right]$, where m is the man's mass, g is the acceleration due to gravity, and k is the factor of proportionality in the air resistance $-kv$ (v being velocity).

ARTICLE 18–9

1. $y = C_1 + C_2 e^{-2x}$ 2. $y = C_1 e^{-2x} + C_2 e^{-3x}$

3. $y = C_1 e^{-x} + C_2 e^{-5x}$ 4. $y = C_1 e^{3x} + C_2 e^{-x}$

5. $y = e^{-x/2}[C_1 \cos (x\sqrt{3}/2) + C_2 \sin (x\sqrt{3}/2)]$

6. $y = (C_1 + C_2 x)e^{2x}$ 7. $y = (C_1 + C_2 x)e^{-3x}$

8. $y = e^{3x}(C_1 \cos x + C_2 \sin x)$

9. $y = e^x(C_1 \cos \sqrt{3}x + C_2 \sin \sqrt{3}x)$

10. $y = C_1 e^{2x} + C_2 e^{8x}$

ARTICLE 18–10

1. $y = \dfrac{x^2}{2} - x + C_1 + C_2 e^{-x}$

2. $y = \cos x \sinh^{-1} (\tan x) + C_1 \cos x + C_2 \sin x$

3. $y = -\tfrac{1}{2} x \cos x + C_1 \cos x + C_2 \sin x$

4. $y = \tfrac{1}{4} e^x + e^{-x}(C_1 + C_2 x)$ 5. $y = e^{-x}(C_1 + C_2 x + \tfrac{1}{2} x^2)$

6. $y = C_1 e^x + C_2 e^{-x} - x$ 7. $y = C_1 e^x + C_2 e^{-x} + \dfrac{x}{2} e^x$

8. $y = C_1 e^x + C_2 e^{-x} - \tfrac{1}{2} \sin x$

9. $y = e^{-2x}(C_1 \cos x + C_2 \sin x) + 2$

10. $y = e^{-2x}(C_1 \cos x + C_2 \sin x) + \tfrac{1}{5} x + \tfrac{6}{25}$

ARTICLE 18–11

1. $y = C_1 + C_2 e^x + C_3 e^{2x}$

2. $y = C_1 e^x + e^{-x/2}[C_2 \cos (x\sqrt{3}/2) + C_3 \sin (x\sqrt{3}/2)]$

3. $y = (C_1 + C_2 x)e^{\sqrt{2}x} + (C_3 + C_4 x)e^{-\sqrt{2}x}$

4. $y = C_1 e^{2x} + C_2 e^{-2x} + C_3 \cos 2x + C_4 \sin 2x$

5. $y = e^{\sqrt{2}x}(C_1 \cos \sqrt{2}x + C_2 \sin \sqrt{2}x) + e^{-\sqrt{2}x}(C_3 \cos \sqrt{2}x + C_4 \sin \sqrt{2}x)$

6. $y = e^x \left(\dfrac{x^2}{6} + C_1 x + C_2 \right) + C_3 e^{-2x}$

7. $y = (C_1 + C_2 x + C_3 x^2 + C_4 x^3) e^x + 7$

8. $y = e^{x/\sqrt{2}} \left(C_1 \cos \dfrac{x}{\sqrt{2}} + C_2 \sin \dfrac{x}{\sqrt{2}} \right)$
$$+ e^{-x/\sqrt{2}} \left(C_3 \cos \dfrac{x}{\sqrt{2}} + C_4 \sin \dfrac{x}{\sqrt{2}} \right) + x + 1$$

ARTICLE 18–12

1. $x = x_0 \cos \omega t + \dfrac{v_0}{\omega} \sin \omega t = \sqrt{x_0^2 + \dfrac{v_0^2}{\omega^2}} \sin (\omega t + \phi),$

where $\omega = \sqrt{k/m}$, $\phi = \tan^{-1} \dfrac{\omega x_0}{v_0}$.

2. $x = 0.288 \sin (13.9t)$; x in feet, t in sec.

3. (a) $I = C_1 \cos \omega t + C_2 \sin \omega t$

(b) $I = C_1 \cos \omega t + C_2 \sin \omega t + \dfrac{A\alpha}{L(\omega^2 - \alpha^2)} \cos \alpha t$

(c) $I = C_1 \cos \omega t + C_2 \sin \omega t + \dfrac{A}{2L} t \sin \omega t$

(d) $I = e^{-5t}(C_1 \cos 149t + C_2 \sin 149t)$

4. $\theta = \theta_0 \cos (\sqrt{g/l}\, t)$

5. $\theta = \theta_0 \cos \omega t + \dfrac{v_0}{\omega} \sin \omega t$, where $\omega = \sqrt{2k/mr^2}$.

6. $C = 5.3$ (lb sec/ft)

7. (a) $x = C_1 \cos \omega t + C_2 \sin \omega t + \dfrac{\omega^2 A}{\omega^2 - \alpha^2} \sin \alpha t$, where $\omega = \sqrt{k/m}$.

(b) $x = C_1 \cos \omega t + C_2 \sin \omega t - \dfrac{\omega A}{2} t \cos \omega t$, with $\omega = \sqrt{k/m}$.

ARTICLE 18–13

5. (a) $e^{-10} = 0.000045$, (b) $1 - e^{-4} = 0.9817$

6. (a) 0.67   (b) 0.33   (c) 0.98

7. (a) 10   (b) $e^{-10} \sum\limits_{n=0}^{5} \dfrac{(10)^n}{n!} \approx 0.067$

8. (a) 0.270   (b) 0.180   (c) 0.368   (d) 0.073

9. 0.195

CHAPTER 18: MISCELLANEOUS

1. $\ln (c \ln y) = -\tan^{-1} x$

2. $y = [cx^3 + 2(x + 1)^3][(x + 1)^3 - cx^3]^{-1}$

3. $y = \ln (c - \frac{1}{3}e^{-3x})$

4. $ky + \sqrt{k^2 y^2 - 1} = ce^{kx}$

5. $y^2 + \sqrt{y^4 + 1} = ce^{2x}$

6. $x^2 + xy - y^2 = c$

7. $y^2 = 2x^2 \ln (cx)$

8. $y + \sqrt{x^2 + y^2} = cx^2$

9. $y = x \tan^{-1} (\ln cx)$

10. $y = xe^{\sqrt{2 \ln cx}}$

11. $y = (x^2 + 2)/4 + cx^{-2}$

12. $y - x \sec y = c$

13. $y = \cosh x \ln (c \cosh x)$

14. $y = \frac{1}{6}(2x^3 + 3x^2 + c)(x + 1)^{-2}$

15. $y^3 + 3xy^2 + 3(x + y) = c$

16. $x^3 + 3xy + 3e^y = c$

17. $x^3 + 3xy^2 + 3 \sinh y = c$

18. $e^x + x \ln y + y = c$

19. $x^2 + e^y(x^2 + y^2 - 2y + 2) = c$

20. $2x \tan^{-1} (y/x) + y \ln (x^2 + y^2) - 2 \cos x - (y + 1)^2 = c$

21. $y = c \tan (cx + cd)$, or $y = c \dfrac{1 + e^{2c(x+d)}}{1 - e^{2c(x+d)}}$

22. $y = c_1 \cos 2x + c_2 \sin 2x$

23. $y = -\ln |\cos (x + c)| + d$

24. $x = e^{-y/2}[c_1 \cosh (y\sqrt{5}/2) + c_2 \sinh (y\sqrt{5}/2)]$

25. $y = \frac{1}{2} (\ln cx)^2 + d$

26. $y = c_1 e^x + c_2 e^{3x}$

27. $y = c_1 + (c_2 x + c_3)e^x$

28. $y = c_1 \sin 2x + c_2 \cos 2x + (x/2) \sin 2x + \frac{1}{4} \cos 2x \ln \cos 2x$

29. $y = c_1 e^{-x} + (c_2 + x/3)e^{2x}$

30. $y = e^x(c_1 \cos 2x + c_2 \sin 2x) + \frac{1}{8}e^{-x}$

31. $y = c_1 \sqrt{x} + c_2/\sqrt{x}$

33. $\frac{3}{2}x^2 + y^2 = d$

34. $x^2 + (y - d)^2 = d^2$

35. $y^2 = d^2 + 2 dx$

36. $y = 10 \cos 10t + 50 \sin 10t$

APPENDIX

FORMULAS FROM ELEMENTARY MATHEMATICS

A. Algebra.

1. *Laws of exponents.*

$$a^m a^n = a^{m+n}, \ (ab)^m = a^m b^m, \ (a^m)^n = a^{mn}, \ a^{m/n} = \sqrt[n]{a^m}.$$

If $a \neq 0$: $\dfrac{a^m}{a^n} = a^{m-n}, \ a^0 = 1, \ a^{-m} = \dfrac{1}{a^m}.$

2. *Zero.*

$a \cdot 0 = 0 \cdot a = 0$ for any finite number a.

If $a \neq 0$, $\dfrac{0}{a} = 0, \ 0^a = 0, \ a^0 = 1.$

Division by zero is not defined.

3. *Fractions.*

$$\frac{a}{b} + \frac{c}{d} = \frac{ad + bc}{bd}, \ \frac{a}{b} \cdot \frac{c}{d} = \frac{ac}{bd}, \ \frac{a/b}{c/d} = \frac{a}{b} \cdot \frac{d}{c}, \ \frac{-a}{b} = -\frac{a}{b} = \frac{a}{-b}.$$

$$\frac{(a/b) + (c/d)}{(e/f) + (g/h)} = \frac{(a/b) + (c/d)}{(e/f) + (g/h)} \cdot \frac{bdfh}{bdfh} = \frac{(ad + bc)fh}{(eh + fg)bd}.$$

4. *Binomial Theorem, for $n =$ positive integer.*

$$(a + b)^n = a^n + na^{n-1}b + \frac{n(n-1)}{1 \cdot 2} a^{n-2}b^2$$

$$+ \frac{n(n-1)(n-2)}{1 \cdot 2 \cdot 3} a^{n-3}b^3 + \cdots + nab^{n-1} + b^n.$$

5. *Proportionality factor.* If y is proportional to x, or y varies directly as x, then $y = kx$ for some constant k, called the *proportionality factor.*

6. *Remainder Theorem and Factor Theorem.* If the polynomial $f(x)$ is divided by $x - r$ until a remainder R independent of x is obtained, then $R = f(r)$. In particular, $x - r$ is a *factor* of $f(x)$ if and only if r is a *root* of the equation $f(x) = 0$.

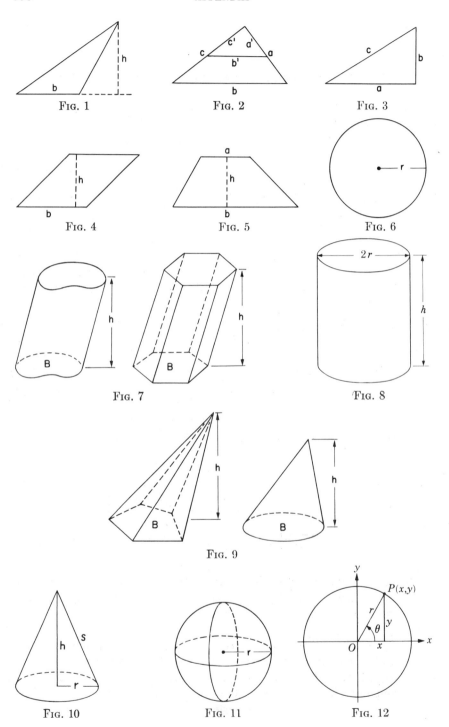

FIG. 1   FIG. 2   FIG. 3
FIG. 4   FIG. 5   FIG. 6
FIG. 7   FIG. 8
FIG. 9
FIG. 10   FIG. 11   FIG. 12

7. *Quadratic formula.* If $a \neq 0$, the roots of the equation $ax^2 + bx + c = 0$ are given by the formula

$$x = \frac{-b \pm \sqrt{b^2 - 4ac}}{2a}.$$

B. **Geometry.** (A = area, B = area of base, C = circumference, S = lateral area or surface area, V = volume.)

1. *Triangle.* $A = \frac{1}{2}bh$. (Fig. 1)

2. *Similar triangles.* $\dfrac{a'}{a} = \dfrac{b'}{b} = \dfrac{c'}{c}.$ (Fig. 2)

3. *Theorem of Pythagoras.* $c^2 = a^2 + b^2$. (Fig. 3)

4. *Parallelogram.* $A = bh$. (Fig. 4)

5. *Trapezoid.* $A = \frac{1}{2}(a + b)h$. (Fig. 5)

6. *Circle.* $A = \pi r^2$, $C = 2\pi r$. (Fig. 6)

7. *Any cylinder or prism with parallel bases.* $V = Bh$. (Fig. 7)

8. *Right circular cylinder.* $V = \pi r^2 h$, $S = 2\pi rh$. (Fig. 8)

9. *Any cone or pyramid.* $V = \frac{1}{3}Bh$. (Fig. 9)

10. *Right circular cone.* $V = \frac{1}{3}\pi r^2 h$, $S = \pi rs$. (Fig. 10)

11. *Sphere.* $V = \frac{4}{3}\pi r^3$, $A = 4\pi r^2$. (Fig. 11)

C. **Trigonometry.**

1. *Definitions and fundamental identities.* (Fig. 12)

$$\sin \theta = \frac{y}{r} = \frac{1}{\csc \theta}.$$

$$\cos \theta = \frac{x}{r} = \frac{1}{\sec \theta}.$$

$$\tan \theta = \frac{y}{x} = \frac{1}{\cot \theta}.$$

$\sin (-\theta) = -\sin \theta$, $\cos (-\theta) = \cos \theta$.

$\sin^2 \theta + \cos^2 \theta = 1$.

$\sin 2\theta = 2 \sin \theta \cos \theta$, $\cos 2\theta = \cos^2 \theta - \sin^2 \theta$.

$\sin (\alpha + \beta) = \sin \alpha \cos \beta + \cos \alpha \sin \beta$.

$\cos (\alpha + \beta) = \cos \alpha \cos \beta - \sin \alpha \sin \beta$.

2. *Angles and sides of triangle.*

Law of cosines: $a^2 = b^2 + c^2 - 2bc \cos A$.

Law of sines: $\dfrac{\sin A}{a} = \dfrac{\sin B}{b} = \dfrac{\sin C}{c}$.

Area $= \frac{1}{2}bc \sin A = \frac{1}{2}ac \sin B = \frac{1}{2}ab \sin C$.

TABLE 1

NATURAL TRIGONOMETRIC FUNCTIONS

Angle					Angle				
De-gree	Ra-dian	Sine	Co-sine	Tan-gent	De-gree	Ra-dian	Sine	Co-sine	Tan-gent
0°	0.000	0.000	1.000	0.000					
1°	0.017	0.017	1.000	0.017	46°	0.803	0.719	0.695	1.036
2°	0.035	0.035	0.999	0.035	47°	0.820	0.731	0.682	1.072
3°	0.052	0.052	0.999	0.052	48°	0.838	0.743	0.669	1.111
4°	0.070	0.070	0.998	0.070	49°	0.855	0.755	0.656	1.150
5°	0.087	0.087	0.996	0.087	50°	0.873	0.766	0.643	1.192
6°	0.105	0.105	0.995	0.105	51°	0.890	0.777	0.629	1.235
7°	0.122	0.122	0.993	0.123	52°	0.908	0.788	0.616	1.280
8°	0.140	0.139	0.990	0.141	53°	0.925	0.799	0.602	1.327
9°	0.157	0.156	0.988	0.158	54°	0.942	0.809	0.588	1.376
10°	0.175	0.174	0.985	0.176	55°	0.960	0.819	0.574	1.428
11°	0.192	0.191	0.982	0.194	56°	0.977	0.829	0.559	1.483
12°	0.209	0.208	0.978	0.213	57°	0.995	0.839	0.545	1.540
13°	0.227	0.225	0.974	0.231	58°	1.012	0.848	0.530	1.600
14°	0.244	0.242	0.970	0.249	59°	1.030	0.857	0.515	1.664
15°	0.262	0.259	0.966	0.268	60°	1.047	0.866	0.500	1.732
16°	0.279	0.276	0.961	0.287	61°	1.065	0.875	0.485	1.804
17°	0.297	0.292	0.956	0.306	62°	1.082	0.883	0.469	1.881
18°	0.314	0.309	0.951	0.325	63°	1.100	0.891	0.454	1.963
19°	0.332	0.326	0.946	0.344	64°	1.117	0.899	0.438	2.050
20°	0.349	0.342	0.940	0.364	65°	1.134	0.906	0.423	2.145
21°	0.367	0.358	0.934	0.384	66°	1.152	0.914	0.407	2.246
22°	0.384	0.375	0.927	0.404	67°	1.169	0.921	0.391	2.356
23°	0.401	0.391	0.921	0.424	68°	1.187	0.927	0.375	2.475
24°	0.419	0.407	0.914	0.445	69°	1.204	0.934	0.358	2.605
25°	0.436	0.423	0.906	0.466	70°	1.222	0.940	0.342	2.748
26°	0.454	0.438	0.899	0.488	71°	1.239	0.946	0.326	2.904
27°	0.471	0.454	0.891	0.510	72°	1.257	0.951	0.309	3.078
28°	0.489	0.469	0.883	0.532	73°	1.274	0.956	0.292	3.271
29°	0.506	0.485	0.875	0.554	74°	1.292	0.961	0.276	3.487
30°	0.524	0.500	0.866	0.577	75°	1.309	0.966	0.259	3.732
31°	0.541	0.515	0.857	0.601	76°	1.326	0.970	0.242	4.011
32°	0.559	0.530	0.848	0.625	77°	1.344	0.974	0.225	4.332
33°	0.576	0.545	0.839	0.649	78°	1.361	0.978	0.208	4.705
34°	0.593	0.559	0.829	0.675	79°	1.379	0.982	0.191	5.145
35°	0.611	0.574	0.819	0.700	80°	1.396	0.985	0.174	5.671
36°	0.628	0.588	0.809	0.727	81°	1.414	0.988	0.156	6.314
37°	0.646	0.602	0.799	0.754	82°	1.431	0.990	0.139	7.115
38°	0.663	0.616	0.788	0.781	83°	1.449	0.993	0.122	8.144
39°	0.681	0.629	0.777	0.810	84°	1.466	0.995	0.105	9.514
40°	0.698	0.643	0.766	0.839	85°	1.484	0.996	0.087	11.43
41°	0.716	0.656	0.755	0.869	86°	1.501	0.998	0.070	14.30
42°	0.733	0.669	0.743	0.900	87°	1.518	0.999	0.052	19.08
43°	0.750	0.682	0.731	0.933	88°	1.536	0.999	0.035	28.64
44°	0.768	0.695	0.719	0.966	89°	1.553	1.000	0.017	57.29
45°	0.785	0.707	0.707	1.000	90°	1.571	1.000	0.000	

TABLE 2

EXPONENTIAL FUNCTIONS

x	e^x	e^{-x}	x	e^x	e^{-x}
0.00	1.0000	1.0000	2.5	12.182	0.0821
0.05	1.0513	0.9512	2.6	13.464	0.0743
0.10	1.1052	0.9048	2.7	14.880	0.0672
0.15	1.1618	0.8607	2.8	16.445	0.0608
0.20	1.2214	0.8187	2.9	18.174	0.0550
0.25	1.2840	0.7788	3.0	20.086	0.0498
0.30	1.3499	0.7408	3.1	22.198	0.0450
0.35	1.4191	0.7047	3.2	24.533	0.0408
0.40	1.4918	0.6703	3.3	27.113	0.0369
0.45	1.5683	0.6376	3.4	29.964	0.0334
0.50	1.6487	0.6065	3.5	33.115	0.0302
0.55	1.7333	0.5769	3.6	36.598	0.0273
0.60	1.8221	0.5488	3.7	40.447	0.0247
0.65	1.9155	0.5220	3.8	44.701	0.0224
0.70	2.0138	0.4966	3.9	49.402	0.0202
0.75	2.1170	0.4724	4.0	54.598	0.0183
0.80	2.2255	0.4493	4.1	60.340	0.0166
0.85	2.3396	0.4274	4.2	66.686	0.0150
0.90	2.4596	0.4066	4.3	73.700	0.0136
0.95	2.5857	0.3867	4.4	81.451	0.0123
1.0	2.7183	0.3679	4.5	90.017	0.0111
1.1	3.0042	0.3329	4.6	99.484	0.0101
1.2	3.3201	0.3012	4.7	109.95	0.0091
1.3	3.6693	0.2725	4.8	121.51	0.0082
1.4	4.0552	0.2466	4.9	134.29	0.0074
1.5	4.4817	0.2231	5	148.41	0.0067
1.6	4.9530	0.2019	6	403.43	0.0025
1.7	5.4739	0.1827	7	1096.6	0.0009
1.8	6.0496	0.1653	8	2981.0	0.0003
1.9	6.6859	0.1496	9	8103.1	0.0001
2.0	7.3891	0.1353	10	22026	0.00005
2.1	8.1662	0.1225			
2.2	9.0250	0.1108			
2.3	9.9742	0.1003			
2.4	11.023	0.0907			

TABLE 3

NATURAL LOGARITHMS OF NUMBERS

n	$\log_e n$	n	$\log_e n$	n	$\log_e n$
0.0	*	4.5	1.5041	9.0	2.1972
0.1	7.6974	4.6	1.5261	9.1	2.2083
0.2	8.3906	4.7	1.5476	9.2	2.2192
0.3	8.7960	4.8	1.5686	9.3	2.2300
0.4	9.0837	4.9	1.5892	9.4	2.2407
0.5	9.3069	5.0	1.6094	9.5	2.2513
0.6	9.4892	5.1	1.6292	9.6	2.2618
0.7	9.6433	5.2	1.6487	9.7	2.2721
0.8	9.7769	5.3	1.6677	9.8	2.2824
0.9	9.8946	5.4	1.6864	9.9	2.2925
1.0	0.0000	5.5	1.7047	10	2.3026
1.1	0.0953	5.6	1.7228	11	2.3979
1.2	0.1823	5.7	1.7405	12	2.4849
1.3	0.2624	5.8	1.7579	13	2.5649
1.4	0.3365	5.9	1.7750	14	2.6391
1.5	0.4055	6.0	1.7918	15	2.7081
1.6	0.4700	6.1	1.8083	16	2.7726
1.7	0.5306	6.2	1.8245	17	2.8332
1.8	0.5878	6.3	1.8405	18	2.8904
1.9	0.6419	6.4	1.8563	19	2.9444
2.0	0.6931	6.5	1.8718	20	2.9957
2.1	0.7419	6.6	1.8871	25	3.2189
2.2	0.7885	6.7	1.9021	30	3.4012
2.3	0.8329	6.8	1.9169	35	3.5553
2.4	0.8755	6.9	1.9315	40	3.6889
2.5	0.9163	7.0	1.9459	45	3.8067
2.6	0.9555	7.1	1.9601	50	3.9120
2.7	0.9933	7.2	1.9741	55	4.0073
2.8	1.0296	7.3	1.9879	60	4.0943
2.9	1.0647	7.4	2.0015	65	4.1744
3.0	1.0986	7.5	2.0149	70	4.2485
3.1	1.1314	7.6	2.0281	75	4.3175
3.2	1.1632	7.7	2.0412	80	4.3820
3.3	1.1939	7.8	2.0541	85	4.4427
3.4	1.2238	7.9	2.0669	90	4.4998
3.5	1.2528	8.0	2.0794	95	4.5539
3.6	1.2809	8.1	2.0919	100	4.6052
3.7	1.3083	8.2	2.1041		
3.8	1.3350	8.3	2.1163		
3.9	1.3610	8.4	2.1282		
4.0	1.3863	8.5	2.1401		
4.1	1.4110	8.6	2.1518		
4.2	1.4351	8.7	2.1633		
4.3	1.4586	8.8	2.1748		
4.4	1.4816	8.9	2.1861		

INDEX

(Numbers in parentheses refer to problems on the indicated pages)